HEAT AND MASS TRANSFER

(A textbook for the students preparing for B.E., B.Tech., B.Sc. Engg.,
A.M.I.E., U.P.S.C. (Engg. Services) and GATE Examinations)
in

SI UNITS

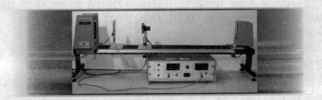

R.K. RAJPUT

M.E. (Hons.), Gold Medalist; Grad. (Mech. Engg. & Elec. Engg.); M.I.E. (India);
M.S.E.S.I.; M.I.S.T.E.; C.E. (India)
Recipient of :
"Best Teacher (Academic) Award"
"Distinguished Author Award"
"Jawahar Lal Nehru Memorial Gold Medal"
for an Outstanding Research Paper
(Institution of Engineers–India)
Principal (Formerly)
Punjab College of Information Technology
PATIALA

S. CHAND & COMPANY LTD.

(An ISO 9001 : 2000 Company)

RAM NAGAR, NEW DELHI - 110 055

S. CHAND & COMPANY LTD.

(An ISO 9001 : 2000 Company)

Head Office : 7361, RAM NAGAR, NEW DELHI - 110 055
Phones : 23672080-81-82; Fax : 91-11-23677446
Shop at: **schandgroup.com**
E-mail: **schand@vsnl.com**

Branches :

- 1st Floor, Heritage, Near Gujarat Vidhyapeeth, Ashram Road,
  Ahmedabad-380 014. Ph. 27541965, 27542369
- No. 6, Ahuja Chambers, 1st Cross, Kumara Krupa Road,
  Bangalore-560 001. Ph : 22268048, 22354008
- 152, Anna Salai, Chennai-600 002. Ph : 28460026
- S.C.O. 6, 7 & 8, Sector 9D, Chandigarh-160017, Ph-2749376, 2749377
- 1st Floor, Bhartia Tower, Badambadi, Cuttack-753 009, Ph-2332580; 2332581
- 1st Floor, 52-A, Rajpur Road, Dehradun-248 011. Ph : 2740889, 2740861
- Pan Bazar, Guwahati-781 001. Ph : 2522155
- Sultan Bazar, Hyderabad-500 195. Ph : 24651135, 24744815
- Mai Hiran Gate, Jalandhar - 144008 . Ph. 2401630
- 613-7, M.G. Road, Ernakulam, Kochi-682 035. Ph : 2381740
- 285/J, Bipin Bihari Ganguli Street, Kolkata-700 012. Ph : 22367459, 22373914
- Mahabeer Market, 25 Gwynne Road, Aminabad, Lucknow-226 018. Ph : 2626801, 2284815
- Blackie House, 103/5, Walchand Hirachand Marg , Opp. G.P.O., Mumbai-400 001.
  Ph : 22690881, 22610885
- 3, Gandhi Sagar East, Nagpur-440 002. Ph : 2723901
- 104, Citicentre Ashok, Govind Mitra Road, Patna-800 004. Ph : 2300489, 2302100

Marketing Offices :

- 238-A M.P. Nagar, Zone 1, Bhopal - 462 011. Ph : 5274723.
- A-14 Janta Store Shopping Complex, University Marg, Bapu Nagar, Jaipur - 302 015,
  Phone : 0141-2709153

First Edition 1999
Subsequent Editions & Reprints 2001, 2002, 2003, 2004, 2005
Third Revised Edition 2006

First Multicolour Illustrative Revised Edition 2006
Reprint 2006

ISBN : 81-219-2617-3
Code :10 314

PRINTED IN INDIA

By Rajendra Ravindra Printers (Pvt.) Ltd., 7361, Ram Nagar, New Delhi-110 055
and published by S. Chand & Company Ltd. 7361, Ram Nagar, New Delhi-110 055

To My Wife Ramesh Rajput

PREFACE TO THE THIRD EDITION

I am pleased to present the **"Third edition"** of this treatise on **"Heat and Mass Transfer"**. The entire book has been thoroughly revised and a large number of solved examples under the heading **"Additional /Typical Worked Examples"** (Questions selected from various Universities and Competitive Examinations) have been added at the end of the book. Besides this the **"Questions Bank"** including *"Objective type questions"* has been enriched with additional questions drawn from latest competitive examinations (U.P.S.C., GATE etc.) to make this book a still more useful and comprehensive unit in all respects.

As ever before, I take this opportunity to thank my publisher Sh. Ravindra Kumar Gupta, CMD, and Sh. Navin Joshi, GM (Sales & Marketing) of S. Chand & Company Ltd. for the personal interest they took in printing this book.

I also thank the editorial staff of S. Chand & Company Ltd., especially Mr. Shishir Bhatnagar, Editor, Mr. Rupesh Kumar Gupta, Mr. Riyaz Baqar Asst. Editors (Science & Technology), Mr. Chander Shekhar, for their help in converting the book into multicolour edition and Mr. Dhan Singh Karki for Designing and Layouting this book.

Any suggestions for improvement of this book will be thankfully acknowledged and incorporated in the next edition.

R.K. RAJPUT
(AUTHOR)

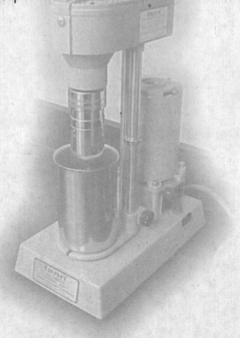

PREFACE TO THE FIRST EDITION

This treatise on **"Heat and Mass Transfer"** contains comprehensive treatment of the subject matter in simple, lucid and direct language. It envelopes a large number of solved problems, properly graded, including typical examples from examination point of view.

The book comprises 13 chapters. All chapters are saturated with much needed text supported by simple and self explanatory figures. A large number of *Worked Examples* (including *Typical Examples* selected from various Indian Universities Examinations question papers), *Highlights*, *Objective Type Question, Theoretical Questions* and *Unsolved Examples* have been added to make the book a comprehensive and a complete unit in all respects.

The book will prove to be a boon to the students preparing for engineering undergraduate, A.M.I.E., U.P.S.C. and other competitive examinations.

The author's thanks are due to his wife Ramesh Rajput for extending all co-operation during preparation of the manuscript and proof reading.

In the end the author wishes to express his gratitude to Shri Ravindra Kumar Gupta, Director, S.Chand & Company Ltd., New Delhi for taking a lot of pains in bringing out the book with very good presentation in a short span of time.

Although every care has been taken to make the book free of errors both in text as well as in solved examples, yet the author shall feel obliged if errors present are brought to his notice. Constructive criticism of the book will be warmly received.

R.K. RAJPUT
(AUTHOR)

CONTENTS

PART 1 : HEAT TRANSFER BY "CONDUCTION"

4. CONDUCTION-UNSTEADY-STATE (TRANSIENT)   290—336

PART II : HEAT TRANSFER BY "CONVECTION"

5. INTRODUCTION TO HYDRODYNAMICS   339—351

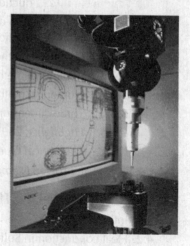

PART III : HEAT TRANSFER BY "RADIATION"

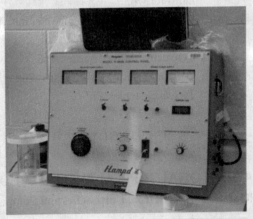

PART IV : MASS TRANSFER

PART V : OBJECTIVE TYPE QUESTIONS BANK WITH ANSWERS

NOMENCLATURE

A	Area	Q	Heat transfer rate per unit time
c	Specific heat	Q'	Total heat transfer
c_p	specific heat at constant pressure	Q_g	Heat generated per unit time
c_v	Specific heat at constant volume	Q_g'	Total heat generated
C	Mass concentration	R	Characteristic gas constant
C_{fx}	Local skin friction coefficient	R_{th}	Thermal resistance
$\overline{C}_f$	Average skin friction coefficient	$(R_{th})_{cond.}$	Conductive thermal resistance
		$(R_{th})_{conv.}$	Convective thermal resistance
D	Diffusion coefficient	$(R_{th})_{rad.}$	Radiative thermal resistance
D, d	Diameter	t	temperature
E	Total emissive power	T	Absolute temperature
E_b	Emissive power of a black body	U	Overall heat transfer coefficient
E_λ	Monochromatic emissive power	x	Mole fraction

E_b Emissive power of a black body

E_λ Monochromatic emissive power

Greek Notations

f	Interchange factor		
F	Correction factor		
G	Irradiation	$\alpha\left(=\dfrac{k}{\rho c}\right)$	Thermal diffusivity; Absorptivity
G	Universal gas constant		
h_{mc}	Mass transfer coefficient based upon concentration	β	Coefficient of volume expansion; Temperature coefficient of thermal conductivity
h_{mp}	Mass transfer coefficient based upon pressure	τ	Time; Transmittivity
J	Radiosity	τ_{th}	Thermal time constant
k	Thermal conductivity	θ	Temperature difference; Momentum thickness
L	Length	θ_m	Log-mean temperature difference
m	Mass	δ	Hydrodynamic boundary layer thickness
$\dot{m}$	Mass flow rate		
M	Molecular weight	δ^*	Displacement thickness
m^*	Mass fraction	δ_e	Energy thickness
N	Mass flux of species	δ_{th}	Thermal boundary layer thickness
p	Pressure	ψ	Stream function
P	Perimeter	ϕ	Velocity potential
q	Heat transfer per unit area per unit time	σ	Stefan-Boltzmann constant $(=5.67 \times 10^{-8}\ \text{W/m}^2\text{K}^4)$
q_g	Heat generated per unit volume per unit time		

ρ	Reflectivity; Mass density	
ϵ	Emissivity	
λ	Wavelength	
Ω	Collision integral	

Dimensionless Groups

$Bi\left(=\dfrac{hL}{k}\right)$ Biot number

$Gr\left(=\dfrac{L^3 g\beta\Delta t}{v^2}\right)$ Grashof number

$Gz\left(=\dfrac{mc_p}{Lk}\right)$ Graetz number

$Le\left(=\dfrac{\alpha}{D}\right)$ Lewis number

$Nu\left(=\dfrac{hx}{h}\right)$ Nusselt number

$\bar{Nu}\left(=\dfrac{\bar{h}x}{k}\right)$ Average Nusselt number

$Pe\left(=Re.Pr=\dfrac{LV}{\alpha}\right)$ Peclet number

$Pr\left(=\dfrac{c_p\mu}{k}=\dfrac{v}{\alpha}\right)$ Prandtl number

$Re\left(=\dfrac{\rho Ux}{\mu}\right)$ Reynolds number

$Sh=\dfrac{h_m \cdot x}{D}$ Sherwood number

$Sc\left(=\dfrac{v}{D}\right)$ Schmidt number

$St\left(=\dfrac{h}{\rho Vc_p}\right)$ Stanton number

Subscripts

$i, 1$	Inner or inlet conditions
$0, 2$	Outer or outlet conditions
hf	Hot fluid
cf	Cold fluid
w	Wall conditions

CHAPTER 1

Basic Concepts

1.1. HEAT TRANSFER–GENERAL ASPECTS

1.1.1. HEAT

*"The energy in transit is termed **heat**"*

While Aristotle was of the opinion that fire was one of the four primary elements, Plato thought that the heat was sort of motion of particles; accordingly there are two theories of heat. Any theory should be able to explain the facts given below :

(*i*) Whenever there is an exchange of heat, heat is consumed (heat lost by the hot body is always equal to heat gained by the cold body).

(*ii*) The heat flow takes place from higher to lower temperature.

(*iii*) The substances expand on heating.

(*iv*) In order to change the state of a body form solid to liquid or liquid to gas without rise in temperature, certain amount of heat is required.

(*v*) When a body is heated or cooled its weight does not change.

According to the **modern or dynamical theory of heat:** *"Heat is a form of energy. The molecules of a substance are in parallel motion. The mean kinetic energy per molecule of the substance is proportional to its absolute temperature"*.

A molecule may consist of one or two or many atoms depending upon the nature of the gas. The force of attraction between the molecules of a perfect gas is negligible. The atoms in a molecule vibrate with respect to one another, consequently a molecule has '*vibrational energy*'. The whole molecule may rotate about one or more axes, so it can have 'rotational energy'. A molecule has 'translational energy' due to its motion. Thus kinetic energy of a molecule is the sum of its translational, rotational and vibrational energies. Summarily *heat energy given to a substance is used in increasing its internal energy*. Increase in internal energy causes increase in kinetic energy or potential energy or increase in both the energies. Due to increase in kinetic energy of a molecule, its translational, vibrational or rotational energy may increase.

1.1.2. IMPORTANCE OF HEAT TRANSFER

Heat transfer may be defined as :

"*The transmission of energy from one region to another as a result of temperature gradient*".

In *heat transfer* the driving potential is *temperature difference* whereas in *mass transfer* the driving potential is *concentration difference*. In *mass transfer* we concentrate upon *mass motion which result in changes in composition*, and are *caused by the variations in concentrations of the various constituent species*. This transfer, in literature, is also known as "**diffusion**".

The *study of heat transfer* in carried out for the follows *purposes* :

1.   To estimate the rate of flow of energy as heat through the boundary of a system under study (both under steady and transient conditions).

2.   To determine the temperature field under steady and transient conditions.

In almost every branch of engineering, heat transfer (and mass transfer) problems are encountered which cannot be solved by thermodynamic reasoning alone but require an analysis based on heat transfer principles. The *areas covered* under the discipline of *heat transfer* are :

● Design of thermal and nuclear power plants including heat engines, steam generators, condensers and other heat exchange equipments, catalytic converters, heat shields for space vehicles, furnaces, electronic equipments etc.

● Internal combustion engines.

● Refrigeration and air conditioning units.

● Design of cooling systems for electric motors, generators and transformers.

● Heating and cooling of fluids etc. in chemical operations.

● Construction of dams and structures; minimisation of building-heat losses using improved insulation techniques.

● Thermal control of space vehicles.

● Heat treatment of metals.

● Dispersion of atmospheric pollutants.

1.1.3. THERMODYNAMICS
1.1.3.1. Definition

Thermodynamics may be defined as follows:

"*Thermodynamics is an axiomatic science which deals with the relations among heat, work and properties of system which are in equilibrium. It describes state and changes in state of physical systems.*"

Thermodynamic, basically entails four laws or axioms known as Zeroth, First, Second and Third law of thermodynamics.

● *First law* throws light on *concept of internal energy*.

● Zeroth law deals with *thermal equilibrium* and establishes a *concept of temperature*.

- Second law indicates the limit of *converting heat into work* and introduces the *principle of increase of entropy*.
- Third law defines *absolute zero of entropy*.

These laws are based on experimental observations and have no *mathematical proof*. Like all physical laws, these laws are based on *logical reasoning*.

1.1.3.2. Thermodynamic systems

System, boundary and surroundings :

System. A system is a *finite quantity of matter or a prescribed region of space* (Refer Fig. 1.1).

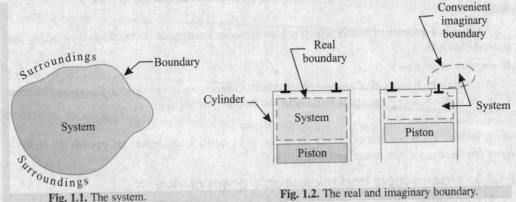

Fig. 1.1. The system.   Fig. 1.2. The real and imaginary boundary.

Boundary. The *actual or hypothetical envelop enclosing the system* is the boundary of the system. The boundary may be fixed or it may move, as and when a system containing a gas is compressed or expanded. The boundary may be *real or imaginary*. It is not difficult to envtisage a real boundary but an example of imaginary boundary would be one drawn around a system consisting of a fresh mixture about to enter the cylinder of an I.C engine together with remanants of the last cylinder charge after the exhaust process (Fig 1.2).

Refer to Fig. 1.3. If the boundary of the system is impervious to the flow of matter, it is called a *closed system*. An example of this system is mass of gas or vapour contained in an engine cylinder, the boundary of which is drawn by the cylinder walls, the cylinder head and piston crown. Here the *boundary is continuous and no matter may enter or leave*.

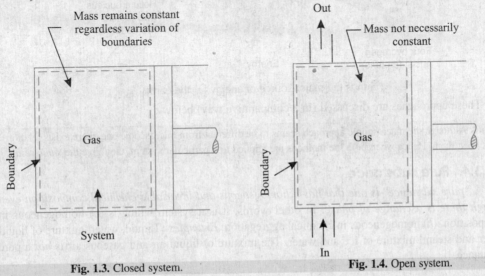

Fig. 1.3. Closed system.   Fig. 1.4. Open system.

Open system :

Refer figure 1.4. An open system is one in which *matter flows into or out of the system*. Most of the engineering systems are open.

Isolated system :

An isolated system is that system *which exchanges neither energy nor matter with any other system or with environment.*

Adiabatic system :

An adiabatic system is one *which is thermally insulated from its surroundings*. It can, however, *exchange work with its surroundings*. If it does not, it becomes an isolated system.

Phase :

A phase is a quantity of matter which is homogeneous throughout in chemical composition and physical structure.

Homogeneous system :

A system which consists of a single phase is termed as homogeneous system. *Examples* : Mixture of air and water vapour, water plus nitric acid and octane plus heptane.

Heterogeneous system :

A system which consists of two or more phases is called a heterogeneous system. *Examples* : Water plus steam, ice plus water and water plus oil.

1.1.3.3. Macroscopic and microscopic points of view

Thermodynamic studies are undertaken by the following two different approaches :

1. Macroscopic approach—(*Macro* mean *big or total*)
2. Microscopic approach—(*Micro* means *small*)

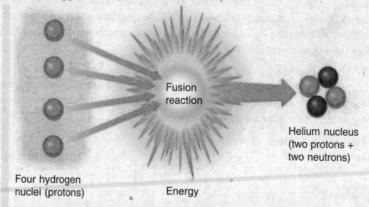

Four hydrogen nuclei (protons)

Fusion reaction

Energy

Helium nucleus (two protons + two neutrons)

Sun is the major source of energy for the earth.

These approaches are discussed (in a comparative way) below :

Note. Although the macroscopic approach seems to be different from microscopic one, there exists relation between them. Hence when both the methods are applied to a particular system, they give the *same result*.

1.1.3.4. Pure substance

A *"pure substance"* is one that has a *homogeneous and invariable chemical composition even though there is a change of phase*. In other words, it is a system which is (*a*) homogeneous in composition, (*b*) homogeneous in chemical aggregation. *Examples* : Liquid, water, mixture of liquid water and steam, mixture of ice and water. The mixture of liquid air and gaseous air is *not* a pure substance.

S.No.	Macroscopic approach	Microscopic approach
1.	In this approach a certain quantity of matter is considered without taking into account the events occuring at molecular level. In other words this approach to thermo-dynamics is concerned with *gross or overall behaviour.* This is known as *"Classical thermodynamics".*	The approach considers that the system is matter of a very large number of discrete particles known as *molecules.* These molecule have different velocities and energies. The values of these energies are constantly changing with time. This approach to thermodynamics which is concerned directly with the *structure of the matter* is known as *"Statistical thermo-dynamics".*
2.	The analysis of macroscopic system requires simple mathematical formulae.	The behaviour of the system is found by using statistical methods as the number of molecules is very large. So advanced statistical and mathematical methods are needed to explain the change in the system.
3.	The values of the properties of the system are their average values. For example, consider a sample of a gas in a closed container. The *pressure* of the gas is the average value of the pressure exerted by millions of individual molecules. Similarly the *temperature* of this gas is the average value of translational kinetic energies of millions of individual molecules. These properties like *pressure* and *temperature* can be measured very easily. The *changes* in *properties can be felt by our senses.*	The properties like *velocity, momentum,* impulse kinetic energy, force of impact etc. which describe the molecule *cannot be easily measured by instruments. Our senses cannot feel them.*
4.	In order to describe a system only a few properties are needed.	Large number of variables are needed to describe a system. So the approach is complicated.

1.1.3.5. Thermodynamic equilibrium

A system is in *thermodynamic equilibrium* if the temperature and pressure at all points are same; there should be no velocity gradient; the chemical equilibrium is also necessary. Systems under temperature and pressure equilibrium but not under chemical equilibrium are sometimes said to be in metastable equilibrium conditions. *It is only under thermodynamic equilibrium conditions that the properties of a system can be fixed.*

Thus for attaining a state of *thermodynamic equilibrium* the following three types of equilibrium states must be achieved :

1. Thermal equilibrium. The temperature of the system does not change with time and has same value at all points of the system.

2. Mechanical equilibrium. There are no unbalanced forces within the system or between the surroundings. The pressure in the system is same at all points and does not change with respect to time.

3. **Chemical equilibrium.** No chemical reaction takes place in the system and the chemical composition which is same throughout the system does not vary with time.

1.1.3.6. Properties of systems

A *"property of a system"* is *a characteristic of the system which depends upon its state, but not upon how the state is reached.* There are two sorts of property :

1. **Intensive properties.** These properties *do not depend on the mass of the system. Example* : Temperature and pressure.

2. **Extensive properties.** These properties *depend on the mass of the system. Example* : Volume. Extensive properties are often divided by mass associated with them to obtain the intensive poroperties. For example, if the volume of a system of mass m is V, then the specific volume of matter within the system is $\dfrac{V}{m} = v$ which is an intensive property.

1.1.3.7. State

"State" is *the condition of the system at an instant of time as described or measured by its properties. Or each unique condition of a system is called a "state".*

It follows from the definition of state that each property has a single value at each state. Stated differently, all properties are *state* or *point functions.* Therefore, all properties are identical for identical states.

On the basis of the above discussion, we can determine if a given variable is *property* or not by applying the following tests :

- A **variable** *is a property, if and only if, it has a single value at each equilibrium state.*
- A *variable* is a property, if and only if, the change in its value between any two prescribed equilibrium states is single-valued.

Therefore, *any variable whose change is fixed by the end states is a "property".*

1.1.3.8. Process

A process occurs when the system undergoes a change in a state or an energy transfer at a steady state. A process may be *non-flow* in which a fixed mass within the defined boundary is undergoing a change of state. *Example* : A substance which is being heated in a closed cylinder undergoes a non-flow process (Fig. 1.3.). *Closed systems undergo non-flow processes.* A process may be a flow process

Petroleum, Coal, etc. are energy sources which originally obtained the energy from the Sun.

in which mass is entering and leaving through the boundary of an open system. In a steady flow process (Fig. 1.4.) mass is crossing the boundary from surroundings at entry, and an equal mass is crossing the boundary at the exit so that the total mass of the system remains constant. In an open system it is necessary to take account of the work delivered from the surroundings to the system at entry to cause the mass to enter, and also, of the work delivered from the system at surroundings to cause the mass to leave, as well as any heat or work crossing the boundary of the system.

　　Quasi-static process. Quasi means 'almost'. A quasi-static process is also called a *reversible process. This process is a succession of equilibrium states and infinite slowness is its characteristic feature.*

1.1.3.9. Cycle

　　Any process or series of processes whose end states are identical is termed a **cycle**. The processes through which the system has passed can be shown on a state diagram, but a complete section of the path requires in addition a statement of the heat and work crossing the boundary of the system. Fig.1.5 shows such a cycle in which a system commencing at condition '1' changes in pressure and volume through a path 1-2-3 and returns to its initial condition '1'.

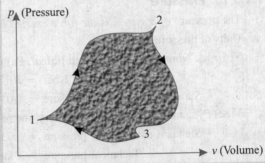

Fig. 1.5. Cycle of operations.

1.1.3.10. Point function

　　When two properties locate a point on the graph (coordinate axes) then those properties are called as *point function.*

　　Examples. Pressure, temperature, volume etc.

$$\int_1^2 dV = V_2 - V_1 \text{ (an } exact \ differential)$$

1.1.3.11. Path function

　　There are certain quantities which cannot be located on a graph by a *point* but are given by the *area* or so, on that graph. In that case, the area on the graph, pertaining to the particular process, is a function of the path of the process. Such quantities are called *path functions.*

　　Examples : Heat, work etc.

　　Heat and work are *inexact differentials*. Their change cannot be written as differences between their end states.

Thus $\qquad \int_1^2 \delta Q \neq Q_2 - Q_1$ and is shown as $_1Q_2$ or Q_{1-2}

Similarly $\qquad \int_1^2 \delta W \neq W_2 - W_1$, and is shown as $_1W_2$ or W_{1-2}

Note. The operator δ is used to denote inexact differentials and operator d is used to denote exact differentials.

1.1.3.12. Temperature

　　The temperature is a thermal state of a body which distinguishes a hot body from a cold body. The temperature of a body is *proportional to the stored molecular energy i.e.,* the average molecular kinetic energy of the molecules in a system. (A particular molecule does not have a temperature, it has energy; the gas as a system has temperature).

Instruments for measuring ordinary temperatures are known as thermometers and those for measuring high temperatures are known as *pyrometers*.

It has been found that a gas will not occupy any volume at a certain temperature. This temperature is known as *absolute zero temperature*. The temperatures measured with absolute zero as basis are called *absolute temperatures*. Absolute temperature is stated in degree centigrade. The point of absolute temperature is found to occur at 273°C (app.) below the freezing point of water.

Then, Absolute temperature = Thermometer reading in °C + 273.

Absolute temperature in degree centigrade is known as degree kelvin, denoted by K (SI units).

1.1.3.13. Pressure

The pressure *of a system is the force exerted by the system on unit area of boundaries.*
Units of pressure are :

SI Units. N/m² (sometimes called *pascal*, Pa) or bar

$$1 \text{ bar} = 10^5 \text{ N/m}^2 = 10^5 \text{ Pa}$$

Standard atmospheric pressure = 1.01325 bar = 0.76 m Hg.

MKS System. kgf/cm², mm of mercury, metre or mm of water column.

Standard atmospheric pressure = 1.033 kgf/cm² (= 760 mm of Hg)

Technical pressure = 1 kgf/cm².

The pressure gauges, vacuum gauges or manometers are used for measuring fluid pressure. These devices indicate pressure relative to atmospheric pressure and this pressure is known as *gauge pressure*. To get absolute pressure, atmospheric pressure is *added* to the gauge pressure. In other words,

Absolute pressure = Gauge pressure + atmospheric pressure.

Vaccum is defined as the *absence of pressure*. A *perfect vacuum* is obtained when *absolute pressure is zero*, at this instant *molecular momentum is zero*.

Energy, Work and Heat

1.1.3.14. Energy

"*Energy*" is a general term embracing *energy in transition and stored energy*. The stored energy of a substance may be in the forms of *mechanical energy* and *internal energy* (other forms of stored energy may be chemical energy and electrical energy). Part of the stored energy may take the form of either potential energy (which is the gravitational energy due to height above a chosen datum line) or kinetic energy due to velocity. The balance part of the energy is known as *internal energy*. In a *non-*

Piston and piston rod.

flow process usually there is no change of potential or kinetic energy and hence change of mechanical energy will not enter the calculations. In a *flow process*, however, there may be changes in both potential and kinetic energy and these must be taken into account while considering the changes of stored energy. *Heat and work* are the forms of energy in transition. These are the only forms in which energy can cross the boundaries of a system. Neither heat nor work can exist as stored energy.

1.1.3.15. Work

Work is said to be done when a *force moves through a distance*. If a part of the boundary of a system undergoes a displacement under the action of a pressure, the work done W is the product of the force (pressure × area), and the distance it moves in the direction of the force. Fig. 1.6 (*a*) illustrates this with the conventional piston and cylinder arrangement, the heavy line defining the boundary of the system. Fig. 1.6 (b) illustrates another way in which work might be applied to a system. A force is exerted by the paddle as it changes the momentum of the fluid, and since this force moves during rotation of the paddle room work is done.

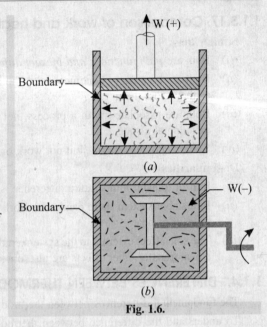

(a)

(b)

Fig. 1.6.

Work is a transient quantity which only appears at the boundary while a change of state is taking place within a system. Work is 'something' which appears at the boundary when a system changes its state due to the movement of a part of the boundary under the action of a force.

Sign convention :

- If the work is done *by* the system *on* the surroundings, *e.g.*, when a fluid expands pushing a piston outwards, the work is said to be *positive*.

i.e.,　　　　　*Work output of the system = + W*

- If the work is done *on* the system by the surroundings, *e.g.*, when a force is applied to a rotating handle, or to a piston to compress a fluid, the work is said to be *negative*.

i.e.,　　　　　*Work input to system = – W*

1.1.3.16. Heat

Heat (denoted by the symbol Q), may be, defined in an analogous way to work as follows :

"Heat is 'something' which appears at the boundary when a system changes its state due to a difference in temperature between the system and its surroundings".

Heat, like work, is a transient quantity which only appears at the boundary while a change is taking place within the system.

It is apparent that neither δW or δQ are exact differentials and, therefore, any integration of elemental quantities of work or heat which appear during a change from state 1 to state 2 must be written as

$$\int_1^2 \delta W = W_{1-2} \text{ or } {}_1W_2 \text{ (or } W\text{), and}$$

$$\int_1^2 \delta Q = Q_{1-2} \text{ or } {}_1Q_2 \text{ (or } Q\text{)}$$

Sign convention :

If the heat flows *into* a system *from* the surroundings, the quantity is said to be *positive* and conversely, if heat flows *from* the system to the surroundings it is said to be *negative*.

In other words :

　　　　Heat received by the system = + Q

　　Heat rejected or given up by the system = – Q.

1.1.3.17. Comparison of work and heat

Similarities :

(i) Both are *path functions and inexact differentials*.

(ii) Both are boundary phenomenon *i.e.*, both are recognized at the boundaries of the system as they cross them.

(iii) Both are associated with a process, not a state. Unlike properties, work or heat has no meaning at a state.

(iv) Systems possess energy, but not work or heat.

Dissimilarities :

(i) In heat transfer temperature difference is required.

(ii) In a stable system there cannot be work transfer, however, there is no restriction for the transfer of heat.

(iii) The sole effect external to the system could be reduced to rise of a weight but in the case of a heat transfer other effects are also observed.

1.1.4. DIFFERENCES BETWEEN THERMODYNAMICS AND HEAT TRANSFER

The fundamental differences between thermodynamics and heat transfer are given below :

To understand the difference between thermodynamics and heat transfer, let us consider the cooling of a hot steel bar which is placed in a water bath. *Thermodynamics* may be used to predict the final equilibrium temperature of the steel bar-water combination; however, it will not help us to find out how long it takes to reach this equilibrium condition or what the temperature of the bar will be after a certain length of time before the equilibrium condition is attained. *Heat transfer* on the other hand, may be used to *predict* the *temperatures of both the bar and the water as a function of time*.

Heat transfer theory *combines thermodynamics and rate equations together* (to quantify the rate at which heat transfer occurs in terms of the degree of non-equilibrium).

	Thermodynamics	Heat transfer
1.	It deals with the *equilibrium states* of matter, and precludes the existence of a temperature gradient.	It is inherently a *non-equilibrium process* (since a temperature gradient must exist for exchange of heat to take place).
2.	When a system changes from one equilibrium state to another, thermodynamics helps to determine the quantity of work and heat interactions. It describes how much heat is to be exchanged during a process but does not hint how the same could be achieved.	It helps to *predict the distribution of temperature* and to *determine the rate at which energy is transferred* across a surface of interest due to temperature gradients at the surface, and difference of temperature between different surfaces.

1.1.5. BASIC LAWS GOVERNING HEAT TRANSFER

The following are the *basic laws* which govern heat transfer :

1. First law of thermodynamics :

In the early part of nineteenth century the scientists developed the concept of energy and hypothesis that it can neither be created nor destroyed; this came to be known as the '*law of the conservation of energy*'. *The first law of thermodynamics* is merely one statement of this general law/principle with particular reference to heat energy and mechanical work *i.e.*, work, and is *stated* as follows :

"When a system undergoes a thermodynamic cycle then the net heat supplied to the system from the surroundings is equal to the net work done by the system on its surroundings.

$$\oint dQ = \oint dW$$

where $\oint$ represents the sum for the complete cycle".

The first law of thermodynamics applies to *reversible as well as irresversible transformations.* For non-cylic process, a more general formulation of first law of thermodynamics is required. A new concept which involves a term called *internal energy* fulfills this need. As per this law, the relationships for closed and open systems are as follows :

Closed system : The net flow of heat across the system boundary + heat generated inside the system = change in the internal energy of system.

Open system : The net energy transported through a control volume + energy generated within the control volume = change in the internal energy in the control volume.

2. Second law of thermodynamics:

It states that *"heat will flow naturally from one reservoir to another at a lower temperature, but not in opposite direction without assistance".*

This law establishes the direction of energy transport as heat and postulates that the flow of energy as heat through a system boundary will always be in the direction of lower temperature (or along negative temperature gradient).

3. *Law of conservation of mass.* This law is used to determine the parameters of flow.

4. *Newton's laws of motion.* These laws are used to determine fluid flow parameters.

In a steam engine coal burns producing heat, heat generates steam which is finally converted into mechanical energy. Steam engine is an external combustion engine.

5. *The rate equations.* These equations are made applicable depending upon the mode of heat transfer being considered.

1.1.6. MODES OF HEAT TRANSFER

Heat transfer which is defined as the *transmission of energy from one region to another as a result of temperature gradient* takes place by the following three modes :

(*i*) Conduction;   (*ii*) Convection;   (*iii*) Radiation.

Heat transmission, in majority of real situations, occurs as a result of combinations of these modes of heat transfer. *Example* : The water in a boiler shell receives its heat from the fire-bed by conducted, convected and radiated heat from the fire to the shell, conducted heat through the shell and conducted and convected heat from the inner shell wall, to the water. *Heat always flows in the direction of lower temperature.*

The above three modes are similar in that a temperature differential must exist and the heat exchange is in the direction of decreasing temperature; each method, however, has different controlling laws.

Conduction :

"Conduction" is the *transfer of heat from one part of a substance to another part of the same*

substance, or from one substance to another in physical contact with it, without appreciable displacement of molecules forming the substance.

In *solids*, the heat is conducted by the following *two mechanisms* :

(*i*) *By lattice vibration* (the faster moving molecules or atoms in the hottest part of a body transfer heat by impacts some of their energy to adjacent molecules).

(*ii*) *By transport of free electrons* (Free electrons provide an energy flux in the direction of decreasing temperature — For metals, especially good electrical conductors, the electrtonic mechanism is responsible for the major portion of the heat flux except at low temperature).

In case of *gases*, the mechanism of heat conduction is simple. The kinetic energy of a molecule is a function of temperature. These molecules are in a continuous random motion exchanging energy and momentum. When a molecule from the high temperature region collides with a molecule from the low temperature region, it loses energy by collisions.

In liquids, the mechanism of heat is nearer to that of gases. However, the molecules are more closely spaced and intermolecular forces come into play.

Convection :

"Convection" is the transfer of heat within a fluid by mixing of one portion of the fluid with another.

- Convection is possible only in a fluid medium and is *directly linked with the transport of medium itself.*
- Convection constitutes the *macroform* of the heat transfer since macroscopic particles of a fluid moving in space cause the heat exchange.
- The effectiveness of heat transfer by convection depends largely upon the mixing motion of the fluid.

This mode of heat transfer is met with in situations where energy is transferred as heat to a flowing fluid at any surface over which flow occurs. This mode is *basically conduction in a very thin fluid layer at the surface and then mixing caused by the flow.* The heat flow depends on the properties of fluid and is independent of the properties of the material of the surface. However, the shape of the surface will influence the flow and hence the heat transfer.

Free or natural convection. Free or natural convection occurs when the fluid circulates by virtue of the natural differences in densities of hot and cold fluids; the denser portions of the fluid move downward because of the greater force of gravity, as compared with the force on the less dense.

Forced convection. When the work is done to blow or pump the fluid, it is said to be *forced convection.*

Radiation :

"Radiation" is the transfer of heat through space or matter by means other than conduction or convection.

Radiation heat is thought of as *electromagnetic waves or quanta* (as convenient) an emanation of the same nature as light and radio waves. *All bodies radiate heat; so a transfer of heat by radiation occurs because hot body emits more heat than it receives and a cold body receives more heat than it emits.* Radiant *energy* (being electromagnetic radiation) *requires no medium for propagation and will pass through vaccum.*

Note: The rapidly oscillating molecules of the hot body produce electromagnetic waves in hypothetical medium called *ether*. These waves are identical with light waves, radio waves and X-rays, differ from them only in *wavelength* and travel with an approximate velocity of 3×10^8 m/s. These waves carry energy with them and *transfer it to the relatively slow- moving molecules of the cold body* on which they happen to fall. The molecular energy of the later increases and results in a rise of its temperature. Heat travelling by radiation is known as *radiant heat.*

The properties of radiant heat in general, are similar to those of light. Some of the properties are :

(*i*)   It does not require the presence of a material medium for its transmission.

(*ii*)   Radiant heat can be reflected from the surfaces and obeys the ordinary laws of reflection.

(*iii*)   It travels with velocity of light.

(*iv*)   Like light, it shows intereference, diffraction and polarisation etc.

(*v*)   It follows the law of inverse square.

The wavelength of heat radiations is longer than that of light waves, hence they are invisible to the eye.

1.2. HEAT TRANSFER BY CONDUCTION

1.2.1. FOURIER'S LAWS OF HEAT CONDUCTION

Fourier's law of heat conduction is an emperical law based on observation and states as follows :

"*The rate of flow of heat through a simple homogeneous solid is directly proportional to the area of the section at right angles to the direction of heat flow, and to change of temperature with respect to the length of the path of the heat flow*".

Mathematically, it can be represented by the equation :

$$Q \propto A . \frac{dt}{dx}$$

where, Q = Heat flow through a body per unit time (in watts), W,

A = Surface area of heat flow (*perpendeneous to the direction of flow*), m^2,

dt = Temperature difference of the faces of block (homogeneous solid) of thickness 'dx' through which heat flows, °C or K, and

dx = Thickness of body in the direction of flow, m.

Thus, $$Q = - k . A \frac{dt}{dx}$$ ...(1.1)

where, k = Constant of proportionality and is known as *thermal conductivity of the body*.

The – ve sign of k [eqn. (1.1)] is to take care of the decreasing temperature alongwith the direction of increasing thickness or the direction of heat flow. The temperature gradient $\frac{dt}{dx}$ is *always negative along positive x direction and, therefore, the value as Q becomes* + ve.

Assumptions :

The following are the assumptions on which Fourier's law is based :

1.   Conduction of heat takes place under *steady state conditions*.

2.   The heat flow is unidirectional.

3.   The temperatures gradient is *constant* and the temperature profile is *linear*.

4.   There is no internal heat generation.

5.   The bounding surfaces are isothermal in character.

6.   The material is homogeneous and isotropic (*i.e.*, the value of thermal conductivity is *constant in all directions*).

Some essential features of Fourier's law :

Following are some essential features of Fourier's law :

1.   It is applicable to all matter (may be solid, liquid or gas).

2.   It is based on experimental evidence and cannot be derived from first principle.

3. It is a vector expression indicating that heat flow rate is in the direction of decreasing temperature and is normal to an isotherm.

4. It helps to define thermal conductivity 'k' (transport property) of the medium through which heat is conducted.

1.2.2. THERMAL CONDUCTIVITY OF MATERIALS

From eqn. (1.1), we have

$$k = \frac{Q}{A} \cdot \frac{dx}{dt}$$

The value of $k = 1$ when $Q = 1$, $A = 1$ and $\dfrac{dt}{dx} = 1$

Now $k = \dfrac{Q}{1} \cdot \dfrac{dx}{dt}$ (unit of k : $W \times \dfrac{1}{m^2} \times \dfrac{m}{K\,(or\,°C)} = W/mK$. or $W/m°C$)

Thus, the **thermal conductivity** *of a material is defined as follows* :

"The amount of energy conducted through a body of unit area, and unit thickness in unit time when the difference in temperature between the faces causing heat flow is unit temperature difference".

It follows from eqn. (1.1) that materials with high thermal conductivities are good conductors of heat, whereas materials with low thermal conductivities are good thermal insulator. *Conduction of heat occurs most readily in pure metals, less so in alloys, and much less readily in non-metals.* The very low thermal conductivities of certain thermal insulators *e.g.*, cork is due to their porosity, the air trapped within the material acting as an insulator.

Thermal conductivity (a property of material) depends essentially upon the following *factors* :

    (*i*) Material structure   (*ii*) Moisture content

    (*ii*) Density of the material   (*iv*) Pressure and temperature (operating conditions).

Thermal conductivities (average values at normal pressure and temperature) of some common materials are as under :

Material	Thermal conductivity (k) (W/mK)	Material	Thermal conductivity (k) (W/mK)
1. Silver	410	8. Asbestos sheet	0.17
2. Copper	385	9. Ash	0.12
3. Aluminium	225	10. Cork, felt	0.05 – 0.10
4. Cast iron	55–65	11. Saw dust	0.07
5. Steel	20–45	12. Glass wool	0.03
6. Concrete	1.20	13. Water	0.55 – 0.7
7. Glass (window)	0.75	14. Freon	0.0083

Following points *regarding thermal conductivity – its variation for different materials and under different conditions are worth noting* :

1. Thermal conductivity of a material is due to flow of free electrons (in case of *metals*) and lattice vibrational waves (in case of *fluids*).

2. Thermal conductivity in case of *pure metals* is the highest ($k = 10$ to 400 W/m°C). It decreases with increase in impurity.

The range of k for other materials is as follows :

$$\text{Alloys : } k = 12 \text{ to } 120 \text{ W/m °C}$$
$$\text{Heat insulating and building materials : } k = 0.023 \text{ to } 2.9 \text{ W/m°C}$$
$$\text{Liquids : } k = 0.2 \text{ to } 0.5 \text{ W/m°C}$$
$$\text{Gases and vapours : } k = 0.006 \text{ to } 0.05 \text{ W/m°C}$$

3. Thermal conductivity of a metal varies considerably when it (metal) is heat treated or mechanically processed / formed.

4. Thermal conductivity of *most metals decreases with the increase in temperature (aluminium and uranium being the exceptions)*.

   – In most of *liquids* the value of thermal conductivity tends to decrease with temperature (water being an exception) due to decrease in density with increase in temperature.

   – In case of gases the value of thermal conductivity *increases with temperature*.

   Gases with higher molecular weights have smaller thermal conductivities than with lower molecular weights. This is because the mean molecular path of gas molecules decreases with increase in density and k is directly proportional to the mean free path of the molecule.

5. The dependence of thermal conductivity (k) on temperature, for most materials is almost linear;

   $$k = k_0 (1 + \beta t) \qquad \qquad ...(1.2)$$

   where, k_0 = Thermal conductivity at 0°C, and

   β = Temperature coefficient of thermal conductivity, 1/°C (It is usually *posi- tive for non-metals and insulating materials* (magnesite bricks being the exception) and *negative for metallic conductors* (aluminium and certain non-ferrous alloys are the exceptions).

6. In case of solids and liquids, thermal conductivity (k) is only very weakly dependent on pressure; in case of gases the value of k is independent of pressure (near standard atmospheric).

7. In case of non-metallic solids :

   – Thermal conductivity of porous materials depends upon the type of gas or liquid present in the voids.

   – Thermal conductivity of a damp material is considerably higher than that of the dry material and water taken individually.

   – Thermal conductivity increases with increase in density.

8. The Wiedemann and Franz law (based on experiment results), regarding thermal and electrical conductivities of a material, states as follows :

   "The ratio of the thermal and electrical conductivi-

Diesel engine is an Internal Combustion (IC) engine where fuel burns inside the cylinder.

ties is the same for all metals at the same temperature; and that the ratio is directly proportional to the absolute temperature of the metal."

Mathematically, $\qquad \dfrac{k}{\sigma} \propto T$

or, $\qquad \dfrac{k}{\sigma T} = C \qquad\qquad\qquad\qquad\qquad\qquad\qquad$ ...(1.3)

where, $\quad k$ = Thermal conductivity of metal at temperature T(K),

$\qquad\quad \sigma$ = Electrical conductivity of metal at temperature T (K), and

$\qquad\quad C$ = Constant (for all metals), referred to as Lorenz number

$\qquad\qquad$ (= 2.45×10^{-8} WΩ/K^2; Ω stands for ohms).

This law conveys that the materials which are *good conductors of electrticity are also good conductors of heat.*

1.2.3. THERMAL RESITANCE (R_{th})

When two physical systems are described by similar equations and have similar boundary conditions, these are said to be *analogous*. The heat transfer processes may be compared by *analogy* with the flow of electricity in an electrical resistance. As the flow of electric current in the electrical resistance is directly proportional to potential difference (dV); similarly heat flow rate, Q, is directly proportional to temperature difference (dt), the driving force for heat conduction through a medium.

As per Ohm's law (in elctric-circuit theory), we have

$$\text{Current } (I) = \frac{\text{Potential difference } (dV)}{\text{Electrical resistance } (R)} \qquad\qquad ...(1.4)$$

By analogy, the heat flow equation (Fourier's equation) may be written as

$$\text{Heat flow rate } (Q) = \frac{\text{Temperature difference } (dt)}{\left(\dfrac{dx}{kA}\right)} \qquad\qquad ...(1.5)$$

By comparing eqns. (1.4) and (1.5), we find that I is analogous to, Q, dV is analogous to dt and R is analogous to the quantity $\left(\dfrac{dx}{kA}\right)$. The quantity $\dfrac{dx}{kA}$ is called **thermal conduction resistance** (R_{th})$_{\text{cond.}}$ *i.e.,*

$$(R_{th})_{\text{cond.}} = \frac{dx}{kA}$$

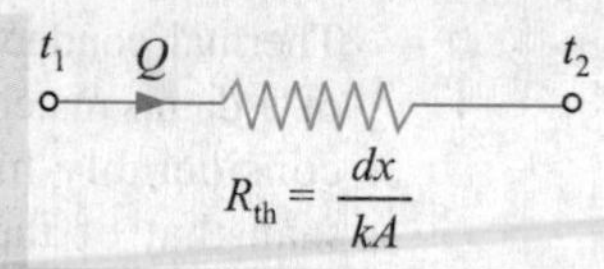

$$R_{th} = \frac{dx}{kA}$$

Fig. 1.7.

- The reciprocal of the thermal resistance is called *thermal conductance*.

- It may be noted that *rules for combining electrical resistances in series and parallel apply equally well to thermal resistances.*

The concept of thermal resistance is quite helpful while making calculations for flow of heat.

Example 1.1. *Calculate the rate of heat transfer per unit area through a copper plate 45 mm thick, whose one face is maintained at 350°C and the other face at 50°C. Take thermal conductivity of copper as 370 W/m°C.*

Solution. Temperature difference, dt (= $t_2 - t_1$) = (50 – 350)

$\qquad\qquad$ Thickness of copper plate, L = 45 mm = 0.045 m

$\qquad\qquad$ Thermal conductivity of copper, k = 370 W/m°C

Rate of heat-transfer per unit area, q :

From Fourier's law

$$Q = -kA\frac{dt}{dx} = -kA\frac{(t_2 - t_1)}{L}$$

...(Eqn. 1.1)

or,

$$q = \frac{Q}{A} = -k\frac{dt}{dx}$$

$$= -370 \times \frac{(50 - 350)}{0.045}$$

$$= 2.466 \times 10^6 \text{ W/m}^2 \text{ or}$$

2.466 MW/m² (Ans.)

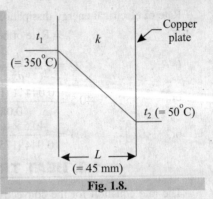

Fig. 1.8.

Example 1.2. *A plane wall is 150 mm thick and its wall area is 4.5 m². If its conductivity is 9.35 W/m°C and surface temperatures are steady at 150°C and 45°C, determine :*

(*i*) *Heat flow across the plane wall;*

(*ii*) *Temperature gradient in the flow direction.*

Solution. Thickness of the plane wall,

$$L = 150 \text{ mm}$$
$$= 0.15 \text{ m}$$

Area of the wall, $A = 4.5 \text{ m}^2$

Temperature difference, $dt = t_2 - t_1 = 45 - 150 = -105°C$

Thermal conductivity of wall material,

$$k = 9.35 \text{ W/m°C}$$

(*i*) **Heat flow across the plane wall, Q :**

As per Fourier's law,

$$Q = -kA\frac{dt}{dx} = -kA\frac{(t_2 - t_1)}{L}$$

$$= -9.35 \times 4.5 \times \frac{(-105)}{0.15} = \textbf{29452.5 W}$$

(*ii*) **Temperature gradient, $\frac{dt}{dx}$:**

From Fourier's law, we have

$$\frac{dt}{dx} = -\frac{Q}{kA} = \frac{29452.5}{9.35 \times 4.5} = \textbf{- 700°C/m}$$

Example 1.3. *The following data relate to an oven :*

Thickness of side wall of the oven $= 82.5$ mm

Thermal conductivity of wall insulation $= 0.044$ W/m°C

Temperature on inside of the wall $= 175°C$

Energy dissipated by the electrical coil

within the oven $= 40.5$ W

Determine the area of wall surface, perpendicular to heat flow, so that temperature on the other side of the wall does not exceed 75°C.

Solution. *Given* : $x = 82.5 \text{ mm} = 0.0825 \text{ m}$; $k = 0.044 \text{ W/m°C}$; $t_1 = 175°C$; $t_2 = 75°C$; $Q = 40.5\text{W}$

Area of the wall surface, A :

Assuming one-dimentional steady state heat conduction,

Rate of electrical energy dissipation in the oven.

= Rate of heat transfer (conduction) across the wall

i.e.

$$Q = -\, kA \frac{dt}{dx} = -\, kA \frac{(t_2 - t_1)}{x} = \frac{kA\,(t_1 - t_2)}{x}$$

or,

$$40.5 = \frac{0.044\ A\ (175 - 75)}{0.0825}$$

or,

$$A = \frac{40.5 \times 0.0825}{0.044\ (175 - 75)} = \textbf{0.759 m}^2$$

1.3. HEAT TRANSFER BY CONVECTION

The rate equation for the convective heat transfer (regardless of particular nature) between a surface and an adjacent fluid is prescribed by *Newton's law of cooling (Refer Fig. 1.9)*

$$Q = hA\,(t_s - t_f) \qquad\qquad ...(1.6)$$

where,

Q = Rate of conductive heat transfer,

A = Area exposed to heat transfer,

t_s = Surface temperature,

t_f = Fluid temperature, and

h = Co-efficient of conductive heat transfer.

The units of h are,

$$h = \frac{Q}{A\,(t_s - t_f)} = \frac{W}{m^2\,°C} \quad \text{or} \quad W/m^2\,°C$$

or, $W/m^2 K$

The coefficient of convective heat transfer 'h' (also known as *film heat transfer coefficient*) may be defined as *"the amount of heat transmitted for a unit temperature difference between the fluid and unit area of surface in unit time."*

The value of 'h' depends on the following factors :

(*i*) Thermodynamic and transport properties (*e.g.* viscosity, density, specific heat etc.).

(*ii*) Nature of fluid flow.

(*iii*) Geometry of the surface.

(*iv*) Prevailing thermal conditions.

Since 'h' depends upon several factors, it is difficult to frame a single equation to satisfy all the variations, however, by dimensional analysis an equation for the purpose can be obtained.

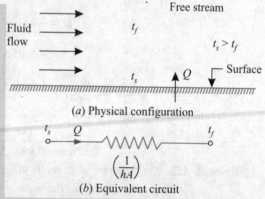

(*a*) Physical configuration

(*b*) Equivalent circuit

Fig. 1.9. Convective heat-transfer

The *mechanisms of convection* in which phase changes are involved lead to the important *fields of boiling and condensation*. Refer Fig. 1.9 (*b*). The quantity $\dfrac{1}{hA} \left[Q = \dfrac{t_s - t_f}{(1/\,hA)} \; ...\text{Eqn (1.6)} \right]$ is called **convection thermal resistance** [$(R_{th})_{conv}$.] to heat flow.

Example 1.4. *A hot plate 1m × 1.5 m is maintained at 300°C. Air at 20°C blows over the plate. If the convective heat transfer coefficient is 20W/m²°C, calculate the rate of heat transfer.*

Solution. Area of the plate exposed to heat transfer, $A = 1 \times 1.5 = 1.5$ m^2

Plate surface temperature, $t_s = 300°C$

Temperature of air (fluid), $t_f = 20°C$

Connvective heat-transfer coefficient, $h = 20$ W/m^2 °C

Rate of heat transfer, Q :

From Newton's law of cooling,

$$Q = hA\,(t_s - t_f)$$
$$= 20 \times 1.5\,(300 - 20) = 8400 \text{ W or } \mathbf{8.4 \text{ kW}}$$

Example 1.5. *A wire 1.5 mm in diameter and 150 mm long is submerged in water at atmospheric pressure. An electric current is passed through the wire and is increased until the water boils at 100°C. Under the condition if convective heat transfer coefficient is 4500 W/m^2°C find how much electric power must be supplied to the wire to maintain the wire surface at 120°C ?*

Solution. Diameter of the wire, $d = 1.5$ mm $= 0.0015$ m

Length of the wire, $L = 150$ mm $= 0.15$ m

∴ Surface area of the wire (exposed to heat transfer),

$A = \pi\,d\,L = \pi \times 0.0015 \times 0.15 = 7.068 \times 10^{-4}$ m^2

Wire surface temperature, $t_s = 120°C$

Water temperature, $t_f = 100°C$

Convective heat transfer coefficient, $h = 4500$ W/m^2 °C

Electric power to be supplied :

Electric power which must be supplied = Total convection loss (Q)

∴ $Q = hA\,(t_s - t_f) = 4500 \times 7.068 \times 10^{-4}\,(120 - 100) = \mathbf{63.6 \text{ W}}$

1.4. HEAT TRANFER BY RADIATION

Laws of Radiation :

1. **Wien's law.** It states that *the wavelength λ_m corresponding to the maximum energy is inversely proportional to the absolute temperature T of the hot body.*

    i.e., $\lambda_m \propto \dfrac{1}{T}$ or, $\lambda_m T = $ constant   ...(1.7)

2. **Kirchhoff's law.** It states that the *emissivity of the body at a particular temperature is numerically equal to its absorptivity for radiant energy from body at the same temperature.*

3. **The Stefan-Boltzmann law.** The law states that *the emissive power of a black body is directly proportional to fourth power of its absolute temperature.*

    i.e., $Q \propto T^4$ ...(1.8)

    Refer Fig. 1.10 (a)

    $Q = F\sigma A\,(T_1^4 - T_2^4)$ ...(1.9)

    where, $F = $ A factor depending on geom-
    etry and surface properties,

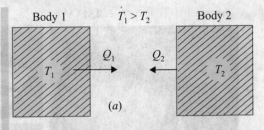

$T_1 > T_2$

Body 1   Body 2

Q_1 Q_2

T_1 T_2

(a)

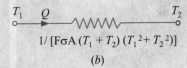

T_1 Q T_2

$1/\,[F\sigma A\,(T_1 + T_2)\,(T_1{}^2 + T_2{}^2)]$

(b)

Fig. 1.10. Heat transfer by radiation.

σ = Stefan-Boltzmann constant

$= 5.67 \times 10^{-8}$ W/m²K⁴,

A = Area, m², and

T_1, T_2 = Temperatures, degrees kelvin (K).

This equation can also be rewritten as :

$$Q = \frac{T_1 - T_2}{1/[F \sigma A (T_1 + T_2) (T_1^2 + T_2^2)]}$$ ...(1.10)

where denominator is **radiation thermal resistance**, $(R_{th})_{rad}$. [Fig. 1.10 (b)]

i.e., $(R_{th})_{rad} = 1/[F \sigma A (T_1 + T_2) (T_1^2 + T_2^2)]$

The values of F are available for simple configurations in the form of charts and tables.

$F = 1$ ... for simple cases of black surface enclosed by other surface

F = emissivity (ε) ... for non-black surface enclosed by other surface.

[*Emissivity* (ε) is defined as the ratio of heat radiated by a surface to that of an ideal surface.]

Example 1.6. *A surface having an area of 1.5 m^2 and maintained at 300°C exchanges heat by radiation with another surface at 40°C. The value of factor due to the geometric location and emissivity is 0.52. Determine :*

(i) *Heat lost by radiation,*

(ii) *The value of thermal resistance, and*

(iii) *The value of equivalent convection coefficient.*

Solution. *Given :* $A = 1.5$ m²; $T_1 = t_1 + 273 = 300 + 273 = 573$K; $T_2 = t_2 + 273 = 40 + 273 = 313$K; $F = 0.52$.

(*i*) **Heat lost by radiation, Q :**

$$Q = F \sigma A (T_1^4 - T_2^4)$$ ...[Eqn. (1.9)]

(where $\sigma = 5.67 \times 10^{-8}$ W/m² K⁴)

or, $Q = 0.52 \times 5.67 \times 10^{-8} \times 1.5 [(573)^4 - (313)^4]$

$$= 0.52 \times 5.67 \times 1.5 \left[\left(\frac{573}{100} \right)^4 - \left(\frac{313}{100} \right)^4 \right]$$

(Please note this step)

or, $Q = \mathbf{4343}$ **W**

These appliances are used to radiate heat in the winter.

(ii) **The value of thermal resistance, (Rth)rad :**

We know that,
$$Q = \frac{(T_1 - T_2)}{(R_{th})_{rad}} \qquad \text{...[Eqn. (1.10)]}$$

∴
$$(R_{th})_{rad.} = \frac{(T_1 - T_2)}{Q} = \frac{(573 - 313)}{4343} = \textbf{0.0598 °C/W}$$

(iii) **The value of equivalent convection coefficient, hr :**
$$Q = h_r A (t_1 - t_2)$$

or,
$$h_r = \frac{Q}{A(t_1 - t_2)} = \frac{4343}{1.5(300 - 40)} = \textbf{11.13 W/m}^2\,\textbf{°C}$$

$$
\left[
\begin{array}{l}
\text{Alternatively,} \qquad h_r = F\sigma(T_1 + T_2)(T_1^2 + T_2^2) \qquad \text{...From eqn. (1.10)} \\[6pt]
\qquad\qquad = 0.52 \times 5.67 \times 10^{-8}(573 + 313)(573^2 + 313^2) \\[6pt]
\qquad\qquad = \textbf{11.13 W/m}^2\,\textbf{°C}
\end{array}
\right.
$$

Example 1.7. *A carbon steel plate (thermal conductivity = 45 W/m°C) 600 mm × 900 mm × 25 mm is maintained at 310°C. Air at 15°C blows over the hot plate. If convection heat transfer coefficient is 22 W/m² °C and 250 W is lost from the plate surface by radiation, calculate the inside plate temperature.*

Solution.   Area of the plate exposed to heat transfer,
$$A = 600 \text{ mm} \times 900 \text{ mm} = 0.6 \times 0.9 = 0.54 \text{ m}^2$$

Thickness of the plate, $L = 25 \text{ mm} = 0.025 \text{ m}$

Surface temperature of the plate, $t_s = 310°C$

Temperature of air (fluid), $t_f = 15°C$

Convective heat transfer coefficient,
$$h = 22 \text{ W/m}^2\text{°C}$$

Heat lost from the plate surface by radiation,
$$Q_{rad.} = 250 \text{W}$$

Thermal conductivity, $k = 45 \text{ W/m °C}$

Inside plate temperature, t_i :

In this case the heat conducted through the plate is removed from the plate surface by a *combination of convection and radiation.*

Heat conducted through the plate = Convection heat losses + radiation heat losses.

or,
$$Q_{cond.} = Q_{conv.} + Q_{rad.}$$

$$-kA\frac{dt}{dx} = hA(t_s - t_f) + F\sigma A(T_s^4 - T_f^4)$$

or,
$$-45 \times 0.54 \times \frac{(t_s - t_i)}{L} = 22 \times 0.54(310 - 15) + 250 \text{ (given)}$$

or,
$$-45 \times 0.54 \times \frac{(310 - t_i)}{0.025} = 22 \times 0.54 \times 295 + 250$$

or,
$$972(t_i - 310) = 3754.6$$

or,
$$t_i = \frac{3754.6}{972} + 310 = \textbf{313.86°C}$$

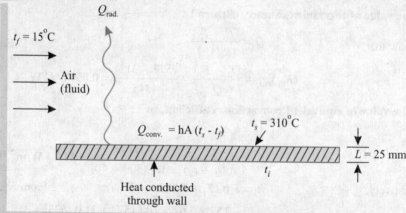

Fig. 1.11. Combination of conduction, convection and radiation heat transfer.

Example 1.8. *A surface at 250°C exposed to the surroundings at 110°C convects and radiates heat to the surroundings. The convection coefficient and radiation factor are 75W/m²°C and unity respectively. If the heat is conducted to the surface through a solid of conductivity 10W/m°C, what is the temperature gradient at the surface in the solid ?*

Solution. Temperature of the surface, t_s = 250°C

Temperature of the surroundings, t_{sur} = 110°C

The convection co-efficient, h = 5W/m²°C

Radiation factor, F = 1

Boltzmann constant, σ = 5.67 × 10⁻⁸ W/m²K⁴

Conductivity of the solid, k = 10W/m°C

Temperature gradient, $\dfrac{dt}{dx}$:

Heat conducted through the plate = Convection heat losses + radiation heat losses

i.e., $Q_{cond.} = Q_{conv.} + Q_{rad.}$ $- kA \dfrac{dt}{dx} = hA (t_s - t_{sur}) + F\sigma A (T_s^4 - T_{sur}^4)$

Substituting the values, we have

$$- 10 \times \frac{dt}{dx} = 75 (250 - 110) + 1 \times 5.67 \times 10^{-8} [(250 + 273)^4 - (110 + 273)^4]$$

$$- 10 \times \frac{dt}{dx} = 10500 + 5.67 \left[\left(\frac{523}{100} \right)^4 - \left(\frac{383}{100} \right)^4 \right]$$

$$= 10500 + 3022.1 = 13522.1$$

∴ $\dfrac{dt}{dx} = - \dfrac{13522.1}{10} = $ **– 1352.21 °C/m**

HIGHLIGHTS

1. The energy in transit is termed *heat.*

2. *Heat transfer may be defined as "The transmission of energy from one region to another as a result of temperature gradient."*

3. The study of heat transfer is carried out for the following *purposes* :

    (*i*) To estimate the rate of flow of energy as heat through the boundary of a system under study (both steady and transient conditions).

    (*ii*) To determine the temperature field under steady and transient conditions.

4. *Thermodynamics* is an axiomatic science which deals with the relations among heat, work and properties of system which are in *equilibrium*. It describes state and changes in state of physical systems. It basically entails four laws or axioms known as Zeroth, First, Second and third law of thermodynamics.

5. Heat transfer theory combines thermodynamics and rate equations together (to quantify the rate at which heat transfer occurs in terms of the degree of non-equilibrium).

6. Basic laws which govern the heat transfer are :

   (*i*)   First laws of thermodynamics   (*ii*)   Second law of thermodynamics
   (*iii*) Law of conservation of mass   (*iv*)   Newton's laws of motion
   (*v*)   The rate equations.

7. Heat transfer takes place by the following three modes :

   (*i*)   Conduction   (*ii*)   Convection   (*iii*)   Radiation.

   'Conduction' is the transfer of heat from one part of a substance to another part of the same substance, or from one substance to another in physical contact with it, without appreciable displacement of molecules forming the substance.

   'Convection' is the transfer of heat within a fluid by mixing of one portion of the fluid with another. Convection is possible only in a fluid medium and is directly linked with the transport of medium itself.

   'Radiation' is the transfer of heat through space or matter by means other than conduction or convection. Radiant energy (being electromagnetic radiation) requires no medium for propagation and will pass through a vaccum.

8. *Fourier's law of heat conduction states* : "The rate of flow of heat through a single homogeneous solid is directly proportional to the area of the section at right angles to the direction of heat flow, and to change of temperature with respect to the length of path of the heat flow".

   Mathematically,
   $$Q = -kA\frac{dt}{dx}$$

   where,
   Q = Heat flow through a body per unit time, W,

   A = Surface area of heat flow (perpendicular to the direction of flow), m²,

   dt = Temperature difference of the faces of the block,

   dx = Thickness of the body, and

   k = Thermal conductivity of the body.

   The –ve sign of k is to take care of the decreasing temperature along with the direction of increasing thickness or the direction of heat flow.

9. The *thermal conductivity* (k) of a material is defined as : "The amount of energy conducted through a body of unit area, and unit thickness in unit time when the difference in temperature between the faces causing heat flow is unit temperature difference."

10. The rate equation for the convective heat transfer (regardless of particular nature) between a surface and an adjacent fluid is prescribed Newton's law of cooling :

    $$Q = hA\,(t_s - t_f)$$

    where,
    Q = Rate of convective heat transfer,

    A = Area exposed to heat transfer,

    t_s = Surface temperature,

    t_f = Fluid temperature, and

    h = Coefficient of convective heat transfer.

    Units of h : W/m²°C or W/m²K

11. The *Stefan-Boltzmann law states* : "The emissive power of a black body is directly proportional to fourth power of its absolute temperature."

12. *Thermal resistance* (R_{th}) :

Conduction thermal resistance, $(R_{th})_{cond.} = \dfrac{dx}{kA}$

Convection thermal resistance, $(R_{th})_{conv.} = \dfrac{1}{hA}$

Radiation thermal resistance, $(R_{th})_{rad.} = \dfrac{1}{1/[F\,\sigma\,A\,(T_1 + T_2)\,(T_1^2 + T_2^2)]}$

THEORETICAL QUESTIONS

1. Define the following terms :
    (i) Heat   (ii) Heat transfer   (iii) Thermodynamics.
2. What is the difference between thermodynamics and heat transfer ?
3. Enumerate the basic laws which govern the heat transfer.
4. Name and explain briefly the various modes of heat transfer.
5. What is conduction heat transfer ? How does it differ from convective heat transfer ?
6. What is the significance of heat transfer ?
7. Enumerate some important areas which are covered under the discipline of heat transfer.
8. What is the difference between the 'natural' and 'forced' convection ?
9. What is 'Fourier's law of conduction'? State also the assumptions on which this law is based.
10. State some essential features of Fourier's law.
11. How is thermal conductivity of a material defined ? What are its units ?
12. What is thermal resistance ?
13. What is 'Newton's law of cooling ?
14. What is Stefan's Boltzmann law ?

UNSOLVED EXAMPLES

1. The inner surface of a plane brick wall is at 40°C and the outer surface is at 20°C. Calculate the rate of heat transfer per m² of surface area of the wall, which is 250 mm thick. The thermal conductivity of the brick is 0.52 W/m°C.   (**Ans.** 41.6 W/m²)
2. A plane wall (thermal conductivity = 10.2 W/m°C) of 100 mm thickness and area 3m² has steady surface temperature of 170°C and 100°C. Determine :
    (i) The rate of heat flow across the plane wall;
    (ii) The temperature gradient in the flow direction.   [**Ans.** (i) 21.42 kW; (ii) – 700°C/m]
3. Determine the heat transfer by convection over a surface of 0.75 m² if the surface is at 200°C and the fluid is at 80°C. The value of convective heat transfer is 25 W/m² °C.   [**Ans.** 2.25 kW]
4. A surface of area 3m² and at 200°C exchanges heat with another surface at 30°C by radiation. If the value of factor due to the geometric location and emissivity is 0.69, determine :
    (i) The rate of heat transfer,
    (ii) The value of thermal resistance, and
    (iii) The equivalent convection coefficient. [**Ans.** (i) 4885.6W; (ii) 0.0348 °C/W; (iii) 9.58 W/m² °C]
5. A surface at 200°C exposed to the surroundings at 60°C convects and radiates heat to the surroundings. The convection coefficient and radiation factor are 80W/m² °C and unity respectively. If the heat is conducted to the surface through a solid of conductivity 15W/m °C what is the temperature gradient at the surface ?   (**Ans.** – 889.4 °C/m)

PART I

HEAT TRANSFER
BY CONDUCTION

Heat conduction with internal heat generation.

Conduction–Steady–State One Dimension

2

2.1. INTRODUCTION

In this chapter an attempt will be made to derive general heat conduction equation and examine the applications of Fourier's law of heat conduction to the calculation of heat flow in some simple one-dimensional systems. Under the category of one-dimensional systems several different physical shapes may fall; *when the temperature of the body is a function only of radial distance and is independent of azimuth angle or axial distance cylindrical and spherical systems are treated as one-dimensional.* In case of problems of two-dimensional nature the effect of a second-space coordinate may be so small that it may be neglected and the heat-flow problems of multi-dimensional type may be approximated with a one-dimensional analysis; in such cases the differential equations are simplified and as a consequence of this simplification much easier solution in available.

2.2. GENERAL HEAT CONDUCTION EQUATION IN CARTESIAN COORDINATES

Consider an infinitesimal rectangular parallelopiped (volume element) of sides dx, dy and dz parallel, respectively, to the three axes (X, Y, Z) in a medium in which temperature is varying with location and time as shown in Fig. 2.1.

Let, t = Temperature at the left face *ABCD*; this temperature may be assumed uniform over the entire surface, since the area of this face can be made arbitrarily *small*, and

$\dfrac{dt}{dx}$ = Temperature changes and rate of change along *X*-direction.

Then, $\left(\dfrac{\partial t}{\partial x}\right) dx$ = Change of temperature through distance dx, and

$t + \left(\dfrac{\partial t}{\partial x}\right) dx$ = emperature on the right face *EFGH* (at a distance dx from the left face *ABCD*).

Further, let, k_x, k_y, k_z = Thermal conductivities (direction characteristics of the material) along *X*, *Y* and *Z* axes.

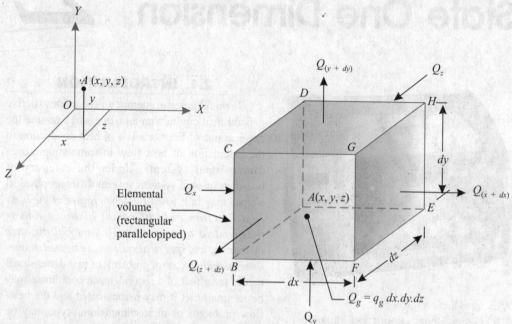

Fig. 2.1. Elemental volume for three-dimensional heat conduction analysis - Cartesian coordinates.

If the directional characterisitics of a material are equal/same, it is called an *"Isotropic material"* and if unequal/different *"Anisotropic material"*.

q_g = Heat generated per unit volume per unit time.

Inside the control volume there may be heat sources due to flow of electric current in electric motors and generators, nuclear fission etc.

(**Note :** q_g may be function of position or time, or both).

ρ = Mass density of material, and

c = Specific heat of the material.

Energy balance/equation for volume element :

Net heat accumulated in the element due to conduction of heat from all the coordinate directions considered (*A*) + heat generated within the element (*B*) = Energy stored in the element (*C*). ...(1)

Let, Q = Rate of heat flow in a direction, and

$Q' = (Q.d\tau)$ = Total heat flow (flux) in that direction (in time $d\tau$).

A. *Net heat accumulated in the element due to conduction of heat from all the directions considered*:

Quantity of heat flowing into the element from the left face *ABCD* during the time interval $d\tau$ in *X*-direction is given by :

Heat influx,
$$Q'_x = -k_x \, (dy.dz) \, \frac{\partial t}{\partial x} \cdot d\tau \qquad \qquad ...(i)$$

During the same time interval $d\tau$ the heat flowing out of the right face of control volume (*EFGH*) will be :

Heat efflux,
$$Q'_{(x+dx)} = Q'_x + \frac{\partial}{\partial x} \, (Q'_x) \, dx \qquad \qquad ...(ii)$$

∴   Heat accumulation in the element due to heat flow in *X*-direction,

$$dQ'_x = Q'_x - \left[Q'_x + \frac{\partial}{\partial x} \, (Q'_x) \, dx \right] \qquad \qquad \text{[Subtracting } (ii) \text{ from } (i)\text{]}$$

$$= -\frac{\partial}{\partial x} \, (Q'_x) \, dx$$

$$= -\frac{\partial}{\partial x} \left[-k_x \, (dy.dz) \, \frac{\partial t}{\partial x} \cdot d\tau \right] dx$$

$$= \frac{\partial}{\partial x} \left[-k_x \, \frac{\partial t}{\partial x} \right] dx.dy.dz.d\tau \qquad \qquad ...(2.1)$$

Similarly the heat accumulated due to heat flow by conduction along *Y* and *Z* directions in time $d\tau$ will be :

$$dQ'_y = \frac{\partial}{\partial y} \left[k_y \, \frac{\partial t}{\partial y} \right] dx.dy.dz.d\tau \qquad \qquad ...(2.2)$$

$$dQ'_z = \frac{\partial}{\partial z} \left[k_z \, \frac{\partial t}{\partial z} \right] dx.dy.dz.d\tau \qquad \qquad ...(2.3)$$

Boilers in a plant. A good boiler should efficiently take the heat from the fuel and minimise loss of heat from inside to outside.

∴ *Net heat accumulated* in the element due to conduction of heat from all the coordinate directions considered

$$= \frac{\partial}{\partial x}\left[k_x \frac{\partial t}{\partial x}\right] dx.dy.dz.d\tau + \frac{\partial}{\partial y}\left[k_y \frac{\partial t}{\partial y}\right] dx.dy.dz.d\tau + \frac{\partial}{\partial z}\left[k_z \frac{\partial t}{\partial z}\right] dx.dy.dz.d\tau$$

$$= \left[\frac{\partial}{\partial x}\left(k_x \frac{\partial t}{\partial x}\right) + \frac{\partial}{\partial y}\left(k_y \frac{\partial t}{\partial y}\right) + \frac{\partial}{\partial z}\left(k_z \frac{\partial t}{\partial z}\right)\right] dx.dy.dz.d\tau \qquad ...(2.4)$$

B. *Total heat generated within the element* (Q_g') :

The total heat generated in the element is given by

$$Q_g' = q_g\,(dx.dy.dz)\,d\tau \qquad ...(2.5)$$

C. *Energy stored in the element* :

The total heat accumulated in the element due to heat flow along coordinate axes (Eqn. 2.4) and the heat generated within the element (Eqn. 2.5) together serve to increase the thermal energy of the element/lattice. This increase in thermal energy is given by

$$\rho\,(dx.dy.dz)\,c.\frac{\partial t}{\partial \tau}.\,d\tau \qquad ...(2.6)$$

[∵   Heat stored in the body = Mass of the body × specific heat of the body material × rise in the temperature of body].

Now, substituting eqns. (2.4), (2.5), (2.6), in the eqn. (1), we have

$$\left[\frac{\partial}{\partial x}\left(k_x \frac{\partial t}{\partial x}\right) + \frac{\partial}{\partial y}\left(k_y \frac{\partial t}{\partial y}\right) + \frac{\partial}{\partial z}\left(k_z \frac{\partial t}{\partial z}\right)\right] dx.dy.dz.d\tau + q_g\,(dx.dy.dz.)d\tau = \rho\,(dx.dy.dz)\,c.\frac{\partial t}{\partial \tau}.\,d\tau$$

Dividing both sides by $dx.dy.dz.d\tau$, we have

$$\frac{\partial}{\partial x}\left(k_x \frac{\partial t}{\partial x}\right) + \frac{\partial}{\partial y}\left(k_y \frac{\partial t}{\partial y}\right) + \frac{\partial}{\partial z}\left(k_z \frac{\partial t}{\partial z}\right) + q_g = \rho.c.\frac{\partial t}{\partial \tau} \qquad ...(2.7)$$

or, using the vector operator ∇, we get

$$\nabla .(k\nabla t) + q_g = \rho.c.\frac{\partial t}{\partial \tau} \qquad ...[2.7\,(a)]$$

This is known as the **general heat conduction equation** for **'non-homogeneous material'**, **'self heat generating'** and **'unsteady three-dimensional heat flow'**. This equation establishes in *differential form the relationship between the time and space variation of temperature at any point of solid through which heat flow by conduction takes place.*

General heat conduction equation for constant thermal conductivity :

In case of homogeneous (in which properties *e.g.*, specific heat, density, thermal conductivity etc. are same everywhere in the material) and isotropic (in which properties are independent of surface orientation) material, $k_x = k_y = k_z = k$ and diffusion equation Eqn. (2.7) becomes

$$\frac{\partial^2 t}{\partial x^2} + \frac{\partial^2 t}{\partial y^2} + \frac{\partial^2 t}{\partial z^2} + \frac{q_g}{k} = \frac{\rho.c}{k}\cdot\frac{\partial t}{\partial \tau} = \frac{1}{\alpha}\cdot\frac{\partial t}{\partial \tau} \qquad ...(2.8)$$

where,
$$\alpha = \frac{k}{\rho.c} = \frac{\text{Thermal conductivity}}{\text{Thermal capacity}}$$

The quantity,
$$\alpha = \frac{k}{\rho.c}$$ is known as **thermal diffusivity**.

–   The larger the value of α, the faster will the heat diffuse through the material and its temperature will change with time. This will result either due to a high value of thermal conductivity k or a low value of heat capacity $\rho.c$. A low value of heat capacity means the less amount of heat entering the element, would be absorbed and used to raise its temperature and more would be available for onward transmission. Metals and gases have relatively high value of α and their response to temperature changes is quite rapid. The non-metallic solids and liquids respond slowly to temperature changes because of their relatively small value of thermal diffusivity.

– Thermal diffusivity is an important characteristic quantity for *unsteady conduction situations*.

Eqn. (2.8) by using Laplacian ∇^2, may be written as :

$$\nabla^2 t + \frac{q_g}{k} = \frac{1}{\alpha} \cdot \frac{\partial t}{\partial \tau} \qquad \qquad ...[2.8\ (a)]$$

Eqn. (2.8), governs the temperature distribution under unsteady heat flow through a material which is homogeneous and isotropic.

Other simplified forms of heat conduction equation in cartesian coordinates :

(i) For the case when *no internal source of heat generation is present*, Eqn. (2.8) reduces to

$$\frac{\partial^2 t}{\partial x^2} + \frac{\partial^2 t}{\partial y^2} + \frac{\partial^2 t}{\partial z^2} = \frac{1}{\alpha} \cdot \frac{\partial t}{\partial \tau} \quad \text{[Unsteady state} \left(\frac{\partial t}{\partial \tau} \neq 0 \right) \text{ heat flow with no}$$

internal heat generation]

or, $$\nabla^2 t = \frac{1}{\alpha} \cdot \frac{\partial t}{\partial \tau} \quad \textbf{(Fourier's equation)} \qquad\qquad ...(2.9)$$

(ii) Under the situations when temperature does not depend on time, the conduction then takes place in the steady state $\left(i.e., \dfrac{\partial t}{\partial \tau} = 0 \right)$ and the eqn. (2.8) reduces to

$$\frac{\partial^2 t}{\partial x^2} + \frac{\partial^2 t}{\partial y^2} + \frac{\partial^2 t}{\partial z^2} + \frac{q_g}{k} = 0$$

or, $$\nabla^2 t + \frac{q_g}{k} = 0 \quad \textbf{(Poisson's equation)} \qquad\qquad ...(2.10)$$

In the absence of internal heat generation, Eqn. (2.10) reduces to

$$\frac{\partial^2 t}{\partial x^2} + \frac{\partial^2 t}{\partial y^2} + \frac{\partial^2 t}{\partial z^2} = 0$$

or, $$\nabla^2 t = 0 \quad \textbf{(Laplace equation)} \qquad\qquad ...(2.11)$$

(iii) *Steady state and one-dimensional heat transfer:*

$$\frac{\partial^2 t}{\partial x^2} + \frac{q_g}{k} = 0 \qquad\qquad ...(2.12)$$

(iv) *Steady state, one-dimensional, without internal heat generation*

$$\frac{\partial^2 t}{\partial x^2} = 0 \qquad\qquad ...(2.13)$$

(v) *Steady state, two dimensional, without internal heat generation*

$$\frac{\partial^2 t}{\partial x^2} + \frac{\partial^2 t}{\partial y^2} = 0 \qquad\qquad ...(2.14)$$

(vi) *Unsteady state, one dimensional, without internal heat generation*

$$\frac{\partial^2 t}{\partial x^2} = \frac{1}{\alpha} \cdot \frac{\partial t}{\partial \tau} \qquad\qquad ...(2.15)$$

2.3. GENERAL HEAT CONDUCTION EQUATION IN CYLINDRICAL COORDINATES

While dealing with problems of conduction of heat through systems having cylindrical geometries (*e.g.*, rods and pipes) it is convenient to use cylindrical coordinates.

Consider an elemental volume having the coordinates (r, ϕ, z), for three-dimensional heat conduction analysis, as shown in Fig. 2.2.

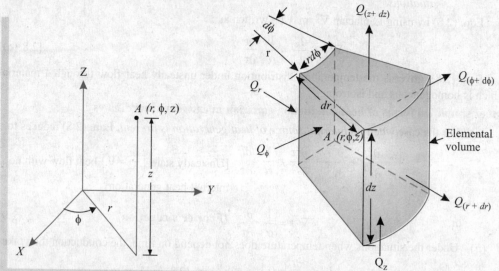

Fig. 2.2. Elemental volume for three-dimensional heat conduction analysis - Cylindrical coordinates.

The volume of the element $= rd\phi.dr.dz$

Let, q_g = Heat generation (uniform) per unit volume per unit time.

Further, let us assume that k (thermal conductivity), ρ (density), c (specific heat) do not alter with position.

A. *Net heat accumulated in the element due to conduction of heat from all the coordinate directions considered :*

Heat flow in radial direction $(x–\phi)$ plane :

Heat influx, $$Q'_r = -k\,(rd\phi.dz)\,\frac{\partial t}{\partial r}.d\tau \qquad\qquad ...(i)$$

Heat efflux, $$Q'_{(r+dr)} = Q'_r + \frac{\partial}{\partial r}\,(Q_r)\,dr \qquad\qquad ...(ii)$$

∴ Heat accumulation in the element due to heat flow in *radial direction,*

$$dQ'_r = Q'_r - Q'_{(r+dr)} \qquad\qquad \text{[subtracting (ii) from (i)]}$$

$$= -\frac{\partial}{\partial r}\,(Q'_r)\,dr$$

$$= -\frac{\partial}{\partial r}\left[-k\,(rd\phi.dz)\,\frac{\partial t}{\partial r}.d\tau\right]dr$$

$$= k\,(dr.d\phi.dz)\,\frac{\partial}{\partial r}\left(r\cdot\frac{\partial t}{\partial r}\right)d\tau$$

$$= k\,(dr.d\phi.dz)\left(r\,\frac{\partial^2 t}{\partial r^2} + \frac{\partial t}{\partial r}\right)d\tau$$

$$= k \ (dr.rd\phi.dz) \left[\frac{\partial^2 t}{\partial r^2} + \frac{1}{r} \frac{\partial t}{\partial r} \right] d\tau \qquad \text{...(2.16)}$$

Heat flow in *tangential direction (r–z) plane* :

Heat influx, $\qquad\qquad Q'_\phi = - k \ (dr.dz) \ \dfrac{\partial t}{r.\partial\phi} \ d\tau \qquad \text{...(iii)}$

Heat efflux, $\qquad Q'_{(\phi + d\phi)} = Q'_\phi + \dfrac{\partial}{r.\partial\phi} \ (Q'_\phi) \ rd\phi \qquad \text{...(iv)}$

Heat accumulated in the element due to heat flow in *tangential direction*,

$dQ'_\phi = Q'_\phi - Q'_{(\phi + d\phi)}$ $\qquad\qquad$ [subtracting (iv) from (iii)]

$$= - \frac{\partial}{r.\partial\phi} \ (Q_\phi) \ r.d\phi$$

$$= - \frac{\partial}{r.\partial\phi} \left[- k \ (dr.dz) \ \frac{\partial t}{r.\partial\phi} \ . \ d\tau \right] r.d\phi$$

$$= k \ (dr.d\phi.dz) \ \frac{\partial t}{\partial\phi} \left(\frac{1}{r} \ . \ \frac{\partial t}{\partial\phi} \right) d\tau$$

$$= k \ (dr.rd\phi.dz) \ \frac{1}{r^2} \ . \ \frac{\partial^2 t}{\partial\phi^2} \ . \ d\tau$$

Heat flow in *axial direction (r-ϕ plane)* :

Heat influx, $\qquad Q'_z = - k \ (r.d\phi.dr) \ \dfrac{\partial t}{\partial z} \ d\tau \quad \text{...(v)}$

Heat efflux, $Q'_{(z + dz)} = Q'_z + \dfrac{\partial}{\partial z} \ (Q'_z) \ dz \qquad \text{...(vi)}$

Heat accumulated in the element due to heat flow in *axial direction*,

Piston assembly. The fins around the cylinder are meant to spread the heat and speed-up cooling.

[subtracting (vi) from (v)]

$$dQ'_z = Q'_z - Q'_{(z + dz)}$$

$$= - \frac{\partial}{\partial z} \left[- k \ (r.d\phi.dr) \ \frac{\partial t}{\partial z} \ . \ d\tau \right] dz$$

$$= k \ (dr.rd\phi.dz) \ \frac{\partial^2 t}{\partial z^2} \ . \ d\tau \qquad \text{...(2.18)}$$

Net heat accumulated in the element

$$= k.dr.rd\phi.dz \left[\frac{\partial^2 t}{\partial r^2} + \frac{1}{r} \ . \ \frac{\partial t}{\partial r} + \frac{1}{r^2} \ . \ \frac{\partial^2 t}{\partial\phi^2} + \frac{\partial^2 t}{\partial z^2} \right] d\tau \qquad \text{...(2.19)}$$

B. *Heat generated within the element (Q'_g)* :

The total heat generated within the element is given by

$$Q'_g = q_g \ (dr.rd\phi.dz).d\tau \qquad \text{...(2.20)}$$

C. *Energy stored in the element* :

The increase in thermal energy in the element is equal to

$$= \rho (dr.rd\phi.dz).c. \frac{\partial t}{\partial\tau} \ . \ d\tau \qquad \text{...(2.21)}$$

Now, $\qquad$ (A) + (B) = (C) $\qquad\qquad\qquad\qquad\qquad$ ... Energy balance/equation

$\therefore \qquad k.dr.rd\phi.dz \left[\dfrac{\partial^2 t}{\partial r^2} + \dfrac{1}{r} \ . \ \dfrac{\partial t}{\partial r} + \dfrac{1}{r^2} \ . \ \dfrac{\partial^2 t}{\partial\phi^2} + \dfrac{\partial^2 t}{\partial z^2} \right] d\tau + q_g \ (dr.rd\phi.dz).d\tau$

$$= \rho (dr.rd\phi.dz).c. \frac{\partial t}{\partial\tau} \ . \ d\tau$$

Dividing both sides by $dr.rd\phi.dz.d\tau$, we have

$$k\left[\frac{\partial^2 t}{\partial r^2} + \frac{1}{r}\cdot\frac{\partial t}{\partial r} + \frac{1}{r^2}\cdot\frac{\partial^2 t}{\partial\phi^2} + \frac{\partial^2 t}{\partial z^2}\right] + q_g = \rho.c.\frac{\partial t}{\partial\tau}$$

or, $$\left[\frac{\partial^2 t}{\partial r^2} + \frac{1}{r}\cdot\frac{\partial t}{\partial r} + \frac{1}{r^2}\cdot\frac{\partial^2 t}{\partial\phi^2} + \frac{\partial^2 t}{\partial z^2}\right] + \frac{q_g}{k} = \frac{\rho c}{k}\cdot\frac{\partial t}{\partial\tau} = \frac{1}{\alpha}\cdot\frac{\partial t}{\partial\tau} \qquad \text{...(2.22)}$$

Equation (2.22) is the **general heat conduction equation in cylindrical coordinates**.

In case there are no *heat sources* present and the heat flow is *steady* and *one-dimensional*, then eqn. (2.22) reduces to

$$\frac{\partial^2 t}{\partial r^2} + \frac{1}{r}\cdot\frac{\partial t}{\partial r} = 0 \qquad \text{...(2.23)}$$

or, $$\frac{\partial^2 t}{\partial r^2} + \frac{1}{r}\cdot\frac{dt}{dr} = 0$$

or, $$\frac{1}{r}\cdot\frac{d}{dr}\left(r\cdot\frac{dt}{dr}\right) = 0$$

Since $\dfrac{1}{r} \neq 0$, therefore,

$$\frac{d}{dr}\left(r\cdot\frac{dt}{dr}\right) \quad \text{or} \quad r\cdot\frac{dt}{dr} = \text{constant} \qquad \text{...(2.24)}$$

Equation (2.22) can also be derived by transformation of coordinates, as follows :

$$x = r\cos\phi, \; y = r\sin\phi \text{ and } z = z$$

Now, by chain rule :

$$\frac{\partial t}{\partial r} = \frac{\partial t}{\partial x}\cdot\frac{\partial x}{\partial r} + \frac{\partial t}{\partial y}\cdot\frac{\partial y}{\partial r} = \frac{\partial t}{\partial x}\cos\phi + \frac{\partial t}{\partial y}\sin\phi$$

or, $$\cos\phi\frac{\partial t}{\partial r} = \cos^2\phi\cdot\frac{\partial t}{\partial x} + \sin\phi.\cos\phi\cdot\frac{\partial t}{\partial y} \qquad \text{...(i)}$$

$$\text{(Multiplying both sides by } \cos\phi)$$

Also, $$\frac{\partial t}{\partial\phi} = \frac{\partial t}{\partial x}\cdot\frac{\partial x}{\partial\phi} + \frac{\partial t}{\partial y}\cdot\frac{\partial y}{\partial\phi} = \frac{\partial t}{\partial x}(-r\sin\phi) + \frac{\partial t}{\partial y}(r\cos\phi)$$

or, $$\frac{\sin\phi}{r}\cdot\frac{\partial t}{\partial\phi} = -\sin^2\phi\frac{\partial t}{\partial x} + \sin\phi.\cos\phi\cdot\frac{\partial t}{\partial y} \qquad \text{...(ii)}$$

$$\text{(Multiplying both sides by } \frac{\sin\phi}{r})$$

From Eqns. (i) and (ii), we have

$$\frac{\sin\phi}{r}\cdot\frac{\partial t}{\partial\phi} = -\sin^2\phi\frac{\partial t}{\partial x} + \left[\cos\phi\cdot\frac{\partial t}{\partial r} - \cos^2\phi\frac{\partial t}{\partial x}\right]$$

$$= -\frac{\partial t}{\partial x} + \cos\phi\frac{\partial t}{\partial r}$$

$\therefore$ $$\frac{\partial t}{\partial x} = \cos\phi\frac{\partial t}{\partial r} - \frac{\sin\phi}{r}\cdot\frac{\partial t}{\partial\phi} \qquad \text{...(iii)}$$

Differentiating both sides with respect to x, we have

$$\frac{\partial}{\partial x}\left(\frac{\partial t}{\partial x}\right) = \frac{\partial}{\partial x}\left[\cos\phi\cdot\frac{\partial t}{\partial r} - \frac{\sin\phi}{r}\cdot\frac{\partial t}{\partial\phi}\right]$$

or, $\dfrac{\partial^2 t}{\partial x^2} = \cos\phi \cdot \dfrac{\partial}{\partial r}\left(\dfrac{\partial t}{\partial x}\right) - \dfrac{\sin\phi}{r}\cdot\dfrac{\partial}{\partial\phi}\left(\dfrac{\partial t}{\partial x}\right)$

$\qquad = \cos\phi \cdot \dfrac{\partial}{\partial r}\left(\cos\phi\cdot\dfrac{\partial t}{\partial r} - \dfrac{\sin\phi}{r}\cdot\dfrac{\partial t}{\partial\phi}\right) - \dfrac{\sin\phi}{r}\cdot\dfrac{\partial}{\partial\phi}\left(\cos\phi\cdot\dfrac{\partial t}{\partial r} - \dfrac{\sin\phi}{r}\cdot\dfrac{\partial t}{\partial\phi}\right)$

$\qquad\qquad\qquad$ [Substituting the value of $\dfrac{\partial t}{\partial x}$ from (iii)]

$\qquad = \cos^2\phi\cdot\dfrac{\partial^2 t}{\partial r^2} - \dfrac{\cos\phi\cdot\sin\phi}{r^2}\cdot\dfrac{\partial t}{\partial\phi} + \dfrac{\sin^2\phi}{r}\cdot\dfrac{\partial t}{\partial r} + \dfrac{\sin^2\phi}{r^2}\cdot\dfrac{\partial^2 t}{d\phi^2} + \dfrac{\sin\phi\cdot\cos\phi}{r^2}\cdot\dfrac{\partial t}{\partial\phi}$

$\qquad\qquad\qquad\qquad\qquad\qquad\qquad\qquad\qquad\qquad\qquad\qquad\qquad\qquad ...(iv)$

Similarly, $\dfrac{\partial^2 t}{\partial y^2} = \sin^2\phi\cdot\dfrac{\partial^2 t}{\partial r^2} + \dfrac{\cos^2\phi}{r}\cdot\dfrac{\partial t}{\partial r} - \dfrac{\cos\phi\cdot\sin\phi}{r^2}\cdot\dfrac{\partial t}{\partial\phi} + \dfrac{\cos^2\phi}{r^2}\cdot\dfrac{\partial^2 t}{\partial\phi^2} - \dfrac{\cos\phi\cdot\sin\phi}{r^2}\cdot\dfrac{\partial t}{\partial\phi}$

$\qquad\qquad\qquad\qquad\qquad\qquad\qquad\qquad\qquad\qquad\qquad\qquad\qquad\qquad ...(v)$

By adding (iii) and (iv), we get

$$\dfrac{\partial^2 t}{\partial x^2} + \dfrac{\partial^2 t}{\partial y^2} = \dfrac{\partial^2 t}{\partial r^2} + \dfrac{1}{r}\cdot\dfrac{\partial t}{\partial r} + \dfrac{1}{r^2}\cdot\dfrac{\partial^2 t}{\partial\phi^2}$$

Substituting it in eqn. (2.8), we get,

$$\left[\dfrac{\partial^2 t}{\partial r^2} + \dfrac{1}{r}\cdot\dfrac{\partial t}{\partial r} + \dfrac{1}{r^2}\cdot\dfrac{\partial^2 t}{\partial\phi^2} + \dfrac{\partial^2 t}{\partial z^2}\right] + \dfrac{q_g}{k} = \dfrac{1}{\alpha}\cdot\dfrac{\partial t}{\partial\tau}$$

which is the same as eqn. (2.22)

2.4. GENERAL HEAT CONDUCTION EQUATION IN SPHERICAL COORDINATES

Consider an elemental volume having the coordinates (r, ϕ, θ), for three dimensional heat conduction analysis, as shown in Fig. 2.3.

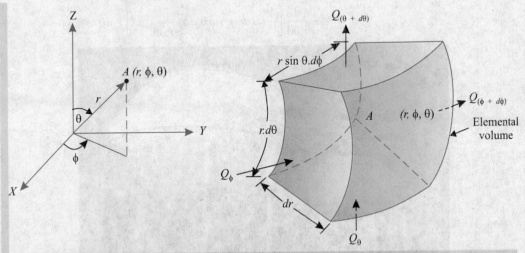

Fig. 2.3. Elemental volume for three-dimensional heat conduction analysis - Spherical coordinates.

The volume of the element $= dr.rd\theta.r\sin\theta\, d\phi$

Let, $\qquad\qquad q_g$ = Heat generation (uniform) per unit volume per unit time.

Further let us assume that k (thermal conductivity), ρ (density), c (specific heat) do not alter with position.

A. *Net heat accumulated in the element due to conduction of heat from all the coordinate directions considered :*

Heat flow through *r–θ* plane; *φ-direction* :

Heat influx,
$$Q'_\phi = -k\,(dr.rd\theta)\,\frac{\partial t}{r.\sin\theta.\partial\phi}\,d\tau \qquad\qquad ...(i)$$

Heat efflux,
$$Q'_{(\phi+d\phi)} = Q'_\phi + \frac{\partial}{r.\sin\theta.\partial\phi}\,(Q'_\phi)\,r\,\sin\theta.d\phi \qquad\qquad ...(ii)$$

∴   Heat accumulated in the element due to heat flow in the φ-direction,

$$dQ'_\phi = Q'_\phi - Q'_{(\phi+d\phi)} \qquad\qquad\qquad \text{[subtracting } (ii) \text{ from } (i)]$$

$$= -\frac{1}{r\sin\theta}\cdot\frac{\partial}{\partial\phi}\,(Q'_\phi)\,r\,\sin\theta.d\phi$$

$$= -\frac{1}{r\sin\theta}\cdot\frac{\partial}{\partial\phi}\left[-k\,(dr.rd\theta)\,\frac{1}{r\sin\theta}\cdot\frac{\partial t}{\partial\phi}.d\tau\right]r\,\sin\theta.d\phi$$

$$= k\,(dr.rd\theta.r\sin\theta.d\phi)\,\frac{1}{r^2\sin^2\theta}\cdot\frac{\partial^2 t}{\partial\phi^2}\,d\tau \qquad\qquad ...(2.25)$$

Heat flow in *r–φ* plane, *θ-direction* :

Heat influx,
$$Q'_\theta = -k\,(dr.\,r\,\sin\theta.\,d\phi)\,\frac{\partial t}{r\partial\theta}\cdot d\tau \qquad\qquad ...(iii)$$

Heat efflux,
$$Q'_{(\theta+d\theta)} = Q'_\theta + \frac{\partial}{r\partial\theta}\,(Q'_\theta)\,rd\theta \qquad\qquad ...(iv)$$

∴   Heat accumulated in the element due to heat flow in the θ-direction,

$$dQ'_\theta = Q'_\theta - Q'_{(\theta+d\theta)} \qquad\qquad\qquad \text{[subtracting } (iv) \text{ from } (iii)]$$

$$= -\frac{\partial}{r.\partial\theta}\,(Q'_\theta)\,r.d\theta$$

$$= -\frac{\partial}{r.\partial\theta}\left[-k\,(dr.r\,\sin\theta.d\phi)\,\frac{\partial t}{r.\partial\theta}.d\tau\right]r.d\theta$$

Spherical vessels.

$$= \frac{k}{r} \frac{dr.rd\phi.rd\theta}{r} \frac{\partial}{\partial\theta}\left[\sin\theta \cdot \frac{\partial t}{\partial\theta}\right] d\tau$$

$$= k\,(dr.rd\theta.r\sin\theta.d\phi)\,\frac{1}{r^2\sin\theta} \cdot \frac{\partial}{\partial\theta}\left[\sin\theta \cdot \frac{\partial t}{\partial\theta}\right] d\tau \qquad \qquad ...(2.26)$$

Heat flow in θ-φ *plane, r-direction* :

Heat influx, $\qquad Q'_r = -k\,(rd\theta.r\sin\theta.d\phi)\,\dfrac{\partial t}{\partial r} \cdot \partial\tau \qquad \qquad \qquad ...(v)$

Heat efflux, $\quad Q'_{(r+dr)} = Q'_r + \dfrac{\partial}{\partial r}(Q'_r)\,dr \qquad \qquad \qquad \qquad \qquad ...(vi)$

∴   Heat accumulation in the element due to heat flow in the *r-direction*,

$$dQ'_r = Q'_r - Q'_{(r+dr)} \qquad\qquad\qquad\qquad \text{[subtracting } (vi) \text{ from } (v)]$$

$$= -\frac{\partial}{\partial r}(Q'_r)\,dr$$

$$= -\frac{\partial}{\partial r}\left[-k\,(rd\theta.r\sin\theta.d\phi)\,\frac{\partial t}{\partial r} \cdot d\tau\right] dr$$

$$= k\,d\theta.\sin\theta.d\phi\,dr\,\frac{\partial}{\partial r}\left[r^2 \cdot \frac{\partial t}{\partial r}\right] d\tau$$

$$= k\,(dr.rd\theta.r\sin\theta.d\phi)\,\frac{1}{r^2} \cdot \frac{\partial}{\partial r}\left[r^2 \cdot \frac{\partial t}{\partial r}\right] d\tau \qquad \qquad ...(2.27)$$

Net heat accumulated in the element

$$= k\,dr.rd\theta.r\sin\theta.d\phi\left[\frac{1}{r^2\sin^2\theta} \cdot \frac{\partial^2 t}{\partial\phi^2} + \frac{1}{r^2\sin\theta} \cdot \frac{\partial}{\partial\theta}\left(\sin\theta.\frac{\partial t}{\partial\theta}\right) + \frac{1}{r^2} \cdot \frac{\partial}{\partial r}\left(r^2 \cdot \frac{\partial t}{\partial r}\right)\right] d\tau$$

$$...(2.28)$$

B. *Heat generated within the element* (Q'_g) :

The total heat generated within the element is given by,

$$Q'_g = q_g\,(dr.rd\theta.r\sin\theta.d\phi) \qquad \qquad ...(2.29)$$

C. *Energy stored in the element* :

The increase in thermal energy in the element is equal to

$$\rho\,(dr.rd\theta.r\sin\theta.d\phi)\,c.\frac{\partial t}{\partial\tau} \cdot d\tau \qquad \qquad ...(2.30)$$

Now, $(A) + (B) = (C)$ $\qquad\qquad\qquad\qquad\qquad\qquad\qquad$ ...Energy balance/equation

$$\therefore \quad k\,dr.rd\theta.r\sin\theta.d\phi\left[\frac{1}{r^2\sin^2\theta} \cdot \frac{\partial^2 t}{\partial\phi^2} + \frac{1}{r^2\sin\theta} \cdot \frac{\partial}{\partial\theta}\left(\sin\theta.\frac{\partial t}{\partial\theta}\right) + \frac{1}{r^2} \cdot \frac{\partial}{\partial r}\left(r^2.\frac{\partial t}{\partial r}\right)\right].d\tau$$

$$+ q_g\,(dr.rd\theta.r\sin\theta.d\phi) = \rho\,(dr.rd\theta.r\sin\theta.d\phi)\,c.\frac{\partial t}{\partial\tau}.d\tau$$

Dividing both sides by $k.(dr.rd\theta.\,r\sin\theta.d\phi)d\tau$, we get

$$\left[\frac{1}{r^2\sin^2\theta} \cdot \frac{\partial^2 t}{\partial\phi^2} + \frac{1}{r^2\sin\theta} \cdot \frac{\partial}{\partial\theta}\left(\sin\theta \cdot \frac{\partial t}{\partial\theta}\right) + \frac{1}{r^2} \cdot \frac{\partial}{\partial r}\left(r^2 \cdot \frac{\partial t}{\partial r}\right)\right] + \frac{q_g}{k}$$

$$= \frac{\rho c}{k} \cdot \frac{\partial t}{\partial\tau} = \frac{1}{\alpha} \cdot \frac{\partial t}{\partial\tau} \qquad \qquad ...(2.31)$$

Equation (2.31) is the **general heat conduction equation in spherical coordinates.**

In case there are not *heat sources present* and the heat flow is *steady* and *one-dimensional*, then eqn. (2.31) reduces to

$$\frac{1}{r^2} \cdot \frac{d}{dr}\left(r^2 \cdot \frac{dt}{dr}\right) = 0 \qquad \qquad ...(2.32)$$

Equation (2.31) can also be derived by transformation of coordinates as follows :

$$x = r \sin \theta \sin \phi \; ; \; y = r \sin \theta \cos \phi \; ; \; z = r \cos \theta$$

2.5. HEAT CONDUCTION THROUGH PLANE AND COMPOSITE WALLS

2.5.1. HEAT CONDUCTION THROUGH A PLANE WALL

Case I : Uniform thermal conductivity

Refer to Fig. 2.4 (a) Consider a plane wall of homogeneous material through which heat is flowing *only in x-direction.*

Let,
- L = Thickness of the plane wall,
- A = Cross-sectional area of the wall,
- k = Thermal conductivity of the wall material, and
- t_1, t_2 = Temperatures maintained at the two faces 1 and 2 of the wall, respectively.

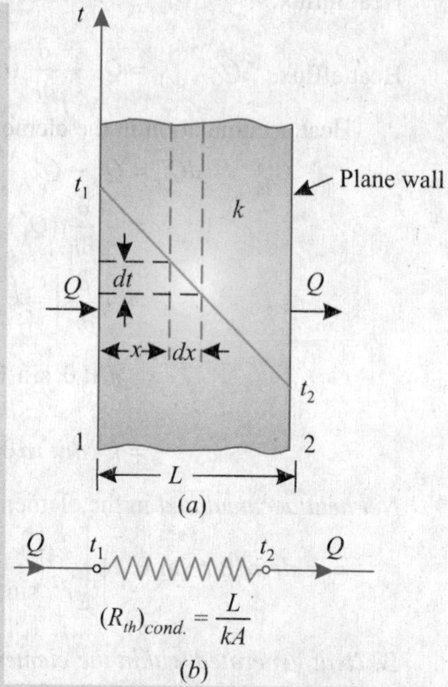

The general heat conduction equation in cartesian coordinates is given by

$$\frac{\partial^2 t}{dx^2} + \frac{\partial^2 t}{dy^2} + \frac{\partial^2 t}{dz^2} + \frac{q_g}{k} = \frac{1}{\alpha} \cdot \frac{\partial t}{\partial \tau}$$

...[Eqn. 2.8]

If the heat conduction takes place under the conditions, steady state $\left(\frac{\partial t}{\partial \tau} = 0\right)$, one-dimensional $\left[\frac{\partial^2 t}{\partial y^2} = \frac{\partial^2 t}{\partial z^2} = 0\right]$ and with no internal heat generation $\left(\frac{q_g}{k} = 0\right)$ then the above equation is reduced to

$$\frac{\partial^2 t}{dx^2} = 0, \quad \text{or} \quad \frac{d^2 t}{dx^2} = 0 \qquad ...(2.33)$$

By integrating the above differential twice, we have

$$\frac{dt}{dx} = C_1 \quad \text{and} \quad t = C_1 x + C_2 \qquad ...(2.34)$$

where C_1 and C_2 are the arbitrary constants. The values of these constants may be calculated from the known boundary conditions as follows :

At $x = 0$ $t = t_1$
At $x = L$ $t = t_2$

Substituting the values in the eqn. (2.34), we get

$$t_1 = O + C_2 \quad \text{and} \quad t_2 = C_1 L + C_2$$

After simplification, we have, $C_2 = t_1$ and $C_1 = \dfrac{t_2 - t_1}{L}$

Thus, the eqn. (2.34) reduces to :

$$t = \left(\frac{t_2 - t_1}{L}\right) x + t_1 \qquad ...(2.35)$$

$(R_{th})_{cond.} = \dfrac{L}{kA}$

(b)

Fig. 2.4. Heat conduction through a plane wall.

The eqn. (2.35) indicates that *temperature distribution across a wall is linear* and is *independent of thermal conductivity*. Now heat through the plane wall can be found by using Fourier's equation as follows :

$$Q = -kA \frac{dt}{dx} \quad \text{(where, } \frac{dt}{dx} = \text{Temperature gradient)}$$

... [Eqn.(1.1)]

But,

$$\frac{dt}{dx} = \frac{d}{dx}\left[\left(\frac{t_2 - t_1}{L}\right)x + t_1\right] = \frac{t_2 - t_1}{L}$$

$$\therefore \qquad Q = -kA \frac{(t_2 - t_1)}{L} = \frac{kA(t_1 - t_2)}{L} \qquad \qquad ...(2.36)$$

Eqn (2.36) can be written as :

$$Q = \frac{(t_1 - t_2)}{(L/kA)} = \frac{(t_1 - t_2)}{(R_{th})_{cond.}} \qquad \qquad ...(2.37)$$

where, $(R_{th})_{cond.}$ = Thermal resistance to heat conduction. Fig. 2.4 (*b*) shows the *equivalent thermal circuit* for heat flow through the plane wall.

Let us now find out the condition when instead of space, weight is the main criterion for selection of the insulation of a plane wall.

Thermal resistance (conduction) of the wall, $(R_{th})_{cond.} = \dfrac{L}{kA}$ ...(*i*)

Weight of the wall, $W = \rho A L$ ...(*ii*)

Eliminating L from (*i*) and (*ii*), we get

$$W = \rho A.(R_{th})_{cond.} \, kA = (\rho.k)A^2.(R_{th})_{cond.} \qquad \qquad ...(2.38)$$

The eqn., (2.38) stipulates the condition that, for a specified thermal resistance, the *lightest insulation will be one which has the smallest product of density (ρ) and thermal conductivity (k).*

Case II. Variable thermal conductivity

A. *Temperature variation in terms of surface temperatures* (t_1, t_2) :

A diesel engine is more efficient due to internal combustion and better heat.

Let the thermal conductivity vary with temperature according to the relation

$$k = k_0 (1 + \beta t) \qquad \qquad ...(2.39)$$

[In most of the cases, the thermal conductivity is found to vary *linearly with temperature*]

where, k_0 = Thermal conductivity at zero temperature.

When the effect of temperature on thermal conductivity is considered, the Fourier's equation,

$$Q = -kA \frac{dt}{dx} \text{ is written as :}$$

$$Q = -k_0 (1 + \beta t) \frac{dt}{dx} . A \qquad \qquad ...(2.40)$$

or, $$\frac{Q}{A} . dx = -k_0 (1 + \beta t) dt$$

or, $$\frac{Q}{A} \int_0^L dx = -k_0 \int_{t_1}^{t_2} (1 + \beta t) dt$$

or, $$\frac{Q.L}{A} = -k_0 \left[t + \frac{\beta}{2} t^2 \right]_{t_1}^{t_2}$$

or, $$\frac{Q.L}{A} = -k_0 \left[(t_2 - t_1) + \frac{\beta}{2} (t_2^2 - t_1^2) \right] \qquad \qquad ...(2.41)$$

$$= k_0 \left[(t_1 - t_2) + \frac{\beta}{2} (t_1 - t_2)(t_1 + t_2) \right]$$

$$= k_0 \left[1 + \frac{\beta}{2} (t_1 + t_2) \right] (t_1 - t_2)$$

$$= k_0 [1 + \beta t_m] (t_1 - t_2) \qquad \qquad \text{where } t_m = \frac{t_1 + t_2}{2}$$

$$\therefore \qquad \qquad Q = k_0 (1 + \beta t_m). \frac{A (t_1 - t_2)}{L}$$

From eqn. (2.39) t is replaced by t_m, then

$$k_m = k_0 (1 + \beta t_m) \qquad \qquad ...(2.42)$$

$$\therefore \qquad \qquad Q = k_m A \left[\frac{t_1 - t_2}{L} \right] \qquad \qquad ...(2.43)$$

where k_m is known as *mean thermal conductivity* of the wall material.

Further, if t is the temperature of the surface at a distance x from the left surface (Fig. 2.5), then eqn. (2.41) becomes

$$\frac{Qx}{A} = -k_0 \left[(t - t_1) + \frac{\beta}{2} (t^2 - t_1^2) \right] \qquad \qquad ...(2.44)$$

Form eqns. (2.41) and (2.44), we have

$$\left[(t_2 - t_1) + \frac{\beta}{2} (t_2^2 - t_1^2) \right] \frac{X}{L} = \left[(t - t_1) + \frac{\beta}{2} (t^2 - t_1^2) \right]$$

[Equating the values of Q and rearranging]

Solving the above equation for t, we get

$$t = \frac{1}{\beta} \left[(1 + \beta t_1)^2 - \{(1 + \beta t_1)^2 - (1 + \beta t_2)^2\} \frac{x}{L} \right]^{1/2} - \frac{1}{\beta} \qquad ...(2.45)$$

B. *Temperature variation in terms of heat flux (Q) :*

Fourier's equation for heat conduction is given by

$$Q = -kA.\frac{dt}{dx} = -k_0(1+\beta t)A.\frac{dt}{dx}$$

or, $\qquad Q.dx = -k_0(1+\beta t)A.dt$

Integrating both sides, we get

$$Q.x = -k_0 A\left(t + \frac{\beta}{2}t^2\right) + C \qquad\qquad ...(i)$$

(where, C = Constant of integration)

To evaluate C, applying the condition : At $x = 0$, $t = t_1$, we get

$$C = k_0 A\left(t_1 + \frac{\beta}{2}t_1^2\right)$$

Substituting the values of the constant C in (i), we get

$$Q.x = -k_0 A\left(t + \frac{\beta}{2}t^2\right) + k_0 A\left(t_1 + \frac{\beta}{2}t_1^2\right)$$

Dividing both sides by $k_0 A$ and rearranging, we obtain,

$$\frac{\beta}{2}t^2 + t + \left[\frac{Q.x}{k_0 A} - \left(t_1 + \frac{\beta}{2}t_1^2\right)\right] = 0$$

By solving the above quadratic equation, we have

$$\therefore \qquad t = \frac{-1 + \sqrt{1 - 4\times\dfrac{\beta}{2}\left[\dfrac{Q.x}{k_0 A} - \left(t_1 + \dfrac{\beta}{2}t_1^2\right)\right]}}{2\times\left(\dfrac{\beta}{2}\right)}$$

or, $\qquad t = -\dfrac{1}{\beta} + \left[\dfrac{1}{\beta^2} - \dfrac{2}{\beta}\left(\dfrac{Q.x}{k_0 A} - t_1 - \dfrac{\beta}{2}t_1^2\right)\right]^{1/2}$

$$= -\frac{1}{\beta} + \left[\frac{1}{\beta^2} - \frac{2}{\beta}t_1 + t_1^2 - \frac{2Q.x}{\beta k_0 A}\right]^{1/2}$$

$$= -\frac{1}{\beta} + \left[\left(t_1 + \frac{1}{\beta}\right)^2 - \frac{2Q.x}{\beta k_0 A}\right]^{1/2}$$

Hence,

$$t = -\frac{1}{\beta} + \left[\left(t_1 + \frac{1}{\beta}\right)^2 - \frac{2Q.x}{\beta k_0 A}\right]^{1/2}$$

$$...(2.46)$$

In most of the practical applications where the variation of temperature is small, the average value of k for the given temperature range is commonly used as given in eqn. (2.42).

If the variation of k with temperature is *not linear*, then

$$k = k_0 f(t), \text{ and}$$

$$\frac{Q}{A}\int_0^L dx = -\int_{t_1}^{t_2} [k_0 f(t)\, dt$$

or, $\qquad Q = \dfrac{A}{L}\left[-\int_{t_1}^{t_2}[k_0 f(t)\, dt]\right] \qquad ...(2.47)$

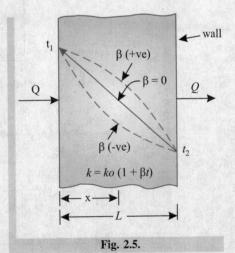

Fig. 2.5.

But,
$$Q = k_m A \left(\frac{t_1 - t_2}{L} \right)$$
...[Eqn. (2.43)]

Equating these eqns. (2.47) and (2.43), we have

$$k_m = \frac{1}{(t_1 - t_2)} \left[\int_{t_1}^{t_2} [k_0 \, f(t) \, dt] \right]$$

$$= \frac{1}{(t_1 - t_2)} \int_{t_2}^{t_1} [k_0 \, f(t) \, dt] \qquad \qquad ...(2.48)$$

The effect of $+ \beta$ and $- \beta$ on temperature is depicted in Fig. 2.5.

2.5.2. HEAT CONDUCTION THROUGH A COMPOSITE WALL

Refer to Fig. 2.6 (*a*). Consider the transmission of heat through a composite wall consisting of a number of slabs.

Let, L_A, L_B, L_C = Thicknesses of slabs A, B and C respectively (also called path lengths),

k_A, k_B, k_C = Thermal conductivities of the slabs A, B, and C respectively,

$t_1, t_4 \,(t_1 > t_4)$ = Temperatures at the wall surfaces 1 and 4 respectively, and

t_2, t_3 = Temperatures at the interfaces 2 and 3 respectively.

Since the quantity of heat transmitted per unit time through each slab/layer is same, we have,

$$Q = \frac{k_A . A \,(t_1 - t_2)}{L_A} = \frac{k_B \, . \, A \,(t_2 - t_3)}{L_B} = \frac{k_C \, . \, A \,(t_3 - t_4)}{L_C}$$

(Assuming that there is a perfect contact between the layers and no temperature drop occurs across the interface between the materials).

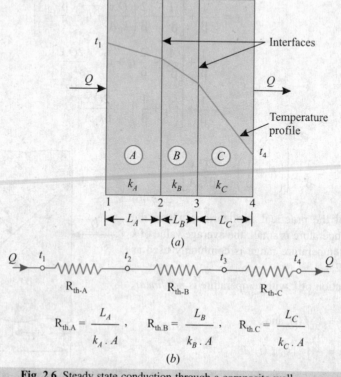

(*a*)

$$R_{th.A} = \frac{L_A}{k_A . A} \,, \qquad R_{th.B} = \frac{L_B}{k_B . A} \,, \qquad R_{th.C} = \frac{L_C}{k_C . A}$$

(*b*)

Fig. 2.6. Steady state conduction through a composite wall.

Rearranging the above expression, we get

$$t_1 - t_2 = \frac{Q \cdot L_A}{k_A \cdot A} \qquad \qquad \qquad \dots(i)$$

$$t_2 - t_3 = \frac{Q \cdot L_B}{k_B \cdot A} \qquad \qquad \qquad \dots(ii)$$

$$t_3 - t_4 = \frac{Q \cdot L_c}{k_C \cdot A} \qquad \qquad \qquad \dots(iii)$$

Adding (*i*), (*ii*) and (*iii*), we have

$$(t_1 - t_4) = Q \left[\frac{L_A}{k_A \cdot A} + \frac{L_B}{k_B \cdot A} + \frac{L_C}{k_C \cdot A} \right]$$

or,

$$Q = \frac{A (t_1 - t_4)}{\left[\dfrac{L_A}{k_A} + \dfrac{L_B}{k_B} + \dfrac{L_C}{k_C} \right]} \qquad \qquad \dots(2.49)$$

or,

$$Q = \frac{(t_1 - t_4)}{\left[\dfrac{L_A}{k_A \cdot A} + \dfrac{L_B}{k_B \cdot A} + \dfrac{L_C}{k_C \cdot A} \right]} = \frac{(t_1 - t_4)}{\left[R_{th-A} + R_{th-B} + R_{th-C} \right]} \qquad \dots[2.49\ (a)]$$

If the composite wall consists of *n* slabs/layers, then

$$Q = \frac{[t_1 - t_{(n+1)}]}{\displaystyle\sum_1^n \frac{L}{kA}} \qquad \qquad \dots(2.50)$$

In order to solve more complex problems involving both series and parallel thermal resistances, the electrical analogy may be used. A typical problem and its analogous electric circuit are shown in Fig. 2.7.

$$Q = \frac{\Delta t_{overall}}{\sum R_{th}} \qquad \qquad \dots(2.51)$$

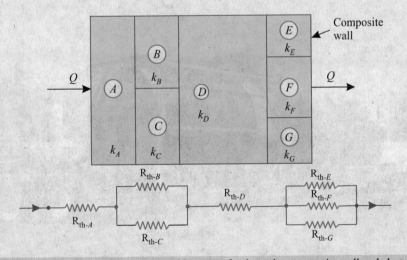

Fig. 2.7. Series and parallel one-dimensional heat transfer through a composite wall and electrical analog.

Thermal contact resistance. In a composite (multi-layer) wall, the calculations of heat flow are made on the assumptions : (*i*) The contact between the adjacent layers is perfect, (*ii*) At the interface there is no fall of temperature, and (*iii*) At the interface the temperature is continuous, although there is discontinuity in temperature gradient. In real systems, however, due to surface roughness and void spaces (usually filled with air) the contact surfaces *touch only at discrete locations*. Thus there is not a single plane of contact, which means that the area available for the flow of heat at the interface will be small compared to geometric face area. Due to this reduced area and presence of air voids, *a large resistance to heat flow at the interface occurs*. This resistance is known as *thermal contact resistance* and it causes temperature drop between two materials at the interface as shown in Fig. 2.8.

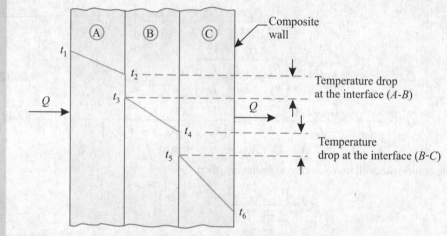

Fig. 2.8. Temperature drops at the interfaces.

Refer to Fig. 2.8. The contact resistances are given by

$$(R_{th-AB})_{cont.} = \frac{(t_2 - t_3)}{Q/A} \qquad \text{and} \qquad (R_{th-BC})_{cont.} = \frac{(t_4 - t_5)}{Q/A}$$

Boiler is being transported.

2.5.3. THE OVERALL HEAT-TRANSFER COEFFICIENT

While dealing with the problems of fluid to fluid heat transfer across a metal boundary, it is usual to adopt an overall heat transfer coefficient U which *gives the heat transmitted per unit area per unit time per degree temperature difference between the bulk fluids on each side of the metal.*

Refer to Fig. 2.9

Let,

L = Thickness of the metal wall,

k = Thermal conductivity of the wall material,

t_1 = Temperature of the surface–1,

t_2 = Temperature of the surface–2,

t_{hf} = Temperature of the hot fluid,

t_{cf} = Temperature of the cold fluid,

h_{hf} = Heat transfer coefficient from hot fluid to metal surface, and

h_{cf} = Heat transfer coefficient from metal surface to cold fluid.

(The suffices *hf* and *cf* stand for hot fluid and cold fluid respectively.)

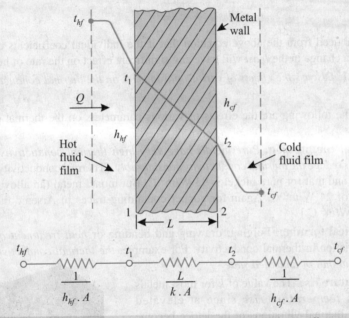

Fig. 2.9. The overall heat transfer through a plane wall.

The equations of heat flow through the fluid and the metal surface are given by

$$Q = h_{hf}\, A\, (t_{hf} - t_1) \qquad \qquad ...(i)$$

$$Q = \frac{k.A\,(t_1 - t_2)}{L} \qquad \qquad ...(ii)$$

$$Q = h_{cf}\, A\, (t_2 - t_{cf}) \qquad \qquad ...(iii)$$

By rearranging (*i*), (*ii*) and (*iii*), we get

$$t_{hf} - t_1 = \frac{Q}{h_{hf}\,.A} \qquad \qquad ...(iv)$$

$$t_1 - t_2 = \frac{QL}{k\,.A} \qquad \qquad ...(v)$$

$$t_2 - t_{cf} = \frac{Q}{k_{cf} \cdot A} \qquad\qquad ...(vi)$$

Adding (iv), (v) and (vi) we get

$$t_{hf} - t_{cf} = Q \left[\frac{1}{h_{hf} \cdot A} + \frac{L}{k \cdot A} + \frac{1}{h_{cf} \cdot A} \right]$$

or,

$$Q = \frac{A\,(t_{hf} - t_{cf})}{\dfrac{1}{h_{hf}} + \dfrac{L}{k} + \dfrac{1}{h_{cf}}} \qquad\qquad ...(2.52)$$

If U is the overall coefficient of heat transfer, then

$$Q = U.A\,(t_{hf} - t_{cf}) = \frac{A\,(t_{hf} - t_{cf})}{\dfrac{1}{h_{hf}} + \dfrac{L}{k} + \dfrac{1}{h_{cf}}}$$

or,

$$U = \frac{1}{\dfrac{1}{h_{hf}} + \dfrac{L}{k} + \dfrac{1}{h_{cf}}} \qquad\qquad ...(2.53)$$

It may be noticed from the above equation that if the individual coefficients differ greatly in magnitude only a change in the *least* will have any significant effect on the rate of heat transfer.

Example 2.1. *Discuss the effects of various parameters on the thermal conductivity of solids.*

(AMIE Summer, 2001)

Solution. The following are the effects of various parameters on the thermal conductivity of solids.

1. **Chemical composition.** *Pure metals have very high thermal conductivity. Impurities or alloying elements reduce the thermal conductivity considerably.* [Thermal conductivity of pure copper is 385 W/m° C, and that for pure nickel is 93 W/m° C. But monel metal (an alloy of 30% Ni and 70% Cu) has k of 24 W/m° C. Again for copper containing traces of Arsenic the value of k is reduced to 142 W/m° C.]

2. **Mechanical forming.** Forging, drawing and bending or *heat treatment of metals* cause considerable variation in thermal conductivity. For example, *the thermal conductivity of hardened steel is lower than that of annealed state.*

3. **Temperature rise.** The value of k for most metals *decreases with temperature rise* since at elevated temperatures the thermal vibrations of the lattice become higher that retard the motion of free electrons.

4. **Non-metallic solids.** Non-metallic solids have k *much lower* than that for metals. For many of the building materials (concrete, stone, brick, glass wool, cork etc.) the thermal conductivity may vary from sample to sample due to variations in structure, composition, density and porosity.

Fire brick

5. **Presence of air.** The thermal conductivity is *reduced* due to the presence of air filled pores or cavities.

6. **Dampness.** Thermal conductivity of a damp material is *considerably higher* than that of dry material.

7. **Density.** Thermal conductivity of insulating powder, asbestos etc. increases with density growth. Thermal conductivity of snow is also proportional to its density.

Example 2.2. *The inner surface of a plane brick wall is at 60°C and the outer surface is at 35°C. Calculate the rate of heat transfer per m² of surface area of the wall, which is 220 mm thick. The thermal conductivity of the brick is 0.51 W/m°C.*

(AMIE Winter, 2000)

Solution. Temperature of the inner surface of the wall, $t_1 = 60°C$

Temperature of the outer surface of the wall, $t_2 = 35°C$

The thickness of the wall, $L = 220$ mm $= 0.22$ m

Thermal conductivity of the brick,
$$k = 0.51 \text{ W/m°C}$$

Rate of heat transfer per m², q :

Rate of heat transfer per unit area,

$$q = \frac{Q}{A} = \frac{k\,(t_1 - t_2)}{L}$$

or

$$q = \frac{0.51 \times (60 - 35)}{0.22} = \textbf{57.95 W/m}^2 \textbf{ (Ans.)}$$

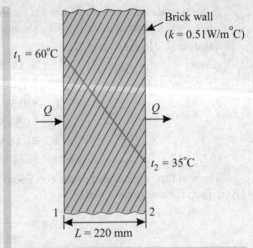

Fig. 2.10.

Example 2.3. *Consider a slab of thickness L = 0.25 m. One surface is kept at 100°C and the other surface at 0°C. Determine the net flux across the slab if the slab is made from pure copper. Thermal conductivity of copper may be taken as 387.6 W/m K.*

(AMIE Winter, 1998)

Solution. *Given* : $L = 0.25$ m; $t_1 = 100°C$; $t_2 = 0°C$; $k = 387.6$ W/m K.

From Fourier's law,

$$Q = -kA\,\frac{dt}{dx} \quad ...\text{[Eqn. (1.1)]}$$

Net flux,
$$q = \frac{Q}{A} = -k \cdot \frac{(t_2 - t_1)}{L}$$

$$= -387.6 \times \frac{(0 - 100)}{0.25}$$

$$= \textbf{1.55} \times \textbf{10}^5 \textbf{ W/m}^2 \quad \textbf{(Ans.)}$$

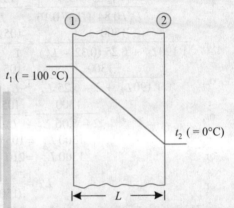

Fig. 2.11.

Example 2.4. *A reactor's wall, 320 mm thick, is made up of an inner layer of fire brick (k = 0.84 W/m°C) covered with a layer of insulation (k = 0.16 W/m°C). The reactor operates at a temperature of 1325°C and the ambient temperature is 25°C.*

(i) Determine the thickness of fire brick and insulation which gives minimum heat loss;

(ii) Calculate the heat loss presuming that the insulating material has a maximum temperature of 1200°C.

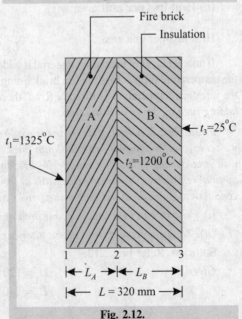

Fig. 2.12.

If the calculated heat loss is not acceptable, then state whether addition of another layer of insulation would provide a satisfactory solution.

Solution.   Refer to Fig. 2.12.

Given :
$$t_1 = 1325°C; t_2 = 1200°C, t_3 = 25°C$$
$$L_A + L_B = L = 320 \text{ mm or } 0.32 \text{ m}$$

∴
$$L_B = (0.32 - L_A); \qquad\qquad\qquad ...(i)$$
$$k_A = 0.84 \text{ W/m°C};$$
$$k_B = 0.16 \text{ W/m°C}.$$

(i) $L_A : L_B$:

The heat flux, under steady state conditions, is constant throughout the wall and is same for each layer. Then for *unit area* of wall,

$$q = \frac{t_1 - t_3}{L_A/k_A + L_B/k_B} = \frac{t_1 - t_2}{L_A/k_A} = \frac{t_2 - t_3}{L_B/k_B}$$

Considering first two quantities, we have

$$\frac{(1325 - 25)}{L_A/0.84 + L_B/0.16} = \frac{(1325 - 1200)}{L_A/0.84}$$

or,
$$\frac{1300}{1.190 L_A + 6.25 (0.32 - L_A)} = \frac{105}{L_A}$$

or,
$$\frac{1300}{1.190 L_A + 2 - 6.25 L_A} = \frac{105}{L_A}$$

or,
$$\frac{1300}{2 - 5.06 L_A} = \frac{105}{L_A}$$

or, $1300 L_A = 105 (2 - 5.06 L_A)$

or, $1300 L_A = 210 - 531.3 L_A$

or,
$$L_A = \frac{210}{(1300 + 531.3)} = 0.1146 \text{ m or } \textbf{114.6 mm}$$

∴ Thickness of insulation $L_B = 320 - 114.6 = \textbf{205.4 mm (Ans.)}$

(ii) Heat loss per unit area, q :

Heat loss per unit area, $q = \dfrac{t_1 - t_2}{L_A/k_A} = \dfrac{1325 - 1200}{0.1146/0.84} = \textbf{916.23 W/m}^2 \textbf{ (Ans.)}$

If another layer of insulating material is added, the heat loss from the wall will reduce; consequently the temperature drop across the fire brick lining will drop and the interface temperature t_2 will rise. As the interface temperature is *already fixed*, therefore, a *satisfactory solution will not be available by adding another layer of insulation.*

Example 2.5. *A wall of a furnace is made up of inside layer of silica brick 120 mm thick covered with a layer of magnesite brick 240 mm thick. The temperatures at the inside surface of silica brick wall and outside surface of magnesite brick wall are 725°C and 110°C respectively. The contact thermal resistance between the two walls at the interface is 0.0035°C/W per unit wall area. If thermal conductivities of silica and magnesite bricks are 1.7 W/m°C and 5.8 W/m°C, calculate.*

(i)   *The rate of heat loss per unit area of walls, and*

(ii) *The temperature drop at the interface.*

Solution. Refer Fig. 2.13.

Given :
$$L_A = 120 \text{ mm} = 0.12 \text{ m};$$
$$L_B = 240 \text{ mm} = 0.24 \text{ m};$$

$k_A = 1.7$ W/m°C; $k_B = 5.8$ W/m°C

The contact thermal resistance $(R_{th})_{cont.}$

$= 0.0035$°C/W

The temperature at the inside surface of silica brick wall, $t_1 = 725$°C

The temperature at the outside surface of the magnesite brick wall, $t_4 = 110$°C

(i) **The rate of heat loss per unit area of wall, q :**

$$q = \frac{\Delta t}{\Sigma R_{th}} = \frac{\Delta t}{R_{th-A} + (R_{th})_{cont.} + R_{th-B}}$$

$$= \frac{(t_1 - t_4)}{L_A / k_A + 0.0035 + L_B / k_B}$$

$$= \frac{(725 - 110)}{0.12/1.7 + 0.0035 + 0.24/5.8}$$

$$= \frac{615}{0.0706 + 0.0035 + 0.0414}$$

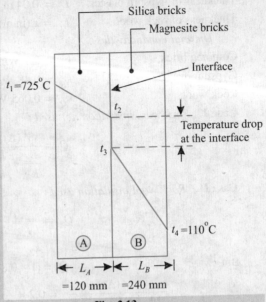

Fig. 2.13.

$$= 5324.67 \text{ W/m}^2$$

∴ The rate of heat loss per unit area of wall, $q = 5324.67$ W/m² **(Ans.)**

(ii) **The temperature drop at the interface, $(t_2 - t_3)$:**

As the same heat flows through each layer of composite wall, therefore,

$$q = \frac{t_1 - t_2}{L_A / k_A} = \frac{t_3 - t_4}{L_B / k_B}$$

or, $$5324.67 = \frac{(725 - t_2)}{0.12/1.7}$$

or, $t_2 = 725 - 5324.67 \times \dfrac{0.12}{1.7} = 349.14$°C

Similarly, $$5324.67 = \frac{(t_3 - 110)}{0.24/5.8}$$

or, $t_3 = 110 + 5324.67 \times \dfrac{0.24}{5.8} = 330.33$°C

Hence, the temperature drop at the interface $= t_2 - t_3$

$$= 349.14 - 330.33 = \textbf{18.81°C} \quad \textbf{(Ans.)}$$

Example 2.6. *An exterior wall of a house may be approximated by a 0.1 m layer of common brick (k = 0.7 W/m°C) followed by a 0.04m layer of gypsum plaster (k = 0.48 W/m°C). What thickness of loosely packed rock wool insulation (k = 0.065 W/m°C) should be added to reduce the heat loss or (gain) through the wall by 80 per cent ?* **(AMIE Summer, 1999)**

Solution. Refer to Fig. 2.14.

Thickness of common brick, $\quad L_A = 0.1$ m

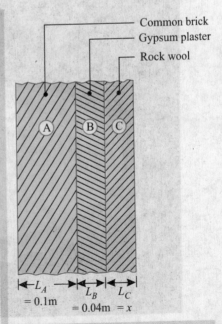

Fig. 2.14.

Thickness of gypsum plaster, $L_B = 0.04$ m

Thickness of rock wool, $L_C = x$ (in m) =?

    Thermal conductivities :

Common brick, $k_A = 0.7$ W/m°C;

Gypsum plaster, $k_B = 0.48$ W/m°C;

Rock wool, $k_C = 0.065$ W/m°C.

Case I. *Rock wool insulation not used :*

$$Q_1 = \frac{A(\Delta t)}{\dfrac{L_A}{k_A} + \dfrac{L_B}{k_B}} = \frac{A(\Delta t)}{\dfrac{0.1}{0.7} + \dfrac{0.04}{0.48}} \qquad \ldots(i)$$

Case II. *Rock wool insulation used :*

$$Q_2 = \frac{A(\Delta t)}{\dfrac{L_A}{k_A} + \dfrac{L_B}{k_B} + \dfrac{L_C}{k_C}} = \frac{A(\Delta t)}{\dfrac{0.1}{0.7} + \dfrac{0.04}{0.48} + \dfrac{x}{0.065}} \qquad \ldots(ii)$$

But, $Q_2 = (1 - 0.8) Q_1 = 0.2 \, Q_1$ *...(given)*

∴

$$\frac{A(\Delta t)}{\dfrac{0.1}{0.7} + \dfrac{0.04}{0.48} + \dfrac{x}{0.065}} = 0.2 \times \frac{A(\Delta t)}{\dfrac{0.1}{0.7} + \dfrac{0.04}{0.48}}$$

or, $\dfrac{0.1}{0.7} + \dfrac{0.04}{0.48} = 0.2 \left[\dfrac{0.1}{0.7} + \dfrac{0.04}{0.48} + \dfrac{x}{0.065} \right]$

or, $0.1428 + 0.0833 = 0.2 \, [0.1428 + 0.0833 + 15.385x]$

or, $0.2261 = 0.2 \, (0.2261 + 15.385 \, x)$

or, $x = 0.0588$ m or 58.8 mm

Thus, the *thickness of rock wool insulation should be* **58.8 mm**   **(Ans.)**

Induction furnace.

Example 2.7. *A furnace wall consists of 200 mm layer of refractory bricks, 6 mm layer of steel plate and a 100 mm layer of insulation bricks. The maximum temperature of the wall is 1150°C on the furnace side and the minimum temperature is 40°C on the outermost side of the wall. An accurate energy balance over the furnace shows that the heat loss from the wall is 400 W/m². It is known that there is a thin layer of air between the layers of refractory bricks and steel plate. Thermal conductivities for the three layers are 1.52, 45 and 0.138 W/m°C respectively. Find :*

(i) To how many millimeters of insulation brick is the air layer equivalent?

(ii) What is the temperature of the outer surface of the steel plate?

(AMIE Winter, 1996)

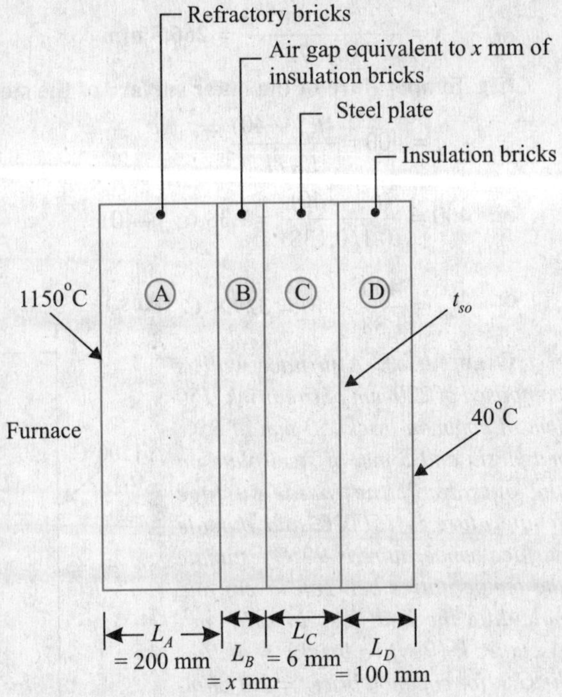

Fig. 2.15.

Solution. Refer Fig. 2.15.

Thickness of refractory bricks,

$$L_A = 200 \text{ mm} = 0.2 \text{ m}$$

Thickness of steel plate,

$$L_C = 6 \text{ mm} = 0.006 \text{ m}$$

Thickness of insulation bricks, $L_D = 100 \text{ mm} = 0.1 \text{ m}$

Difference of temperature beetween the innermost and outermost sides of the wall,

$$\Delta t = 1150 - 40 = 1110°C$$

Thermal conductivities :

$$k_A = 1.52 \text{ W/m°C}; \quad k_B = k_D = 0.138 \text{ W/m°C}; \quad k_C = 45 \text{ W/m°C}$$

Heat loss from the wall, $q = 400 \text{ W/m}^2$

(i) The value of x ($= L_C$) :

We know,

$$Q = \frac{A \cdot \Delta t}{\Sigma \dfrac{L}{k}} \qquad \text{or} \qquad \frac{Q}{A} = q = \frac{\Delta t}{\Sigma \dfrac{L}{k}}$$

or,

$$400 = \frac{1110}{\dfrac{L_A}{k_A} + \dfrac{L_B}{k_B} + \dfrac{L_C}{k_C} + \dfrac{L_D}{k_D}}$$

or,

$$400 = \frac{1110}{\dfrac{0.2}{1.52} + \dfrac{(x/1000)}{0.138} + \dfrac{0.006}{45} + \dfrac{0.1}{0.138}}$$

$$= \frac{1110}{0.1316 + 0.0072x + 0.00013 + 0.7246} = \frac{1110}{0.8563 + 0.0072x}$$

or,

$$0.8563 + 0.0072\, x = \frac{1110}{400} = 2.775$$

or, $x = \dfrac{2.775 - 0.8563}{0.0072} = \textbf{266.5 mm}$ **(Ans.)**

(ii) **Temperature of the outer surface of the steel plate** t_{so}:

$$q = 400 = \frac{(t_{so} - 40)}{L_D / k_D}$$

or, $400 = \dfrac{(t_{so} - 40)}{(0.1/0.138)} = 1.38\,(t_{so} - 40)$

or, $t_{so} = \dfrac{400}{1.38} + 40 = \textbf{329.8°C}$ **(Ans.)**

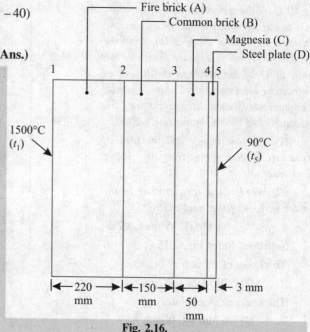

Fig. 2.16.

Example 2.8. *A furnace wall is composed of 220 mm of fire brick, 150 mm of common brick, 50 mm of 85% magnesia and 3 mm of steel plate on the outside. If the inside surface temperature is 1500°C and outside surface temperature is 90°C, estimate the temperatures between layers and calculate the heat loss in kJ/h- m². Assume, k (for fire brick) = 4kJ/m-h-°C, k(for common brick) = 2.8 kJ/m-h-°C, k (for 85% magnesia) = 0.24 kJ/m-h-°C, and k (steel) = 240 kJ/m-h-°C.*

(AMIE, Winter, 1997)

Solution. Given : $L_A = 220$ mm = 0.22 m; $L_B = 150$ mm = 0.15 m; $L_C = 50$ mm = 0.05m; $L_D = 3$ mm = 0.003 m

$$t_1 = 1500°C,\ t_5 = 90°C;$$
$$k_A = 4\ kJ/mh°C;\ k_B = 2.8\ kJ/mh°C$$
$$k_C = 0.24\ kJ/mh°C;\ k_D = 240\ kJ/mh°C.$$

Heat loss in kJ/hm² :

The equivalent thermal resistances of various layers are :

$$R_{th-A} = \frac{L_A}{k_A} = \frac{0.22}{4} = 0.055\ m^2h°C/kJ$$

$$R_{th-B} = \frac{L_B}{k_B} = \frac{0.15}{2.8} = 0.05357\ m^2h°C/kJ$$

$$R_{th-C} = \frac{L_C}{k_C} = \frac{0.05}{0.24} = 0.2083\ m^2h°C/kJ$$

$$R_{th-D} = \frac{L_D}{k_D} = \frac{0.003}{240} = 1.25 \times 10^{-5}\ m^2h°C/kJ$$

Total thermal resistance,

$$(R_{th})_{total} = 0.055 + 0.05357 + 0.2083 + 1.25 \times 10^{-5} = 0.3169\ m^2h°C/kJ$$

Heat loss, $q = \dfrac{(t_1 - t_5)}{(R_{th})_{total}} = \dfrac{(1500 - 90)}{0.3169} = \textbf{4449.35 kJ/hm}^2$ **(Ans.)**

Temperatures between layers :

Also,
$$q = \frac{t_4 - t_5}{R_{th-D}}$$

or $\quad t_4 = t_5 + q\,R_{th-D} = 90 + 4449.35 \times 1.25 \times 10^{-5} = \mathbf{90.056°C}$ (Ans.)

Similarly, $\quad t_3 = t_4 + q\,R_{th-C} = 90.056 + 444.35 \times 0.2083 = \mathbf{1016.86°C}$

and $\quad t_2 = t_3 + q\,R_{th-B} = 1016.86 + 4449.35 \times 0.05357 = \mathbf{1255.2°C}$

[Check $\quad t_1 = t_2 + q\,R_{th-A} = 1255.2 + 4449.35 \times 0.55 \simeq 1500°C$]

Example 2.9. *A metal piece of length l has a cross-section of a sector of a circle of radius r and included angle of* θ. *Its two ends are maintained at temperatures* t_1 *and* t_2 $(t_1 > t_2)$. *Find the expression for heat flow through the metal piece, assuming that the conductivity of metal varies with temperature according to relation,*

$$k = k_0(1 - \beta t).$$

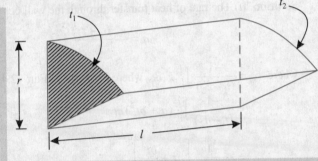

Fig. 2.17.

Also assume that $\dfrac{\partial t}{\partial \theta} = 0$ *and* $\dfrac{\partial t}{\partial r} = 0$ *and outer surfaces of the slab except the end surfaces are completely insulated.*

What will be the rate of heat transfer if l = 600 mm, r = 120 mm, θ *= 60°,* t_1 *= 125°C,* t_2 *= 25°C and* k_0 *= 115 W/m°C and* β *= 10⁻⁴ ?*

Solution. As per given conditions,
$$Q = \frac{kA(t_1 - t_2)}{l}$$

The area through which heat is flowing is given by,

$$A = \pi r^2 \times \frac{\theta}{2\pi} = \frac{r^2\theta}{2}$$

where θ is in radians.

$$k_m = k_0(1 - \beta t_m) \text{ where } t_m = \frac{t_1 + t_2}{2}$$

as its variation is linear.

$$\therefore Q = \frac{k_m}{l}\left(\frac{r^2 \cdot \theta}{2}\right)(t_1 - t_2) \qquad ...(i)$$

Rate of heat transfer, Q :

Given : l = 600 mm = 0.6 m; r = 120 mm

= 0.12 m, $\theta = 60° = \dfrac{\pi}{3}$ rad., t_1 = 125°C, t_2 = 25°C, k_0 = 115 W/m°C and β = 10⁻⁴.

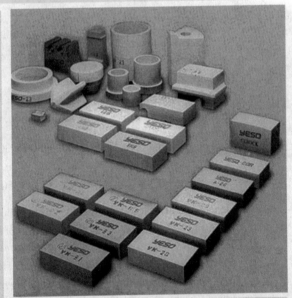

Insulating fire bricks.

$$\therefore k_m = k_0(1 - \beta t_m) = 115\left[1 - 10^{-4}\left(\frac{125 + 25}{2}\right)\right] = 114.14 \text{ W/m°C}$$

Subsituting the proper values in the expression (i), we have

$$Q = \frac{114.14}{0.6} \left(\frac{0.12^2 \times \frac{\pi}{3}}{2} \right) (125 - 25) = \mathbf{143.43\,W} \quad \text{(Ans.)}$$

Example 2.10. *(i) Derive an expression for the heat loss per m^2 of the surface area for a furnace wall (Fig. 2.18), when the thermal conductivity varies with temperature according to the relation :*

$$k = (a + bt^2) \text{ W/m}°C, \qquad \text{where } t \text{ is in } °C$$

(ii) Find the rate of heat transfer through the wall, if $L = 0.2$ m, $t_1 = 300°C$, $t_2 = 30°C$ and $a = 0.3$ and $b = 5 \times 10^{-6}$.

(Maharashtra University)

Solution. *(i)* The rate of heat transfer through the wall per m^2 is given by

$$q = \frac{k_m (t_1 - t_2)}{L}$$

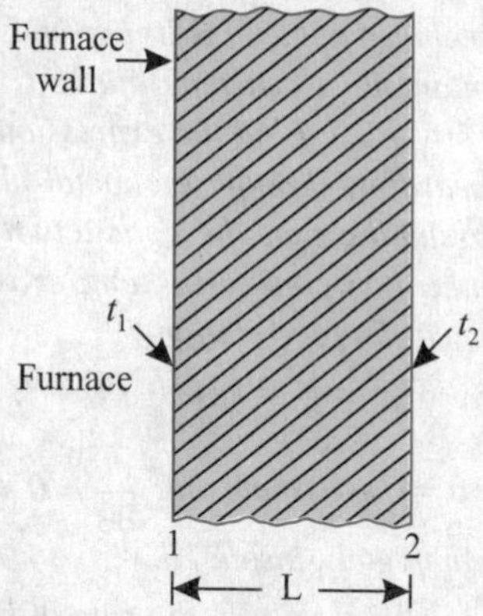

where $k_m = \dfrac{-1}{(t_1 - t_2)} \displaystyle\int_{t_1}^{t_2} k \cdot dt$, where $k = f(t)$ ...[Eqn. (2.47)]

$$= \frac{-1}{(t_1 - t_2)} \int_{t_1}^{t_2} (a + bt^2)\, dt$$

$$= \frac{-1}{(t_1 - t_2)} \left[at + \frac{bt^3}{3} \right]_{t_1}^{t_2}$$

$$= \frac{-1}{(t_1 - t_2)} \left[a(t_2 - t_1) + \frac{b}{3}(t_2^3 - t_1^3) \right]$$

$$= \frac{-1}{(t_1 - t_2)} (t_2 - t_1) \left[a + \frac{b}{3}(t_2^2 + t_1 t_2 + t_1^2) \right]$$

$$= a + \frac{b}{3} \left[t_1^2 + t_1 t_2 + t_2^2 \right]$$

$$\therefore \qquad q = \left[a + \frac{b}{3}(t_1^2 + t_1 t_2 + t_2^2) \right] \left[\frac{t_1 - t_2}{L} \right] \quad \textit{...Required expression. (Ans.)}$$

Furnace wall

Furnace

Fig. 2.18.

(ii) **Rate of heat transfer per m^2, q :**

Thickness of wall, $L = 0.2$m; $t_1 = 300°C$; $t_2 = 30°C$; $a = 0.3$ and $b = 5 \times 10^{-6}$.

Substituting these values in the said equation, we have

$$q = \left[0.3 + \frac{5 \times 10^{-6}}{3} (300^2 + 300 \times 30 + 30^2) \right] \left[\frac{(300 - 30)}{0.2} \right]$$

$$= \left(0.3 + \frac{5 \times 10^{-6}}{3} \times 99900 \right) \times 1350 = 629.77 \text{ W/m}^2$$

Hence, rate of heat transfer per m^2 through the wall = **629.77 W/m²** **(Ans.)**

Example 2.11. *The surfaces of a plane wall of thickness L are maintained at temperatures t_1 and t_2. The thermal conductivity of wall material varies according to the relation: $k = k_0 t^2$.*

(i) Derive an expression to find the steady state conduction through the wall.

(ii) Find the temperature at which mean thermal conductivity be evaluated in order to get the same heat flow by its substitution in the simplified Fourier's equation.

Solution.   Thickness of wall $= L$

Temperatures of surfaces $= t_1, t_2$

Relation of variation of thermal conductivity $k = k_0 t^2$

(i) Expression for heat conduction through wall :

Heat conduction through a plane wall is given by (Fourier's law)

$$Q = -k\, A \frac{dt}{dx}$$

$$= -k_0 t^2 \cdot A \frac{dt}{dx}$$

By rearranging and integrating, we get

$$\int_0^L Q.dx = -k_0\, A \int_{t_1}^{t_2} t^2\, dt$$

$$Q|x|_0^L = -k_0\, A \left[\frac{t^3}{3}\right]_{t_1}^{t_2}$$

$$QL = \frac{-k_0 A}{3}\left(t_2^{\,3} - t_1^{\,3}\right)$$

or,
$$Q = \frac{k_0\, A}{3L}\left(t_1^{\,3} - t_2^{\,3}\right) \quad ...\textit{Required expression.}$$

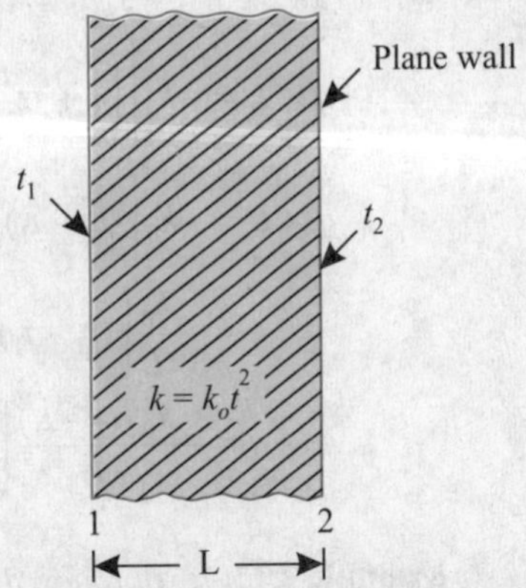

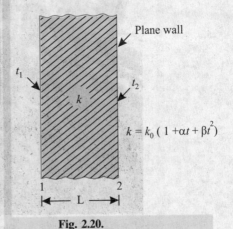

Plane wall

$k = k_0 t^2$

Fig. 2.19.

(ii) Temperature, t_m :

If the above heat flow is to be obtained by substituting mean value of thermal conductivity in the simplified Fourier's equation, we have

$$\frac{k_0\, A}{3L}\left(t_1^{\,3} - t_2^{\,3}\right) = \frac{k_m\, A(t_1 - t_2)}{L}$$

$$= \frac{k_0\, t_m^2\, A(t_1 - t_2)}{L}$$

or,
$$t_m^{\,2} = \left[\frac{k_0\, A}{3L}(t_1^{\,3} - t_2^{\,3})\right] \times \left[\frac{L}{k_0\, A(t_1 - t_2)}\right]$$

$$= \frac{t_1^{\,3} - t_2^{\,3}}{3(t_1 - t_2)} = \frac{(t_1 - t_2)(t_1^{\,2} + t_1 t_2 + t_2^{\,2})}{3(t_1 - t_2)} = \frac{t_1^{\,2} + t_1 t_2 + t_2^{\,2}}{3}$$

∴
$$t_m = \sqrt{\frac{t_1^{\,2} + t_2^{\,2} + t_1 t_2}{3}} \quad ...\textit{Required temperature.} \ \textbf{(Ans.)}$$

Example 2.12. *The variation of thermal conductivity of a wall material is given by*

$$k = k_0\,(1 + \alpha t + \beta t^2)$$

If the thickness of the wall is L and its two surfaces are maintained at temperatures t_1 and t_2, find an expression for the steady state one-dimensional heat flow through the wall.

Solution. The rate of heat transfer through a wall per unit area is given by

$$q = -k \cdot \frac{dt}{dx} \quad ...\text{Fourier's equation}$$

$$= -k_0\,(1 + \alpha t + \beta t^2) \cdot \frac{dt}{dx}$$

or,
$$q.\,dx = -k_0\,(1 + \alpha t + \beta t^2)\,.\,dt$$

Plane wall

$k = k_0\,(1 + \alpha t + \beta t^2)$

Fig. 2.20.

Integrating both sides we get

$$q \int_0^L dx = -k_0 \int_{t_1}^{t_2} (1 + \alpha t + \beta t^2) dt$$

$$q \times L = -k_0 \left[\left(t + \alpha \frac{t^2}{2} + \beta . \frac{t^3}{3} \right) \right]_{t_1}^{t_2}$$

$$q \times L = -k_0 \left[(t_2 - t_1) + \frac{\alpha}{2}(t_2^2 - t_1^2) + \frac{\beta}{3}(t_2^3 - t_1^3) \right]$$

$$q = -\frac{k_0}{L} \left[(t_2 - t_1) + \frac{\alpha}{2}(t_2 - t_1)(t_2 + t_1) + \frac{\beta}{3}(t_2 - t_1)(t_1^2 + t_2^2 + t_1 t_2) \right]$$

$$q = -\frac{k_0(t_2 - t_1)}{L} \left[1 + \frac{\alpha}{2}(t_1 + t_2) + \frac{\beta}{3}(t_1^2 + t_2^2 + t_1 t_2) \right] \text{ ...Required expression.}$$

(Ans.)

Example 2.13. *It is proposed to carry pressurized water through a pipe imbeded in a 1.2 m thick wall whose surfaces are held at constant temperatures of 200°C and 60°C respectively. It is desired to locate the pipe in wall where the temperature is 120°C, find how far from the hot surface should the pipe be imbedded ? The thermal conductivity of the wall material varies with the temperature according to the relation, k = 0.28 (1 + 0.036t) where t is in degree celsius and k is in W/m°C.*

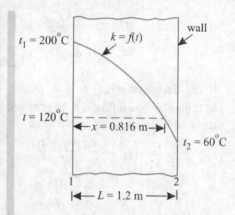

Fig. 2.21.

Solution. Thickness of wall, $\quad L = 1.2$ m

Temperatures of wall surfaces $\quad t_1 = 200°C;$

$$t_2 = 60°C$$

Temperature, $\qquad\qquad t = 120°C$

Relation for conductivity $\qquad k = 0.28 (1 + 0.036t)$

Pipework inside a factory.

The rate of heat transfer through a plane wall of variable thermal conductivity is given by

$$Q = k_m \cdot \frac{A}{L}(t_1 - t_2)$$

$$= k_0 \left[1 + \frac{\alpha}{2}(t_1 + t_2) \right] \frac{A}{L}(t_1 - t_2)$$

Now, when　$t_2 = 60°C$,　　$L = 1.2$ m

and, when　$t_2 = 120°C$,　　$L = x$ (unknown)

Substituting the values and equating the two expressions, we have

$$0.28\left[1 + \frac{0.036}{2}(200 + 60)\right]\frac{A}{1.2}(200 - 60) = 0.28\left[1 + \frac{0.036}{2}(200 + 120)\right]\frac{A}{x}(200 - 120)$$

$$185.54 = \frac{151.42}{x} \quad \text{or} \quad \frac{151.42}{185.54} = 0.816\,\text{m}$$

Hence the pipe should be imbedded 0.816 m *from the hot wall surface.* **(Ans.)**

Example 2.14. *Find the steady state heat flux through the composite slab as shown in the Fig. 2.22 and the interface temperature. The thermal conductivities of the two materials vary with temperature as given below :*

$k_A = 0.05\,(1 + 0.0065t)$ *W/m°C; $k_B = 0.04\,(1 + 0.0076t\,)$ W/m°C, where temperatures are in °C.* **[M.U.]**

Solution.　　$t_1 = 600°C; t_3 = 300°C$

$L_A = 50$ mm $= 0.05$m

$L_B = 100$ mm $= 0.1$m

$$k_{mA} = k_{OA}\left[1 + \alpha_A\left(\frac{t_1 + t_2}{2}\right)\right]$$

$$= 0.05\left[1 + 0.0065\left(\frac{t_1 + t_2}{2}\right)\right]$$

$$k_{mB} = k_{OB}\left[1 + \alpha_B\left(\frac{t_2 + t_3}{2}\right)\right]$$

$$= 0.04\left[1 + 0.0075\left(\frac{t_2 + t_3}{2}\right)\right]$$

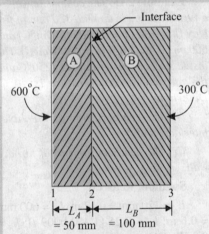

Fig. 2.22.

Interface temperature, t_2 :

Rate of heat transfer per m^2,

$$q = \frac{Q}{A} = \frac{(t_1 - t_2)}{(L_A / k_{mA})} = \frac{(t_2 - t_3)}{(L_B / k_{mB})} \qquad \text{...(1)}$$

Now substituting the values of k_{mA} and k_{mB} in eqn (1), we get

$$\frac{(600 - t_2)}{0.05\left[1 + 0.0065\left(\dfrac{600 + t_2}{2}\right)\right]} = \frac{(t_2 - 300)}{0.1\left[0.04\left[1 + 0.0075\left(\dfrac{t_2 + 300}{2}\right)\right]\right.}$$

or, $(600 - t_2)\left[1 + 0.0065\left(\dfrac{600 + t_2}{2}\right)\right] = 0.4\,(t_2 - 300)\left[1 + 0.0075\left(\dfrac{t_2 + 300}{2}\right)\right]$

or, $(600 - t_2)\left[\dfrac{5.9 + 0.0065\,t_2}{2}\right] = (t_2 - 300)\left[\dfrac{4.25 + 0.0075\,t_2}{2}\right] \times 0.4$

or, $(600 - t_2)(5.9 + 0.0065\, t_2) = (t_2 - 300)(1.7 + 0.003\, t_2)$

or, $3540 + 3.9t_2 - 5.9t_2 - 0.0065t_2^2 = 1.7\, t_2 + 0.003\, t_2^2 - 510 - 0.9\, t_2$

or, $0.0095\, t_2^2 + 2.8\, t_2 - 4050 = 0$

or, $t_2^2 + 294.7\, t_2 - 426315 = 0$

or, $$t_2 = \frac{-294.7 \pm \sqrt{294.7^2 + 4 \times 426316}}{2}$$

$$= \frac{-294.7 \pm 1338.7}{2} = 522°C$$

∴ $$k_{mA} = 0.05\left[1 + 0.0065\left(\frac{600 + 522}{2}\right)\right] = 0.2323 \text{ W}/m°C$$

Rate of heat transfer per m^2, q :

The steady state heat flow through the composite slab,

$$q = \frac{(t_1 - t_2)}{(L_A / k_{mA})} = \frac{(600 - 522)}{(0.05/0.2323)} = \textbf{362.39 W/m}^2 \textbf{ (Ans.)}$$

Example 2.15. *The composite wall of a furnace is made up with 120 mm of fire clay [k = 0.25 (1 + 0.0009 t) W/m°C] and 600 mm of red brick (k = 0.8 W/m°C). The inside surface temperature is 1250°C and the outside air temperature is 40°C. Determine :*

(i) The temperature at the layer interface, and

(ii) The heat loss for 1m² of furnace wall.

Solution. Refer Fig. 2.23.

$L_A = 120$ mm $= 0.12$ m; $L_B = 600$ mm $= 0.6$ m; $k_A = 0.25\,[1 + 0.0009\,t]$; $k_B = 0.8$ W/m°C; $\Delta t = (t_1 - t_{air}) = 1250 - 40 = 1210°C$.

(i) The temperature at layer interface, t_2 :

Average/mean thermal conductivity of fire clay,

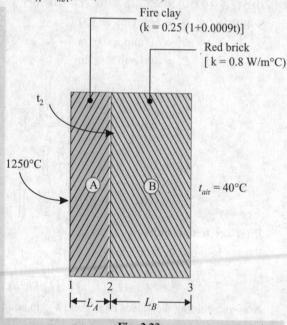

Fig. 2.23.

$$(k_A)_m = 0.25\left[1 + 0.0009\left(\frac{1250 + t_2}{2}\right)\right]$$

$$= 0.25\,[1 + 0.00045\,(1250 + t_2)]$$

∴ Thermal resistance of fire clay,

$$R_{th-A} = \frac{L_A}{(k_A)_m\, A} = \frac{0.12}{0.25[1 + 0.00045(1250 + t_2)] \times 1} = \frac{1}{2.083 + 0.000937(1250 + t_2)}$$

Similarly, thermal resistance of red brick,

$$R_{th-B} = \frac{L_B}{k_B \cdot A} = \frac{0.6}{0.8 \times 1} = 0.75$$

Heat loss for $1 m^2$ of furnace wall,

$$Q = \frac{\Delta t}{\Sigma R_{th}} = \frac{\Delta t}{R_{th-A} + R_{th-B}}$$

$$= \frac{1210}{\dfrac{1}{2.083 + 0.000937\,(1250 + t_2)} + 0.75} \qquad \text{...}(i)$$

Under steady state conditions the same amount of heat flows through each layer. Then considering heat flow through the red brick, we have

$$Q = \frac{(t_2 - 40)}{k_B} = \frac{(t_2 - 40)}{0.8} \qquad \text{...}(ii)$$

From expression (i) and (ii), we obtain

$$\frac{1210}{\dfrac{1}{2.083 + 0.000937\,(1250 + t_2)} + 0.75} = \frac{(t_2 - 40)}{0.8}$$

or, $$\frac{1210[2.083 + 0.000937\,(1250 + t_2)]}{1 + 0.75[2.083 + 0.000937\,(1250 + t_2)]} = \frac{t_2 - 40}{0.8}$$

or, $$\frac{1210[3.254 + 0.000937\,t_2]}{1 + 1.562 + 0.878 + 0.000703\,t_2} = \frac{(t_2 - 40)}{0.8}$$

or, $$\frac{3937.34 + 1.134\,t_2}{3.44 + 0.000703\,t_2} = \frac{(t_2 - 40)}{0.8}$$

or, $$0.8\,(3937.34 + 1.134\ t_2) = (t_2 - 40)\,(3.44 + 0.000703\ t_2)$$

or, $$3149.87 + 0.907\ t_2 = 3.44\ t_2 + 0.000703\ t_2^2 - 137.6 - 0.0281\ t_2$$

or, $$0.000703\ t_2^2 + 2.505\ t_2 - 3287.47 = 0$$

or, $$t_2 = \frac{-2.505 + \sqrt{(2.505)^2 + 4 \times 0.000703 \times 3287.47}}{2 \times 0.000703} = \textbf{1020.24°C} \ \textbf{(Ans.)}$$

(*ii*) **Heat loss, Q :**

Heat loss for 1 m² of the furnace wall,

$$Q = \frac{(t_2 - 40)}{R_{th-B}} = \frac{(1020.24 - 40)}{0.75} = \textbf{1306.98 W} \ \textbf{(Ans.)}$$

Example 2.16. *Find the heat flow rate through the composite wall as shown in Fig. 2.24 Assume one dimensional flow.*

$k_A = 150 \ W/m°C,$

$k_B = 30 \ W/m°C,$

$k_C = 65 \ W/m°C, \text{ and}$

$k_D = 50 \ W/m°C$

(M.U. Winter, 2000)

Solution. The thermal circuit for heat flow in the given composite system (shown in Fig. 2.24) has been illustrated in Fig. 2.25.

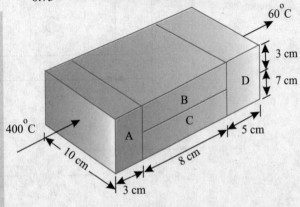

Fig. 2.24.

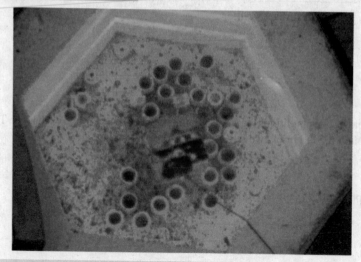

Furnance view from top.

Thickness :

$L_A = 3 \text{ cm} = 0.03 \text{ m}; L_B = L_C = 8 \text{ cm} = 0.08 \text{ m}; L_D = 5 \text{ cm} = 0.05 \text{ m}$

Areas :

$$A_A = 0.1 \times 0.1 = 0.01 \text{m}^2 ; \qquad A_B = 0.1 \times 0.03 = 0.003 \text{m}^2$$
$$A_C = 0.1 \times 0.07 = 0.007 \text{m}^2 ; \qquad A_D = 0.1 \times 0.1 = 0.01 \text{m}^2$$

Heat flow rate, Q :

The thermal resistances are given by,

$$R_{th-A} = \frac{L_A}{k_A A_A} = \frac{0.03}{150 \times 0.01} = 0.02$$

$$R_{th-B} = \frac{L_B}{k_B A_B} = \frac{0.08}{30 \times 0.003} = 0.89$$

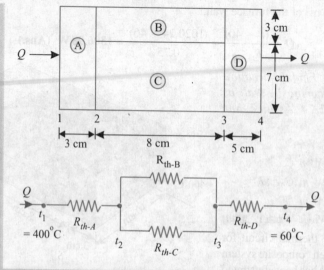

Fig. 2.25. Thermal circuit.

$$R_{th-C} = \frac{L_C}{k_C \, A_C} = \frac{0.08}{65 \times 0.007} = 0.176$$

$$R_{th-D} = \frac{L_D}{k_D \, A_D} = \frac{0.05}{50 \times 0.01} = 0.1$$

The equivalent thermal resistance for the parallel thermal resistance R_{th-B} and R_{th-C} is given by

$$\frac{1}{(R_{th})_{eq}} = \frac{1}{R_{th-B}} + \frac{1}{R_{th-C}} = \frac{1}{0.89} + \frac{1}{0.176} = 6.805$$

$$\therefore \qquad (R_{th})_{eq.} = \frac{1}{6.805} = 0.147$$

Now, the total thermal resistance is given by

$$(R_{th})_{total} = R_{th-A} + (R_{th})_{eq.} + R_{th-D} = 0.02 + 0.147 + 0.1 = 0.267$$

$$\therefore \qquad Q = \frac{(\Delta t)_{overall}}{(R_{th})_{total}} = \frac{(400-60)}{0.267} = \textbf{1273.4 W} \ \ \textbf{(Ans.)}$$

Example 2.17. *The insulation boards for air-conditioning purposes are made of three layers, middle being of packed grass 10 cm thick (k = 0.02 W/m°C) and the sides are made of plywood each of 2 cm thickness (k = 0.12 W/m°C). They are glued with each other.*

(i) Determine the heat flow per m² area if one surface is at 35°C and other surface is at 20°C. Neglect the resistance of glue.

(ii) Instead of glue, if these three pieces are bolted by four steel bolts of 1 cm diameter at the corner (k = 40 W/m°C) per m² area of the board then find the heat flow per m² area of the combined board. **(M.U., 2001)**

Solution. (*i*) **When the layers are glued :**
Refer Fig. 2.26.

Thickness of each of the plywood layer, $L_A = L_C = 2$ cm $= 0.02$ m

Thickness of grass layer,

$L_B = 10$ cm $= 0.1$ m

Thermal conductivities :

$k_A = k_C = 0.12$ W/m°C;

$k_B = 0.02$ W/m°C;

Temperatures : $t_1 = 35°C$; $t_4 = 20°C$

Heat flow per m² area, q :

$$q = \frac{(t_1 - t_4)}{R_{th-A} + R_{th-B} + R_{th-C}}$$

$$= \frac{(t_1 - t_4)}{\dfrac{L_A}{k_A \cdot A} + \dfrac{L_B}{k_B \cdot A} + \dfrac{L_C}{k_C \cdot A}}$$

$$= \frac{(35-20)}{\dfrac{0.02}{0.12 \times 1} + \dfrac{0.1}{0.02 \times 1} + \dfrac{0.02}{0.12 \times 1}}$$

$$= \frac{15}{0.167 + 5.0 + 0.167} = \textbf{2.81 W/m}^2 \ \ \textbf{(Ans.)}$$

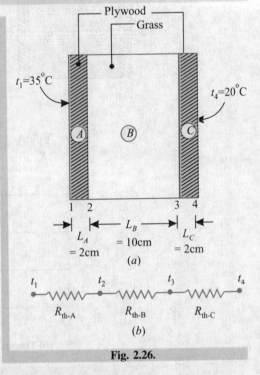

Fig. 2.26.

(ii) **When the layers are joined by steel bolts :** Refer to Fig. 2.27.

Number of steel bolts used = 4

Diameter of each bolt, d_b = 1cm = 0.01 m

$$\therefore \text{ Area of each bolt, } A_b = \frac{\pi}{4} \times 0.01^2 = 7.854 \times 10^{-5} \text{ m}^2$$

Thermal conductivity of bolt material, k_D = 40 W/m°C

The equivalent thermal resistance $(R_{th})_{eq.}$ of the thermal circuit for the system is given by

$$\frac{1}{(R_{th})_{eq}} = \frac{1}{(R_{th-A} + R_{th-B} + R_{th-C})} + \frac{4}{R_{th-D}}$$

where

$$R_{th-D} = \frac{(L_A + L_B + L_C)}{k_D \cdot A_b} = \frac{0.02 + 0.1 + 0.02}{40 \times 7.854 \times 10^{-5}} = 44.56°C/W$$

$$\therefore \qquad \frac{1}{(R_{th})_{eq}} = \frac{1}{(0.167 + 5.0 + 0.167)} + \frac{4}{44.56} = 0.187 + 0.089 = 0.276$$

or,

$$(R_{th})_{eq.} \text{ or } (R_{th})_{total} = \frac{1}{0.276} = 3.623°C/W$$

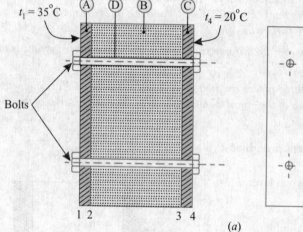
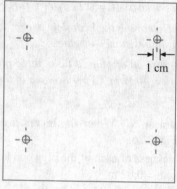

(a)

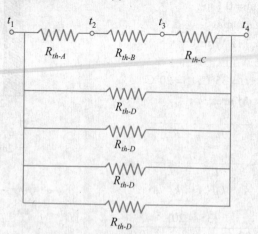

(b) Thermal circuit for the system.

Fig. 2.27.

Heat flow per m² area, q :

$$q = \frac{(t_1 - t_4)}{(R_{th})_{total}} = \frac{(35 - 20)}{3.623} = 4.14 \text{ W/m}^2 \text{ (Ans.)}$$

Example 2.18. *Two slabs, each 120 mm thick, have thermal conductivities of 14.5 W/m°C and 210 W/m°C. These are placed in contact, but due to roughness, only 30 percent of area is in contact and the gap in the remaining area is 0.025 mm thick and is filled with air. If the temperature of the face of the hot surface is at 220°C and the outside side surface of other slab is at 30°C, determine :*

(i) *Heat flow through the composite system.*

(ii) *The contact resistance and temperature drop in contact.*

Assume that the conductivity of air is 0.032 W/m°C and that half of the contact (of the contact area) is due to either metal.

Solution. $L_A = 120 \text{ mm} = 0.12 \text{ m};$ $\quad L_{A_1} = 0.025 \text{ mm} = 0.000025 \text{ m}$

$\qquad\quad L_B = 120 \text{ mm} = 0.12 \text{ m};$ $\quad L_{B_1} = 0.025 \text{ mm} = 0.000025 \text{ m}$

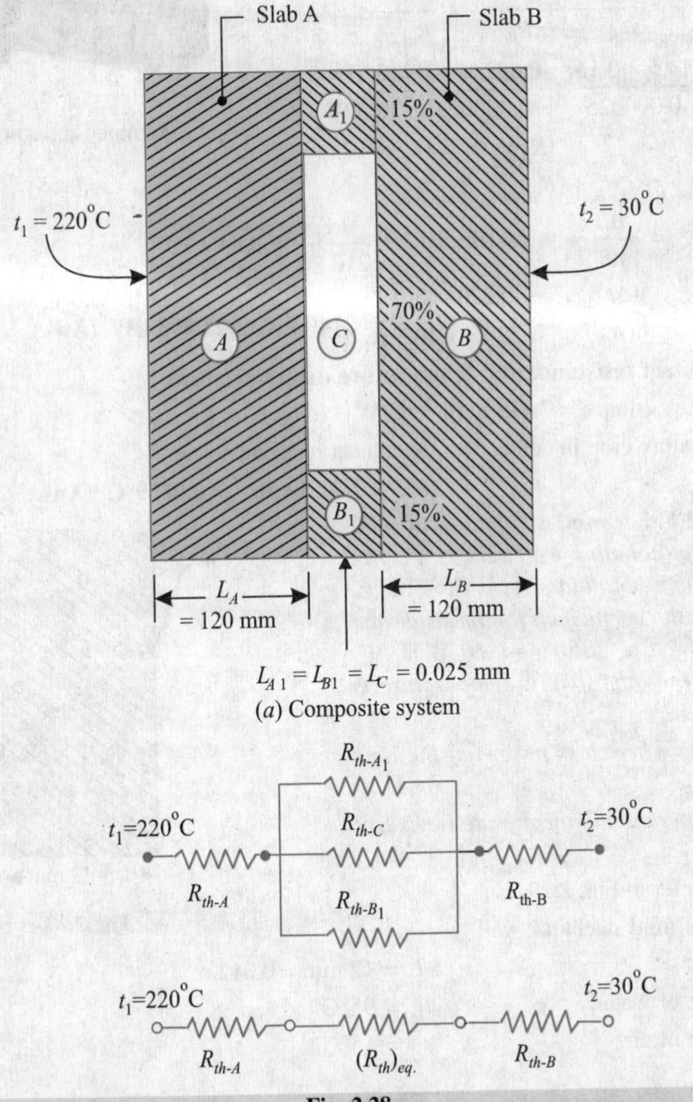

$L_{A1} = L_{B1} = L_C = 0.025 \text{ mm}$

(a) Composite system

Fig. 2.28.

L_C $= 0.025$ mm $= 0.000025$ m;

$k_A = k_{A_1} = 14.5$ W/m°C;

$k_B = k_{B_1} = 210$ W/m°C;

$k_C = 0.032$ W/m°C; $t_1 = 220$°C; $t_2 = 30$°C

(i) Heat flow through the system, Q :

$$R_{th-A} = \frac{0.12}{14.5 \times 1}$$

$$R_{th-A_1} = \frac{0.000025}{14.5 \times 0.15}, \quad R_{th-C} = \frac{0.000025}{0.032 \times 0.7}$$

$$R_{th-B_1} = \frac{0.000025}{210 \times 0.15}; \quad R_{th-B} = \frac{0.12}{210 \times 1}$$

$$\frac{1}{(R_{th})_{eq}} = \frac{1}{R_{th-A_1}} + \frac{1}{R_{th-C}} + \frac{1}{R_{th-B_1}}$$

$$\frac{1}{(R_{th})_{eq}} = \frac{14.5 \times 0.15}{0.000025} + \frac{0.032 \times 0.7}{0.000025} + \frac{210 \times 0.15}{0.000025}$$

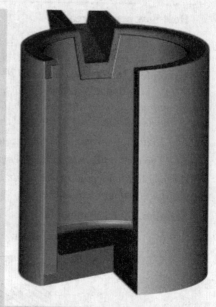

Rammed induction furnace.

or, $(R_{th})_{eq} = 7.419 \times 10^{-7}$

or, $(R_{th})_{total} = R_{th-A} + (R_{th})_{eq} + R_{th-B}$

$$= \frac{0.12}{14.5 \times 1} + 7.419 \times 10^{-7} + \frac{0.12}{210 \times 1} \approx 8.84 \times 10^{-3}$$

Hence, $Q = \dfrac{(\Delta t)_{overall}}{(R_{th})_{total}} = \dfrac{(220 - 30)}{8.84 \times 10^{-3}} = 21493$ W or **21.493 kW** **(Ans.)**

(ii) The contact resistance and temperature drop in contact :

The contact resistance = **7.419×10^{-7} °C/W**   **(Ans.)**

The temperature drop in contact = $Q \times$ contact resistance

$$= 21493 \times 7.419 \times 10^{-7} = \textbf{0.0159°C} \textbf{ (Ans.)}$$

Example 2.19. *A mild steel tank of wall thickness 12 mm contains water at 95°C. The thermal conductivity of mild steel is 50 W/m°C, and the heat transfer coefficients for the inside and outside the tank are 2850 and 10 W/m²°C, respectively. If the atmospheric temperature is 15°C, calculate :*

(i) The rate of heat loss per m² of the tank surface area.

(ii) The temperature of the outside surface of the tank.

Solution. Refer to Fig. 2.29.

Thickness of mild steel tank wall

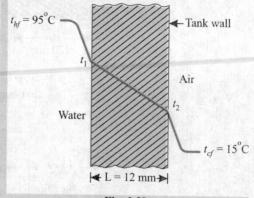

Fig. 2.29.

$$L = 12 \text{ mm} = 0.012 \text{ m}$$

Temperature of water, $t_{hf} = 95$°C

Temperature of air, $t_{cf} = 15$°C

Thermal conductivity of mild steel,
$$k = 50 \text{ W/m°C}$$

Heat transfer coefficients :

Hot fluid (water), h_{hf} = 2850 W/m²°C

Cold fluid (air), h_{cf} = 10 W/m²°C.

(i) Rate of heat loss per m² of the tank surface area, q:

Rate of heat loss per m² of tank surface,
$$q = UA\,(t_{hf} - t_{cf})$$

The overall heat transfer coefficient, U is found from the relation,

$$\frac{1}{U} = \frac{1}{h_{hf}} + \frac{L}{k} + \frac{1}{h_{cf}} = \frac{1}{2850} + \frac{0.012}{50} + \frac{1}{10}$$

$$= 0.0003508 + 0.00024 + 0.1 = 0.1006$$

$$\therefore \quad U = \frac{1}{0.1006} = 9.94 \text{ W/m}^2\text{°C}$$

Bricked induction furnace.

$$\therefore \quad q = 9.94 \times 1 \times (95 - 15) = \textbf{795.2 W/m}^2 \textbf{ (Ans.)}$$

(ii) Temperature of the outside surface of the tank, t_2:

We know that, $q = h_{cf} \times 1 \times (t_2 - t_{cf})$

or, $795.2 = 10\,(t_2 - 15)$

or, $t_2 = \dfrac{795.2}{10} + 15 = \textbf{94.52°C}$ (Ans.)

Example 2.20. *An electric hot plate is maintained at a temperature of 350°C, and is used to keep a solution boiling at 95°C. The solution is contained in a cast-iron vessel of wall thickness 25 mm, which is enamelled inside to a thickness of 0.8 mm. The heat transfer coefficient for the boiling solution is 5.5 kW/m²K, and the thermal conductivities of the cast iron and enamel are 50 and 1.05 W/mK, respectively. Calculate :*

(i) The overall heat transfer coefficient.

(ii) The rate of heat transfer per unit area.   (GATE, 1993)

Solution. *Given :* t_{heater} = 350°C; $t_{solution}$ = 95°C; $(\Delta x)_{C.I.}$ = 25 mm = 0.025 m;

$(\Delta x)_{enamel}$ = 0.8 mm = 0.8 × 10⁻³ m; $h_{solution}$ = 5.5 kW/m²K; $k_{C.I.}$ = 50 W/mK;

k_{enamel} = 1.05 W/mK.

Refer Fig. 2.30.

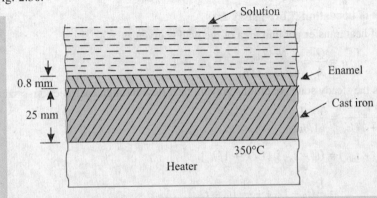

Fig. 2.30.

(i) The overall heat transfer coefficient, U :

$$\frac{1}{U} = \frac{(\Delta x)_{C.I.}}{k_{C.I.}} + \frac{(\Delta x)_{enamel}}{k_{enamel}} + \frac{1}{h_{solution}}$$

$$= \left(\frac{0.025}{50} + \frac{0.8 \times 10^{-3}}{1.05} + \frac{1}{5.5 \times 10^3} \right) = 1.444 \times 10^{-3} \text{ W}$$

$\therefore$ $U = 692.5 \text{ W/m}^2\text{K}$ **(Ans.)**

(ii) The rate of heat transfer per unit area, Q :

$$Q = UA \, (t_{heater} - t_{solution})$$

$$= 692.5 \times 1 \times (350 - 9.5) = 176587.5 \text{ W/m}^2 \approx \mathbf{176.6 \text{ kW/m}^2} \quad \textbf{(Ans.)}$$

Example 2.21. *The maximum operating temperature of a kitchen oven is set at 310°C. Due to seasonal variations, the kitchen temperature may vary from 12°C to 32°C. If the average heat transfer coefficient between the outside oven surface and kitchen air is 12 W/ m²°C, determine the necessary thickness of fibre glass (k = 0.036 W/m°C) insulation to ensure that the outside surface temperature of oven does not exceed 45°C. Assume that the steady state conditions prevail and the thermal resistance of metal wall is negligible.*

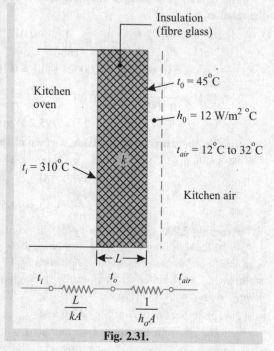

Fig. 2.31.

Solution. Refer Fig. 2.31.

Maximum temperature of kitchen oven,

$$t_i = 310°C$$

Outside surface temperature of oven,

$$t_0 = 45°C$$

Kitchen air temperature,

$$t_{air} = 12°C \text{ to } 32°C$$

Thermal conductivity of insulating material (fibre glass)

$$k = 0.036 \text{W/m°C}$$

Heat transfer coefficient,

$$h_o = 12 \text{W/m}^2°C.$$

Thickness of insulation (fibre glass), L :

The rate of heat transfer per unit area of the wall is given as

$$q = \frac{Q}{A} = \frac{t_i - t_{air}}{L/k + 1/h_0}$$

Further, as the steady state conditions prevail, heat flow through each section is same.

$$\therefore \quad \frac{t_i - t_{air}}{L/k + 1/h_0} = \frac{t_0 - t_{air}}{1/h_0}$$

or, $$\frac{1}{h_0}(t_i - t_{air}) = (t_0 - t_{air}) \, [L/k + 1/h_0]$$

$$= \frac{L}{k}(t_0 - t_{air}) + \frac{1}{h_0}(t_0 - t_{air})$$

or $\quad \dfrac{1}{h_0}[(t_i - t_{air}) - (t_0 - t_{air})] = \dfrac{L}{k}(t_0 - t_{air})$

or $\quad\quad\quad \dfrac{1}{h_0}(t_i - t_0) = \dfrac{L}{k}(t_0 - t_{air})$

or $\quad\quad\quad L = \dfrac{k}{h_0}\left[\dfrac{t_i - t_0}{t_0 - t_{air}}\right]$

The thickness of insulation (fibre glass) will be large for $t_{air} = 32°C$.

$\therefore \quad\quad\quad L = \dfrac{0.036}{12}\left[\dfrac{310 - 45}{45 - 32}\right] = 0.06115$ m or **61.15 mm**   **(Ans.)**

Example 2.22. *Hot gases at 1020°C flow past the upper surface of a gas turbine blade (the blade to be considered as a flat plate 1.2 mm thick) and the lower surface is cooled by air bled off the compressor. The thermal conductivity of blade material is 12 W/m°C and the heat transfer coefficients (convective) at the upper and lower surfaces are 2750 W/m²°C and 1400 W/m²°C respectively. Assuming steady state conditions have reached and the metallurgical considerations limit the blade temperature to 900°C, estimate the temperature of coolant-air.*

Solution. Temperature of hot gases (fluid) $\quad t_{hf} = 1020°C$

$\quad\quad\quad$ Thickness of blade, $L = 1.2$ mm $= 0.0012$ m

$\quad\quad$ Thermal conductivity of blade material, $k = 12$ W/m°C

Convective heat transfer coefficients :

$\quad\quad\quad\quad\quad$ Upper surface, $h_{hf} = 2750$ W/m²°C

$\quad\quad\quad\quad\quad$ Lower surface, $h_{cf} = 1400$ W/m²°C

Temperature at the upper surface of the blade,

$$t_1 = 900°C.$$

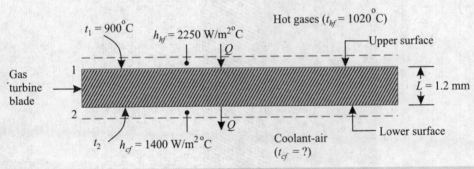

Fig. 2.32.

Temperature of the coolant air, t_{cf} :

The rate of heat transfer per unit area,

$$Q = h_{hf} \cdot A\,(t_{hf} - t_1)$$
$$= 2750 \times 1\,(1020 - 900) = 330000 \text{ W/m}^2$$

Since the heat transfer takes place under steady state conditions, therefore, this heat would be conducted across the gas turbine blade. Using Fourier's law of heat conduction, we have

$$Q = \dfrac{kA(t_1 - t_2)}{L}$$

where, t_2 = Temperature of the lower surface.

or, $\quad\quad\quad 330000 = \dfrac{12 \times 1 \times (900 - t_2)}{0.0012}$

or, $t_2 = 900 - \dfrac{330000 \times 0.0012}{12} = 867°C$

As the heat conducted across the blade would be transferred to the coolant-air, therefore,

$$Q = h_{cf} \cdot A\,(t_2 - t_{cf})$$

$$330000 = 1400 \times 1\,(867 - t_{cf})$$

$$\therefore \quad t_{cf} = 867 - \dfrac{330000}{1400} = \textbf{631.28°C}$$

(Ans.)

Example 2.23. *A metal plate of 4mm thickness (k = 95.5 W/m°C) is exposed to vapour at 100°C on one side and cooling water at 25°C on the opposite side. The heat transfer coefficients on vapour side and water side are 14500 W/m²°C and 2250 W/m²°C respectively. Determine :*

(i) The rate of heat transfer,

(ii) The overall heat transfer coefficient, and

(iii) Temperature drop at each side of heat transfer.

Gas turbine blades.

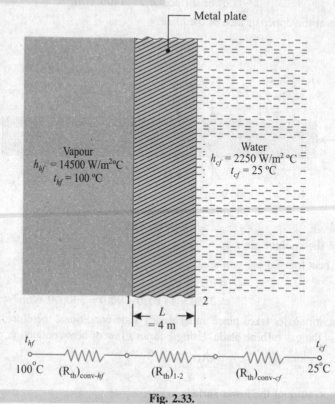

Metal plate

Vapour
h_{hf} = 14500 W/m²°C
t_{hf} = 100 °C

Water
h_{cf} = 2250 W/m² °C
t_{cf} = 25 °C

L = 4 m

t_{hf} t_{cf}

100°C $(R_{th})_{conv\text{-}hf}$ $(R_{th})_{1\text{-}2}$ $(R_{th})_{conv\text{-}cf}$ 25°C

Fig. 2.33.

Solution. Thickness of metal plate, $L = 4 \text{ mm} = 0.004 \text{ m}$

Thermal conductivity of plate material, $k = 95.5 \text{ W/m°C}$

Temperature of vapour (hot fluid), $h_{hf} = 100°C$

Temperature of water (cold fluid), $t_{cf} = 25°C$

Heat transfer coefficients :

Vapour side, $h_{hf} = 14500 \text{ W/m}^2\text{°C}$

Water side, $h_{cf} = 2250 \text{ W/m}^2\text{°C}$

(i) The rate of heat transfer per m², q :

$$q = \frac{(\Delta t)_{overall}}{(R_{th})_{total}} = \frac{(t_{hf} - t_{cf})}{(R_{th})_{total}}$$

$$= \frac{(t_{hf} - t_{cf})}{(R_{th})_{conv.-hf} + (R_{th})_{1-2} + (R_{th})_{conv.-cf}}$$

$$= \frac{(100 - 25)}{\dfrac{1}{h_{hf}} + \dfrac{L}{k} + \dfrac{1}{h_{cf}}}$$

$$= \frac{75}{\dfrac{1}{14500} + \dfrac{0.004}{95.5} + \dfrac{1}{2250}}$$

$$= \frac{75}{6.896 \times 10^{-5} + 4.188 \times 10^{-5} + 44.444 \times 10^{-5}}$$

$$= 1.35 \times 10^5 \text{ W/m}^2$$

Hence, rate of heat transfer, $q = \mathbf{1.35 \times 10^5 \text{ W/m}^2}$ **(Ans.)**

(ii) The overall heat transfer coefficient, U:

The rate of heat transfer through a composite system is given by

$$Q = U.A. (\Delta t)_{overall}$$

or, $$U = \frac{Q}{A.(\Delta t)} = \frac{q}{\Delta t} = \frac{1.35 \times 10^5}{(100 - 25)} = \mathbf{1800 \text{ W/m}^2\text{°C}} \text{ (Ans.)}$$

(iii) Temperature drop at each side of heat transfer :

We know that $q = q_{hf} = q_{1-2} = q_{cf} = 1.35 \times 10^5 \text{ W/m}^2$

Now, $$q_{hf} = \frac{(\Delta t)_{hf}}{(R_{th})_{conv.-cf}}$$

or, $$(\Delta t)_{hf} = 1.35 \times 10^5 \times \frac{1}{14500} = 9.31°C$$

i.e., Temperature drop in vapour film = **9.31°C** **(Ans.)**

Similarly, $$q_{1-2} = \frac{(\Delta t)_{1-2}}{(R_{th})_{1-2}} \text{ or } (\Delta t)_{1-2} = 1.35 \times 10^5 \times \frac{0.004}{95.5} = 5.65°C$$

i.e., Temperature drop in the *metal* = **5.65°C** **(Ans.)**

and, $$q_{cf} = \frac{(\Delta t)_{cf}}{(R_{th})_{conv-cf}}$$

or, $$(\Delta t)_{cf} = 1.35 \times 10^5 \times \frac{1}{2250} = 60°C$$

i.e., Temperature drop in the *water film* = **60°C (Ans.)**

Example 2.24. *The interior of a refrigerator having inside dimensions of 0.5 m × 0.5 m base area and 1m height, is to be maintained at 6°C. The walls of the refrigerator are constructed of two mild steel sheets 3mm thick (k = 46.5 W/m°C) with 50 mm of glass wool insulation (k = 0.046 W/m°C) between them. If the average heat transfer coefficients at the outer and inner surfaces are 11.6 W/m²°C and 14.5 W/m²°C respectively, calculate :*

(i) *The rate at which heat must be removed from the interior to maintain the specified temperature in the kitchen at 25°C, and*

(ii) *The temperature on the outer surface of the metal sheet.*

Solution. Refer to Fig. 2.34.

$$L_A = L_C = 3\text{mm} = 0.003 \text{ m}$$
$$L_B = 50 \text{ mm} = 0.05 \text{ m}$$
$$k_A = k_C = 46.5 \text{ W/m°C};$$
$$k_B = 0.046 \text{ W/m° C}$$
$$h_0 = 11.6 \text{ W/m}^2\text{°C}; h_i = 14.5 \text{ W/m}^2\text{°C}$$
$$t_0 = 25\text{°C}; t_i = 6\text{°C}.$$

The total area through which heat is coming into the refrigerator,

$$A = 0.5 \times 0.5 \times 2 + 0.5 \times 1 \times 4 = 2.5 \text{ m}^2$$

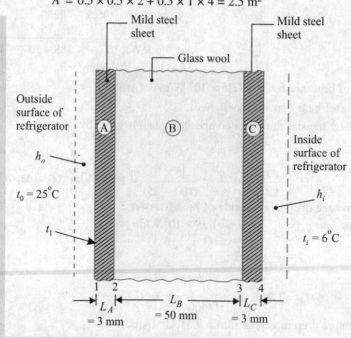

Fig. 2.34.

(i) **The rate of removal of heat, Q :**

$$Q = \frac{A(t_0 - t_i)}{\dfrac{1}{h_0} + \dfrac{L_A}{k_A} + \dfrac{L_B}{k_B} + \dfrac{L_C}{k_C} + \dfrac{1}{h_i}}$$

$$= \frac{2.5(25 - 6)}{\dfrac{1}{11.6} + \dfrac{0.003}{46.5} + \dfrac{0.05}{0.046} + \dfrac{0.003}{46.5} + \dfrac{1}{14.5}} = \textbf{38.2 W} \textbf{(Ans.)}$$

(*ii*) **The temperature at the outer surface of the metal sheet, t :**

$$Q = h_0 A (25 - t_1)$$

or, $\quad 38.2 = 11.6 \times 2.5 (25 - t_1)$

or, $\quad t_1 = 25 - \dfrac{38.2}{11.6 \times 2.5} = 23.68°C \quad \text{(Ans.)}$

Example 2.25. *Calculate the rate of heat flow per m^2 through a furnace wall consisting of 200 mm thick inner layer of chrome brick, a centre layer of kaolin brick 100 mm thick and an outer layer of masonry brick 100 mm thick. The unit surface conductance at the inner surface is 74 $W/m^2°C$ and the outer surface temperature is 70°C. The temperature of the gases inside the furnace is 1670°C. What temperatures prevail at the inner and outer surfaces of the centre layer ?*

Take : $k_{chrome\ brick}$ = 1.25 $W/m°C$; $k_{kaolin\ brick}$ = 0.074 $W/m°C$; $k_{masonry\ brick}$ = 0.555 $W/m°C$

Assume steady heat flow. (M.U.)

Solution. Thickness of chrome bricks, L_A = 200 mm = 0.2 m

Thickness of kaolin bricks, L_B = 100 mm = 0.1 m

Thickness of masonry bricks, L_C = 100 mm = 0.1m

Thermal conductivities : k_A = 1.25 W/m°C;

k_B = 0.074 W/m°C; k_C = 0.555 W/m°C;

The unit surface conductance, h_{hf} = 74 W/m²°C

Temperature of hot fluid, $\qquad t_{hf} (= t_g)$ = 1670°C

Temperature of the outer surface, $\qquad t_4$ = 70°C

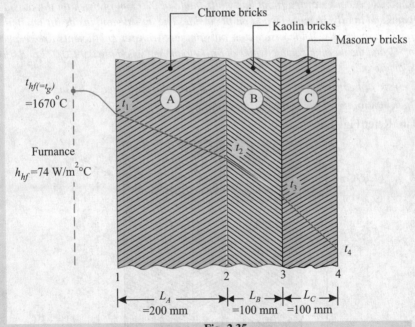

Fig. 2.35

(*i*) **Rate of heat flow per m^2, q :**

$$q = \frac{(t_{hf} - t_4)}{\dfrac{1}{h_{hf}} + \dfrac{L_A}{k_A} + \dfrac{L_B}{k_B} + \dfrac{L_C}{k_C}}$$

$$= \frac{(1670 - 70)}{\frac{1}{74} + \frac{0.2}{1.25} + \frac{0.1}{0.074} + \frac{0.1}{0.555}}$$

$$= \frac{1600}{0.0135 + 0.16 + 1.351 + 0.1802}$$

$$= \textbf{938.58 W/m}^2 \quad \textbf{(Ans.)}$$

Close-up view of turbine blades.

(ii) **Temperatures; t_2, t_3 :**

The heat flow is given by

$$q = \frac{(t_{hf} - t_1)}{1/h_{hf}} = \frac{(t_1 - t_2)}{L_A/k_A} = \frac{(t_2 - t_3)}{(L_B/k_B)}$$

∴ $938.58 = \dfrac{1670 - t_1}{1/74}$

or $t_1 = 1670 - 938.58 \times \dfrac{1}{74} = 1657.3°C$

Similarly, $938.58 = \dfrac{(1657.3 - t_2)}{0.2/1.25}$ or $t_2 = 1657.3 - 938.58 \times \dfrac{0.2}{1.25} = \textbf{1507.1°C}$ **(Ans)**

$938.58 = \dfrac{(1507.1 - t_3)}{(0.1/0.074)}$ or $t_3 = 1507.1 - 938.58 \times \dfrac{0.1}{0.074} = \textbf{238.7°C}$ **(Ans.)**

Example 2.26. *A cold storage room has walls made of 220 mm of brick on the outside, 90 mm of plastic foam, and finally 16 mm of wood on the inside. The outside and inside air temperatures are 25°C and –3°C respectively. If the inside and outside heat transfer coefficients are respectively 30 and 11 W/m²°C, and the thermal conductivities of brick, foam and wood are 0.99, 0.022 and 0.17 W/m°C respectively, determine :*

(i)   The rate of heat removal by refrigeration if the total wall area is 85 m²;

(ii) The temperature of the inside surface of the brick.

Solution. Refer Fig. 2.36.

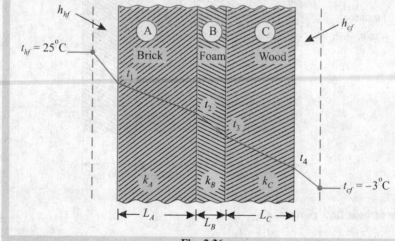

Fig. 2.36.

Thickness of brick wall, $L_A = 220 \text{ mm} = 0.22 \text{ m}$

Thickness of plastic foam, $L_B = 90 \text{ mm} = 0.09 \text{ m}$

Thickness of wood, $L_C = 16$ mm $= 0.016$ m

Temperature of hot fluid (air), $t_{hf} = 25°C$

Temperature cold fluid (air), $t_{cf} = -3°C$

Heat transfer coefficients :

Hot fluid (air), $h_{hf} = 11$ W/m²°C

Cold fluid (air), $h_{cf} = 30$ W/m²°C

Thermal conductivities :

Brick, $k_A = 0.99$ W/m°C

Foam, $k_B = 0.022$ W/m°C

Wood, $k_C = 0.17$ W/m°C

Total wall area, $A = 85$ m²

(i) Rate of heat transfer, Q :

$$Q = UA (t_{hf} - t_{cf})$$

The overall heat transfer co-efficient (U) may be found from the following relation :

$$\frac{1}{U} = \frac{1}{h_{hf}} + \frac{L_A}{k_A} + \frac{L_B}{k_B} + \frac{L_C}{k_C} + \frac{1}{h_{cf}}$$

$$= \frac{1}{11} + \frac{0.22}{0.99} + \frac{0.09}{0.022} + \frac{0.06}{0.17} + \frac{1}{30}$$

$$= 0.091 + 0.222 + 4.091 + 0.094 + 0.033 = 4.531$$

$$\therefore U = \frac{1}{4.531} = 0.2207 \text{ W/m}^2°C$$

$$\therefore Q = 0.2207 \times 85 [25 - (-3)] = \textbf{525.26 W} \textbf{ (Ans.)}$$

(ii) Temperature of inside surface of the brick, t_2 :

$$Q = U.A (t_{hf} - t_2)$$

or, $$525.26 = \left[\frac{1}{\frac{1}{h_{hf}} + \frac{L_A}{k_A}} \right] A(t_{hf} - t_2)$$

$$= \left[\frac{1}{\frac{1}{11} + \frac{0.22}{0.99}} \right] \times 85 (25 - t_2) = 271.45(25 - t_2)$$

$$\therefore t_2 = 25 - \frac{525.26}{271.45} = \textbf{23.06°C} \textbf{ (Ans.)}$$

Example 2.27. *A furnace wall is made of composite wall of total thickness 550 mm. The inside layer is made of refractory material (K = 2.3 W/mK) and outside layer is made of an insulating material (K = 0.2 W/mK). The mean temperature of the glass inside the furnace is 900°C and inter-face temperature is 520°C. The heat transfer coefficient between the gases and inner surface can be taken as 230 W/m² °C and between the outside surface and atmosphere as 46 W/m²°C. Taking air temperature = 30°C, calculate :*

(i) Required thickness of each layer,

(ii) The rate of heat loss per m² area, and

(iii) The temperatures of surface exposed to gases and of surface exposed to atmosphere.

(B.U., Dec., 2002)

Solution. *Given :* Total thickness of wall, $L_A + L_B = 550$ mm $= 0.55$ m; $k_A = 2.3$ W/mK; $k_B = 0.2$ W/mK; $t_{hf} = 900°C$; $t_2 = 520°C$; $h_{hf} = 230$ W/m²°C; $h_{cf} = 46$ W/m²°C; $t_{cf} = 30°C$.

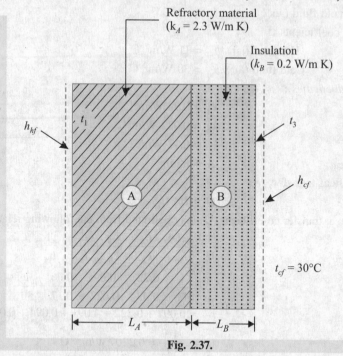

Refractory material ($k_A = 2.3$ W/m K)

Insulation ($k_B = 0.2$ W/m K)

Fig. 2.37.

Thickness of each layer, L_A, L_B :

The heat flow rate,

$$q = \frac{Q}{A} = \frac{t_{hf} - t_2}{\dfrac{1}{h_{hf}} + \dfrac{L_A}{k_A}}$$

$$= \frac{t_2 - t_{cf}}{\dfrac{0.55 - L_A}{k_B} + \dfrac{1}{h_{cf}}}$$

Equating (*i*) and (*ii*) we get,

$$\frac{t_{hf} - t_2}{\dfrac{1}{h_{hf}} + \dfrac{L_A}{k_A}} = \frac{t_2 - t_{cf}}{\dfrac{0.55 - L_A}{k_B} + \dfrac{1}{h_{cf}}}$$

$$\frac{900 - 520}{\dfrac{1}{230} + \dfrac{L_A}{2.3}} = \frac{520 - 30}{\dfrac{0.55 - L_A}{0.22} + \dfrac{1}{46}}$$

$$380\left[\frac{0.55 - L_A}{0.2} + \frac{1}{46}\right] = 490\left[\frac{1}{230} + \frac{L_A}{2.3}\right]$$

$$1045 - 1900 L_A + 8.26 = 2.13 + 213 L_A$$

$$2113 L_A = 1051.13$$

or, $L_A = 0.497$ m or **497 mm**   **(Ans.)**

and, $L_B = 550 - 497$ m $= $ **53 mm**   **(Ans.)**

(i) The rate of heat loss per m² area, q :

$$q = \frac{t_{hf} - t_2}{\dfrac{1}{h_{hf}} + \dfrac{L_A}{k_A}} = \frac{900 - 520}{\dfrac{1}{230} + \dfrac{0.497}{2.3}}$$

$$= \frac{380}{0.004348 + 0.216} = \textbf{1724.5 W/m}^2 \qquad \textbf{(Ans.)}$$

Example 2.28. *The inside temperature of furnace wall, 200 mm thick, is 1350°C. The mean thermal conductivity of wall material is 1.35 W/m°C. The heat transfer coefficient of the outside surface is a function of temperature difference and is given by*

$$h = 7.85 + 0.08 \, \Delta t$$

where Δt is the temperature difference between outside wall surface and surroundings. Determine the rate of heat transfer per unit area if the surrounding temperature is 40°C.

Solution. Thickness of wall,

$$L = 200 \text{ mm} = 0.2\text{m}$$

Temperature of inner surface of wall,

$$t_1 = 1400°C$$

Temperature of air (cold fluid),

$$t_{cf} = 40°C$$

Mean thermal conductivity of wall material,

$$k = 1.35 \text{ W/m°C}$$

Rate of heat transfer per unit area, q :

$$q = \frac{(t_1 - t_2)}{L/k} = \frac{(t_2 - t_{cf})}{1/h}$$

$$\frac{(1350 - t_2)}{0.2/1.35} = h(t_2 - 40)$$

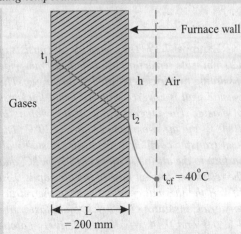

Fig. 2.38.

Furnace walls and electric wils.

or, $\qquad$ $6.75\,(1350 - t_2) = [7.85 + 0.08\,(t_2 - 40)]\,(t_2 - 40)$

or, $\qquad$ $9112.5 - 6.75t_2 = 7.85\,(t_2 - 40) + 0.08\,(t_2 - 40)^2$

or, $\qquad$ $9112.5 - 6.75t_2 = 7.85t_2 - 314 + 0.08\,(t_2{}^2 - 80t_2 + 1600)$

or, $\qquad$ $t_2{}^2 - 80t_2 + 1600 = \dfrac{9112.5 - 6.75t_2 - 7.85t_2 + 314}{0.08}$

$$= 117831 - 182.5\,t_2$$

or, $\qquad$ $t_2{}^2 + 102.5t_2 - 116231 = 0$

or, $\qquad$ $t_2 = \dfrac{-102.5 \pm \sqrt{(102.5)^2 + 4 \times 116231}}{2}$

$$= \dfrac{-102.5 \pm 689.5}{2} = 293.5°C$$

$\therefore$ $\qquad$ $q = \dfrac{(1350 - 293.5)}{0.2/1.35} = 7131.37 \text{ W/m}^2$ **(Ans.)**

Exampel 2.29. *The furnace wall consists of 120 mm wide refractory brick and 120 mm wide insulating fire brick separated by an air gap. The outside wall is covered with a 12 mm thickness of plaster. The inner surface of the wall is at 1090°C and the room temperature is 20°C. The heat transfer coefficient from the outside wall surface to the air in the room is 18 W/m²°C, and the resistance to heat flow of the air gap is 0.16 K/W. If the thermal conductivities of the refractory brick, insulating fire brick, and plaster are 1.6, 0.3 and 0.14 W/mK, respectively calculate :*

(i) Rate at which heat is lost per m² of the wall surface;

(ii) Each interface temperature; and

(iii) Temperature of the outside surface of the wall.

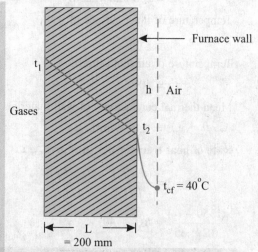

Fig. 2.39.

Solution. Refer Fig. 2.39.

Thickness of refractory brick, $L_A = 120 \text{ mm} = 0.12 \text{ m}$

Thickness of insulating fire brick, $L_B = 120 \text{ mm} = 0.12 \text{ m}$

Thickness of plaster, $L_C = 12 \text{ mm} = 0.012 \text{ m}$

Heat transfer coefficient from the outside wall surface to the air in the room,

$$h_{cf} = 18 \text{ W/m}^2°C$$

Resistance of air gap to heat flow $= 0.16 \text{ K/W}$

Thermal conductivities :

Refractory brick, $k_A = 1.6 \text{ W/m°C}$

Insulating fire brick, $k_B = 0.3 \text{ W/m°C}$

Plaster, $k_C = 0.14 \text{ W/m°C}.$

Temperatures : $t_{hf} = 1090°C;\ t_{cf} = 20°C$

Consider 1m² of surface area.

(i) Rate of heat loss per m^2 of surface area, q :

$$q = \frac{(t_{hf} - t_{cf})}{\dfrac{L_A}{k_A} + \text{air gap resistance} + \dfrac{L_B}{k_B} + \dfrac{L_C}{k_C} + \dfrac{1}{h_{cf}}}$$

$$= \frac{(1090 - 20)}{\dfrac{0.12}{1.6} + 0.16 + \dfrac{0.12}{0.3} + \dfrac{0.012}{0.14} + \dfrac{1}{18}}$$

$$= \frac{1070}{0.075 + 0.16 + 0.4 + 0.0857 + 0.0555} = 1378.5 \text{ W or } 1.3785 \text{ kW}$$

i.e., Rate of heat loss per m^2 of surface area = **1.3785 kW**   (Ans.)

(ii) Temperatures at interfaces, t_2, t_3, t_4:

$$Q = 1378.5 = \frac{1090 - t_2}{L_A / k_A} = \frac{1090 - t_2}{0.12/1.6} = \frac{1090 - t_2}{0.075}$$

$\therefore$ $t_2 = 1090 - 1378.5 \times 0.075 = \textbf{986.6°C}$ (Ans.)

Also, $Q = 1378.5 = \dfrac{t_2 - t_3}{\text{air gap resistance}} = \dfrac{986.6 - t_3}{0.16}$

$\therefore$ $t_3 = 986.6 - 1378.5 \times 0.16 = \textbf{766.04°C}$ (Ans.)

Again, $Q = 1378.5 = \dfrac{t_3 - t_4}{L_B / k_B} = \dfrac{766.04 - t_4}{0.12/0.3} = \dfrac{766.04 - t_4}{0.4}$

$\therefore$ $t_4 = 766.04 - 1378.5 \times 0.4 = \textbf{214.64°C}$ (Ans.)

(iii) Temperature of the outside surface of the wall, t_5 :

$$Q = 1378.5 = \frac{t_4 - t_5}{L_C / k_C} = \frac{214.64 - t_5}{0.012/0.14} = \frac{214.64 - t_5}{0.0857}$$

$\therefore$ $t_5 = 214.64 - 1378.5 \times 0.0857 = \textbf{96.5°C}$ (Ans.)

Example 2.30. *A furnace wall is made up of three layers of thicknesses 250 mm, 100 mm and 150 mm with thermal conductivities of 1.65, k and 9.2 W/m°C respectively. The inside is exposed to gases at 1250°C with a convection coefficient of 25 W/m²°C and the inside surface is at 1100°C, the outside surface is exposed to air at 25°C with convection coefficient of 12 W/m²°C. Determine :*

(i) *The unknown thermal conductivity 'k';*

(ii) *The overall heat transfer coefficient;*

(iii) *All surface temperatures.*

Solution. L_A = 250 mm = 0.25 m;

L_B = 100 mm = 0.1 m;

L_C = 150 mm = 0.15 m;

k_A = 1.65 W/m°C;

k_C = 9.2 W/m°C;

t_{hf} = 1250°C, t_1 = 1100°C;

h_{hf} = 25 W/m²°C; h_{cf} = 12 W/m²°C.

(i) Thermal conductivity, k $(= k_B)$:

The rate of heat transfer per unit area of the furnace wall,

$$q = h_{hf}(t_{hf} - t_1)$$
$$= 25(1250 - 1100) = 3750 \text{ W/m}^2$$

Also,

$$q = \frac{(\Delta t)_{overall}}{(R_{th})_{total}}$$

or

$$q = \frac{(t_{hf} - t_{cf})}{(R_{th})_{conv-hf} - R_{th-A} + R_{th-B} + R_{th-C} + (R_{th})_{conv-cf}}$$

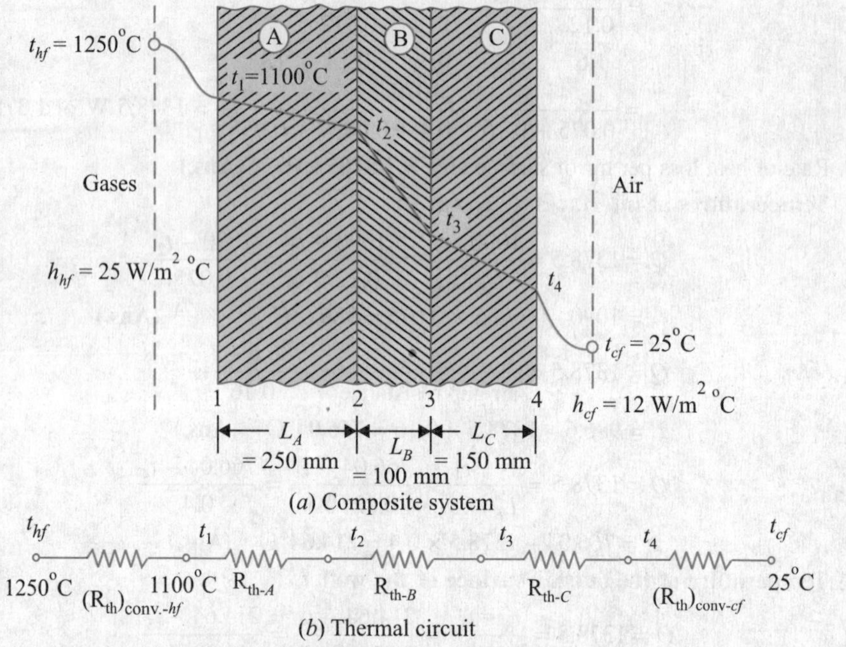

(a) Composite system

(b) Thermal circuit

Fig. 2.40.

or,

$$3750 = \frac{(1250 - 25)}{\dfrac{1}{h_{hf}} + \dfrac{L_A}{k_A} + \dfrac{L_B}{k_B} + \dfrac{L_C}{k_C} + \dfrac{1}{h_{cf}}}$$

or,

$$3750 = \frac{1225}{\dfrac{1}{25} + \dfrac{0.25}{1.65} + \dfrac{0.1}{k_B} + \dfrac{0.15}{9.2} + \dfrac{1}{12}}$$

$$= \frac{1225}{0.04 + 0.1515 + \dfrac{0.1}{k_B} + 0.0163 + 0.0833} = \frac{1225}{0.2911 + \dfrac{0.1}{k_B}}$$

or,

$$3750 \left(0.289 + \frac{0.1}{k_B} \right) = 1225$$

or,

$$\frac{0.1}{k_B} = \frac{1225}{3750} - 0.2911 = 0.0355$$

∴

$$k_B = k = \frac{0.1}{0.0355}$$

$$= 2.817 \ W/m°C \quad \textbf{(Ans.)}$$

(ii) The overall heat transfer coefficient, U :

The overall heat transfer coefficient, $U = \dfrac{1}{(R_{th})_{total}}$

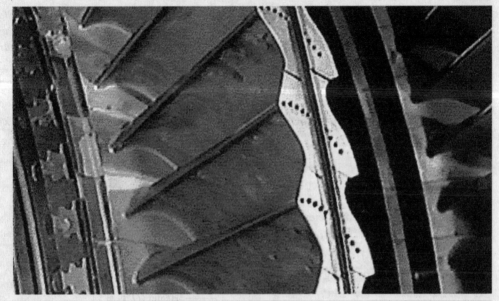

Effects of heat on turbine blades is an important consideration while designing.

Now, $(R_{th})_{\text{total}} = \dfrac{1}{25} + \dfrac{0.25}{1.65} + \dfrac{0.1}{2.817} + \dfrac{0.15}{9.2} + \dfrac{1}{12}$

$= 0.04 + 0.1515 + 0.0355 + 0.0163 + 0.0833 = 0.3266\ °C\ m^2/W$

$\therefore$ $U = \dfrac{1}{(R_{th})_{\text{total}}} = \dfrac{1}{0.3266} = \mathbf{3.06\ W/m^{2\,°}C}$ **(Ans.)**

(iii) All surface temperatures; t_1, t_2, t_3, t_4 :

$$q = q_A = q_B = q_C$$

or, $3750 = \dfrac{(t_1 - t_2)}{L_A / k_A} = \dfrac{(t_2 - t_3)}{L_B / k_B} = \dfrac{(t_3 - t_4)}{L_C / k_C}$

or, $3750 = \dfrac{(1100 - t_2)}{0.25/1.65}$

or, $t_2 = 1100 - 3750 \times \dfrac{0.25}{1.65} = \mathbf{531.8°C}$ **(Ans.)**

Similarly, $3750 = \dfrac{(531.8 - t_3)}{0.1/2.817}$

or, $t_3 = 531.8 - 3750 \times \dfrac{0.1}{2.817} = \mathbf{398.6°C}$ **(Ans.)**

and $3750 = \dfrac{(398.6 - t_4)}{(0.15/9.2)}$

or, $t_4 = 398.6 - 3750 \times \dfrac{0.5}{9.2} = \mathbf{337.5°C}$ **(Ans.)**

[Check using outside convection,

$$q = \dfrac{(337.5 - 25)}{1/h_{cf}} = \dfrac{(337.5 - 25)}{1/12} = 3750\ W/m^2\,]$$

Example 2.31. *A square plate heater (15 cm × 15 cm) is inserted between two slabs. Slab A is 2 cm thick (k = 50 W/m°C) and slab B is 1 cm thick (k = 0.2 W/m°C). The outside heat transfer coefficients on side A and side B are 200 W/m²°C and 50 W/m²°C respectively. The temperature of surrounding air is 25°C. If rating of heater is 1kW, find :*

(i) Maximum temperature in the system;

(ii) Outer surface temperature of two slabs.

Draw an equivalent electrcal circuit. (M.U., 2001)

Solution. Refer to Fig. 2.41.

Thickness of slab A,	$L_A = 2\text{cm} = 0.02\text{m}$
Thickness of slab B,	$L_B = 1\text{cm} = 0.01\text{m}$
Thermal conductivities,	$k_A = 50 \text{ W/m°C}; k_B = 0.2 \text{ W/m°C}$

Overall heat transfer co-efficients : $h_1 = 200 \text{ W/m}^2\text{°C}; h_2 = 50 \text{ W/m}^2\text{°C}$

Area of the plate $= 0.15 × 0.15 = 0.0225 \text{ m}^2$

Rating of heater $= 1\text{kW} = 1000 \text{ W}$

Temperature of surrounding air, $t_a = 25\text{°C}$

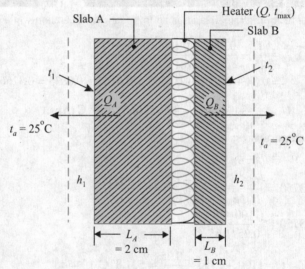

(a) Slabs and the heater

(b) The equivalent electrical/thermal circuit

Fig. 2.41.

(i)   Maximum temperature in the system, t_{max} :

For steady state heat flow, we have

Q = Heat flow through slab $A(Q_A)$ + heat flow through slab $B(Q_B)$

$$= \frac{(t_{max} - t_a)}{\dfrac{L_A}{k_A . A} + \dfrac{1}{h_1 . A}} + \frac{(t_{max} - t_a)}{\dfrac{L_B}{k_B . A} + \dfrac{1}{h_2 . A}} = A(t_{max} - t_a)\left[\frac{1}{\dfrac{L_A}{k_A} + \dfrac{1}{h_1}} + \frac{1}{\dfrac{L_B}{k_B} + \dfrac{1}{h_2}}\right]$$

Substituting the values in the above equation, we get,

$$1000 = 0.0225(t_{max} - 25)\left[\frac{1}{\frac{0.02}{50}+\frac{1}{200}} + \frac{1}{\frac{0.01}{0.2}+\frac{1}{50}}\right]$$

$$= 0.0225(t_{max} - 25)\left[\frac{1}{(0.0004 + 0.005)} + \frac{1}{(0.05 + 0.02)}\right]$$

$$= 0.0225\,(t_{max} - 25) \times 199.47$$

$$\therefore \quad t_{max} = 25 + \frac{100}{0.0225 \times 199.47} = \textbf{247.8° C (Ans.)}$$

(ii) **Outer surface temperature of two slabs; t_1, t_2:**

$$Q_A = \frac{k_A . A(t_{max} - t_1)}{L_A} = h_i . A(t_1 - t_a)$$

or, $$\frac{50(247.8 - t_1)}{0.02} = 200(t_1 - 25)$$

or, $$2500\,(247.8 - t_1) = 200\,(t_1 - 25)$$

or, $$247.8 - t_1 = \frac{200}{2500}(t_1 - 25) = 0.08\,t_1 - 2$$

or, $$1.08\,t_1 = 249.8$$

$$\therefore \quad t_1 = \frac{249.8}{1.08} = \textbf{231.3° C (Ans.)}$$

Similarly, $$Q_B = \frac{k_B . A(t_{max} - t_2)}{L_B} = h_2 . A(t_2 - t_a)$$

or, $$\frac{0.2(247.8 - t_2)}{0.01} = 50(t_2 - 25)$$

or, $$20\,(247.8 - t_2) = 50\,(t_2 - 25)$$

or, $$(247.8 - t_2) = \frac{50}{20}(t_2 - 25) = 2.5\,t_2 - 62.5$$

or, $$3.5\,t_2 = 310.3$$

$$\therefore \quad t_2 = \frac{310.3}{3.5} = \textbf{88.6° C (Ans.)}$$

Equivalent electrical/thermal circuit is shown in Fig. 2.41 (b).

Example 2.32. *The following data relate to furnace of a steam boiler :*

Temperature of gases in the furnace .... *1300°C*

Temperature of air in the boiler room .... *30°C*

Thickness of refractory material .... *250 mm*

The heat transfer coefficient from gases to refractory wall .... *30 W/m²°C*

The heat transfer coefficient from outside surface to surrounding air .... *10W/m²°C*

Thermal conductivity of refractory material : k = 0.28 (1 + 0.000833 t) W/m°C

Thermal conductivity of diatomite layer : k = 0.113 (1 + 0.000206 t) W/m°C

Estimate the thickness of the diatomite layer of setting so that the loss of heat to the surroundings should not exceed 750 W/m².

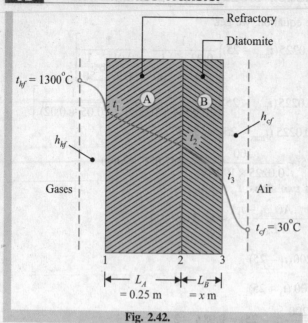

Refractory

Diatomite

$t_{hf} = 1300°C$

A

B

h_{cf}

t_1

t_2

t_3

h_{hf}

Gases

Air

$t_{cf} = 30°C$

1   2   3

$\leftarrow L_A \rightarrow \leftarrow L_B \rightarrow$
$= 0.25$ m $= x$ m

Fig. 2.42.

Electric resistance furnace.

Solution. Refer to Fig. 2.42.

Given : $t_{hf} = 1300°C$; $t_{cf} = 30°C$; $L_A = 250$ mm $= 0.25$ m; $h_{hf} = 30$ W/m²°C; $h_{cf} = 10$ W/m²°C.
Thermal conductivities :

$$k_A = 0.28(1 + 0.000833\, t)\text{W/m°C}$$
$$k_B = 0.113(1 + 0.000206\, t)\text{W/m°C}$$

Loss of heat to the surroundings, $q = 750$ W/m²

Thickness of diatomite layer, L_B $(=x)$:

The rate of heat transfer per m^2 through the composite furnace wall is given by,

$$q = \frac{(t_{hf} - t_1)}{1/h_{hf}} = \frac{(t_3 - t_{cf})}{1/h_{cf}} = \frac{(t_1 - t_{cf})}{L_A/k_{mA}} = \frac{(t_2 - t_3)}{L_B/k_{mB}}$$

where,

$$k_{mA} = k_{oA}\left[1 + \alpha_A\left(\frac{t_1 + t_2}{2}\right)\right]$$

and,

$$k_{mB} = k_{oB}\left[1 + \alpha_B\left(\frac{t_2 + t_3}{2}\right)\right]$$

∴

$$750 = \frac{(1300 - t_1)}{1/30} \qquad \text{or} \qquad t_1 = 1300 - 750 \times \frac{1}{30} = 1275°C$$

Again,

$$750 = \frac{(t_3 - 30)}{1/10} \qquad \text{or} \qquad t_3 = 30 + 750 \times \frac{1}{10} = 105°C$$

Now, using the following equation,

$$\frac{(t_3 - t_{cf})}{1/h_{cf}} = \frac{k_{mA}(t_1 - t_2)}{L_A}$$

or,

$$h_{cf}(t_3 - t_{cf}) = \frac{k_{mA}(t_1 - t_2)}{L_A}$$

Substituting the value of k_{mA} in the above equation, we have

$$h_{cf}(t_3 - t_{cf}) = \frac{k_o A\left[1 + \alpha_A\left(\dfrac{t_1 + t_2}{2}\right)\right]}{L_A}(t_1 - t_2)$$

$$10(105 - 30) = \frac{0.28\left[1 + 0.000833\left(\dfrac{1275 + t_2}{2}\right)\right]}{0.25}(1275 - t_2)$$

$$750 = 1.12\left[1 + 0.000833\left(\frac{1275 + t_2}{2}\right)\right](1275 - t_2)$$

or,

$$\frac{750}{1.12} = [1 + 0.0004165(1275 + t_2)](1275 - t_2)$$

$$669.6 = (1275 - t_2) + 0.0004165\,[(1275)^2 - (t_2)^2]$$

$$669.6 = (1275 - t_2) + 677 - 0.0004165\,t_2^2$$

$$0.0004165\,t_2^2 + t_2 - 1282.5 = 0$$

∴

$$t_2 = \frac{-1 \pm \sqrt{1 + 4 \times 0.0004165 \times 1282.5}}{2 \times 0.0004165} = 925.6°C \text{ (ignoring –ve sign)}$$

$$k_{mB} = 0.113\left[1 + 0.000206\left(\frac{925.6 + 105}{2}\right)\right] = 0.125\,W/m°C$$

$$k_{mA} = 0.28\left[1 + 0.000833\left(\frac{1275 + 925.6}{2}\right)\right] = 0.536\,W/m°C$$

Now using the following equation, we have :

$$\frac{(t_1 - t_2)}{L_A / k_{mA}} = \frac{(t_2 - t_3)}{L_B / k_{mB}}$$

or,

$$\frac{k_{mA}(t_1 - t_2)}{L_A} = \frac{k_{mB}(t_2 - t_3)}{L_B}$$

or,

$$\frac{0.536(1275 - 925.6)}{0.25} = \frac{0.125(925.6 - 105)}{x}$$

or,

$$749.11 = \frac{102.57}{x} \qquad ∴ \quad x = \frac{102.57}{749.11} = 0.137\,m \text{ or } 137\,mm$$

Hence, *thickness of diatomite layer* = **137 mm. (Ans.)**

Example 2.33. *Fig. 2.43 shows the temperature distribution through a furnace wall consisting of fire brick and high temperature block insulation and steel plate. If the thermal conductivity of the fire brick is 1.13 W/m°C, determine :*

(i) *Rate of heat per unit area of furnace wall;*

(ii) *Thermal conductivities of block insulation and steel;*

(iii) *Combined convective and radiative heat transfer coefficient for the outside surface of the furnace wall;*

(iv) *Heat exchange by radiation between the hot gases and inside surface of furnace wall. The absorptivity and emissivity of the fire brick wall surface is 0.82.*

(v) *Convective heat transfer coefficient for the inside surface of the furnace wall.*

Solution. Refer to Fig. 2.43.

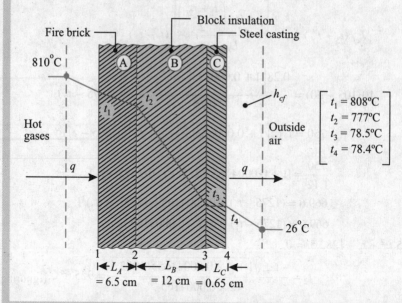

Fig. 2.43.

Given :
$$t_{hf} = 810°C; t_1 = 808°C; t_2 = 777°C; t_3 = 78.5°C; t_4 = 78.4°C; t_{cf} = 26°C$$
$$L_A = 6.5 \text{ cm} = 0.065 \text{ m}; L_B = 12 \text{ cm} = 0.12 \text{ m};$$
$$L_C = 0.65 \text{ cm} = 0.0065 \text{ m}$$
$$k_A = 1.13 \text{ W/m°C}$$
$$\varepsilon_{\text{fire brick}} = 0.82$$
$$\sigma = 5.67 \times 10^{-8} \text{ W/m}^2\text{K}^4$$

(i) **Rate of heat transfer per unit area of furnace wall, q :**

For steady state heat flux for resistances in series,

$$q = q_{hf} = q_A = q_B = q_C = q_{cf}$$

∴
$$q = q_A = \frac{t_1 - t_2}{L_A / k_A} = \frac{(808 - 777)}{\dfrac{0.065}{1.13}} = \textbf{538.9 W/m}^2$$

(ii) **Thermal conductivities of block insulation (k_B) and steel (k_C) :**

$$q_B = \frac{(t_2 - t_3)}{L_B / k_B} = \frac{k_B (t_2 - t_3)}{L_B}$$

or,
$$k_B = \frac{q_B \, L_B}{(t_2 - t_3)} = \frac{538.9 \times 0.12}{(777 - 78.5)} = \textbf{0.0926 W/m°C} \;\textbf{(Ans.)}$$

Similarly,
$$k_C = \frac{q_C \, L_C}{(t_3 - t_4)} = \frac{538.9 \times 0.0065}{(78.5 - 78.4)} = \textbf{35 W/m°C} \;\textbf{(Ans.)}$$

(iii) **Combined convective and radiative coefficient on the outside surface, h_0 :**

$$(h_{\text{rad}})_0 + (h_{\text{conv}}) = h_0 = \frac{q}{t_4 - t_{cf}} = \frac{538.9}{78.4 - 26} = \textbf{10.28 W/m}^{2\circ}\textbf{ C} \;\textbf{(Ans.)}$$

(iv) **Heat exchange by radiation, $q_{rad.}$:**

Assuming the emissivity of hot gases as unity, the net radiation heat gain of wall per unit area is given by

$$q_{rad.} = \varepsilon\sigma\left((T_{hf})^4 - (T_1)^4\right)$$

$$= 0.82 \times 5.67 \times 10^{-8}\ [(810 + 273)^4 - (808 + 273)^4]$$

$$= 0.82 \times 5.67 \left[\left(\frac{810 + 273}{100}\right)^4 - \left(\frac{808 + 273}{100}\right)^4\right] = \textbf{471.2 W/m}^2\ \textbf{(Ans.)}$$

(v) **Convective heat transfer coefficient for the inside surface of the furnace wall ($h_{conv.}$) :**

As convective and radiative heat transfers between gases and wall are in parallel, therefore

$$q = (q_{rad}) + (q_{conv.})_i$$

or $\qquad (q_{conv.})_i = q - q_{rad.} = 538.9 - 471.2 = 67.7\ \text{W/m}^2°\text{C}$

∴ Convective heat transfer coefficient on the inside surface,

$$(h_{conv.})_i = \frac{(q_{conv.})_i}{t_{hf} - t_1} = \frac{67.7}{810 - 808} = \textbf{33.85 W/m}^2°\textbf{C}\quad\textbf{(Ans.)}$$

Example 2.34. *The following data relate to a large rectangular combustion chamber for a furnace made of 220 mm common brick, lined on the inside with 220 mm thick layer of magnesite brick :*

Temperature of gases = 1300°C; Temperature of surrounding air = 40°C; Radiation coefficient, inside surface = 17.5 W/m²°C; convection coefficient, inside surface = 16.4 W/m²°C; Radiation coefficient, outside surface = 7.2 W/m² °C; convection co-efficient, outside surface = 11.5 W/m²°C; Thermal conductivity of common brick = 0.65 W/m°C; Thermal conductivity of magnesite brick = 3.5 W/m°C.

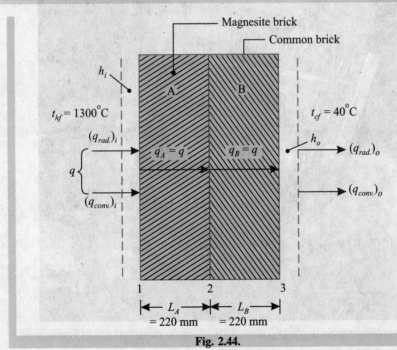

Fig. 2.44.

Determine the following :

(i) Rate of heat transfer through the wall per unit area;

(ii) Maximum temperature to which common brick is subjected.

Solution. *Given :* $L_A = 220$ mm $= 0.22$ m; $L_B = 220$ mm $= 0.22$ m

$$k_A = 3.5 \text{ W/m°C}; \qquad\qquad k_B = 0.65 \text{ W/m°C}$$

$$t_{hf} = 1300°C; \; t_{cf} = 40°C; \;\; (h_{conv.})_i = 16.4 \text{ W/m}^2°C;$$

$$(h_{conv.})_0 = 11.5 \text{ W/m}^2°C; \qquad (h_{rad.})i = 17.5 \text{ W/m}^2°C;$$

$$(h_{rad.})_0 = 7.2 \text{ W/m}^2°C;$$

(i) Rate of heat transfer through the wall per unit area, q :

Since the convective and radiative resistances are in parallel, therefore :

$$q = (q_{conv.} + q_{rad.})_i = q_A = q_B = (q_{conv.} + q_{rad.})_0$$

$$= \frac{(\Delta t)_{overall}}{(R_{th})_{total}} = \frac{(t_{hf} - t_{cf})}{(R_{th})_{total}} \qquad\qquad ...(i)$$

Also, $\qquad\qquad h_i = (h_{conv.} + h_{rad.})_i = 16.4 + 17.5 = 33.9 \text{ W/m}^2°C$

$$h_o = (h_{conv.} + h_{rad.})_o = 11.5 + 7.2 = 18.7 \text{ W/m}^2°C$$

$$(R_{th})_{total} = \frac{1}{h_i} + \frac{L_A}{k_A} + \frac{L_B}{k_B} + \frac{1}{h_o}$$

$$= \frac{1}{33.9} + \frac{0.22}{3.5} + \frac{0.22}{0.65} + \frac{1}{18.7}$$

$$= 0.0295 + 0.0628 + 0.3385 + 0.0535 = 0.4843 \text{ m}^2°C/W$$

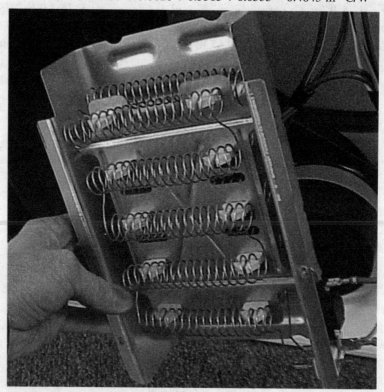

In an electric dryer the heat transmission is mainly by radiation and convection.

Substituting the values in (i), we get

$$q = \frac{(1300 - 40)}{0.4843} = \mathbf{2601.7 \ W/m^2} \quad \textbf{(Ans.)}$$

(*ii*) **Maximum temperature to which common brick is subjected, t_2 :**

$$q = h_i \, (t_{hf} - t_1) = \frac{(t_1 - t_2)}{L_A / k_A}$$

or, $\qquad 2601.7 = 33.9 \, (1300 - t_1)$

or, $\qquad t_1 = 1300 - \dfrac{2601}{33.9} = 1223.27°\text{C}$

and, $\qquad 2601.7 = \dfrac{(1223.27 - t_2)}{(0.22/3.5)}$

or, $\qquad t_2 = 1223.27 - 2601.7 \times \dfrac{0.22}{3.5}$

$$= \mathbf{1059.73°C \ (Ans.)}$$

2.6. HEAT CONDUCTION THROUGH HOLLOW AND COMPOSITE CYLINDERS

2.6.1. HEAT CONDUCTION THROUGH A HOLLOW CYLINDER

Case I. Uniform conductivity :

Refer to Fig. 2.45. Consider a hollow cylinder made of material having constant thermal conductivity and insulated at both ends.

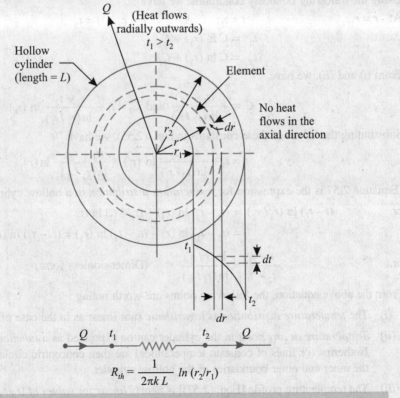

Fig. 2.45.

Let, r_1, r_2 = Inner and outer radii;

     t_1, t_2 = Temperatures of inner and outer surfaces, and

     k = Constant thermal conductivity within the given temperature range.

The general heat conduction equation in cylindrical coordinates is given by,

$$\left[\frac{\partial^2}{\partial r^2} + \frac{1}{r} \cdot \frac{\partial t}{\partial r} + \frac{1}{r^2} \cdot \frac{\partial t}{\partial \phi^2} + \frac{\partial^2 t}{\partial z^2}\right] + \frac{q_g}{k} = \frac{1}{\alpha} \cdot \frac{\partial t}{\partial \tau} \qquad \text{...(Eqn. 2.22)}$$

For steady state $\left(\frac{\partial t}{\partial \tau} = 0\right)$, unidirectional $[t \neq f(\phi, x)]$ heat flow in radial direction and with no internal heat generation ($q_g = 0$), the above equation reduces to

$$\frac{d^2 t}{dr^2} + \frac{1}{r} \cdot \frac{dt}{dr} = 0$$

or,
$$\frac{1}{r} \cdot \frac{d}{dr}\left[r \cdot \frac{dt}{dr}\right] = 0$$

Since, $\frac{1}{r} \neq 0$, therefore, $\frac{d}{dr}\left(r \cdot \frac{dt}{dr}\right) = 0$

or,
$$r \cdot \frac{dt}{dr} = C \text{ (a constant)} \qquad \text{...(2.54)}$$

Integrating the above equation, we get

$$t = C \ln(r) + C_1 \qquad \text{...(2.55)}$$

(where C_1 = Constant of integration)

Using the following boundary conditions, we have :

At $r = r_1$, $t = t_1$;   At $r = r_2$, $t = t_2$

$\therefore$
$$t_1 = C \ln(r_1) + C_1 \qquad \text{...(i)}$$
$$t_2 = C \ln(r_2) + C_1 \qquad \text{...(ii)}$$

From (i) and (ii), we have

$$C = -\frac{(t_1 - t_2)}{\ln(r_2/r_1)} \text{ and } C_1 = t_1 + \frac{t_1 - t_2}{\ln(r_2/r_1)} \ln(r_1) \qquad \text{...(2.56)}$$

Substituting the values of these constants in eqn. (2.55), we have

$$t = t_1 + \frac{t_1 - t_2}{\ln(r_2/r_1)} \ln(r_1) - \frac{(t_1 - t_2)}{\ln(r_2/r_1)} \cdot \ln(r) \qquad \text{...(2.57)}$$

[Equation 2.57 is the expression for *temperature distribution* in a hollow cylinder].

or, $(t - t_1) \ln(r_2/r_1) = (t_1 - t_2) \ln(r_1) - (t_1 - t_2) \ln(r)$

                 $= (t_2 - t_1) \ln(r) - (t_2 - t_1) \ln(r_1) = (t_2 - t_1) \ln(r/r_1)$

or,
$$\frac{t - t_1}{t_2 - t_1} = \frac{\ln(r/r_1)}{\ln(r_2/r_1)} \qquad \text{(Dimensionless form)} \qquad \text{...(2.58)}$$

From the above equation, the following points are worth noting :

  (i)   The *temperature distribution is logarithmic* (not linear as in the case of plane wall).

 (ii)   *Temperature at any point* in the cylinder can be expressed as a *function of radius only*. Isotherms (or lines of constant temperatures) are then concentric circles lying between the inner and outer boundaries of the hollow cylinder.

(iii)   The temperature profile [Eqn. (2.57)] is *nearly linear for values of (r_2/r_1) of the order of unity, but decidedly non-linear for large values of (r_2/r_1)*

Determination of conduction heat transfer rate (Q) :

The conduction heat transfer rate is determined by utilizing the temperature distribution [Eqn. (2.57)] in conjunction with Fourier's equation as follows :

$$Q = -kA \frac{dt}{dr}$$

$$= -kA \frac{d}{dr}\left[t_1 + \frac{t_1 - t_2}{\ln(r_2/r_1)} \ln(r_1) - \frac{(t_1 - t_2)}{\ln(r_2/r_1)} \ln(r) \right]$$

[Substituting the value of t from Eqn. (2.57)]

$$= -k(2\pi r.L)\left[\frac{-(t_1 - t_2)}{r \ln(r_2/r_1)} \right]$$

$$= 2\pi k L \frac{(t_1 - t_2)}{\ln(r_2/r_1)} = \frac{(t_1 - t_2)}{\frac{\ln(r_2/r_1)}{2\pi k L}}\left[= \frac{\Delta t}{R_{th}} \right] \qquad (\text{where}, \ R_{th} = \frac{\ln(r_2/r_1)}{2\pi k L})$$

Hence, $$Q = \frac{(t_1 - t_2)}{\frac{\ln(r_2/r_1)}{2\pi k L}}$$

...(2.59)

Alternative method :

Refer to Fig. 2.45 Consider an element at radius 'r' and thickness 'dr' for a length of the hollow cylinder through which heat is transmitted. Let dt be the temperature drop over the element.

Area through which heat is transmitted, $A = 2\pi r. L$.

Path length $= dr$ (over which the temperature falls is dt)

$$\therefore \qquad Q = -kA \cdot \left(\frac{dt}{dr} \right)$$

$$= -k.2\pi r.L \frac{dt}{dr} \text{ per unit time}$$

Induction eddy current heating.

or,
$$Q.\frac{dr}{r} = -k.2\pi L.dt$$

Integrating both sides, we get

$$Q\int_{r_1}^{r_2} \frac{dr}{r} = -k.2\pi L \int_{t_1}^{t_2} dt$$

or,
$$Q[\ln(r)]_{r_1}^{r_2} = -k.2\pi L[t]_{t_1}^{t_2}$$

or,
$$Q.\ln(r_2/r_1) = -k.2\pi L(t_2 - t_1) = k.2\pi L(t_1 - t_2)$$

∴
$$Q = \frac{k.2\pi L(t_1 - t_2)}{\ln(r_2/r_1)} = \frac{(t_1 - t_2)}{\left[\dfrac{\ln(r_2/r_1)}{2\pi k L}\right]} \qquad ...(2.60)$$

Case II. Variable thermal conductivity :

A. *Temperature variation in terms of interface temperatures* (t_1, t_2) :
The heat flux equation is given by

$$Q = -kA\frac{dt}{dr} \qquad \text{[where } k = k_0(1 + \beta t)\text{]}$$

$$= -k_0(1 + \beta t)2\pi.r.L.\frac{dt}{dr}$$

or,
$$Q.\frac{dr}{r} = -k_0.2\pi L(1 + \beta t)dt \qquad ...(2.61)$$

Integrating both sides, we have

$$Q\int_{r_1}^{r_2}\frac{dr}{r} = -k_0.2\pi L\int_{t_1}^{t_2}(1 + \beta t)dt$$

$$Q[\ln(r)]_{r_1}^{r_2} = -k_0.2\pi L\left[t + \beta.\frac{t^2}{2}\right]_{t_1}^{t_2}$$

$$Q.\ln(r_2/r_1) = -k_0.2\pi L\left[(t_2 - t_1) + \frac{\beta}{2}(t_2^2 - t_1^2)\right]$$

$$= -k_0.2\pi L\left[(t_2 - t_1) + \frac{\beta}{2}(t_2 + t_1)(t_2 - t_1)\right]$$

$$= k_0.2\pi L\left[1 + \frac{\beta}{2}(t_1 + t_2)\right][t_1 - t_2]$$

∴
$$Q = \frac{k_0.2\pi L\left[1 + \dfrac{\beta}{2}(t_1 + t_2)\right][t_1 - t_2]}{\ln(r_2/r_1)} \qquad ...(2.62)$$

Integrating between r_1 and r, we obtain

$$Q = \frac{k_0.2\pi L\left[1 + \dfrac{\beta}{2}(t_1 + t)\right][t_1 - t]}{\ln(r/r_1)} \qquad ...(2.63)$$

Equating eqns. (2.62) and (2.63), we get

$$\frac{k_0.2\pi L\left[1 + \dfrac{\beta}{2}(t_1 + t_2)\right][t_1 - t_2]}{\ln(r_2/r_1)} = \frac{k_0.2\pi L\left[1 + \dfrac{\beta}{2}(t_1 + t)\right][t_1 - t]}{\ln(r/r_1)}$$

or, $\quad \ln(r/r_1)\left[(t_1 - t_2) + \dfrac{\beta}{2}(t_1^2 - t_2^2)\right] = \ln(r_2/r_1)\left[(t_1 - t) + \dfrac{\beta}{2}(t_1^2 - t^2)\right]$

or, $\quad (t_1 - t) + \dfrac{\beta}{2}(t_1^2 - t^2) = \dfrac{\ln(r/r_1)}{\ln(r_2/r_1)}\left[(t_1 - t_2) + \dfrac{\beta}{2}(t_1^2 - t_2^2)\right]$

or, $\quad (t_1 - t) + \dfrac{\beta}{2}t_1^2 - \dfrac{\beta}{2}t^2 = \dfrac{\ln(r/r_1)}{\ln(r_2/r_1)}\left[(t_1 - t_2) + \dfrac{\beta}{2}(t_1^2 - t_2^2)\right]$

or, $\quad \dfrac{\beta}{2}t^2 + t - \left[t_1 + \dfrac{\beta}{2}t_1^2 - \dfrac{\ln(r/r_1)}{\ln(r_2/r_1)}\left\{(t_1 - t_2) + \dfrac{\beta}{2}(t_1^2 - t_2^2)\right\}\right]$

or, $\quad t = \dfrac{-1 \pm \sqrt{1^2 + 4.\dfrac{\beta}{2}\left[t_1 + \dfrac{\beta}{2}t_1^2 - \dfrac{\ln(r/r_1)}{\ln(r_2/r_1)}\left\{(t_1 - t_2) + \dfrac{\beta}{2}(t_1^2 - t_2^2)\right\}\right]}}{2 \times \dfrac{\beta}{2}}$

or, $\quad t = -\dfrac{1}{\beta} \pm \dfrac{1}{\beta}\left[(1 + 2\beta t_1 + 2\beta t_1^2) - \dfrac{\ln(r/r_1)}{\ln(r_2/r_1)} \cdot 2\beta\left\{(t_1 - t_2) + \dfrac{\beta}{2}(t_1^2 - t_2^2)\right\}\right]^{1/2}$

$\quad = -\dfrac{1}{\beta} \pm \dfrac{1}{\beta}\left[(1 + \beta t_1)^2 - \dfrac{\ln(r/r_1)}{\ln(r_2/r_1)}\left\{2\beta t_1 - 2\beta t_2 + \beta t_1^2 - \beta t_2^2\right\}\right]^{1/2}$

$\quad = -\dfrac{1}{\beta} \pm \dfrac{1}{\beta}\left[(1 + \beta t_1)^2 - \dfrac{\ln(r/r_1)}{\ln(r_2/r_1)}\left\{\beta t_1^2 + 2\beta t_1 + 1 - 1 - 2\beta t_2 - \beta t_2^2\right\}\right]^{1/2}$

[Note this step please]

$\quad = -\dfrac{1}{\beta} \pm \dfrac{1}{\beta}\left[(1 + \beta t_1)^2 - \dfrac{\ln(r/r_1)}{\ln(r_2/r_1)}\left\{(1 + \beta t_1)^2 - (1 + \beta t_2)^2\right\}\right]^{1/2}$

i.e., $\quad t = -\dfrac{1}{\beta} \pm \dfrac{1}{\beta}\left[(1 + \beta t_1)^2 - \dfrac{\ln(r/r_1)}{\ln(r_2/r_1)}\left\{(1 + \beta t_1)^2 - (1 + \beta t_2)^2\right\}\right]^{1/2}$ ...(2.64)

Since, $t = t_2$ where $r = r_2$, therefore, only the +ve sign in the above expression can be used.

Hence, $\quad t = \dfrac{1}{\beta}\left[(1 + \beta t_1)^2 - \dfrac{\ln(r/r_1)}{\ln(r_2/r_1)}\left\{(1 + \beta t_1)^2 - (1 + \beta t_2)^2\right\}\right]^{1/2} - \dfrac{1}{\beta}$ ...(2.65)

B. *Temperature variation in terms of heat. flux (Q) :*

Fourier's equation for heat conduction is given as

$$Q = -kA.\dfrac{dt}{dr}$$

or, $$Q = -k_0(1 + \beta t).2\pi r.L\dfrac{dt}{dr}$$

Rearranging the above equation, we get

$$Q.\dfrac{dr}{r} = -k_0.2\pi L(1 + \beta t)\,dt$$

Integrating both sides, we obtain

$$Q \ln(r) = -k_0.2\pi L\left(t + \dfrac{\beta r^2}{2}\right) + C$$

(where C = Constant of integration)

To evaluate the constant of integration (C), using the following boundary condition, we have :

At $r = r_1, \quad t = t_1$

$$C = k_0 . 2\pi L \left(t_1 + \frac{\beta t_1^2}{2} \right) + Q \ln (r_1)$$

$$\therefore \qquad Q \ln (r) = -k_0 . 2\pi L \left(t_1 + \frac{\beta t^2}{2} \right) + k_0 . 2\pi L \left(t_1 + \frac{\beta t_1^2}{2} \right) + Q \ln (r_1)$$

or, $\qquad Q \ln (r) - Q \ln (r_1) = -k_0 . 2\pi L \left(t + \frac{\beta t^2}{2} \right) + k_0 . 2\pi L \left(t_1 + \frac{\beta t_1^2}{2} \right)$

or, $\qquad Q \ln (r/r_1) = k_0 . 2\pi L \left[\left(t_1 + \frac{\beta t_1^2}{2} \right) - \left(t + \frac{\beta t^2}{2} \right) \right]$

or $\qquad \dfrac{Q \ln (r/r_1)}{k_0 . 2\pi L} = \left(t_1 + \frac{\beta t_1^2}{2} \right) - \left(t + \frac{\beta t^2}{2} \right)$

or, $\qquad \dfrac{\beta t^2}{2} + t + \left[\dfrac{Q \ln (r/r_1)}{k_0 . 2\pi L} - \left(t_1 + \frac{\beta t_1^2}{2} \right) \right] = 0$

Solving the above quadratic equation for 't', we get

$$t = \frac{-1 + \sqrt{1 - 4 \times \dfrac{\beta}{2} \times \left[\{Q . \ln (r/r_1)/(k_2 . 2\pi L)\} - \left\{ t_1 + (\beta t_1^2/2) \right\} \right]}}{2 \times \dfrac{\beta}{2}}$$

$$= -\frac{1}{\beta} + \sqrt{\frac{1}{\beta^2} - \frac{2}{\beta} \left[\frac{Q \ln (r/r_1)}{k_0 . 2\pi L} - \left(t_1 + \frac{\beta t_1^2}{2} \right) \right]}$$

$$= -\frac{1}{\beta} + \sqrt{\frac{1}{\beta^2} - \frac{2}{\beta} t_1 + t_1^2 - \frac{Q \ln (r/r_1)}{\beta . k_0 . \pi L}}$$

Cut-out view of a boiler.

$$= -\frac{1}{\beta} + \sqrt{\left(t_1 + \frac{1}{\beta}\right)^2 - \frac{Q}{\beta k_0} \cdot \frac{\ln(r/r_1)}{\pi L}}$$

i.e.,

$$t = -\frac{1}{\beta} + \left[\left(t_1 + \frac{1}{\beta}\right)^2 - \frac{Q}{\beta k_0} \cdot \frac{\ln(r/r_1)}{\pi L}\right]^{\frac{1}{2}} \qquad \qquad ...(2.66)$$

2.6.1.1. LOGARITHMIC MEAN AREA FOR THE HOLLOW CYLINDER

Invariably it is considered convenient to have an expression for the heat flow through a hollow cylinder of the same form as that for a plane wall. Then thickness will be equal to $(r_2 - r_1)$ and the area A will be an equivalent area A_m as shown in the Fig. 2.46. Now, expressions for heat flow through the hollow cylinder and plane wall will be as follows :

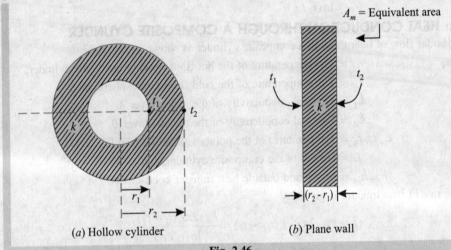

(a) Hollow cylinder

(b) Plane wall

Fig. 2.46.

$$Q = \frac{(t_1 - t_2)}{\dfrac{\ln(r_2/r_1)}{2\pi k L}} \qquad \qquad \text{... Heat flow through cylinder.}$$

$$Q = \frac{(t_1 - t_2)}{\dfrac{(r_2 - r_1)}{k A_m}} \qquad \qquad \text{... Heat flow through plane wall.}$$

A_m is so chosen that heat flow through cylinder and plane wall will be equal for the same thermal potential.

$\therefore$

$$\frac{(t_1 - t_2)}{\dfrac{\ln(r_2/r_1)}{2\pi k L}} = \frac{(t_1 - t_2)}{\dfrac{(r_2 - r_1)}{k A_m}}$$

or,

$$\frac{\ln(r_2/r_1)}{2\pi k L} = \frac{(r_2 - r_1)}{k A_m}$$

or,

$$A_m = \frac{2\pi L(r_2 - r_1)}{\ln(r_2/r_1)} = \frac{2\pi L r_2 - 2\pi L r_1}{\ln(2\pi L r_2/2\pi L r_1)}$$

or,

$$A_m = \frac{A_0 - A_i}{\ln(A_0 - A_i)} \qquad \qquad ...(2.67)$$

where A_i and A_o are inside and outside surface areas of the cylinder.

The expression is known as *logarithmic mean area* of the plane wall and the hollow cylinder. By the use of this expression a cylinder can be transformed into a plane wall and the problem can be solved easily.

If, $\dfrac{A_0}{A_i} < 2$, then we can take,

$$A_{av.} = \frac{A_i + A_0}{2} \quad \text{which is within 4\% of } A_m \qquad (\text{where, } A_{av.} = \text{Average area})$$

Further, $A_m = 2\pi r_m L = \dfrac{2\pi L(r_2 - r_1)}{\ln(r_2/r_1)}$

Obviously, *logarithmic mean radius* of the hollow cylinder is

$$r_m = \frac{(r_2 - r_1)}{\ln(r_2/r_1)} \qquad\qquad ..(2.68)$$

2.6.2. HEAT CONDUCTION THROUGH A COMPOSITE CYLINDER

Consider flow of heat through a composite cylinder as shown in Fig. 2.47.

Let, t_{hf} = The temperature of the hot fluid flowing inside the cylinder,
t_{cf} = The temperature of the cold fluid (atmospheric air),
k_A = Thermal conductivity of the inside layer A,
k_B = Thermal conductivity of the outside layer B,
t_1, t_2, t_3 = Temperatures at the points 1, 2, and 3 (see Fig. 2.47)
L = Length of the composite cylinder, and
h_{hf}, h_{cf} = Inside and outside heat transfer coefficients.

The rate of heat transfer is given by

$$Q = h_{hf} . 2\pi r_1 . L(t_{hf} - t_1) = \frac{k_A . 2\pi L(t_1 - t_2)}{\ln(r_2/r_1)}$$

$$= \frac{k_B . 2\pi L(t_2 - t_3)}{\ln(r_3/r_2)} = h_{cf} . 2\pi r_3 . L(t_3 - t_{cf})$$

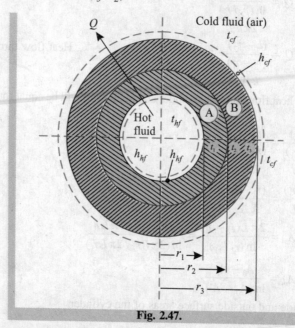

Fig. 2.47.

Rearranging the above expression, we get

$$t_{hf} - t_1 = \frac{Q}{h_{hf} \cdot r_1 \cdot 2\pi L} \qquad \qquad ...(i)$$

$$t_1 - t_2 = \frac{Q}{\dfrac{k_A \cdot 2\pi L}{\ln(r_2/r_1)}} \qquad \qquad ...(ii)$$

$$t_2 - t_3 = \frac{Q}{\dfrac{k_B \cdot 2\pi L}{\ln(r_3/r_2)}} \qquad \qquad ...(iii)$$

$$t_3 - t_{cf} = \frac{Q}{h_{cf} \cdot r_3 \cdot 2\pi L} \qquad \qquad ...(iv)$$

Adding (i), (ii), (iii) and (iv), we have

$$\frac{Q}{2\pi L}\left[\frac{1}{h_{hf} \cdot r_1} + \frac{1}{\dfrac{k_A}{\ln(r_2/r_1)}} + \frac{1}{\dfrac{k_B}{\ln(r_3/r_2)}} + \frac{1}{h_{cf} \cdot r_3} \right] = t_{hf} - t_{cf}$$

$$\therefore \qquad Q = \frac{2\pi L(t_{hf} - t_{cf})}{\left[\dfrac{1}{h_{hf} \cdot r_1} + \dfrac{1}{\dfrac{k_A}{\ln(r_2/r_1)}} + \dfrac{1}{\dfrac{k_B}{\ln(r_3/r_2)}} + \dfrac{1}{h_{cf} \cdot r_3} \right]}$$

or, $$Q = \frac{2\pi L(t_{hf} - t_{cf})}{\left[\dfrac{1}{h_{hf} \cdot r_1} + \dfrac{\ln(r_2/r_1)}{k_A} + \dfrac{\ln(r_3/r_2)}{k_B} + \dfrac{1}{h_{cf}/r_3} \right]} \qquad ...(2.69)$$

If there are 'n' concentric cylinders, then

$$Q = \frac{2\pi L(t_{hf} - t_{cf})}{\left[\dfrac{1}{h_{hf} \cdot r_1} + \sum_{n=1}^{n=n} \dfrac{1}{k_n}\ln\{r_{(n+1)}/r_n\} + \dfrac{1}{h_{cf} \cdot r_{(n+1)}} \right]} \qquad ...(2.70)$$

If inside and outside heat transfer coefficients are not considered then the above equation can be written as

$$Q = \frac{2\pi L\left[t_1 - t_{(n+1)} \right]}{\displaystyle\sum_{n=1}^{n=n} \dfrac{1}{k_n}\ln\left[r_{(n+1)}/r_n \right]} \qquad ...(2.71)$$

Example 2.35. *A thick walled tube of stainless steel with 20 mm inner diameter and 40 mm outer diameter is convered with a 30 mm layer of asbestos insulation (k = 0.2 W/m°C). If the inside wall temperature of the pipe is maintained at 600°C and the outside insulation at 1000°C, calculate the heat loss per metre of length.* **(AMIE Summer, 1997)**

Solution. Refer to Fig. 2.48.

Given: $$r_1 = \frac{20}{2} = 10\,\text{mm}$$

$$= 0.01\,\text{m}$$

$$r_2 = \frac{40}{2} = 20\,\text{mm}$$

$$= 0.02 \text{ m}$$
$$r_3 = 20 + 30 = 50 \text{ mm}$$
$$= 0.05 \text{m}$$
$$t_1 = 600° \text{ C}$$
$$t_3 = 1000° \text{ C}$$
$$k_B = 0.2 \text{ W/m°C}$$

Heat transfer per metre of a length, Q/L :

$$Q = \frac{2\pi L (t_1 - t_3)}{\dfrac{\ln (r_2 / r_1)}{k_A} + \dfrac{\ln (r_3 / r_2)}{k_B}}$$

Since the thermal conductivity of stainless steel is not given, therefore, neglecting the resistance offered by stainless steel to heat transfer across the tube, we have

$$\frac{Q}{L} = \frac{2\pi (t_1 - t_3)}{\dfrac{\ln (r_3 / r_2)}{k_B}} = \frac{2\pi (600 - 1000)}{\dfrac{\ln (0.05 / 0.02)}{0.2}}$$

$$= -548.57 \text{ W/m} \quad \textbf{(Ans.)}$$

Negative sign indicates that the heat transfer takes place *radially inward*.

Example 2.36. *A steel pipe with 50 mm OD is covered with a 6.4 mm asbestos insulation [k = 0.166 W/mK] followed by a 25 mm layer of fiber-glass insulation [k = 0.0485 W/mK]. The pipe wall temperature is 393 K and the outside insulation temperature is 311 K. Calculate the interface temperature between the asbestos and fiber-glass.*

(AMIE Summer, 1998)

Solution.

Given : $r_1 = \dfrac{50}{2} = 25 \text{ mm} = 0.025 \text{ m};$

$$r_2 = r_1 + 6.4 = 25 + 6.4$$
$$= 31.4 \text{ mm or } 0.0314 \text{ m};$$
$$r_3 = r_2 + 25 = 31.4 + 25$$
$$= 56.4 \text{ mm} = 0.0564 \text{ m};$$
$$T_1 = 393 \text{ K}; T_3 = 311 \text{ K}$$
$$k_A = 0.166 \text{ W/mK};$$
$$k_B = 0.0485 \text{ W/mK}.$$

Interface temperature between the asbestos and fiber-glass, t_2 :

We know that, $Q = \dfrac{2\pi L (T_1 - T_3)}{\dfrac{\ln (r_2 / r_1)}{k_A} + \dfrac{\ln (r_3 / r_2)}{k_B}}$

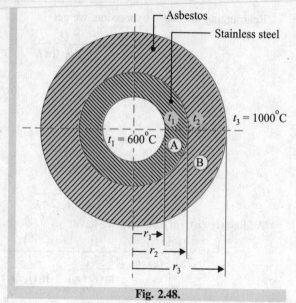

Fig. 2.48.

Stove for heating.

$$\frac{Q}{L} = \frac{2\pi(T_1 - T_3)}{\frac{\ln(r_2/r_1)}{k_A} + \frac{\ln(r_3/r_2)}{k_B}}$$

$$= \frac{2\pi(393 - 311)}{\frac{\ln(0.0314/0.025)}{0.166} + \frac{\ln(0.0564/0.0314)}{0.0485}}$$

$$= \frac{515.22}{1.373 + 12.075} = 38.31\,\text{W/m}$$

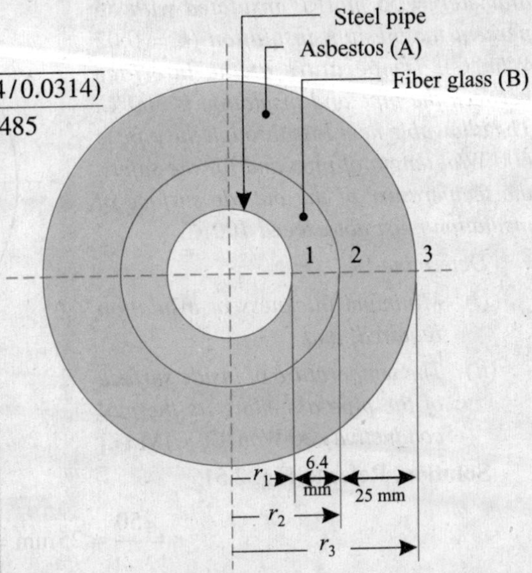

Also, $\dfrac{Q}{L} = \dfrac{2\pi(T_1 - T_2)}{\dfrac{\ln(r_2/r_1)}{k_A}}$

or, $38.31 = \dfrac{2\pi(393 - T_2)}{\left[\dfrac{\ln(0.0314/0.025)}{0.166}\right]}$

$$38.31 = \frac{2\pi(393 - T_2)}{1.373}$$

$\therefore \quad T_2 = 393 - \dfrac{38.31 \times 1.373}{2\pi} = 384.6\,\text{K}$

or, $\quad t_2 = 384.6 - 273 = \mathbf{111.6°\,C}$ **(Ans.)**

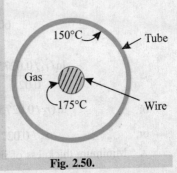

Steel pipe
Asbestos (A)
Fiber glass (B)

1 2 3

r_1→ 6.4 mm ← 25 mm →
r_2 →
r_3 →

Fig. 2.49.

Example 2.37. *A gas filled tube has 2 mm inside diameter and 25 cm length. The gas is heated by an electrical wire of diameter 50 microns (0.05 mm) located along the axis of the tube. Current and voltage drop across the heating element are 0.5 amps and 4 volts, respectively. If the measured wire and inside tube wall temperatures are 175°C and 150°C respectively, find the thermal conductivity of the gas filling the tube.* (GATE, 1998)

Solution. *Given* : Inside radius of the tube, $\quad r_t = 2\,\text{mm}$

Length of the tube, $\quad L = 25\,\text{cm} = 0.25\,\text{m}$

Radius of the electric wire, $\quad r_w = 0.025\,\text{mm}$

Inside tube temperature, $\quad t_t = 150°C$

Wire temperature, $\quad t_w = 175°C$

Current through the element $= 0.5\,\text{A}$

Voltage across the element $= 4\,\text{V}$

Thermal conductivity of the gas, k :

Heat transferred through a cylinder,

$$Q = \frac{2\pi k L(t_w - t_t)}{\ln(r_t/r_w)}$$

$$= \frac{2\pi k \times 0.25\,(175 - 150)}{\ln(1/0.025)} = 10.645\,\text{kW} \quad ...(i)$$

Also, $\quad Q = VI = 4 \times 0.5 = 2.0\,\text{W}$ $\quad\quad ...(ii)$

From (*i*) and (*ii*), we get

$\quad 10.645\,k = 2.0$

or, $\quad k = \mathbf{0.188\,W/m°C.}$ **(Ans.)**

150°C ← Tube

Gas

175°C ← Wire

Fig. 2.50.

Example 2.38. *A standard cast iron pipe (inner diameter = 50 mm and outer diameter = 55 mm) is insulated with 85 percent magnesium insulation (k = 0.02 W/m°C). Temperature at the interface between the pipe and insulation is 300°C. The allowable heat loss through the pipe is 600 W/m length of pipe and for the safety, the temperature of the outside surface of insulation must not exceed 100°C.*

Determine :

(i) *Minimum thickness of insulation required, and*

(ii) *The temperature of inside surface of the pipe assuming its thermal conductivity 20 W/m°C.* [M.U.]

Solution. Refer to Fig. 2.51.

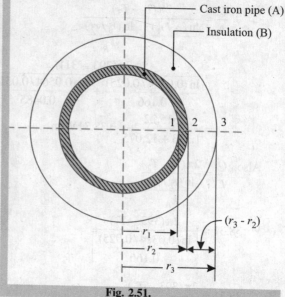

Fig. 2.51.

$$r_1 = \frac{50}{2} = 25 \, \text{mm} = 0.025 \, \text{m}$$

$$r_2 = \frac{55}{2} = 27.5 \, \text{mm} = 0.0275 \, \text{m}$$

$$k_A = 20 \, \text{W/m°C}, \; k_B = 0.02 \, \text{W/m°C}$$

$$t_2 = 300°C, \; t_3 = 100°C$$

Heat loss per metre length of pipe $Q/L = 600$ W/m

(i) Minimum thickness of insulation required, $(r_3 - r_2)$:

$$Q = \frac{2\pi L (t_1 - t_2)}{\dfrac{\ln(r_2/r_1)}{k_A}} = \frac{2\pi L (t_2 - t_3)}{\dfrac{\ln(r_3/r_2)}{k_B}}$$

or,

$$\frac{Q}{L} = \frac{2\pi (t_1 - t_2)}{\dfrac{\ln(r_2/r_1)}{k_A}} = \frac{2\pi (t_2 - t_3)}{\dfrac{\ln(r_3/r_2)}{k_B}}$$

$$600 = \frac{2\pi (t_1 - 300)}{\dfrac{\ln(0.0275/0.025)}{20}} = \frac{2\pi (300 - 100)}{\dfrac{\ln(r_3/0.0275)}{0.02}}$$

∴

$$\frac{\ln(r_3/0.0275)}{0.02} = \frac{2\pi (300 - 100)}{600}$$

or,

$$\ln(r_3/0.0275) = 0.02 \left[\frac{2\pi (300 - 100)}{600} \right] = 0.04188$$

or,

$$r_3/0.0275 = 1.0427 \quad \text{or} \quad r_3 = 0.0287 \, \text{m or } 28.7 \, \text{mm}$$

∴ Minimum thickness of insulation required

$$= r_3 - r_2 = 28.7 - 27.5 = \mathbf{1.2 \, mm} \quad \textbf{(Ans.)}$$

(ii) The temperature of inside surface of the pipe, t_1 :

$$600 = \frac{2\pi (t_1 - 300)}{\dfrac{\ln(0.0275/0.025)}{20}} = \frac{2\pi (t_1 - 300)}{0.00476}$$

$$t_1 = \frac{600 \times 0.00476}{2\pi} + 300 = 300.45°\text{C} \text{ (Ans.)}$$

Example 2.39. *A pipe (k = 180 W/m°C) having inner and outer diameters 80 mm and 100 mm respectively is located in a space at 25°C. Hot gases at temperature 160°C flow through the pipe. Neglecting surface heat transfer coefficients, calculate :*

   (i) *The heat loss through the pipe per unit length,*

  (ii) *The temperature at a point halfway between the inner and outer surfaces, and*

 (iii) *The surface area normal to the direction of heat flow so that the heat transfer through the pipe can be determined by considering material of pipe as a plane wall of the same thickness.*

Solution. Inner diameter of the pipe, $\qquad r_i = \dfrac{80}{2} = 40\,\text{mm} = 0.04\,\text{m}$

Outer diameter of the pipe, $\qquad r_o = \dfrac{100}{2} = 50\,\text{mm} = 0.05\,\text{m}$

Temperature of hot gases, $\qquad t_i = 160°\text{C}$

Temperature of space in which the pipe is located, $t_o = 25°\text{C}$.

Thermal conductivity of pipe material, $\qquad k = 180 \text{ W/m°C}$

(*i*) **The heat loss through the pipe per unit length, Q :**

$$Q = \frac{\Delta t}{R_{th}} = \frac{(160 - 25)}{\left[\dfrac{\ln(r_o/r_i)}{2\pi k L} \right]} = \frac{135}{\dfrac{\ln(0.05/0.04)}{2\pi \times 180 \times 1}} = 684229 \text{ W (Ans.)}$$

(*ii*) **The temperature at a point halfway between the inner and outer surfaces, t :**

Radius at halfway through the pipe wall,

$$r = \frac{r_i + r_0}{2} = \frac{40 + 50}{2} = 45\,\text{mm} = 0.045\,\text{m}$$

Thermal resistance of the pipe upto its mid-plane

$$= \frac{\ln(r/r_i)}{2\pi k L} = \frac{\ln(0.045/0.04)}{2\pi \times 180 \times 1} = 0.0414 \times 10^{-4} \text{ °C/W}$$

As same heat flows through each section

$$684229 = \frac{(t_i - t)}{1.0414 \times 10^{-4}} = \frac{(160 - t)}{1.0414 \times 10^{-4}}$$

$$\therefore \qquad t = 160 - 684229 \times 1.0414 \times 10^{-4} = 88.74°\text{C} \text{ (Ans.)}$$

Alternatively : $\qquad \dfrac{t - t_1}{t_2 - t_1} = \dfrac{\ln(r/r_i)}{\ln(r_o/r_i)}$ $\qquad$ ...[Eqn. 2.58]

$$\frac{(t - 160)}{(25 - 160)} = \frac{\ln(0.045/0.04)}{\ln(0.05/0.04)} = 0.5278$$

or, $\qquad t = 160 + (25 - 160) \times 0.5278 = 88.74°\text{C}$

(*iii*) **Equivalent log-mean area, A_m :**

$$A_m = \frac{A_o - A_i}{\ln(A_o/A_i)} = \frac{2\pi L(r_0 - r_i)}{\ln(r_o/r_i)} = \frac{2\pi \times 1 \times (0.05 - 0.04)}{\ln(0.05/0.04)} = 0.2816\,\text{m}^2$$

Check : $\qquad Q = \dfrac{k A_m (t_i - t_0)}{(r_o - r_i)} = \dfrac{180 \times 0.2616 (160 - 25)}{(0.05 - 0.04)} = 684288 \text{ W}$

which is approximately same as calculated above.

Example 2.40. *A 240 mm steam main, 210 metres long is covered with 50 mm of high tempera-ture insulation (k = 0.092 W/m°C) and 40 mm of low temperature insulation (k = 0.062 W/m°C). The inner and outer surface temperatures as measured are 390°C and 40°C respectively. Calculate :*

   (i)   The total heat loss per hour,

   (ii)   The heat loss per m² of pipe surface,

   (iii)   The total heat loss per m² of outer surface, and

   (iv)   The temperature between two layers of insulation.

   Neglect heat conduction through pipe material.

Solution. Refer to Fig. 2.52.

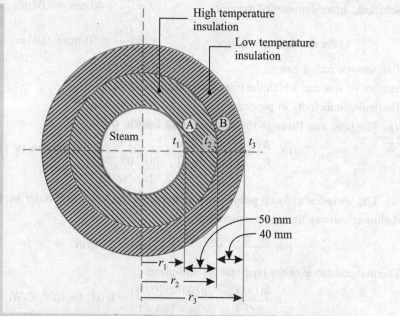

Fig, 2.52.

Pipe network in a factory.

Given :

$$r_1 = \frac{240}{2} = 120 \text{ mm} = 0.12 \text{ m}$$

$$r_2 = 120 + 50 = 170 \text{ mm} = 0.17 \text{ m}$$

$$r_3 = 120 + 50 + 40 = 210 \text{ mm} = 0.21 \text{ m}$$

$$k_A = 0.092 \text{ W/m°C}; \ k_B = 0.062 \text{ W/m°C}$$

$$t_1 = 390°C; \ t_3 = 40°C$$

Length of steam main, $L = 210$ m.

(i) Total heat loss per hour :

$$Q = \frac{2\pi L(t_1 - t_3)}{\left[\dfrac{\ln(r_2/r_1)}{k_A} + \dfrac{\ln(r_3/r_2)}{k_B}\right]} \qquad \text{[Eqn. (2.71)]}$$

$$= \frac{2\pi \times 210(390 - 40)}{\left[\dfrac{\ln(0.17/0.12)}{0.092} + \dfrac{\ln(0.21/0.17)}{0.062}\right]}$$

$$= \frac{461814}{(3.786 + 3.408)} = 64194.3 \text{ W}$$

$$= \frac{64194.3 \times 3600}{1000} = 231099.5 \text{ kJ/h}$$

i.e., The total heat loss per hour = **231099.5 kJ/h** **(Ans.)**

(ii) Total heat loss per m² of the pipe surface :

Total heat loss per m² of the surface

$$= \frac{231099.5}{2\pi r_1 . L} = \frac{231099.5}{2\pi \times 0.12 \times 210} = 1459.55 \text{ kJ/h} \ \text{(Ans.)}$$

(iii) Total heat loss per m² of the outer surface :

Total heat loss per m² of the outer surface

$$= \frac{231099.5}{2\pi r_3 . L} = \frac{231099.5}{2\pi \times 0.21 \times 210} = 834.03 \text{ kJ/h} \ \text{(Ans.)}$$

(iv) The temperature between two layers, t_2 :

$$Q = \frac{2\pi L(t_1 - t_2)}{\left[\dfrac{\ln(r_2/r_1)}{k_A}\right]}$$

$$64194.3 = \frac{2\pi \times 210(390 - t_2)}{\left[\dfrac{\ln(0.17/0.12)}{0.092}\right]} = 348.5(390 - t_2)$$

$$\therefore \quad t_2 = 390 - \frac{64194.3}{348.5} = 205.8°C \ \text{(Ans.)}$$

Example 2.41. *A steam pipe of outer diameter 120 mm is covered with two layers of lagging, inside layer 45 mm thick (k = 0.08W/m°C) and outside layer 30 mm thick (k = 0.12 W/m°C). The pipe conveys steam at a pressure of 20 bar with 50°C superheat. The outside temperature of lagging is 25°C. If the steam pipe is 30m long, determine :*

(i) Heat lost per hour, and

(ii) Interface temperature of lagging.

The thermal resistance of steam pipe may be neglected.

Solution. Refer to Fig. 2.53.

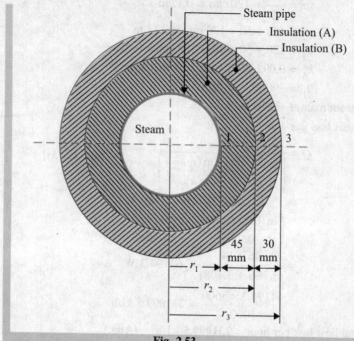

Fig. 2.53.

$$r_1 = \frac{120}{2} = 60\,\text{mm} = 0.06\,\text{m}$$

$$r_2 = 60 + 45 = 105 \text{ mm} = 0.105 \text{ m}$$

$$r_3 = 105 + 30 = 135 \text{ mm} = 0.135 \text{ m}$$

$$k_A = 0.08 \text{ W/m°C}; \ k_B = 0.12 \text{ W/m°C}$$

$$t_3 = 25°\text{C}; \ L \text{ (length of pipe)} = 30 \text{ m}$$

Corresponding to 20 bar (from steam tables),

$$t_{sat} \text{ (saturation temp.)} = 212.4°\text{C}$$

∴   Temperature of steam, $t_1 = t_{sat} + 50 = 212.4 + 50 = 262.4°\text{C}$

(i) Heat lost per hour :

The rate of heat transfer is given by

$$Q = \frac{2\pi L (t_1 - t_3)}{\dfrac{\ln (r_2 / r_1)}{k_A} + \dfrac{\ln (r_3 / r_2)}{k_B}}$$

$$= \frac{2\pi \times 30 (262.4 - 25)}{\dfrac{\ln (0.105/0.06)}{0.08} + \dfrac{\ln (0.135/0.105)}{0.12}}$$

$$= 4923 \text{ W (or J/s)}$$

∴   Heat lost per hour $= \dfrac{4923 \times 3600}{1000}$

$$= \textbf{17722.8 kJ/h}   \textbf{(Ans.)}$$

(ii) **Interface temperature of lagging, t_2 :**

$$Q = \frac{2\pi L(t_1 - t_2)}{\dfrac{\ln(r_2/r_1)}{k_A}}$$

or, $$4923 = \frac{2\pi \times 30(262.4 - t_2)}{\dfrac{\ln(0.105/0.06)}{0.08}}$$

or, $$(262.4 - t_2) = \frac{4923}{2\pi \times 30} \times \frac{\ln(0.105/0.06)}{0.08} = 182.69$$

$$\therefore \qquad t_2 = 262.4 - 182.69 = \mathbf{79.71°C} \ \textbf{(Ans.)}$$

Example 2.42. *A steam pipe of outside diameter 80 mm and 25 m long conveys 800 kg of steam per hour at a pressure of 22 bar. The steam enters the pipe with a dryness fraction of 0.99 and is to leave the other end of the pipe with the minimum dryness fraction of 0.97. This is to be accomplished by using a lagging material (k = 0.2 W/m°C), determine its minimum thickness to meet the necessary conditions, if the temperature of the outside surface of lagging is 25°C.*

Assume that there is no pressure drop across the pipe and the resistance of the pipe material is negligible.

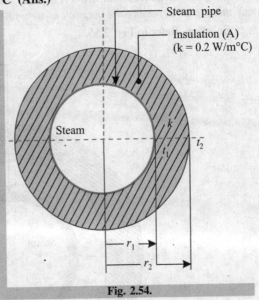

Fig. 2.54.

Solution. Refer to Fig. 2.54.

$$r_1 = \frac{80}{2}\,\text{mm} = 0.04\,\text{m},$$
$$k = 0.2 \ \text{W/m°C}$$

Length of pipe, $L = 25\text{m}$, $t_2 = 25°C$

Minimum thickness of insulation, $(r_2 - r_1)$:

From steam tables, corresponding to 22 bar pressure :

$$t_{sat}\,(= t_1) = 217.2°C, \ h_{fg} = 1868.1 \ \text{kJ/kg}$$

$\therefore$ Heat loss per kg of steam passing through the pipe

$$= (0.99 - 0.97) \times 1868.1 = 37.36 \ \text{kJ/kg}$$

Total heat loss through the pipe per second

$$= 37.36 \times \frac{800}{3600} = 8.302 \ \text{kJ/s or } 8302 \ \text{J/s or } 8302 \ \text{W}$$

Heat loss through the pipe (neglecting pipe thermal resistance) is given by

$$Q = \frac{2\pi L(t_1 - t_2)}{\dfrac{\ln(r_2/r_1)}{k}} = \frac{2\pi \times 25 \times (217.2 - 25)}{\dfrac{\ln(r_2/r_1)}{0.2}}$$

or, $$8302 = \frac{6038.14}{\ln(r_2/r_1)} \qquad \text{or} \quad \ln(r_2/r_1) = \frac{6038.14}{8302} = 0.72731$$

$\therefore \qquad \dfrac{r_2}{r_1} = 2.069 \qquad \text{or} \qquad r_2 = 40 \times 2.069 = 82.76 \ \text{mm}$

$\therefore$ Minimum thickness of insulation $= r_2 - r_1$

$$= 82.76 - 40 = \textbf{42.76 mm (Ans.)}$$

Example 2.43. *A steam pipe (inner diameter = 150 mm and outer diameter = 160 mm) having thermal conductivity 58 W/m°C is covered with two layers of insulation, of thickness 30 mm and 50 mm respectively and thermal conductivities 0.18 W/m°C and 0.09 W/m°C respectively. The temperature of inner surface of steam pipe is 320°C and that of the outer surface of the insulation layers is 40°C.*

(i) Determine the quantity of heat lost per metre length of steam pipe and layer contact temperature, and

(ii) If the condition of the steam is dry and saturated, find the quality of the steam coming out of one metre pipe assuming the quantity of steam flowing is 0.32 kg/min.

Solution. Refer to Fig. 2.55.

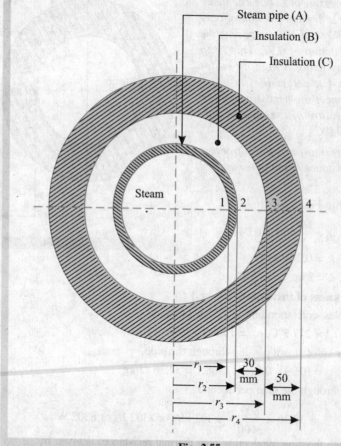

Fig. 2.55.

$$r_1 = \frac{150}{2} = 75\,\text{mm} = 0.075\,\text{m}$$

$$r_2 = \frac{160}{2} = 80\,\text{mm} = 0.08\,\text{m}$$

$$r_3 = 80 + 30 = 110\,\text{mm} = 0.11\,\text{m}$$

$$r_4 = 110 + 50 = 160\,\text{mm} = 0.16\,\text{m}$$

$$t_1 = 320° \text{ C}, t_4 = 40°C$$
$$k_A = 58 \text{ W/m°C}$$
$$k_B = 0.18 \text{ W/m°C}, k_C = 0.09 \text{ W/m°C}$$

(i) **Quantity of heat lost per meter (Q) and layer contact temperatures (t_2, t_3):**

Quantity of heat lost is given by

$$Q = \frac{2\pi L(t_1 - t_4)}{\dfrac{\ln(r_2/r_1)}{k_A} + \dfrac{\ln(r_3/r_2)}{k_B} + \dfrac{\ln(r_4/r_3)}{k_C}}$$

$$= \frac{2\pi \times 1 \times (320 - 40)}{\dfrac{\ln(0.08/0.075)}{58} + \dfrac{\ln(0.11/0.08)}{0.18} + \dfrac{\ln(0.16/0.11)}{0.09}} = 296.5 \text{ W/m} \quad \textbf{(Ans).}$$

Also, $$Q = \frac{2\pi \times 1(t_1 - t_2)}{\dfrac{\ln(r_2/r_1)}{k_A}} = \frac{2\pi \times 1(t_2 - t_3)}{\dfrac{\ln(r_3/r_2)}{k_B}} = \frac{2\pi \times 1(t_3 - t_4)}{\dfrac{\ln(r_4/r_3)}{k_C}}$$

∴ $$296.5 = \frac{2\pi(320 - t_2)}{\dfrac{\ln(r_2/r_1)}{k_A}} \quad \text{or} \quad t_2 = 320 - \frac{296.5}{2\pi} \times \frac{\ln(r_2/r_1)}{k_A}$$

$$= 320 - \frac{296.5}{2\pi} \times \frac{\ln(0.08/0.75)}{58} = \textbf{319.95° C (Ans.)}$$

Similarly, $$296.5 = \frac{2\pi(319.95 - t_3)}{\dfrac{\ln(r_3/r_2)}{k_B}}$$

or, $$t_3 = 319.95 - \frac{296.5}{2\pi} \times \frac{\ln(r_3/r_2)}{k_B} = 319.95 - \frac{296.5}{2\pi} \times \frac{\ln(0.11/0.08)}{0.18} = \textbf{236.5° C (Ans.)}$$

(ii) **Quality of steam coming out of one metre pipe, x :**

Total heat of steam when it is saturated at 320°C = 2703 kJ/kg ...from steam tables

Heat carried by steam per minute after losing heat in the pipe

$$= 0.32(\text{kg/min}) \times 2703 (\text{kJ/kg}) - \frac{296.5 \times 60}{1000} (\text{kJ/min}) = 847.17 \text{ kJ/min}$$

Now $$847.17 = 0.32 (h_f + x h_{fg})$$

Corresponding to 320°C saturation temperature, from steam tables, we have

$$h_f = 1463 \text{ kJ/kg}, h_{fg} = 1240 \text{ kJ/kg}$$

∴ $$847.17 = 0.32 (1463 + x \times 1240) = 468.16 + 396.8x$$

or, $$x = \frac{(847.17 - 468.16)}{396.8} = 0.955 \quad \textbf{(Ans.)}$$

Example 2.44. *Thermal conductivity, k, of a certain material is given by $k = a + bT + cT^2$ where a, b, c are constants and T is the absolute temperature. Derive an expression for heat flow per unit length of a hollow cylinder made of this material. Assume that inner and outer radii of the cylinder are r_1 and r_2 respectively and the cylinder ends are perfectly insulated.* (AMIE Summer, 2000)

Solution. Refer to Fig. 2.56. Consider a hollow ring at radius r, and thickness dr of the hollow cylinder. The radius heat flow across the ring, per unit length, is given by

$$Q = -kA_r \frac{dT}{dr} = -k \times 2\pi r \times \frac{dT}{dr}$$

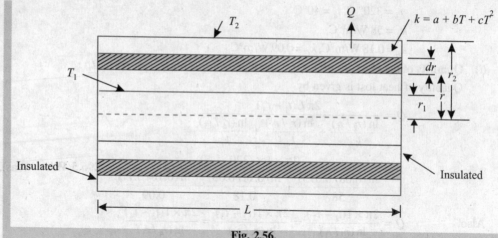

Fig. 2.56.

or,
$$Q\frac{dr}{r} = -2\pi(a + bT + cT^2)\,dT$$

Integrating from inner to outer radius, we get

$$Q\int_{r_1}^{r_2}\frac{dr}{r} = -2\pi\int_{T_1}^{T_2}(a + bt + cT^2)\,dT$$

or,
$$Q\ln\left(\frac{r_2}{r_1}\right) = 2\pi\left[a\,(T_1 - T_2) + \frac{b}{2}(T_1^2 - T_2^2) + \frac{c}{3}(T_1^3 - T_2^3)\right]$$

or,
$$Q = \frac{2\pi(T_1 - T_2)\left[a + \dfrac{b}{2}(T_1 + T_2) + \dfrac{c}{3}(T_1^2 + T_1 T_2 + T_2^2)\right]}{\ln\left(\dfrac{r_2}{r_1}\right)}$$

which is the *required expression*. **(Ans.)**

Example 2.45. *At a certain time, the temperature distribution in a long cylindrical fire tube, inner radius 30 cm and outer radius 50 cm, is given by*

$$t = 800 + 1000\,r - 5000\,r^2$$

where (t) is in (°C) and (r) in (m). The thermal conductivity and thermal diffusivity of tube material are 58 W/m-K °C and 0.004 m²/h, respectively. Find :

   (i)   *Rate of heat flow at inside and outside surfaces per unit length;*

  (ii)   *Rate of heat storage per unit length;*

 (iii)   *Rate of change of temperature at inner and outer surfaces.*   **(AMIE Winter, 1999)**

Solution. Given : $r_1 = 30$ cm $= 0.3$ m; $r_2 = 50$ cm $= 0.5$ m, $k = 58$ W/m° C; $\alpha = 0.004$ m²/h

 (i)   **Rate of heat flow per unit length :**

Temperature distribution, $t = 800 + 1000\,r - 5000\,r^2$ ...(Given)

$$\frac{dt}{dr} = 1000 - 10000\,r$$

Rate of heat flow at inside surface (1), per unit length,

$$Q_1 = -k\,A_1\frac{dt}{dr}\bigg|_{r = r_1} = -k\,2\pi r_1 \cdot \frac{dt}{dr}\bigg|_{r = 0.3}$$

$$= -k \times 2\pi r_1\,(1000 - 10000\,r_1)$$

$$= -58 \times 2\pi \times 0.3 \,(1000 - 10000 \times 0.3)$$

$$= \mathbf{2.1865 \times 10^5 \ W/m}, \textit{ in outward direction} \text{ (as it is positive) (\textbf{Ans.})}$$

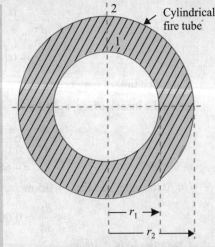

2 Cylindrical fire tube

Similarly, rate of heat flow at outer surface (2), per unit length,

$$Q_2 = -k \times 2\pi r_2 \,(1000 - 10000 \, r_2)$$

$$= -58 \times 2\pi \times 0.5 \,(1000 - 10000 \times 0.5)$$

$$= \mathbf{7.2885 \times 10^5 \ W/m}, \textit{ outward direction} \text{ (as it is positive) (\textbf{Ans.})}$$

(ii) Rate of heat storage per unit length :

As the heat leaving Q_2 is greater than heat entering Q_1, there is decrease in the heat contents.

In other words, the rate of heat storage is negative. It is equal to

r_1

r_2

Fig. 2.57.

$$Q_1 - Q_2 = 2.1865 \times 10^5 - 7.2885 \times 10^5 = \mathbf{-5.102 \times 10^5 \ W/m \ (Ans.)}$$

(iii) Rate of change of temperature at inner and outer surfaces :

We know that,

$$\frac{dt}{d\tau} = \frac{\alpha}{r} \frac{d}{dr}\left(r \frac{dt}{dr}\right) \qquad \qquad \qquad ...(i)$$

$$\frac{dt}{dr} = 1000 - 10000 \, r$$

$$\frac{d}{dr}\left(r \frac{dt}{dr}\right) = \frac{d}{dr}(1000 \, r - 10000 \, r^2) = 1000 - 20000 \, r \qquad ...(ii)$$

Electric arc furnace for producing steel.

$$\frac{dt}{d\tau} = \frac{\alpha}{r}(1000 - 20000\,r), \qquad \text{by using (i) and (ii)}$$

$$= \alpha\left(\frac{1000}{r} - 20000\right)$$

Rate of change of temperature :

(*a*) At the inner surface, $r = 0.3$ m

$$\frac{dt}{d\tau} = \alpha\left(\frac{1000}{0.3} - 20000\right) = 0.004\left(\frac{1000}{0.3} - 20000\right)$$

$$= -66.67°\text{C/h}, \quad (i.e., \textbf{decrease}) \quad \textbf{(Ans.)}$$

(*b*) At the outer surface, $r = 0.5$ m

$$= \frac{dt}{d\tau} = 0.004\left(\frac{1000}{0.5} - 20000\right) = -72°\text{C/h}, (i.e., \textbf{decrease}) \quad \textbf{(Ans.)}$$

Example 2.46. *A steam pipe of 220 mm outer diameter is carrying steam at 280°C. It is insulated with a material having thermal conductivity k = 0.06 (1 + 0.0018 t) where k is in W/m°C and t is °C. If the insulation thickness is 50 mm and the temperature of the outer surface is 50°C, determine:*

  (*i*) *The heat flow per metre length of the pipe, and*

  (*ii*) *The temperature at the mid thickness.*

Solution. Refer to Fig. 2.58.

$$r_1 = \frac{220}{2} = 110\,\text{mm}$$

$$= 0.11\,\text{m}; \, r_2 = 110 + 50$$

$$= 160\,\text{mm} = 0.16\,\text{m}$$

$$k = 0.06\,(1 + 0.0018\,t)$$

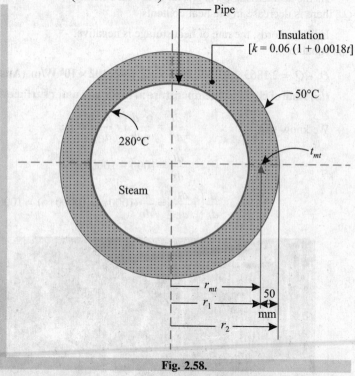

Fig. 2.58.

(*i*) **The heat flow per metre length of pipe, Q :**

$$Q = \frac{\Delta t}{\dfrac{\ln(r_2/r_1)}{2\pi k_m L}} \qquad \qquad ...(i)$$

where

$$k_m = 0.06\left[1 + 0.0018\left(\frac{280 + 50}{2}\right)\right]$$

$$= 0.0778 \text{ W/m°C}$$

$$\therefore \qquad Q = \frac{(280 - 50)}{\dfrac{\ln(0.16/0.11)}{2\pi \times 0.778 \times 1}} = \textbf{300.06 W/m (Ans.)}$$

(ii) **The temperature at the mid thickness, t_{mt} :**

$$Q = \frac{(280 - t_{mt})}{\dfrac{\ln(r_{mt}/r_1)}{2\pi k_m \times 1}} \quad \left[\begin{array}{l}\text{where } r_{mt} = \text{radius at mid thickness/plane} \\ = \left(\dfrac{r_1 + r_2}{2}\right) = \left(\dfrac{0.11 + 0.16}{2}\right) = 0.135\,\text{m}\end{array}\right]$$

$$300.06 = \frac{2\pi k_m (280 - t_{mt})}{\ln(0.135/0.11)} = \frac{2\pi \times 0.06\left[1 + 0.0018\left(\dfrac{280 + t_{mt}}{2}\right)(280 - t_{mt})\right]}{0.2048}$$

or, $\qquad [1 + 0.0009(280 + t_{mt})](280 - t_{mt}) = \dfrac{300.06 \times 0.2048}{2\pi \times 0.06} = 163$

or, $\qquad (1 + 0.252 + 0.0009\,t_{mt})(280 - t_{mt}) = 163$

or, $\qquad (1.252 + 0.0009\,t_{mt})(280 - t_{mt}) = 163$

or, $\qquad 350.56 - 1.252\,t_{mt} + 0.252\,t_{mt} - 0.0009\,t_{mt}^2 = 163$

or, $\qquad 0.0009\,t_{mt}^2 + t_{mt} - 187.56 = 0$

or, $\qquad t_{mt} = \dfrac{-1 + \sqrt{1 + 4 \times 0.0009 \times 187.56}}{2 \times 0.0009} = 163.5°C$

∴ $\qquad$ Temperature at the mid thickness, $t_{mt} = \mathbf{163.5°C}$ **(Ans.)**

$$\left[\text{Check } Q = \frac{(280 - 163.5)}{\ln(0.135/0.11)} \times 2\pi \times 0.06\left\{1 + 0.0018\left(\frac{280 + 163.5}{2}\right)\right\} = 300.06\,\text{W}\right]$$

Example 2.47. *An insulated steam pipe having outside diameter of 30 mm is to be covered with two layers of insulation, each having thickness of 20 mm. The thermal conductivity of one material is 5 times that of the other.*

Assuming that the inner and outer surface temperatures of composite insulation are fixed, how much will heat transfer be increased when better insulation material is next to the pipe than it is outer layer? (M.U.)

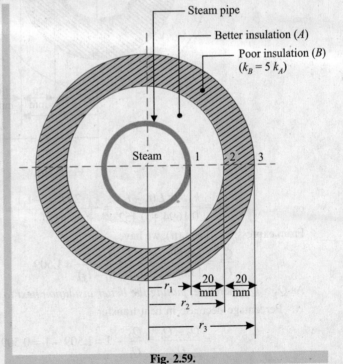

Fig. 2.59.

Solution. Case I. When better insulation is inside :

Refer to Fig. 2.59.

$r_1 = \dfrac{30}{2} = 15\,\text{mm} = 0.015\,\text{m};$

$r_2 = 15 + 20 = 35\,\text{mm} = 0.035\,\text{m};$

$r_3 = 35 + 20 = 55\,\text{mm} = 0.055\,\text{m}$

$k_B = 5k_A$

Heat lost through the pipe is given by

$$Q_1 = \frac{2\pi L(t_1 - t_3)}{\dfrac{\ln(r_2/r_1)}{k_A} + \dfrac{\ln(r_3/r_2)}{k_B}} = \frac{2\pi L(t_1 - t_3)}{\dfrac{\ln(0.035/0.015)}{k_A} + \dfrac{\ln(0.055/0.035)}{5k_A}}$$

or, $\quad Q_1 = \dfrac{k_A.\,2\pi L(t_1 - t_3)}{0.8473 + 0.0904} = \dfrac{k_A.2\pi L(t_1 - t_3)}{0.9377} = 1.066\,2\pi L k_A\,(t_1 - t_3)$ ...(i)

Case II. When better insulation is outside : Refer to Fig. 260.

$$Q_2 = \frac{2\pi L(t_1 - t_3)}{\dfrac{\ln(r_2/r_1)}{k_B} + \dfrac{\ln(r_3/r_2)}{k_A}} = \frac{2\pi L(t_1 - t_3)}{\dfrac{\ln(0.035/0.015)}{5k_A} + \dfrac{\ln(0.055/0.035)}{k_A}}$$

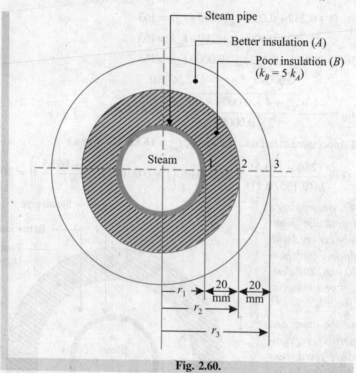

- Steam pipe
- Better insulation (A)
- Poor insulation (B) $(k_B = 5\,k_A)$

Steam

20 mm | 20 mm

r_1

r_2

r_3

Fig. 2.60.

or, $\quad Q_2 = \dfrac{k_A.2\pi L(t_1 - t_3)}{0.1694 + 0.452} = \dfrac{k_A.2\pi L(t_1 - t_3)}{0.6214} = 1.609\,2\pi L.k_A\,(t_1 - t_3)$ ...(ii)

From expression (i) and (ii), we have,

$$\frac{Q_2}{Q_1} = \frac{1.609 \times 2\pi L.k_A\,(t_1 - t_3)}{1.066 \times 2\pi L.k_A\,(t_1 - t_3)} = 1.509$$

As $Q_2 > Q_1$, therefore, *putting the better insulation next to the pipe decreases the heat flow.*

∴ Percentage decrease in heat transfer

$$= \frac{Q_2 - Q_1}{Q_1} = \frac{Q_2}{Q_1} - 1 = 1.509 - 1 = 0.509 \text{ or } \mathbf{50.9\%} \text{ (Ans.)}$$

Example 2.48. *Hot air at a temperature of 65°C is flowing through a steel pipe of 120 mm diameter. The pipe is covered with two layers of different insulating materials of thickness 60 mm and 40 mm, and their corresponding thermal conductivities are 0.24 and 0.4 W/m°C. The inside and outside heat transfer coefficients are 60 W/m°C and 12 W/m°C respectively. The atmosphere is at 20°C. Find the rate of heat loss from 60 m length of pipe.*

Solution. Refer to Fig. 2.61.

Given : $r_1 = \dfrac{120}{2} = 60\,mm = 0.06\,m$

$r_2 = 60 + 60 = 120\,mm = 0.12\,m$

$r_3 = 60 + 60 + 40 = 160\,mm = 0.16\,m$

$k_A = 0.24\,W/m°C$; $k_B = 0.4\,W/m°C$

$h_{hf} = 60\,W/m^2°C$; $h_{cf} = 12\,W/m^2°C$

$t_{hf} = 65°C$; $t_{cf} = 20°C$

Length of pipe, $L = 60\,m$

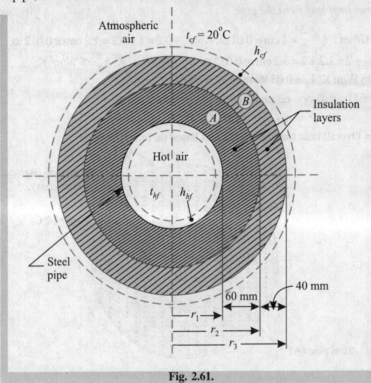

Fig. 2.61.

Rate of heat loss, Q :

Rate of heat loss is given by

$$Q = \frac{2\pi L (t_{hf} - t_{cf})}{\left[\dfrac{1}{h_{hf} \cdot r_1} + \dfrac{\ln(r_2/r_1)}{k_A} + \dfrac{\ln(r_3/r_2)}{k_B} + \dfrac{1}{h_{cf} \cdot r_3}\right]} \qquad \text{[Eqn. (2.69)]}$$

$$= \frac{2\pi \times 60(65 - 20)}{\left[\dfrac{1}{60 \times 0.06} + \dfrac{\ln(0.12/0.06)}{0.24} + \dfrac{\ln(0.16/0.12)}{0.4} + \dfrac{1}{12 \times 0.16}\right]}$$

$$= \frac{16964.6}{0.2777 + 2.8881 + 0.7192 + 0.5208} = 3850.5\,W$$

i.e., Rate of heat loss = **3850.5 W** **(Ans.)**

Example 2.49. *Calculate the overall heat transfer coefficient (based on inner diameter) for a steel pipe covered with fiber glass insulation. The following data are given :*

ID of pipe = 2 cm

Thickness of pipe = 0.2 cm

Thickness of insulation = 2 cm

Heat transfer coefficient (inside) = 10 W/m² K

Heat transfer coefficient (outside) = 5 W/m² K

Conductivity of insulation = 0.05 W/m K

Conductivity of steel = 46 W/m K

Inside fluid temperature = 200°C

Ambient temperature = 30°C

Also find net heat loss from the pipe.   (AMIE Summer, 2002)

Solution. Given : $r_1 = \dfrac{2}{2} = 1$ cm $= 0.01$ m; $r_2 = r_1 + 0.2 = 1 + 0.2 = 1.2$ cm or 0.012 m,

$r_3 = r_2 + 2 = 1.2 + 2 = 3.2$ cm or 0.032 m, $h_{hf} = 10$ W/m² K; $h_{cf} = 5$ W/m² K;

$k_A = 46$ W/m K; $k_B = 0.05$ W/m K; $t_{hf} = 200°C$; $t_{cf} = 30°C$.

Overall heat transfer co-efficient, U_i :

$$Q = A_i\, U_i\, \Delta t = 2\pi r_1\, L U_i\, (t_{hf} - t_{cf})$$

where U_i = Overall heat transfer coefficient based on inner diameter.

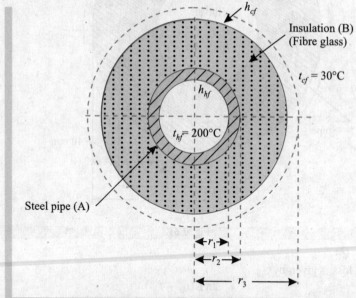

Fig. 2.62.

$$U_i = \cfrac{1}{\dfrac{1}{h_{hf}} + \dfrac{r_1}{k_A}\ln\!\left(\dfrac{r_2}{r_1}\right) + \dfrac{r_1}{k_B}\ln\!\left(\dfrac{r_3}{r_2}\right) + \dfrac{r_1}{r_3}\cdot\dfrac{1}{h_{cf}}}$$

$$= \cfrac{1}{\dfrac{1}{10} + \dfrac{0.01}{46}\ln\!\left(\dfrac{0.012}{0.01}\right) + \dfrac{0.01}{0.05}\ln\!\left(\dfrac{0.032}{0.012}\right) + \dfrac{0.01}{0.032}\times\dfrac{1}{5}}$$

$$= \cfrac{1}{0.1 + 3.96\times10^{-5} + 0.19616 + 0.0625}$$

$$= \dfrac{1}{0.3587} = \mathbf{2.788\ W/m^2 K}\ \ \textbf{(Ans.)}$$

Heat loss/m length, Q/L :

$$\frac{Q}{L} = 2\pi\, r_1 \times U_i \times (t_{hf} - t_{cf})$$

$$= 2\pi \times 0.01 \times 2.788\,(200 - 30) = \mathbf{29.78\ W/m\ (Ans.)}$$

Example 2.50. *An aluminium pipe carries steam at 110°C. The pipe (k = 185 W/m°C) has an inner diameter of 100 mm and outer diameter of 120 mm. The pipe is located in a room where the ambient air temperature is 30°C and the convective heat transfer coefficient between the pipe and air is 15 W/ m²°C. Determine the heat transfer rate per unit length of pipe.*

To reduce the heat loss from the pipe, it is covered with a 50 mm thick layer of insulation (k = 0.20 W/m°C). Determine the heat transfer rate per unit length from the insulated pipe. Assume that the convective resistance of the steam is negligible. **(AMIE Summer, 1999)**

Solution. Case I. Refer to Fig. 2.63.

Given :
$$r_1 = \frac{100}{2} = 50\ \text{mm}$$
$$= 0.05\ \text{m}$$
$$r_2 = \frac{120}{2} = 60\ \text{mm}$$
$$= 0.06\ \text{m}$$

Temperature of steam (hot fluid),
$$t_{hf} = 110°C$$

Temperature of ambient air (cold fluid),
$$t_{cf} = 30°C$$

Thermal conductivity of pipe material,
$$k = 185\ \text{W/m°C}$$

Heat transfer coefficient between the pipe and air,
$$h_{cf} = 15\ \text{W/m}^2°C$$

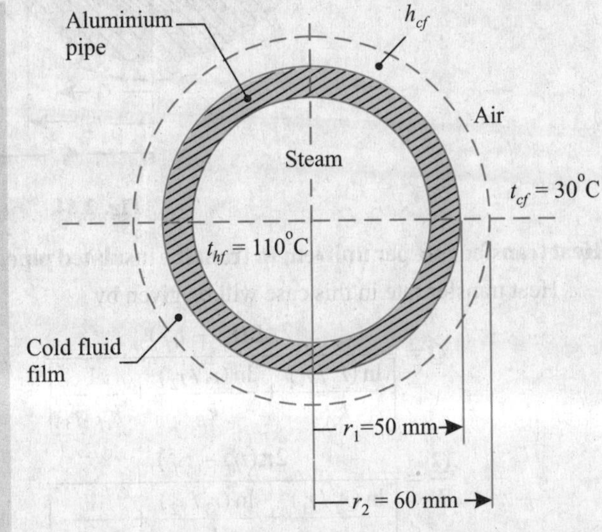

Fig. 2.63.

Heat transfer rate per unit length of pipe, Q/L :

Heat transfer rate is given by,

$$Q = \frac{2\pi L(t_{hf} - t_{cf})}{\left[\dfrac{\ln(r_2/r_1)}{k_A} + \dfrac{1}{h_{cf}\cdot r_2}\right]} \qquad \text{[Eqn. (2.69)]}$$

or,
$$\frac{Q}{L} = \frac{2\pi L(t_{hf} - t_{cf})}{\left[\dfrac{\ln(r_2/r_1)}{k_A} + \dfrac{1}{h_{cf}\cdot r_2}\right]} = \frac{2\pi(110 - 30)}{\left[\dfrac{\ln(0.06/0.05)}{185} + \dfrac{1}{15 \times 0.06}\right]} = 451.99\ \text{W/m}$$

*i.e., Heat transfer rate per unit length of pipe = **451.99 W/m** (Ans.)*

Case II : Refer to Fig. 2.64.

$$r_1 = 50\ \text{mm} = 0.05\ \text{m}; \qquad\qquad r_2 = 60\ \text{mm} = 0.06\ \text{m}$$
$$r_3 = 60 + 50 = 110\ \text{mm} = 0.11\ \text{m}; \qquad k_A = 185\ \text{W/m°C}$$
$$k_B = 0.20\ \text{W/m°C}; \qquad\qquad h_{cf} = 15\ \text{W/m}^2°C$$

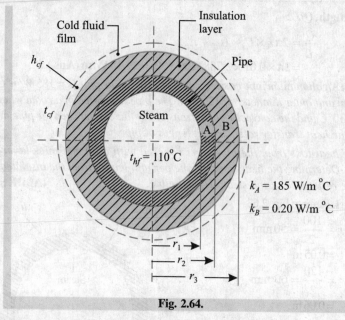

Fig. 2.64.

Heat transfer rate per unit length from the insulated pipe, Q/L :

Heat transfer rate in this case will be given by

$$Q = \frac{2\pi L (t_{hf} - t_{cf})}{\left[\dfrac{\ln (r_2 / r_1)}{k_A} + \dfrac{\ln (r_3 / r_2)}{k_B} + \dfrac{1}{h_{cf} \cdot r_3} \right]}$$

$$\frac{Q}{L} = \frac{2\pi (t_{hf} - t_{cf})}{\left[\dfrac{\ln (r_2 / r_1)}{k_A} + \dfrac{\ln (r_3 / r_2)}{k_B} + \dfrac{1}{h_{cf} \cdot r_3} \right]}$$

Substituting the given data is the above equation, we have,

$$\frac{Q}{L} = \frac{2\pi (110 - 30)}{\left[\dfrac{\ln (0.06/0.05)}{185} + \dfrac{\ln (0.11/0.06)}{0.20} + \dfrac{1}{15 \times 0.11} \right]}$$

$$= \frac{502.65}{0.000985 + 3.030679 + 0.606060} = 138.18 \, \text{W/m}$$

i.e., Heat transfer rate per unit length of insulated pipe = **138.18 W/m**   (Ans.)

Example 2.51. *A 150 mm steam pipe has inside diameter of 120 mm and outside diameter of 160 mm. It is insulated at the outside with asbestos. The steam temperature is 150°C and the air temperature is 20°C. h (steam side) = 100 W/m²°C, h (air side) = 30 W/m²°C, k (asbestos) = 0.8 W/m°C and k (steel) = 42 W/m°C. How thick should the asbestos be provided in order to limit the heat loses to 2.1 kW/m² ?*   (AMIE Winter, 2002)

Solution. Refer to Fig. 2.65.

Given : $r_1 = \dfrac{120}{2} = 60 \, \text{mm} = 0.06 \, \text{m}$

$r_2 = \dfrac{160}{2} = 80 \, \text{mm} = 0.08 \, \text{m}$

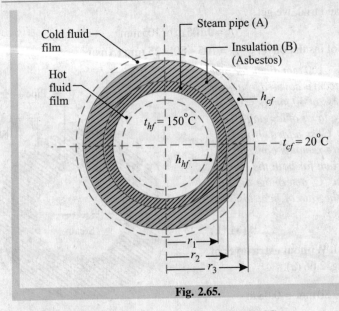

Fig. 2.65.

k_A = 42 W/m°C; k_B = 0.8 W/m°C

t_{hf} = 150°C; t_{cf} = 20°C

h_{hf} = 100 W/m²°C; h_{cf} = 30 W/m²°C

Heat loss = 2.1 kW/m²

Thickness of insulation (asbestos), $(r_3 - r_2)$:

Area for heat transfer = $2\pi r L$ (where L = length of the pipe)

∴   Heat loss = $2.1 \times 2\pi rL$ kW

$= 2.1 \times 2\pi \times 0.075 \times L = 0.989\, L$ kW

$= 0.989\, L \times 10^3$ watts

$$\left(\text{where } r, \text{ mean radius} = \frac{150}{2} = 75 \text{ mm or 0.075 m ... given}\right]$$

Heat transfer rate in such a case is given by

$$Q = \frac{2\pi L(t_{hf} - t_{cf})}{\left[\dfrac{1}{h_{hf} \cdot r_1} + \dfrac{\ln(r_2/r_1)}{k_A} + \dfrac{\ln(r_3/r_2)}{k_B} + \dfrac{1}{h_{cf} \cdot r_3}\right]} \qquad \text{[Eqn. 2.69]}$$

$$0.989\, L \times 10^3 = \frac{2\pi L(150 - 20)}{\left[\dfrac{1}{100 \times 0.06} + \dfrac{\ln(0.08/0.06)}{42} + \dfrac{\ln(r_3/0.08)}{0.8} + \dfrac{1}{30 \times r_3}\right]}$$

$$0.989 \times 10^3 = \frac{816.81}{\left[0.16666 + 0.00685 + \dfrac{\ln(r_3/0.08)}{0.8} + \dfrac{1}{30\, r_3}\right]}$$

or, $\dfrac{\ln(r_3/0.08)}{0.8} + \dfrac{1}{30\, r_3} = \dfrac{816.81}{0.989 \times 10^3} - (0.16666 + 0.00685) = 0.6524$

or, $1.25 \ln(r_3/0.08) + \dfrac{1}{30\, r_3} - 0.6524 = 0$

Solving by hit and trial, we get

$$r_3 \approx 0.105 \text{ m or } 105 \text{ mm}$$

∴ Thickness of insulation $= r_3 - r_2 = 105 - 80 = 25$ **mm (Ans.)**

Example 2.52. *A 160 mm diameter pipe carrying saturated steam is covered by a layer of lagging of thickness of 40 mm (k = 0.8 W/ m°C). Later, an extra layer of lagging 10 mm thick (k = 1.2 W/m° C) is added. If the surrounding temperature remains constant and heat transfer coefficient for both the lagging materials is 10 W/m²°C, determine the percentage change in the rate of heat loss due to extra lagging layer.*

(M.U.)

Solution. Case I. Without extra layer of lagging : Refer to Fig. 2.66 (a).

$$r_1 = \frac{160}{2} = 80 \text{ mm} = 0.08 \text{ m}$$

$$r_2 = 80 + 40 = 120 \text{ mm} = 0.12 \text{ m}$$

$$k_A = 0.8 \text{ W/m°C}, h_0 = 10 \text{ W/m}^2\text{°C}$$

Let, t_s = Temperature of steam, and

t_a = Temperature of air.

Considering *unit length of pipe* in both the cases (Case I and Case II) and neglecting internal heat transfer coefficient (being not given) and also neglecting the resistance of the pipe (as thickness and conductivity of the pipe are not given), the heat flow rate is given as

$$Q_1 = \frac{2\pi(t_s - t_a)}{\dfrac{\ln(r_2/r_1)}{k_A} + \dfrac{1}{h_0 \cdot r_2}}$$

$$= \frac{2\pi(t_s - t_a)}{\dfrac{\ln(0.12/0.08)}{0.8} + \dfrac{1}{10 \times 0.12}}$$

$$= \frac{2\pi(t_s - t_a)}{1.340} \qquad ...(i)$$

Case II. With extra layer of lagging :
Refer to Fig. 2.66 (b).

$$r_3 = 120 + 10 = 130 \text{ mm} = 0.13 \text{ m}$$

$$k_B = 1.2 \text{ W/m°C}, h_0 = 10 \text{ W/m}^2\text{°C}$$

$$Q_2 = \frac{2\pi(t_s - t_a)}{\dfrac{\ln(r_2/r_1)}{k_A} + \dfrac{\ln(r_3/r_2)}{k_B} + \dfrac{1}{h_0 \cdot r_3}}$$

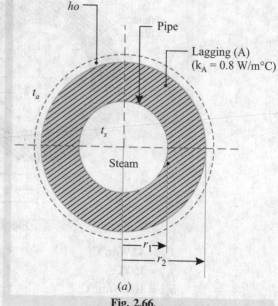

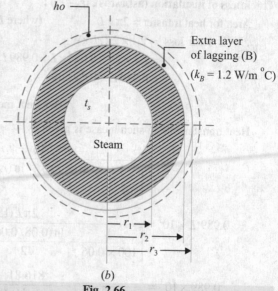

(a)

Fig. 2.66.

(b)

Fig. 2.66.

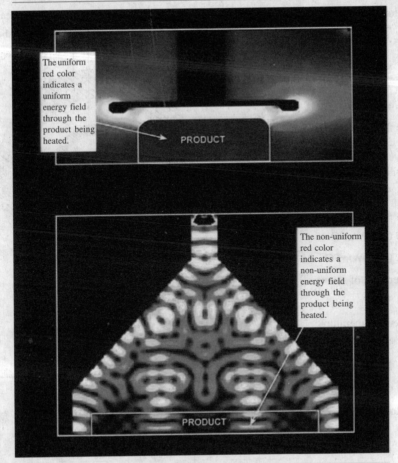

The uniform red color indicates a uniform energy field through the product being heated.

PRODUCT

The non-uniform red color indicates a non-uniform energy field through the product being heated.

PRODUCT

Dielectric heating.

$$= \frac{2\pi(t_s - t_a)}{\dfrac{\ln(0.12/0.08)}{0.8} + \dfrac{\ln(0.13/0.12)}{1.2} + \dfrac{1}{10 \times 0.13}}$$

$$= \frac{2\pi(t_s - t_a)}{1.343} \qquad\qquad ...(ii)$$

The percentage decrease in heat flow due to extra addition of insulation can be calculated using eqns. (i) and (ii) as follows :

$$\frac{Q_1 - Q_2}{Q_1} = \left[\frac{(1/1.34) - (1/1.343)}{(1/1.34)}\right] = 0.00223 \text{ or } \mathbf{0.223\%} \quad \textbf{(Ans.)}$$

Example 2.53. *A steam pipe (k = 45 W/m°C) having 70 mm inside diameter and 85 mm outside diameter is lagged with two insulation layers; the layer in contact with the pipe is 35 mm asbestos (k = 0.15 W/m°C) and it is covered with 25 mm thick magnesia insulation (k = 0.075 W/m°C). The heat transfer coefficients for the inside and outside surfaces are 220 W/m²°C and 6.5 W/m²°C respectively. If the temperature of steam is 350°C and the ambient temperature is 30°C, calculate :*

(i)   *The steady loss of heat for 50 m length of the pipe;*

(ii) *The overall heat transfer coefficients based on inside and outside surfaces of the lagged steam main.*

Solution. Refer to Fig. 2.67.

$$r_1 = \frac{70}{2} = 35 \text{ mm or } 0.035 \text{ m}$$

$$r_2 = \frac{85}{2} = 42.5 \text{ mm or } 0.0425 \text{ m}$$

$$r_3 = 42.5 + 35$$
$$= 77.5 \text{ mm or } 0.0775 \text{ m}$$

$$r_4 = 77.5 + 25$$
$$= 102.5 \text{ mm or } 0.1025 \text{ m}$$

$$L = 50 \text{ m}$$

$$k_A = 45 \text{ W/m°C}$$

$$k_B = 0.15 \text{ W/m°C}$$

$$k_C = 0.075 \text{ W/m°C}$$

Temperature of steam,

$$t_{hf} = 350°C$$

Ambient temperature,

$$t_{cf} = 30°C$$

$$h_{hf} = 220 \text{ W/m}^2°C,$$

$$h_{cf} = 6.5 \text{ W/m}^2°C.$$

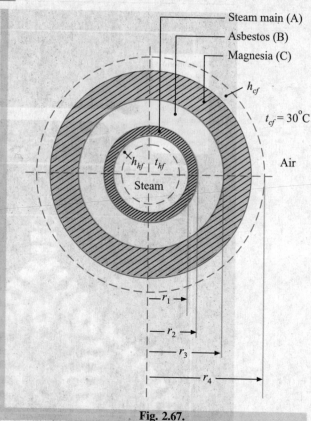

Fig. 2.67.

(i) **Loss of heat, Q :**

$$Q = \frac{2\pi L (t_{hf} - t_{cf})}{\dfrac{1}{h_{hf} \cdot r_1} + \dfrac{\ln(r_2/r_1)}{k_A} + \dfrac{\ln(r_3/r_2)}{k_B} + \dfrac{\ln(r_4/r_3)}{k_C} + \dfrac{1}{h_{cf} \cdot r_4}}$$

$$= \frac{2\pi \times 50 (350 - 30)}{\dfrac{1}{220 \times 0.035} + \dfrac{\ln(0.0425/0.035)}{45} + \dfrac{\ln(0.0775/0.0425)}{0.15} + \dfrac{\ln(0.1025/0.0775)}{0.075} + \dfrac{1}{6.5 \times 0.1025}}$$

$$= \frac{100530.96}{0.129870 + 0.00431 + 4.00516 + 3.72779 + 1.50094} = 10731.23 \text{ W}$$

i.e., Loss of heat for 50 m of length = **10731.23 W**   **(Ans.)**

(ii) **The overall heat transfer coefficients, U_o, U_i :**

The loss of heat can also be expressed as follows :

$$Q = U_o A_o \Delta t = U_i A_i \Delta t$$

Where U_o and U_i are the overall heat transfer co-efficients based on the outside area A_o and inside area A_i respectively.

∴

$$U_0 = \frac{Q}{A_o \cdot \Delta t} = \frac{10731.23}{2\pi r_4 L \times \Delta t}$$

$$= \frac{10731.23}{2\pi \times 0.1025 \times 50 (350 - 30)} = \textbf{1.0414 W/m}^2\textbf{°C} \quad \textbf{(Ans.)}$$

Similarly,

$$U_i = \frac{Q}{A_i \cdot \Delta t} = \frac{10731.23}{2\pi r_1 L \times \Delta t} = \frac{10731.23}{2\pi \times 0.035 \times 50 (350 - 30)}$$

$$= \textbf{3.05 W/m}^2\textbf{°C} \quad \textbf{(Ans.)}$$

Example 2.54. *A steel pipe is carrying steam at a pressure of 30 bar. Its outside diameter is 90 mm and is lagged with a layer of material 45 mm thick (k = 0.05 W/m°C). The ambient temperature is 20°C and the surface of the lagging has a heat transfer coefficient of 8.4 W/m²°C. Neglecting resistance due to pipe material and due to steam film on the inside of steam pipe, find the thickness of the lagging (k = 0.07 W/m°C) which must be added to reduce the steam condensation rate by 50 percent if the surface coefficient remains unchanged.*

Solution. Case I. Single layer of insulation : Refer to Fig. 2.68.

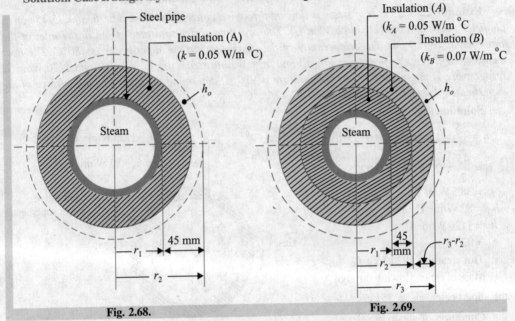

Fig. 2.68. Fig. 2.69.

$$r_1 = \frac{90}{2} = 45\,\text{mm} = 0.045\,\text{m}, \quad r_2 = 45 + 45 = 90\,\text{mm} = 0.09\,\text{m}$$

$$h_0 = 8.4\,\text{W/m}^2\text{°C}, \quad k_A = 0.05\,\text{W/m°C}$$

The total thermal resistance is given by

$$\Sigma R_{th} = R_{th-A} + (R_{th})_{\text{conv.}}$$

$$= \frac{\ln(r_2/r_1)}{2\pi k_A.L} + \frac{1}{2\pi r_2 L.h_0}$$

$$= \frac{\ln(0.09/0.045)}{2\pi \times 0.05 \times 1} + \frac{1}{2\pi \times 0.09 \times 1 \times 8.4}$$

$$= 2.206 + 0.210 = 2.416\text{°C/W per metre length}$$

Case II. Two layers of insulation : Refer Fig. 2.69.

$$\Sigma R_{th} = R_{th-A} + R_{th-B} + (R_{th})_{\text{conv.}}$$

$$= \frac{\ln(r_2/r_1)}{2\pi k_A.L} + \frac{\ln(r_3/r_2)}{2\pi k_B.L} + \frac{1}{2\pi r_3.L.h_o}$$

$$= \frac{\ln(0.09/0.045)}{2\pi \times 0.05 \times 1} + \frac{\ln(r_3/0.09)}{2\pi \times 0.07 \times 1} + \frac{1}{2\pi r_3 \times 8.4}$$

$$= 2.206 + 2.274 \ln(r_3/0.09) + \frac{0.019}{r_3}$$

When condensation is to be reduced by 50 percent, the thermal resistance to heat flow must become two times,

i.e.,
$$2.206 + 2.274 \ln (r_3 / 0.09) + \frac{0.019}{r_3} = 2 \times 2.416$$

$$2.274 \ln (r_3 / 0.09) + \frac{0.019}{r_3} = 2.626$$

By hit and trial, we get

$$r_3 \approx 0.275 \text{ m or } 275 \text{ mm}$$

Hence thickness of insulation $(B) = (r_3 - r_2) = 275 - 90 = \textbf{185 mm (Ans.)}$

Example 2.55. *55 kg/s of steam is flowing through a convective steam superheater 35/45 mm in diameter made of steel (k = 38.5 W/m°C). The pressure of dry saturated steam at the inlet of the superheater is 120 bar. The temperature of the steam leaving the superheater is 480°C. The heat transfer coefficients from the gas to wall and from wall to steam are 82 W/m²°C and 1120 W/m²°C respectively. If the mean flue gas temperature is 920°C, determine the outer heating surface of the superheater. Take: c_{ps} (for steam) = 1.92 kJ/kg°C.*

Solution. Refer to Fig. 2.70.

$$r_1 = \frac{35}{2} = 17.5 \text{ mm} = 0.0175 \text{ m}$$

$$r_2 = \frac{45}{2} = 22.5 \text{ mm} = 0.0225 \text{ m}$$

$k = 38.5 \text{ W/m°C}$

$h_o = 82 \text{ W/m}^2\text{°C}$

$h_i = 1120 \text{ W/m}^2\text{°C}$

$t_o = 920\text{°C}$

c_{ps} (for steam) = 192 kJ/kg°C

Mass of steam flowing through the superheater, $\dot{m}_s = 55 \text{ kg/s}$

Condition of steam at inlet of the superheater; $p = 120$ bar, dryness fraction $(x) = 1$

The temperature of steam leaving the superheater, $t_{sup} = 480\text{°C}$.

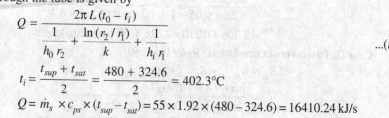

Steel
$(k = 38.5 \text{ W/m}^\circ\text{C})$

$h_i = 1120 \text{ W/m}^2 \text{ }^\circ\text{C}$

$h_o = 82 \text{ W/m}^2 \text{ }^\circ\text{C}$

Convective steam superheater

t_o

Gases t_i Steam

r_1

r_2

Fig. 2.70.

Outer heating surface of the superheater :

From steam tables, corresponding to 120 bar,

Saturation temperature, $t_{sat.} = 324.6\text{°C}$

The heat flow through the tube is given by

$$Q = \frac{2\pi L (t_0 - t_i)}{\dfrac{1}{h_0 \, r_2} + \dfrac{\ln (r_2 / r_1)}{k} + \dfrac{1}{h_i \, r_1}} \qquad \ldots(i)$$

where,
$$t_i = \frac{t_{sup} + t_{sat}}{2} = \frac{480 + 324.6}{2} = 402.3\text{°C}$$

and,
$$Q = \dot{m}_s \times c_{ps} \times (t_{sup} - t_{sat}) = 55 \times 1.92 \times (480 - 324.6) = 16410.24 \text{ kJ/s}$$

Substituting the proper values in eqn. (i), we have

$$16410.24 \times 10^3 = \frac{2\pi L (920 - 402.3)}{\dfrac{1}{82 \times 0.0225} + \dfrac{\ln (0.0225 / 0.0175)}{38.5} + \dfrac{1}{1120 \times 0.0175}}$$

$$= \frac{3252.8 \, L}{0.5995} = 5425.8 \, L$$

or, $$L = \frac{16410.24 \times 10^3}{5425.8} = 3024\,\text{m}$$

∴ Outer surface area of the superheater $= 2\pi r_2 L$

$$= 2\pi \times 0.0225 \times 3024 = \mathbf{427.5\,m^2} \quad \textbf{(Ans.)}$$

Example 2.56. *A pipe having outer diameter 250 mm is insulated by a material of thermal conductivity of 0.48 W/m°C. The insulation of outside diameter 500 mm, due to restriction of space, is placed with an eccentricity of 60 mm. Determing the heat loss for a length of 10 m if inner and outer surfaces are at temperatures of 280°C and 50°C respectively.*

Solution. Refer to Fig. 2.71.

$$r_1 = \frac{250}{2} = 125\,\text{mm} = 0.125\,\text{m};$$

$$r_2 = \frac{500}{2} = 250\,\text{mm} = 0.25\,\text{m}$$

Eccentricity, $e = 60\,\text{mm} = 0.06\,\text{m}$

Length of pipe, $L = 10\,\text{m}$

Thermal conductivity of insulation,

$k = 0.48\,\text{W/m°C}$

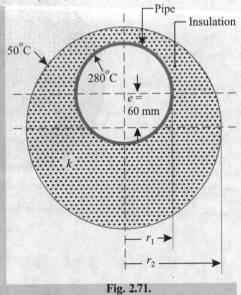

Fig. 2.71.

Heat loss, Q :

$$Q = \frac{\Delta t}{R_{th}} \qquad \qquad \qquad \qquad ...(i)$$

The thermal resistance (R_{th}) in this case is given by (from hand book)

$$R_{th} = \frac{1}{2\pi k L} \ln\left[\frac{\{(r_2 + r_1)^2 - e^2\}^{1/2} + \{(r_2 - r_1)^2 - e^2\}^{1/2}}{\{(r_2 + r_1)^2 - e^2\}^{1/2} - \{(r_2 - r_1)^2 - e^2\}^{1/2}}\right]$$

$$= \frac{1}{2\pi \times 0.48 \times 10} \ln\left[\frac{\{(0.250 + 0.125)^2 - (0.06)^2\}^{1/2} + \{(0.250 - 0.125)^2 - (0.06)^2\}^{1/2}}{\{(0.250 + 0.125)^2 (0.06)^2\}^{1/2} - \{(0.250 - 0.125)^2 - (0.06)^2\}^{1/2}}\right]$$

$$= \frac{1}{2\pi \times 0.48 \times 10} \ln\left[\frac{0.3702 + 0.1096}{0.3702 - 0.1096}\right] = 0.0202°\text{C/W}$$

Substituting the proper values in expression (i), we have

$$Q = \frac{(280 - 50)}{0.0202} = \mathbf{11386\,W} \qquad \textbf{(Ans.)}$$

Example 2.57. *A current of 950 amperes is flowing through a long copper rod of 25 mm diameter, having an electrical resistance of 22×10^{-6} ohm per metre length. The rod is insulated to a radius of 17 mm with fibrous cotton (k = 0.058 W/m°C) which is further covered by a layer of plastic (k = 0.42 W/m°C). The heat transfer coefficient between the plastic and the surroundings is 20.5 W/m²°C and the temperature of surroundings is 15°C. Determine :*

(i) The thickness of the plastic layer which gives minimum temperature in a cotton insulation.

(ii) The temperature of copper rod and the maximum temperature in the plastic layer, for the condition as at (i).

Solution. Refer to Fig. 2.72.

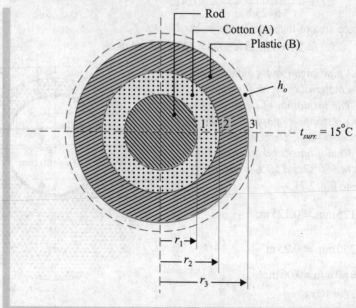

Fig. 2.72

$$r_1 = \frac{25}{2} = 12.5\,\text{mm} = 0.0125\,\text{m}$$

$$r_2 = 17\,\text{mm} = 0.017\,\text{m}$$

$$k_A = 0.058\,\text{W/m°C}; k_B = 0.42\,\text{W/m°C}$$

$$h_o = 20.5\,\text{W/m}^2\text{°C}; t_{surr.} = 15\text{°C}$$

(i) The thickness of plastic layer which gives minimum temperature in cotton insulation :
For the given system the heat transfer rate is given by

$$Q = \frac{\Delta t}{\Sigma R_{th}} = \frac{\Delta t}{\dfrac{\ln(r_2/r_1)}{2\pi k_A . L} + \dfrac{\ln(r_3/r_2)}{2\pi k_B . L} + \dfrac{1}{2\pi r_3 L . h_o}}$$

The effect of insulation (plastic) can be studied by differentiating the total thermal resistance (ΣR_{th}) w.r.t. r_3 and setting the derivative equal to zero.

i.e.,
$$\frac{d(\Sigma R_{th})}{dr_3} = \frac{d}{dr_3}\left[\frac{\ln(r_2/r_1)}{2\pi k_A L} + \frac{\ln(r_3/r_2)}{2\pi k_B L} + \frac{1}{2\pi r_3 L . h_o}\right] = 0$$

or,
$$\frac{1}{2\pi k_B L . r_3} - \frac{1}{2\pi L . h_0 . r_3^2} = 0$$

or,
$$r_3 = \frac{k_B}{h_o}$$

Let us find second derivative to determine whether the foregoing result maximises or minimises the total resistance.

$$\frac{d^2(\Sigma R_{th})}{dr_3^2} = -\frac{1}{2\pi k_B L . r_3^2} + \frac{1}{\pi h_0 L r_3^3}$$

At
$$r_3 = \frac{k_B}{h_0}$$

$$\frac{d^2(\Sigma R_{th})}{dr_3^2} = -\frac{1}{2\pi k_B L} . \left[\frac{h_0}{k_B}\right]^2 + \frac{1}{\pi h_o L}\left[\frac{h_0}{k_B}\right]^3 \quad \text{which is obviously +ve.}$$

Thus $r_3 = \dfrac{k_B}{h_o}$ represents the condition for minimum thermal resistance (*i.e.*, maximum heat flow rate) and hence *minimum temperature in the cotton insulation.*

$$\therefore \qquad r_3 = \dfrac{k_B}{h_o} = \dfrac{0.42}{20.5} = 0.02048 \text{ m or } 20.48 \text{ mm}$$

Hence, thickness of plastic insulation = 20.48 – 17 = **3.48 mm**   (**Ans.**)

(*ii*) **Temperature of copper rod (t_1) and maximum temperature in the plastic layer (t_2):**

Heat generated in the copper rod due to flow of current

$$= I^2 R = 950^2 \times 22 \times 10^{-6} = 19.855 \text{ W/m}$$

($\because R = 22 \times 10^{-6}$ ohm per metre length $\qquad\qquad$ ... given)

Total thermal resistance,

$$(\Sigma R_{th}) = \dfrac{\ln(r_2/r_1)}{2\pi k_A.L} + \dfrac{\ln(r_3/r_2)}{2\pi k_B.L} + \dfrac{1}{2\pi r_3 L.h_o}$$

$$= \dfrac{\ln(0.017/0.0125)}{2\pi \times 0.058 \times 1} + \dfrac{\ln(0.02048/0.017)}{2\pi \times 0.42 \times 1} + \dfrac{1}{2\pi \times 0.02048 \times 1 \times 20.5}$$

$$= 1.293 \degree \text{C/W}$$

Heat flow through the composite system, $Q = \dfrac{\Delta t}{\Sigma R_{th}} = \dfrac{t_1 - t_{surr.}}{\Sigma R_{th}} = \dfrac{t_1 - 15}{1.293}$

This heat flow, under steady conditions, equals the heat generated in the copper rod due to flow of current.

$$\therefore \qquad \dfrac{t_1 - 15}{1.293} = 19.855 \text{ or } t_1 = 19.855 \times 1.293 + 15 = \mathbf{40.67 \degree C} \qquad (\mathbf{Ans.})$$

Similarly, $\dfrac{(t_1 - t_2)}{\dfrac{\ln(r_2/r_1)}{2\pi k_A.L}} = 19.855$ or $\dfrac{(40.67 - t_2)}{\dfrac{\ln(0.017/0.0125)}{2\pi \times 0.058 \times 1}} = 19.855$

or, $\qquad t_2 = 40.67 - 19.855 \times \dfrac{\ln(0.017/0.0125)}{2\pi \times 0.058} = \mathbf{23.9 \degree C} \qquad (\mathbf{Ans.})$

Example 2.58. (*i*) *Find an expression for distribution of temperature and heat flow due to conduction in a circular conical rod with diameter at any section given by D = cx where x is the distance measured from the apex of the cone and c is a certain numerical constant. Assume that lateral surface is well insulated, there is no internal heat generation and heat flow takes place under steady state conditions.*

(*ii*) *What will be the heat flow rate if the smaller and longer ends are located at x_1 = 50 mm and x_2 = 250 mm and have temperatures 400°C and 200°C respectively ?*

Take : c = 0.22 and k (average thermal conductivity) = 3.6 W/m°C.

Solution. Refer to Fig. 2.73. *Since the lateral surface is well insulated, the conduction of heat is one-dimensional (x-direction),* using Fourier's equation, we have

$$Q = -k.A\dfrac{dt}{dx} = -k.\dfrac{\pi}{4}D^2 \times \dfrac{dt}{dx}$$

or $\qquad Q = -k \times \dfrac{\pi}{4} \times c^2 x^2 \times \dfrac{dt}{dx} \qquad\qquad (\because D = cx \text{ ...given})$

Rearranging the above equation, we get

$$-k dt = \dfrac{4Q\, dx}{\pi c^2 x^2}$$

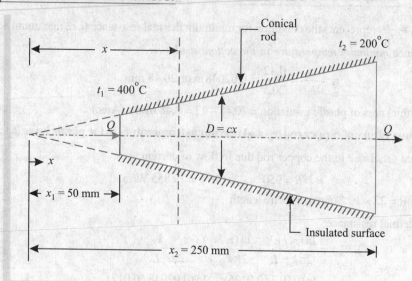

Fig. 2.73.

Integrating both sides, we have

$$-k \int_{t_1}^{t} dt = \frac{4Q}{\pi c^2} \int_{x_1}^{x} \frac{dx}{x^2}$$

or $\qquad -k(t - t_1) = \frac{4Q}{\pi c^2} \left[\frac{x^{-2+1}}{-2+1} \right]_{x_1}^{x} = \frac{4Q}{\pi c^2} \left[-\frac{1}{x} \right]_{x_1}^{x}$

or $\qquad -k(t - t_1) = \frac{4Q}{\pi c^2} \left(\frac{1}{x_1} - \frac{1}{x} \right)$

or $\qquad t = t_1 - \frac{4Q}{\pi c^2 k} \left(\frac{1}{x_1} - \frac{1}{x} \right)$ ...(i)

At $x = x_2$, where $t = t_2$, the above expression becomes

$$t_2 = t_1 - \frac{4Q}{\pi c^2 k} \left(\frac{1}{x_1} - \frac{1}{x_2} \right)$$ ...(ii)

or *Heat flow rate,* $\qquad Q = \dfrac{\pi c^2 k (t_1 - t_2)}{4 \left(\dfrac{1}{x_1} - \dfrac{1}{x_2} \right)}$ ...(iii)

By substituting Q in (i), we get the temperature distribution as follows :

$$t = t_1 + (t_1 - t_2) \left[\frac{\left(\dfrac{1}{x} - \dfrac{1}{x_1} \right)}{\left(\dfrac{1}{x_1} - \dfrac{1}{x_2} \right)} \right]$$ ...*Required expression.* **(Ans.)**

(ii) *Given* : $x_1 = 50$ mm $= 0.05$ m; $x_2 = 250$ mm $= 0.25$ m; $t_1 = 400°C$; $t_2 = 200°C$; $c = 0.22$; $k = 3.6$ W/m°C.

Heat flow rate, Q :

Substituting the various values in expression (iii), we have

$$Q = \frac{\pi \times 0.22^2 \times 3.6 (400 - 200)}{4 \left(\dfrac{1}{0.05} - \dfrac{1}{0.25} \right)} = \frac{109.48}{64} = \mathbf{1.71\,W} \text{ (Ans.)}$$

Example 2.59. *Heat is conducted through a tapered circular rod of 200 mm length. The ends A and B having diameters 50 mm and 25 mm are maintained at 27°C and 227°C respectively. k (rod material) = 40 W/m°C. Find :*

(i) Heat conducted through the rod.

(ii) The temperature at the mid-point of the end.

Assume there is no temperature gradient at a particular cross-section and there is no heat transfer through the peripheral surface. (M.U.)

Solution. *Given :* $L = 200 \text{ mm} = 0.2 \text{ m}; D_1 = 50 \text{ mm} = 0.05 \text{ m}; D_2 = 25 \text{ mm} = 0.025 \text{ m};$

$$t_1 = 227°C; t_2 = 27°C; k = 40 \text{ W/m°C}.$$

(i) Heat conducted through the rod, Q :

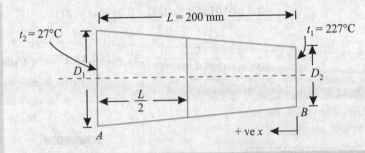

Fig. 2.74.

The heat flow through the rod is given by

$$Q = \frac{k \pi R_1 R_2 (t_1 - t_2)}{L} \qquad ...(i)$$

$$= \frac{40 \times \pi \times 0.025 \times 0.0125 \times (227 - 27)}{0.2} = \mathbf{39.27 \text{ W}} \text{ (Ans.)}$$

(ii) The temperature at the mid-point of the rod, t :

Now, $$R_x = R_2 + (R_1 - R_2)\frac{x}{L}$$

In power plants turbines and pipes function under high temperatures and pressures.

$$(R_x)_{x=\frac{1}{2}} = R_2 + (R_1 - R_2) \times \frac{1}{2} = R_2 + \frac{R_1}{2} - \frac{R_2}{2} = \left(\frac{R_1 + R_2}{2}\right)$$

Now substituting the value of $(R_x)_{x=\frac{L}{2}}$ in the eqn. (i) for R_1 and t for t_1 and $L = \frac{L}{2}$, we get

$$Q = \frac{k\pi\left(\dfrac{R_2 + R_1}{2}\right)R_2\,(t - t_2)}{L/2} = \frac{k\pi(R_1 + R_2)\,R_2\,(t - t_2)}{L}$$

where t is the temperature at $x = \dfrac{L}{2}$

Now substituting the values in the above equation, we get

$$39.27 = \frac{40 \times \pi (0.0125 + 0.025) \times 0.0125 (t - 27)}{0.2}$$

or,

$$t = \frac{39.27 \times 0.2}{40 \times (0.0125 + 0.025)} + 27 = \textbf{160.33° C} \qquad \textbf{(Ans.)}$$

Note. *For steady state heat flow, Q remains constant at all sections.*

Example 2.60. *The following data relate to a gas turbine rotor :*

Radius of the rotor = 550 mm; Thickness of rotor- varies linearly from 160 mm at the centre to 60 mm at the outer periphery where blades are attached; Temperatures indicated by the thermocouples attached to the rotor at radial distances of 90 mm and 450 mm = 330°C and 645°C respectively; Thermal conductivity of rotor material = 0.345 W/m°C.

(i) Starting from the basic principles, determine the radial heat flow rate through the runner;

(ii) Determine the percentage change in heat flow rate that would occur if the rotor has a uniform thickness of 60 mm.

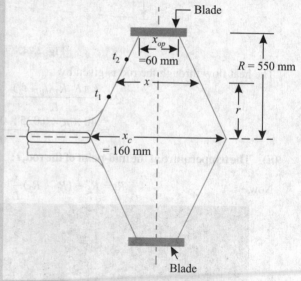

Fig. 2.75. Gas turbine rotor.

Solution. Refer to Fig. 2.75.

Radius of the rotor, $\quad R = 550\,\text{mm} = 0.55\,\text{m}$

Thickness of the rotor – varies linearly :

At the centre, $\quad\quad x_c = 160\,\text{mm} = 0.16\,\text{m}$

At the outer periphery, $\quad x_{op} = 60\,\text{mm} = 0.06\,\text{m}$

Temperatures indicated by the thermocouples :

At radial distance, $\quad\quad r_1 = 90\,\text{mm or } 0.09\,\text{m}\,;\, t_1 = 330°\text{C}$

At radial distance, $\quad\quad r_2 = 450\,\text{mm or } 0.45\,\text{m}\,;\, t_2 = 645°\text{C}$

Thermal conductivity of rotor material, $k = 0.345\,\text{W/m°C}$.

(i) **Radial heat flow rate through the runner, Q :**

The thickness of rotor changes from x_c to x_{op} from the centre to outer periphery; therefore, the thickness of rotor at a distance r from the centre,

$$x = x_c - \left[\frac{x_c - x_{op}}{R}\right] r = x_c - zr$$

where, $z \ (a \ constant) = \dfrac{x_c - x_{op}}{R}$

Heat conducted at radius r,

$$Q = -k \, A.\frac{dt}{dr} = -k.2\pi r \,(x_c - zr)\frac{dt}{dr}$$

Rearranging and integrating within the given limits, we have

$$-\int_{t_1}^{t_2} dt = \frac{Q}{2\pi k}\int_{r_1}^{r_2}\frac{dr}{r(x_c - zr)}$$

The right hand integral is of the form

$$\int \frac{dx}{x(a-bx)} = \frac{1}{a}\ln\left(\frac{x}{a-bx}\right)$$

$$\therefore \qquad t_1 - t_2 = \frac{Q}{2\pi k}\left[\frac{1}{x_c}\ln\left(\frac{r}{x_c - zr}\right)\right]_{r_1}^{r_2}$$

$$= \frac{Q}{2\pi k x_c}\left[\ln\left(\frac{r_2}{x_c - zr_2}\right) - \ln\left(\frac{r_1}{x_c - zr_1}\right)\right]$$

$$= \frac{Q}{2\pi k x_c}\ln\left[\frac{r_2}{r_1}\left\{\frac{x_c - zr_1}{x_c - zr_2}\right\}\right]$$

$$\therefore \qquad Q = \frac{2\pi k x_c\,(t_1 - t_2)}{\ln\left[\dfrac{r_2}{r_1}\left\{\dfrac{x_c - zr_1}{x_c - zr_2}\right\}\right]} \qquad\qquad ...(i)$$

Now, $z = \dfrac{x_c - x_{op}}{R} = \dfrac{0.16 - 0.06}{0.55} = 0.182$

Substituting the given data in the expression (i), we get

$$Q = \frac{2\pi \times 0.345 \times 0.16\,(330 - 645)}{\ln\left[\dfrac{0.45}{0.09}\left\{\dfrac{0.16 - 0.182 \times 0.09}{0.16 - 0.182 \times 0.45}\right\}\right]}$$

$$= \frac{-109.252}{\ln\left[5 \times \dfrac{0.1436}{0.0781}\right]} = -\,\textbf{49.25 W} \ \ \textbf{(Ans.)}$$

Negative sign indicates that the heat flow is *radially inward*.

(ii) **Percentage change in heat flow rate if the rotor has uniform thickness of 60 mm :**

For a rotor of uniform thickness x_{op}

$$Q = -k.2\pi r . x_{op}.\frac{dt}{dr}$$

Rearranging and integrating within the given limits, we have

$$-\int_{t_1}^{t_2} dt = \frac{Q}{2\pi k \, x_{op}}\int_{r_1}^{r_2}\frac{dr}{r}$$

or $$(t_1 - t_2) = \frac{Q}{2\pi k\, x_{op}} \ln(r_2/r_1)$$

$$\therefore \qquad Q = \frac{2\pi k\, x_{op}\,(t_1 - t_2)}{\ln(r_2/r_1)} \qquad \qquad ...(ii)$$

This expression (ii) is identical to the heat flow equation through a hollow cylinder of length x_{op}.
Substituting the given data in the above expression, we have

$$Q = \frac{2\pi \times 0.345 \times 0.06(330 - 645)}{\ln(0.45/0.09)} = -25.45\,\text{W}$$

$\therefore$ Percentage change in heat flow rate

$$= \frac{49.25 - 25.45}{49.25} = 0.4832 \qquad \text{or} \quad \textbf{48.32\%} \qquad \textbf{(Ans.)}$$

2.7. HEAT CONDUCTION THROUGH HOLLOW AND COMPOSITE SPHERES

2.7.1. HEAT CONDUCTION THROUGH HOLLOW SPHERE

Case I. Uniform conductivity :

Refer Fig. 2.76. Consider a hollow sphere made of material having constant thermal conductivity.

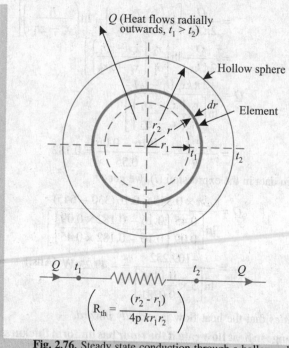

Fig. 2.76. Steady state conduction through a hollow sphere.

Let, r_1, r_2 = Inner and outer radii,

   t_1, t_2 = Temperatures of inner and outer surfaces, and

   k = Constant thermal conductivity of the material with the given temperature range.

The general heat conduction equation in spherical coordinates is given as follows :

$$\frac{1}{r^2}\frac{\partial}{\partial r}\left(r^2\frac{\partial t}{\partial r}\right) + \frac{1}{r^2\sin^2\phi}\cdot\frac{\partial^2 t}{\partial\phi^2} + \frac{1}{r^2\sin\theta}\frac{\partial}{\partial\theta}\left(\sin\theta\frac{\partial t}{\partial\theta}\right) + \frac{q_g}{k} = \frac{1}{\alpha}\cdot\frac{\partial t}{\partial\tau} \qquad ...[\text{Eqn. 2.31}]$$

For steady state $\left(\dfrac{\partial t}{\partial \tau}=0\right)$, unidirectional heat flow in the radial direction $\{t \neq f(\theta, \phi)\}$ and with no heat generation $(q_g = 0)$, the above equation reduces to

$$\frac{1}{r^2}\frac{d}{dr}\left(r^2 \cdot \frac{dt}{dr}\right)=0$$

or, $\qquad \dfrac{d}{dr}\left(r^2 \cdot \dfrac{dt}{dr}\right)=0 \qquad$ as $\qquad \dfrac{1}{r^2} \neq 0$

or, $\qquad r^2 \cdot \dfrac{dt}{dr} = C$ (a constant) $\hspace{4cm}$ ...(2.72)

Integrating the above equation, we obtain

$$t = -\frac{C}{r}+C_1 \hspace{5cm} ...(2.73)$$

(where C_1 = a constant of integration)

Using the following boundary conditions, we have

At $r = r_1, t = t_1$; At $r = r_2, t = t_2$

∴ $\hspace{3cm} t_1 = -\dfrac{C}{r_1}+C_1 \hspace{4.5cm} ...(i)$

$\hspace{3cm} t_2 = -\dfrac{C}{r_2}+C_1 \hspace{4.5cm} ...(ii)$

From (i) and (ii), we have

$$C = \frac{(t_1 - t_2)\, r_1\, r_2}{r_1 - r_2}$$

and, $\hspace{2cm} C_1 = t_1 + \dfrac{(t_1 - t_2)\, r_1\, r_2}{r_1\,(r_1 - r_2)}$

Substituting the values of these constants in eqn. (2.73), we get

$$t = -\frac{(t_1 - t_2)\, r_1\, r_2}{r\,(r_1 - r_2)} + t_1 + \frac{(t_1 - t_2)\, r_1\, r_2}{r_1\,(r_1 - r_2)}$$

or, $\hspace{1.5cm} t = -\dfrac{(t_1 - t_2)}{r\,(1/r_2 - 1/r_1)} + t_1 + \dfrac{(t_1 - t_2)}{r_1\,(1/r_2 - 1/r_1)}$

or, $\hspace{1.5cm} t = t_1 + \dfrac{(t_1 - t_2)}{(1/r_2 - 1/r_1)}\left[\dfrac{1}{r_1} - \dfrac{1}{r}\right] \hspace{2.5cm} ...(2.74)$

or, $\hspace{1.5cm} \dfrac{t - t_1}{t_2 - t_1} = \dfrac{1/r - 1/r_1}{1/r_2 - 1/r_1}$

or, $\hspace{1.5cm} \dfrac{t - t_1}{t_2 - t_1} = \dfrac{r_2}{r}\left[\dfrac{r - r_1}{r_2 - r_1}\right] \qquad$ [Dimensionless form] $\hspace{1cm} ...(2.75)$

From the eqn. (2.75) it is evident that the temperature distribution associated with radial conduction through a sphere is represented by a *hyperbola*.

Determination of conduction heat transfer rate, Q :

The conduction heat transfer rate is determined by using the temperature distribution expression [Eqn. (2.75)] in conjuction with Fourier's equation as follows :

$$Q = -kA\frac{dt}{dr}$$

$$= -k.4\pi r^2 \cdot \frac{d}{dr}\left[t_1 + \frac{(t_1 - t_2)}{(1/r_2 - 1/r_1)}\left(\frac{1}{r_1} - \frac{1}{r}\right)\right]$$

$$= -k.4\pi r^2 . \frac{t_1 - t_2}{(1/r_2 - 1/r_1)} \times -\left(-\frac{1}{r^2}\right)$$

$$= -k.4\pi r^2 . \frac{(t_1 - t_2)}{\left(\dfrac{r_1 - r_2}{r_1 . r_2}\right)} \times \frac{1}{r^2}$$

$$= -4\pi k \frac{(t_1 - t_2) r_1 r_2}{(r_1 - r_2)} = \frac{4\pi k (t_1 - t_2) r_1 r_2}{(r_2 - r_1)} = \frac{(t_1 - t_2)}{(r_2 - r_1)/4\pi k r_1 r_2}$$

i.e.
$$Q = \frac{(t_1 - t_2)}{\left[\dfrac{(r_2 - r_1)}{4\pi k r_1 r_2}\right]} \left[= \frac{\Delta t}{R_{th}}\right] \qquad ...(2.76)$$

where the term $(r_2 - r_1)/4\pi k r_1 r_2$ is the thermal resistance (R_{th}) for heat conduction through a hollow sphere.

Alternative method :

Refer Fig. 2.76. Consider a small element of thickness dr at any radius r.

Area through which the heat is transmitted, $A = 4\pi r^2$

$\therefore \qquad\qquad Q = -k.4\pi r^2 . \dfrac{dt}{dr}$

Rearranging and integrating the above equation, we obtain

$$Q \int_{r_1}^{r_2} \frac{dr}{r^2} = -4\pi k \int_{t_1}^{t_2} dt$$

or, $\qquad Q\left[\dfrac{r^{-2+1}}{-2+1}\right]_{r_1}^{r_2} = -4\pi k [t]_{t_1}^{t_2}$

or, $\qquad -Q\left(\dfrac{1}{r_2} - \dfrac{1}{r_1}\right) = -4\pi k (t_2 - t_1)$

or, $\qquad \dfrac{Q(r_2 - r_1)}{r_1 r_2} = 4\pi k (t_1 - t_2)$

or, $\qquad Q = \dfrac{4\pi k r_1 r_2 (t_1 - t_2)}{(r_2 - r_1)} = \dfrac{t_1 - t_2}{\left[\dfrac{(r_2 - r_1)}{4\pi k r_1 r_2}\right]} \qquad ...(2.77)$

Case II. Variable conductivity :

A. *Temperature variation in terms of surface temperatures, t_1, t_2 :*

By adopting the similar procedure as was followed in case of a hollow cylinder, we would obtain the following expressions for the rate of heat transfer (Q) and temperature variation in a hollow sphere in terms of surface temperatures (t_1, t_2).

$$Q = \frac{4\pi k_0 r_1 r_2}{(r_2 - r_1)}\left[1 + \frac{\beta}{2}(t_1 + t_2)\right](t_1 - t_2) \qquad ...(2.78)$$

and,
$$t = \frac{1}{\beta}\left[(1 + \beta t_1)^2 - \left(\frac{r - r_1}{r_2 - r_1}\right)\left(\frac{r_2}{r}\right)\{(1 + \beta t_1)^2 - (1 + \beta t_2)^2\}\right]^{1/2} - \frac{1}{\beta} \qquad ...(2.79)$$

B. *Temperature variation in terms of heat flux (Q) :*

By using the same approach as was adopted in case of hollow cylinder, we would obtain the following expression

$$t = -\frac{1}{\beta} + \left[\left(t_1 - \frac{1}{\beta}\right)^2 - \frac{Q}{\beta k_0}\cdot\frac{1}{2\pi}\left(\frac{1}{r_1} - \frac{1}{r}\right)\right]^{1/2} \qquad ...(2.80)$$

2.7.1.1. Logarithmic mean area for the hollow sphere

Adopting the same concept as used for hollow cylinder, we can write

$$Q_{sphere} = \frac{(t_1 - t_2)}{\left[\dfrac{(r_2 - r_1)}{4\pi k\, r_1\, r_2}\right]}$$

$$Q_{plane\ wall} = \frac{(t_1 - t_2)}{\left(\dfrac{(r_2 - r_1)}{k\, A_m}\right)}$$

A_m *is so chosen that the heat flow through cylinder and plane wall will be equal for the same thermal potential.*

∴

$$Q_{sphere} = Q_{plane\ wall}$$

$$\frac{(t_1 - t_2)}{\left[\dfrac{(r_2 - r_1)}{4\pi k\, r_1\, r_2}\right]} = \frac{(t_1 - t_2)}{\left[\dfrac{r_2 - r_1}{k\, A_m}\right]}$$

or,

$$\frac{r_2 - r_1}{4\pi k\, r_1\, r_2} = \frac{r_2 - r_1}{k\, A_m}$$

or,

$$A_m = 4\pi\, r_1\, r_2$$

or,

$$A_m^2 = (4\pi\, r_1\, r_2)^2 = (4\pi\, r_1^2) \times (4\pi\, r_2^2)$$

or,

$$A_m^2 = A_i \times A_0$$

or,

$$A_m = \sqrt{A_i\, A_0} \qquad ...(2.81)$$

Further,

$$A_m = 4\pi\, r_m^2 = 4\pi\, r_1\, r_2$$

A combined cycle power plant. In power plants heat and mass transfer plays important role.

or,
$$r_m = \sqrt{r_1\, r_2}$$

(where r_m = logarithmic mean radius of hollow sphere).

2.7.2. HEAT CONDUCTION THROUGH A COMPOSITE SPHERE

Considering Fig. 2.77 as cross-section of a composite sphere, the heat flow equation can be written as follows

$$Q = h_{hf} \cdot 4\pi r_1^2\,(t_{hf} - t_1) = \frac{4\pi k_A\, r_1\, r_2\,(t_1 - t_2)}{(r_2 - r_1)} = \frac{4\pi k_B\, r_2\, r_3\,(t_2 - t_3)}{(r_3 - r_2)}$$

$$= h_{cf} \cdot 4\pi r_3^2\,(t_3 - t_{cf})$$

By rearranging the above equation we have

$$t_{hf} - t_1 = \frac{Q}{h_{hf} \cdot 4\pi r_1^2} \qquad\qquad \ldots(i)$$

$$t_1 - t_2 = \frac{Q(r_2 - r_1)}{4\pi k_A \cdot r_1\, r_2} \qquad\qquad \ldots(ii)$$

$$t_2 - t_3 = \frac{Q(r_3 - r_2)}{4\pi k_B \cdot r_2\, r_3} \qquad\qquad \ldots(iii)$$

$$t_3 - t_{cf} = \frac{Q}{h_{cf} \cdot 4\pi r_3^2} \qquad\qquad \ldots(iv)$$

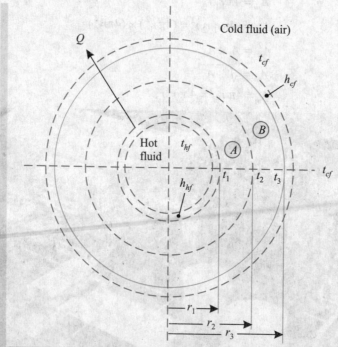

Fig. 2.77. Steady state conduction through a composite sphere.

Adding (i), (ii), (iii), and (iv), we get

$$\frac{Q}{4\pi}\left[\frac{1}{h_{hf} \cdot r_1^2} + \frac{(r_2 - r_1)}{k_A \cdot r_1\, r_2} + \frac{(r_3 - r_2)}{k_B \cdot r_2\, r_3} + \frac{1}{h_{cf} \cdot r_3^2}\right] = t_{hf} - t_{cf}$$

$$\therefore \qquad Q = \frac{4\pi(t_{hf} - t_{cf})}{\left[\dfrac{1}{h_{hf} \cdot r_1^2} + \dfrac{(r_2 - r_1)}{k_A \cdot r_1 r_2} + \dfrac{(r_3 - r_2)}{k_B \cdot r_2 r_3} + \dfrac{1}{h_{cf} \cdot r_3^2}\right]} \qquad ...(2.82)$$

If there are n concentric spheres then the above equation can be written as follows

$$Q = \frac{4\pi(t_{hf} - t_{cf})}{\left[\dfrac{1}{h_{hf} \cdot r_1^2} + \displaystyle\sum_{n=1}^{n=n}\left\{\dfrac{r_{(n+1)} - r_n}{k_n \cdot r_n \cdot r_{(n+1)}}\right\} + \dfrac{1}{h_{cf} \cdot r_{(n+1)}^2}\right]} \qquad ...(2.83)$$

If inside and outside heat transfer coefficients are not considered, then the above equation can be written as follows :

$$Q = \frac{4\pi(t_1 - t_{n+1})}{\displaystyle\sum_{n=1}^{n=n}\left[\dfrac{r_{(n+1)} - r_n}{k_n \cdot r_n \cdot r_{(n+1)}}\right]} \qquad ...(2.84)$$

Example 2.61. *A spherical shaped vessel of 1.4 m diameter is 90 mm thick. Find the rate of heat leakage, if the temperature difference between the inner and outer surfaces is 220°C. Thermal conductivity of the material of the sphere is 0.083 W/m°C.*

Solution. Refer to Fig. 2.78.

$$r_2 = \frac{1.4}{2} = 0.7 \, \text{m}.$$

$$r_1 = 0.7 - \frac{90}{1000} = 0.61 \, \text{m}$$

$$t_1 - t_2 = 220°C;$$
$$k = 0.083 \, \text{W/m°C}$$

The rate of heat transfer/leakage is given by

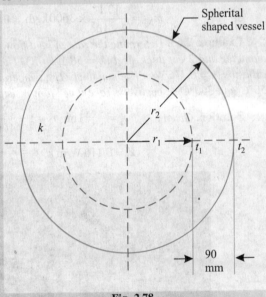

Fig. 2.78.

$$Q = \frac{(t_1 - t_2)}{\left[\dfrac{(r_2 - r_1)}{4\pi k r_1 r_2}\right]} \qquad \text{...Fig.}$$
$$(2.76)$$

$$= \frac{220}{\left[\dfrac{(0.7 - 0.61)}{4\pi \times 0.083 \times 0.61 \times 0.7}\right]}$$

$$= 1088.67 \, \text{W}$$

i.e., Rate of heat leakage = **1088.67 W** (Ans.)

Example 2.62. *A spherical thin walled metallic container is used to store liquid N_2 at $-196°C$. The container has a diameter of 0.5 m and is covered with an evacuated reflective insulation composed of silica powder. The insulation is 25 mm thick and its outer layer is exposed to air at 27°C. The convective heat transfer coefficient on outer surface $= 20 \, W/m^2 °C$. Latent heat of evaporation of $N_2 = 2 \times 10^5 \, J/kg$. Density of $N_2 = 804 \, kg/m^3$.*

k (silica powder) = 0.0017 W/m°C.

Find out the rate of heat transfer and rate of N_2 boil-off. (N.U., 1998)

Solution. *Given :* $t_1 = -196°C; t_2 = 27°C; r_1 = \dfrac{0.5}{2} = 0.25 \, \text{m};$

$$r_2 = r_1 + 0.025 = 0.25 + 0.025 = 0.275 \, \text{m};$$

$h_0 = 20 \ \text{W/m}^2{}^\circ\text{C}; \ h_{fg \ N_2}$

$= 2 \times 10^5 \ \text{J/kg}; \ \rho_{N_2} = 804 \ \text{kg/m}^3;$

$k = 0.0017 \ \text{W/m}^\circ\text{C}.$

Rate of heat transfer, Q :

The heat flow is given by

$$Q = \frac{(t_1 - t_a)}{\dfrac{(r_2 - r_1)}{4\pi k \, r_1 \, r_2} + \dfrac{1}{h_0 \times 4\pi r_2^2}}$$

$$= \frac{(-196 - 27)}{\dfrac{(0.275 - 0.25)}{4\pi \times 0.0017 \times 0.25 \times 0.275} + \dfrac{1}{20 \times 4\pi \times 0.275^2}}$$

$$= \frac{-223}{17.022 + 0.0526} = -13.1 \ \text{W}$$

The – ve sign indicates that the heat *flows in.*

$\therefore \qquad m_{N_2} \times h_{fg} = 13.1$

or $\qquad m_{N_2} = \dfrac{13.1}{2 \times 10^5} \times 3600 \ \text{kg/h} = \mathbf{0.2358 \ kg/h}$ **(Ans.)**

Fig. 2.79.

Example 2.63. *Determine the rate of heat flow through a spherical boiler wall which is 2 m in diameter and 2 cm thick steel (k = 58 W/m K). The outside surface of boiler wall is covered with asbestos (k = 0.116 W/m K) 5mm thick. The temperature of outer surface and that of fluid inside are 50°C and 300°C respectively. Take inner film resistance as 0.0023 K/W.*   (N.U. Summer, 2000)

Solution. *Given :* $\qquad r_1 = \dfrac{2}{2} = 1 \ \text{m}; \ r_2 = 1 + \dfrac{2}{100} = 1.02 \ \text{m}; \ k_A = 58 \ \text{W/m K};$

$$k_B = 0.116 \ \text{W/m k}; \ r_3 = r_2 + \dfrac{5}{100} = 1.02 + 0.005 = 0.025 \ \text{m}$$

Spherical vessels.

$Q = h_1 A_1 (t_i - t_1)$ as heat flows from fluid to inner surface by convection only.

or,
$$Q = \frac{t_i - t_1}{\dfrac{1}{h_i A_1}}$$

where, $\dfrac{1}{h_i A_1}$ is inner film resistance.

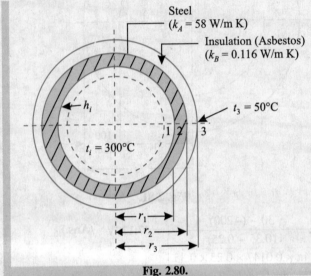

Fig. 2.80.

∴
$$Q = \frac{(t_i - t_3)}{\dfrac{1}{h_i A_1} + \dfrac{(r_2 - r_1)}{4\pi k_A r_1 r_2} + \dfrac{(r_3 - r_2)}{4\pi k_B r_2 r_3}}$$

$$= \frac{(300 - 50)}{0.0023 + \dfrac{(1.02 - 1.0)}{4\pi \times 58 \times 1.0 \times 1.02} + \dfrac{(1.025 - 1.02)}{4\pi \times 0.116 \times 1.02 \times 1.025}}$$

$$= \frac{250}{0.0023 + 2.6902 \times 10^{-5} + 0.0032808} = 44581\,\text{W} = \textbf{4.581\,kW} \quad \textbf{(Ans.)}$$

Example 2.64. *A spherical container having outer diameter 500 mm is insulated by 100 mm thick layer of material with thermal conductivity $k = 0.03\,(1 + 0.006\,t)$ W/m°C, where t is in °C. If the surface temperature of sphere is $-200°C$ and temperature of outer surface is 30°C, determine the heat flow in.*

Solution. Refer to Fig. 2.81.

Given : $r_1 = 250\,\text{mm} = 0.25\,\text{m},\ r_2 = 250 + 100 = 350\,\text{mm} = 0.35\,\text{m}$

           $k = 0.03\,(1 + 0.006\,t)$

Heat flow, Q :

$$Q = \frac{\Delta t}{\left[\dfrac{(r_2 - r_1)}{4\pi k_m\, r_1\, r_2}\right]}$$

where, $k_m = 0.03\left[1 + 0.006\left(\dfrac{-200 + 30}{2}\right)\right] = 0.0147\,\text{W/m°C}$

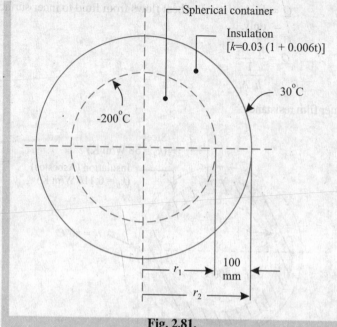

Fig. 2.81.

$$\therefore \qquad Q = \dfrac{30 - (-200)}{\left[\dfrac{(0.35 - 0.25)}{4\pi \times 0.0147 \times 0.25 \times 0.35}\right]} = 37.17\,\text{W} \quad \textbf{(Ans.)}$$

Example 2.65. *The inside and outside surfaces of a hollow sphere of radii r_1 and r_2 are maintained at t_1 and t_2 respectively. The thermal conductivity of sphere material varies with temperature as given below :*

$$k = k_0\,(1 + \alpha t + \beta t^2)$$

Derive an expression for total heat flow rate through the sphere.   **(P.U., 2001)**

Solution. Considering steady state conduction through a hollow sphere $r = r$ and of thickness $\dfrac{dr}{dt}$, we can write

$$Q = -kA\frac{dt}{dr} = -k \times 4\pi r^2 \times \frac{dt}{dr}$$

Substituting the given value of k in the above equation, we get

$$Q = -k_0\,(1 + \alpha t + \beta t^2) \times 4\pi r^2 \times \frac{dt}{dr}$$

$$\therefore \quad \frac{Q}{4\pi} \times \frac{dr}{r^2} = -k_0\,(1 + \alpha t + \beta t^2)\,dt$$

Integrating the above equation in the given range, we get

$$\frac{Q}{4\pi}\int_{r_1}^{r_2}\frac{dr}{r^2} = -k_0\int_{t_1}^{t_2}(1 + \alpha t + \beta t^2)\,dt$$

$$\therefore \quad \frac{Q}{4\pi}\left[-\frac{1}{r}\right]_{r_1}^{r_2} = -k_0\left[\left(t + \alpha\frac{t^2}{2} + \beta\frac{t^3}{3}\right)\right]_{t_1}^{t_2}$$

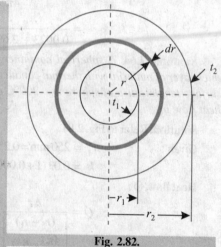

Fig. 2.82.

$$\frac{Q}{4\pi}\left(\frac{1}{r_2}-\frac{1}{r_1}\right)=k_0\left[(t_2-t_1)+\alpha\left(\frac{t_2^2-t_1^2}{2}\right)+\frac{\beta}{3}(t_2^3-t_1^3)\right]$$

or,

$$\frac{Q}{4\pi}\left(\frac{r_1-r_2}{r_1\,r_2}\right)=-k_0\left[(t_1-t_2)+\frac{\alpha}{2}\left(t_1^2-t_2^2\right)+\frac{\beta}{3}(t_1^3-t_2^3)\right]$$

or,

$$\frac{Q}{4\pi}\left(\frac{r_2-r_1}{r_1\,r_2}\right)=-k_0\,(t_1-t_2)\left[1+\frac{\alpha}{2}(t_1+t_2)+\frac{\beta}{3}(t_1^2+t_1\,t_2+t_2^2)\right]$$

or,

$$Q=\frac{4\pi\,r_1\,r_2}{r_2-r_1}\times k_0\,(t_1-t_2)\left[1+\frac{\alpha}{2}(t_1+t_2)+\frac{\beta}{3}(t_1^2+t_1\,t_2+t_2^2)\right]$$

...Required expression (Ans.)

Example 2.66. *The inside and outside surfaces of a hollow sphere, having inner and outer radii r_1 and r_2 respectively, are maintained at uniform temperatures t_1 and t_2. Find the rate of heat transfer through the sphere if the conductivity of the material of which the sphere is made varies according to relation :*

$$k = k_1 + (k_2 - k_1)\,[(t - t_1)\,/\,(t_2 - t_1)]$$

Solution. Fourier's equation for unidirectional steady state heat conduction is given as :

$$Q = -kA\frac{dt}{dr} \qquad\qquad ...(i)$$

where $A = 4\,\pi r^2$ (area normal to radial direction).

Now, by substituting the values of A and k in eqn. (i), we get

$$Q = -[k_1 + (k_2 - k_1)\{(t - t_1)/(t_2 - t_1)\}]\times 4\pi r^2\times\frac{dt}{dr}$$

or,

$$Q\cdot\frac{dr}{r^2} = -4\pi\left[k_1 + (k_2 - k_1)\,\{(t - t_1)/(t_2 - t_1)\}\right]dt$$

Integrating both sides, we get

$$Q\int_{r_1}^{r_2}\frac{dr}{r^2} = -4\pi\int_{t_1}^{t_2}\left[k_1 + (k_2 - k_1)\left\{\frac{(t - t_1)}{(t_2 - t_1)}\right\}\right]dt$$

$$-Q\left[\frac{1}{r}\right]_{r_1}^{r_2} = -4\pi\left[k_1 t + \frac{k_2 - k_1}{t_2 - t_1}\left\{\frac{t^2}{2} - t\cdot t_1\right\}\right]_{t_1}^{t_2}$$

Furnace.

$$-Q\left[\frac{1}{r_2} - \frac{1}{r_1}\right] = -4\pi\left[k_1(t_2 - t_1) + \frac{k_2 - k_1}{t_2 - t_1}\left(\frac{t_2^2 - t_1^2}{2}\right) - t_1\left(\frac{k_2 - k_1}{t_2 - t_1}\right)(t_2 - t_1)\right]$$

$$Q \cdot \frac{(r_2 - r_1)}{r_1 r_2} = -4\pi\left[k_1(t_2 - t_1) + \frac{(k_2 - k_1)}{2}(t_2 + t_1) - t_1(k_2 - k_1)\right]$$

$$= -4\pi\left[k_1(t_2 - t_1) + \frac{(k_2 - k_1)}{2}(t_2 + t_1 - 2t_1)\right]$$

$$= -4\pi\left[k_1(t_2 - t_1) + \frac{k_2 - k_1}{2}(t_2 - t_1)\right]$$

$$= -4\pi(t_2 - t_1)\left[k_1 + \frac{k_2 - k_1}{2}\right]$$

$$= -4\pi(t_1 - t_2)\left(\frac{k_1 + k_2}{2}\right)$$

$\therefore \qquad Q = 4\pi r_1 r_2\left(\frac{k_1 + k_2}{2}\right)\left(\frac{t_1 - t_2}{r_2 - r_1}\right)$ ...*Required expression.* **(Ans.)**

Example 2.67. *Show that for small objects transferring heat to the surrounding, the minimum Nusselt number is equal to 2.* **(M.U., 2002)**

Solution. Consider a small body as *sphere*.

The heat flow by conduction through a sphere is given by

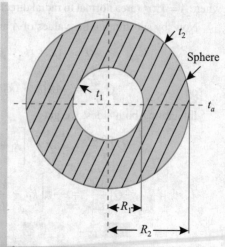

$$Q = \frac{t_1 - t_2}{\dfrac{R_2 - R_1}{4\pi k R_1 R_2}} = \frac{t_1 - t_2}{R_{\text{th} - \text{cond.}}}$$

Fig. 2.83.

The heat conducted at $r = R_2$ is further convected to the surrounding air and it is given by

$$Q = \frac{t_2 - t_a}{\dfrac{1}{4\pi R_2^2 h}} = \frac{t_2 - t_a}{R_{\text{th} - \text{conv.}}}$$

where $R_{\text{th-cond.}}$ and $R_{\text{th-conv.}}$ are conduction and convection resistances respectively.

$$R_{\text{th} - \text{cond.}} = \frac{1}{4\pi k}\left(\frac{1}{R_1} - \frac{1}{R_2}\right) \qquad ...(i)$$

Now the surrounding fluid will be considered a spherical shell of radius r and infinite outside radius. If we neglect the motion of the fluid, the only mechanism of heat transfer will be conduction through the small sphere and the resistance of this shell to heat flow [by substituting $R_1 = r$ and $R_2 = \infty$] in eqn. (*i*)], will be

$$R_{\text{th} - \text{cond.}} = \frac{1}{4\pi k}\left(\frac{1}{r} - \frac{1}{\infty}\right) = \frac{1}{4\pi r k}$$

$\therefore \qquad Q = \dfrac{t_2 - t_a}{\dfrac{1}{4\pi r k}};$ where t_2 is the surface temperature.

The heat flow is also given by introducing h as

$$Q = \frac{t_2 - t_a}{\dfrac{1}{4\pi r^2 h}}$$ ...(ii)

Now equating (i) and (ii), we get

$$\frac{t_2 - t_a}{\dfrac{1}{4\pi r k}} = \frac{t_2 - t_a}{\dfrac{1}{4\pi r^2 h}}$$

or, $$4\pi r^2 h = 4\pi rk$$

or, $$h = \frac{k}{r} = \frac{2k}{d}$$

∴ $$\frac{hd}{k} = 2$$

where $\dfrac{hd}{k}$ is known as Nusselt number (Nu).

∴   **Nu = 2**   (Ans.)

Example 2.68. *A Cylindrical tank of 1.0 m diameter and 5 m total length has hemispherical ends. It contains liquid oxygen which has boiling point and heat of vaporisation –180°C and 210 kJ/kg respectively. It is required to insulate the tank so as to reduce the boil-off rate of oxygen in steady state to 14 kg/h. Determine the thermal conductivity of the insulating material if its maximum thickness is limited to 70 mm. Assume room temperature outside the insulation as 25°C.*

Solution. Refer to Fig. 2.84.

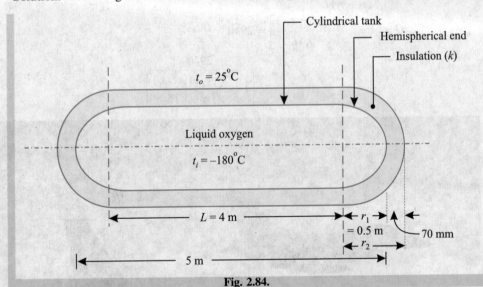

Fig. 2.84.

$$r_1 = \frac{1.0}{2} = 0.5\,\text{m};\quad r_2 = 0.5 + \frac{70}{1000} = 0.57\,\text{m};\quad t_i = -180°C;\, t_0 = 25°C$$

Boil-off rate of liquid oxygen = 14 kg/h

Heat of vaporisation of liquid oxygen, $h_{fg} = 210$ kJ/kg

Thermal conductivity of insulating material, k :

For the *cylindrical section* of the tank,

$$Q_{cyl.} = \frac{(t_0 - t_i)}{\dfrac{\ln(r_2/r_1)}{k \cdot 2\pi L}}$$

or,
$$(t_0 - t_i) = \frac{\ln(r_2/r_1)}{2\pi k L} \times Q_{cyl.} \qquad \ldots(i)$$

For the *hemispherical ends*,

$$Q_{ends} = \frac{(t_0 - t_i)}{\dfrac{(r_2 - r_1)}{k \cdot 4\pi r_1 r_2}}$$

or,
$$(t_0 - t_i) = \frac{r_2 - r_1}{4\pi k r_1 r_2} \times Q_{ends} \qquad \ldots(ii)$$

Equating expressions (i) and (ii), we have

$$\frac{\ln(r_2/r_1)}{2\pi k L} \times Q_{cyl} = \frac{r_2 - r_1}{4\pi k r_1 r_2} \times Q_{ends}$$

or,
$$Q_{ends} = \frac{\ln(r_2/r_1)}{2\pi k L} \times \frac{4\pi k r_1 r_2}{(r_2 - r_1)} \times Q_{cyL}$$

$$= \frac{2 r_1 r_2 \ln(r_2/r_1)}{(r_2 - r_1)L} \times Q_{cyl.}$$

Also
$$Q_{cyl.} + Q_{ends} = Q_{boil} = 14 \times 210 = 2940$$

or,
$$Q_{cyl.} + \frac{2 r_1 r_2 \ln(r_2/r_1)}{(r_2 - r_1)L} \times Q_{cyl.} = 2940$$

or,
$$Q_{cyl.}\left[1 + \frac{2 r_1 r_2 \ln(r_2/r_1)}{(r_2 - r_1)L}\right] = 2940$$

or,
$$Q_{cyl.} = \frac{2940}{\left[1 + \dfrac{2 r_1 r_2 \ln(r_2/r_1)}{(r_2 - r_1)L}\right]}$$

The air fuel tanker as shown above while flying. The temperatures at which they operate plays an important role in designing.

Also, $\qquad L + 2r_1 = 5$ or $L + 2 \times 0.5 = 5$ $\quad \therefore L = 4.0\,\text{m}$

$$\therefore \qquad Q_{cyl.} = \cfrac{2940}{\left[1 + \cfrac{2 \times 0.5 \times 0.57 \times \ln(0.57/0.5)}{(0.57 - 0.5) \times 4}\right]}$$

$$= 2320.9\,\text{kJ/h} = \frac{2320.9 \times 1000}{3600}\,\text{W} = 644.69\,\text{W}$$

From expression (i), we have

$$k = \frac{\ln(r_2/r_1)}{2\pi L(t_o - t_i)} \times Q_{cyl.}$$

$$= \frac{\ln(0.57/0.5)}{2\pi \times 4[25 - (-180)]} \times 644.69 = \mathbf{0.0164\ W/m°C}\ \ \textbf{(Ans.)}$$

Example 2.69. *A cylindrical tank with hemispherical ends is used to store liquid oxygen at* −183° C. *The diameter of the tank is 1.5 m and the total length is 8 m. The tank is covered with a 10 cm thick layer of insulation. Determine the thermal conductivity of the insulation, so that the boil-off rate does not exceed 10.8 kg/h. The latent heat of vapourisation of liquid oxygen is 214 kJ/kg. Assume that the outer surface temperature of the insulation is 27°C and that the thermal resistance of the wall of the tank is negligible.* **(U.P.S.C., 1994)**

Solution. Heat generated during boiling of oxygen,

$$Q_{\text{boil}} = 10.8 \times 214 = 2311.2\,\text{kJ/h}$$

Let t_0 be the room temperature outside of insulation and t_i be the temperature of liquid oxygen inside the tank.

For the cylindrical section of the tank,

$$Q_{cyl} = \frac{2\pi k\,L_{cyl}\,(t_0 - t_i)}{\ln(r_2/r_1)}$$

or, $\qquad (t_0 - t_i) = \dfrac{\ln(r_2/r_1)}{2\pi k\,L_{cyl}} \times Q_{cyl}$ $\hspace{3cm}$ ...(i)

For the two spherical ends, $\quad Q_{\text{ends}} = \dfrac{t_0 - t_i}{(r_2 - r_1)/(4\pi k\,r_1\,r_2)}$

$$= \frac{4\pi k\,r_1\,r_2\,(t_0 - t_i)}{(r_2 - r_1)}$$

or, $\qquad (t_0 - t_i) = \dfrac{r_2 - r_1}{4\pi k\,r_1\,r_2} \times Q_{\text{ends}}$ $\hspace{3cm}$ ...(ii)

From eqns. (i) and (ii), we get

$$\frac{\ln(r_2/r_1)}{2\pi k\,L_{cyl}} \times Q_{cyl} = \frac{r_2 - r_1}{4\pi k\,r_1\,r_2} \times Q_{\text{ends}}$$

$$\therefore \qquad Q_{\text{ends}} = \frac{2r_1\,r_2 \times \ln(r_2/r_1)}{(r_2 - r_1)L_{cyl}} \times Q_{cyl}$$

Now $\qquad Q_{cyl} + Q_{\text{ends}} = Q_{\text{boil}} = 2311.2$

or, $\quad Q_{cyl} + \dfrac{2r_1\,r_2 \times \ln(r_2/r_1)}{(r_2 - r_1)L_{cyl}} \times Q_{cyl} = 2311.2$

$$\therefore \qquad Q_{cyl} = \cfrac{2311.2}{1 + \left[\cfrac{2r_1\,r_2 \times \ln(r_2/r_1)}{(r_2 - r_1)L_{cyl}}\right]} \hspace{2cm} \text{...(iii)}$$

From the given geometry of the tank,

$$r_1 = \frac{1.5}{2} = 0.75\,\text{m};\ r_2 = 0.75 + 0.10 = 0.85\,\text{m};\ L_{cyl} = 8 - 1.5 = 6.5\,\text{m}$$

Substituting the values in eqn. (*iii*), we get

$$Q_{cyl} = \cfrac{2311.2}{1 + \left[\cfrac{2 \times 0.75 \times 0.85 \times \ln(0.85/0.75)}{(0.85 - 0.75) \times 6.5}\right]} = \frac{2311.2}{1 + 0.2455}$$

$$= 1855.6\,\text{kJ/h} = 515.44\,\text{J/s}$$

Now, from eqn. (*i*), we have

$$k = \frac{\ln(r/r_1)}{(t_0 - t_i)\,2\pi\,L_{cyl}} \times Q_{cyl} = \frac{\ln(0.85/0.75)}{[27 - (-183)]2\pi \times 6.5} \times 515.44$$

$$= 7.522 \times 10^{-3}\,\text{W/m K}$$

Hence, the *thermal conductivity of the insulation*, **k = 7.522 × 10⁻³ W/m K** (Ans.)

2.8. CRITICAL THICKNESS OF INSULATION

2.8.1. INSULATION-GENERAL ASPECTS

Definition. A *material which retards the flow of heat with reasonable effectiveness* is known as *'Insulation'*. Insulation serves the following *two purposes* :

(*i*)   It prevents the heat flow from the system to the surroundings;

(*ii*)   It prevents the heat flow from the surroundings to the system.

Applications :

The *fields of application* of insulations are :

(*i*)   Boilers and steam pipes;

(*ii*)   Airconditioning systems;

(*iii*)   Food preserving stores and refrigerators;

(*iv*)   Insulating bricks (employed in various types of furnaces);

(*v*)   Preservation of liquid gases etc.

Factors affecting thermal conductivity :

Some of the important factors which affect thermal conductivity (*k*) of the insulators (*the value of k should be always low to reduce the rate of heat flow*) are as follows :

1.   *Temperature.* For most of the insulating materials, the value of *k increases with increase in temperature.*

2.   *Density.* There is no mathematical relationship between *k* and ρ (density). The common understanding that high density insulating materials will have higher values of *k* is not always true.

3.   *Direction of heat flow.* For most of the insulating materials (except few like wood) the effect of direction of heat flow on the values of *k* is negligible.

4.   *Moisture.* It is always considered necessary to prevent ingress of moisture in the insulating materials, during service. it is, however, difficult to find the effect of moisture on the values of *k* of different insulating materials.

5.   *Air pressure.* It has been found that the value of *k decreases with decrease in pressure.*

6.   *Convection in insulators.* The value of *k* increases due to the phenomenon of convection in insulators.

2.8.2. CRITICAL THICKNESS OF INSULATION

The addition of insulation always increases the conductive thermal resistance. But when the the the total thermal resistance is made of conductive thermal resistance $[(R_{th})_{cond.}]$ and convective thermal resistance $[(R_{th})_{conv.}]$, the addition of insulation in *some cases* may *reduce the convective thermal resistance due to increase in surface area*, as in the case of a cylinder and sphere, and the total thermal resistance may actually decrease resulting in increased heat flow. It may be shown that the thermal resistance actually decreases and then increases in some cases.

"The thickness upto which heat flow increases and after which heat flow decreases is termed as **Critical thickness**. *In case of cylinders and spheres it is called* **'Critical radius'**.

A. Critical thickness of insulation for cylinder :

Consider a solid cylinder of radius r_1 insulated with an insulation of thickness $(r_2 - r_1)$ as shown in Fig. 2.85.

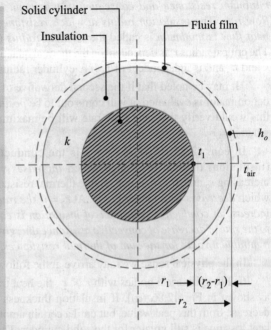

Fig. 2.85. Critical thickness of insulation for cylinder.

Let, L = Length of the cylinder,

t_1 = Surface temperature of the cylinder,

t_{air} = Temperature of air,

h_o = Heat transfer coefficient at the outer surface of the insulation, and

k = Thermal conductivity of insulating material.

Then the rate of heat transfer from the surface of the solid cylinder to the surroundings is given by

$$Q = \frac{2\pi L (t_1 - t_{air})}{\dfrac{\ln (r_2 / r_1)}{k} + \dfrac{1}{h_0 \cdot r_2}} \qquad \qquad ...(2.85)$$

From Eqn. (2.85) it is evident that as r_2 increases, the factor $\dfrac{\ln (r_2 / r_1)}{k}$ increases but the factor $\dfrac{1}{h_0 \cdot r_2}$ decreases. Thus Q becomes *maximum* when the *denominator* $\left[\dfrac{\ln (r_2 / r_1)}{k} + \dfrac{1}{h_o \cdot r_2}\right]$ becomes *minimum*. The required condition is

$$\frac{d}{dr_2}\left[\frac{\ln (r_2 / r_1)}{k} + \frac{1}{h_o \cdot r_2}\right] = 0 \qquad (r_2 \text{ being the only variable})$$

$$\therefore \qquad \frac{1}{k}\cdot\frac{1}{r_2} + \frac{1}{h_o}\left(-\frac{1}{r_2^{\,2}}\right) = 0$$

or, $$\frac{1}{k} - \frac{1}{h_o \cdot r_2} = 0 \qquad \text{or} \qquad h_o \cdot r_2 = k$$

or, $$r_2\, (= r_c) = \frac{k}{h_o} \qquad \qquad ...(2.86)$$

The above relation represents the *condition for minimum resistance and consequently*maximum heat flow rate*. The *insulation radius at which resistance to heat flow is minimum* is called the '*critical radius* (r_c)'. The critical radius r_c is dependent on the thermal quantities k and h_o and is independent of r_1 (*i.e.* cylinder radius).

*It may be noted that if the second derivative of the denominator is evaluated, it will come out to be *positive*; this would verify that heat flow rate will be maximum, when $r_2 = r_c$.

In eqn. (2.85) ln $(r_2 / r_1) / k$ is the conduction (insulation) thermal resistance which *increases* with increasing r_2 and $1/h_o.r_2$ is convective thermal resistance which *decreases* with increasing r_2. *At $r_2 = r_c$ the rate of increase of conductive resistance of insulation is equal to the rate of decrease of convective resistance thus giving a minimum value for the sum of thermal resistances.*

Underground cables.

In the physical sense we may arrive at the following *conclusions* :

(*i*) For cylindrical bodies with $r_1 < r_c$, the heat transfer increases by adding insulation till $r_2 = r_c$ as shown in Fig. [2.86 (*a*)]. If insulation thickness is further increased, the rate of heat loss will decrease from this peak value, but until a certain amount of insulation denoted by r_2' at b is added, the heat loss rate is still greater for the solid cylinder. This happens when r_1 is small and r_c is large, *viz.*, the thermal conductivity of the insulation k is high (poor insulating material) and h_o is low. *A practical application would be the insulation of electric cables which should be a good insulator for current but poor for heat.*

(*ii*) For cylindrical bodies with $r_1 > r_c$, the heat transfer decreases by adding insulation [Fig.2.86 (*b*)]. This happens when r_1 is large and r_c is small, *viz.*, a good insulating material is used with low k and h_0 is high. In *steam and refrigeration pipes* heat insulation is the main objective. For insulation to be properly effective in restricting heat transmission, the *outer radius must be greater than or equal to the critical radius.*

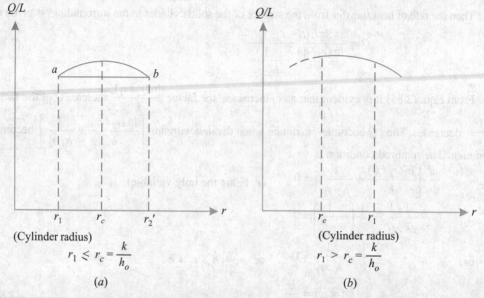

Fig. 2.86. Dependence of heat loss on insulation thickness.

B. Critical thickness of insulation for sphere :

Refer to Fig. 2.87. The equation of heat flow through a sphere with insulation is given as

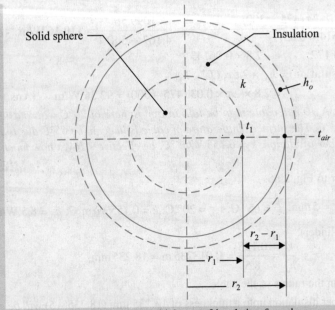

Solid sphere

Insulation

k

h_o

t_1

t_{air}

$r_2 - r_1$

r_1

r_2

Fig. 2.87. Critical thickness of insulation for sphere.

$$Q = \frac{(t_1 - t_{air})}{\left[\dfrac{r_2 - r_1}{4\pi k\, r_1\, r_2}\right] + \dfrac{1}{4\pi r_2^2 \cdot h_o}}$$

Adopting the same procedure as that of a cylinder, we have

$$\frac{d}{dr_2}\left[\frac{r_2 - r_1}{4\pi k\, r_1\, r_2} + \frac{1}{4\pi r_2^2 \cdot h_o}\right] = 0$$

or,

$$\frac{d}{dr_2}\left[\frac{1}{k\, r_1} - \frac{1}{k\, r_2} + \frac{1}{r_2^2\, h_o}\right] = 0$$

or,

$$\frac{1}{k\, r_2^2} - \frac{2}{r_2^3\, h_o} = 0$$

or,

$$r_2^3\, h_o = 2k\, r_2^2$$

or,

$$r_2\,(= r_c) = \frac{2k}{h_o} \qquad\qquad\qquad ...(2.87)$$

Example 2.70. *Calculate the critical radius of insulation for asbestos [k = 0.172 W/m K] surrounding a pipe and exposed to room air at 300 K with h = 2.8 W/m K. Calculate the heat loss from a 475 K, 60 mm diameter pipe when covered with the critical radius of insulation and without insulation.*

(AMIE, Summer, 1998)

Solution. *Given :* $k = 0.172$ W/m K; $T_1 = 475$ K; $T_2 = 300$ K;

$$h_0 = 2.8 \text{ W/m}^2 \text{ K};\ r_1 = \frac{60}{2} = 30\,\text{mm} = 0.03\,\text{m}.$$

The critical radius of insulation,

$$r_c = \frac{k}{h_0} = \frac{0.172}{2.8} = 0.06143\,\text{m} \quad \text{or} \quad \textbf{61.43 mm} \quad \textbf{(Ans.)}$$

$$Q \text{ (with insulation)} = \frac{2\pi(T_1 - T_2)}{\dfrac{\ln(r_c/r_1)}{k} + \dfrac{1}{h_0 r_c}}$$

$$= \frac{2\pi(475 - 300)}{\dfrac{\ln(0.06143/0.03)}{0.172} + \dfrac{1}{2.8 \times 0.06143}} = \frac{1099.56}{4.167 + 5.814} = \textbf{110.16 W/m} \quad \textbf{(Ans.)}$$

$$Q \text{ (without insulation)} = h_0 \times 2\pi r_1 (T_1 - T_2)$$
$$= 2.8 \times 2\pi \times 0.03 (475 - 300) = \textbf{92.36 W/m} \quad \textbf{(Ans.)}$$

Example 2.71. *A 10 mm cable is to be laid in atmosphere of 20°C with outside heat transfer coefficient 8.5 W/m²°C. The surface temperature of cable is likely to be 65°C due to heat generation within. Will the rubber insulation, k = 0.155 W/m °C, be effective ? If yes how much ?*

(AMIE Winter, 1999)

Solution. Refer to Fig. 2.85.

Given : $r_1 = \dfrac{10}{2} = 5\,mm$; $t_1 = 65°\,C$; $t_{air} = 20°\,C$; $k = 0.155\,W/m°C$; $h_0 = 8.5\,W/m^2°C$

For a cable (cylinder),

$$r_c = \frac{k}{h_0} = \frac{0.155}{8.5} = 0.018235\,m = 18.235\,mm,$$

r_c is greater than the radius of the cable.

Hence, the rubber insulation upto a thickness of 13.235 mm (18.235 – 5) *will be effective in heat dissipation.* **(Ans.)**

The maximum heat dissipation per m length of the cable will be

$$\frac{Q_{max}}{L} = \frac{2\pi(t_1 - t_{air})}{\dfrac{\ln(r_c/k_1)}{k} + \dfrac{1}{h_0 r_c}}$$

$$= \frac{2\pi(65 - 20)}{\dfrac{\ln(18.235/5)}{0.155} + \dfrac{1}{8.5 \times 0.018235}} = \frac{282.74}{8.348 + 6.452} = \textbf{19.1 W/m} \quad \textbf{(Ans.)}$$

Example 2.72. *A small electric heating application uses wire of 2 mm diameter with 0.8 mm thick insulation (k = 0.12 W/m°C). The heat transfer coefficient (h_o) on the insulated surface is 35 W/m²°C. Determine the critical thickness of insulation in this case and the percentage change in the heat transfer rate if the critical thickness is used, assuming the temperature difference between the surface of the wire and surrounding air remains unchanged.*

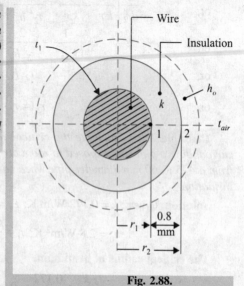

Solution. Refer to Fig. 2.88.

$$r_1 = \frac{2}{2} = 1\,mm = 0.001\,m$$

$$r_2 = 1 + 0.8 = 1.8\,mm = 0.0018\,m$$

$$k = 0.12\,W/m°C, h_o = 35\,W/m^2\,°C.$$

Critical thickness of insulation :

The critical radius of insulation is given by

Fig. 2.88.

Underground Cables.

$$r_c = \frac{k}{h_0} = \frac{0.12}{35} = 3.43 \times 10^{-3} \text{ m or } 3.43 \text{ mm.}$$

Percentage change in heat transfer rate :

Case I. The heat flow through an insulated wire is given by

$$Q_1 = \frac{2\pi L(t_1 - t_{air})}{\dfrac{\ln(r_2/r_1)}{k} + \dfrac{1}{h_0 \cdot r_2}} = \frac{2\pi L(t_1 - t_{air})}{\dfrac{\ln L(0.0018/0.001)}{0.12} + \dfrac{1}{35 \times 0.0018}} = \frac{2\pi L(t_1 - t_{air})}{20.77} \qquad ...(i)$$

Case II. The heat flow through an insulated wire, when *critical thickness is used*, is given by

$$Q_2 = \frac{2\pi L(t_1 - t_{air})}{\dfrac{\ln(r_c/r_1)}{k} + \dfrac{1}{h_0 \cdot r_c}} = \frac{2\pi L(t_1 - t_{air})}{\dfrac{\ln(0.00343/0.001)}{0.12} + \dfrac{1}{35 \times 0.00343}}$$

$$= \frac{2\pi L(t_1 - t_{air})}{18.6}$$

∴ Percentage increase in heat flow by using critical thickness of insulation

$$= \frac{Q_2 - Q_1}{Q_1} \times 100 = \frac{\dfrac{1}{18.6} - \dfrac{1}{20.77}}{\dfrac{1}{20.77}} \times 100 = \mathbf{11.6\%} \qquad \textbf{(Ans.)}$$

Example 2.73. *A wire of 6.5 mm diameter at a temperature of 60°C is to be insulated by a material having k = 0.174 W/m°C. Convection heat transfer coefficient (h_o) = 8.722 W/m²°C. The ambient temperature is 20°C. For maximum heat loss, what is the minimum thickness of insulation and heat loss per metre length? Also find percentage increase in the heat dissipation too.* (M.U.)

Solution. Refer to Fig. 2.89.

$$r_1 = \frac{6.5}{2} = 3.25 \text{ mm} = 0.00325 \text{ m}$$

$$k = 0.174 \text{ W/m°C,}$$

$$h_o = 8.722 \text{ W/m}^2\text{°C.}$$

For maximum heat loss, the minimum insulation thickness corresponds to critical radius of insulation which is given by

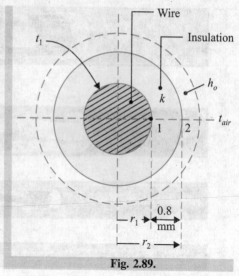

$$r_c = \frac{k}{h_0} = \frac{0.174}{8.722} = 0.01995\,m \text{ or } 19.95\,mm$$

∴ *Minimum insulation thickness*

$$= r_c - r_1 = 19.95 - 3.25 = \textbf{16.7 mm (Ans.)}$$

Heat loss per metre length :

Case I. Without insulation :

$$Q_1 = \frac{2\pi L(t_1 - t_{air})}{\dfrac{1}{h_o \cdot r_1}} = \frac{2\pi \times 1(60 - 20)}{\dfrac{1}{8.722 \times 0.00325}}$$

$$= 7.124 \text{ W/m}$$

Fig. 2.89.

Case II. With insulation when critical thickness is used :

$$Q_2 = \frac{2\pi L(t_1 - t_{air})}{\dfrac{\ln(r_c/r_1)}{k} + \dfrac{1}{h_o \cdot r_c}} = \frac{2\pi \times 1 \times (60 - 20)}{\dfrac{\ln(0.01995/0.00325)}{0.174} + \dfrac{1}{8.722 \times 0.01995}}$$

$$= 15.537 \text{ W/m}$$

∴ Percentage increase in heat dissipation $= \dfrac{Q_2 - Q_1}{Q_1} \times 100$

$$= \frac{(15.537 - 7.124)}{7.124} \times 100 = \textbf{118.09\%} \qquad \textbf{(Ans.)}$$

Example 2.74. *A refrigerant suction line having outer diameter 30 mm is required to be thermally insulated. The outside air film coefficient of heat transfer is 12 W/m²°C. The thermal conductivity of insulation is 0.3 W/m°C.*

(i) *Determine whether the insulation will be effective;*

(ii) *Estimate the maximum value of thermal conductivity of insulating material to reduce heat transfer;*

(iii) *Determine the thickness of cork insulation to reduce the heat transfer to 22 percent if the thermal conductivity of cork is 0.038 W/m°C.*

Solution. *Given :* $r_0 = \dfrac{30}{2} = 15\,mm = 0.015\,m$; $h_o = 12$ W/m² °C; $k_{insu.} = 0.3$W/m°C; $k_{cork} = 0.038$ W/m°C.

(i) The critical radius, $r_c = \dfrac{k_{insu.}}{h_o} = \dfrac{0.30}{12} = 0.025\,m$ or 25 mm or 25 mm

Since $r_o = 15$ mm $< r_c$, therefore, heat transfer will increase by adding this insulation and thus it is **not effective. (Ans.)**

(ii) For *insulation to be effective* : $r_o \geq r_c$

or, $\qquad 0.015 \geq \dfrac{k_{insu.}}{12}$

or, $\qquad k_{insu} \leq (0.015 \times 12) = \textbf{0.18 W/m°C (Ans.)}$

(iii) Consider *unit length* of pipe.

For base pipe $\qquad Q = h_o.A.\Delta t = h_o \times 2\pi r_o \times 1 \times \Delta t$

For pipe with cork-insulation, $\qquad Q_{C1} = \dfrac{\Delta t}{\dfrac{\ln(r_{C1/r_o})}{2\pi k_{C1}} + \dfrac{1}{2\pi r_{C1} \cdot h_o}} = 0.22Q$

(where r_{CI} = radius of cork-insulation layer)

or, $\qquad \dfrac{\Delta t}{\dfrac{\ln(r_{CI}/r_o)}{2\pi k_{CI}} + \dfrac{1}{2\pi r_{CI} \cdot h_o}} = 0.22 \times h_0 \times 2\pi r_0 \times 1 \times \Delta t$

or, $\qquad \dfrac{\ln(r_{CI}/r_o)}{2\pi k_{CI}} + \dfrac{1}{2\pi r_{CI} \cdot h_o} = \dfrac{1}{0.22 \times h_o \times 2\pi r_o}$

or, $\qquad \dfrac{\ln(r_{CI}/r_o)}{k_{CI}} + \dfrac{1}{12\, r_{CI}} = \dfrac{1}{0.22 \times 12 \times 0.015} = 25.25$

or, $\qquad \dfrac{\ln(r_{CI}/0.015)}{0.038} + \dfrac{1}{12\, r_{CI}} = 25.25$

Solving by trial and error, we have

$$r_{CI} = 0.036 \text{ m or } 36 \text{ mm}$$

∴ Thickness of cork-insulation $\qquad = r_{CI} - r_o = 36 - 15 = \textbf{21 mm (Ans.)}$

Example 2.75. *A uniform sheathing of plastic insulation (k = 0.18 W/m°C) is applied to an electric cable of 8mm diameter. The convective film coefficient on the surface of bare cable as well as insulated cable was estimated as 12.5 W/m²°C and a surface temperature of 45°C was observed when the cable was directly exposed to ambient air 20°C. Determine :*

(i) The thickness of insulation to keep the wire as cool as possible;

(ii) The surface temperature of insulated cable if the intensity of current flowing through the conductor remains unchanged.

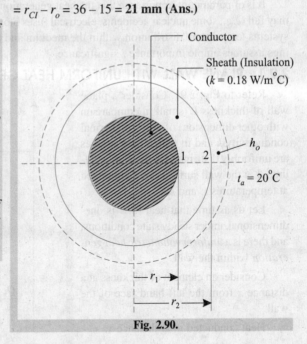

Fig. 2.90.

Solution. Refer to Fig. 2.90.

$r_1 = \dfrac{8}{2} = 4 \text{ mm} = 0.004 \text{ m};$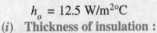

$k = 0.18 \text{ W/m°C}$

$h_o = 12.5 \text{ W/m}^2\text{°C}$

(i) Thickness of insulation :

In order to keep the wire as cool as possible, the required condition corresponds to that for critical radius of insulation,

i.e., $\qquad r_2 = r_c = \dfrac{k}{h_o} = \dfrac{0.18}{12.5} = 0.0144 \text{ m or } 14.4 \text{ mm}$

∴ Thickness of insulation, $= r_2 - r_1 = 14.4 - 4 = \textbf{10.4 mm} \qquad$ **(Ans.)**

(ii) Surface temperature of insulated cable, t_2 :

For a bare wire, the heat flow (per metre length) is given by

$$Q_1 = h_o\, A\, \Delta t = 12.5 \times (2\pi \times 0.004 \times 1) \times (45 - 20) = 7.85 \text{ W/m}$$

In case of the sheathed (insulated) cable, the heat flow (per metre length) is given as

$$Q_2 = \frac{2\pi\, L\,(t_2 - 20)}{\dfrac{1}{h_o \cdot r_2} + \dfrac{\ln(r_2/r_1)}{k}} = \frac{2\pi \times 1\,(t_2 - 20)}{\dfrac{1}{2.5 \times 0.0144} + \dfrac{\ln(0.044/0.004)}{0.18}} = 0.495\,(t_2 - 20)$$

Since the intensity of current flowing through the conductor remains unaltered, therefore,

$$Q_1 = Q_2 = (I^2 R)$$
$$7.85 = 0.495\,(t_2 - 20)$$

or
$$t_2 = 20 + \frac{7.85}{0.495} = 35.86°C \qquad \textbf{(Ans.)}$$

2.9. HEAT CONDUCTION WITH INTERNAL HEAT GENERATION

Following are some of the cases where heat generation and heat conduction are encountered :

(*i*) Fuel rods – nuclear reactor;

(*ii*) Electrical conductors;

(*iii*) Chemical and combustion processes;

(*iv*) Drying and setting of concrete.

It is of paramount importance that the heat generation rate be controlled otherwise the equipment may fail (*e.g.*, some nuclear accidents, electrical fuses blowing out). Thus, in the design of the thermal systems temperature distribution within the medium and the rate of heat dissipation to the surroundings assumes ample importance / significance.

2.9.1. PLANE WALL WITH UNIFORM HEAT GENERATION

Refer to Fig. 2.91. Consider a plane wall of thickness L (small in comparison with other dimension) of uniform thermal conductivity k and in which heat sources are uniformly distributed in the whole volume. Let the wall surfaces are maintained at temperatures t_1 and t_2.

Let us assume that heat flow is one-dimensional, under steady state conditions, and there is a *uniform volumetric heat generation* within the wall.

Consider an element of thickness at a distance x from the left hand face of the wall.

Heat conducted in at distance x,

$$Q_x = -kA\frac{dt}{dx}$$

Heat generated in the element,

$$Q_g = A \cdot dx\ q_g$$

(where q_g = heat generated per unit volume per unit time in the element)

Heat conducted out at distance

$(x + dx)$, $Q_{(x+dx)} = Q_x + \dfrac{d}{dx}(Q_x)\,dx$

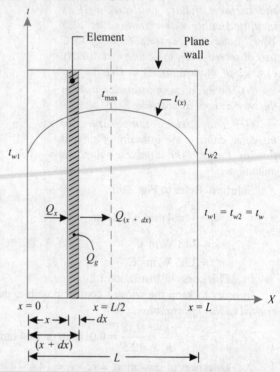

Fig. 2.91. Plane wall uniform heat generation. Both the surfaces maintained at a common temperature.

As Q_g represents an energy increase in the volume element, an energy balance on the element of thick dx is given by

$$Q_x + Q_g = Q_{(x+dx)}$$

$$= Q_x + \frac{d}{dx}(Q_x)\,dx$$

or,

$$Q_g = \frac{d}{dx}(Q_x)\,dx$$

or,

$$q_g \cdot A \cdot dx = \frac{d}{dx}\left[-kA\frac{dt}{dx}\right]dx$$

$$= -kA \cdot \frac{d^2t}{dx^2} \cdot dx$$

or,

$$\frac{d^2t}{dx^2} + \frac{q_g}{k} = 0 \qquad\qquad ...(2.88)$$

Eqn. (2.88) may also be obtained from eqn. (2.8) by assuming one-dimensional steady state conditions.

The first and second integration of Eqn. (2.88) gives respectively

$$\frac{dt}{dx} = -\frac{q_g}{k}x + C_1 \qquad\qquad ...(2.89)$$

$$t = -\frac{q_g}{2k}x^2 + C_1 x + C_2 \qquad\qquad (2.90)$$

Case I. Both the surfaces have the same temperature :

Refer to Fig. 2.92.

At $x = 0$ $\qquad\qquad t = t_1 = t_w$, and

At $x = L$ $\qquad\qquad t = t_2 = t_w$

(where t_w = temperature of the wall surface).

Using these boundary conditions in eqn. (2.90), we get

$$C_2 = t_w \text{ and } C_1 = \frac{q_g}{2k}\cdot L$$

Substituting these values of C_1 and C_2 in eqn. (2.90), we have

$$t = -\frac{q_g}{2k}x^2 + \frac{q_g}{2k}\cdot L\cdot x + t_w$$

or,

$$t = \frac{q_g}{2k}(L - x)x + t_w \qquad\qquad ...(2.91)$$

In order to determine the location of the maximum temperature, differentiating the eqn. (2.91) w.r.t x and equating the derivative to *zero*, we have

$$\frac{dt}{dx} = \frac{q_g}{2k}(L - 2x) = 0$$

Since,

$$\frac{q_g}{2k} \neq 0, \text{ therefore,}$$

$$L - 2x = 0 \qquad\qquad \text{or} \qquad\qquad x = \frac{L}{2}$$

Thus the *distribution of temperature* given by eqn. (2.91) is the *parabolic* and *symmetrical* about the midplane. The maximum temperature occurs at $x = \dfrac{L}{2}$ and its value equals

$$t_{max} = \left[\frac{q_g}{2k}(L - x)x\right]_{x = \frac{L}{2}} + t_w$$

or,
$$= \left[\frac{q_g}{2k} \left(L - \frac{L}{2} \right) \frac{L}{2} \right] + t_w$$

i.e.
$$t_{max} = \frac{q_g}{8k} \cdot L^2 + t_w \qquad \qquad ...(2.92)$$

Heat transfer then takes place towards both the surfaces, and for each surface it is given by

$$Q = -kA \left(\frac{dt}{dx} \right)_{x=0 \text{ or } x=L}$$

$$= -kA \left[\frac{q_g}{2k} (L - 2x) \right]_{x=0 \text{ or } x=L}$$

i.e.,
$$Q = \frac{AL}{2} \cdot q_g \qquad \qquad ...(2.93)$$

When both the surfaces are considered,

$$Q = 2 \times \frac{AL}{2} q_g = A.L.q_g \qquad \qquad ...[2.93\,(a)]$$

Also heat conducted to *each wall surface* is further dissipated to the surrounding atmosphere at temperature t_a,

Thus,
$$\frac{AL}{2} \cdot q_g = hA \,(t_w - t_a)$$

or,
$$t_w = t_a + \frac{q_g}{2h} \cdot L \qquad \qquad ...(2.94)$$

Substituting this value of t_w in eqn. (2.91), we obtain

$$t = t_a + \frac{q_g}{2h} \cdot L + \frac{q_g}{2k} (L - x) \, x \qquad \qquad ...(2.95)$$

At
$$x = L/2 \text{ i.e., at the midplane :}$$

$$t = t_{max} = t_a + \frac{q_g}{2h} \cdot L + \frac{q_g \, L^2}{8k}$$

or,
$$t_{max} = t_a + q_g \left[\frac{L}{2h} + \frac{L^2}{8k} \right] \qquad \qquad ...[2.95\,(a)]$$

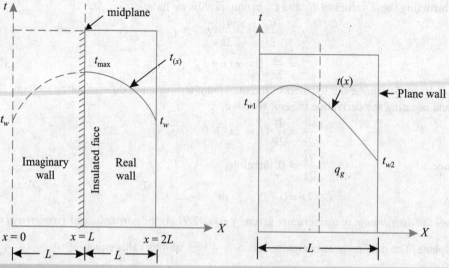

Fig. 2.92. Heat conduction in an insulated wall.   **Fig. 2.93.** Plane wall with uniform heat generation—Both the surfaces of the wall having different temperatures.

The eqn. (2.95) also works well in case of conduction in an *insulated wall* Fig. (2.92).

The following boundary conditions apply in the full *hypothetical wall* of thickness $2L$:

$$\text{At } x = L \qquad \frac{dt}{dx} = 0$$

$$\text{At } x = 2L \qquad t = t_w$$

The location $x = L$ refers to the mid-plane of the hypothetical wall (or insulated face of given wall).

Eqns. (2.91) and (2.92) for temperature distribution and maximum temperature at the mid- plane (insulated end of the given wall) respectively can be written as

Vertical tank.

$$t = \frac{q_g}{2k}(2L - x)\,x + t_w \qquad ...(2.96)$$

$$t_{max} = \frac{q_g}{2k}L^2 + t_w \qquad ...(2.97)$$

[Substituting L = 2L in eqn. (2.91) and (2.92)]

Case II. Both the surfaces of the wall have different temperatures :

Refer to Fig. 2.93

The boundary conditions are :

$$\text{At } x = 0 \qquad\qquad\qquad t = t_{w1}$$

$$\text{At } x = L \qquad\qquad\qquad t = t_{w2}$$

Substituting these values in eqn. (2.90), we obtain the values of constant C_1 and C_2 as :

$$C_2 = t_{w1}; \qquad C_1 = \frac{t_{w2} - t_{w1}}{L} + \frac{q_g}{2k}\cdot L$$

Inserting these values in eqn. (2.90), we get

$$t = -\frac{q_g}{2k}x^2 + \frac{t_{w2} - t_{w1}}{L}x + \frac{q_g}{2k}L\cdot x + t_{w1}$$

$$= \frac{q_g}{2k}L\cdot x - \frac{q_g}{2k}x^2 + \frac{x}{L}(t_{w2} - t_{w1}) + t_1$$

or,

$$t = \left[\frac{q_g}{2k}(L - x) + \frac{t_{w2} - t_{w1}}{L}\right]x + t_{w1} \qquad ...(2.98)$$

The temperature distribution, in dimensionless form can be obtained by making the following transformations :

$$t - t_{w2} = \frac{q_g}{2k}L^2\left[\frac{x}{L} - \left(\frac{x}{L}\right)^2\right] + \frac{x}{L}(t_{w2} - t_{w1}) + (t_{w1} - t_{w2})$$

or,

$$\frac{t - t_{w2}}{t_1 - t_{w2}} = \frac{q_g}{2k}\cdot\frac{L^2}{(t_{w1} - t_{w2})}\left[\frac{x}{L} - \left(\frac{x}{L}\right)^2\right] - \frac{x}{L} + 1$$

or,

$$\frac{t - t_{w2}}{t_{w1} - t_{w2}} = \frac{q_g}{2k}\cdot\frac{L^2}{(t_{w1} - t_{w2})}\cdot\frac{x}{L}\left[1 - \frac{x}{L}\right] + \left[1 - \frac{x}{L}\right]$$

Replacing the parameter $\dfrac{q_g}{2k}\cdot\dfrac{L^2}{(t - t_{w2})}$ (a constant) by a factor Z, we have

$$\frac{t - t_{w2}}{t_{w1} - t_{w2}} = Z \cdot \frac{x}{L}\left[1 - \frac{x}{L}\right] + \left[1 - \frac{x}{L}\right]$$

or,

$$\frac{t - t_{w2}}{t_{w1} - t_{w2}} = \left[1 - \frac{x}{L}\right]\left[\frac{Z x}{L} + 1\right] \qquad \qquad ...(2.99)$$

In order to get maximum temperature and its location, differentiating Eqn. (2.99) w.r.t x and equating the derivative to zero, we have

$$\frac{dt}{d(x/L)} = \left(1 - \frac{x}{L}\right)Z + \left(\frac{Zx}{L} + 1\right)(-1) = 0$$

or, $Z - \dfrac{Zx}{L} - \dfrac{Zx}{L} - 1 = 0$

or, $\dfrac{2Zx}{L} = Z - 1$

or, $\dfrac{x}{L} = \dfrac{Z - 1}{2Z} \qquad ...(2.100)$

Thus the maximum value of temperature occurs at $\dfrac{x}{L} = \dfrac{Z-1}{2Z}$ and its value is given by:

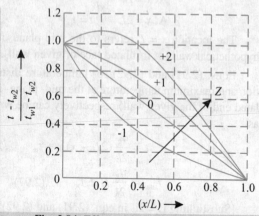

Fig. 2.94. Effect of factor Z on the temperature distribution in the plane wall.

$$\frac{t_{max} - t_{w2}}{t_{w1} - t_{w2}} = \left[1 - \frac{Z-1}{2Z}\right]\left[Z \times \left(\frac{Z-1}{2Z}\right) + 1\right]$$

or,

$$\frac{t_{max} - t_{w2}}{t_{w1} - t_{w2}} = \left(\frac{Z+1}{2Z}\right)\left(\frac{Z+1}{2}\right)$$

$$= \frac{(Z+1)^2}{4Z} \qquad \qquad ...(2.101)$$

Fig. 2.94 shows the effect of factor Z on the temperature distribution in the plane wall. The following points emerge :

- As the value of Z *increases* the slope of the curve changes; obviously the direction of heat flow can be reversed by an adequately large value of q_g.
- When Z = 0, the temperature distribution is *linear* (*i.e.*, no internal heat generation).
- When the value of Z is *negative*, q_g represents *absorption of heat* within the wall/body.

Case III. Current carrying electrical conductor :

When electrical current passes through a conductor, heat is generated (Q_g) in it and is given by

$$Q_g = I^2 R, \text{ where } R = \frac{\rho L}{A}$$

where,
I = Current flowing in the conductor,
R = Electrical resistance,
ρ = Specific resistance or resistivity,
L = Length of the conductor, and
A = Area of cross-section of the conductor.

Also, $Q_g = q_g \times A \times L$

∴ $q_g \times A \times L = I^2 \times \dfrac{\rho L}{A}$ or, $q_g = I^2 \times \dfrac{\rho L}{A} \times \dfrac{1}{AL} = \dfrac{I^2 \rho}{A^2}$

or, $$q_g = \left(\frac{I}{A}\right)^2 \rho = J^2 \rho = \frac{J^2}{k_e} \qquad \qquad ...(2.102)$$

where, J = Current density;

k_e = Electrical conductivity (reciprocal of ρ).

Example 2.76. *The rate of heat generation in a slab of thickness 160 mm ($k = 180$ W/m°C) is 1.2×10^6 W/m³. If the temperature of each of the surface of solid is 120°C, determine :*

(i) The temperature at the mid and quarter planes;

(ii) The heat flow rate and temperature gradients at the mid and quarter planes.

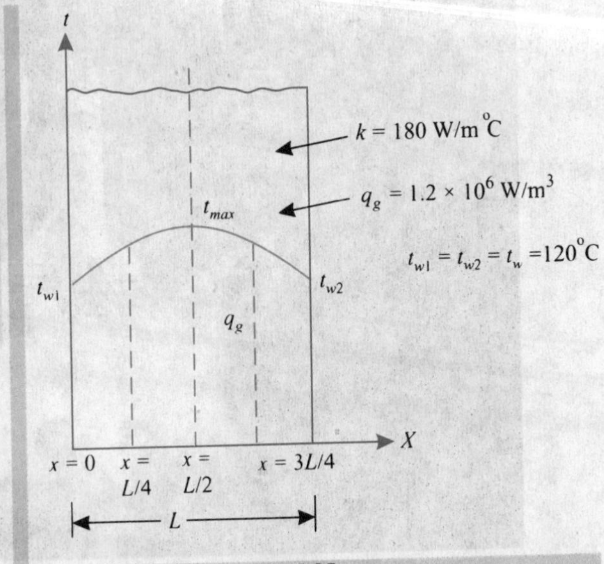

Solution. Refer to Fig. 2.95.

Thickness of slab, $L = 160$ mm

$\qquad = 0.16$ m

The rate of heat transfer,

$\qquad q_g = 1.2 \times 10^6$ W/m³

Thermal conductivity of slabs,

$\qquad k = 180$ W/m°C

$k = 180$ W/m °C

$q_g = 1.2 \times 10^6$ W/m³

$t_{w1} = t_{w2} = t_w = 120°$C

Fig. 2.95.

The temperature of each surface,

$\qquad t_1 = t_2 = t_w = 120°$C

(where t_w = temperature of the wall surface)

The temperature at the mid and quarter planes :

The temperature distribution is given by:

$$t = \frac{q_g}{2k}(L - x)x + t_w \qquad \qquad ...[\text{Eqn. (2.91)}]$$

At mid plane: $x = \dfrac{L}{2}$

$\therefore \qquad t_{mp} = \dfrac{1.2 \times 10^6}{2 \times 180}\left(L - \dfrac{L}{2}\right) \times \dfrac{L}{2} + 120$

or, $\qquad t_{mp} = \dfrac{1.2 \times 10^6}{2 \times 180}\left(0.16 - \dfrac{0.16}{2}\right) \times \dfrac{0.16}{2} + 120 = \mathbf{141.33° C}$ **(Ans.)**

At quarter planes : $\quad x = L/4$ and $x = 3L/4$

$\therefore \qquad t_{qP_{(x = L/4)}} = \dfrac{1.2 \times 10^6}{2 \times 180}\left(L - \dfrac{L}{4}\right) \times \dfrac{L}{4} + 120$

or, $\qquad t_{qP_{(x = L/4)}} = \dfrac{1.2 \times 10^6}{2 \times 180}\left(0.16 - \dfrac{0.16}{4}\right) \times \dfrac{0.16}{4} + 120 = \mathbf{136° C}$ **(Ans.)**

Similarly $\quad t_{qP_{(x = 3L/4)}} = \dfrac{1.2 \times 10^6}{2 \times 180}\left(L - \dfrac{3L}{4}\right) \times \dfrac{3L}{4} + 120 = \mathbf{136° C}$ **(Ans.)**

(ii) **The heat flow rate and temperature gradients at the mid and quarter planes :**

For unit area, *i.e.*, $1m^2$

Heat flow : $\quad Q_{(x=L/2)} = q_g \times A \times x$

Space shuttle carries oxygen and hydrogen in tanks which hold the gases below −150°C

$$= 12 \times 10^6 \times 1 \times (0.16/2) = \textbf{96000 W/m}^2 \textbf{ (Ans.)}$$

$$Q_{(x=L/4)} = 1.2 \times 10^6 \times 1 \times (0.16/4) = \textbf{48000 W/m}^2 \textbf{ (Ans.)}$$

Temperature gradients : $\quad Q = -kA \cdot \dfrac{dt}{dx} \quad \text{or} \quad \dfrac{dt}{dx} = -\dfrac{Q}{kA}$

$$\left(\frac{dt}{dx}\right)_{x=L/2} = -\frac{96000}{180 \times 1} = \textbf{−533.3° C/m} \quad \textbf{(Ans.)}$$

$$\left(\frac{d}{dx}\right)_{x=L/4} = -\frac{48000}{180 \times 1} = \textbf{−266.67° C/m} \quad \textbf{(Ans.)}$$

Example 2.77. *A meat slab of 25 mm thickness having k = 1W/m°C is heated with the help of microwave heating for roasting the meat slab. The centre temperature of the slab is maintained at 100°C when surrounding temperature is 30°C. The heat transfer coefficient on the surface of meat slab is 20W/m²°C. Find out the microwave heating capacity in W/m³.* [N.U. Summer, 1998]

Solution. Thickness of meat slab, L = 25 mm = 0.025 m

Thermal conductivity of meat, k = 1W/m°C

The centre temperature of the slab, t_{max} = 100°C

Surrounding temperature, t_a = 30°C

The heat transfer coefficient; h = 20 W/m²°C.

The microwave heat capacity q_g :

The maximum temperature occurs at the centre of the slab only and is given by

$$t_{max} = t_a + q_g \left[\frac{L}{2h} + \frac{L^2}{8k}\right]$$

$$\qquad\qquad\qquad\qquad\qquad\qquad\qquad ...[\text{Eqn. 2.95 }(a)]$$

Substituting the proper values, we obtain

$$100 = 30 + q_g \left[\frac{0.025}{2 \times 20} + \frac{0.025^2}{8 \times 1} \right] = 30 + 0.000703\, q_g$$

$$\therefore \qquad q_g = \frac{100 - 30}{0.000703} = 99573 \text{ W/m}^3 \text{ or } \textbf{99.573kW/m}^3 \qquad \textbf{(Ans.)}$$

Example 2.78. *A plate 2 cm thick and 10 cm wide is used to heat a fluid at 30°C. The heat generation rate inside the plate is 7×10^6 W/m³. Determine the heat transfer coefficient to maintain the temperature of the plate below 180°C. Given k(plate) = 26 W/m°C. Neglect heat losses from the edge of the plate.* (AMIE Summer, 1998)

Solution. Thickness of the plate, $b = 2$ cm $= 0.02$ m

Temperature of fluid to be heated, $t_a = 30°C$

Heat generation rate, $q_g = 7 \times 10^6$ W/m³

Maximum temperature of the plate, $t_{max} = 180°C$

Thermal conductivity of plate material, $k = 26$ W/m°C.

Heat transfer coefficient, h :

Using the following relation, we have

$$t_{max} = t_a + q_g \left[\frac{L}{2h} + \frac{L^2}{8k} \right] \qquad \qquad \text{...[Eqn. 2.95 (a)]}$$

$$180 = 30 + 7 \times 10^6 \left[\frac{0.02}{2h} + \frac{0.02^2}{8 \times 26} \right]$$

or,
$$\frac{0.02}{2h} = \frac{(180 - 30)}{7 \times 10^6} - \frac{0.02^2}{8 \times 26} = 1.95 \times 10^{-5}$$

$$h = \frac{0.02}{2 \times 1.95 \times 10^{-5}} = \textbf{512.8 W/m}^2\textbf{°C} \quad \textbf{(Ans.)}$$

Example 2.79. *The temperatures on the two surfaces of a 25 mm thick steel plate, (k = 48 W/m°C) having a uniform volumetric heat generation of 30×10^6 W/m³, are 180°C and 120°C. Neglecting the end effects, determine the following :*

(i) *The temperature distribution across the plate;*

(ii) *The value and position of the maximum temperature, and*

(iii) *The flow of heat from each surface of the plate.*

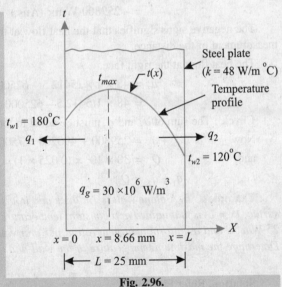

Fig. 2.96.

Solution. Refer to Fig. 2.96.

$L = 25$ mm $= 0.025$ m;

$t_{w1} = 180°C; t_{w2} = 120°C$

$q_g = 30 \times 10^6$ W/m³;

$k = 48$ W/m°C.

(*i*) **The temperature distribution across the plate :**

The temperature distribution, when both the surfaces of the wall have different temperatures, is given by

$$t = \left[\frac{q_g}{2k}(L - x) + \frac{(t_{w2} - t_{w1})}{L} \right] x + t_{w1} \qquad \qquad \text{...[Fig. (2.98)]}$$

Substituting the values, we have

$$t = \left[\frac{30 \times 10^6}{2 \times 48}(0.025 - x) + \frac{(120 - 180)}{0.025} \right] x + 180$$

$$= [312500 \, (0.025 - x) - 2400]x + 180$$

$$= [7812.5 - 312500x - 2400]x + 180$$

or, $\qquad \qquad t = 180 + 5412.5x - 312500\,x^2$ ...*Required temperature distribution.* **(Ans.)**

(where temperature t is in °C and the distance x is in metres)

The temperature distribution is *parabolic.*

(*ii*) **The value and position of the maximum temperature; t_{max}, x :**

In order to determine the position of maximum temperature, differentiating the above expression and equating it to zero, we obtain

$$\frac{dt}{dx} = 5412.5 - 625000\,x = 0$$

∴ $\qquad \qquad x = \frac{5412.5}{625000} = \textbf{0.00866\,m or 8.66\,mm}$ **(Ans.)**

The value of maximum temperature,

$$t_{max} = 180 + 5412.5 \times 0.00866 - 312500 \times 0.00866^2 = \textbf{203.44°C} \quad \textbf{(Ans.)}$$

(*iii*) **The flow of heat from each surface of the plate, q_1, q_2 :**

The heat flow at the left face ($x = 0$)

$$q_1 = -k\,A \left(\frac{dt}{dx} \right)_{x = 0}$$

$$= -48 \times 1 \times (5412.5 - 625000\,x)_{x = 0}$$

$$= \textbf{-259800 W/m}^2 \textbf{ (Ans.)}$$

The negative signs signifies that the heat flow at the left face is in a direction *opposite* to that of measurement of the distance.

The heat flow at the right face,

$$q_2 = 48 \times 1 \times (5412.5 - 625000\,x)_{x = 0.025}$$

$$= 48 \times 1(5412.5 - 625000 \times 0.025) = \textbf{-490200 W/m}^2 \textbf{ (Ans.)}$$

Check : The sum of q_1 and q_2 must be equal to total heat generated per unit length of plate.

Now $\qquad \qquad q_1 + q_2 = 259800 + 490200 = 750000 \text{ W/m}^2,$

and $\qquad \qquad Q_g = 30 \times 10^6 \times (0.025 \times 1) = 750000 \text{ W/m}^2$

i.e. $\qquad \qquad q_1 + q_2 = Q_g$

Example 2.80. *A plane wall is 1m thick and it has one surface ($x = 0$) insulated while the other surface ($x = L$) is maintained at a constant temperature of 350°C. The thermal conductivity of wall is 25 W/m°C and a uniform heat generation per unit volume of 500 W/m³ exists throughout the wall. Determine the maximum temperature in the wall and the location of the plane where it occurs.*

(AMIE Summer, 1999)

Solution. Refer Fig. 2.97.

$L = 1$ m; $t_1 = 350°C$; $k = 25$ W/m°C,

Heat generated per unit volume

per unit time, $q_g = 500$ W/m³.

Maximum temperature and its location, t_{max}, x:

The differential equation controlling heat flow by conduction when the body is generating heat is given by

$$\frac{d^2t}{dx^2} + \frac{q_g}{k} = 0 \qquad ...(i)$$

Integrating eqn. (i) twice, we have

$$\frac{dt}{dx} + \frac{q_g}{k} \cdot x = C_1 \qquad ...(ii)$$

$$t + \frac{q_g}{k} \cdot \frac{x^2}{2} = C_1 x + C_2 \qquad ...(iii)$$

(where C_1, C_2 = constants of integration).

In order to evaluate C_1 and C_2, using the following boundary conditions, we have

At $\qquad x = L, \dfrac{dt}{dx} = 0$

$\therefore \qquad C_1 = 0 \qquad$ [From eqn. (ii)]

At $\qquad x = L, t = t_1$

$\therefore \qquad C_2 = t_1 + \dfrac{q_g}{k} \cdot \dfrac{L^2}{2} \quad$ [From eqn. (iii)]

Substituting the values of C_1 and C_2 in eqn. (iii), we have

$$t + \frac{q_g}{k} \cdot \frac{x^2}{2} = t_1 + \frac{q_g}{k} \cdot \frac{L^2}{2}$$

or, $\qquad t = t_1 + \dfrac{q_g}{k} \left[\dfrac{L^2}{2} - \dfrac{x^2}{2} \right]$

or, $\qquad t = t_1 + \dfrac{q_g}{k} \cdot \dfrac{L^2}{2} \left[1 - \left(\dfrac{x}{2} \right)^2 \right] \qquad ...(iv)$

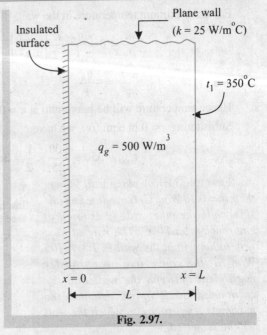

Plane wall ($k = 25$ W/m°C)

Insulated surface

$t_1 = 350°$C

$q_g = 500$ W/m³

$x = 0$ $\qquad$ $x = L$

L

Fig. 2.97.

Another air-to-air refuelling operation by an air oil-tanker.

For the maximum temperature in the wall,

$$\frac{dt}{dx} = 0 = \frac{q_g}{k} \cdot \frac{L^2}{2} \left[-\frac{2x}{L^2} \right] \qquad \text{or} \qquad x = 0$$

and

$$\frac{d^2 t}{dx^2} = -\frac{q_g}{k}$$

Hence temperature will be maximum at $x = 0$

Substituting $x = 0$ in eqn. (iv), we have

$$t_{max} = 350 + \frac{500}{25} \times \frac{1}{2} = \mathbf{360° C}$$

Example 2.81. *A plane wall 90 mm thick ($k = 0.18$ W/m°C) is insulated on one side while the other side is exposed to environment at 80°C. The rate of heat generation within the wall is 1.3×10^5 W/m³. If the convective heat transfer coefficient between the wall and the environment is 520 W/m²°C, determine the maximum temperature to which the wall will be subjected.*

Solution. Refer Fig. 2.98

$$L = 90 \text{ mm} = 0.09 \text{ m},$$

$$k = 0.18 \text{ W/m°C}$$

$$h = 520 \text{ W/m}^2°C$$

Temperature of environment,

$$t_a = 80°C$$

The rate of heat generation,

$$q_g = 1.3 \times 10^5 \text{ W/m}^3$$

Maximum temperature, t_{max} :

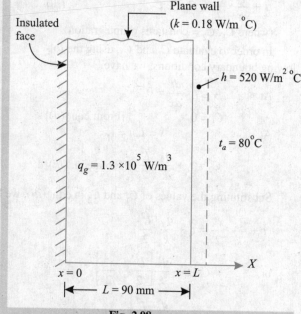

Fig. 2.98.

One dimensional, steady state heat conduction equation is given by

$$\frac{d^2 t}{dx^2} + \frac{q_g}{k} = 0 \qquad ..(i)$$

Integrating the above equation twice, we have

$$\frac{dt}{dx} = -\frac{q_g}{k} \cdot x + C_1 \qquad ...(ii)$$

$$t = -\frac{q_g}{k} \cdot \frac{x^2}{2} + C_1 x + C_2 \qquad ...(iii)$$

(where $\dot{C_1}, C_2$ = constants of integration)

In order to evaluate C_1 and C_2, using the following boundary conditions, we have

(*i*)   At $x = 0, \dfrac{dt}{dx} = 0$ $\therefore C_1 = 0$

(*ii*) At $x = L$, the heat conduction equals the convective heat flow to the environment.

i.e $-kA \left. \dfrac{dt}{dx} \right|_{x = L} = h A[t_{(L)} - t_a]$

              $-\left. \dfrac{dt}{dx} \right|_{x = L} = \dfrac{h}{k}[t_{(L)} - t_a] \qquad ...(iv)$

Again from eqn (ii),

$$\left.\frac{dt}{dx}\right|_{x=L} = -\frac{q_g}{k}\cdot L \qquad ...(v)$$

From eqns. (iv) and (v), we obtain

$$-\frac{h}{k}\left[t_{(L)} - t_a\right] = -\frac{q_g}{k}\cdot L$$

$$t_{(L)} = t_a + \frac{q_g}{h}\cdot L$$

Substituting into eqn. (iii), we have

$$t_{(L)} = t_a + \frac{q_g}{h}\cdot L = -\frac{q_g}{2k}\cdot L^2 + C_2$$

$$\therefore \qquad C_2 = t_a + \frac{q_g}{h}\cdot L + \frac{q_g}{2k}\cdot L^2 \qquad ...(vi)$$

Inserting the values of constants C_1 and C_2 in eqn. (iii), we get

$$t = -\frac{q_g}{2k}\cdot x^2 + t_a + \frac{q_g}{h}\cdot L + \frac{q_g}{2k}\cdot L^2$$

or,

$$t = t_a + \frac{q_g}{h}\cdot L + \frac{q_g}{2k}(L^2 - x^2) \qquad ...(vii)$$

The maximum temperature occurs at the insulated wall boundary i.e., $x = 0$

$$\therefore \qquad t_{max} = t_a + \frac{q_g}{h}\cdot L + \frac{q_g}{2k}\cdot L^2 \qquad ...(viii)$$

Substituting the proper values, we have

$$t_{max} = 80 + \frac{1.3 \times 10^5}{520} \times 0.09 + \frac{1.3 \times 10^5}{2 \times 0.18} \times (0.09)^2$$

$$= 3027.5°C \quad \text{(Ans.)}$$

Example 2.82. *A plane wall 'X' ($k = 75$ W/m°C) is 60 mm thick and has volumetric heat genera-tion of 1.5×10^6 W/m³. It is insulated on one side while the other side is in contact with surface of another wall 'Y' ($k = 150$ W/m°C) which is 30 mm thick and has no heat generation. The non-contact surface of wall 'Y' is exposed to a cooling fluid at 20°C. If the convective heat transfer coefficient between wall 'Y' and fluid is 950 W/m²°C, determine :*

(i) *The temperature at the insulated surface;*

(ii) *The temperature at the cooled surface of the composite wall.*

Solution. Refer Fig. 2.99. $k_X = 75$ W/m°C; $L_X = 60$ mm $= 0.06$ m

$$k_Y = 150 \text{ W/m°C}; L_Y = 30 \text{ mm} = 0.03 \text{ m}$$

$$h = 950 \text{ W/m}^2\text{°C}; t_{cf} = 20°C.$$

(i) **The temperature at the insulated surface, t_o :**

The heat generated in wall X per unit area,

$$Q_g = q_g \cdot A \cdot L_X = 1.5 \times 10^6 \times 1 \times 0.06 = 90000 \text{ W/m}^2$$

As the left face of the wall X is *insulated*, the flow of heat through this surface is nil and all the heat generated would pass through wall Y and finally dissipated to cooling fluid.

i.e.

$$90000 = h.A (t_2 - t_{cf})$$

$$= 950 \times 1 \times (t_2 - 20)$$

or,

$$t_2 = \frac{90000}{950} + 20 = 114.7°C$$

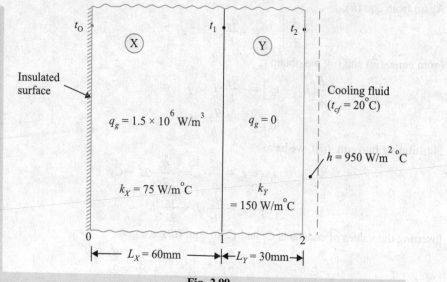

Fig. 2.99.

Cosidering heat flow through wall Y, we have

$$Q = \frac{k_Y \cdot A (t_1 - t_2)}{L_Y}$$

or, $$90000 = \frac{150 \times 1 \times (t_1 - 114.7)}{0.03} = 5000 (t_1 - 114.7)$$

or, $$t_1 = \frac{90000}{5000} + 114.7 = 132.7°C$$

The temperature of the insulated surface of the wall X is given by,

Air force helicopters carry huge amounts of fuel in their tankers, which need to be safely protected from temperature variations.

$$t_o = \frac{q_g}{2k_X} \cdot L_X^2 + t_1 \qquad \qquad \text{...[Refer eqn. (2.97)]}$$

or,
$$t_o = \frac{1.5 \times 10^6}{2 \times 75} \times (0.06)^2 + 132.7 = \mathbf{168.7^\circ C} \quad \text{(Ans.)}$$

Example 2.83. *The inside surface (x = 0) of a flat plate is insulated and the outside surface (x = L) is maintained at a uniform temperature T_2, and the heat generation term is in the form of g (x) = $g_0\ e^{-\gamma x}$ W/m³ where g_0 and γ are constants and x is measured from the insulated inside surface. Develop :*

(i) An expression for the temperature distribution in the plate, and

(ii) An expression for the temperature at the insulated surface (i.e., x = 0) of the plate.

(AMIE Winter, 1998)

Solution. The applicable differential equation is

$$\frac{d^2t}{dx^2} + \frac{q_g}{k} = 0 \qquad \qquad \text{...[Eqn. (2.88)]}$$

or,
$$\frac{d^2t}{dx^2} + \frac{g_0 e^{-\gamma x}}{k} = 0$$

or,
$$\frac{d^2t}{dx^2} = \frac{g_0 e^{-\gamma x}}{k}$$

Integrating w.r.t. x, we get

$$\frac{dt}{dx} = -\frac{g_0}{k} \times \frac{e^{-\gamma x}}{-\gamma} + C_1$$

At $x = 0$, $\dfrac{dt}{dx} = 0$ (insulated)

∴
$$C_1 = -\frac{g_0}{k\gamma}$$

∴
$$\frac{dt}{dx} = -\frac{g_0}{k} \times \frac{e^{-\gamma x}}{-\gamma} - \frac{g_0}{k\gamma}$$

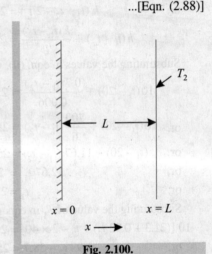

Fig. 2.100.

Integrating again w.r.t. x, we have

$$t = +\frac{g_0}{k\gamma} \times \frac{e^{-\gamma x}}{(-\gamma)} - \frac{g_0}{k\gamma}x + C_2$$

At $x = L$, $t = T_2$

Substituting the values, we get

$$T_2 = -\frac{g_0}{k\gamma^2} \cdot e^{-\gamma L} - \frac{g_0}{k\gamma}L + C_2$$

or,
$$C_2 = T_2 + \frac{g_0}{k\gamma^2}e^{-\gamma L} + \frac{g_0}{k\gamma}L$$

∴
$$L = -\frac{g_0}{k\gamma^2} \cdot e^{-\gamma x} - \frac{g_0}{k\gamma}x + T_2 + \frac{g_0}{k\gamma^2}e^{-\gamma L} + \frac{g_0}{k\gamma}L$$

(*i*) Thus, expression for this temperature distribution in the plate,

$$t = T_2 + \frac{g_0}{k\gamma}(L - x) + \frac{g_0}{k\gamma^2}(e^{-\gamma L} - e^{-\gamma x}) \quad \text{(Ans.)}$$

(*ii*) The expression for temperature at the insulated surface (x = 0) is :

$$t_0 = T_2 + \frac{g_0}{k\gamma}L + \frac{g_0}{k\gamma^2}(e^{-\gamma L} - 1) \quad \text{(Ans.)}$$

Example 2.84. *A sheet of glass coated on one side with an exceedingly thin but transparent electrically conducting layer is mounted vertically in a room where air is at 20°C. An electric current is passed through the conducting layer to generate heat at the rate of 2.5 kW/m² of conducting material.*

If the mean heat transfer coefficient on both sides of the sheet is 10 kW/m² °C, find the temperature on both sides of the glass. The glass thickness is 6 mm and neglect the thickness of conducting layer.

Take k (glass) = 0.7 W/m K. (A.U. Winter, 2000)

Solution. *Given :* $t_a = 20°C; q = 2.5$ kW/m² = 2500 W/m²; $h = 10$ W/m²°C;
$$k = 0.7 \text{ W/m K}; L = 6 \text{ mm} = 0.006 \text{ m}$$

Temperatures, t_1, t_2 :

Consider surface area of 1 m^2.

$$h(t_1 - t_a) + h(t_2 - t_a) = 2500$$

or,
$$h(t_1 + t_2 - 2 t_a) = 2500 \quad ...(i)$$

$$h(t_1 - t_a) + \frac{k(t_1 - t_2)}{L} = 2500 \quad ...(ii)$$

Substituting the values in eqn. (*ii*), we get

$$10(t_1 - 20) + \frac{0.7(t_1 - t_2)}{0.006} = 2500$$

or, $10(t_1 - 20) + \dfrac{700}{6}(t_1 - t_2) = 2500$

or, $(t_1 - 20) + 11.67(t_1 - t_2) = 250$

or, $12.67 \, t_1 = 270 + 11.67 \, t_2$

or, $t_1 = 21.3 + 0.92 \, t_2$

Substituting the value of T_1 in eqn. (*i*), we get

$10 [(21.3 + 0.92 \, t_2) + t_2 - 2 \times 40] = 2500$

or, $1.92 \, t_2 - 58.7 = 250$

or, $t_2 = \dfrac{250 + 58.7}{1.92} = \textbf{160.78° C}$ **(Ans.)**

$t_1 = 21.3 + 0.92 \times 160.78 = \textbf{169.22°C}$ **(Ans.)**

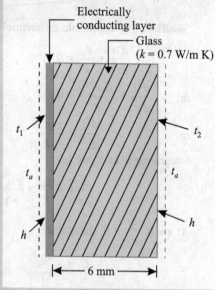

Fig. 2.101.

Example 2.85. *A plane wall is a composite of three materials a, b and c. The wall of materials generates heat at a rate of* 2×10^6 *W/m². The other details are :*

$$L_a = 5 \text{ cm}; L_b = 3 \text{ cm}; L_c = 1.5 \text{ cm};$$
$$k_a = 190 \text{ W/mK}; k_b = 150 \text{ W/m K and } k_c = 50 \text{ W/m K.}$$

The inner surface of material 'a' is well insulated and outer surface of material 'c' is cooled by water stream with $t_w = 50°C$, *and h = 2000 W/m²°C.*

The wall materials of 'b' and 'c' have no heat generation. Determine the temperature of insulated surface and temperature of cooled surface. (N.M.U. Winter, 1998)

Solution. *Given :* $q_g = 2 \times 10^6$ W/m²; $L_a = 5$ cm = 0.05 m; $L_b = 3$ cm = 0.03 m;
$$L_c = 1.5 \text{ cm} = 0.015 \text{ m}; k_a = 190 \text{ W/m K}; k_b = 150 \text{ W/m K};$$
$$k_c = 50 \text{ W/m K}; t_w = 50°C; h = 200 \text{ W/m²°C.}$$

Under steady state condition, the heat generated in slab is passed through a composite slab.

$\therefore$ $\qquad q_g = \dfrac{Q}{A}$ = Heat generated per unit surface area of a.

$\therefore$ Volume of slab 'a' per m^2 of surface area,

$$V = 1 \times 0.05 = 0.05 \text{ m}^3$$

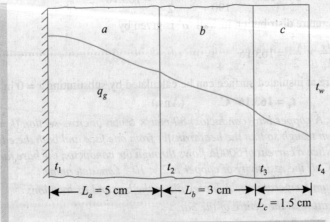

Fig. 2.102.

$\therefore$ Heat generated $V \times q_g = 0.05 \times 2 \times 10^6 = 10^5$ W/m^2

$$Q = \frac{(t_2 - t_w)}{\dfrac{L_b}{k_b} + \dfrac{L_c}{k_c} + \dfrac{1}{h_0}}$$

$$10^5 = \frac{(t_2 - 50)}{\dfrac{0.03}{150} + \dfrac{0.015}{50} + \dfrac{1}{2000}} = \frac{(t_2 - 50)}{2 \times 10^{-4} + 3 \times 10^{-4} + 5 \times 10^{-4}} = \frac{t_2 - 50}{10^{-3}}$$

$\therefore$ $\quad t_2 = 10^5 \times 10^{-3} + 50 = 150°C$

We can also write

$$q = \frac{t_2 - t_3}{\dfrac{L_b}{k_b}} = \frac{t_3 - t_4}{\dfrac{L_c}{k_c}}$$

$\therefore$ $\quad t_3 = t_2 - 10^5 \times \dfrac{L_b}{k_b} = 150 - 10^5 \times \dfrac{0.03}{150} = 150 - 20 = 130°C$

$\therefore$ $\quad t_4 = t_3 - 10^5 \times \dfrac{L_c}{k_c} = 130 - 10^5 \times \dfrac{0.015}{50} = 100° C$ **(Ans.)**

The temperature distribution in a generating slab is given by

$$\frac{d^2 t}{dx^2} + \frac{q_g}{k} = 0 \qquad \text{[Eqn. (2.88)]}$$

The first and second integration of the above equation gives respectively,

$$\frac{dt}{dx} + \frac{q_g}{k} \cdot x = C_1 \qquad \qquad ...(i)$$

$$t + \frac{q_g}{k} \cdot \frac{x^2}{2} = C_1 x + C_2 \qquad \qquad ...(ii)$$

The boundary conditions are :

1. $\qquad \qquad \dfrac{dt}{dx} = 0$ at $x = 0$ $\qquad \therefore C_1 = 0$

2. $t = 150°C$ at $x = 0.05$ m

$\therefore$ $C_2 = 150 + \dfrac{2 \times 10^6}{190} \times \dfrac{0.05^2}{2} = 163.16$

$\therefore$ The temperature distribution in wall 'a' is given by

$$t + \frac{q_g}{k_a} \times \frac{x^2}{2} = 163.16$$

[From eqn. (ii)]

The temperature at insulated surface can be calculated by substituting $x = 0$ in the above eqn.

$\therefore$ $t_1 = \textbf{163.16° C.}$ **(Ans.)**

Example 2.86. *A copper bar (conductor) 80 mm × 6 mm in cross-section (k = 370 W/m°C) is lying in an insulation trough so that the heat transfer from one face and both the edges is negligible. It is observed that when a current of 5000A flows through the conductor, the bare face has a constant temperature of 45°C. If the resistivity of copper is 2 × 10⁻⁸ Ωm, determine :*

(i) The maximum temperature which prevails in the bar and its location;

(ii) The temperature at the centre of the bar.

Solution. Refer Fig. 2.103.

Given : Cross-section of the conductor = 80 mm × 6 mm or 0.08 m × 0.006 m

Thermal conductivity of copper, $k = 370$ W/m°C

Resistivity of copper,

$\rho = 2 \times 10^{-8}$ Ωm

Temperature of bare face, $t = 45°C$

Current flowing in the conductor, $I = 5000$ A

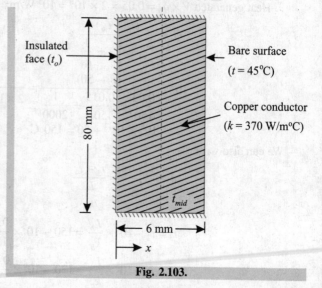

Fig. 2.103.

(*i*) **The value of maximum temperature and its location :**

In case of one-dimensional and steady state heat flow, the heat conduction equation may be written as :

$$\frac{d^2t}{dx^2} + \frac{q_g}{k} = 0 \quad ...(i)$$

(where q_g = rate of heat generation per unit volume per unit time)

Integrating eqn. (*i*), twice, we have

$$\frac{dt}{dx} = -\frac{\dot{q_g}}{k}x + C_1 \quad\quad\quad ...(ii)$$

$$t = -\frac{q_g}{k} \cdot \frac{x^2}{2} + C_1 x + C_2 \quad\quad\quad ...(iii)$$

(where C_1, C_2 = constants of integration).

The values of the constants C_1 and C_2 can be found out by using the following boundary conditions :

(i)   At $x = 0$, $\dfrac{dt}{dx} = 0$ $\therefore C_1 = 0$

(ii)   At $x = 0.006$ m, $t = 45°C$

Amount of heat generated per unit time,

Cylindrical vessel on a rail - wagon.

$$Q_g = I^2 R = I^2 \times \frac{\rho l}{a}$$

$$\therefore \quad q_g = \frac{Q_g}{a \times l} = I^2 \times \left(\frac{\rho l}{a}\right) \times \frac{1}{al} = \left(\frac{I}{a}\right)^2 \cdot \rho$$

(where a = cross-sectional area of the conductor through which current is flowing.)

or, $\qquad q_g = \left(\frac{5000}{0.08 \times 0.006}\right)^2 \times 2 \times 10^{-8} = 2.17 \times 10^6 \text{ W/m}^3$

$\therefore$ From eqn. (iii), we have

$$C_2 = t + \frac{q_g}{k} \cdot \frac{x^2}{2} = 45 + \frac{2.17 \times 10^6}{370} \times \frac{0.006^2}{2} = 45.105$$

Substituting the values of C_1 and C_2 in eqn. (iii), we get the expression for temperature distribution as follows :

$$t = -\frac{q_g}{k} \cdot \frac{x^2}{2} + 45.105 \qquad \qquad ...(iv)$$

The *maximum temperature occurs at the insulated face* ($x = 0$) and its value is

$$t_{max} = \textbf{45.105°C}$$

[Substituting $x = 0$ in eqn. (iv)]

(ii) **The temperature at the centre of the bar, t_{mid} :**

At the midpoint, $\qquad x = \dfrac{0.006}{2} = 0.003 \text{ m}$

$\therefore \qquad t_{mid} = -\dfrac{2.17 \times 10^6}{370} \times \dfrac{0.003^2}{2} + 45.105 = \textbf{45.078° C} \qquad$ **(Ans.)**

[Substituting $x = 0.003$ m in eqn (iv)]

2.9.2. DIELECTRIC HEATING

Dielectric heating is a method of quickly heating insulating materials packed between the plates (of an electric condenser) to which a *high frequency, high voltage alternating current is applied.* The *temperature rise is uniform* and the *internal heat generated is of equal intensity on the surface and the core.*

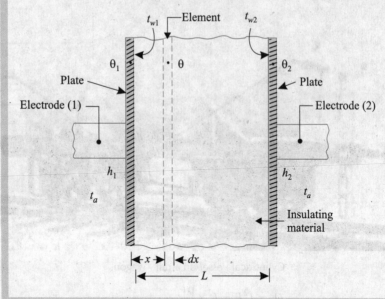

Fig. 2.104. Dielectric heating.

The heat generated :

- is *directly proportional* to the *area of condenser plates*, *voltage* and *frequency*;
- is inversely proportional to the distance between the plates;
- per unit volume of the material is constant.

The method of dielectric heating entails the following **advantages** : (*i*) More economical, (*ii*) No pollution (*iii*) High efficiency and (*iv*) Greater safety.

Dielectric heating refers to the situation that corresponds to the conduction in a plane wall with uniform internal heat source.

Consider an insulating material (say wool) placed between the two plates of an electric condenser as shown in the Fig. 2.104.

Let, L = Thickness of slab (insulating material),

        θ_1 = Temperature of electrode (1) above ambient temperature [= $(t_{w1} - t_a)$],

        θ_2 = Temperature of electrode (2) above the ambient temperature [= $(t_{w2} - t_a)$],

  h_1, h_2 = Heat transfer coefficients on the surfaces of plates of the electric condenser, and

      q_g = Heat generated per unit volume of dielectric medium (wool).

Consider an element of thickness dx at a distance x from the left hand plate (see Fig. 2.104); θ being the difference between the temperature of wool and the ambient temperature.

$$\text{Heat conducted in at a distance } x, \; Q_x = -k \cdot A \cdot \frac{d\theta}{dx}$$

$$\text{Heat generated due to dielectric heating, } Q_g = q_g \, A. \, dx$$

$$\text{Heat conducted out at distance } (x + dx), \; Q_{(x+dx)} = Q_x + \frac{d}{dx}(Q_x)\,dx$$

For steady state heat conduction, we have

$$Q_x + Q_g = Q_{(x+dx)}$$

or,
$$Q_x + q_g . A . dx = Q_x + \frac{d}{dx}(Q_x) dx$$

or,
$$q_g . A dx = \frac{d}{dx}\left[-k A \frac{d\theta}{dx}\right] dx$$

$$= -k A \frac{d^2\theta}{dx^2} dx$$

or,
$$\frac{d^2\theta}{dx^2} + \frac{q_g}{k} = 0 \qquad \qquad ...(i)$$

Integrating eqn. (i) twice, we have

$$\frac{d\theta}{dx} + \frac{q_g}{k} . x = C_1 \qquad \qquad ...(ii)$$

$$\theta + \frac{q_g}{k} . \frac{x^2}{2} = C_1 x + C_2 \qquad \qquad ...(iii)$$

(where C_1 and C_2 = constants of integration).

C_1 and C_2 are evaluated from known boundary conditions as follows :

Heat conducted at $x = 0$ = heat convected to the surrounding at ambient temperature t_a

i.e.
$$-kA \frac{d\theta}{dx}\bigg|_{x=0} = h_1 A(t_{w1} - t_a)$$

$$kAC_1 = h_1 A\theta_1 \qquad \qquad \text{[Using Eqn. }(ii)\text{]}$$

or,
$$C_1 = \frac{h_1 \theta_1}{k}$$

∴
$$\theta = \frac{q_g}{2} . \frac{x^2}{2} = \frac{h_1 \theta_1}{k} . x + C_2$$

Also, at $x = 0$, $\theta = \theta_1$ ∴ $C_2 = \theta_1$

Thus temperature distribution may be written as

$$\theta = -\frac{q_g}{k} . \frac{x^2}{2} + \frac{h_1 \theta_1}{k} . x + \theta_1 \qquad \qquad ...(iv)$$

[substituting the values of C_1 and C_2 in eqn (iii)]

Again, At $x = L$, $\theta = \theta_2$ ...Electrode (2)

∴
$$\theta_2 = -\frac{q_g}{k} . \frac{L^2}{2} + \frac{h_1 \theta_1}{k} . L + \theta_1 \qquad \qquad ...(2.103)$$

[Substituting $x = L$ in eqn. (iv)]

Under steady state conditions :

Total heat generated within insulating material

= surface heat loss from both the electrodes

∴
$$q_g A.L = h_1 A (t_{w1} - t_a) + h_2 A (t_{w2} - t_a)$$

or,
$$q_g L = h_1 \theta_1 + h_2 \theta_2 \qquad \qquad ...(2.104)$$

The values of the temperature t_{w1} and t_{w2} can be found out by solving eqns. (2.103) and (2.104).

Example 2.87. *A 70 mm thick slab of insulation material (k = 0.42 W/m°C) is placed between and is in contact with two parallel electrodes, and is then subjected to dielectric heating (high frequency) at a uniform rate of 40800 W/m³. On the attainment of steady state conditions, the coefficients of combined radiation and convection for the exposed surfaces are 12.5 W/m²°C and 14.5 W/m² °C respectively. If the ambient temperature is 20°C, determine :*

(i) Surface temperatures;

(ii) *Location and magnitude of maximum temperature in the system.*

Assume the flow of heat to be unidirectional and each electrode to be at a uniform temperature equal to that of the slab with which it is in contact.

Solution. Refer to Fig. 2.104.

$$L = 70 \text{ mm} = 0.07 \text{ m}; \ k = 0.42 \text{ W/m°C}; \ q_g = 40800 \text{ W/m}^3$$
$$h_1 = 12.5 \text{ W/m}^2\text{°C}; \ h_2 = 14.5 \text{ W/m}^2\text{°C}; \ t_a = 20\text{°C}.$$

(i) Surface temperatures t_{w1}, t_{w2} :

The temperature distribution, in case of dielectric heating, is given by

$$\theta = -\frac{q_g}{k} \cdot \frac{x^2}{2} + \frac{h_1 \theta_1}{k} \cdot x + \theta_1$$

$$= -\frac{40800}{0.42} \cdot \frac{x^2}{2} + \frac{12.5\theta_1}{0.42} x + \theta_1$$

or, $\theta = -48571.4x^2 + 29.76 \ \theta_1 x + \theta_1$ ...(i)

At $x = 0.07\text{m}, \ \theta = \theta_2$

$\therefore$ $\theta_2 = -48571.4 \times (0.07)^2 + 29.76 \times 0.07 \ \theta_1 + \theta_1$

or, $\theta_2 = -238 + 3.08 \ \theta_1$ ...(ii)

Under steady state conditions,

Heat generated due to dielectric heating

= heat lost due to convection from the electrode surfaces

or, $q_g.A.L = h_1.A.\theta_1 + h_2.A.\theta_2$

or, $q_g.L = h_1.\theta_1 + h_2.\theta_2$

or, $40800 \times 0.07 = 12.5 \ \theta_1 + 14.5 \ \theta_2$

or, $196.96 = 0.862 \ \theta_1 + \theta_2$

or, $\theta_2 = 196.96 - 0.862\theta_1$ ...(iii)

From eqns. (ii) and (iii), we have

$$-238 + 3.08 \ \theta_1 = 196.96 - 0.862 \ \theta_1$$

or, $\theta_1 = \dfrac{(238 + 196.96)}{(3.08 + 0.862)} = 110.34\text{°C}$

and $\theta_2 = -238 + 3.08 \times 110.34 = 101.85\text{°C}$ [From eqn. (ii)]

Thus, the electrode temperatures are :

$\theta_1 = t_{w1} - t_a$ $\therefore$ $t_{w1} = \theta_1 + t_a = 110.34 + 20 = \mathbf{130.34°C}$ **(Ans.)**

$\theta_2 = t_{w2} - t_a$ $\therefore$ $t_{w2} = \theta_2 + t_a = 101.85 + 20 = \mathbf{121.85°C}$ **(Ans.)**

(ii) Location and magnitude of maximum temperature; x, t_{max} :

The location of maximum temperature can be obtained by differentiating eqn. (i) w.r.t. x and equating the derivative to zero.

Thus, $\dfrac{d\theta}{dx} = \dfrac{d}{dx}\left[-48571.4x^2 + 29.76\theta_1 \cdot x + \theta_1\right]$

or, $\dfrac{d\theta}{dx} = -48571.4 \times 2x + 29.76\theta_1 = 0$

or, $x = \dfrac{29.76\theta_1}{48571.4 \times 2} = \dfrac{29.76 \times 110.34}{48571.4 \times 2} = 0.0338\text{m}$ or 33.8 mm (from left hand electrode)

$\therefore$ $t_{max} = -48571.4 \times 0.0338^2 + 29.76 \times 110.4 \times 0.0338 + 110.4$

$= \mathbf{165.96°C}$ **(Ans.)**

2.9.3. CYLINDER WITH UNIFORM HEAT GENERATION

Refer to Fig. 2.105. Consider a cylindrical rod in which one-dimensional radial conduction is taking place under steady state conditions.

Let, R = Radius of the rod,

L = Length of the rod,

k = Thermal conductivity (uni-form),

q_g = Uniform volumetric heat gen-eration per unit volume per unit time,

h = Heat transfer coefficient, and

t_a = Ambient temperature.

In order to obtain temperature distribution, consider an *element* of radius r and thickness dr as shown in Fig. 2.105.

Heat conducted in at radius r,

$$Q_r = -k \cdot 2\pi r L \cdot \frac{dt}{dr}$$

Heat generated in the element,

$$Q_g = q_g \cdot 2\pi \, r.dr.L$$

Heat conducted out at radius, $r + dr$,

$$Q_{(r + dr)} = Q_r + \frac{d}{dr}(Q_r)\,dr$$

Under steady state conditions,

$$Q_r + Q_g = Q_{(r + dr)}$$

$$= Q_r + \frac{d}{dr}(Q_r)\,dr$$

$\therefore$ $$Q_g = \frac{d}{dr}(Q_r)\,dr$$

$$q_g \cdot 2\pi r.dr.L = \frac{d}{dr}\left[-k.2\pi r L.\frac{dt}{dr}\right]dr$$

or $$\frac{d}{dr}\left[r.\frac{dt}{dr}\right] = -\frac{q_g}{k} \cdot r \qquad\qquad ...(2.105)$$

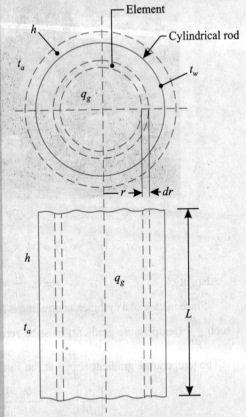

Fig. 2.105. Heat conduction in a solid cylinder with heat generation.

[Eqn. (2.105) may also be obtained from eqn. 2.22 assuming steady state uni-directional heat conduction in radial direction].

Intergrating the above equation twice, we obtain

$$r.\frac{dt}{dr} = -\frac{q_g}{k} \cdot \frac{r^2}{2} + C_1$$

or, $$\frac{dt}{dr} = -\frac{q_g}{k} \cdot \frac{r}{2} + \frac{C_1}{r} \qquad\qquad ...(2.106)$$

$$t = -\frac{q_g}{k} \cdot \frac{r^2}{4} + C_1 \log_e{}^r + C_2 \qquad\qquad ...(2.107)$$

(where C_1 and C_2 = constants of integration).

The constants C_1 and C_2 are evaluated from the boundary conditions, as follows :

(i) At $r = R$, $t = t_w$

(ii) Heat generated = Heat lost by conduction at the rod surface

Tank of a compressor.

i.e.
$$q_g \times (\pi R^2 \times L) = -k \times 2\pi RL \times \left[\frac{dt}{dr}\right]_{r=R}$$

Also, at
$$r = 0, \quad \frac{dt}{dr} = 0$$

Since in case of a cylinder, centre line is line of symmetry for temperature distribution and as such $\dfrac{dt}{dr}$ (temperature gradient) must be zero.

The temperature gradient $\left(\dfrac{dt}{dr}\right)$ at the surface (*i.e.* at $r = R$) is given by

$$\left[\frac{dt}{dr}\right]_{r=R} = -\frac{q_g}{k} \cdot \frac{R}{2} + \frac{C_1}{R}$$

Also from boundary condition (*ii*), we have

$$\left[\frac{dt}{dr}\right]_{r=R} = -\frac{q_g}{k} \cdot \frac{R}{2}$$

$$\therefore \qquad -\frac{q_g}{k} \cdot \frac{R}{2} + \frac{C_1}{R} = -\frac{q_g}{k} \cdot \frac{R}{2} \qquad \text{or} \qquad C_1 = 0$$

Applying the boundary condition (*i*) [*i.e.* at $r = R, t = t_w$] to eqn. (2.107), we obtain,

$$t_w = -\frac{q_g}{k} \cdot \frac{R^2}{4} + C_2$$

or,
$$C_2 = t_w + \frac{q_g}{k} \cdot \frac{R^2}{4}$$

Substituting the values of C_1 and C_2 in eqn. (2.107), we have the general solution for temperature distribution as

$$t = -\frac{q_g}{k} \cdot \frac{r^2}{4} + t_w + \frac{q_g}{k} \cdot \frac{R^2}{4}$$

or,
$$t = t_w + \frac{q_g}{4k}[R^2 - r^2] \qquad\qquad ...(2.108)$$

It is evident from eqn. (2.108) that temperature distribution is *parabolic* and the maximum temperature occurs at the centre of the rod ($r = 0$) and its value is given by

$$t_{max} = t_w + \frac{q_g}{4k} \cdot R^2 \qquad \text{...(2.109)}$$

By combining eqns. (2.108) and (2.109), we arrive at the following dimensionless form of temperature distribution :

$$\frac{t - t_w}{t_{max} - t_w} = \frac{\dfrac{q_g}{4k}(R^2 - r^2)}{\dfrac{q_g}{4k} \cdot R^2} = \frac{R^2 - r^2}{R^2} = 1 - \left(\frac{r}{R}\right)^2$$

i.e.

$$\frac{t - t_w}{t_{max} - t_w} = 1 - \left(\frac{r}{R}\right)^2 \qquad \text{...(2.110)}$$

Also, energy generated within the rod (per unit time)

= Energy dissipated (per unit time) by convection at the rod boundary

i.e. $q_g \times (\pi R^2 \times L) = h \times 2\pi RL\,(t_w - t_a)$

or,

$$t_w = t_a + \frac{q_g}{2h} \cdot R \qquad \text{...(2.111)}$$

Inserting the value of t_w in eqn. (2.108), we obtain the temperature distribution (in terms of t_a) as

$$t = t_a + \frac{q_g}{2h} \cdot R + \frac{q_g}{4k}[R^2 - r^2] \qquad \text{...(2.112)}$$

The value of t_{max}, at $r = 0$, is given by

$$t_{max} = t_a + \frac{q_g}{2h} \cdot R + \frac{q_g}{4k} \cdot R^2 \qquad \text{...(2.113)}$$

Example 2.88. *A current of 300 amperes passes through a stainless steel wire of 2.5 mm diameter and k = 20 W/m°C. The resistivity of the wire is 70 × 10⁻⁸ Ωm and the length of the wire is 2m. If the wire is submerged in a fluid maintained at 50°C and convective heat transfer coefficient at the wire surface is 4000 W/m²°C, calculate the steady state temperature at the centre and at the surface of wire.* (M.U)

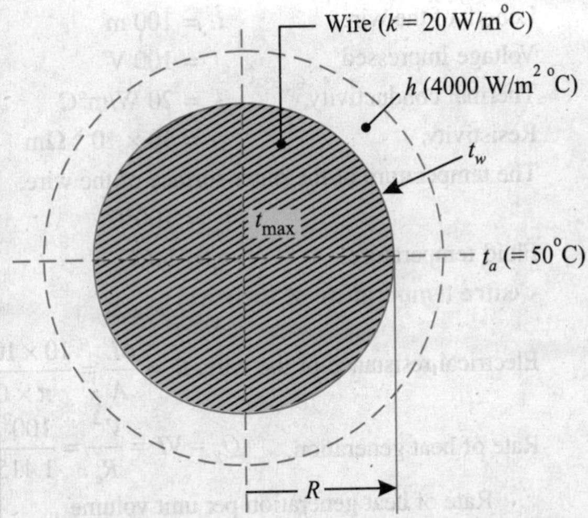

Fig. 2.106.

Solution. Refer to Fig. 2.106.

$$R = \frac{2.5}{2} = 1.25\,\text{mm} = 0.00125\,\text{m};$$

$$k = 20 \text{ W/m°C},$$

resistivity, $\rho = 70 \times 10^{-8}\,\Omega m$

$$L = 2\text{m},\ t_a = 50°C,\ \text{Current},$$

$$I = 300 \text{ amp}.$$

Temperature at the surface of wire (t_w) and at the centre of wire (t_{max}) :

Rate of heat generation,

$$Q_g = I^2 R_e = I^2 \times \frac{\rho L}{A}$$

(where R_e = electrical resistance)

Rate of heat generation per unit volume;

$$q_g = \frac{Q_g}{AL} = I^2 \times \frac{\rho L}{A} \times \frac{1}{AL} = \rho \left(\frac{I}{A}\right)^2$$

$$= 70 \times 10^{-8} \left[\frac{300}{\pi \times 0.00125^2}\right]^2$$

$$= 26.14 \times 10^8 \text{ W/m}^3$$

Temperature at the surface of wire is given by

$$t_w = t_a + \frac{q_g}{2h} \cdot R \qquad\qquad ...\text{[Eqn. (2.111)]}$$

or,
$$t_w = 50 + \frac{26.14 \times 10^8}{2 \times 4000} \times 0.00125 = \mathbf{458.44°C} \quad \textbf{(Ans.)}$$

Temperature at the centre of wire is given by

$$t_{max} = t_w + \frac{q_g}{4k} \cdot R^2 \qquad\qquad \text{[Eqn. (12.109)]}$$

or,
$$t_{max} = 458.44 + \frac{26.14 \times 10^8}{4 \times 20} \times (0.00125)^2 = \mathbf{509.5°C} \quad \textbf{(Ans.)}$$

Example 2.89. *A 3 mm diameter stainless steel wire (k = 20 W/m°C, resistivity, $\rho = 10 \times 10^{-8}$ Ωm) 100 metres long has a voltage of 100 V impressed on it. The outer surface of the wire is maintained at 100°C. Calculate the centre temperature of the wire. If the heated wire is submerged in a fluid maintained at 50°C, find the heat transfer coefficient on the surface of the wire.* (M.U.)

Solution. Radius of stainless steel wire, $R = \dfrac{3}{2} = 1.5$ mm $= 0.0015$ m

Length of the wire, $L = 100$ m

Voltage impressed $= 100$ V

Thermal conductivity, $k = 20$ W/m°C

Resistivity, $\rho = 10 \times 10^{-8}$ Ωm

The temperature of the outer surface of the wire,

$$t_w = 100°C$$

Fluid temperature, $t_a = 50°C.$

Centre temperature of the wire, t_{max} :

Electrical resistance of the wire, $R_e = \dfrac{\rho L}{A} = \dfrac{10 \times 10^{-8} \times 100}{\pi \times 0.0015^2} = 1.415\,\Omega$

Rate of heat generation, $Q_g = VI = \dfrac{V^2}{R_e} = \dfrac{100^2}{1.415} = 7067$ W

∴ Rate of heat generation per unit volume

$$q_g = \frac{Q_g}{AL} = \frac{7067}{\pi \times 0.0015^2 \times 100} = 9.998 \times 10^6 \text{ W/m}^3$$

The centre temperature is given by

$$t_{max} = t_w + \frac{q_g}{4k} \cdot R^2 \qquad\qquad ...\text{[Fig. (2.109)]}$$

$$= 100 + \frac{9.998 \times 10^6}{4 \times 20} \times 0.0015^2 = 100.28°C$$

Heat transfer coefficient, h :

$$t_w = t_a + \frac{q_g}{2h} \cdot R \qquad\qquad ...[\text{Eqn. (2.111)}]$$

$$100 = 50 + \frac{9.998 \times 10^6}{2h} \times 0.0015$$

or,

$$(100 - 50) = \frac{7498.5}{h}$$

$\therefore$

$$h = \frac{7498.5}{50} = \textbf{149.97 W/m}^{2\circ}\textbf{C} \qquad \textbf{(Ans.)}$$

Example 2.90. *One metre long Nichrome wire of resistivity $1\mu\Omega m$ is to dissipate power of 10 kW in the surrounding fluid which is at 80°C. Find the diameter of the wire if the maximum operating temperature of the wire is 1000°C.* (M.U.)

Take $h = 1000 \; W/m^2°C$ and k (wire) = 60 W/m°C.

Solution:

Length of wire, $L = 1$ m

Resistivity of wire material, $\rho = 1\mu\Omega m$

Power to be dissipated, $P = 10$ kW

Temperature of surrounding fluid, $t_a = 80°C$

Maximum operating temperature of the wire, $t_{max} = 1000°C$

Heat transfer coefficient, $h = 1000 \; W/m^2 \; °C$

Thermal conductivity of wire, $k = 60 \; W/m^2 \; °C$.

Diameter of the wire, D :

The maximum temperature is given by

$$t_{max} = t_a + \frac{q_g}{2h} \times R + \frac{q_g}{4k} \times R^2 \qquad\qquad ...[\text{Eqn.(2.113)}]$$

(where, R = radius of the wire).

Tanker truck.

The rate of heat generation per unit volume

$$q_g = \frac{P}{\text{Volume of wire}} = \frac{10 \times 1000}{\pi R^2 \times L} = \frac{10 \times 1000}{\pi \times R^2 \times 1} = \frac{10000}{\pi R^2}$$

Substituting the relevant values in the above equation, we have

$$1000 = 80 + \frac{10000}{\pi R^2 \times 2 \times 1000} \times R + \frac{10000}{\pi R^2 \times 4 \times 60} \times R^2$$

$$(1000 - 80) = \frac{1.59}{R} + 13.26$$

or, $R = 1.75 \times 10^{-3}$ m or 1.75 mm

∴   Diameter of the wire, $D = 2 \times 1.75 = \textbf{3.5 mm}$ **(Ans.)**

Example 2.91. *The meat rolls of 25 mm diameter having k = 1 W/m°C are heated up with the help of microwave heating for roasting. The centre temperature of the rolls in maintained at 100°C when the surrounding temperature is 30°C. The heat transfer coefficient on the surface of the meat roll is 20 W/m² °C. Find the microwave heating capacity required in W/m³.*

Solution. $R = \dfrac{25}{2} = 12.5$ mm or 0.0125 m; $k = 1$W/m°C; $t_{max} = 100°$ C; $t_a = 30°$C;

$h = 20$ W/m²°C.

Microwave heating capacity, q_g :

The maximum temperature occurs at the centre and is given by

$$t_{max} = t_a + \frac{q_g}{2h} \times R + \frac{q_g}{4k} \times R^2 \qquad \text{...[Eqn. (2.113)]}$$

$$100 = 30 + \frac{q_g}{2 \times 20} \times 0.0125 + \frac{q_g}{4 \times 1} \times 0.0125^2$$

$$(100 - 30) = 0.0003125 \, q_g + 0.00003906 \, q_g$$

or, $$q_g = \frac{(100 - 30)}{(0.0003125 + 0.00003906)} = \textbf{1.991} \times \textbf{10}^5 \textbf{ W/m}^3$$

Example 2.92. *(a) Prove that the maximum temperature at the centre of wire, carrying electrical current, is given by the relation :*

$$t_{max} = t_w + \frac{J^2}{4k \cdot k_e} \cdot R^2$$

where t_w = surface temperature; J = current density; k, k_e = thermal and electrical conductivities of the wire material respectively; R = radius of the wire.

(b) A 3 mm dia. copper wire 10 m long, is carrying electric current and has a surface temperature of 25°C. The thermal and electrical conductivities of copper are 375 W/m°C and 5.1 × 10⁷ Ωm respectively. Determine the voltage if the temperature rise at the wire axis is limited to 15°C.

Solution. *(a)* The maximum temperature in case of a cylindrical wire conductor occurs at the centre and is given by [Eqn. (2.109)].

$$t_{max} = t_w + \frac{q_g}{4k} \cdot R^2 \qquad \text{...(i)}$$

Total volumetric heat generated $= I^2 R_e = I^2 \times \dfrac{\rho L}{A} = \left(\dfrac{I^2 L}{A}\right)\dfrac{1}{k_e}$

[where, R_e = electrical resistance of the conductor, ρ electrical resistivity $= \dfrac{1}{k_e}$]

∴   Heat generated per unit volume,

$$q_g = \frac{\left(\dfrac{I^2 L}{A}\right)\dfrac{1}{k_e}}{AL} = \left(\frac{I}{A}\right)^2 \times \frac{1}{k_e} = \frac{J^2}{k_e} \qquad\qquad ...(ii)$$

(where $J = I/A$)

From Eqns. (i) and (ii), we have

$$t_{max} = t_w + \frac{J^2}{4 k k_e} \cdot R^2 \qquad\qquad \textbf{(Proved)} \qquad\qquad ...(iii)$$

(b) Given : $R = \dfrac{3}{2} = 1.5\,\text{mm} = 0.0015\,\text{m};\ L = 10\,\text{m};\ t_{max} - t_w = 15°\text{C};\ k = 375\ \text{W/m°C}$

$k_e = 5.1 \times 10^7\ \Omega m$

Voltage drop : $\quad J^2 = \dfrac{(t_{max} - t_w) \times 4 k k_e}{R^2} \qquad\qquad$ [From eqn. (iii)]

$$= \frac{15 \times 4 \times 375 \times 5.1 \times 10^7}{(0.0015)^2} = 5.1 \times 10^{17}$$

∴   Current density, $\qquad J = 7.14 \times 10^8\ \text{amperes/m}^2$

Voltage drop $\qquad IR_e = (J.A).\left(\dfrac{\rho L}{A}\right) = J\rho L = \dfrac{JL}{k_e} = \dfrac{7.14 \times 10^8 \times 10}{5.1 \times 10^7}$

$$= \textbf{140 volts (Ans.)}$$

Example 2.93. *The heat generating rate per unit volume, q_g, at any radius, r, of a solid rod is given by*

$$q_g = q_0 \left[1 - \left(\frac{r}{R}\right)^2\right]$$

where q_0 is the heat generation rate at the centre of the rod of radius R. Find out an expression for maximum temperature at the centre of a rod 40 cm diameter, when heat generating rate at the centre is 24 × 10⁶ kJ/m³-h and temp. at the surface of the rod is 20°C. Assume K for the material of the rod as 200 kJ/m-h-°C. (AMIE Winter, 2001)

Solution. The governing differential equation is

$$\frac{d}{dr}\left[r \cdot \frac{dt}{dr}\right] = -\frac{q_g}{k} \cdot r \qquad\qquad \text{[Eqn. (2.105)]}$$

$$\frac{d}{dr}\left[r \cdot \frac{dt}{dr}\right] + \frac{r}{k} q_0 \left\{1 - \left(\frac{r}{R}\right)^2\right\} = 0 \qquad\qquad \text{(substituting for } q_g)$$

Integrating, we get

$$r \cdot \frac{dt}{dr} = -\frac{q_0}{k}\left[\frac{r^2}{2} - \frac{r^4}{4R^2}\right] + C_1$$

$$\frac{dt}{dr} = -\frac{q_0}{k}\left[\frac{r}{2} - \frac{r^3}{4R^2}\right] + \frac{C_1}{r}$$

Since at $r = 0$, $\dfrac{dt}{dr} = 0$ ∴ $C_1 = 0$

Integrating again, we get

$$t = -\frac{q_0}{k}\left[\frac{r^2}{4} - \frac{r^4}{16R^2}\right] + C_2 \qquad\qquad ...(i)$$

At $r = R$, $t = t_s$ where t_s is surface temperature.

$\therefore$
$$t_s = -\frac{q_0}{k}\left[\frac{R^2}{4} - \frac{R^4}{16R^2}\right] + C_2$$

or,
$$C_2 = t_s + \frac{q_0}{k} \times \frac{3}{16}R^2$$

From (i) as occurs at $r = 0$

$$t_{max} = C_2$$

or,
$$t_{max} = t_s + \frac{3}{16}\frac{q_0}{k}R^2 \text{ is the } \textbf{\textit{required expression.}} \quad \textbf{(Ans.)}$$

Substituting the numerical values,

$$t_{max} = 20 + \frac{3}{16} \times \frac{24 \times 10^6}{200} \times \left(\frac{40}{2 \times 100}\right)^2 = \textbf{920°C.} \quad \textbf{(Ans.)}$$

Example 2.94. *A long hollow cylinder has inner and outer radii 50 mm and 150 mm resepctively. It generates heat at a rate of 1 kW/m³ (k = 0.5 W/m°C). If the maximum temperature occurs at radius of 100 mm and temperature of outer surface is 50°C, find :*

(i) Temperature at inner surface, and

(ii) Maximum temperature in the cylinder.
(P.U. 2001)

Solution. Refer to Fig. 2.107.

$r_1 = 50$ mm $= 0.05$ m; $r_2 = 150$ mm $= 0.15$ m

q_g (rate of heat generation) $= 1$ kW/m³ $= 1000$ W/m³

$k = 0.5$ W/m°C; $t_2 = 50$°C.

t_1, t_{max} :

Consider an element of hollow cylinder at a radius r and thickness dr and length L.

Heat conducted at radius r,

$$Q_r = -k \times 2\pi r L \times \frac{dt}{dr}$$

Heat generated in the element,

$$Q_g = q_g \times 2\pi r L \times dr$$

Heat conducted at radius $(r + dr)$,

$$Q_{(r+dr)} = Q_r + \frac{d}{dr}(Q_r)\,dr$$

For steady state conduction of heat flow,

$$Q_r + Q_g = Q_{(r+dr)}$$

or, $Q_r + Q_g = Q_r + \dfrac{d}{dr}(Q_r)\,dr$

or, $Q_g = \dfrac{d}{dr}(Q_r)\,dr$

or,

$$q_g \times 2\pi r L \times dr = \frac{d}{dr}\left[-2\pi r L k \times \frac{dt}{dr}\right]dr$$

$$r q_g = -k\frac{d}{dr}\left(r\frac{dt}{dr}\right)$$

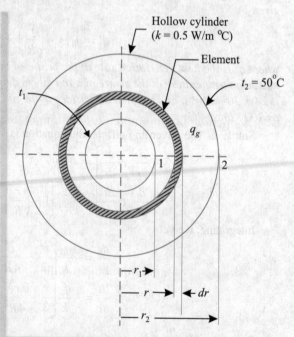

Fig. 2.107. Heat generation in hollow cylinder.

or,
$$k \frac{d}{dr}\left(r\frac{dt}{dr}\right) + rq_g = 0$$

or,
$$k\left[r\frac{d^2t}{dr^2} + \frac{dt}{dr}\right] + rq_g = 0$$

or,
$$r\frac{d^2t}{dr^2} + \frac{dt}{dr} + \frac{q_g r}{k} = 0$$

or,
$$\frac{d}{dr}\left(r\cdot\frac{dt}{dr}\right) + \frac{q_g r}{k} = 0 \qquad \qquad ...(i)$$

Integrating eqn. (i) twice, we have

$$r\frac{dt}{dr} + \frac{q_g}{k}\cdot\frac{r^2}{2} = C_1$$

or,
$$\frac{dt}{dr} + \frac{q_g}{k}\cdot\frac{r}{2} = \frac{C_1}{r} \qquad \qquad ...(ii)$$

and,
$$t + \frac{q_g}{k}\cdot\frac{r^2}{4} = C_1 \ln r + C_2 \qquad \qquad ...(iii)$$

(where C_1, C_2 = constants of integration)

For evaluating the constants, let us use the following boundary conditions as follows :

(i) At $r = 0.1$ m, $\dfrac{dt}{dr} = 0$ (condition for maximum temperature) ...(Given)

$$\frac{dt}{dr} = -\frac{q_g}{k}\cdot\frac{r}{2} + \frac{C_1}{r} = 0 \qquad \text{[From Eqn. (ii)]}$$

$\therefore$
$$C_1 = \frac{q_g}{k}\cdot\frac{r^2}{2} = \frac{1000}{0.5} \times \frac{0.1^2}{2} = 10$$

(ii) At $r = r_2 = 0.15$ m, $t = t_2 = 50°C$

$$t_2 + \frac{q_g}{k} \times \frac{0.15^2}{4} = 10 \ln (0.15) + C_2 \qquad \text{[From eqn. (iii)]}$$

Fuel tanks.

or, $\quad 50 + \dfrac{1000}{0.5} \times \dfrac{0.15^2}{4} = 10 \ln (0.15) + C_2$

or, $\qquad\qquad C_2 = 80.22$

Substituting the values of C_i and C_2 in eqn. (iii), we have, at $r = r_1 = 0.05$ m

$$t_1 + \dfrac{1000}{0.5} \dfrac{0.05^2}{4} = 10 \ln (0.05) + 80.22$$

$\therefore \qquad\qquad t_1 = 49°C$ **(Ans.)**

Again, substituting the values in eqn. (iii) at $r = 0.1$ m, we have

$$t_{max} + \dfrac{1000}{0.5} \times \dfrac{0.1^2}{4} = 10 \ln (0.1) + 80.22$$

$\therefore \qquad\qquad t_{max} = 52.2°C$ **(Ans.)**

Example 2.95. *A chemical reaction takes place in a packed bed ($k = 0.6$ W/m°C) between two coaxial cylinders with radii 15 mm and 45 mm. The inner surface is at 580°C and it is insulated. Assuming the reaction rate of 0.55 MW/m³ in the reactor volume, find the temperature at the outer surface of the reactor.*

Solution. Refer to Fig. 2.108. $r_1 = 15$ mm $= 0.015$ m; $r_2 = 45$ mm $= 0.045$ m, q_g (heat generation rate) $= 0.55$ MW/m³; $t_1 = 580°C$.

Temperature at the outer surface, t_2 :

For the given problem, the controlling differential equation is given by

$$\dfrac{d}{dr}\left[r \dfrac{dt}{dr} \right] + \dfrac{q_g}{k} r = 0$$
...[Eqn. (2.105)]

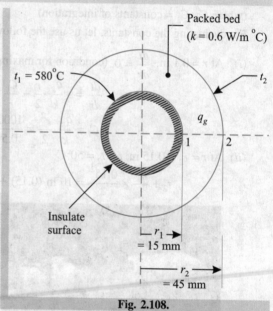

Fig. 2.108.

Integrating the above equation twice, we obtain

$$r \dfrac{dt}{dr} + \dfrac{q_g}{k} \cdot \dfrac{r^2}{2} = C_1$$

or, $\qquad \dfrac{dt}{dr} + \dfrac{q_g}{k} \dfrac{r}{2} = \dfrac{C_1}{r}$ ...(i)

or, $\qquad t + \dfrac{q_g}{k} \cdot \dfrac{r^2}{4} = C_1 \ln (r) + C_2$

...(ii)

(where $C_1, C_2 =$ constants of integration)

In order to evaluate C_1 and C_2, using the following boundary conditions, we have

At $\qquad\qquad r = r_1, \quad \dfrac{dt}{dr} = 0$

$\therefore \qquad\qquad C_1 = \dfrac{q_g}{k} \cdot \dfrac{r_1^2}{2} \cdot$ [From eqn (i)]

At $\qquad\qquad r = r_1, \qquad t = t_1$

$\therefore \qquad t_1 + \dfrac{q_g}{k} \cdot \dfrac{r_1^2}{4} = \dfrac{q_g}{k} \cdot \dfrac{r_1^2}{2} \ln (r) + C_2$

[Substituting the values in eqn. (ii)]

or, $\qquad C_2 = t_1 + \dfrac{q_g}{k} \cdot \dfrac{r_1^2}{4} - \dfrac{q_g}{k} \cdot \dfrac{r_1^2}{2} \ln (r) = t_1 - \dfrac{q_g}{k} \cdot \dfrac{r_1^2}{2}\left[\ln (r_1) - \dfrac{1}{2} \right]$

Substituting the values of the integration constants in eqn. (*ii*), we have

$$t + \frac{q_g}{k} \cdot \frac{r^2}{4} = \frac{q_g}{k} \cdot \frac{r_1^2}{2} \ln(r) + t_1 - \frac{q_g}{k} \cdot \frac{r_1^2}{2} \left[\ln(r_1) - \frac{1}{2} \right]$$

$$t + \frac{q_g}{k} \cdot \frac{r^2}{4} = t_1 + \frac{q_g}{k} \cdot \frac{r_1^2}{2} \ln(r/r_1) + \frac{q_g}{k} \cdot \frac{r_1^2}{4}$$

or,
$$t = t_1 + \frac{q_g}{k} \cdot \frac{r_1^2}{2} \ln(r/r_1) + \frac{q_g}{k \cdot 4} \cdot r_1^2 \left[1 - \left(\frac{r}{r_1} \right)^2 \right] \quad \dots(iii)$$

Substituting the values in eqn. (*iii*) as $t = t_2$ when $r = r_2$, we have

$$t_2 = 580 + \frac{0.55 \times 10^6}{0.6} \times \frac{0.015^2}{2} \ln(0.045/0.015) + \frac{0.55 \times 10^6}{0.6} \times \frac{0.015^2}{4} \left[1 - \left(\frac{0.045}{0.015} \right)^2 \right]$$

or,
$$t_2 = 580 + 113.29 - 412.5 = \textbf{280.79°C} \quad \textbf{(Ans.)}$$

Example 2.96. *A nuclear fuel element is in the form of hollow cylinder insulated at the inner surface. Its inner and outer radii are 50 mm and 100 mm respectively. Outer surface gives heat to the fluid at 50°C where the unit surface conductance is 100 W/m² °C. The thermal conductivity of material is 50 W/m°C. Find the rate of heat generation so that maximum temperature in the system will not exceed 200°C.* (P.U., 1996)

Solution. Refer to Fig. 2.109.

Given : $r_1 = 50$ mm $= 0.05$ m; $r_2 = 100$ mm $= 0.1$ m;

$$t_a = 50°C, k = 50 \text{ W/m°C}, h = 100 \text{ W/m}^2 °C; t_1 (t_{max}) = 200°C.$$

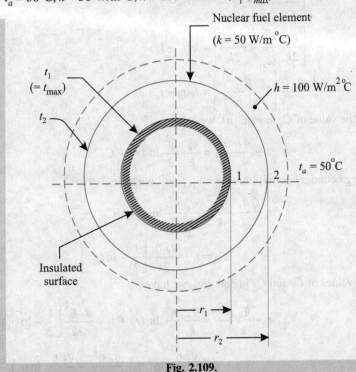

Fig. 2.109.

Rate of heat generation, q_g :

For the given problem the controlling differential equation is

$$\frac{d}{dt}\left(r \cdot \frac{dt}{dr} \right) + \frac{q_g}{k} \cdot r = 0 \quad \dots\text{[Eqn. 2.105]}$$

Integrating the above equation twice, we have

$$r \cdot \frac{dt}{dr} + \frac{q_g}{k} \cdot \frac{r^2}{2} = C_1$$

or,

$$\frac{dt}{dr} + \frac{q_g}{k} \cdot \frac{r}{2} = \frac{C_1}{r} \qquad \qquad ...(i)$$

and,

$$t + \frac{q_g}{k} \cdot \frac{r^2}{4} = C_1 \ln(r) + C_2 \qquad \qquad ...(ii)$$

(where C_1, C_2 = constants of integration).

Applying boundary condition; at $\quad r = r_1, \quad \dfrac{dt}{dr} = 0$, we have,

$$C_1 = \frac{q_g}{k} \cdot \frac{r_1^2}{2} \qquad \qquad ...[\text{From Eqn. } (i)]$$

Applying the following boundary condition, we have,

(Heat conducted)$_{r=r_2}$ = Heat convected from the outer bondary to the surrounding fluid.

or, $\qquad -k \times (2\pi r_2 \times 1) \times \left(\dfrac{dt}{dr}\right)_{r=r_2} = h \times (2\pi r_2 \times 1) \times (t_2 - t_a)$

$$\text{(considering unit length of cylinder)}$$

or, $\qquad -k \left[\dfrac{C_1}{r} - \dfrac{q_g}{k} \cdot \dfrac{r}{2}\right]_{r=r_2} = h(t_2 - t_a)$

or, $\qquad -k \left[\dfrac{q_g}{2k} \cdot \dfrac{r_1^2}{r_2} - \dfrac{q_g \, r_2}{2k}\right] = h(t_2 - t_a)$

or, $\qquad \dfrac{q_g \, r_2}{2}\left[1 - \left(\dfrac{r_1}{r_2}\right)^2\right] = h(t_2 - t_a) \qquad \qquad ...(iii)$

Substituting the value of C_1 in eqn. (ii), we have

$$t + \frac{q_g}{k} \cdot \frac{r^2}{4} = \frac{q_g}{k} \cdot \frac{r_1^2}{2} \ln(r) + C_2 \qquad \qquad ...(iv)$$

Now, applying boundary condition, at $r = r_1$, $t = t_1$, we have

$$t_1 + \frac{q_g}{k} \cdot \frac{r_1^2}{4} = \frac{q_g}{k} \cdot \frac{r_1^2}{2} \ln(r_1) + C_2$$

$\therefore \qquad\qquad\qquad C_2 = t_1 + \dfrac{q_g \, r_1^2}{2k}\left[\dfrac{1}{2} - \ln(r_1)\right]$

Inserting the values of C_1 and C_2 in eqn. (iv), we have

$$t + \frac{q_g}{k} \cdot \frac{r^2}{4} = \frac{q_g}{k} \cdot \frac{r_1^2}{2} \ln(r) + t_1 + \frac{q_g \, r_1^2}{2k}\left[\frac{1}{2} - \ln(r_1)\right]$$

or, $\qquad t - t_1 = \dfrac{q_g \, r_1^2}{2k} \ln(r) + \dfrac{q_g \, r_1^2}{4k} - \dfrac{q_g \, r_1^2}{2k} \ln(r_1) - \dfrac{q_g \, r^2}{4k}$

or, $\qquad t - t_1 = \dfrac{q_g \, r_1^2}{4k}\left[1 - \left(\dfrac{r}{r_1}\right)^2\right] + \dfrac{q_g \, r_1^2}{2k} \ln(r/r_1) \qquad \qquad ...(v)$

At $r = r_2$, $t = t_2$; the eqn. (v) becomes

$$t_2 - t_1 = \frac{q_g r_1^2}{4k}\left[1 - \left(\frac{r_2}{r_1}\right)^2\right] + \frac{q_g r_1^2}{2k}\ln(r_2/r_1)$$

$$\therefore \qquad t_1 - t_2 = \frac{q_g r_1^2}{4k}\left[\left(\frac{r_2}{r_1}\right)^2 - 1\right] - \frac{q_g r_1^2}{2k}\ln(r_2/r_1)$$

or, $$t_1 - t_2 = \frac{q_g r_1^2}{4k}\left[\left(\frac{r_2}{r_1}\right)^2 - 2\ln(r_2/r_1) - 1\right] \qquad \qquad ...(vi)$$

Substituting the value of t_2 from eqn. (*iii*) in eqn. (*vi*), we have

$$t_1 - \left[t_a + \frac{q_g r_2}{2h}\left\{1 - \left(\frac{r_1}{r_2}\right)^2\right\}\right] = \frac{q_g r_1^2}{4k}\left[\left(\frac{r_2}{r_1}\right)^2 - 2\ln(r_2/r_1) - 1\right] \qquad ...(vii)$$

Now, inserting the proper values in (*vii*), we obtain

$$200 - \left[50 + \frac{q_g \times 0.1}{2 \times 100}\left\{1 - \left(\frac{0.05}{0.1}\right)^2\right\}\right] = \frac{q_g \times 0.05^2}{4 \times 50}\left[\left(\frac{0.1}{0.05}\right)^2 - 2\ln(0.1/0.05) - 1\right]$$

$$200 - [50 + 0.000375\,q_g] = 0.0000125\,q_g\,[4 - 1.386 - 1]$$

or, $$150 - 0.000375\,q_g = 0.00002\,q_g$$

$$\therefore \qquad q_g = \frac{150}{(0.000375 + 0.00002)}$$

$$= 3.797 \times 10^5 \text{ W/m}^3 \text{ (Ans.)}$$

Example 2.97. (*a*) *Establish a relation for the temperature as the function of the radial coordinate r, for a hollow cylinder (thermal conductivity k) having inner and outer radii r_1 and r_2 respectively; it is perfectly insulated at its outer radius and is held at a temperature t_1 by a coolant at the inner radius. Electrical energy is dissipated at the constant rate of q_g per unit volume. Assume that the temperature distribution is primarily radial and heat transfer takes place under steady state conditions.*

(*b*) *A hollow conductor (k = 18 W/m°C) of inner and outer radii 50 mm and 65 mm has an electrical resistance of 0.024 ohm per metre. It is perfectly insulated at its outer radius. The cooling fluid at the inside is at 40°C. Determine the maximum allowable current if the temperature is not to exceed 52°C.*

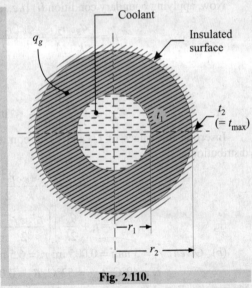

Fig. 2.110.

Solution. (*a*) The heat conduction equation is given by

$$\frac{d^2t}{dr^2} + \frac{1}{r}\cdot\frac{dt}{dr} + \frac{q_g}{k} = 0$$

or $$\frac{d}{dr}\left[r\cdot\frac{dt}{dr}\right] = -\frac{q_g}{k}r$$

Integrating the above equation twice, we have

$$r\frac{dt}{dr} = -\frac{q_g}{k}\cdot\frac{r^2}{2} + C_1$$

or, $\quad \dfrac{dt}{dr} = -\dfrac{q_g}{k}\cdot\dfrac{r}{2} + \dfrac{C_1}{r}$ ...(1)

and $\quad t = -\dfrac{q_g}{k}\cdot\dfrac{r^2}{4} + C_1 \ln (r) + C_2$ ...(2)

(where C_1, C_2 = constants of integration).

The values of C_1 and C_2 are determined from the following boundary conditions as follows :

(*i*) At $r = r_1, t = t_1$

(*ii*) At $r = r_2$, the heat flow is zero (since the conductor is insulated at the outer radius)

$$i.e. \quad \dfrac{dt}{dr} = 0 \qquad \left[\begin{array}{l} \text{From Fourier's law} \\[4pt] Q = -kA \cdot \dfrac{dt}{dr} \end{array}\right]$$

$$\therefore \qquad 0 = -\dfrac{q_g}{k}\cdot\dfrac{r_2}{2} + \dfrac{C_1}{r_2}$$

...[From eqn. (1)]

Fuel oil tank.

or, $\qquad C_1 = \dfrac{q_g}{k}\cdot\dfrac{r_2^2}{2}$

Now, applying boundary condition (*i*) [*i.e.*, at $r = r_1, t = t_1$] to eqn. (2), we have

$$t_1 = -\dfrac{q_g}{k}\cdot\dfrac{r_2^2}{4} + \dfrac{q_g}{k}\cdot\dfrac{r_2^2}{2} \ln (r_1) + C_2$$

$$\left[\text{Substituting } C_1 = \dfrac{q_g}{k}\cdot\dfrac{r_2^2}{2}\right]$$

or, $\qquad C_2 = t_1 + \dfrac{q_g}{2k}\left[\dfrac{r_1^2}{2} - r_2^2 \ln (r_1)\right]$

Inserting the values of C_1 and C_2 in eqn. (2), we have the general solution for temperature distribution as

$$t = -\dfrac{q_g}{k}\cdot\dfrac{r^2}{4} + \dfrac{q_g}{k}\cdot\dfrac{r_2^2}{2} \ln (r) + t_1 + \dfrac{q_g}{2k}\left[\dfrac{r_1^2}{2} - r_2^2 \ln (r_1)\right]$$

or, $\qquad t = t_1 + \dfrac{q_g}{2k}\cdot\left[\left(\dfrac{r_1^2 - r^2}{2}\right) + r_2^2 \ln (r/r_1)\right]$ ...(3)

(*b*) *Given* : $r_1 = 5$ mm $= 0.005$ m; $r_2 = 6.5$ mm $= 0.0065$ m, $k = 18$ W/m°C

$\qquad t_1 = 40$°C, $t_{max} = 52$°C, $R_e = 0.024$ ohms per metre.

Maximum allowable current, I :

The maximum temperature occurs at the insulated boundary, *i.e.*, at $r = r_2$. The eqn. (3) then takes the form

$$t_{max} = t_1 + \dfrac{q_g}{2k}\cdot\left[\left(\dfrac{r_1^2 - r_2^2}{2}\right) + r_2^2 \ln (r_2 / r_1)\right]$$

$$52 = 40 + \dfrac{q_g}{2 \times 18}\left[\left(\dfrac{0.005^2 - 0.0065^2}{2}\right) + 0.0065^2 \times \ln (0.0065/0.005)\right]$$

or, $\qquad 52 = 40 + \dfrac{q_g}{36}\left[-8.625 \times 10^{-6} \times 11.085 \times 10^{-6}\right]$

or,
$$12 = \frac{q_g}{36} \times 2.46 \times 10^{-6}$$

or,
$$q_g = \frac{12 \times 36}{2.46 \times 10^{-6}} = 175.61 \times 10^6 \text{ W/m}^3$$

Total volumetric heat generation $= 175.61 \times 10^6 \times \frac{\pi}{4}\left[(0.0065)^2 - (0.005)^2\right]$

$$= 2379.2 \text{ W per metre length of the conductor.}$$

Also heat generated $= I^2 R_e$

$$= I^2 \times 0.024 \text{ watts per metre length}$$

$\therefore$ $\qquad I^2 \times 0.024 = 2379.2$

or $\qquad I = \left(\frac{2379.2}{0.024}\right)^{1/2} = \textbf{314.85 A}$ $\qquad$ **(Ans.)**

Example 2.98. *A steel rod* *(k = 40 W/m°C) 30 mm diameter and 300 mm long separates two large steel plates maintained at 100°C and 75°C. The space between the plates is filled with insulation which also insulates the circumference of the rod. Voltage difference exits between the two plates due to which current flows through the rod and the electrical energy is dissipated at a rate of 12 W. Determine :*

(i) The maximum temperature in the rod, and its point of occurence;

(ii) The heat flux at each end.

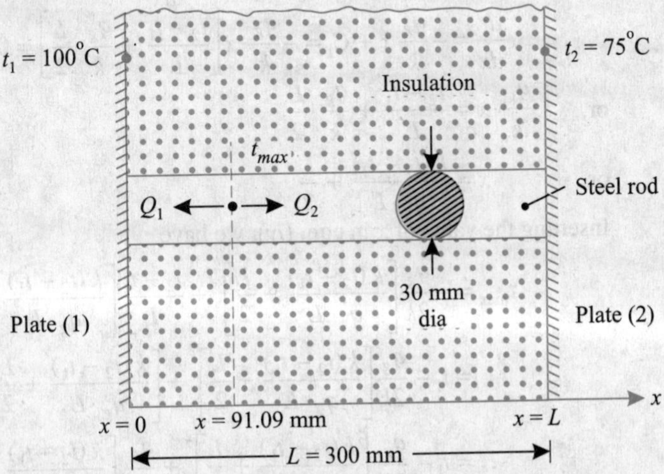

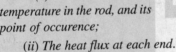

Fig. 2.111.

Solution. Refer to Fig. 2.111.

$t_1 = 100°C$; $t_2 = 75°C$; $k = 40$ W/m°C.

The rate of dissipation of electrical energy $= 12$W

$\therefore$ Heat generated per unit volume, $q_g = \dfrac{12}{\dfrac{\pi}{4} \times 0.03^2 \times 0.30} = 56588 \text{ W/m}^3$

(i) The maximum temperature in the rod (t_{max}) and its point of occurence (x) :

The heat conduction equation for steel rod is given by

$$\frac{d^2 t}{dx^2} + \frac{q_g}{k} = 0 \qquad\qquad ...(i)$$

Integrating eqn. (i) twice, we obtain

$$\frac{dt}{dx} + \frac{q_g}{k} \cdot x = C_1 \qquad\qquad ...(ii)$$

$$t + \frac{q_g}{k}\cdot\frac{x^2}{2} = C_1 x + C_2 \qquad \text{...(iii)}$$

(where C_1, C_2 = constants of integration).

In order to evaluate C_1 and C_2, using the following boundary conditions, we have

(i) At $x = 0$, $\qquad t = t_1 \qquad \therefore \qquad C_2 = t_1$

(ii) At $x = L$, $\qquad t = t_2$

$$\therefore \quad t_2 + \frac{q_g}{k}\cdot\frac{L^2}{2} = C_1 L + t_1 \quad \text{or} \quad C_1 = \frac{t_2 - t_1}{L} + \frac{q_g}{k}\cdot\frac{L}{2}$$

Substituting the values of C_1 and C_2 in eqn. (iii), we get

$$t = -\frac{q_g}{k}\cdot\frac{x^2}{2} + \left[\frac{t_2 - t_1}{L} + \frac{q_g}{k}\cdot\frac{L}{2}\right]x + t_1 \qquad \text{...(iv)}$$

The maximum temperature occurs where $\dfrac{dt}{dx} = 0$

$$\therefore \qquad \frac{dt}{dx} = -\frac{q_g}{k}x + C_1 = -\frac{q_g}{k}\cdot x\left[\frac{t_2 - t_1}{L} + \frac{q_g}{k}\cdot\frac{L}{2}\right] = 0 \qquad \text{...from eqn. (ii)}$$

or, $\qquad \dfrac{q_g}{k}\cdot x = \dfrac{t_2 - t_1}{L} + \dfrac{q_g}{k}\cdot\dfrac{L}{2}$

or, $\qquad x = \dfrac{k(t_2 - t_1)}{q_g \cdot L} + \dfrac{L}{2} \qquad \text{...(v)}$

Inserting the value of x in eqn. (iv), we have

$$t_{max} = -\frac{q_g}{2k}\left[\frac{k(t_2-t_1)}{q_g\cdot L}+\frac{L}{2}\right]^2 + \frac{t_2-t_1}{L}\left[\frac{k(t_2-t_1)}{q_g\cdot L}+\frac{L}{2}\right] + \frac{q_g L}{2k}\left[\frac{k(t_2-t_1)}{q_g\cdot L}+\frac{L}{2}\right] + t_1$$

$$= t_1 - \frac{q_g}{2k}\left[\frac{k(t_2-t_1)}{q_g\cdot L}+\frac{L}{2}\right]^2 + \left[\frac{k(t_2-t_1)}{q_g\cdot L}+\frac{L}{2}\right]\left[\frac{q_g\cdot L}{2k}+\frac{t_2-t_1}{L}\right]$$

$$= t_1 - \frac{q_g}{2k}\left[\frac{k(t_2-t_1)}{q_g\cdot L}+\frac{L}{2}\right]^2 + \frac{q_g}{k}\left[\frac{k(t_2-t_1)}{q_g\cdot L}+\frac{L}{2}\right]^2$$

or, $\qquad t_{max} = t_1 + \dfrac{q_g}{2k}\left[\dfrac{k(t_2-t_1)}{q_g\cdot L}+\dfrac{L}{2}\right]^2 \qquad \text{...(vi)}$

Substituting the proper values in eqn. (vi), we get

$$t_{max} = 100 + \frac{56588}{2\times 40}\left[\frac{40(75-100)}{56588\times 0.3}+\frac{0.3}{2}\right]^2 = 105.8°\text{C} \quad \textbf{(Ans.)}$$

The distance x at which t_{max} occurs is given by

$$x = \frac{k(t_2 - t_1)}{q_g\cdot L} + \frac{L}{2} \qquad \text{...[Eqn. (v)]}$$

$$= \frac{40(75-100)}{56588\times 0.3} + \frac{0.3}{2} = 0.09109\,\text{m or } \textbf{91.09 mm} \quad \textbf{(Ans.)}$$

(ii) **The heat flux at each end :**

The heat flow from the rod at $x = 0$,

$$Q_1 = -kA\left.\frac{dt}{dx}\right|_{x=0}$$

$$= -kA\left[-\frac{q_g \cdot x}{k} + \frac{t_2 - t_1}{L} + \frac{q_g}{k}\cdot\frac{L}{2}\right]_{x=0}$$

$$= -40 \times \frac{\pi}{4} \times 0.03^2\left[\frac{75-100}{0.3} + \frac{56588}{40}\times\frac{0.3}{2}\right] = -3.64\,\text{W}$$

(–ve sign indicates that the heat flows in a direction *opposite* to that of *x*-direction). The heat flow from the rod at $x = L$ (=0.3m),

$$Q_2 = -k\,A\left.\frac{dt}{dx}\right|_{x=L}$$

$$= -kA\left[-\frac{q_g \cdot L}{k} + \frac{t_2 - t_1}{L} + \frac{q_g}{k}\cdot\frac{L}{2}\right]$$

$$= -kA\left[\frac{t_2 - t_1}{L} - \frac{q_g}{k}\cdot\frac{L}{2}\right]$$

$$= -40 \times \frac{\pi}{4} \times 0.03^2\left[\frac{75-100}{0.3} - \frac{56588}{40}\times\frac{0.3}{2}\right] = 8.36\,\text{W} \qquad \textbf{(Ans.)}$$

[Check : The sum of Q_1 and Q_2 should be equal to Q_g, i.e., $Q_1 + Q_2 = 3.64 + 8.36 = 12\text{W}$ i.e., Q_g]

Example 2.99. *The rate of heat generation per unit volume in a long cylinder of radius R is given by*

$$q_g = a + br^2$$

where a and b are constants and r is any radius. The cylinder is undergoing heat transfer with a medium at a temperature t_a and surface heat transfer coefficient is h. Find the steady state temperature distribution in the solid. (M.U.)

Solution. For the given problem, the controlling differential equation is given by

$$\frac{d}{dr}\left(r\cdot\frac{dt}{dr}\right) + \frac{q_g}{k}\cdot r = 0$$

...[Eqn. (2.105)]

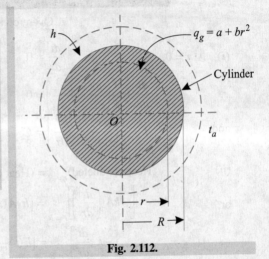

Fig. 2.112.

Substituting the value of q_g, we have

$$\frac{d}{dr}\left(r\frac{dt}{dr}\right) + \frac{r}{k}(a + br^2) = 0$$

Integrating the above equation, we get

$$r\frac{dt}{dr} + \frac{1}{k}\left(\frac{ar^2}{2} + \frac{br^4}{4}\right) = C_1 \qquad \text{...(i)}$$

or,

$$\frac{dt}{dr} + \frac{1}{k}\left(\frac{ar}{2} + \frac{br^3}{4}\right) = \frac{C_1}{r}$$

Integrating again, we get

$$t + \frac{1}{k}\left[\frac{ar^2}{4} + \frac{br^4}{16}\right] = C_1 \ln(r) + C_2 \qquad \text{...(ii)}$$

(where C_1, C_2 = constants of integration).

The boundary conditions for finding C_1 and C_2 are :

Overground oil storage tanks.

(*i*) At $r = 0$, $\qquad\qquad \dfrac{dt}{dr} = 0 \qquad\qquad \therefore C_1 = 0 \qquad$ [from eqn. (*i*)]

$\therefore \qquad \dfrac{dt}{dr} + \dfrac{1}{k}\left(\dfrac{ar}{2} + \dfrac{br^3}{4} \right) = 0 \qquad\qquad\qquad$ ...(*iii*)

and $\qquad t + \dfrac{1}{k}\left[\dfrac{a r^2}{4} + \dfrac{br^4}{16} \right] = C_2 \qquad\qquad\qquad$ ...(*iv*)

$\qquad\qquad\qquad\qquad\qquad\qquad\qquad\qquad\qquad$ [From eqn. (*ii*)]

(*ii*) $\qquad$ (Heat conducted)$_{r = R}$ = (Heat convected)$_{r = R}$

or, $\qquad \left[-kA \cdot \left(\dfrac{dt}{dr} \right) \right]_{r = R} = \left[h \cdot A (t - t_a) \right]_{r = R}$

$\qquad\qquad \left[-k \cdot \dfrac{dt}{dr} \right]_{r = R} = \left[h (t - t_a) \right]_{r = R}$

Substituting the values from eqns. (*iii*) and (*iv*) for $\dfrac{dt}{dr}$ and t in the above equation for $r = R$, we get

$$-k\left[-\dfrac{1}{k}\left(\dfrac{aR}{2} + \dfrac{bR^3}{4} \right) \right] = h\left[C_2 - \dfrac{1}{k}\left(\dfrac{aR^2}{4} + \dfrac{bR^4}{16} \right) - t_a \right]$$

$\therefore \qquad\qquad \dfrac{R}{2h}\left[a + \dfrac{bR^2}{2} \right] = C_2 - \dfrac{R^2}{4k}\left[a + \dfrac{bR^2}{4} \right] - t_a$

or, $\qquad\qquad C_2 = t_a + \dfrac{R}{2h}\left[a + \dfrac{bR^2}{2} \right] + \dfrac{R^2}{4k}\left[a + \dfrac{b R^2}{4} \right]$

Now, substituting this value in eqn. (*iv*), we obtain

$$t + \dfrac{r^2}{4k}\left[a + \dfrac{br^2}{4} \right] = t_a + \dfrac{R}{2h}\left[a + \dfrac{bR^2}{2} \right] + \dfrac{R^2}{4k}\left[a + \dfrac{bR^2}{4} \right]$$

$\therefore \qquad\qquad t - t_a = \dfrac{R}{2h}\left[a + \dfrac{bR^2}{2} \right] + \left[\dfrac{aR^2}{4k} + \dfrac{bR^4}{16k} \right] - \left[\dfrac{ar^2}{4k} + \dfrac{br^4}{16k} \right]$

or,

$$t - t_a = \frac{R}{2h}\left[a + \frac{bR^2}{2}\right] + \frac{aR^2}{4k}\left[1 - \left(\frac{r}{R}\right)^2\right] + \frac{bR^4}{16k}\left[1 - \left(\frac{r}{R}\right)^4\right]$$

...(Temperature distribution)   (Ans.)

Example 2.100. *A copper conductor ($k = 380$ W/m°C, resistivity $\rho = 2 \times 10^{-8}$ W m) having inner and outer radii 1.0 cm and 2.25 cm respectively is carrying a current density of 4800 amperes/cm². The conductor is internally cooled and a constant temperature of 65°C is maintained at the inner surface and there is no heat transfer through insulation surrounding the conductor. Determine:*

(i) The maximum temperature of the conductor and the radius at which it occurs, and

(ii) The internal heat transfer rate.

Solution. Refer to Fig. 2.113.

$r_1 = 1.0$ cm; $r_2 = 2.25$ cm; J (current density) = 4800 amp/cm² or 4800 × 10⁴ amp/m²

$k = 380$ W/m°C; $\rho = 2 \times 10^{-8}$ Ωm; $t_o = 65°C$.

(i) **The maximum temperature of the conductor and the radius at which it occurs; t_{max}, r :**

Total volumetric heat generated

$$= I^2 R = I^2 \cdot \frac{\rho L}{A}$$

Heat generated per unit volume,

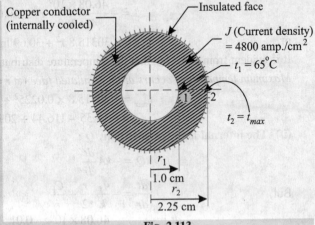

Fig. 2.113.

Copper conductor (internally cooled)
Insulated face
J (Current density) = 4800 amp./cm²
$t_1 = 65°C$
$t_2 = t_{max}$
r_1 1.0 cm
r_2 2.25 cm

$$q_g = \frac{I^2 \cdot \frac{\rho L}{A}}{A \times L} = I^2 \cdot \frac{\rho L}{A} \times \frac{1}{AL} = \rho\left(\frac{I}{A}\right)^2$$

$$= \rho J^2 = 2 \times 10^{-8} \times [4800 \times 10^4]^2 = 46.08 \times 10^6 \text{ W/m}^3$$

The differential equation describing the temperature distribution through a cylindrical conductor is given by

$$\frac{d}{dr}\left(r\frac{dt}{dr}\right) + \frac{q_g}{k} \cdot r = 0$$

Integrating eqn. (i) twice, we get

$$r\frac{dt}{dr} + \frac{q_g}{k} \cdot \frac{r^2}{2} = C_1 \qquad ...(ii)$$

or,

$$\frac{dt}{dr} + \frac{q_g}{k} \cdot \frac{r}{2} = \frac{C_1}{r}$$

and,

$$t + \frac{q_g}{k} \cdot \frac{r^2}{4} = C_1 \ln(r) + C_2$$

or,

$$t = -\frac{q_g}{k} \cdot \frac{r^2}{4} + C_1 \ln(r) + C_2 \qquad ...(iii)$$

(where C_1, C_2 = constants of integration).

The values of C_1 and C_2 are found from the following boundary conditions :

(i) At $r = r_2 = 2.25$ cm (or 0.0225 m), $\frac{dt}{dr} = 0$ (since the face is insulated and there is no heat transfer).

$$\therefore \qquad C_1 = \frac{q_g}{k} \cdot \frac{r^2}{2} = \frac{46.08 \times 10^6}{380} \times \frac{0.0225^2}{2} = 30.69. \quad \text{...[From eqn. (}ii\text{)]}$$

(ii) At $r = r_1 = 1.0$ cm (or 0.01 m), $t = t_1 = 65°C$

$$65 = -\frac{46.08 \times 10^6}{380} \times \frac{0.01^2}{4} + 30.69 \ln(0.01) + C_2$$

$$\therefore \qquad C_2 = 65 + \frac{46.08 \times 10^6}{380} \times \frac{0.01^2}{4} - 30.69 \ln(0.01) = 209.36°C$$

Substituting the values of C_1 and C_2 in eqn. (iii) we get the temperature distribution through the conductor as

$$t = -\frac{46.08 \times 10^6}{4 \times 380} r^2 + 30.69 \ln(r) + 209.36$$

or, $\qquad\qquad t = -30315.8 \, r^2 + 30.69 \ln(r) + 209.36 \qquad\qquad\qquad$ ...(iv)

It is evident from eqn. (iv), that the temperature distribution is *parabolic*.

Maximum temperature occurs at the insulated face (at **$r = r_2 = 0.0225$ m**) and its value equals,

$$t_{max} = -30315.8 \times 0.0225^2 + 30.69 \ln(0.0225) + 209.36$$

$$= -15.35 - 116.44 + 209.36 = \textbf{77.57°C} \qquad \textbf{(Ans.)}$$

(ii) **The internal heat transfer rate, Q :**

$$Q = -kA \frac{dt}{dr}$$

But, $\qquad\qquad \dfrac{dt}{dr} = -\dfrac{q_g}{k} \cdot \dfrac{r}{2} + \dfrac{C_1}{r} \qquad\qquad\qquad$ [From eqn. (ii)]

$$\therefore \qquad \left. \frac{dt}{dr} \right|_{r=0.01} = -\frac{46.08 \times 10^6}{380} \times \frac{0.01}{2} + \frac{30.69}{0.01} = 2462.68$$

$\therefore \quad Q = -380 \times (2\pi \times 0.01 \times 1) \times 2462.68 \approx \textbf{58800 W/m}$

($-$ ve sign indicates that heat flow is radially *inwards*.)

[Check : Internal heat transfer $= q_g \times [\pi \, (0.0225^2 - 0.01^2) \times 1]$

$= 46.08 \times 10^6 \, [\, \pi \, (0.0225^2 - 0.01^2) \times 1] \approx \textbf{58800 W/m}]$

Example 2.101. *A hollow cylinder having inner and outer radii r_1 and r_2 respectively is developing heat uniformly, q_g per unit volume per unit time. The conductivity of the cylinder material is given by; $k = k_o \, (1 + \beta t)$. If the outside surface temperature is t_w, prove that the temperature distribution in cylinder is given by*

$$t = -\frac{1}{\beta} + \sqrt{\left(\frac{1}{\beta} + t_w\right)^2 - \frac{q_g \, r_1^2}{2\beta k_o}\left[\left(\frac{r}{r_1}\right)^2 + 2\ln(r_2/r) - \left(\frac{r_2}{r_1}\right)^2\right]}$$

Solution. Refer to Fig. 2.114.

Heat generation rate between $r = r_1$ and $r = r =$ heat conducted at $r = r$

$$(q_g)_r = q_g \times \pi \, (r^2 - r_1^2) \times 1$$

$$= -k_0 \, (1 + \beta t) \, 2\pi r \times 1 \times \frac{dt}{dr} \quad \text{(Considering unit length of the cylinder)}$$

$$\left(\frac{r^2 - r_1^2}{r}\right) \cdot \frac{q_g}{2k_o} \cdot dr = -(1 + \beta t) \, dt$$

$$-\left(r - \frac{r_1^2}{r}\right) \cdot \frac{q}{2k_o} \cdot dr = (1 + \beta t) \, dt$$

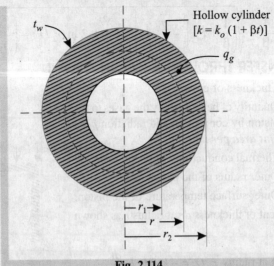

t_w

Hollow cylinder
$[k = k_o(1 + \beta t)]$

q_g

r_1

r

r_2

Fig. 2.114.

Integrating both sides, we have

$$\int (1 + \beta t)\, dt = -\frac{q_g}{2k_o} \int \left(r - \frac{r_1^2}{r} \right) dr$$

or,

$$t + \beta \cdot \frac{t^2}{2} = -\frac{q_g}{2k_o} \left[\frac{r^2}{2} - r_1^2 \ln(r) \right] + C \qquad ..(i)$$

(where C = constant of integration).

Using boundary condition (for finding the constant C), at $r = r, t = t_w$, we have

$$C = t_w + \frac{\beta}{2} \cdot t_w^2 + \frac{q_g}{2k_o} \left[\frac{r_2^2}{2} - r_1^2 \ln(r_2) \right]$$

Substituting the value of C in eqn. (i), we have

$$t + \frac{\beta}{2} \cdot t^2 = -\frac{q_g}{2k_0} \left[\frac{r^2}{2} - r_1^2 \ln(r) \right] + t_w + \frac{\beta}{2} t_w^2 + \frac{q_g}{2k_0} \cdot \left[\frac{r_2^2}{2} - r_1^2 \ln(r_2) \right]$$

or, $\dfrac{\beta}{2} \cdot t^2 + t + \dfrac{q_g}{2k_o} \left[\dfrac{r^2}{2} - r_1^2 \ln(r) \right] - t_w - \dfrac{\beta}{2} \cdot t_w^2 - \dfrac{q_g}{2k_o} \left[\dfrac{r_2^2}{2} - r_1^2 \ln(r_2) \right]$

or, $\dfrac{\beta}{2} \cdot t^2 + t - \left[\dfrac{\beta}{2} \cdot t_w^2 + t_w + \dfrac{q_g}{2k_o} \left\{ \dfrac{r_2^2 - r^2}{2} - r_1^2 \ln(r_2/r) \right\} \right] = 0$

or,

$$t = \frac{-1 + \sqrt{1 + 4 \times \dfrac{\beta}{2} \left[\dfrac{\beta}{2} t_w^2 + t_w + \dfrac{q_g}{2k_o} \left\{ \dfrac{r_2^2 - r^2}{2} - r_1^2 \ln(r_2/r) \right\} \right]}}{\beta}$$

or,

$$t = -\frac{1}{\beta} + \sqrt{\left\{ \left(\frac{1}{\beta} \right)^2 + t_w^2 + \frac{2}{\beta} t_w \right\} + \frac{2}{\beta} \cdot \frac{q_g}{2k_o} \left\{ \frac{r_2^2 - r^2}{2} - r_1^2 \ln(r_2/r) \right\}}$$

$$= -\frac{1}{\beta} + \sqrt{\left(\frac{1}{\beta} + t_w \right)^2 - \frac{q_g}{\beta k_o} \left[\frac{r^2}{2} + r_1^2 \ln(r_2/r) - \frac{r_2^2}{2} \right]}$$

or, $$t = -\frac{1}{\beta} + \sqrt{\left(\frac{1}{\beta} + t_w\right)^2 - \frac{q_g\, r_1^2}{2\beta k_o}\left[\left(\frac{r}{r_1}\right)^2 + 2\ln(r_2/r) - \left(\frac{r_2^2}{r_1}\right)^2\right]}$$ ....(Proved)

2.9.4. HEAT TRANSFER THROUGH A PISTON CROWN

Let, b = Thickness of crown,

q_g = Quantity of heat given by the gases to the piston by convection and radiation *per unit area per unit time*,

k = Thermal conductivity of piston material,

R = Outer radius of the piston, and

t_o = Outer surface temperature of the piston.

Consider an element of thickness dr at radius r as shown in Fig. 2.115.

Heat conducted in at radius r, $Q_r = -k.2\pi r b.\dfrac{dt}{dr}$.

Heat given by the gases to the piston, $Q_g = q_g \times 2\pi\, r.dr$

Heat conducted out at radius $(r + dr)$, $Q_{(r+dr)}$

$$= Q_r + \frac{d}{dr}(Q_r)dr$$

For steady state heat conduction, we have

$$Q_r + Q_g = Q_{(r + dr)}$$

$$= Q_r + \frac{d}{dr}(Q_r)\,dr$$

or, $$Q_g = \frac{d}{dr}(Q_r)\,dr$$

or, $$q_g \times 2\pi r.dr = \frac{d}{dr}\left[-k \times 2\pi rb \cdot \frac{dt}{dr}\right]dr$$

or, $$q_g \times r = \frac{d}{dr}\left[-kb \cdot r \cdot \frac{dt}{dr}\right]$$

or, $$\frac{d}{dr}\left[r\,\frac{dt}{dr}\right] + \frac{q_g}{kb} \cdot r = 0 \qquad \text{...}(i)$$

Integrating eqn. (i) twice, we obtain

$$r \cdot \frac{dt}{dr} + \frac{q_g}{kb} \cdot \frac{r^2}{2} = C_1 \qquad \text{...}(ii)$$

or, $$\frac{dt}{dr} + \frac{q_g}{kb} \cdot \frac{r}{2} = \frac{C_1}{r}$$

and, $$t + \frac{q_g}{kb} \cdot \frac{r^2}{4} = C_1 \ln(r) + C_2 \text{ ...}(iii)$$

(where C_1 and C_2 = constants of integration).

The values of C_1 and C_2 can be found out from the following boundary conditions, as follows :

(i) At $r = 0$, $\dfrac{dt}{dr} = 0$ $\therefore C_1 =$ [From eqn. (ii)]

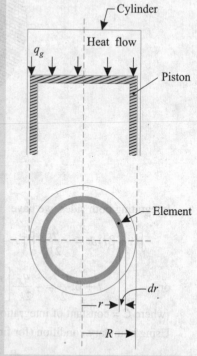

Fig. 2.115. Heat transfer through a piston crown.

Piston crown.

(ii) At $r = R$, $t = t_o$ $\therefore \; C_2 = t_0 + \dfrac{q_g}{kb} \cdot \dfrac{R^2}{4}$ [From eqn. (iii)]

Substituting the values of C_1 and C_2 in eqn (iii), we have

$$t + \frac{q_g}{kb} \cdot \frac{r^2}{4} = t_o + \frac{q_g}{kb} \cdot \frac{R^2}{4}$$

or,
$$t = t_o + \frac{q_g}{4kb}(R^2 - r^2) \qquad \qquad ...(2.114)$$

It is evident from eqn. (2.114) that the temperature distribution is parabolic and the maximum temperature which occurs at the centre of the piston crown ($r = 0$), is given by

$$t_{\max} = t_o + \frac{q_g}{4kb} \cdot R^2 \qquad \qquad ... (2.115)$$

If the total heat given by the gases to the piston crown is denoted by Q, then

$$Q = q_g \times \pi R^2 \text{ or } q_g = \frac{Q}{\pi R^2}$$

$\therefore$
$$t_{max} = t_0 + \frac{Q}{\pi R^2} \times \frac{1}{4kb} \times R^2$$

or,
$$t_{max} = t_0 + \frac{Q}{4\pi k b} \qquad \qquad ...(2.116)$$

From eqn. (2.114) the thickness of the piston crown can be calculated.

i.e.,
$$b = \frac{Q}{4\pi k (t_{\max} - t_0)} \qquad \qquad ...(2.117)$$

2.9.5. HEAT CONDUCTION WITH HEAT GENERATION IN NUCLEAR CYLINDRICAL FUEL ROD

A. Nuclear cylindrical fuel rod *without* cladding :

The internal heat generation for a cylindrical fuel rod is generally given by (not being uniform)

$$q_g = q_0\left[1 - \left(\frac{r}{R_{fr}}\right)^2\right]$$

where, q_g = Heat generation rate at radius r,

q_o = Heat generation rate at the centre of the rod ($r = 0$), and

R_{fr} = Outer radius of the fuel rod.

One-dimensional, steady state heat transfer in radial direction is given by

$$\frac{d}{dr}\left[r \cdot \frac{dt}{dr}\right] + \frac{q_g}{k} \cdot r = 0$$

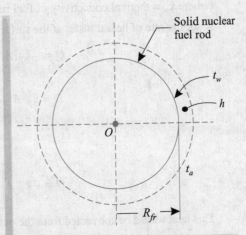

Fig. 2.116. Nuclear cylindrical fuel rod. .

or $\dfrac{d}{dr}\left[r \cdot \dfrac{dt}{dr}\right] + \dfrac{q_0}{k}\left[1 - \left(\dfrac{r}{R_{fr}}\right)^2\right] r = 0$ ...(i)

Integrating eqn. (i), we have

$$r \cdot \frac{dt}{dr} + \frac{q_0}{k}\left[\frac{r^2}{2} - \frac{r^4}{4R{fr}^2}\right] = C_1 \qquad \qquad ...(ii)$$

or, $\quad \dfrac{dt}{dr} + \dfrac{q_o}{k}\left[\dfrac{r}{2} - \dfrac{r^3}{4R_{fr}^2}\right] = \dfrac{C_1}{r}$

Integrating again, we obtain

$$t + \dfrac{q_o}{k}\left[\dfrac{r^2}{4} - \dfrac{r^4}{16R_{fr}^2}\right] = C_1 \ln(r) + C_2 \qquad \ldots(iii)$$

(where C_1, C_2 = constants of integration).

Using the following boundary conditions, we have

(i)   At $r = 0$, $\qquad \dfrac{dt}{dr} = 0 \quad \therefore C_1 = 0$ $\qquad\qquad$ [From eqn. (ii)]

(ii) At $r = 0$, $\qquad t = t_{max} \quad \therefore C_2 = t_{max}$ $\qquad\qquad$ [From eqn. (iii)]

Substituting these values of the constants in eqn. (iii), we get

$$t + \dfrac{q_o}{k}\left[\dfrac{r^2}{4} - \dfrac{r^4}{16R_{fr}^2}\right] = t_{max}$$

or, $\quad t - t_{max} = -\dfrac{q_o}{k}\left[\dfrac{r^2}{4} - \dfrac{r^4}{16R_{fr}^2}\right] \qquad \ldots(iv)$

If t_w is the temperature at the outer surface of the rod *i.e.*, at $r = R_{fr}$, then

$$t_w - t_{max} = -\dfrac{q_o}{k_{fr}}\left[\dfrac{R_{fr}^2}{4} - \dfrac{R_{fr}^4}{16R_{fr}^2}\right] = -\dfrac{q_o}{k}\left[\dfrac{R_{fr}^2}{4} - \dfrac{R_{fr}^2}{16}\right]$$

or, $\quad t_w - t_{max} = -\dfrac{3q_0 R_{fr}^2}{16k_{fr}} \qquad \ldots(2.118)$

(where k_{fr} = thermal coductivity of fuel rod material).

Also, the rate of heat transfer at the surface of the rod,

$$Q = -k_{fr}\, A\, \left.\dfrac{dt}{dr}\right|_{r = R_{fr}}$$

$$= k_{fr}\, A\left[-\dfrac{q_o}{k_{fr}}\left\{\dfrac{r}{2} - \dfrac{r^3}{4R_{fr}^2}\right\}\right]_{r = R_{fr}}$$

[Substituting the value of $\dfrac{dt}{dr}$ from eqn. (ii)]

or, $\quad Q = -k_{fr}\, A\left[-\dfrac{q_0}{k_{fr}}\left\{\dfrac{R_{fr}}{2} - \dfrac{R_{fr}^3}{4R_{fr}^2}\right\}\right] = \dfrac{q_0\, A R_{fr}}{4} \qquad \ldots(2.119)$

This heat would be convected from the outside surface of the rod, under steady state conditions.

$\therefore \qquad \dfrac{q_o\, A R_{fr}}{4} = h A (t_w - t_a)$

[where h = convective heat transfer coefficient and

$\quad t_a$ = ambient temperature.]

or, $\quad t_w = t_a + \dfrac{q_o\, A R_{fr}}{4hA} = t_a + \dfrac{q_o R_{fr}}{4h} \qquad \ldots(v)$

Inserting this value of t_w in eqn. (2.118), we obtain

$$\left[t_a + \frac{q_o R_{fr}}{4h} \right] - t_{max} = -\frac{3 q_o R_{fr}^2}{16 k_{fr}}$$

or, $$t_{max} - t_a = \frac{3 q_o R_{fr}^2}{16 k_{fr}} + \frac{q_o R_{fr}}{4h}$$

or, $$t_{max} - t_a = \frac{q_o R_{fr}}{4} \left[\frac{3 R_{fr}}{4 k_{fr}} + \frac{1}{h} \right] \qquad \qquad \qquad ...(2.120)$$

B. Nuclear cylindrical fuel rod with cladding :

When nuclear fuel elements happen to come in contact with the cooling medium they are likely to get damaged owing to oxidation. In order to check this damage the fuel elements are usually covered with pretective material known as 'cladding'.

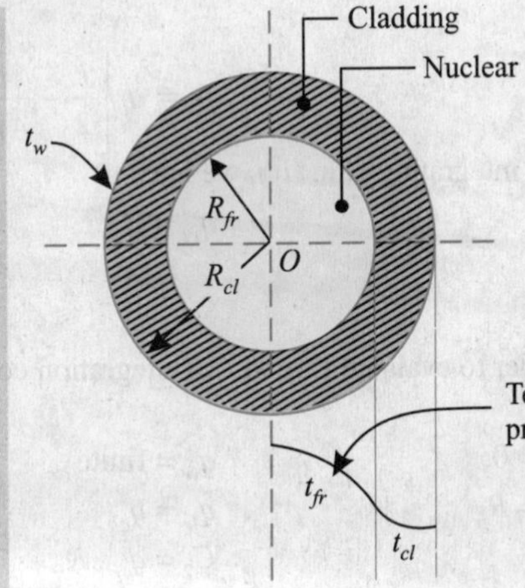

Refer to Fig. 2.117. The heat generated per unit volume in the nuclear fuel rod is given by

$$q_g = q_o \left[1 - \frac{r}{R_{fr}} \right]^2$$

Fig. 2.117. Nuclear cylindrical fuel rod with cladding.

where, q_g = Heat generation rate at radius r,

q_o = Heat generation rate at the centre of the rod ($r = 0$), and

R_{fr} = Outer radius of fuel rod.

Let, R_{cl} = Outer radius of cladding,

q_{cl} = Heat generation rate in the cladding,

q_{fr} = Heat generation rate in the fuel rod,

k_{fr} = Thermal conductivity of fuel rod material, and

k_{cl} = Thermal conductivity of cladding material.

One-dimensional steady state heat conduction in radial direction is given by

$$\frac{d}{dr} \left[r \frac{dt}{dr} \right] + \frac{q_g}{k} r = 0 \qquad \qquad \qquad ...(i)$$

Also, heat flow rate per unit area, $q \left(= \frac{Q}{A} \right)$ is given by

$$q = -k \cdot \frac{dt}{dr} \qquad \text{or} \qquad \frac{dt}{dr} = -\frac{q}{k}$$

Substituting $\dfrac{dt}{dr} = -\dfrac{q}{k}$ in eqn. (i) we have

$$\frac{d}{dr} \left[-\frac{rq}{k} \right] + \frac{q_g}{k} \cdot r = 0 \qquad \qquad \text{(assuming } k \text{ to be constant)}$$

or, $$\frac{d}{dr} (rq) = q_g \cdot r \qquad \qquad \qquad ...(ii)$$

or, $$\frac{d}{dr} (r \cdot q_{fr}) = q_g \cdot r \qquad \qquad \qquad ...\text{for fuel rod}$$

or,
$$\frac{d}{dr}(r.q_{fr}) = q_o \left[1 - \left(\frac{r}{R_{fr}}\right)^2\right] r \qquad ...(iii)$$

Since there is no internal heat generation in cladding, therefore,
$$\frac{d}{dr}(r.q_{cl}) = 0 \qquad ...(iv)$$

Integrating eqn (iii), we obtain
$$r.q_{fr} = q_o \left[\frac{r^2}{2} - \frac{r^4}{4R_{fr}^2}\right] + C_1 \qquad ...(v)$$

or,
$$q_{fr} = q_o \left[\frac{r}{2} - \frac{r^3}{4R_{fr}^2}\right] + \frac{C_1}{r} \qquad ...(vi)$$

Now, integrating eqn. (iv), we have
$$r.q_{cl} = C_2 \qquad ...(vii)$$

or,
$$q_{cl} = \frac{C_2}{r} \qquad ...(viii)$$

In order to evaluate C_1 and C_2 (integration constants), using the following boundary conditions, we have

At $r = 0$, $\qquad q_{fr} = $ finite $\qquad \therefore \; C_1 = 0$ $\qquad$ ...[From eqn. (v)]

At $r = R_{fr}$ $\qquad q_{fr} = q_{cl}$

$\therefore \qquad C_2 = q_{fr} \cdot R_{fr}$ $\qquad\qquad$ ....[from eqn. (vii)]

$$= q_o \left[\frac{R_{fr}}{2} - \frac{R_{fr}^3}{4R_{fr}^2}\right] R_{fr}$$

[substititing the value of q_{fr} from eqn. (vi)]

Nuclear power plant.

or, $$C_2 = \frac{q_o}{4} \cdot R_{fr}^2$$

∴ The rate of heat flow through fuel rod, $q_{fr} = -k_{fr} \cdot \dfrac{dt_{fr}}{dr} = q_o \left[\dfrac{r}{2} - \dfrac{r^3}{4 R_{fr}^2} \right]$ ...(ix)

and, the rate of heat flow through the cladding, $q_{cl} = -k_{cl} \cdot \dfrac{dt_{cl}}{dr} = \dfrac{q_o}{4r} \cdot R_{fr}^2$ ...(x)

By integrating eqns. (ix) and (x), we get the temperatures t_{fr} and t_{cl} as follows :

$$t_{fr} = \frac{q_o}{k_{fr}} \left[\frac{r^4}{16 R_{fr}^2} - \frac{r^2}{4} \right] + C_3$$ ...(xi)

and, $$t_{cl} = -\frac{q_o}{4k_{cl}} R_{fr}^2 \ln(r) + C_4$$ ...(xii)

(where C_3, C_4 = constants of intergration)

(i) Applying the boundary condition : At $r = R_{cl}$, $t_{cl} = t_w$

(outside surface temperature of the system),

we have $$C_4 = t_w + \frac{q_o}{4k_{cl}} \cdot R_{fr}^2 \ln(R_{cl})$$ [From

eqn. (xii)]

∴ $$t_{cl} = -\frac{q_o}{4k_{cl}} R_{fr}^2 \ln(r) + t_w + \frac{q_o}{4k_{cl}} \cdot R_{fr}^2 \ln(R_{cl})$$

or, $$(t_{cl} - t_w) = \frac{q_o}{4k_{cl}} \cdot R_{fr}^2 \ln(R_{cl}/r)$$ ...(xiii)

(ii) Applying boundary condition, at $r = R_{fr}$, $t_{cl} = t_{fr}$ to eqn. (xi), we have

$$t_{fr} = \frac{q_o}{k_{fr}} \left[\frac{R_{fr}^4}{16 R_{fr}^2} - \frac{R_{fr}^2}{4} \right] + C_3 = t_{cl}$$

or, $$\frac{q_o}{k_{fr}} \left[\frac{R_{fr}^4}{16 R_{fr}^2} - \frac{R_{fr}^2}{4} \right] + C_3 = -\frac{q_o}{4k_{cl}} R_{fr}^2 \ln(R_{fr}) + C_4$$

or, $$\frac{q_o}{k_{fr}} \left[\frac{R_{fr}^4}{16 R_{fr}^2} - \frac{R_{fr}^2}{4} \right] + C_3 = -\frac{q_o}{4k_{cl}} \cdot R_{fr}^2 \ln(R_{fr}) + t_w + \frac{q_o}{4k_{cl}} \cdot R_{fr}^2 \ln(R_{cl})$$

(substituting the value of C_4)

or, $$\frac{q_o}{k_{fr}} \left[\frac{R_{fr}^2}{16} - \frac{R_{fr}^2}{4} \right] + C_3 = t_w + \frac{q_o}{4k_{cl}} \cdot R_{fr}^2 \cdot \ln(R_{cl}/R_{fr})$$

or, $$\frac{q_o R_{fr}^2}{4k_{fr}} \left[-\frac{3}{4} \right] + C_3 = t_w + \frac{q_o}{4k_{cl}} \cdot R_{fr}^2 \cdot \ln(R_{cl}/R_{fr})$$

or, $$C_3 = t_w + \frac{q_o R_{fr}^2}{4} \left[\frac{3}{4k_{fr}} + \frac{1}{k_{cl}} \cdot \ln(R_{cl}/R_{fr}) \right]$$

Subsituting the value of C_3 in eqn. (xi), we get

$$t_{fr} = \frac{q_o}{k_{fr}} \left[\frac{r^4}{16 R_{fr}^2} - \frac{r^2}{4} \right] + t_w + \frac{q_o R_{fr}^2}{4} \left[\frac{3}{4k_{fr}} + \frac{1}{k_{cl}} \cdot \ln(R_{cl}/R_{fr}) \right]$$ ...(xiv)

The maximum value of temperature (t_{max}) which occurs at the centre of the rod at (at $r = 0$), is given by

$$t_{max} = t_w + \frac{q_o R_{fr}^2}{4} \left[\frac{3}{4k_{fr}} + \frac{1}{k_{cl}} \cdot \ln (R_{cl}/R_{fr}) \right]$$ ...(2.121)

Example 2.102. *In a cylindrical fuel rod of nuclear reactor, the internal heat generation is given by*

$$q_g = q_o \left[1 - \left(\frac{r}{R_{fr}} \right)^2 \right]$$

where R_{fr} is the radius of the fuel rod.

Calculate the temperature drop from the centre to the surface of a 25 mm diameter fuel rod having k = 20 W/m°C when the rate of heat generation from the surface = 0.25 MW/m².

(P.U. 1997)

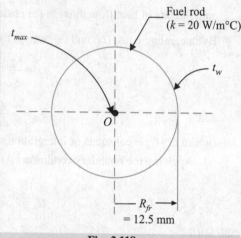

Fig. 2.118.

Solution. Radius of the fuel rod,

$$R_{fr} = \frac{25}{2} = 12.5\,\text{mm} = 0.0125\,\text{m}$$

Thermal conductivity, k_{fr} = 20 W/m°C

The rate of heat generation from the surface = 0.25 MW/m²

Temperature drop from the centre to the surface of the rod :

Let, t_{max} = Maximum temperature at the centre of the rod $(r = 0)$,

   t_w = Temperature at the surface of the fuel rod,

   q_o = Heat generation rate at the centre $(r = 0)$, and

   qg = Heat generation rate at a radius r.

Heat generation rate from the surface = Heat transfer rate from the surface of the rod,

$$Q = 0.25\ \text{MW/m}^2$$

Nuclear reactor.

But, $$Q = \frac{q_0 \, A R_{fr}}{4}$$ ...[Eqn. (2.119)]

or, $$0.25 \times 10^6 = \frac{q_0 \times 1 \times 0.0125}{4}$$

$$\therefore \qquad q_0 = \frac{0.25 \times 10^6 \times 4}{0.0125} = 80 \times 10^6 \text{ W/m}^3$$

Also, $$t_{max} - t_w = \frac{3 q_0 \, R_{fr}^2}{16 k_{fr}}$$ ...[Eqn. (2.118)]

or, $$(t_{max} - t_w) = \frac{3 \times 80 \times 10^6 \times 0.0125^2}{16 \times 20} = \textbf{117.2°C}$$ (**Ans.**)

Example 2.103. *The rate of heat generation in a cylindrical fuel rod of a nuclear reactor is given by* $q_g = [1 - (r/R_{fr})^2]$, *where* q_g *and* q_o *are the heat generation rates at any radius r and at the centre respectively and* R_{fr} *is the outside radius of the fuel rod. Derive a relation for the temperature drop from the centre line to the outside surface of the rod. Determine this temperature drop for 35 mm outside diameter rod (k = 24 W/m°C) if heat is removed from the outside surface at the rate of* 2.5×10^6 W/m². *What will be surface heat transfer coefficient if the maximum wall surface temperature is limited to 180°C and the temperature of the fluid surrounding the rod is 70°C.*

Solution. Outside radius of the fuel rod, $R_{fr} = \dfrac{35}{2} = 17.5 \text{mm} = 0.0175 \text{ m}$

Thermal conductivity of fuel rod, $k_{fr} = 24$ W/m°C

Rate of heat removal, $\dfrac{Q}{A} = 2.5 \times 10^6$ W/m²

Maximum wall surface temperature, $t_w = 180°$C

Temperature of fluid surrounding the rod, $t_a = 70°$C

Temperature drop, $(t_{max} - t_w)$:

The heat flow at the outside surface of the fuel rod is given by

$$Q = \frac{q_o \, A R_{fr}}{4}$$ ...[Eqn. (2.119)]

or, $$\frac{Q}{A} = \frac{q_o \, R_{fr}}{4}$$

$$\therefore \qquad q_o = \frac{Q}{A} \times \frac{4}{R_{fr}} = 2.5 \times 10^6 \times \frac{4}{0.0175} = 5.714 \times 10^8 \text{ W/m}^3$$

The temperature drop from the centre line $(t = t_{max})$ to the outside surface $(t = t_w)$ of the fuel rod is given by

$$t_{max} - t_w = \frac{3 q_o \, R_{fr}^2}{16 k_{fr}}$$ ...[Eqn. (2.118)]

or, $$t_{max} - t_w = \frac{3 \times 5.714 \times 10^8 \times 0.0175^2}{16 \times 24} = \textbf{1367°C}$$ (**Ans.**)

Surface heat transfer coefficient, h :

$$Q = hA \, (t_w - t_a)$$

$$h = \frac{Q}{A} \cdot \frac{1}{(t_w - t_a)} = 2.5 \times 10^6 \times \frac{1}{(180 - 70)} = \textbf{22727 W/m}^2\textbf{°C}$$ (**Ans.**)

2.9.6. SPHERE WITH UNIFORM HEAT GENERATION

Consider one dimensional radial conduction of heat, under steady state conditions, through a sphere having uniform heat generation.

Let, R = Outside radius of sphere,

k = Thermal conductivity (uniform),

q_g = Uniform heat generation per unit volume, per unit time within the solid,

t_w = Temperature of the outside surface (wall) of the sphere, and

t_a = Ambient temperature.

Consider an element at radius r and thickness, dr as shown in Fig. 2.119.

Heat conducted in at radius r,

$$Q_r = -kA\frac{dt}{dr} = -k \times 4\pi r^2 \cdot \frac{dt}{dr}$$

Heat generated in the element,

$$Q_g = q_g \times A \times dr = q_g \times 4\pi r^2 \times dr$$

Heat conducted out at radius $(r + dr)$

$$Q_{(r+dr)} = Q_r + \frac{d}{dr}(Q_r)\,dr$$

Under steady state conditions, we have

$$Q_r + Q_g = Q_{(r+dr)}$$

$$= Q_r + \frac{d}{dr}(Q_r).dr$$

or, $$Q_g = \frac{d}{dr}(Q_r)\,dr$$

or, $$q_g \times 4\pi r^2 \times dr = \frac{d}{dr}\left[-4\pi k\,r^2 \cdot \frac{dt}{dr}\right]dr$$

or, $$q_g \times 4\pi r^2 \times dr = -4\pi k \frac{d}{dr}\left[r^2 \cdot \frac{dt}{dr}\right]dr$$

or, $$\frac{1}{r^2}\frac{d}{dr}\left[r^2 \cdot \frac{dt}{dr}\right] + \frac{q_g}{k} = 0 \qquad \ldots(i)$$

(Heat flow equation)

or, $$\frac{1}{r^2}\left[r^2 \cdot \frac{d^2t}{dr^2} + 2r \cdot \frac{dt}{dr}\right] + \frac{q_g}{k} = 0$$

or, $$\frac{d^2t}{dr^2} + \frac{2}{r} \times \frac{dt}{dr} + \frac{q_g}{k} = 0$$

or, $$r\frac{d^2t}{dt^2} + 2\frac{dt}{dr} + \frac{q_g r}{k} = 0 \qquad \text{(multiplying both sides by } r)$$

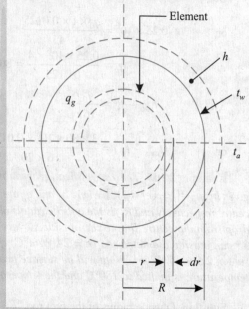

Fig. 2.119. Sphere with uniform heat generation.

or,
$$r\frac{d^2t}{dr^2} + \frac{dt}{dr} + \frac{dt}{dr} + \frac{q_g r}{k} = 0$$

or,
$$\frac{dt}{dr}\left(r\frac{dt}{dr}\right) + \frac{dt}{dr} + \frac{q_g r}{k} = 0$$

Integrating both sides, we have

$$r\frac{dt}{dr} + t + \frac{q_g}{k}\cdot\frac{r^2}{2} = C_1 \qquad\qquad\qquad ...(ii)$$

or,
$$\frac{d}{dr}(rt) + \frac{q_g}{k}\cdot\frac{r^2}{2} = C_1$$

Integrating again, we have

$$rt + \frac{q_g}{k}\cdot\frac{r^3}{6} = C_1 r + C_2 \qquad\qquad\qquad ...(iii)$$

(where C_1, C_2 = constants of integration).

At the centre of sphere, $r = 0$ $\qquad \therefore \qquad C_2 = 0$ $\qquad\qquad$ [From eqn. (iii)]

Applying boundary condition, at $r = R$, $t = t_w$ to eqn. (iii), we have

$$Rt_w + \frac{q_g}{k}\cdot\frac{R^3}{6} = C_1 R \qquad\qquad\qquad (\because C_2 = 0)$$

or,
$$C_1 = t_w + \frac{q_g}{6k} R^2$$

By substituting the values of C_1 and C_2 in eqn. (iii), we have the temperature distribution as

$$rt + \frac{q_g}{k}\cdot\frac{r^3}{6} = \left[t_w + \frac{q_g}{6k}R^2\right]r$$

or,
$$t + \frac{q_g}{6k}\cdot r^2 = t_w + \frac{q_g}{6k} R^2$$

or,
$$t = t_w + \frac{q_g}{6k}(R^2 - r^2) \qquad\qquad\qquad ...(2.122)$$

From eqn. (2.122) it is evident that the temperature distribution is *parabolic*; the maximum temperature occurs at the centre ($r = 0$) and its value is given by

$$t_{max} = t_w + \frac{q_g}{6k} R^2 \qquad\qquad\qquad ...(2.123)$$

From eqns. (2.122) and (2.123), we have

$$\frac{t - t_w}{t_{max} - t_w} = \frac{R^2 - r^2}{R^2} = 1 - \left(\frac{r}{R}\right)^2$$

i.e.,
$$\frac{t - t_w}{t_{max} - t_w} = 1 - \left(\frac{r}{R}\right)^2 \qquad\qquad\qquad ...(2.124)$$

(temperature distribution in *dimensionless form*)

Invoking Fourier's equation (to evaluate heat flow), we have

$$Q = -kA\left(\frac{dt}{dr}\right)_{r=R}$$

$$= -k \times 4\pi R^2 \times \frac{d}{dr}\left[t_w + \frac{q_g}{6k}(R^2 - r^2)\right]_{r=R}$$

[substituting the value of t from eqn. (2.122)]

$$= -k \times 4\pi R^2 \left[\frac{q_g}{6k}(-2r) \right]_{r=R} = k \times 4\pi R^2 \times \frac{q_g}{3k} \cdot R$$

or,

$$Q = \frac{4}{3}\pi R^3 \times q_g$$

(= volume of sphere × heat generation capacity)   ...(iv)

Thus heat conducted is equal to heat generated. Under steady state conditions the heat conducted (or generated) should be equal to the heat convected from the outer surface of the sphere.

i.e.,

$$q_g \times \frac{4}{3}\pi R^3 = h \times 4\pi R^2 (t_w - t_a)$$

or,

$$t_w = t_a + \frac{q_g R}{3h}$$

    ...(2.125)

Inserting this value of t_w in eqn. 2.122, we have

$$t = t_a + \frac{q_g R}{3h} + \frac{q_g}{6k}(R^2 - r^2)$$

    ...(2.126)

The maximum temperature, $t_{max} = t_a + \frac{q_g}{3k} \cdot R + \frac{q_g}{6k} \cdot R^2$ (at $r = 0$)   ...(2.127)

Example 2.104. *An approximately spherical shaped orange (k = 0.23 W/m°C), 90 mm in diameter, undergoes riping process and generates 5100 W/m³ of energy. If external surface of the orange is at 8°C, determine :*

(i) Temperature at the centre of the orange, and

(ii) Heat flow from the outer surface of the orange.

Solution. Outside radius of the orange, $R = \dfrac{90}{2} = 45$ mm $= 0.045$ m

Rate of heat generation, $q_g = 5100$ W/m³

The temperature at the outer surface of the orange, $t_w = 8°C$

(i) Temperature at the centre of the orange, t_{max} :

$$t_{max} = t_w + \frac{q_g}{6k} R^2$$

    ...[Eqn. (2.123)]

or,

$$t_{max} = 8 + \frac{5100}{(6 \times 0.23)} \times (0.045)^2 = \mathbf{15.48°C} \ \ \mathbf{(Ans.)}$$

(ii) Heat flow from the outer surface of the orange, Q :

Heat conducted = Heat generated

∴

$$Q = q_g \times \frac{4}{3}\pi R^3$$

or,

$$Q = 5100 \times \frac{4}{3}\pi \times (0.045)^3 = \mathbf{1.946\,W} \ \ \mathbf{(Ans.)}$$

Example 2.105. *Write down Fourier equation for heat conduction in spherical coordinate system. Hence, deduce an expression for steady state heat conduction in radial direction through a solid sphere of radius R with a uniform volumetric heat generation of q_g W/m³ at the centre. Assume thermal conductivity of the material of the cylinder to be constant.*   **(AMIE Summer, 2000)**

Solution. For constant thermal conductivity k, the general heat conduction equation in spherical coordinates is given as

$$\left[\frac{1}{r^2\sin^2\theta}\cdot\frac{\partial^2 t}{\partial\phi^2}+\frac{1}{r^2\sin\theta}\cdot\frac{\partial}{\partial\theta}\left\{\sin\theta\cdot\frac{\partial t}{\partial\theta}\right\}+\frac{1}{r^2}\cdot\frac{\partial}{\partial r}\left(r^2\cdot\frac{\partial t}{\partial r}\right)\right]+\frac{q_g}{k}=\frac{1}{\alpha}\cdot\frac{\partial t}{\partial\tau}$$

...[Eqn. (2.31)]

For steady state heat conduction in radial direction,

$$\frac{\partial t}{\partial\phi}\equiv 0,\ \frac{\partial t}{\partial\theta}\equiv 0,\ \text{and}\ \frac{\partial t}{\partial\tau}\equiv 0$$

Hence, the above equation reduces to

$$\frac{1}{r^2}\frac{d}{dr}\left(r^2\frac{dt}{dr}\right)+\frac{q_g}{k}=0$$

or

$$\frac{d}{dr}\left(r^2\frac{dt}{dr}\right)+\frac{q_g}{k}r^2=0$$

Integrating both sides, we get

$$r^2\frac{dt}{dr}+\frac{q_g}{k}\cdot\frac{r^3}{3}=C_1 \qquad ...(i)$$

At the centre, $\quad r=0,\ \dfrac{dt}{dr}=0$

$\therefore \qquad\qquad C_1=0$

The eqn. (i), therefore, reduces to

$$\frac{dt}{dr}=-\frac{q_g}{k}\cdot\frac{r}{3} \qquad ...(ii)$$

Heat conduction in radial direction, at any radius r, is

$$Q=-kA_r\frac{dt}{dr}$$

where, A_r = surface area of a sphere = $4\pi\,r^2$

Containment vessel at an operating nuclear power plant.

$\therefore \qquad Q=-k\,(4\pi r^2)\left(-\dfrac{q_g}{k}\cdot\dfrac{r}{3}\right)$, using eqn. (i)

$$=\frac{4}{3}\pi r^3\,q_g,\ \text{which is the required expression.}$$

Hence, heat conducted at the surface $=\dfrac{4}{3}\pi R^3\,q_g \quad$ **(Ans.)** $\qquad\qquad$ (Here $r=R$)

2.10. HEAT TRANSFER FROM EXTENDED SURFACES (FINS)

2.10.1. INTRODUCTION

Whenever the available surface is found *inadequate* to transfer the required quantity of heat with the available temperature drop and convective heat transfer coefficient, *extended surfaces* or *fins are used*. This practice, Invariably, is found necessary in heat transfer between a surface and gas as the convective heat transfer coefficient is rather low in these situations. The *finned surfaces* are widely used in :

(*i*) Economisers for steam power plants;

(*ii*) Convectors for steam and hot-water heating systems;

(*iii*) Radiators of automobiles;

(*iv*) Air-cooled engine cylinder heads;

(v) Cooling coils and condenser coils in refrigerators and air conditioners;

(vi) Small capacity compressors;

(vii) Electric motor bodies;

(viii) Transformers and electronic equipments etc.

In practice all kinds of shapes and sizes of fins are employed; some common types of fin configurations are shown in Fig. 2.120.

Radiators of automobiles.

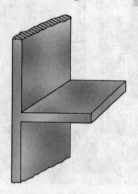

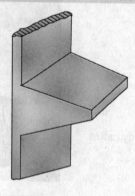

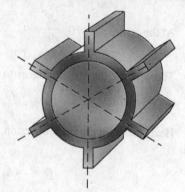

(i) Uniform straight fin   (ii) Tapered straight fin   (iii) Splines

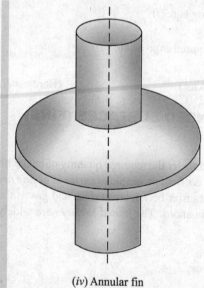

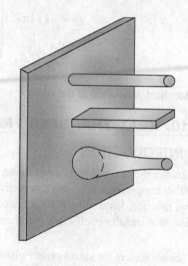

(iv) Annular fin   (v) Pin fins (spines)

Fig. 2.120. Common types of fin configurations.

For the proper design of fins, the knowledge of temperature distribution along the fin is necessary. In this article the mathematical analysis for finding out the temperature distribution and heat flow from different types of fins is dealt with.

The following **assumptions** are made for the analysis of heat flow through the fin :

1. Steady state heat conduction.

2. No heat generation within the fin.

3. Uniform heat transfer coefficient (h) over the entire surface of the fin.

4. Homogeneous and isotropic fin material (*i.e.* thermal conductivity of material constant).

5. Negligible contact thermal resistance.

6. Heat conduction one-dimensional.

7. Negligible radiation.

2.10.2. HEAT FLOW THROUGH "RECTANGULAR FIN"

Consider a rectangular fin protruding from a wall surface as shown in Fig. 2.121.

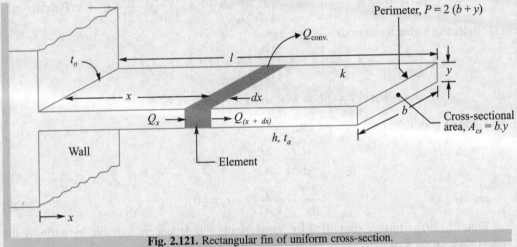

Fig. 2.121. Rectangular fin of uniform cross-section.

Let, l = Length of the fin (perpendicular to surface from which heat is to be removed),

b = Width of the fin (parallel to the surface from which heat is to be removed),

y = Thickness of the fin,

P = Perimeter of the fin [$=2(b + y)$],

A_{cs} = Area of cross-section ($=by$),

t_o = Temperature at the base of the fin, and

t_a = Temperature of the ambient/surrounding fluid,

k = Thermal conductivity (constant), and

h = Heat transfer coefficient (convective).

In order to determine the governing differential equation for the fins, shown in Fig. 2.121, consider the heat flow to and from an element dx thick at a distance x from the base.

Heat conducted into the element at plane x,

$$Q_x = -k\, A_{cs} \left[\frac{dt}{dx}\right]_x \qquad \qquad ...(i)$$

Heat conducted out of the element at plane ($x + dx$)

$$Q_{(x + dx)} = -k A_{cs} \left[\frac{dt}{dx} \right]_{x + dx} \qquad \qquad ...(ii)$$

Heat convected out of the element between the planes x and $(x + dx)$,

$$Q_{conv} = h (P . dx) (t - t_a)$$

Applying an energy balance on the element, we can write

$$Q_x = Q_{(x+dx)} + Q_{conv.}$$

$$-k A_{cs} \left[\frac{dt}{dx} \right]_x = -k A_{cs} \left[\frac{dt}{dx} \right]_{x + dx} + h (P . dx) (t - t_a) \qquad \qquad ...(2.128)$$

Making a Taylor's expansion of the temperature gradient at $(x + dx)$ in terms of that at x, we get

$$\left(\frac{dt}{dx} \right)_{x + dx} = \left(\frac{dt}{dx} \right)_x + \frac{d}{dx} \left(\frac{dt}{dx} \right)_x dx + \frac{d^2}{dx^2} \left(\frac{dt}{dx} \right) \frac{(dx)^2}{2!} + ...$$

Substituting this in eqn. (2.128), we have

$$-k A_{cs} \left[\frac{dt}{dx} \right]_x = -k A_{cs} \left[\frac{dt}{dx} \right]_x - k A_{CS} \left[\frac{d^2 t}{dx^2} \right]_x dx - k A_{cs} \left[\frac{d^3 t}{dx^3} \right] \frac{(dx)^2}{2!} + .. + h (P . dx) (t - t_a)$$

Neglecting higher terms as $dx \to 0$, we have

$$-k A_{cs} \left[\frac{dt}{dx} \right] = -k A_{cs} \left[\frac{dt}{dx} \right] - k A_{cs} \left[\frac{d^2 t}{dx^2} \right] dx + h (P . dx) (t - t_a)$$

$$k A_{cs} \left[\frac{d^2 t}{dx^2} \right] dx - h (P . dx) (t - t_a) = 0$$

Dividing both sides by $A_{cs} dx$, we get,

$$k \frac{d^2 t}{dx^2} - \frac{hP}{A_{cs}} (t - t_a) = 0$$

or,
$$\frac{d^2 t}{dx^2} - \frac{h P}{k A_{cs}} (t - t_a) = 0 \qquad \qquad ...(2.129)$$

Eqn. (2.129) is further simplified by transforming the dependent variable by defining the *temperature excess* θ as,

$$\theta_{(x)} = t_{(x)} - t_{(a)}$$

As the ambient temperature t_a is constant, we get by differentiation

$$\frac{d\theta}{dx} = \frac{dt}{dx} ; \quad \frac{d^2 \theta}{dx^2} = \frac{d^2 t}{dx^2}$$

Thus,
$$\frac{d^2 \theta}{dx^2} - m^2 \theta = 0 \qquad \qquad ...(2.130)$$

where
$$m = \sqrt{\frac{h P}{k A_{cs}}}$$

Eqns. (2.129) and (2.130) represent a general form of the energy equation for one-dimensional heat dissipation from an extended surface (fin). The parameter m, for a given fin, is constant provided the convective film coefficient h is constant over the whole surface and the thermal conductivity k is constant within the temperature range considered. Then the general solution of this linear and homogeneous second order differential equation is of the form :

$$\theta = C_1 e^{mx} + C_2 e^{-mx} \qquad \qquad ...(2.131)$$

or,
$$[t - t_a = C_1 e^{mx} + C_2 e^{-mx}]$$

where C_1 and C_2 are the constants, these are to be determined by using proper boundary conditions.

One boundary condition is :

$$\theta = \theta_o = t_o - t_a \qquad \text{at } x = 0$$

The other boundary condtition depends on the *physical situation*. The following cases may be considered :

Case I. The *fin is infinitely long* and the temperature at the end of the fin is esentially that of the ambient/surrounding fluid.

Case II. The end of the *fin is insulated.*

Case III. The *fin is of finite length* and loses heat by convection.

2.10.2.1. Heat dissipation from an infinitely long fin ($l \to \infty$) :

Refer to Fig. 2.122. In this case the boundary conditions are :

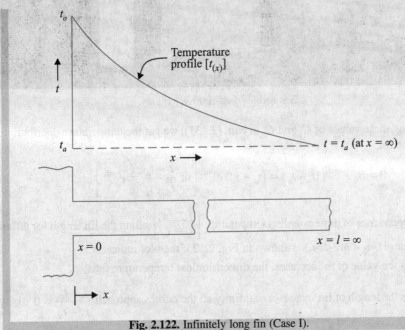

Fig. 2.122. Infinitely long fin (Case I).

(*i*) At $\quad x = 0, \qquad\qquad t = t_o \qquad$ (Temperature at the base of fin equals the temperature of the surface to which fin is attached.)

$$t - t_a = t_o - t_a \qquad\qquad \text{(in terms of excess temperature)}$$

or, At $\quad x = 0, \qquad\qquad \theta = \theta_o$

(*ii*) At $\quad x = \infty, \qquad\qquad t = t_a$

(Temperature at the end of an infinitely long fin equals that of the surroundings)

At $\qquad x = \infty, \qquad\qquad \theta = 0$ (in terms of *excess temperature*)

Substituting these boundary conditions in eqn. (2.131), we get,

$$C_1 + C_2 = \theta_0 \qquad\qquad\qquad\qquad \text{...(}i\text{)}$$
$$C_1 e^{m(\infty)} + C_2\, e^{-m(\infty)} = 0 \qquad\qquad \text{...(}ii\text{)}$$

or, $\qquad\qquad C_1 e^{m(\infty)} + 0 = 0 \qquad \therefore C_1 = 0$

and, $\qquad\qquad\qquad C_2 = \theta_0 \qquad\qquad\qquad\qquad\qquad$ [From eqn. (*i*)]

Gas turbine based power plants.

Inserting these values of C_1 and C_2 in eqn. (2.131), we get the temperature distribution along the length of the fin,

$$\theta = \theta_0 \, e^{-mx}; \; (t - t_a) = (t_o - t_a) e^{-mx} \left[\text{or } \frac{t - t_a}{t_o - t_a} = e^{-mx} \right] \qquad \qquad ...(2.132)$$

The dependence of dimensionless temperature $\left[\dfrac{t - t_a}{t_o - t_a} \right]$ along the fin length for different values of parameter m $(m_1 < m_2 < m_3)$ is shown in Fig. 2.123; the plot indicates :

(i) As the value of m increases, the dimensionless temperature falls;

(ii) As the length of fin increases to infinity all the curves approach $\dfrac{t - t_a}{t_o - t_a} = 0$ *asymptotically.*

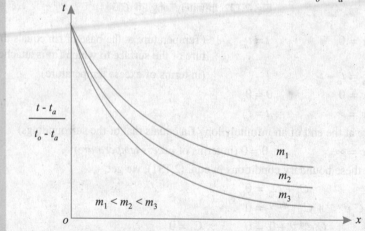

Fig. 2.123. Temperature distribution in a fin.

The heat flow rate can be determined in *either* of the two ways :

(*a*) By considering the heat flow across the root (or base) by conduction;

(*b*) By considering the heat which is transmitted by convection from the surface of the fin to the surrounding fluid.

(*a*) The rate of heat flow across the base of the fin is given by (Fourier's equation)

$$Q_{fin} = -k\, A_{cs} \left[\frac{dt}{dx} \right]_{x=0}$$

$$\left[\frac{dt}{dx} \right]_{x=0} = \left[-m(t_0 - t_a)e^{-mx} \right]_{x=0} = -m(t_0 - t_a) \quad \text{[From eqn. (2.132)]}$$

$$\therefore \qquad\qquad Q_{fin} = -k\, A_{cs} \times [-m\,(t_o - t_a)] = k\, A_{cs}\, m\,(t_o - t_a)$$

i.e., $\qquad\qquad Q_{fin} = k\, A_{cs}\, m\,(t_o - t_a) \qquad\qquad\qquad$ ...(2.133)

or, $\qquad\qquad Q_{fin} = k\, A_{cs} \sqrt{\dfrac{Ph}{kA_{cs}}}\,(t_0 - t_a) \qquad\qquad$ (Substituting for *m*)

or, $\qquad\qquad Q_{fin} = \sqrt{Ph\, k\, A_{cs}}\,(t_0 - t_a) \qquad\qquad$ ...[2.133 (*a*)]

(*b*) *Alternatively* :

$$Q_{fin} = \int_0^\infty h\,(P.dx)(t - t_a) \qquad\qquad \text{...convective rate of heat flow}$$

$$= \int_0^\infty h\, P\,(t_o - t_a)\, e^{-mx}\, dx \qquad\qquad \text{[From Eqn. (2.132)]}$$

$$= h\, P\,(t_o - t_a)\int_0^\infty e^{-mx}\, dx$$

$$= h\, P\,(t_o - t_a)\frac{1}{m} = h\, P\,(t_o - t_a)\sqrt{\frac{k\, A_{cs}}{Ph}} \qquad \text{(Substituting for *m*)}$$

or, $\qquad\qquad Q_{fin} = \sqrt{Ph\, kA_{cs}}\,(t_o - t_a) \qquad\qquad$ ...[Same as Eqn. 2.133 (*a*)]

[An infinitely long fin is one for which $m_l \rightarrow \infty$, and this condition may be approached when $ml > 5$]

From the Eqn. (2.132) it is evident that the temperature falls towards the tip of the fin, thus the area near the fin tip is *not utilised to the extent as the lateral area near the base*. Hence beyond a certain point the increase in the length of the fin *does not contribute much in respect of increase in the dissipation of heat.* Consequently a *tapered fin* is considered to be a *better design* since its lateral area is more near the base/root where temperature difference is high.

Example 2.106. *Calculate the amount of energy required to solder together two very long pieces of bare copper wire 1.5 mm in diameter with solder that melts at 190°C. The wires are positioned vertically in air at 20°C. Assume that the heat transfer coefficient on the wire surface is 20W/m²°C and thermal conductivity of wire alloy is 330 W/m°C.*

Solution. *Given :* $\qquad d = 1.5\text{ mm} = 0.0015\text{ m};\ t_o = 190°C;\ t_a = 20°C;$

$\qquad\qquad\qquad\qquad h = 20\text{ W/m}^2°C;\ k = 330\text{ W/m}°C.$

Energy required to solder :

Area of cross-section, $\qquad A_{cs} = \dfrac{\pi}{4}d^2 = \dfrac{\pi}{4} \times 0.0015^2 = 1.767 \times 10^{-6}\text{ m}^2$

Perimeter, $\qquad\qquad P = \pi\, d = \pi \times 0.0015 = 4.712 \times 10^{-3}\text{ m}$

Heat dissipation from a long fin is given by,

$$Q_{fin} = k\, A_{cs}\, m\,(t_o - t_a) \qquad\qquad \text{...[Eqn. (2.133)]}$$

where, $\qquad m = \sqrt{\dfrac{h\, P}{k\, A_{cs}}} = \sqrt{\dfrac{20}{330} \times \dfrac{4.712 \times 10^{-3}}{1.767 \times 10^{-6}}} = 12.71\text{ m}^{-1}$

$$\therefore \qquad Q_{fin} = 330 \times 1.767 \times 10^{-6} \times 12.71 \,(190 - 20) = 1.26 \text{ W}$$

$\therefore$ Total energy required for two wires $= 2 \times 1.26 = \textbf{2.52 W}$ **(Ans.)**

Example 2.107. *It is required to heat oil to about 300°C for frying purpose. A laddle is used in the frying. The section of the handle is 5 mm $\times$ 18 mm. The surroundings are at 30°C. The conductivity of the material is 205 W/m°C. If the temperature at a distance of 380 mm from the oil should not reach 40°C, determine the convective heat transfer coefficient.*

Solution. Refer to Fig. 2.124. $t_o = 300°C$; $b = 18$ mm $= 0.018$ m; $y = 5$ mm $= 0.005$ m; $l = 380$ mm $= 0.38$ m; $k = 205$ W/m°C; $t_a = 30°C$.

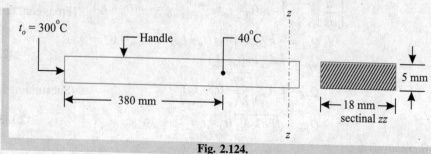

Fig. 2.124.

Convective heat transfer coefficient, h :

Assumming the *fin* to be *long one*, we have

$$\frac{t - t_a}{t_o - t_a} = e^{-mx} \qquad\qquad\qquad\qquad \text{...[Eqn. (2.132)]}$$

or,
$$\frac{t_o - t_a}{t - t_a} = e^{mx}$$

or,
$$\frac{300 - 30}{40 - 30} = e^{m \times 0.38} \qquad\qquad\qquad (\because x = 380 \text{ mm} = 0.38 \text{ m})$$

or,
$$e^{0.38m} = 27 \qquad \text{or} \qquad m = 8.673$$

But,
$$m = \sqrt{\frac{hP}{kA_{cs}}} = 8.673$$

or,
$$\frac{hP}{kA_{cs}} = 75.22$$

or,
$$\frac{h \times [(0.018 + 0.005) \times 2]}{205 \times (0.018 \times 0.005)} = 75.22$$

or,
$$h = \frac{75.22 \times 205 \times (0.018 \times 0.005)}{(0.018 + 0.005) \times 2} = \textbf{30.17 W/m}^2\textbf{°C} \quad \textbf{(Ans.)}$$

Example 2.108. *A temperature rise of 60°C in a circular shaft of 60 mm diameter is caused by the amount of heat generated due to friction in the bearing mounted on the crankshaft. The thermal conductivity of the shaft material is 50 W/m°C and the heat transfer coefficient is 6.5 W/m²°C.*

(i) Develop an expression for the temperature distribution;

(ii) Determine amount of heat transferred through the shaft.

Assume that the shaft is a rod of infinite length.

Solution. Temperature rise, $\qquad \theta_o = 60°C$

Diameter of the shaft, $\qquad\qquad d = 60$ mm $= 0.06$ m

Thermal conductivity of material, $k = 50$ W/m°C

Heat transfer coefficient, $\qquad\qquad h = 6.5$ W/m² °C

(*i*) **Expression for temperature distribution :**

The general expression for temperature distribution for an extended surface is given by

$$\theta = C_1 e^{mx} + C_2 e^{-mx} \qquad\qquad ...[Eqn. (2.131)]$$

Using the following boundary conditions, we have

At $\qquad x = 0,$ $\qquad\qquad \theta = \theta_o$

At $\qquad x = \infty,$ $\qquad\qquad \theta = 0$

$\qquad\qquad C_1 = 0;$ $\qquad\qquad C_2 = \theta_o$

$\therefore \qquad\qquad\qquad \theta = \theta_o\, e^{-mx} ...Required\ expression.$ **(Ans.)**

(*ii*) **Amount of heat transferred, Q :**

$$Q = -k\,A_{cs}\cdot\left.\frac{d\theta}{dx}\right|_{x=0}$$

$$= -k\,A_{cs}\cdot\left[\frac{d}{dx}(\theta_o\, e^{-mx})\right]_{x=0}$$

or, $\qquad\qquad Q = kA_{cs}\, m\theta_0$

where, $\qquad\qquad m = \sqrt{\dfrac{hP}{k\,A_{cs}}} = \sqrt{\dfrac{h}{k}\times\dfrac{\pi d}{\frac{\pi}{4}d^2}}\sqrt{\dfrac{4h}{kd}} = \sqrt{\dfrac{4\times6.5}{50\times0.06}} = 2.944$

$\therefore \qquad\qquad Q = 50\times\left(\dfrac{\pi}{4}\times0.06^2\right)\times2.944\times60 = \mathbf{24.97\,W} \qquad$ **(Ans.)**

Example 2.109. *A very long 25 mm diameter copper rod (k = 380 W/m°C) extends horizontally from a plane heated wall at 120°C. The temperature of the surrounding air is 25°C and the convective heat transfer coefficient is 9.0W/m²°C.*

(*i*) *Determine the heat loss;*

(*ii*) *How long the rod be in order to be considered infinite?*

Solution. $d = 25$ mm $= 0.025$ m; $k = 380$ W/m°C; $t_o = 120$°C; $t_a = 25$°C; $h = 9.0$ W/m²°C.

(*i*) **Heat loss:**

Heat dissipation from an *infinitely long fin* is given by

$$Q_{fin} = k\,A_{cs}\, m\,(t_o - t_a) \qquad\qquad ...[Eqn. (2.133)]$$

where, $\qquad\qquad m = \sqrt{\dfrac{hP}{k\,A_{cs}}} = \sqrt{\dfrac{h\times\pi d}{k\times\frac{\pi}{4}d^2}} = \sqrt{\dfrac{4h}{kd}} = \sqrt{\dfrac{4\times9.0}{380\times0.025}} = 1.946$

$\therefore \qquad\qquad Q_{fin} = k\times\dfrac{\pi}{4}d^2\times\sqrt{\dfrac{4h}{kd}}\,(t_o - t_a)$

$$= 380\times\dfrac{\pi}{4}\times0.025^2\times1.946\,(120 - 25) = \mathbf{34.48\,W} \qquad \textbf{(Ans.)}$$

(*ii*) **Length of the rod (to be considered infinite) :**

Since there is no heat loss from the tip of an infinitely long rod and as such it behaves as if the tip were *insulated*; therefore, an estimate of the validity of this approximation can be made by comparing the following two expressions for the fin :

$$Q_{fin} = kA_{cs}\, m\,(t_o - t_a) \ ...\ infinitely\ long\ fin;$$

$$Q_{fin} = k_{Acs}\, m\,(t_o - t_a)\ \tanh{(ml)} \ ...\ fin\ with\ tip\ insulated.$$

Equivalent results are obtained if $\tanh{(ml)} \ge 0.99$ or $ml \ge 2.646$.

Hence the rod can be considered infinite if

$$l \geq \frac{2.646}{m} = \frac{2.646}{1.946} = 1.36\,m \quad \text{(Ans.)}$$

Example 2.110. *Two long rods of the same diameter, one made of brass (k = 85 W/m°C) and other made of copper (k = 375 W/m°C) have one of their ends inserted into the furnace. Both of the rods are exposed to the same environment. At a distance 105 mm away from the furnace end, the temperature of the brass rod is 120°C. At what distance from the furnace end the same temperature would be reached in the copper rod ?*

(IES-1993)

Solution. $k_1 = 85$ W/m°C; $k_2 = 375$ W/m°C

The controlling differential equation for the heat flow in the rod is given by

$$\frac{d^2\theta}{dx^2} - m^2\theta = 0$$

The general solution is

$$\theta = C_1 e^{mx} + C_2 e^{-mx} \qquad \text{...(1)}$$

The boundary conditions are :

(*i*) At $x = 0$, $\theta = \theta_o$

(*ii*) At $x = \infty$, $\theta = 0$

Using the boundary condition (*ii*), we get

$$0 = C_1 e^{mx} \quad \therefore \ C_1 = 0$$

$$\therefore \qquad \theta = C_2 e^{-mx} \qquad \text{...(2)}$$

[Substituting $C_1 = 0$ in eqn. (1)]

Now using boundary condition (*i*), we get

$$\theta_o = C_2$$

$$\therefore \qquad \theta = \theta_o e^{-mx}$$

[Substituting $C_2 = \theta_o$ in eqn (2)]

or, $$\frac{\theta}{\theta_0} = \frac{t - t_a}{t_o - t_a} = e^{-mx}$$

$$\therefore \qquad t = t_a + (t_o - t_a)e^{-mx} \qquad \text{...(3)}$$

Finned surfaces are widely used in condenser coils in refrigerators.

Now using eqn. (3) for *brass rod*, when $t = 120$°C at $x = 105$ mm $= 0.105$ m, we have

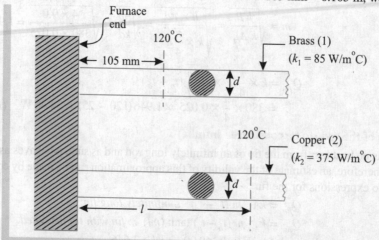

Furnace end

120°C

← 105 mm →

$\uparrow d$

Brass (1)
$(k_1 = 85$ W/m°C)

120°C

$\uparrow d$

Copper (2)
$(k_2 = 375$ W/m°C)

l

Fig. 2.125.

$$\therefore \qquad 120 = t_a + (t_o - t_a)\, e^{(-m_1 \times 0.105)} \qquad \qquad ...(4)$$

Now using eqn. (3) for *copper rod*, when $t = 120°C$ at $x = l$, we have

$$\therefore \qquad 120 = t_a + (t_0 - t_a)\, e^{-m_2 l} \qquad \qquad ...(5)$$

as t_a and t_o are same for both the rods.

Equating (4) and (5), we get

$$e^{-m_1 \times 0.105} = e^{-m_2 l} \qquad \text{or} \qquad 0.105\, m_1 = m_2 l$$

$$\therefore \qquad l = \frac{m_1}{m_2} \times 0.105 \qquad \qquad ...(6)$$

But,

$$m_1 = \sqrt{\frac{hP}{k_1 A_{cs}}} \qquad \text{and} \qquad m_2 = \sqrt{\frac{hP}{k_2 A_{cs}}}$$

and,

$$\frac{m_1}{m_2} = \sqrt{\frac{hP}{k_1 A_{cs}}} \times \sqrt{\frac{k_2 A_{cs}}{hP}} = \sqrt{\frac{k_2}{k_1}} = \sqrt{\frac{375}{85}} = 2.1$$

$$\therefore \qquad l = 2.1 \times 0.105 = 0.22 \text{ m or } \textbf{220 mm} \quad \textbf{(Ans.)}$$

2.10.2.2. Heat dissipation from a fin insulated at the tip :

Fig. 2.126 illustrates a fin of finite length with insulated end (*i.e.* no heat loss from the end of the fin).

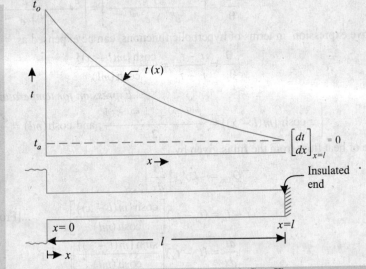

Fig. 2.126. The fin with insulated end (Case II).

The boundary conditions are :

(*i*) At $\quad x = 0, \qquad\qquad \theta = \theta_o$

(*ii*) A $\quad x = l, \qquad\qquad \dfrac{dt}{dx} = 0$

Applying these boundary conditions to eqn. (2.131), we have

$$C_1 + C_2 = \theta_o \qquad \qquad ...(i)$$

Further

$$t - t_a = C_1 e^{mx} + C_2 e^{-mx} \qquad \qquad \text{[Eqn. 2.131]}$$

$$\frac{dt}{dx} = m C_1 e^{mx} - m C_2 e^{-mx}$$

$$\left[\frac{dt}{dx}\right]_{x=l} = m C_1 e^{ml} - m C_2 e^{-ml} = 0$$

$$\therefore \qquad C_1 e^{ml} - C_2 e^{-ml} = 0 \qquad \qquad \text{[As per boundary condition (ii)]}$$

Solving eqns. (*i*) and (*ii*), we have

$$C_2 = \theta_o - C_1 \qquad \text{...[From eqn. (i)]}$$

$$C_1 e^{ml} - (\theta_o - C_1) \, e^{-ml} = 0$$

or, $\qquad C_1 e^{ml} - \theta_o \, e^{-ml} + C_1 \, e^{-ml} = 0$

or, $\qquad C_1 \, (e^{ml} + e^{-ml}) = \theta_o \, e^{-ml}$

or, $\qquad C_1 = \theta_o \left[\dfrac{e^{-ml}}{e^{ml} + e^{-ml}} \right]$

$\therefore \qquad C_2 = \theta_o - \left[\theta_o \left\{ \dfrac{e^{-ml}}{e^{ml} + e^{-ml}} \right\} \right] \qquad \text{...[From eqn. (i)]}$

or, $\qquad C_2 = \theta_o \left[1 - \dfrac{e^{-ml}}{e^{ml} + e^{-ml}} \right] = \theta_o \left[\dfrac{e^{ml}}{e^{ml} + e^{-ml}} \right]$

Inserting the values of C_1 and C_2 in eqn. (2.131), we have

$$\theta = \theta_o \left[\frac{e^{-ml}}{e^{ml} + e^{-ml}} \right] e^{mx} + \theta_o \left[\frac{e^{ml}}{e^{ml} + e^{-ml}} \right] e^{-mx}$$

or, $\qquad \dfrac{\theta}{\theta_o} = \left[\dfrac{e^{m(x-l)} + e^{m(l-x)}}{e^{ml} + e^{-ml}} \right] = \left[\dfrac{e^{m(l-x)} + e^{[-m(l-x)]}}{e^{ml} + e^{-ml}} \right]$

The above expression, in terms of hyperbolic functions, can be expensed as

$$\frac{\theta}{\theta_o} = \frac{t - t_a}{t_o - t_a} = \frac{\cosh\{m(l-x)\}}{\cosh(ml)} \qquad ..(2.134)$$

...*Expression for temperature distribution*

$$\left[\because \cosh\{m(l-x)\} = \frac{e^{m(l-x)} + e^{[-m(l-x)]}}{2}, \text{ and } \cosh(ml) = \frac{e^{ml} + e^{-ml}}{2} \right]$$

The rate of heat flow from the fin is given by

$$Q_{fin} = -k \, A_{cs} \left[\frac{dt}{dx} \right]_{x=0}$$

Now, $\qquad t - t_a = (t_o - t_a) \left[\dfrac{\cosh\{m(l-x)\}}{\cosh(ml)} \right] \qquad \text{...[From eqn. (2.134)]}$

$$\frac{dt}{dx} = (t_o - t_a) \left[\frac{\sinh\{m(l-x)\}}{\cosh(ml)} \right] (-m)$$

$$\left[\because \frac{d}{dx}[\cosh(mx)] = m \sinh(mx) \right]$$

$$\left[\frac{dt}{dx} \right]_{x=0} = -m(t_o - t_a) \tanh(ml)$$

$\therefore \qquad Q_{fin} = kA_{cs} \, m \, (t_o - t_a) \tanh(ml) \qquad ...(2.135)$

(Substituting for m)

or, $\qquad Q_{fin} = \sqrt{PhkA_{cs}} \, (t_o - t_a) \tanh(ml) \qquad ...[2.135\,(a)]$

Example 2.111. *Aluminium fins of rectangular profile are attached on a plane wall with 5 mm spacing. The fins have thickness y = 1 mm, length l = 10 mm, and the thermal conductivity, k = 200 W/m K. The wall is maintained at a temperature 200°C, and the fins dissipate heat by convection into the ambient air at 40°C, with heat transfer coefficient h = 50 W/m²K. Determine the heat loss.*

(AMIE Winter, 1998)

Solution. *Given* : $t = 1$ mm $= 0.001$ m; $l = 10$ mm $= 0.01$ m; $y = 1$ mm $= 0.001$ m;
$k = 200$ W/mK; $t_o = 200°C$; $t_a = 40°C$; $h = 50$ W/m² K.

Heat loss, Q :

$$m = \sqrt{\frac{hP}{kA_{cs}}} = \sqrt{\frac{h(b+y) \times 2}{k(b \times y)}}$$

$$= \sqrt{\frac{h \times 2b}{k \times by}}, \text{ assuming } b \gg y$$

$$= \sqrt{\frac{2h}{ky}} = \sqrt{\frac{2 \times 50}{200 \times 0.001}} = 22.36$$

For unit width of the fin, $(b = 1$ m)

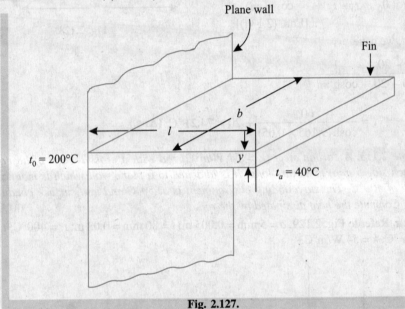

Fig. 2.127.

$$Q = \sqrt{PhkA_{cs}} \ (t_0 - t_a) \ \tanh(ml)$$

$$= \sqrt{(2 \times 1) \times 50 \times 200 \times (1 \times 0.001)} \times (200 - 40) \times \tanh(22.36 \times 0.01)$$

$$= \tanh(0.2236) = \textbf{157.38 W/m} \qquad \textbf{(Ans.)}$$

Example 2.112. *Find out the amount of heat transferred through an iron fin of length 50 mm, width 100 mm and thickness 5 mm. Assume $k = 210$ kJ/mh°C and $h = 42$ kJ/m²h°C for the material of the fin and the temperature at the base of the fin as 80°C. Also determine the temperature at tip of the fin, if the atmosphere temperature is 20°C.* (AMIE, Summer, 2000)

Solution. Given : $l = 50$ mm $= 0.05$ m; $b = 100$ mm $= 0.1$ m; $y = 5$ mm $= 0.005$ m;
$k = 210$ kJ/mh°C; $h = 42$ kJ/m²h°C; $t_0 = 80°C$; $t_a = 20°C$.

Amount of heat transferred through the fin, Q :

Perimeter, $\qquad P = 2(b + y) = 2(0.1 + 0.005) = 0.21$ m

Area, $\qquad A_{cs} = b \times y = 0.1 \times 0.005 = 0.0005$ m²

$$m = \sqrt{\frac{hP}{kA_{cs}}} = \sqrt{\frac{42 \times 0.21}{210 \times 0.0005}} = 9.165$$

$$\therefore \qquad Q_{\text{fin}} = \sqrt{PhkA_{cs}}\,(t_0 - t_a)\tanh{(ml)}$$

$$...[\text{Eqn. (2.135)}]$$

$$= \sqrt{0.21 \times 42 \times 210 \times 0.0005}$$

$$\times (80 - 20)\tanh{(9.165 \times 0.05)}$$

$$= 0.9263 \times 60 \times 0.4286$$

$$= \textbf{24.75 kJ/h (Ans.)}$$

Temperature at the tip of the fin, Q_L :

We know that,

$$\frac{\theta}{\theta_0} = \frac{t - t_a}{t_0 - t_a} = \frac{\cosh{\{m(l - x)\}}}{\cosh{(ml)}}$$

$$...[\text{Eqn. (2.134)}]$$

At $x = l$, we have

$$\frac{t - 20}{80 - 20} = \frac{1}{\cosh{ml}}$$

or, $\qquad t = \dfrac{60}{\cosh{(9.165 \times 0.05)}} + 20 = \textbf{74.21°C (Ans.)}$

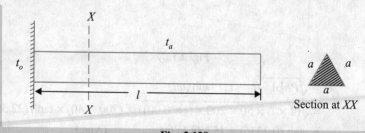

Fig. 2.128.

Example 2.113. *A carbon steel ($k = 54$ W/m°C) rod with a cross-section of an equilateral triangle (each side 5 mm) is 80 mm long. It is attached to a plane wall which is maintained at a temperature of 400°C. The surrounding environment is at 50°C and unit surface conductance is 90 W/m²°C. Compute the heat dissipated by the rod.* (M.U., 1997)

Solution. Refer to Fig. 2.129. $a = 5$ mm $= 0.005$ m; $l = 80$ mm $= 0.08$ m; $t_o = 400°C$; $t_a = 50°C$; $h = 90$ W/m²°C; $k = 54$ W/m°C.

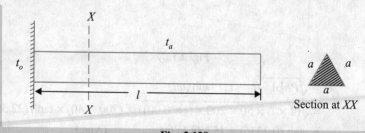

Fig. 2.129.

Heat dissipated by the rod, Q :

The heat flow from the rod (considering tip of the fin to be *insulated*) is given by

$$Q = kA_{cs}\,m\,(t_o - t_a)\tanh{(ml)} \qquad ...[\text{Eqn. (2.135)}]$$

where, $\qquad m = \sqrt{\dfrac{hP}{kA_{cs}}};\, P = 3a, A_{cs} = \dfrac{1}{2} \times a \times \left(\dfrac{\sqrt{3}}{2}a\right) = \dfrac{\sqrt{3}}{4}a^2$

$$\therefore \qquad \frac{P}{A_{cs}} = \frac{3a}{\dfrac{\sqrt{3}}{4} \times a^2} = \frac{4\sqrt{3}}{a} = \frac{6.93}{0.005} = 1386$$

and, $\qquad m = \sqrt{\dfrac{90}{54} \times 1386} = 48.06$

Substituting the values in the above equation, we have

$$Q = 54 \times \left[\frac{\sqrt{3}}{4} \times (0.005)^2 \right] \times 48.06 \times (400 - 50) \tanh(48.06 \times 0.08) = \textbf{9.82 W} \quad \textbf{(Ans.)}$$

Example 2.114. *The aluminium square fins (0.5 mm × 0.5 mm) of 10 mm length are provided on a surface of semiconductor electronic device to carry 1W of energy generated by electronic device. The temperature at the surface of the device should not exceed 80°C when surrounding temperature is 40°C.*

Taking the following data, find the number of fins required to carry out above duty. Neglect the heat loss from the end of fins.

$$k \text{ (aluminium)} = 200 \text{ W/m°C}; \ h = 15 \text{ W/m}^2\text{°C} \hspace{2cm} \text{(M.U.)}$$

Solution. *Given :* A_{cs} (area of cross-section of fin) $= 0.5$ mm $\times 0.5$ mm $= 2.5 \times 10^{-7}$ m^2; $l = 10$ mm $= 0.01$ m; Q (rate of heat transfer) $= 1$ W; $t_0 = 80°C$; $t_a = 40°C$; $k = 200$ W/m°C; $h = 15$ W/m^2°C.

Number of fins required, n :

The heat carried by n number of fins is given by

$$Q_{fins} = n \left[k A_{cs} m (t_o - t_a) \tanh (ml) \right]$$

$$...\text{[Refer Eqn. (2.135)]}$$

Where, $m = \sqrt{\dfrac{hP}{kA_{cs}}} = \sqrt{\dfrac{15 \times \left(4 \times \dfrac{0.5}{1000} \right)}{200 \times 2.5 \times 10^{-7}}} = 24.5$

Aluminium fins.

$$\left[\text{where } P \text{ (perimeter)} = 4 \times \frac{0.5}{1000} \text{ m} \right] \text{ and } ml = 24.5 \times 0.01 = 0.245$$

Substituting the values in the above equation, we have

$$l = n \left[200 \times 2.5 \times 10^{-7} \times 24.5 \ (80 - 40) \tanh (0.245) \right]$$
$$= n \ (200 \times 2.5 \times 10^{-7} \times 24.5 \times 40 \times 0.2402) = 0.01177$$

$$\therefore \hspace{3cm} n = \frac{1}{0.01177} \simeq \textbf{85} \hspace{2cm} \textbf{(Ans.)}$$

Example 2.115. *Pin fins are provided to increase the heat transfer rate from a hot surface. Which of the following arrangement will give higher heat transfer rate ?*

(i)   6 – fins of 10 cm length.

(ii) 12 – fins of 5 cm length.

Take k (fins material) = 200 W/m°C, h = 20 W/m^2°C

Cross-sectional area of fin = 2 cm^2

Perimeter of fin = 4 cm

Fin base temperature = 230°C

Surrounding air temperature = 30°C \hspace{2cm} (Shivaji University, 1997)

Solution. *Given :* $A_{cs} = 2 \times 10^{-4}$ m^2; $P = 0.04$ m, $t_o = 230°C$; $t_a = 30°C$; $k = 200$ W/m°C; $h = 20$ W/m^2°C.

The heat flow through 'n' number of fins is given by

$$Q = n \left[k A_{cs} m (t_0 - t_a) \tanh (ml) \right]$$

where, $\hspace{2cm} m = \sqrt{\dfrac{hP}{kA_{cs}}} = \sqrt{\dfrac{20 \times 0.04}{200 \times 2 \times 10^{-4}}} = 4.47$

(i) *Case I.* $n = 6$ and $l = 10$ cm $= 0.1$ m

$ml = 4.47 \times 0.1 = 0.447$

$\therefore$ $Q_1 = 6 [200 \times 2 \times 10^{-4} \times 4.47 \times (230 - 30) \tanh (0.447)] = 89.99$ W

(ii) *Case II.* $n = 12$ and $l = 5$ cm $= 0.05$ m $ml = 4.47 \times 0.05 = 0.2235$

$\therefore$ $Q_2 = 12 [200 \times 2 \times 10^{-4} \times 4.47 (230 - 30) \tanh (0.2235)] = 94.34$ W

This shows that the rate of heat transfer is higher in second case, therefore, this arrangement **(Case II) is better.**

Example 2.116. *One end of a long rod, 35 mm in diameter, is inserted into a furnace with the other end projecting in the outside air. After the steady state is reached, the temperature of the rod is measured at two points 180 mm apart and found to be 180°C and 145°C. The atmospheric air temperature is 25°C. If the heat transfer coefficient is 65 W/m² °C, calculate the thermal conductivity of the rod.*

Solution. Diameter of the rod, $d = 35$ mm $= 0.035$ m

The atmospheric air temperature, $t_a = 25$°C

Heat transfer coefficient; $h = 65$ W/m²°C

The starting point $x = 0$ is considered at the first point where the temperature is measured; $x = l$ is considered at the outer point. *Assume that the end of the fin is insulated.*

For *insulated end*, we have

$$\frac{\theta}{\theta_o} = \frac{t - t_a}{t_o - t_a} = \frac{\cosh \{m(l - x)\}}{\cosh ml} \qquad \text{...[Eqn. (2.134)]}$$

At $x = l$, this equation, reduces to

or, $$\frac{\theta_l}{\theta_o} = \frac{1}{\cosh ml} \qquad \text{...(i)}$$

Here, $\theta_l = 145 - 25 = 120$°C and $\theta_o = t_o - t_a = 180 - 25 = 155$°C

$\therefore$ $$\frac{120}{155} = \frac{1}{\cosh ml}$$

or, $$\cosh ml = \frac{155}{120} = 1.292 \quad \text{or} \quad ml = 0.747$$

or, $$m = \frac{0.747}{l}$$

But, $$m = \sqrt{\frac{hP}{kA_{cs}}}$$

$\therefore$ $$\sqrt{\frac{hP}{kA_{cs}}} = \frac{0.747}{l}$$

or, $$\frac{hP}{kA_{cs}} = \frac{0.747^2}{l^2}$$

or, $$\frac{h}{k} \cdot \frac{\pi d}{\frac{\pi}{4} d^2} = \frac{0.747^2}{l^2} \quad \text{or} \quad \frac{h}{k} \times \frac{4}{d} = \frac{0.558}{l^2}$$

or, $$k = \frac{4hl^2}{0.558 d} = \frac{4 \times 65 \times 0.18^2}{0.558 \times 0.035} = \textbf{431.34 W/m°C} \qquad \textbf{(Ans.)}$$

[where, $l = 180$ mm $= 0.18$ m (*given*)]

Example 2.117. *An electric motor drives a centrifugal pump which circulates a hot liquid metal at 480°C. The motor is coupled to the pump impeller by a horizontal steel shaft (k = 32 W/m°C) 25 mm in diameter. If the ambient air temperature is 20°C, the temperature of the motor is limited to a maximum value of 55°C and the heat transfer coefficient between the steel shaft and the ambient air is 14.8 W/m²°C, what length of shaft should be specified between the motor and the pump?*

Solution. *Given* : $d = 25$ mm $= 0.025$ m; $t_o = 480°C$; $t_a = 20°C$; $t_1 = 55°C$

$$k = 32 \text{ W/m°C}; h = 14.8 \text{ W/m}^2°C.$$

(The shaft conducts heat from the pump ($t_o = 480°C$) towards motor ($t_1 = 55°C$) and also loses energy from its surface to the surroundings ($t_a = 20°C$) by convection.)

The temperature distribution, treating the shaft as a *fin insulated at the tip*, is given by

$$\frac{\theta}{\theta_o} = \frac{t - t_a}{t_o - t_a} = \frac{\cosh[m(l - x)]}{\cosh(ml)} \qquad \text{[Eqn. 2.134)]}$$

At $x = l$, $t = t_1$; the above equation reduces to

or, $$\frac{t_1 - t_a}{t_o - t_a} = \frac{1}{\cosh(ml)}$$

or, $$\frac{55 - 20}{480 - 20} = \frac{1}{\cosh(ml)} \qquad \text{or} \quad \cosh(ml) = \frac{(480 - 20)}{(55 - 20)} = 13.14$$

∴ $$ml = 3.267$$

But, $$m = \sqrt{\frac{hP}{kA_{cs}}} = \sqrt{\frac{h \times \pi d}{k \times \frac{\pi}{4}d^2}} = \sqrt{\frac{4h}{kd}} = \sqrt{\frac{4 \times 14.8}{32 \times 0.025}} = 8.6 \, \text{m}^{-1}$$

∴ $$8.6 \, l = 3.267$$

Electric motor.

or $l = \dfrac{3.267}{8.6} = 0.3799\,\text{m}$ or   **379.9 mm (Ans.)**

Example 2.118. *The heat exchange, in a certain chemical process, is involved from metal surface to distilled water. A number of thin metal fins, each 70 mm long and 3.5 mm thick, are provided to increase the heat transfer rate and their ends are attached to an insulated wall. In order to prevent ionization of water the metal fins are coated with 0.12 mm thick layer of plaster. The mean water temperature and temperature at the base of the fin are 30°C and 90°C respectively. The thermal conductivities of the fin material and plastic are 205 W/m°C and 0.52 W/m°C respectively. If the heat transfer coefficient between the plastic coating and water is 250 W/m²°C, calculate :*

(i) *The temperature at the tip of fin, and*

(ii) *The fin efficiency.*

Solution. Length of a fin, $l = 70$ mm = 0.07 m

Thickness of fin, $y = 3.5$ mm = 0.0035 m

Thickness of plastic coating, $\delta_p = 0.12$ mm = 0.00012 m

Mean water temperature, $t_a = 30°C$

Temperature at the base of fin, $t_o = 90°C$

Thermal conductivity of fin material, $k_f = 205$ W/m°C

Thermal conductivity of plastic, $k_p = 0.52$ W/m°C

Heat transfer coefficient; $h = 250$ W/m²°C.

(i) **Temperature at the tip of fin, t_l :**

When making calculations for the value of m given by the expression $m = \sqrt{\dfrac{hP}{kA_{cs}}}$, the value of h is replaced by U as a result of resistance to heat transfer due to layer of plastic coating on the metallic fins; thus

$$\frac{1}{U} = \frac{1}{h} + \frac{\delta_p}{k_p} = \frac{1}{250} + \frac{0.00012}{0.52} = 0.00023$$

or, $U = 236.4$ W/m²°C

For fin of rectangular cross-section,

$$m = \sqrt{\frac{2U}{k_f y}} = \sqrt{\frac{236.4 \times 2}{205 \times 0.0035}} = 25.67 \text{ (when } 2y << 2b)$$

For a fin with *insulated tip*,

$$\frac{\theta}{\theta_o} = \frac{t - t_a}{t_o - t_a} = \frac{\cosh m(l - x)}{\cosh ml}$$ [Eqn. (2.134)]

At $x = l$, the above equation reduces to

$$\frac{\theta_l}{\theta_o} = \frac{t_l - 30}{90 - 30} = \frac{1}{\cosh (ml)} = \frac{1}{\cosh (25.67 \times 0.07)} = 0.3227$$

∴ $t_l = 30 + (90 - 30) \times 0.3227 = $ **49.36°C (Ans.)**

(ii) **Fin efficiency, η_{fin} :**

$$\eta_{fin} = \frac{\tanh (ml)}{ml}$$ ...[Eqn. (2.139)]

$$= \frac{\tanh(25.67 \times 0.07)}{(25.67 \times 0.07)} = 0.5267 \text{ or } \textbf{52.67\%} \quad \textbf{(Ans.)}$$

Example 2.119. *A heating unit is made in the form of a vertical tube fitted with rectangular section steel fins. The tube height is 1.2 m and its outer diameter is 60 mm. The fins are 50 mm in height and their thickness is 3 mm. The total number of the fins used is 20. The temperature at the base of a fin is 80°C and surrounding air temperature is 18°C. The heat transfer coefficient on the fin surface and tube surface to the surrounding air is 9.3 W/m²°C. k (fin material) = 55.7 W/m°C*

Calculate the amount of heat transferred from the tube with and without fin.

Solution. *Given* : Height of the tube, $H = 1.2$ m

Outer diameter of the tube, $d_o = 60$ mm $= 0.06$ m

Height of the fin, $l = 50$ mm $= 0.05$ m

Width of the fin, $b (= H) = 1.2$ m

Thickness of the fin, $y = 3$ mm $= 0.003$ m

Total number of fins, $n = 20$

Temperature at the base of the fin, $t_o = 80°C$

Surrounding air temperature, $t_a = 18°C$

Heat transfer coefficient, $h = 9.3$ W/m²°C

Thermal conductivity of fin material, $k = 55.7$ W/m°C.

Heat transferred from the tube with and without fin :

Let Q_1 = Rate of heat flow from the tube surface *without fins.*

Q_2 = Rate of heat flow from the tube surface when *fins are fitted,*

Q_b = Rate of heat convected from the *base,* and

Q_f = Rate of heat convected from the *fins.*

Now, $\quad Q_1 = h\,(\pi d_o H)\,(t_o - t_a)$

$\quad\quad = 9.3 \times (\pi \times 0.06 \times 1.2)\,(80 - 18) = \textbf{130.42 W (Ans.)}$

$\quad\quad Q_b = h\,A_b\,(t_o - t_a)$

where, $\quad A_b = (\pi \times 0.06 \times 1.2) - 20\,(1.2 \times 0.003) = 0.1542$ m²

$\therefore \quad Q_b = 9.3 \times 0.1542\,(80 - 18) = 88.91$ W

$\quad\quad Q_f = n\,kA_{cs}\,m\,(t_o - t_a)\tanh(ml) \quad\quad\quad …[\text{Eqn. (2.135)}]$

(Assuming fin end is *insulated*)

where, $\quad m = \sqrt{\dfrac{hP}{kA_{cs}}} = \sqrt{\dfrac{h}{k} \times \dfrac{(b+y) \times 2}{by}} = \sqrt{\dfrac{9.3}{55.7} \times \dfrac{(1.2+0.003) \times 2}{1.2 \times 0.003}} = 10.56$

and, $\quad ml = 10.56 \times 0.05 = 0.53$

$\therefore \quad Q_f = 20 \times 55.7 \times (1.2 \times 0.003) \times 10.56\,(80 - 18)\tanh(0.53) = 1274.5$ W

and, $\quad Q_2 = Q_b + Q_f = 88.91 + 1274.5 = \textbf{1363.41 W (Ans.)}$

Example 2.120. *A metal tank containing cooling oil is to have its dissipation rate by convection, increased by 70% by adding the fins to the wall surface. The fins will be 5 mm thick and spaced 100 mm apart between the centres. The surface temperature of the tank is 95°C and surrounding atmosphere temperature is 15°C. The natural convection heat transfer coefficient of the surface is 40 W/m²°C. Determine the length (height) of each fin on the assumption that the convection coefficient remains unchanged and surface temperature of the tank is dropped to 90°C when fins are fitted. Take k (metal tank and fin) = 240 W/m°C.*

Neglect the heat transfer from the tips of the fin. (M.U.)

Solution. Consider tank surface of 1m × 1 m as shown in Fig. 2.130.

Let, Q_1 = The rate of heat transfer from the tank surface when fins are *not* fitted,

Q_2 = The amount of heat which will be dissipated per unit time *after fitting the fins*, and [= 1.7 Q_1 .... given]

l = Length of each fin.

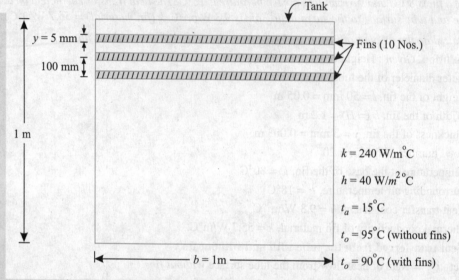

Tank

$y = 5$ mm

100 mm

Fins (10 Nos.)

1 m

$k = 240$ W/m$^\circ$C

$h = 40$ W/m^2 $^\circ$C

$t_a = 15^\circ$C

$t_o = 95^\circ$C (without fins)

$b = 1$m

$t_o = 90^\circ$C (with fins)

Fig. 2.130.

Now, $Q_1 = hA\,(t_o - t_a) = 40 \times 1 \times (95 - 15) = 3200$ W

$Q_2 = 1.7\,Q_1 = 1.7 \times 3200 = 5440$ W

Metal tanks are used in automobile manufacturing facility.

Out of Q_2, part of the heat is dissipated from the base surface and remaining from the fin surfaces.

The number of fins per metre width of the tank = 10 ...(See fig. 2.130)

∴ The base surface left after fitting the fins $= 1 \times 1 - 10\left(\dfrac{5}{1000} \times 1\right) = 0.95\,\text{m}^2$

∴ Q_{base} (the rate of heat transfer from the base surface) = 40 × 0.95 (90 – 15) = 28.50W

∴ Q_{fins} (the rate of heat transfer from the fin surfaces) $= Q_2 - Q_{base}$

$$= 5440 - 2850 = 2590 \text{ W}$$

Also, $Q_{fins} = nkA_{cs}\, m\, (t_o - t_a)\, \tanh\,(ml)$ ...[Eqn. (2.135)]

where, $m = \sqrt{\dfrac{hP}{kA_{cs}}}$ where $\dfrac{P}{A_{cs}} = \dfrac{(b+y)\times 2}{by} = \dfrac{(1+0.005)\times 2}{1 \times 0.005} = 402$

∴ $m = \sqrt{\dfrac{40}{240}} \times 402 = 8.185$

Substituting the values in the above equation, we get

or, $\tanh\,(8.185\,l) = \dfrac{2590}{10 \times 240 \times (1 \times 0.005) \times 8.185 \times (90 - 15)} = 0.351$

or, $8.185\, l = 0.37$

∴ $l = \dfrac{0.37}{8.185} = 0.0452 \text{ m}$ or **45.2 mm** (Ans.)

Example 2.121. *In the Fig. 2.131 are shown copper tubes soldered to steel plate panel (1mm thick); the tubes are parallel to each other and kept 450 mm apart. The steam at 100°C saturation temperature is condensed to water at 100°C passing through the copper tubes. Determine :*

(i) The heat loss per metre length of each tube, and

(ii) The mass of steam condensed per hour if the panel contains 25 tubes.

Take h (air) = 25 W/m²°C; k (steel) = 48 W/m°C; Air temperature = 26°C.

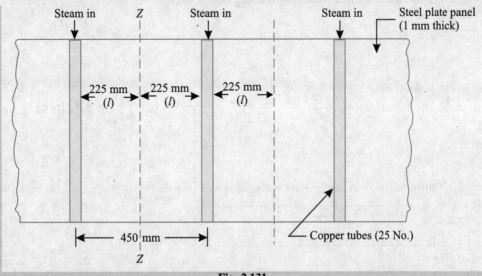

Fig. 2.131.

Solution. Refer to Fig. 2.131.

Thickness of steel plate, y = 1 mm = 0.001 m

Length of the fin, $l = 225$ mm $= 0.225$ m

Temperature at the base of the fin, $t_o = 100°C$

Temperature of air, $t_a = 26°C$

Thermal conductivity of steel, $k = 48$ W/m°C

Heat transfer coefficient for air, $h = 25$ W/m²°C

(*i*) **Heat loss per metre length ($b = 1$ m) of each tube :**

If the panel between the two tubes is considered, the coldest spot will be middle of the two tubes

(at Z–Z) due to symmetry of the tubes arrangement. Therefore, the temperature gradient $\left(\dfrac{dt}{dx}\right)$ at this

point will be zero. The half length of the panel between the two tubes becomes a fin for the tube and each tube will have *two fins* each of 250 mm length/height.

The heat flow though the panel for each tube is given by

$$Q = [k\,A_{cs}\,m\,(t_o - t_a)\tanh(ml)] \times 2$$

where,

$$m = \sqrt{\frac{hP}{kA_{cs}}} = \sqrt{\frac{h}{k} \times \frac{(b+y)\times 2}{b\cdot y}} = \sqrt{\frac{25}{48} \times \frac{(1+0.001)\times 2}{1\times 0.001}} = 32.29$$

∴

$$Q = [48 \times (1 \times 0.001) \times 32.29\,(100 - 26)\tanh(32.29 \times 0.225)] \times 2$$

$$= 229.38\ \text{W} = \textbf{229.38 J/s per metre length of each tube. (Ans.)}$$

(*ii*) **The mass of steam condensed per hour :**

Number of tubes $= 25$ ...(*Given*)

∴ The mass of steam condensed per hour

$$= \frac{(229.38 \times 3600) \times 25}{2257 \times 1000} = \textbf{9.146 kg/h (Ans.)}$$

[where latent heat (h_{fg}) $= 2257$ kJ/kg at 100°C ....from steam tables]

2.10.2.3. Heat dissipation from a fin losing heat at the tip

Fig. 2.132 illustrates a fin of finite length losing heat at the tip.

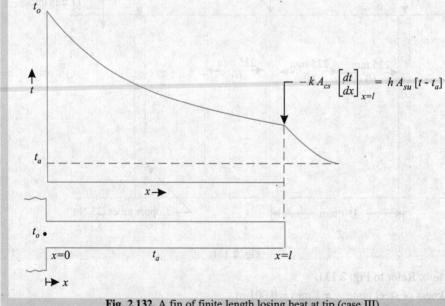

$$-k\,A_{cs}\left[\frac{dt}{dx}\right]_{x=l} = h\,A_{su}\,[t - t_a]$$

Fig. 2.132. A fin of finite length losing heat at tip (case III).

The boundary conditions are :

(i) At $x = 0$, $\theta = \theta_0$

(ii) Heat conducted to the fin at $x = l$

$$= \text{Heat convected from the end to the surroundings.}$$

i.e., $$-k \, A_{cs} \left[\frac{dt}{dx} \right]_{x=l} = h \, A_{su} \, (t - t_a)$$

where A_{cs} (cross-sectional area for heat conduction) equals A_{su} (surface area from which the convective heat transport takes place), at the tip of the fin; *i.e.* $A_{cs} = A_{su}$.

Thus $$\frac{dt}{dx} = -\frac{h\theta}{k} \qquad \text{at } x = l$$

Applying these boundary conditions to eqn. (2.131), we get

$$C_1 + C_2 = \theta_0 \qquad \qquad \text{...(i)}$$

Further $$t - t_a = C_1 e^{mx} + C_2 e^{-mx} \qquad \qquad \text{[Eqn. 2.131]}$$

Differentiating this expression w.r.t. x, we have

$$\frac{dt}{dx} = m \, C_1 e^{mx} - m \, C_2 e^{-mx}$$

$$\left[\frac{dt}{dx} \right]_{x=l} = m \, C_1 e^{ml} - m \, C_2 e^{-ml} = -\frac{h\theta}{k}$$

or, $$C_1 e^{ml} - C_2 e^{-ml} = -\frac{h\theta}{km}$$

or, $$C_1 e^{ml} - C_2 e^{-ml} = -\frac{h}{km} [C_1 e^{ml} + C_2 e^{-ml}] \qquad \qquad \text{...(ii)}$$

$$[\because \theta_{(x=l)} = C_1 e^{ml} + C_2 e^{-ml}]$$

Solving eqns. (i) and (ii), we have

$$C_2 = \theta_o - C_1 \qquad \qquad \text{...[From eqn. (i)]}$$

$$C_1 e^{ml} - (\theta_o - C_1) e^{-ml} = -\frac{h}{km} [C_1 e^{ml} + \theta_o - C_1) e^{-ml}] \qquad \text{...[From eqn. (ii)]}$$

$$C_1 e^{ml} - \theta_o e^{-ml} + C_1 e^{ml} = -\frac{h}{km} \cdot C_1 e^{ml} - \frac{h}{km} \cdot \theta_o \cdot e^{-ml} + \frac{h}{km} \cdot C_1 \cdot e^{-ml}$$

$$C_1 \left[(e^{ml} + e^{-ml}) + \frac{h}{km} e^{ml} - \frac{h}{km} e^{-ml} \right] = \theta_o e^{-ml} - \frac{h}{km} \theta_0 \cdot e^{-ml}$$

$$C_1 \left[(e^{ml} + e^{-ml}) + \frac{h}{km} (e^{ml} - e^{-ml}) \right] = \theta_o e^{-ml} \left[1 - \frac{h}{km} \right]$$

$\therefore$ $$C_1 = \frac{\theta_0 \left[1 - \dfrac{h}{km} \right] e^{-ml}}{\left[(e^{ml} + e^{-ml}) + \dfrac{h}{km} (e^{ml} - e^{-ml}) \right]}$$

and, $$C_2 = \theta_o - \left[\frac{\theta_0 \left(1 - \dfrac{h}{km} \right) e^{-ml}}{(e^{ml} + e^{-ml}) + \dfrac{h}{km} (e^{ml} - e^{-ml})} \right]$$

$$= \theta_o \left[1 - \frac{\left(1 - \dfrac{h}{km}\right) e^{-ml}}{(e^{ml} + e^{-ml}) + \dfrac{h}{km}(e^{ml} - e^{-ml})} \right]$$

$$= \theta_o \left[\frac{(e^{ml} + e^{-ml}) + \dfrac{h}{km}(e^{ml} - e^{-ml}) - e^{-ml} + \dfrac{h}{km}e^{-ml}}{(e^{ml} + e^{-ml}) + \dfrac{h}{km}(e^{ml} - e^{-ml})} \right]$$

$$= \theta_o \left[\frac{e^{ml} + e^{-ml} + \dfrac{h}{km}e^{ml} - \dfrac{h}{km}e^{-ml} - e^{-ml} + \dfrac{h}{km} \cdot e^{-ml}}{(e^{ml} + e^{-ml}) + \dfrac{h}{km}(e^{ml} - e^{-ml})} \right]$$

or, $$C_2 = \frac{\theta_o \left[1 + \dfrac{h}{km}\right] e^{ml}}{\left[(e^{ml} + e^{-ml}) + \dfrac{h}{km}(e^{ml} - e^{-ml})\right]}$$

Substituting these values of constants C_1 and C_2 in eqn. (2.131), we get

$$\theta = C_1 e^{mx} + C_2 e^{-mx} \qquad \qquad \text{...[Eqn (2.129)]}$$

$$\theta = \left[\frac{\theta_o \left(1 - \dfrac{h}{km}\right) e^{-ml}}{(e^{ml} + e^{-ml}) + \dfrac{h}{km}(e^{ml} - e^{-ml})} \right] e^{mx} + \left[\frac{\theta_o \left(1 + \dfrac{h}{km}\right) e^{ml}}{(e^{ml} + e^{-ml}) + \dfrac{h}{km}(e^{ml} - e^{-ml})} \right] e^{-mx}$$

or, $$\frac{\theta}{\theta_o} = \frac{[e^{m(l-x)} + e^{-m(l-x)}] + \dfrac{h}{km}[e^{m(l-x)} - e^{-m(l-x)}]}{[(e^{ml} + e^{-ml}) + \dfrac{h}{km}(e^{ml} - e^{-ml})]}$$

or, $$\frac{\theta}{\theta_o} = \frac{t - t_a}{t_o - t_a} = \frac{\cosh[m(l-x)] + \dfrac{h}{km}[\sinh\{m(l-x)\}]}{\cosh(ml) + \dfrac{h}{km}[\sinh(ml)]} \qquad \text{...(2.136)}$$

The rate of heat flow from the fin is given by

$$Q_{fin} = -k A_{cs} \left[\frac{dt}{dx}\right]_{x=0}$$

Now, $$t - t_a = (t_o - t_a) \left[\frac{\cosh\{m(l-x)\} + \dfrac{h}{km}[\sinh m(l-x)]}{\cosh(ml) + \dfrac{h}{km}\{\sinh(ml)\}} \right]$$

Differentiating the above expression w.r.t. x, we get

$$\frac{dt}{dx} = (t_o - t_a) \left[\frac{-m\sinh\{m(l-x)\} - m\dfrac{h}{km}\{\cosh[m(l-x)]\}}{\cosh(ml) + \dfrac{h}{km}\{\sinh(ml)\}} \right]$$

$$\left[\frac{dt}{dx}\right]_{x=0} = -(t_o - t_a)m\left[\frac{\sinh(ml) + \dfrac{h}{km}\{\cosh(ml)}{\cosh(ml) + \dfrac{h}{km}\{\sinh(ml)\}}\right]$$

$$\therefore \quad Q_{fin} = k\,A_{cs}\,m(t_o - t_a)\left[\frac{\sinh(ml) + \dfrac{h}{km}\{\cosh(ml)\}}{\cosh(ml) + \dfrac{h}{km}\{\sinh(ml)\}}\right]$$

$$= \sqrt{P\,h\,k\,A_{cs}}\,(t_o - t_a)\left[\frac{\sinh(ml) + \dfrac{h}{km}\{\cosh(ml)\}}{\cosh(ml) + \dfrac{h}{km}\{\sinh(ml)\}}\right] \quad \text{(Substituting for } m\text{)}$$

or,
$$Q_{fin} = \sqrt{P\,h\,k\,A_{cs}}\,(t_o - t_a)\left[\frac{\tanh(ml) + \dfrac{h}{km}}{1 + \dfrac{h}{km}\cdot\tanh(ml)}\right] \quad ...(2.135)$$

Example 2.122. *A motor body is 360 mm in diameter (outside) and 240 mm long. Its surface temperatere should not exceed 55°C when dissipating 340 W. Longitudinal fins of 15 mm thickness and 40 mm height are proposed. The convection coefficient is 40 W/m²°C. Determine the number of fins required. Atmospheric temperature is 30°C. Thermal conductivity = 40 W/m°C.*

Solution. Refer to Fig. 2.133, $l = 40$ mm $= 0.04$ m; $b = 240$ mm $= 0.24$ m; $y = 15$ mm $= 0.015$ m; $k = 40$ W/m°C; $h = 40$ W/m²°C, $t_0 = 55$°C; $t_a = 30$°C; $Q_{total} = 340$ W.

The given problem is a case of heat dissipation from a fin losing heat at the tip (*short fin situation*).

The rate of heat transfer in such a case is given by

$$Q_{fin} = \sqrt{P\,h\,k\,A_{cs}}\,(t_o - t_a)\left[\frac{\tanh(ml) + \dfrac{h}{km}}{1 + \dfrac{h}{km}\times\tanh(ml)}\right] \quad ...[\text{Eqn. (2.137)}]$$

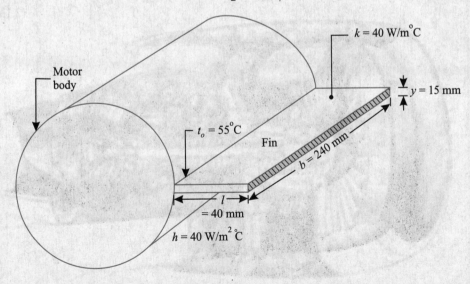

Fig. 2.133

where,

$$m = \sqrt{\frac{hP}{kA_{cs}}} = \sqrt{\frac{h(b+y) \times 2}{k(b \times y)}} = \sqrt{\frac{40 \times (0.24 + 0.015) \times 2}{40 \times (0.24 \times 0.015)}} = 11.9$$

and,

$$ml = 11.9 \times 0.04 = 0.476$$

$$\therefore \quad Q_{fin} = \sqrt{[(0.24 + 0.015) \times 2] \times 40 \times 40 \times (0.24 \times 0.015)} \times (55 - 30)$$

$$\times \left[\frac{\tanh(0.476) + \dfrac{40}{40 \times 11.9}}{1 + \dfrac{40}{40 \times 11.9} \times \tanh(0.476)} \right]$$

$$= 1.714 \times 25 \times \left[\frac{0.443 + 0.084}{1 + 0.084 \times 0.443} \right] = 21.77 \, W$$

$$\therefore \quad \text{Number of fins required} = \frac{Q_{total}}{Q_{fin}} = \frac{340}{21.77} = \textbf{16 fins} \quad \textbf{(Ans.)}$$

Example 2.123. *A turbine blade made of stainless steel (k = 29 W/m°C) is 60 mm long, 500 mm²
cross-sectional area and 120 mm perimeter. The temperature of the root of blade is 480°C and it is
exposed to products of combustion passing through the turbine at 820°C. If the film coefficient
between the blade and the combustion gases is 320 W/m²°C, determine :*

(i) *The temperature at the middle of the blade;*

(ii) *The rate of heat flow from the blade.*

Solution. *Given :* $l = 60$ mm $= 0.06$ m; $A_{cs} = 500$ mm² $= 500 \times 10^{-6}$ m²; $P = 120$ mm $= 0.12$ m;
$t_o = 480°C$; $t_a = 820°C$; $k = 29$ W/m°C; $h = 320$ W/m²°C.

(i) The temperature at the middle of the blade :

The temperature distribution for a fin losing heat at the tip is given by,

$$\frac{\theta}{\theta_o} = \frac{t - t_a}{t_o - t_a} = \frac{\cosh\{m(l - x)\} + \dfrac{h}{km}[\sinh\{m(l - x)\}]}{\cosh(ml) + \dfrac{h}{km}[\sinh(ml)]} \qquad \text{...[Eqn.}$$

$$\text{(2.136)]}$$

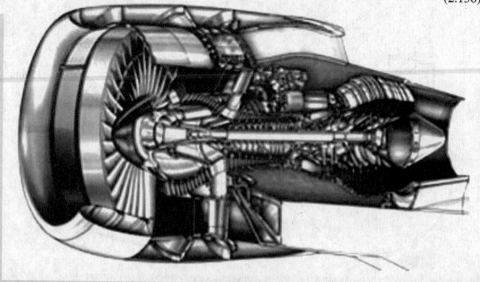

Turbine blades.

where,
$$m = \sqrt{\frac{hP}{kA_{cs}}} = \sqrt{\frac{320 \times 0.12}{29 \times 500 \times 10^{-6}}} = 51.46\,\text{m}^{-1}$$

$$ml = 51.46 \times 0.06 = 3.087$$

$$\frac{h}{km} = \frac{320}{29 \times 51.46} = 0.214$$

At $x = \dfrac{l}{2}$ (middle of the blade), the above equation reduces to

$$\frac{t_{(l/2)} - t_a}{t_o - t_a} = \frac{\cosh\left(\dfrac{ml}{2}\right) + \dfrac{h}{km}\sinh\left(\dfrac{ml}{2}\right)}{\cosh(ml) + \dfrac{h}{km}\sinh(ml)}$$

Substituting the values, we have

$$\frac{t_{(l/2)} - 820}{480 - 820} = \frac{\cosh\left(\dfrac{3.087}{2}\right) + 0.214\sinh\left(\dfrac{3.087}{2}\right)}{\cosh(3.087) + 0.214\sinh(3.087)}$$

$$= \frac{2.925}{13.318} = 0.219$$

∴ $$t_{(l/2)} = 820 + 0.219\,(480 - 820)$$
$$= 745.54°C \qquad \textbf{(Ans.)}$$

(*ii*) **The rate of heat flow from the blade, Q :**

$$Q = k\,A_{cs}\,m\,(t_o - t_a)\left[\frac{\tanh(ml) + \dfrac{h}{km}}{1 + \dfrac{h}{km}\tanh(ml)}\right] \qquad \text{...[Eqn. (2.137)]}$$

$$= 29 \times 500 \times 10^{-6} \times 51.46\,(480 - 820)\left[\frac{\tanh(3.087) + 0.214}{1 + 0.214\tanh(3.087)}\right]$$

$$= -253 \text{ W (Ans.)}$$

The –ve sign indicates that heat flows from the combustion gases to the turbine blade.

Example 2.124. *A fin 5 mm thick and 45 mm long has its base on a plane plate which is maintained at 125°C. The ambient temperature is 25°C. The conductivity of fin material is 55W/m°C and the heat transfer coefficient is 145 W/m²°C. Determine :*

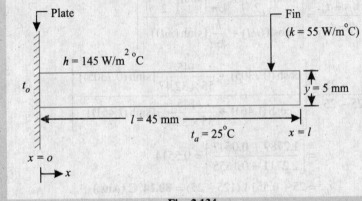

Fig. 2.134.

(i) *Temperature at the end of the fin,*

(ii) *Temperature at the middle of the fin, and*

(iii) *Heat dissipated by the fin (per metre width).*

Solution. Refer to Fig. 2.134.

l = 45 mm = 0.045 m; b = 1m; y = 5mm = 0.005m; k = 55 W/m°C; h = 145 W/m²°C; t_o = 125°C; t_a = 25°C.

(*i*) **Temperature at the end of the fin, t_1 :**

Assuming heat loss by convection from the end of the fin; under this condition, temperature at the end of the fin is given by

$$\frac{\theta}{\theta_o} = \frac{t - t_a}{t_o - t_a} = \left[\frac{\cosh\{m(l - x)\} + \dfrac{h}{km}[\sinh\{m(l - x)\}]}{\cosh(ml) + \dfrac{h}{km}[\sinh(ml)]} \right]_{x=l} \qquad \text{...[Refer Eqn. 2.136]}$$

or,

$$\frac{t_1 - t_a}{t_o - t_a} = \frac{1}{\cosh(ml) + \dfrac{h}{km}[\sinh(ml)]}$$

where,

$$m = \sqrt{\frac{hP}{kA_{cs}}} = \sqrt{\frac{h \times (2b + 2y)}{k \times (b \times y)}} = \sqrt{\frac{h}{k} \times \frac{2}{y}} = \sqrt{\frac{145}{55} \times \frac{2}{0.005}} = 32.47$$

$$(\because 2y \ll 2b)$$

or,

$$ml = 32.47 \times 0.045 = 1.461$$

∴

$$\frac{t_1 - 25}{125 - 25} = \frac{1}{\cosh(1.461) + \dfrac{145}{55 \times 32.47}[\sinh(1.461)]} = 0.41$$

or,

$$t_1 = 25 + 0.41(125 - 25) = 66°C \quad \text{(Ans.)}$$

(*ii*) **Temperature at the middle of the fin, $t_{1/2}$:**

$$\frac{\theta}{\theta_0} = \frac{t - t_a}{t_o - t_a} = \left[\frac{\cosh\{m(l - x)\} + \dfrac{h}{km}[\sinh\{m(l - x)\}]}{\cosh(ml) + \dfrac{h}{km}\{\sinh(ml)\}} \right]_{x=\frac{l}{2}}$$

or,

$$\frac{t_{1/2} - t_a}{t_o - t_a} = \left[\frac{\cosh\left(\dfrac{ml}{2}\right) + \dfrac{h}{km}\left\{\sinh\left(\dfrac{ml}{2}\right)\right\}}{\cosh(ml) + \dfrac{h}{km}\{\sinh(ml)\}} \right]$$

or,

$$\frac{t_{1/2} - 25}{125 - 25} = \left[\frac{\cosh(0.7305) + \dfrac{145}{55 \times 32.47}\{\sinh(0.7305)\}}{\cosh(1.461) + \dfrac{145}{55 \times 32.47}\{\sinh(1.461)\}} \right]$$

$$= \left[\frac{1.2789 + 0.0647}{2.2711 + 0.1655} \right] = 0.5514$$

∴

$$t_{1/2} = 25 + 0.5514(125 - 25) = \mathbf{80.14°C} \text{ (Ans.)}$$

(iii) Total heat dissipated by the fin, Q_{fin} (per metre width) :

$$Q_{fin} = \sqrt{PhkA_{cs}}\ (t_o - t_a)\left[\frac{\tanh(ml) + \dfrac{h}{km}}{1 + \dfrac{h}{km}\cdot\tanh(ml)}\right] \qquad\qquad ...[\text{Eqn. (2.137)}]$$

$$= \sqrt{\{(b + y)\times 2\}\times hk\times(b\times y)}\ (t_o - t_a)\left[\frac{\tanh(ml) + \dfrac{h}{km}}{1 + \dfrac{h}{km}\cdot\tanh(ml)}\right]$$

$$= \sqrt{(1 + 0.005)\times 2\times 145\times 55\times(1\times 0.005)}\ (125 - 25)\left[\frac{\tanh(1.461) + \dfrac{145}{55\times 32.47}}{1 + \dfrac{145}{55\times 32.47}\times\tanh(1.461)}\right]$$

or $\qquad\qquad Q_{fin} = 8.9526\times 100\times\left[\dfrac{0.8978 + 0.0812}{1 + 0.0729}\right] = \mathbf{816.9\,W}\quad$ **(Ans.)**

Example 2.125. *Derive an expression for the temperature distribution along a pin fin insulated at the tip but internally heated by an electric heater uniformly along the length at the rate q_2 W/m^3. The base temperature of the fin is t_o while the surrounding is at a temperature t_a. Can the heat flow from the base towards fin be equal to zero in this case? When?* (M.U.)

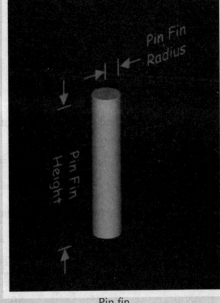

Pin fin.

Solution. Refer to Fig. 2.135. Consider an element of thickness dx and at a distance x from the base of the pin fin.

$$Q_x = -k\,A_{cs}\,\frac{dt}{dx}$$

$$Q_{(x + dx)} = Q_x + \frac{d}{dx}(Q_x)\cdot dx$$

$$Q_{conv.} = h\,(P.dx)\,(t - t_a)$$

$$Q_g = q_g\,(A_{cs}\,.\,dx)$$

For steady state heat flow,

$$Q_x + Q_g = Q_{(x + dx)} + Q_{conv.}$$

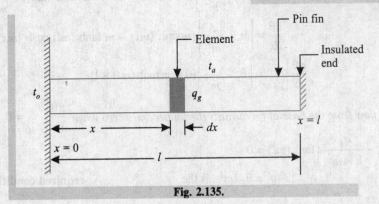

Fig. 2.135.

or, $$Q_x + Q_g = Q_x + \frac{d}{dx}(Q_x) \cdot dx + Q_{conv.}$$

or, $$\frac{d}{dx}(Q_x)\,dx + Q_{conv.} - Q_g = 0$$

or, $$\frac{d}{dx}\left[-kA_{cs}\frac{dt}{dx}\right]dx + h(P.dx)(t - t_a) - q_g(A_{cs}.dx) = 0$$

or, $$-kA_{cs}\frac{d^2t}{dx^2} + hP(t - t_a)\,dx - q_g\,A_{cs}.dx = 0$$

or, $$\frac{d^2t}{dx^2} - \frac{hP}{kA_{cs}}(t - t_a) + \frac{q_g}{k} = 0$$

(Dividing both sides by $k\,A_{cs}$)

Substituting $t - t_a = \theta$, we get

$$\frac{d^2\theta}{dx^2} - m^2\theta + A = 0 \qquad\qquad ...(1)$$

$$\left[\text{where } m^2 = \frac{hP}{kA_{cs}} \text{ and } A = \frac{q_g}{k}\right]$$

The solution of eqn. (1) is

$$\theta = B_1\,e^{mx} + B_2\,e^{-mx} + \frac{A}{m^2}$$

or, $$\theta = C_1\cosh(mx) + C_2\sinh(mx) + \frac{A}{m^2} \qquad\qquad ...(2)$$

where C_1 and C_2 are the constants of integration.
The boundary conditions are :

(i) At $x = 0$, $\theta = \theta_o$

(ii) At $x = l$, $\frac{d\theta}{dx} = 0$

Using the above boundary conditions, we get

$$C_1 = \theta_o - \frac{A}{m^2} \text{ and } C_2 = -C_1\tanh(ml)$$

Substituting the values of C_1 and C_2 in eqn. (2), we get

$$\theta = \left[\theta_o - \frac{A}{m^2}\right][\cosh(mx) - \tanh(ml)\sinh(mx)] + \frac{A}{m^2}$$

or, $$\frac{d\theta}{dx} = \left[\theta_o - \frac{A}{m^2}\right][m\sinh(mx) - m\tanh(ml)\cosh(mx)]$$

$$\therefore \quad \left.\frac{d\theta}{dx}\right|_{x=0} = \left[\theta_o - \frac{A}{m^2}\right][0 - m\tanh(ml) \times 1]$$

The heat flow from the base of fin towards the fin becomes zero when $\left.\dfrac{d\theta}{dx}\right|_{x=0} = 0$

$$\therefore \quad \left(\theta_o - \frac{q_g}{k \times m^2}\right)\tanh(ml) = 0$$

or, $$q_g = \theta_o\,km^2 ...\text{is the} \qquad\qquad \textbf{required condition. (Ans.)}$$

2.10.2.4. Efficiency and effectiveness of fin

Efficiency of fin (η_{fin}) :

The efficiency of a fin is defined as the ratio of the actual heat transferred by the fin to the maximum heat transferable by fin, if entire fin area were at base temperature.

i.e., $\eta_{fin} = \dfrac{\text{Actual heat transferred by the fin } (Q_{fin})}{\text{Maximum heat that would be transferred if whole surface of the fin is maintained at the base temperature } (Q_{max})}$

For a fin which is infinitely long (Art. 2.10.2.1)

$$\eta_{fin} = \frac{\sqrt{PhkA_{cs}}\,(t_o - t_a)}{hPl\,(t_o - t_a)} = \sqrt{\frac{kA_{cs}}{hPl^2}} = \frac{1}{ml} \qquad \text{...(2.138)}$$

For a fin which is insulated at the tip (Art. 2.10.2.2) :

$$\eta_{fin} = \frac{\sqrt{PhkA_{cs}}\,(t_o - t_a)\tanh{(ml)}}{hPl\,(t_o - t_a)} = \frac{\tanh{(ml)}}{ml} \qquad \text{...(2.139)}$$

where, $ml = \sqrt{\dfrac{hP}{kA_{cs}}} \cdot l = \sqrt{\dfrac{h\,(2b + 2y)}{kby}} \cdot l \qquad [\because P = 2\,(b+y)]$

Now, if the fin is sufficiently wide then the term $2b$ will be large compared to $2y$, then

$$ml = \sqrt{\frac{2hb}{kby}} \cdot l = \sqrt{\frac{2h}{ky}} \cdot l = \sqrt{\frac{2h}{kyl}} \cdot l^{3/2} = \sqrt{\frac{2h}{kA_p}} \cdot l^{3/2}$$

where, $y.\,l = A_p = $ Profile area of the fin.

Thus the fin efficiency is a function of ml or $\sqrt{\dfrac{2h}{kA_p}} \cdot l^{3/2}$.

The efficiency of a real rectangular fin which is long, wide and thin can be calculated by replacing l by a corrected length l_c, given by

$$l_c = 1 + \frac{y}{2} \qquad \text{...(2.140)}$$

This corrected length compensates for the fact that there is connective heat loss from the tip of a real fin. The efficiency is then written as

$$\eta_{fin} = \frac{\tanh\left[\sqrt{2h/ky}\left(l + \dfrac{y}{2}\right)\right]}{\sqrt{2h/ky}\left[l + \dfrac{y}{2}\right]} \qquad \text{...(2.141)}$$

The heat flow becomes,

$$Q = \sqrt{hPkA_{cs}}\,(t_o - t_a)\tanh\left[\sqrt{2h/ky}\left(l + \frac{y}{2}\right)\right]$$

$$= \eta_{fin}\sqrt{hPl_c}\,(t_o - t_a) \qquad \text{...(2.142)}$$

The efficiency of a fin forms a criterion for judging the relative merits of fins of different geometrics or materials.

Effectiveness of fin (ε_{fin}) :

Effectiveness of fin is the ratio of the fin heat transfer rate to the heat transfer rate that would exist without a fin.

$$\varepsilon_{fin} = \frac{Q_{with\,fin}}{Q_{without\,fin}} = \frac{\sqrt{PhkA_{cs}}\,(t_o - t_a)}{hA_{cs}\,(t_o - t_a)} = \sqrt{\frac{Pk}{hA_{cs}}} \qquad \text{...(2.143)}$$

(*...in case of infinitely long fin.*)

For a straight rectangular fin of thickness of y and width b,

$$\frac{P}{A_{cs}} = \frac{2(b + y)}{b \cdot y} \simeq \frac{2}{y}$$

$$\therefore \qquad \varepsilon_{fin} = \sqrt{\frac{2k}{hy}} \qquad\qquad\qquad ...(2.144)$$

From the relation for fin effectiveness, following results can be inferred :

1. Fin effectiveness $\sqrt{\dfrac{Pk}{hA_{cs}}}$ should be *greater than unity* if the rate of heat transfer from the primary surface is to be improved. It has been observed that use of fins on surfaces is justified only if $\dfrac{Pk}{hA_{cs}} > 5$.

2. If the ratio of P (perimeter) and A_{cs} (cross-sectional area) is increased the effectiveness of fin is improved. Due to this reason, thin and closely spaced fins are preferred; *the lower limit on the distance between two adjacent fins (pitch) is governed by the thickness of boundary layer that develops on the surface of the fin.*

3. Use of fins is only justified where h is small; finning is hardly justified unless $h < 0.25 \left[\dfrac{kP}{A}\right]$. If the value of h is large (as experienced in boiling, condensation and high velocity fluids), the fins may actually produce a reduction is heat transfer.

4. It is also apparent that the use of fins will be more effective with materials of large thermal conductivities [Although copper is superior to aluminium regarding thermal conductivity, yet fins are generally made of aluminium since it (aluminium) is cheaper in cost and lighter in weight].

Relation between η_{fin} and ε_{fin} :

The performance parameters (*i.e.* η_{fin} and ε_{fin}), in case of a fin *insulated at the tip*, are related to each other by the following expressions :

Efficiency of fin, $\qquad \eta_{fin} = \dfrac{\sqrt{PhkA_{cs}}\,(t_0 - t_a)\tanh(ml)}{hPl\,(t_0 - t_a)} \qquad\qquad ...(i)$

Effectiveness of fin, $\qquad \varepsilon_{fin} = \dfrac{\sqrt{PhkA_{cs}}\,(t_0 - t_a)\tanh(ml)}{hA_{cs}\,(t_o - t_a)} \qquad\qquad ...(ii)$

Dividing eqn. (*ii*) by eqn. (*i*), we have

$$\frac{\varepsilon_{fin}}{\eta_{fin}} = \frac{Pl}{A_{cs}} \qquad\qquad\qquad ...(2.145)$$

or, $\qquad \varepsilon_{fin} = \eta_{fin}\dfrac{Pl}{A_{cs}} = \eta_{fin} \times \dfrac{\text{Surface area of the fin}}{\text{Cross-sectional area of the fin}} \qquad ...(2.145\ (a)]$

It is evident from the above equations that *an increase in fin effectiveness can be obtained by increasing the length of the fin but it decreases the efficiency of the fin on the other hand.*

Example 2.126. *A longitudinal copper fin (k = 380 W/m°C) 600 mm long and 5 mm diameter is exposed to air stream at 20°C. The convective heat transfer coefficient is 20W/m²°C. If the fin base temperature is 150°C, determine :*

(i) *The heat transferred, and*

(ii) *The efficiency of the fin.*

[P.U., 1997]

Solution. Length of the fin, $l = 600$ mm $= 0.6$ m

Diameter of the fin, $d = 5$ mm $= 0.005$ m

The fin base temperature, $t_0 = 150°C$

Air stream temperature, $t_a = 20°C$

Thermal conductivity of fin material, $k = 380$ W/m°C

Convective heat transfer coefficient $h = 20$ W/m^2°C

(i) **The heat transferred, Q :**

Neglecting the heat loss from the end surface, the heat transfer from the fin is given by

$$Q = kA_{cs}\, m\, (t_o - t_a) \tanh (ml) \qquad \text{...[Eqn. (2.135)]}$$

Copper fin.

where

$$m = \sqrt{\frac{hP}{kA_{cs}}} = \sqrt{\frac{h}{2} \times \frac{\pi d}{\frac{\pi}{4}d^2}} = \sqrt{\frac{4h}{kd}} = \sqrt{\frac{4 \times 20}{380 \times 0.005}} = 6.49$$

$$\therefore \quad Q = 380 \times \left(\frac{\pi}{4} \times 0.005^2\right) \times 6.49 \times (150 - 20) \tanh (6.49 \times 0.6) = 6.29 \text{ W}$$

$$= 6.29 \times 3600 = 22644 \text{ J/h or } \mathbf{22.644 \text{ kJ/h}} \quad \textbf{(Ans.)}$$

(ii) **The efficiency of the fin, η_{fin} :**

For a fin which is insulated at the tip is given by

$$\eta_{fin} = \frac{\tanh (ml)}{ml} \qquad \qquad \text{...[Eqn. (2.139)]}$$

$$= \frac{\tanh (6.49 \times 0.6)}{(6.49 \times 0.6)} = 0.2566 \text{ or } \mathbf{25.66\%} \quad \textbf{(Ans.)}$$

Example 2.127. *A steel rod ($k = 32$ W/m°C), 12 mm in diameter and 60 mm long, with an insulated end, is to be used as a spine. It is exposed to surroundings with a temperature of 60°C and a heat transfer coefficient of 55 W/m^2°C. The temperature at the base of fin is 95°C. Determine :*

(i) *The fin efficiency;*

(ii) *The temperature at the edge of the spine;*

(iii) *The heat dissipation.*

Solution. *Given :* $d = 12$ mm $= 0.012$ m; $l = 60$ mm $= 0.06$ m; $t_a = 60°C$; ($k = 32$ W/m°C); $h = 55$ W/m^2°C; $t_o = 95°C$.

(i) **The fin efficiency, η_{fin} :**

$$\eta_{fin} = \frac{\tanh (ml)}{(ml)} \qquad \qquad \text{...[Eqn. (2.139)]}$$

where,

$$m = \sqrt{\frac{hP}{kA_{cs}}} = \sqrt{\frac{h \times \pi d}{k \times \frac{\pi}{4}d^2}} = \sqrt{\frac{4h}{kd}} = \sqrt{\frac{4 \times 55}{32 \times 0.012}} = 23.93$$

$$\therefore \quad \eta_{fin} = \frac{\tanh (23.93 \times 0.06)}{(23.93 \times 0.06)} = 0.6218 \text{ or } \mathbf{62.18\%} \quad \textbf{(Ans.)}$$

(ii) **The temperature at the edge of the spine, t_1 :**

$$\frac{\theta}{\theta_o} = \frac{t - t_a}{t_o - t_a} = \frac{\cosh m(l - x)}{\cosh ml} \qquad \qquad \text{[Eqn. (2.134)]}$$

At $x = l$, the above equation reduces to

$$\frac{\theta_l}{\theta_o} = \frac{t_l - t_a}{t_o - t_a} = \frac{1}{\cosh ml}$$

or,

$$\frac{t_l - 60}{95 - 60} = \frac{1}{\cosh(23.93 \times 0.06)} = 0.45$$

$\therefore$

$$t_1 = 60 + (95 - 60) \times 0.45 = \textbf{75.75°C} \quad \textbf{(Ans.)}$$

(iii) The heat dissipation, Q_{fin} :

$$Q_{fin} = k_{Acs} \, m \, (t_o - t_a) \tanh(ml) \qquad \text{...[Eqn. (2.135)]}$$

$$= 32 \times \frac{\pi}{4} \times (0.012)^2 \times 23.93 \, (95 - 60) \tanh(23.93 \times 0.06) = \textbf{2.7 W} \quad \textbf{(Ans.)}$$

Example 2.128. *Explain whether providing extended surface will always result in increased heat transfer.*
(AMIE Summer, 1999)

Solution. *Providing extended surfaces need not necessarily result in increased heat transfer. There may be situations where adding fins may actually decrease the heat transfer from a given surface. This may be explained as follows :*

Compare the heat transfer rate from a surface with fin to that which would be obtained without a fin. It is called "fin effectiveness" (ε).

$$\varepsilon = \frac{Q_{\text{with fin}}}{Q_{\text{without fin}}}$$

$$= \frac{\sqrt{PhkA_{cs}} \, (t_o - t_a) \tanh(ml)}{h \, A_{cs} \, (t_o - t_a)} \quad \text{for \emph{insulated tip fin.}}$$

If ml is sufficiently large, then (as $\tanh ml \simeq 1.0$)

$$\varepsilon = \sqrt{\frac{Pk}{h \, A_{cs}}} = \sqrt{\frac{k}{h \, L_c}}$$

where $L_c = \dfrac{A_{cs}}{P}$ is the characteristic length.

The addition of fin will increase the heat transfer rate only when $\varepsilon > 1$ or Biot number defined as $\dfrac{h \, L_c}{k} \ll 1$. In other words fin is only effective when 'h' is small or k is large. In boiling and condensation, when 'h' is quite large the fins may actually produce a reduction in heat transfer rate.

Example 2.129. *A composite fin consists of a cylindrical rod (3 mm diameter and 100 mm length) of one material, uniformly covered with another material forming outer diameter 10 mm and length 100 mm.*

k (inner material) = 15 W/m°C; k (outer material) = 45 W/m°C.

h (surface heat transfer coefficient) = 12 W/m²°C.

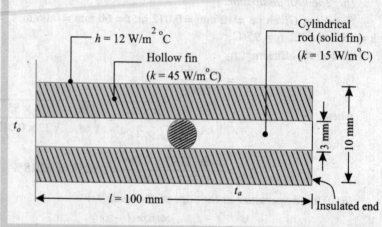

Fig. 2.136.

(i) Determine the effectiveness of the composite fin. Assume no temperature gradient along the radial direction and end is insulated for the composite fin.

(ii) Also find out the expression for the efficiency of this fin and its value for the given data.

Solution. Refer to Fig. 2.136. The composite fin consists of *solid fin* (cylindrical rod) in which heat flows along the axis by conduction only and hollow fin exposed to surroundings.

(i) Effectiveness of the composite fin, ε_{fin} :

The rate of heat transfer for the *solid fin* is given by

$$(Q)_{solid\ fin} = k\,A_{cs} \times \frac{(t_o - t_a)}{l}$$

$$= 15 \times \frac{\pi}{4} \times \left(\frac{3}{1000}\right)^2 \times \frac{(t_o - t_a)}{(100/1000)} = 0.00106(t_o - t_a) \qquad ...(i)$$

$$(Q)_{hollow\ fin} = kA_{cs}\,m\,(t_o - t_a)\tanh(ml)$$

where,

$$m = \sqrt{\frac{hP}{kA_{cs}}} = \sqrt{\frac{12}{45} \times \frac{\pi \times 0.01}{[\pi/4(0.01^2 - 0.003^2)]}} = 10.827$$

$\therefore$

$$ml = 10.827 \times 0.1 = 1.0827$$

$\therefore$

$$(Q)_{hollow\ fin} = 45 \times \frac{\pi}{4}(0.01^2 - 0.003^2) \times 10.827\,(t_o - t_a)\tanh(1.0827)$$

$$= 0.03482\,(t_o - t_a) \times 0.794 = 0.0276\,(t_o - t_a) \qquad ...(ii)$$

The total rate of heat transfer from the composite fin is given by

$$(Q)_{composite\ fin} = (Q)_{solid\ fin} + (Q)_{hollow\ fin}$$

$$= [0.00106\,(t_o - t_a)] + [0.0276\,(t_o - t_a)] = 0.02866\,(t_o - t_a) \qquad ...(iii)$$

The rate of heat transfer from the surface when there is no composite fin,

$$(Q)_{without\ composite\ fin} = hA'_{cs}\,(t_o - t_a)$$

$$= 12 \times \frac{\pi}{4} \times \left(\frac{10}{1000}\right)^2 \times (t_o - t_a) = 0.000942\,(t_o - t_a) \qquad ...(iv)$$

$\therefore$ Effectiveness of the composite fin,

$$\varepsilon_{fin} = \frac{(Q)_{composite\ fin}}{(Q)_{without\ composite\ fin}}$$

$$= \frac{0.02866(t_o - t_a)}{0.000942(t_o - t_a)} = \mathbf{30.42} \qquad \textbf{(Ans.)}$$

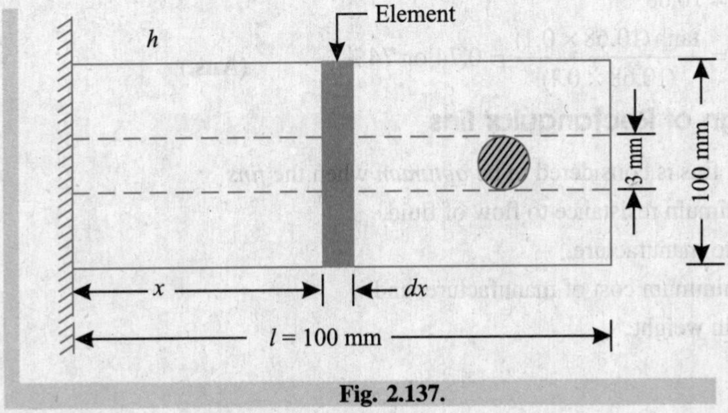

Fig. 2.137.

(ii) **Expression for efficiency of this fin and its value for the given data :**

Let the suffix *sf* stands for solid fin and suffix *hf* for hollow fin.

Refer to Fig. 2.137. Consider an element of thickness dx at a distance x from the base of the composite fin. Then,

Heat conducted in, $Q_x = \left(-k_{sf} A_{sf} \dfrac{dt}{dx}\right) + \left(-k_{hf} \cdot A_{hf} \dfrac{dt}{dx}\right)$

Heat conducted out,

$$Q_{(x+dx)} = \left[-k_{sf} A_{sf} \frac{dt}{dx} + \frac{d}{dx}\left\{-k_{sf} A_{sf} \frac{dt}{dx}\right\}dx\right] + \left[-k_{hf} A_{hf} \frac{dt}{dx} + \frac{d}{dx}\left(-k_{hf} A_{hf} \frac{dt}{dx}\right)dx\right]$$

Heat transfer from the surface,

$$Q_{conv.} = h\,(P \times dx)\,(t - t_a)$$

For steady state : $\qquad Q_x = Q_{(x+dx)} + Q_{conv.}$

or, $\quad k_{sf} A_{sf} \dfrac{d^2t}{dx^2} + k_{hf} A_{sf} \cdot \dfrac{d^2t}{dx^2} = hP\,(t - t_a)$

or, $\quad (k_{sf} A_{sf} + k_{hf} A_{hf}) \dfrac{d^2t}{dx^2} = hP\theta$ $\qquad\qquad\qquad\qquad\qquad (\because \theta = t - t_a)$

or, $\quad (k_{sf} A_{sf} + k_{hf} A_{hf}) \dfrac{d^2\theta}{dx^2} = hP\theta$

or, $\quad \dfrac{d^2\theta}{dx^2} = \dfrac{hP\theta}{k_{sf} A_{sf} + k_{hf} A_{hf}}$

or, $\quad \dfrac{d^2\theta}{dx^2} - m^2\theta = 0$

where, $\qquad m^2 = \dfrac{hP}{k_{sf} A_{sf} + k_{hf} A_{hf}}$

Efficiency of the fin is given by

$$\eta_{fin} = \frac{\tanh\,(ml)}{ml} \qquad\qquad\qquad\qquad ...[\text{Eqn. (2.139)}]$$

Now $\quad m^2 = \dfrac{12 \times (\pi \times 0.01)}{15 \times \left(\dfrac{\pi}{4} \times 0.003^2\right) + 45 \times \dfrac{\pi}{4}(0.01^2 - 0.003^2)} = \dfrac{0.377}{0.000106 + 0.0032} = 114.03$

or, $\quad m = 10.68$

$\therefore \qquad \eta_{fin} = \dfrac{\tanh\,(10.68 \times 0.1)}{(10.68 \times 0.1)} \simeq 0.74 \text{ or } \mathbf{74\%}$ $\qquad$ **(Ans.)**

2.10.2.5. Design of Rectangular fins

The design of fins is considered to be *optimum* when the *fins*

(i) offer minimum resistance to flow of fluid,

(ii) are easy to manufacture,

(iii) require minimum cost of manufacture, and

(iv) are light in weight.

By the use of a fin, surface area is increased due to which heat flow rate increases. *Increase in surface area decreases the surface convection resistance, whereas the conduction resistance increases. The decrease in convection resistance must be greater than the increase in conduction resistance in order to increase the rate of heat transfer from the surface.* In practical applications of fins the surface resistance must be the controlling factor (the

Rectangular fins.

addition of fins might decrease the heat transfer rate under some situations).

Design of the dimensions for a given profile area, to get maximum heat transfer :

Let,

b = Face width of the fin,

y = Thickness of the fin, and

l = Length of the fin.

Then the perimeter, P is expressed as

$$P = (2b + 2y) \simeq 2b \qquad \qquad ...(2.146)$$

(in most practical applications, the width is large as compared to thickness)

The cross-sectional area of the fin is given by

$$A_{cs} = b.y \qquad \qquad ...(2.147)$$

and,

$$m = \sqrt{\frac{hP}{kA_{cs}}} \simeq \sqrt{\frac{h \times 2b}{k \; by}} \simeq \sqrt{\frac{2h}{ky}} \qquad \qquad ...(2.148)$$

Consider the case of *heat dissipation from a fin insulated at the tip.* The expression for heat flow rate in this case is given by

$$Q_{fin} = \sqrt{PhkA_{cs}} \; (t_o - t_a) \tanh (ml) \qquad \text{[Eqn. (2.135)]}$$

$$= \sqrt{PhkA_{cs}} \; \theta_o . \tanh (ml) \qquad (\because \theta = t_o - t_a)$$

$$= \sqrt{2bhkby} \; \theta_o . \tanh \left[\sqrt{\frac{2h}{ky}} . l \right]$$

$$= b \sqrt{2hky} \; . \theta_o . \tanh \left[\sqrt{\frac{2h}{ky}} \times \frac{ly}{y} \right]$$

or,

$$\frac{Q_{fin}}{b} = \theta_o \; \sqrt{2hky} \tanh \left[A_p . \sqrt{\frac{2h}{ky^3}} \right]$$

(where A_p = profile area = ly)

or,

$$q_{fin} = \frac{Q_{fin}}{b} = \text{Heat transfer rate per unit width}$$

or,

$$q_{fin} = \theta_o \; \sqrt{2hky} \tanh \left[A_p . \sqrt{\frac{2h}{ky^3}} \right]$$

For maximum heat transfer, the required condition is

$$\frac{dq_{fin}}{dy} = 0 \text{ (since } q_{fin} \text{ is dependent only on } y, A_p \text{ being constant).}$$

i.e.,

$$\frac{dq_{fin}}{dy} = \frac{d}{dy}\left[\theta_o \sqrt{2hky} \tanh\left\{A_p \cdot \sqrt{\frac{2h}{ky^3}}\right\}\right] = 0$$

or,

$$\frac{dq_{fin}}{dy} = \theta_o \sqrt{2hk}\left[\frac{1}{2\sqrt{y}} \tanh\left(A_p\sqrt{\frac{2h}{k}} \cdot y^{-3/2}\right) + y^{1/2} \operatorname{sech}^2\left(A_p\sqrt{\frac{2h}{k}} \cdot y^{-3/2}\right)\right]$$

$$\times \frac{d}{dy}\left[A_p\sqrt{\frac{2h}{k}} \cdot y^{-3/2}\right] = 0$$

$$\therefore \quad \frac{1}{2\sqrt{y}} \tanh\left[A_p\sqrt{\frac{2h}{k}} \cdot y^{-3/2}\right] + y^{\frac{1}{2}}\operatorname{sech}^2\left[A_p\sqrt{\frac{2h}{k}} \cdot y^{-3/2}\right]\left[A_p\sqrt{\frac{2h}{k}}\left(-\frac{3}{2}\right)y^{-5/2}\right] = 0$$

or,

$$\frac{1}{2\sqrt{y}} \tanh\left[A_p\sqrt{\frac{2h}{k}} \cdot y^{-3/2}\right] - \frac{3}{2}\frac{1}{\sqrt{y}}A_p\sqrt{\frac{2h}{k}} \cdot y^{-3/2} \cdot \operatorname{sech}^2\left[A_p\sqrt{\frac{2h}{k}} \cdot y^{-3/2}\right] = 0$$

or,

$$\tanh\left[A_p\sqrt{\frac{2h}{k}} \cdot y^{-3/2}\right] = 3A_p\sqrt{\frac{2h}{k}} \cdot y^{-3/2} \cdot \operatorname{sech}^2\left[A_p\sqrt{\frac{2h}{k}} \cdot y^{-3/2}\right]$$

or,

$$\frac{\sinh\left[A_p\sqrt{\frac{2h}{k}} \cdot y^{-3/2}\right]}{\cosh\left[A_p\sqrt{\frac{2h}{k}} \cdot y^{-3/2}\right]} = 3A_p\sqrt{\frac{2h}{k}} \cdot y^{-3/2} \cdot \frac{1}{\cosh^2\left[A_p\sqrt{\frac{2h}{k}} \cdot y^{-3/2}\right]}$$

or,

$$\sinh\left[A_p\sqrt{\frac{2h}{k}} \cdot y^{-3/2}\right]\cosh\left[A_p\sqrt{\frac{2h}{k}} \cdot y^{-3/2}\right] = 3 A_p\sqrt{\frac{2h}{k}} \cdot y^{-3/2}$$

or,

$$\sinh\left[2A_p\sqrt{\frac{2h}{k}} \cdot y^{-3/2}\right] = 6 A_p\sqrt{\frac{2h}{k}} \cdot y^{-3/2} \qquad \text{...(2.149)}$$

[Multiplying both sides by 2 and recalling that $\sinh(2x) = 2\sinh(x)\cosh(x)$]

Equation (2.149) can be solved *graphically* and its solution yields :

$$A_p\sqrt{\frac{2h}{k}} \cdot y^{-3/2} = 1.419 \qquad \text{...(2.150)}$$

or,

$$l.y\sqrt{\frac{2h}{k}} \cdot y^{-3/2} = 1.419$$

or,

$$\frac{l}{\sqrt{y}}\sqrt{\frac{2h}{k}} = 1.419$$

or,

$$\frac{l}{y}\sqrt{\frac{2hy}{k}} = 1.419$$

(Multiplying numerator and denomenator by $\sqrt{y}$)

Let,

$$\frac{hy}{2k} = B_i, \text{ where } B_i \text{ is referred to as } \textbf{Biot number.}$$

Then,

$$\frac{2l}{y}B_i = 1.419$$

or,
$$\frac{l}{y} = \frac{1.419}{2\sqrt{B_i}} = \frac{0.7095}{\sqrt{B_i}} \qquad \qquad ...(2.151)$$

where, $\dfrac{l}{y}$ is known as the **optimum ratio**.

Now, consider the case of *heat dissipation from a fin losing heat at the tip*. The expression for heat flow rate in this case is given by,

$$Q_{fin} = \sqrt{PhkA_{cs}} \; (t_o - t_a) \left[\frac{\tanh(ml) + \dfrac{h}{km}}{1 + \dfrac{h}{km} \cdot \tanh(ml)} \right] \qquad ...[\text{Eqn. } (2.137)]$$

$$= \sqrt{PhkA_{cs}} \cdot \theta_o \left[\frac{\tanh(ml) + \dfrac{h}{km}}{1 + \dfrac{h}{km} \cdot \tanh(ml)} \right] \qquad (\because \theta_o = t_o - t_a)$$

The limit of conditions for which addition of fins will increase the rate of heat transfer is given by

$$\frac{dQ_{fin}}{dl} = 0 \qquad \qquad (\text{since } h, k, m, A_{cs}, P \text{ and } \theta o \text{ are constants}).$$

i.e.,
$$\frac{dQ_{fin}}{dl} = \frac{d}{dl} \left[\sqrt{PhkA_{cs}} \cdot \theta_o \left\{ \frac{\tanh(ml) + \dfrac{h}{km}}{1 + \dfrac{h}{km} \cdot \tanh(ml)} \right\} \right]$$

or,
$$\frac{dQ_{fin}}{dl} = \frac{\left[1 + \dfrac{h}{km}\tanh(ml)\right]\dfrac{m}{\cosh^2(ml)} - \left[\tanh(ml) + \dfrac{h}{km}\right]\dfrac{h}{k\cosh^2(ml)}}{\left[1 + \dfrac{h}{km}\tanh(ml)\right]^2} = 0$$

$\therefore$
$$\left[1 + \frac{h}{km}\tanh(ml)\right]\left[\frac{m}{\cosh h^2(ml)}\right] - \left[\tanh(ml) + \frac{h}{km}\right]\left[\frac{h}{k\cosh^2(ml)}\right] = 0$$

or,
$$m + \frac{h}{km}\tanh(ml) - \frac{h}{k}\tanh(ml) - \frac{h^2}{k^2 m} = 0$$

or,
$$m - \frac{h^2}{k^2 m} = 0 \qquad \qquad ...(2.152)$$

Also,
$$m \simeq \sqrt{\frac{2h}{ky}} \qquad \qquad ...[\text{from Eqn. } (2.148)]$$

Then,
$$\sqrt{\frac{2h}{ky} - \frac{h^2}{k^2}} \times \sqrt{\frac{ky}{2h}} = 0$$

or,
$$\frac{2h}{ky} = \frac{h^2}{k^2} \qquad \text{or} \qquad 2hk^2 = ky\, h^2$$

or,
$$\frac{hy}{2k} = 1 \qquad (i.e., \qquad B_i = 1) \qquad \qquad ...(2.153)$$

On rearranging this equation, we get

$$\frac{1}{h} = \frac{(y/2)}{k} \qquad\qquad ...(2.154)$$

where, $\dfrac{1}{h}$ = *Surface convection resistance per unit area*, and

$(y/2)/k$ = Conduction resistance for a plane wall whose thickness is one-half the fin thickness.

- The *heat flow rate will be minimum when these resistances are equal.*
- The *heat flow rate will be minimum when Biot number* (B_i) *is equal to unity and will increase when* $B_i < 1$.

Thus the conditions for *fins to be effective* are :

1. Thermal conductivity (k) should be *large*.
2. Heat transfer coefficient (h) should be *small*.
3. Thickness of the fin (y) should be *small*.

It is *advantageous to use a large number of fins of smaller thickness.*

2.10.3. HEAT FLOW THROUGH "STRAIGHT TRIANGULAR FIN"

The tapered fin is of paramount practical importance since it yields the maximum heat flow per unit weight. Fig. 2.138. shows a straight triangular fin.

Let, l = Length of the fin, between the base and the origin/tip,

     b = Width of the fin (per-pendicular to the paper),

     y = Thickness at the base of the fin (increas-ing uniformly from 0 at the tip to y at the base),

     t = Temperature of the base of the fin,

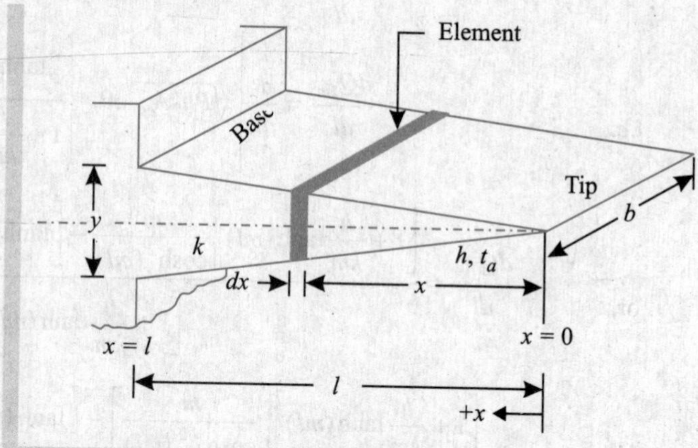

     t_a = Temperature of the ambient/surrounding fluid,

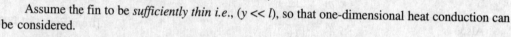

Fig. 2.138.

     k = Thermal conductivity of the material of the fin (constant), and

     h = Heat transfer coefficient (convective).

Assume the fin to be *sufficiently thin i.e., $(y \ll l)$*, so that one-dimensional heat conduction can be considered.

Consider a small element of thickness dx at a distance x from the origin.

$$\text{Area of cross-section, } A_{cs} = \left[\frac{x}{l} \times y\right] \times b \qquad\qquad ...(2.155)$$

$$\text{Perimeter, } P = 2b \qquad\qquad \text{[neglecting the effect of the edges]}$$

Applying energy balance on the element, we get

$$Q_x = Q_{(x+dx)} + Q_{conv.}$$

$$Q_x = Q_x + \frac{d}{dx}(Q_x)dx + hPdx\,(t - t_a)$$

and,

$$\frac{d(Q_x)}{dx} = hP\theta,$$

where ,

$$\theta = (t - t_a)$$

Further,

$$\frac{d\theta}{dx} = \frac{dt}{dx} \quad \text{and} \quad \frac{d^2\theta}{dx^2} = \frac{d^2t}{dx^2}$$

or,

$$\frac{d}{dx}\left(kA_{cs}\frac{dt}{dx}\right) = hP\theta$$

As both A_{cs} and P are functions of x, therefore,

$$kA_{cs}\frac{d^2\theta}{dx^2} + k\frac{dA_{cs}}{dx}\cdot\frac{d\theta}{dx} - hP\theta = 0$$

or,

$$\frac{d^2\theta}{dx^2} + \frac{1}{A_{cs}}\cdot\frac{dA_{cs}}{dx}\cdot\frac{d\theta}{dx} - \frac{hP\theta}{kA_{cs}} = 0 \qquad \text{(Dividing both sides by } kA_{cs}\text{)}$$

or,

$$\frac{d^2\theta}{dx^2} + \frac{1}{xyb}\left(\frac{d}{dx}\right)\left(\frac{xyb}{l}\right)\frac{d\theta}{dx} - \frac{h}{k}\left[\frac{2bl\theta}{xyb}\right] = 0$$

or,

$$\frac{d^2\theta}{dx^2} + \frac{1}{xyb}\left(\frac{yb}{l}\right)\frac{d\theta}{dx} - \frac{h}{k}\frac{2bl\theta}{xyb} = 0$$

or,

$$\frac{d^2\theta}{dx^2} + \frac{1}{x}\cdot\frac{d\theta}{dx} - \frac{2hl}{ky}\cdot\frac{1}{x}\cdot\theta = 0 \qquad \text{...(2.156)}$$

Let,

$$\frac{2hl}{ky} = B^2$$

The eqn. (2.156) becomes

$$\frac{d^2\theta}{dx^2} + \frac{1}{x}\frac{d\theta}{dx} - \frac{B^2}{x}\theta = 0$$

or,

$$x^2\frac{d^2\theta}{dx^2} + x\frac{d\theta}{dx} - B^2x\theta = 0 \qquad \text{...(2.157)}$$

Let us assume z to be new independent variable, such that

$$z = 2B\sqrt{x}, \frac{dz}{dx} = Bx^{-1/2}$$

and,

$$\frac{d\theta}{dx} = \frac{d\theta}{dz}\times\frac{dz}{dx} = Bx^{-1/2}\cdot\frac{d\theta}{dz}$$

Further,

$$\frac{d^2\theta}{dx^2} = \frac{d}{dx}\left(\frac{d\theta}{dx}\right)$$

$$= \frac{d}{dx}\left(Bx^{-1/2}\cdot\frac{d\theta}{dz}\right)$$

$$= B\times -\frac{1}{2}x^{-3/2}\cdot\frac{d\theta}{dz} + Bx^{-1/2}\cdot\frac{d^2\theta}{dz^2}\cdot\frac{dz}{dx}$$

$$= B\left[-\frac{1}{2}x^{-3/2}\frac{d\theta}{dz} + \frac{d^2\theta}{dz^2}Bx^{-1/2}\cdot x^{-1/2}\right] \qquad \left(\because \frac{dz}{dx} = Bx^{-1/2}\right)$$

or,

$$\frac{d^2\theta}{dx^2} = B\left[-\frac{1}{2}x^{-3/2}\frac{d\theta}{dz} + Bx^{-1}\cdot\frac{d^2\theta}{dz^2}\right]$$

Substituting the relevant values in eqn. (2.157), we get

$$x^2 \times B \left[-\frac{1}{2} x^{-3/2} \cdot \frac{d\theta}{dz} + Bx^{-1} \cdot \frac{d^2\theta}{dz^2} \right] + x \times B \times x^{-1/2} \cdot \frac{d\theta}{dz} - B^2 x\theta = 0$$

or, $\quad B \left[-\frac{1}{2} \sqrt{x} \frac{d\theta}{dz} + Bx \cdot \frac{d^2\theta}{dz^2} \right] + B\sqrt{x} \frac{d\theta}{dz} - B^2 x\theta = 0$

or, $\quad -\frac{1}{2} B\sqrt{x} \frac{d\theta}{dz} + B^2 x \frac{d^2\theta}{dz^2} + B\sqrt{x} \frac{d\theta}{dz} - B^2 x\theta = 0$

or, $\quad -\frac{z}{4} \cdot \frac{d\theta}{dz} + \frac{z^2}{4} \cdot \frac{d^2\theta}{dz^2} + \frac{z}{2} \cdot \frac{d\theta}{dz} - \frac{z^2\theta}{4} = 0$ $\qquad$ (Substituting $z = 2 B \sqrt{x}$)

or, $\quad \frac{z^2}{4} \frac{d^2\theta}{dz^2} + \frac{z}{4} \frac{d\theta}{dz} - \frac{z^2\theta}{4} = 0$

or, $\quad z^2 \frac{d^2\theta}{dz^2} + z \frac{d\theta}{dz} - z^2\theta = 0$

or, $\quad \frac{d^2\theta}{dz^2} + \frac{1}{z} \frac{d\theta}{dz} - \theta = 0$ $\qquad$ ...(2.158)

This equation is identical to the modified Bessel's equation of zero order ($n = 0$) and its general solution is

$$\theta = C_1 I_0 (z) + C_2 K_0 (z)$$

or, $\quad \theta = C_1 I_0 (2B \sqrt{x}) + C_1 K_0 (2B \sqrt{x})$ $\qquad$ ...(2.159)

where I_0 and k_0 are modified zero order Bessel's functions of the first and second kind respectively.

The constants of integration C_1 and C_2 can be found by applying the following boundary conditions :

(i) At the base/root : $\qquad$ At $x = l$, $\qquad$ $\theta = \theta_o$

(ii) At the tip : $\qquad$ At $x = 0$, $\qquad$ θ = finite (i.e., the temperature of the fin must be finite everywhere).

From boundary condition (ii), we have

$$\theta = C_1 I_0 (0) + C_2 K_0 (0); \ I_0 (0) = 1; \text{ and } K_0(0) = \infty$$

As θ is finite, $C_2 = 0$, therefore,

$$\theta = C_1 I_0 (2B \sqrt{x})$$ $\qquad$ ...(2.160)

Applying the first boundary condition, we have

$$\theta_o = C_1 I_0 (2B \sqrt{l})$$ $\qquad$ ...(From eqn. (2.145)]

or, $\qquad C_1 = \dfrac{\theta_o}{I_0 (2B\sqrt{l})}$

Substituting the values of C_1 and C_2 in eqn. (2.159), we have

$$\theta = \frac{\theta_o I_0 (2B\sqrt{x})}{I_0 (2B\sqrt{l})}$$ $\qquad$ ...(2.161)

The rate of heat flow through the fin is given by

$$Q = k \left(A_{cs} \frac{d\theta}{dx} \right)_{x=l}$$

From the properties of Bessel's functions, we know that

$$\frac{d\left[I_n(z)\right]}{dx} = I_{(n+1)}(z)\frac{d}{dx}(z)$$

so that for $n = 0$

$$\frac{d\left[I_0(2B\sqrt{x})\right]}{dx} = \left[I_1(2B\sqrt{x})\right]B\,x^{-1/2}$$

$$\therefore \qquad Q = k \times (b \times y) \times \frac{d}{dx}\left[\frac{\theta_o I_0(2B\sqrt{x})}{I_0(2B\sqrt{l})}\right]_{x=l} \quad \text{[using eqn. (2.161)]}$$

or, $\qquad Q = \dfrac{kby\theta_o}{I_0(2B\sqrt{l})}\left[\dfrac{d}{dx}\left\{I_0(2B\sqrt{x})\right\}\right]_{x=l}$

or, $\qquad Q = \dfrac{kby\theta_o}{I_0(2B\sqrt{l})}\left[I_1(2B\sqrt{x})\,Bx^{-1/2}\right]_{x=l}$

or, $\qquad Q = \dfrac{kby\theta_o}{I_0(2B\sqrt{l})}\left[I_1(2B\sqrt{l}) \times \dfrac{B}{\sqrt{l}}\right]$

or, $\qquad Q = \dfrac{kBby\theta_o}{\sqrt{l}} \times \dfrac{I_1(2B\sqrt{l})}{I_0(2B\sqrt{l})} \qquad ..(2.162)$

But $\quad B = \sqrt{\dfrac{2hl}{ky}}$

$$\therefore \qquad Q = \frac{kby\theta_o}{\sqrt{l}} \times \sqrt{\frac{2hl}{ky}} \times \frac{I_1(2B\sqrt{l})}{I_0(2B\sqrt{l})}$$

or, $\quad Q_{fin} = b\sqrt{2hky}\,.\,\theta_o\dfrac{I_1(2B\sqrt{l})}{I_0(2B\sqrt{l})} \qquad\qquad ...(2.163)$

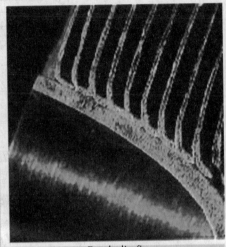
Parabolic fins.

Note: The straight fins can be of rectangular, triangular and parabolic profiles; *parabalic fins* are the *most effective but are difficult to manufacture.*

2.10.4. ESTIMATION OF ERROR IN TEMPERATURE MEASUREMENT IN A THERMOMETER WELL

For estimating error in the value of temperature measured by a thermometer dipped in a thermometer well, the theory of extended surfaces is very helpful. A *thermometer well* is defined as a *small tube welded radially into a pipeline through which a fluid whose temperature is to be measured is flowing.*

Refer to Fig. 2.139.

Let, $\qquad l$ = Length of the well/tube,

$\qquad\qquad d$ = Internal diameter of the well/tube,

$\qquad\qquad \delta$ = Thickness of well/tube,

$\qquad\qquad t_f$ = Temperature of the fluid flowing through the pipe (which is to be measured), and

$\qquad\qquad t_o$ = Temperature of the pipe-wall.

When the temperature of the fluid flowing through the pipeline is higher than the ambient temperature, the heat flows from the fluid towards the tube walls along the well. Consequently the temperature at the bottom of well becomes colder than the fluid flowing around, obviously the temperature shown by the thermometer will not be the true temperature of the fluid. This error may be calculated by assuming the well to be a spine protruding from the wall of a pipe in which fluid is flowing. It may be assumed, for simplicity, that there is no flow of heat from the tip of the well (*i.e.*, the tip of the well is *insulated*). The temperature distribution at any distance x measured from pipe wall along the temperature well is given by

$$\frac{\theta_x}{\theta_o} = \frac{t_x - t_f}{t_o - t_f} = \frac{\cosh\left[m(l - x)\right]}{\cosh(ml)} \qquad \ldots[\text{Eqn. (2.134)}]$$

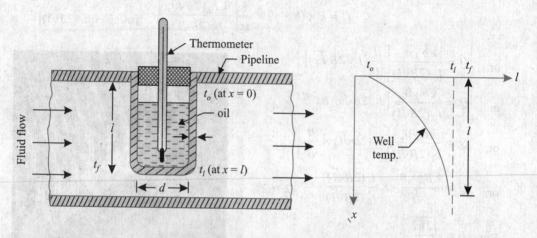

Fig. 2.139. Thermometer well.   Fig. 2.140. Temperature varitation in well.

At $x = l$, we have

$$\frac{t_l - t_f}{t_o - t_f} = \frac{\cosh\left[m(l - l)\right]}{\cosh(ml)} = \frac{1}{\cosh(ml)} \qquad \ldots(2.164)$$

[Thermometeric error]

(where, t_l = Temperature recorded by the thermometer at the bottom of the well.)

Now, perimeter of the well, $P = \pi(d + 2\delta) \simeq \pi d$,

and   cross-sectional area, $A_{cs} = \pi d\,\delta$

$\therefore$ $$\frac{P}{A_{cs}} = \frac{\pi d}{\pi d\,\delta} = \frac{1}{\delta}$$

Then, $$m = \sqrt{\frac{hP}{k\,A_{cs}}} = \sqrt{\frac{h}{k\,\delta}}$$

Thus, the temperature measured by the thermometer is *not* affected by the diameter of the well.

From the Eqn. (2.164) it is obvious that in order to reduce the temperature measurement error, ml should be large necessitating the following :

(*i*) Large value of h (heat transfer coefficient).

(*ii*) Small value of of k (thermal conductivity).

(*iii*) Long and thin well, the pocket (protruding small tube) may be placed obliquely/inclined, if necessary, to provide a longer insertion of thermometer.

Example 2.130. *A mercury thermometer placed in oil well is required to measure temperature of compressed air flowing in a pipe. The well is 140 mm long and is made of steel ($k = 50$ W/m°C) of 1 mm thickness. The temperature recorded by the well is 100°C while pipe wall temperature is 50°C. Heat transfer coefficient between the air and well wall is 30 W/m²°C. Estimate true temperature of air.*

(M.U.)

Solution. Refer to Fig. 2.139.

Given : $l = 140$ mm $= 0.14$ m, $\delta = 1$ mm $= 0.001$ m; $t_l = 100°C$; $t_o = 50°C$; $h = 30$ W/m²°C; $k = 50$ W/m°C.

True temperature of air (fluid) t_f :

The value of t_f is found from the relation,

$$\frac{t_l - t_f}{t_o - t_f} = \frac{1}{\cosh(ml)} \qquad \qquad ...[\text{Eqn. (2.164)}]$$

where,
$$m = \sqrt{\frac{h}{k\delta}} = \sqrt{\frac{30}{50 \times 0.001}} = 24.5$$

and
$$ml = 24.5 \times 0.14 = 3.43$$

Substituting the values, we have

$$\frac{100 - t_f}{50 - t_f} = \frac{1}{\cosh(3.43)} = \frac{1}{15.4545} = 0.0647$$

or, $(100 - t_f) = 0.0647 (50 - t_f)$

or, $100 - t_f = 3.235 - 0.0647\, t_f$

or, $t_f = \mathbf{103.46°C}$ **(Ans.)**

Example 2.131. *A thermometer pocket is inserted in a pipe of 150 mm diameter carrying hot air. The pocket is made of brass (k = 70 W/m°C). The inner and outer diameters of the pocket are 10 mm and 15 mm respectively. The heat transfer coefficient between the pocket and air is given by*

Nu = 0.174 (Re)$^{0.618}$

Take k (air) = 0.035 W/m°C and depth of pocket = 50 mm

Reynolds number (Re) of air flow = 25000

Find the actual error in temperature measurement if the pipe wall is at 50°C and air temperature is 150°C   [N.U., 1997]

Solution. Refer to Fig. 2.141. $d_i = 10$ mm $= 0.01$ m; $d_o = 15$ mm $= 0.015$ m; $l = 50$ mm $= 0.05$ m; $k_{brass} = 70$ W/m°C; $k_{air} = 0.035$ W/m°C; $t_o = 50°C$; $t_f = 150°C$; $Re = 25000$.

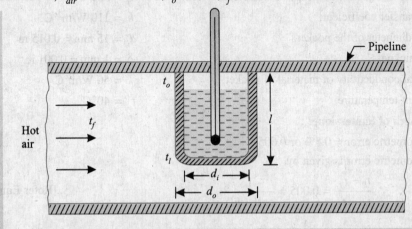

Fig. 2.141.

Actual error in temperature measurement :

Nusselt number, $Nu = 0.174 \, (Re)^{0.618}$ ...(Given.)

or, $Nu = 0.174 \, (25000)^{0.618} = 90.88$

Also
$$Nu = \frac{hd_o}{k_{air}} = 90.88$$

$$\therefore \quad h = \frac{90.88 \times k_{air}}{d_o} = \frac{90.88 \times 0.035}{0.015} = 212 \text{ W/m}^{2\circ}C$$

The temperature recorded by the thermometer (t_l) is found from the relation

$$\frac{t_l - t_f}{t_o - t_f} = \frac{1}{\cosh(ml)} \qquad \qquad \text{...[Eqn. (2.164)]}$$

where,
$$m = \sqrt{\frac{hP}{k_{brass} A_{cs}}} \; ; \quad \frac{P}{A_{cs}} = \frac{\pi d_o}{\frac{\pi}{4}(d_o^2 - d_i^2)} = \frac{4d_0}{d_0^2 - d_i^2} = \frac{4 \times 0.015}{0.015^2 - 0.01^2} = 480$$

$$\therefore \quad m = \sqrt{\frac{212}{70}} \times 480 = 38.13 \text{ and } ml = 38.13 \times 0.05 \approx 1.91$$

Substituting the values in the above equation, we get

$$\frac{t_l - 150}{50 - 150} = \frac{1}{\cosh(1.91)} = \frac{1}{3.4506} = 0.2898$$

$$\therefore \quad t_l = 150 + 0.2898 \, (50 - 150) = 121°C$$

$$\therefore \quad \text{Error in measurement } 150 - 121 = 29°C \quad \textbf{(Ans.)}$$

Example 2.132. *Superheated steam at 330°C is flowing at 20 m/s velocity (h = 110 W/m²°C) through a pipe 120 mm in diameter. The temperature of steam is to be measured by putting a pocket in the pipe of 15 mm diameter (inside) and 1 mm wall thickness. The thermal conductivity of the material of the pocket is 50 W/m°C.*

(i) Determine the length of insertion so that thermometric error is 0.5 percent. Find also the temperature measured if the pipe wall temperature is 40°C.

(ii) What will be the actual error in temperature measurement in °C if the depth of immersion is 55 mm only and the pipe wall temperature is 40°C ?

Solution. Temperature of superheated steam (fluid), $\quad t_f = 330°C$

Heat transfer coefficient; $\quad h = 110 \text{ W/m}^2°C$

Inside diameter of the pocket, $\quad d_i = 15 \text{ mm} = 0.015 \text{ m}$

Wall thickness, $\quad \delta = 1 \text{ mm} = 0.001 \text{ m}$

Thermal conductivity of material of pocket, $\quad k = 50 \text{ W/m°C}$

Ambient temperature, $\quad t_a = 40°C$

(i) Length of immersion, l :

Thermometric error = 0.5% or 0.005 $\qquad \qquad$ ...(Given.)

Thermometric error is given by

$$\frac{t_l - t_f}{t_o - t_f} = 0.005 = \frac{1}{\cosh(ml)} \qquad \qquad \text{...[Refer Eqn. 2.164]}$$

or, $\quad \cosh(ml) = \frac{1}{0.005} = 200$

or, $\quad ml = 6$

where, $\quad m = \sqrt{\frac{hP}{kA_{cs}}} = \sqrt{\frac{h \times \pi d_o}{k \times \frac{\pi}{4}(d_o^2 - d_i^2)}}$

$$= \sqrt{\frac{h}{k} \cdot \frac{4d_o}{d_o^2 - d_i^2}} = \sqrt{\frac{110}{50} \times \frac{4 \times 0.017}{(0.017^2 - 0.015^2)}}$$

$$= 48.35$$

$\therefore \qquad l = \dfrac{6}{m} = \dfrac{6}{48.35} = 0.124 \text{ m}$ or **124 mm**   (Ans.)

As this length is greater than pipe diameter, it is necessary to insert the length *obliquely* in the pipe as shown in Fig. 2.142.

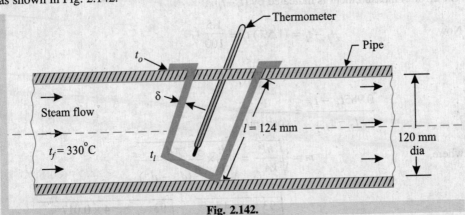

Fig. 2.142.

The temperature measured t_e :

Now, $\qquad \dfrac{t_l - t_f}{t_o - t_f} = \dfrac{1}{\cosh ml}$

or, $\qquad \dfrac{t_l - 330}{40 - 330} = \dfrac{1}{200}$

$\therefore \qquad t_l = 330 + \dfrac{(40 - 330)}{200} = \textbf{328.55°C}$ (Ans.)

(ii) Actual error in temperature measurement when $l = 55$ mm; $(t_l - t_f)$:

$$ml = 46.9 \times 0.055 = 2.579$$

$\therefore \qquad \cosh(ml) = \cosh(2.579) = 6.629$

Now, $\qquad \dfrac{t_l - t_f}{t_o - t_f} = \dfrac{1}{\cosh(ml)} = \dfrac{1}{6.629}$

or, $\qquad (t_l - t_f) = \dfrac{t_o - t_f}{6.629} = \dfrac{40 - 330}{6.629} = \textbf{-43.7°C}$ (Ans.)

Example 2.133. *A steel tube carries steam at a temperature of 320°C. A thermometer pocket of iron (k = 52.3 W/m°C) of inside diameter 15 mm and 1 mm thick is used to measure the temperature. The error to be tolerated is 1.5% of maximum. Estimate the length of the pocket necessary to measure the temperature within this error. The diameter of steel tube is 95 mm. Assume h = 93 W/m²°C and tube wall temperature is 120°C. Suggest a suitable method of locating the thermometer pocket.*

(M.U., 1998)

Solution. *Given :* $t_f = 320$°C; $k = 52.3$ W/m°C; $d_i = 15$ mm $= 0.015$ m; $\delta = 1$ mm $= 0.001$ m; $h = 93$ W/m²°C; $t_o = 120$°C.

$$d_0 = d_i + 2\delta = 15 + 2 \times 1 = 17 \text{ mm} = 0.017 \text{ m}$$

Length of the pocket, l :

The temperature recorded by the thermometer (t_l) is found from the relation

$$\frac{t_l - t_f}{t_o - t_f} = \frac{1}{\cosh(ml)} \qquad\qquad ...[Eqn.\ (2.164)]$$

where, $\qquad\qquad\qquad t_o$ = Wall temperature, and

$\qquad\qquad\qquad\qquad t_f$ = Steam temperature.

The error in measurement is indicated by ($t_f - t_l$).

Now, $\qquad\qquad\qquad t_f - t_l = (1.5\%)\, t_f = \dfrac{1.5}{100}\, t_f$

$\therefore \qquad\qquad\qquad t_l = t_f - \dfrac{1.5}{100}\, t_f = 0.985\, t_f$

$\therefore \qquad\qquad \dfrac{0.985 t_f - t_f}{t_o - t_f} = \dfrac{1}{\cosh(ml)} \qquad\qquad ...(1)$

where, $\qquad\qquad m = \sqrt{\dfrac{hP}{kA_{cs}}} = \sqrt{\dfrac{h}{k} \times \dfrac{\pi d_o}{\dfrac{\pi}{4}(d_o^2 - d_i^2)}}$

$$= \sqrt{\frac{93}{52.3} \times \frac{4 d_o}{d_o^2 - d_i^2}} = \sqrt{\frac{93}{52.3} \times \frac{4 \times 0.017}{(0.017^2 - 0.015^2)}} = 43.5$$

Substituting the value in eqn. (1), we get

$$\frac{0.985 \times 320 - 320}{120 \times 320} = \frac{1}{\cosh(ml)} = \frac{1}{\cosh(43.5l)}$$

or, $\qquad\qquad \cosh(43.5l) = \dfrac{120 \times 320}{0.985 \times 320 - 320} = 41.67$

or, $\qquad\qquad \cosh(43.5l) = 4.423$

or, $\qquad\qquad\qquad l = 0.1016$ or **101.6 mm** (Ans.)

As $l > D$ (95 mm), the pocket should be fitted **inclined**.

2.10.5. HEAT TRANSFER FROM A BAR CONNECTED TO THE TWO HEAT SOURCES AT DIFFERENT TEMPERATURES

Consider the system shown in Fig. 2.143.

Let, $\qquad l$ = Length of the bar connecting two heat sources,

$\qquad A_{cs}$ = Cross-sectional area of the bar (constant),

$\qquad P$ = Perimeter of the bar,

$\qquad t_1$ = Temperature of heat source-1

$\qquad t_2$ = Temperature of heat source-2

$\qquad t_a$ = Temperature of air surrounding the bar,

$\qquad h$ = Heat transfer coefficient on the surface of the bar,

$\qquad k$ = Thermal conductivity of the bar,

$\qquad \theta_1 = t_1 - t_a$, and

$\qquad \theta_2 = t_2 - t_a$.

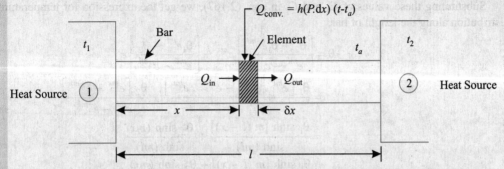

Fig. 2.143. Heeat transfer from a bar connected to heat sources at differernt temperatures.

Consider an infinitesimal element of the bar of thickness dx located at distance x from heat source–1 as shown in Fig. 2.143.

$$Q_{in} = - k \, A_{cs} \frac{dt}{dx};$$

$$Q_{out} = - k \, A_{cs} \left[t + \frac{dt}{dx} \, \delta x \right]$$

$$Q_{conv.} = hP.\delta x \, (t - t_a)$$

Applying energy balance on the element, we have

$$Q_{in} = Q_{out} + Q_{conv}$$

or,

$$- kA_{cs} \cdot \frac{dt}{dx} = - kA_{cs} \frac{d}{dx} \left[t + \frac{dt}{dx} \, \delta x \right] + hP.\, \delta x \, (t - t_a)$$

Upon simplification and rearrangement, we obtain

$$\frac{d^2t}{dx^2} - \frac{hP}{kA_{cs}} (t - t_a) = 0 \qquad \qquad ...(2.165)$$

Replacing the temperature excess $(t - t_a)$ by θ (since the ambient temperature is assumed constant), eqn. 2.165 gets transferred to

$$\frac{d^2\theta}{dx^2} - \frac{hP}{kA_{cs}} \, \theta = 0 \qquad \qquad ...(2.166)$$

The solution to the above differential equation is

$$\theta = C_1 e^{mx} + C_2 \, e^{-mx} \qquad \qquad ...(2.167)$$

where,

$$m = \sqrt{\frac{hP}{kA_{cs}}}$$

The constant C_1 and C_2 are evaluated from the following boundary conditions :

(i) At $x = 0$, $\qquad\qquad\qquad\qquad \theta = \theta_1$

(ii) At $x = l$, $\qquad\qquad\qquad\qquad \theta = \theta_2$

$\therefore$ $\qquad\qquad \theta_1 = C_1 + C_2$ ...[From eqn. (2.167) using boundary condition (i) $\qquad$ ...(a)

$\qquad\qquad \theta_2 = C_1 e^{ml} + C_2 e^{-ml}$...[From eqn. (2.167) using boundary condition (ii) $\quad$ ...(b)

Solving eqns. (a) and (b), we have

$$C_1 = \frac{\theta_2 - \theta_1 e^{-ml}}{e^{-ml} - e^{-ml}} , \qquad C_2 = \frac{\theta_1 e^{ml} - \theta_2}{e^{ml} - e^{-ml}}$$

Substituting these values of C_1 and C_2 in eqn. (2.167), we get the expression for temperature distribution along the length of bar,

$$\theta = \left[\frac{\theta_2 - \theta_1 e^{-ml}}{e^{ml} - e^{-ml}} \right] e^{mx} + \left[\frac{\theta_1 e^{ml} - \theta_2}{e^{ml} - e^{-ml}} \right] e^{-mx}$$

$$= \frac{\theta_1 \left[e^{ml} \cdot e^{-mx} - e^{-ml} \cdot e^{mx} \right]}{e^{ml} - e^{-ml}} + \frac{\theta_2 \left[e^{mx} - e^{-mx} \right]}{e^{ml} - e^{-ml}}$$

$$= \frac{\theta_1 \sinh \left[m (l - x) \right]}{\sinh (ml)} + \frac{\theta_2 \sinh (mx)}{\sinh (ml)}$$

or,

$$\theta = \frac{\theta_1 \sinh \left[m (l - x) \right] + \theta_2 \sinh (mx)}{\sinh (ml)} \qquad \text{...(2.168)}$$

The rate of heat loss is given by

$$Q = \int_0^l hPdx \, (t - t_a) = \int_0^l hPdx \cdot \theta$$

$$= hP \int_0^l \frac{\theta_1 \sinh m(l - x) + \theta_2 \sinh (mx)}{\sinh (ml)} dx$$

$$\text{(substituting for } \theta)$$

$$= \frac{hP}{\sinh (ml)} \left[-\frac{\theta_1 \cdot \cosh \{ m (l - x) \}}{m} + \frac{\theta_2 \cdot \cosh (mx)}{m} \right]_0^l$$

$$= \frac{hP}{\sinh (ml)} \left[-\frac{\theta_1}{m} \{ 1 - \cosh (ml) \} + \frac{\theta_2}{m} \{ \cosh (ml) - 1 \} \right]$$

$$= \frac{hP}{m \sinh (ml)} \left[(\theta_1 + \theta_2) \{ \cosh (ml) - 1 \} \right]$$

But,

$$m = \sqrt{\frac{hP}{kA_{cs}}}$$

$$\therefore \qquad Q = \sqrt{hPkA_{cs}} \, (\theta_1 + \theta_2) \left[\frac{\cosh (ml) - 1}{\sinh (ml)} \right] \qquad \text{...(2.169)}$$

The maximum temperature occurs in the bar where $\frac{d\theta}{dx} = 0$, hence differentiating the eqn. (2.168) we have

$$- m\theta_1 \cosh \{ m (l - x) \} + m\theta_2 \cosh mx = 0$$

or, $\theta \cosh \{ m (l - x) \} = \theta_2 \cosh (mx)$ \qquad \qquad \text{...(2.170)}

The value of x from the above equation gives the position of maximum temperature in the rod.

Example 2.134. *A thin rod of copper (k = 100 W/m°C) 12.5 mm in diameter spans between two parallel plates 150 mm apart. Air flows over the rod providing heat transfer coefficient of 50 W/m²°C. The surface temperature of the plate exceeds the air by 40°C. Determine :*

(i) The excess temperature at the centre of the rod over that of air, and

(ii) The heat lost from the rod in watts. \qquad \qquad (M.U.)

Solution. Refer to Fig. 2.144.

Given : $d = 12.5$ mm $= 0.0125$ m; $l = 150$ mm $= 0.15$ m; $h = 50$ W/m²°C; $k = 100$ W/m°C.

$\qquad \theta_1 = \theta_2 = 40°C$ \qquad \qquad \qquad ...Temperature excess for each plate.

(i) The excess temperature at the centre of the rod over that of air; θ :

The temperature distribution $\theta \, (= t - t_a)$ along the rod is given by

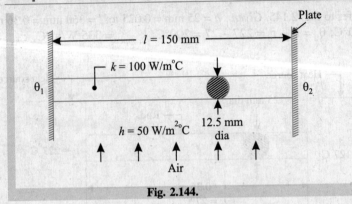

Fig. 2.144.

$$\theta = \frac{\theta_1 \sinh \{m\,(l - x) + \theta_2 \sinh (mx)}{\sinh (ml)} \qquad ...\text{[Eqn. (2.168)]}$$

At, $x = \dfrac{l}{2}$, the value of θ is given by

$$\theta\Big|_{x=\frac{l}{2}} = 2\theta_1 \left[\frac{\sinh (ml/2)}{\sinh (ml)}\right] \qquad ...(i)$$

where, $$m = \sqrt{\frac{hP}{kA_{cs}}} = \sqrt{\frac{h \times \pi d}{k \times \dfrac{\pi}{4}d^2}} = \sqrt{\frac{4h}{kd}} = \sqrt{\frac{4 \times 50}{100 \times 0.0125}} = 12.65$$

∴ $$ml = 12.65 \times 0.15 \simeq 1.9$$

Substituting the proper values in eqn. (i), we have

$$\theta\Big|_{x=\frac{l}{2}} = 2 \times 40 \left[\frac{\sinh (1.9/2)}{\sinh (1.9)}\right] = 80 \times \frac{1.0995}{3.2682} = \mathbf{26.9^\circ C} \quad \textbf{(Ans.)}$$

(ii) **The heat lost from the rod, Q :**

$$Q = \sqrt{hPkA_{cs}}\,(\theta_1 + \theta_2) \left[\frac{\cosh (ml) - 1}{\sinh (ml)}\right] \qquad ...\text{[Eqn. (2.169)]}$$

$$= \sqrt{h \times (\pi d)k \times \left(\frac{\pi}{4}d^2\right)} \times 2\theta_1 \left[\frac{\cosh (ml) - 1}{\sinh (ml)}\right]$$

$$= \sqrt{hk\pi^2 d^3} \times \theta_1 \times \left[\frac{\cosh (ml) - 1}{\cosh (ml)}\right]$$

$$= \sqrt{50 \times 100 \times \pi^2 \times 0.0125^3} \times 40 \times \left[\frac{\cosh (1.9) - 1}{\sinh (1.9)}\right]$$

$$= 0.31 \times 40 \times \left[\frac{3.4177 - 1}{3.2682}\right] = \mathbf{9.17\ W} \quad \textbf{(Ans.)}$$

Example 2.135. *A 25 mm diameter rod of 360 mm length connects two heat sources maintained at 127°C and 227°C respectively. The curved surface of the rod is losing heat to the surrounding air at 27°C. The heat transfer coefficient is 10 W/m²°C. Calculate the loss of heat from the rod if it is made of (i) copper (k = 335 W/m°1C), (ii) steel (k = 40 W/m°C).* (N.U. 1998)

Solution. Refer to Fig. 2.145. *Given :* $d = 25$ mm $= 0.025$ m; $l = 360$ mm $= 0.36$ m; $\theta_1 = t_1 - t_a$ $= 127 - 27 = 100°C$; $\theta_2 = t_2 - t_a = 227 - 27 = 200°C$; $k_{copper} = 335$ W/m°C, $k_{steel} = 40$ W/m°C; $h = 10$ W/m²°C.

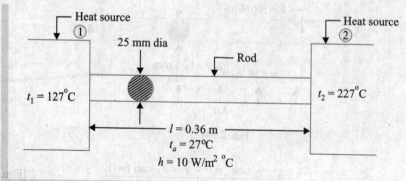

Heat source ①

25 mm dia

Rod

Heat source ②

$t_1 = 127°C$

$t_2 = 227°C$

$l = 0.36$ m
$t_a = 27°C$
$h = 10$ W/m² °C

Fig. 2.145.

(i) **Loss of heat from the copper rod :**
The loss of heat is given by,

$$Q = \sqrt{hPkA_{cs}} \; (\theta_1 + \theta_2) \left[\frac{\cosh (ml) - 1}{\sinh (ml)} \right] \qquad \text{...[Eqn. (2.169)]}$$

where,

$$m = \sqrt{\frac{hP}{kA_{cs}}} \cdot \frac{h \times \pi d}{k \times \frac{\pi}{4} d^2} = \sqrt{\frac{4h}{kd}} = \sqrt{\frac{4 \times 10}{335 \times 0.025}} = 2.185$$

and,

$$ml = 2.185 \times 0.36 = 0.7866,$$
$$P = \pi d = \pi \times 0.025 \text{ m}$$

$$A_{cs} = \frac{\pi}{4} d^2 = \frac{\pi}{4} \times 0.025^2 \text{ m}^2$$

Substituting the values in the above equation, we get

$$Q = \sqrt{10 \times (\pi \times 0.25) \times 335 \times \left(\frac{\pi}{4} \times 0.025^2 \right)} \times (100 + 200) \left[\frac{\cosh (0.7866) - 1}{\sinh (0.7866)} \right]$$

$$= 1.136 \times 300 \times \frac{1.328 - 1}{0.87} = \mathbf{128.48 \text{ W}} \qquad \textbf{(Ans.)}$$

(ii) **Loss of heat from steel rod :**

$$m = \sqrt{\frac{4h}{kd}} = \sqrt{\frac{4 \times 10}{40 \times 0.025}} = 6.32$$
$$ml = 6.32 \times 0.36 = 2.27$$

$$hPkA_{cs} = 10 \times \pi d \times 40 \times \frac{\pi}{4} d^2$$

$$= 10 \times \pi \times 0.025 \times 40 \times \frac{\pi}{4} \times 0.025^2 = 0.0154$$

Substituting the values in eqn. (2.169) above, we get

$$Q = \sqrt{0.0154} \times (100 + 200) \left[\frac{\cosh (2.27) - 1}{\sinh (2.27)} \right]$$

or,

$$Q = 0.124 \times 300 \times \left[\frac{4.89 - 1}{4.79} \right] = \mathbf{30.21 \text{ W}} \qquad \textbf{(Ans.)}$$

Example 2.136. *One end of the copper rod (k = 380 W/m°C) 300 mm long is connected to wall which is maintained at 300°C. The other end is firmly connected to a wall which is maintained at 100°C. Air is blown across the rod so that heat transfer coefficient of 20 W/m²°C is maintained. The diameter of the rod is 15 mm and temperature of air is 40°C. Determine :*

(i) *The net heat transferred to the air in watts;*

(ii) *The heat conducted to the other end which is at 100°C.* [MU, 1999]

Solution. *Refer to Fig. 2.146. Given :* $l = 0.3$ m; $d = 15$ mm $= 0.015$ m, $t_1 = 300°C$; $t_2 = 100°C$, $t_a = 40°C$; $h = 20$ W/m²°C; $k = 380$ W/m°C.

(*i*) **The net rate of heat transfer to the air, Q :**

$$\theta_1 = t_1 - t_a = 300 - 40 = 260°C; \ \theta_2 = t_2 - t_a = 100 - 40 = 60°C$$

The rate of heat flow is given by

$$Q = \sqrt{hPkA_{cs}} \ (\theta_1 + \theta_2) \left[\frac{\cosh{(ml)} - 1}{\sinh{(ml)}}\right] \qquad ...[\text{Eqn. (2.169)}]$$

where,

$$m = \sqrt{\frac{hP}{kA_{cs}}} = \sqrt{\frac{h \times \pi d}{k \times \frac{\pi}{4}d^2}} = \sqrt{\frac{4h}{kd}}$$

$$= \sqrt{\frac{4 \times 20}{380 \times 0.015}} = 3.746$$

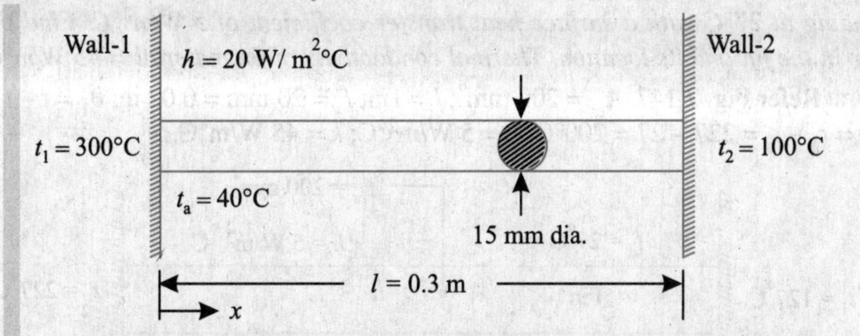

Wall-1 $h = 20$ W/ m²°C   Wall-2

$t_1 = 300°C$

$t_a = 40°C$ $t_2 = 100°C$

15 mm dia.

$l = 0.3$ m

x

Fig. 2.146.

∴ $ml = 3.746 \times 0.3 = 1.12$

$$hPkA_{cs} = 20 \times \pi d \times 380 \times \frac{\pi}{4}d^2$$

$$= 20 \times \pi \times 0.015 \times 380 \times \frac{\pi}{4} \times 0.015^2 = 0.0633$$

Substituting the proper values in the equation, we get

$$Q = \sqrt{0.0633} \times (260 + 60) \left[\frac{\cosh{(1.12)} - 1}{\sinh{(1.12)}}\right]$$

$$= 0.2516 \times 320 \left[\frac{1.6956 - 1}{1.3693}\right] = \textbf{40.9 W (Ans.)}$$

(*ii*) **The heat conducted to the other end which is at 100°C** $[Q_{cond.}]_{x=l}$ **:**

$$[Q_{cond.}]_{x=l} = [Q_{cond.}]_{x=0} - Q \qquad ...(i)$$

The temperature distribution is given by

$$\theta = \frac{\theta_1 \sinh{[m \ (l - x)]} + \theta_2 \sinh{(mx)}}{\sinh{(ml)}} \qquad ...[\text{Eqn. (2.168)}]$$

$$\therefore \qquad \frac{d\theta}{dx} = \left[\frac{-\theta_1 . \cosh m\,(l-x) + \theta_2 . m \cosh (mx)}{\sinh (ml)} \right]$$

and, $$\frac{d\theta}{dx}\bigg|_{x=0} = \left[\frac{-\theta_1 . m \cosh (ml) + \theta_2 . m}{\sinh (ml)} \right]$$

$$\therefore \qquad [Q_{cond.}]_{x=0} = -kA_{cs} \frac{d\theta}{dx}\bigg|_{x=0}$$

or, $$[Q_{cond.}]_{x=0} = kA_{cs}\, m \left[\frac{\theta_1 \cosh (ml) - \theta_2}{\sinh (ml)} \right] \qquad \left[\text{substituting for } \frac{d\theta}{dx}\bigg|_{x=0} \right]$$

Substituting the proper values in eqn. (i), we get

$$[Q_{cond.}]_{x=l} = kA_{cs}\, m \left[\frac{\theta_1 \cosh (ml) - \theta_2}{\sinh (ml)} \right] - Q$$

$$= 380 \times \left(\frac{\pi}{4} \times 0.015^2 \right) \times 3.746 \left[\frac{260 \cosh (1.12) - 60}{\sinh (1.12)} \right] - 40.9$$

or, $$[Q_{cond.}]_{x=l} = 0.2515 \left[\frac{260 \times 1.6956 - 60}{1.3693} \right] - 40.9 = \mathbf{29.05\ W} \quad \textbf{(Ans.)}$$

Example 2.137. *Two ends of a fin of cross-sectional area 200 mm² and length 1m are maintained at 127°C and 227°C. Perimeter is 20 mm. It loses heat from the surface due to natural convection to the surrounding at 27°C with a surface heat transfer coefficient of 5 W/m²°C. Find the minimum temperature in the fin and its location. Thermal conductivity of fin material = 45 W/m°C.*

Solution. Refer Fig. 2.147. A_{cs} = 200 mm²; l = 1m; P = 20 mm = 0.02 m; $\theta_1 = t - t_a = 127 - 27$ = 100°C; $\theta = t_2 - t_a = 227 - 27 = 200°$C; h = 5 W/m²°C; k = 45 W/m°C.

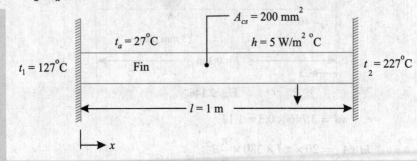

Fig. 2.147.

The temperature distribution for such configuration is given by

$$\theta = (t - t_a) = \frac{\theta_1 \sinh [m\,(l-x)] + \theta_2 \sinh (mx)}{\sinh (ml)} \qquad \text{...[Eqn. (2.168)]}$$

For finding the *position of the minimum temperature*, the required condition is

$$\frac{d\theta}{dx} = 0$$

or, $$\theta_1 \cosh \{m\,(l-x)\} = \theta_2 \cosh (mx) \qquad \text{[Refer eqn. (2.170)]}$$

or, $$\frac{\cosh (mx)}{\cosh \{m\,(l-x)\}} = \frac{\theta_1}{\theta_2} = \frac{100}{200} = 0.5$$

where, $$m = \sqrt{\frac{hP}{kA_{cs}}} = \sqrt{\frac{5 \times 0.02}{45 \times 200 \times 10^{-6}}} = 3.33$$

$$\therefore \qquad \frac{\cosh (3.33x)}{\cosh [3.33 (1-x)]} = 0.5$$

By trial and error method, we get

$$x = 0.39 \text{ m} \quad \text{(Ans.)}$$

Substituting the value of x in the above equation [Eqn. (2.168)], we have

$$\theta = (t - t_a) = \frac{100 \sinh [3.33 (1 - 0.39)] + 200 \sinh (3.33 \times 0.39)}{\sinh (3.33 \times 1)}$$

$$= \frac{100 \sinh (2.03) + 200 \sinh (1.3)}{\sinh (3.33)} = \frac{100 \times 3.7414 + 200 \times 1.6984}{13.9554} = 51.15$$

$$\therefore \qquad t = 51.15 + t_a = 51.15 + 27 = \textbf{78.15°C} \quad \text{(Ans.)}$$

Example 2.138. *The following data were obtained from a single glass cover plate solar heat collector. Mean plate temperature = 70°C. Ambient temperature = 10°C. Back insulation thickness = 5 cm, k (insulation) = 0.05 W/m°C.*

Heat transfer coefficient by convection from plate to cover = 3 W/m²°C.

Equivalent heat transfer coefficient by radiation from plate to cover = 6 W/m²°C.

Convection heat transfer co-efficient from cover to air = 25 W/m²°C.

Equivalent radiant heat transfer co-efficient from cover to air = 5 W/m²°C.

Compare total heat loss per m² area of collector. Assume that the resistance to heat flow by convection at the back surface of the insulation is neglected. **(U.P.S.C., 1993)**

Solution. *Given :* $t_p = 70°C$, $t_a = 10°C$, $h_{cp} = 3$ W/m²°C; $h_{rp} = 6$ W/m²°C; $h_{cc} = 25$ W/m²°C; $h_{rc} = 5$ W/m° C; $k = 0.05$ W/m°C.

The configuration of flat plate collector is shown in Fig. 2.148.

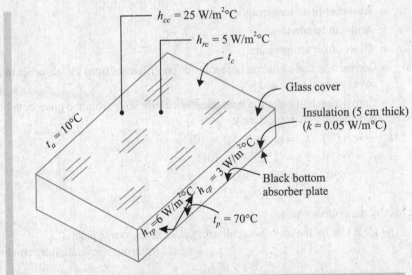

Fig. 2.148. Flat plate heat collector.

Total heat loss per m² area of collector :

Under the steady state condition of the black plate (absorber), and considering the area of collector as unit, we have :

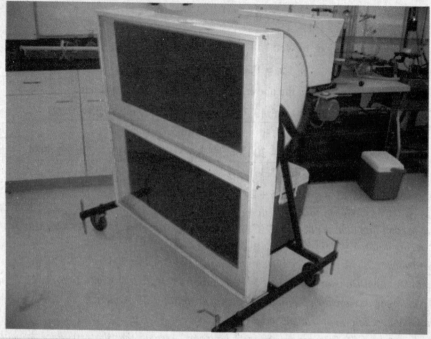

Solar heat collector.

(Heat lost from the absorber plate by convection to cover) + (heat lost by the absorber plate by radiation to the cover) = (Heat lost by the cover to air by convection) + (heat lost by the cover to the air by radiation)

i.e.,

$$h_{cp}(70 - t_c) + h_{rp}(70 - t_c) = h_{cc}(t_c - 10) + h_{rc}(t_c - 10)$$

where, t_p = Absorber plate temperature,

   t_a = Ambient temperature,

   t_c = Glass cover temperature,

   h_{cp}, h_{rp} = Convection and radiation heat transfer co-efficients from the absorber plate to cover respectively, and

   h_{cc}, h_{rc} = Convection and radiation heat transfer co-efficients from the glass cover to the surrounding air respectively.

∴
$$(h_{cp} + h_{rp})(70 - t_c) = (h_{cc} + h_{rc})(t_c - 10)$$
$$(3+6)(70 - t_c) = (25+5)(t_c - 10)$$
$$630 - 9t_c = 30t_c - 300$$

∴
$$t_c = 23.85°C$$

Total heat lost by the collector plate

= Heat lost by the absorber (collector) plate to the cover plate

+ heat lost through insulation by conduction.

$$= (h_{cp} + h_{rp}) \times 1 \times (t_p - t_c) + \frac{k \times 1 \times (t_p - t_a)}{(5/100)}$$

$$= (3 + 6) \times 1 \times (70 - 23.85) + \frac{0.05 \times 1 \times (70 - 10)}{0.05}$$

$$= 415.35 + 60 = \textbf{475.35 W/m}^2 \qquad \textbf{(Ans.)}$$

HIGHLIGHTS

1. General heat conduction equation for 'non-homogeneous material', 'self heat generating' and 'unsteady three-dimensional heat flow'.

$$\nabla \cdot (k\nabla t) + q_g = \rho c \frac{\partial t}{\partial \tau}$$

2. General heat conduction equation for constant thermal conductivity :

$$\frac{\partial^2 t}{\partial x^2} + \frac{\partial^2 t}{\partial y^2} + \frac{\partial^2 t}{\partial z^2} + \frac{q_g}{k} = \frac{\rho c}{k} \cdot \frac{\partial t}{\partial \tau} = \frac{1}{\alpha} \cdot \frac{\partial t}{\partial \tau}$$

where, $$\alpha = \frac{k}{\rho c} = \frac{\text{Thermal conductivity}}{\text{Thermal capacity}}$$

The quantity $\alpha = \dfrac{k}{\rho c}$ is known as *thermal diffusivity*.

$$\frac{\partial^2 t}{dx^2} + \frac{\partial^2 t}{\partial y^2} + \frac{\partial^2 t}{\partial z^2} = \frac{1}{\alpha} \cdot \frac{\partial t}{\partial \tau}$$ ...**Fourier's equation**

$$\left(\text{or } \nabla^2 t = \frac{1}{\alpha} \cdot \frac{\partial t}{\partial \tau} \right)$$

$$\frac{\partial^2 t}{\partial x^2} + \frac{\partial^2 t}{\partial y^2} + \frac{\partial^2 t}{\partial z^2} + \frac{q_g}{k} = 0$$ ...**Poisson's equation**

$$\left(\text{or } \nabla^2 t + \frac{q_g}{k} = 0 \right)$$

$$\frac{\partial^2 t}{\partial x^2} + \frac{\partial^2 t}{\partial y^2} + \frac{\partial^2 t}{\partial z^2} = 0$$ ...**Laplace equation**

$$(\text{or } \nabla^2 t = 0)$$

3. General heat conduction equation in *cylindrical coordinates* :

$$\left[\frac{\partial^2 t}{\partial r^2} + \frac{1}{r} \cdot \frac{\partial t}{\partial r} + \frac{1}{r^2} \cdot \frac{\partial^2 t}{\partial \phi^2} + \frac{\partial^2 t}{\partial z^2} \right] + \frac{q_g}{k} = \frac{\rho c}{k} \cdot \frac{\partial t}{\partial \tau} = \frac{1}{\alpha} \cdot \frac{\partial t}{\partial \tau}$$

4. General heat conduction equation in *spherical coordinates* :

$$\left[\frac{1}{r^2 \sin^2\theta} \cdot \frac{\partial t^2}{\partial \phi^2} + \frac{1}{r^2 \sin\theta} \cdot \frac{\partial}{\partial\theta}\left(\sin\theta \cdot \frac{\partial t}{\partial\theta} \right) + \frac{1}{r^2} \cdot \frac{\partial}{\partial r}\left(r^2 \cdot \frac{\partial t}{\partial r} \right) \right] + \frac{q_g}{k} = \frac{\rho c}{k} \cdot \frac{\partial t}{\partial \tau} = \frac{1}{\alpha} \cdot \frac{\partial t}{\partial \tau}$$

5. Heat conduction through a *composite wall* :

$$Q = \frac{[t_1 - t_{(n+1)}]}{\displaystyle\sum_{1}^{n} \frac{L}{kA}}$$

6. Heat conduction through a *cylinder* :

$$Q = \frac{(t_1 - t_2)}{\dfrac{\ln (r_2 / r_1)}{2\pi kL}}$$

where r_1 and r_2 are the inner and outer radii respectively and L is the length of the cylinder.

7. Logarithmic mean area for the hollow cylinder (A_m) :

$$A_m = \frac{A_o - A_i}{\ln (A_o / A_i)}$$

where A_i and A_o are the inside and outside surface areas of the cylinder.

8. Heat conduction through a *composite cylinder* :

$$Q = \frac{2\pi L \left[t_1 - t_{(n+1)}\right]}{\sum\limits_{n=1}^{n=n} \dfrac{1}{k_n} \ln \left[r_{(n+1)}/r_n\right]}$$

9. Heat conduction through a *hollow sphere* :

$$Q = \frac{(t_1 - t_2)}{\left[\dfrac{(r_2 - r_1)}{4\pi k r_1 r_2}\right]}$$

Logarithmic mean area for the hollow sphere :

$$A_m = \sqrt{A_i A_o}$$

Heat conduction through a *composite sphere* :

$$Q = \frac{4\pi \left(t_{hf} - t_{cf}\right)}{\left[\dfrac{1}{h_{hf} \cdot r_1^2} + \sum\limits_{n=1}^{n=n} \left(\dfrac{r_{(n+1)} - r_n}{k_n \cdot r_n \cdot r_{(n+1)}}\right) + \dfrac{1}{h_{cf} \, r_{(n+1)}^2}\right]}$$

10. *Critical thickness of insulation* :

For a cylinder : $r_2 \, (= r_c) = \dfrac{k}{h_o}$ (where h_o = heat transfer coefficient at the outer surface of the insulation).

The above relation represents the condition for minimum resistance and consequently maximum heat flow rate. The insulation radius at which resistance to heat flow is minimum is called the '*critical radius*'.

For a sphere: $r_2 \, (= r_c) = \dfrac{2k}{h_o}$

11. Heat conduction *with internal heat generation* :

A. Plane wall :

Case I. *Both the surfaces have the same temperature* :

$$t = \frac{q_g}{2k} \, (L - x) \, x + t_w \qquad\qquad ...(i)$$

$$t_{max} = \frac{q_g}{8k} \, L^2 + t_w \qquad\qquad ...(ii)$$

$$\left. \begin{aligned} t &= t_a + \frac{q_g}{h} \, L + \frac{q_g}{2k} \, (L - x) \, x \\[2mm] t_{max} &= t_a + q_g \left[\frac{L}{2h} + \frac{L^2}{8k}\right] \end{aligned} \right\} \text{Considering } h \text{ and } t_a \qquad\begin{aligned} &...(iii) \\[4mm] &...(iv) \end{aligned}$$

(at the mid plane, *i.e.*, $x = L/2$)

$$t = \frac{q_g}{2k} \, (2L - x) \, x + t_w \qquad\qquad ...(v)$$

$$t_{max} = \frac{q_g}{2k} \, L^2 + t_w \qquad\qquad ...(vi)$$

Case II. *Both the surfaces of the wall have different temperatures* :

$$\frac{t - t_{w2}}{t_{w1} - t_{w2}} = \left[1 - \frac{x}{L}\right]\left[\frac{Zx}{L} + 1\right] \qquad\qquad ...(i)$$

$$\frac{t_{max} - t_{w2}}{t_{w1} - t_{w2}} = \frac{(Z+1)^2}{4Z} \qquad \qquad ...(ii)$$

where,
$$Z = \frac{q_g}{2k} \cdot \frac{L^2}{(t_{w1} - t_{w2})}$$

Case III. *Current carrying electrical conductor :*

$$q_g = \frac{J^2}{k_e}$$

where, q_g = Heat generated per unit volume per unit time
  t_w = Temperature of the wall surface
  L = Thickness of the wall
  k = Thermal conductivity of wall material
  h = Heat transfer coefficient
  J = Current density, and
  k_e = Electrical conductivity.

B. Cylinder :

$$t = t_w + \frac{q_g}{4k}[R^2 - r^2] \qquad \qquad ...(i)$$

$$t_{max} = t_w + \frac{q_g}{4k} \cdot R^2 \qquad \qquad ...(ii)$$

$$\frac{t - t_w}{t_{max} - t_w} = \left[1 - \left(\frac{r}{R}\right)^2\right] \qquad \qquad ...(iii)$$

(Temperature distribution in dimensionless form)

$$t_w = t_a + \frac{q_g}{2h} \cdot R \qquad \qquad ...(iv)$$

$$t = t_a + \frac{q_g}{2h} \cdot R + \frac{q_g}{4k}[R^2 - r^2], \text{ considering } h \& t_a \qquad ...(v)$$

$$t_{max} = t_a + \frac{q_g}{2h} \cdot R + \frac{q_g}{4k} \cdot R^2 \qquad \qquad ...(vi)$$

C. Nuclear cylindrical rod :

Case I.   *Without cladding :*

$$t_w - t_{max} = -\frac{3q_o R_{fr}^2}{16 k_{fr}} \qquad \qquad ...(i)$$

$$t_{max} - t_a = \frac{q_o R_{fr}}{4}\left[\frac{3R_{fr}}{4k_{fr}} + \frac{1}{h}\right] \qquad \qquad ...(ii)$$

Case II.   *With cladding*

$$t_{max} = t_w + \frac{q_o R_{fr}^2}{4}\left[\frac{3}{4k_{fr}} + \frac{1}{k_{cl}} \cdot \ln(R_{cl}/R_{fr})\right] \qquad ...(iii)$$

where, q_o = *Heat generation rate at centre of the rod (r = 0),*
  R_{fr} = *Outer radius of the fuel rod,*
  R_{cl} = *Outer radius of cladding,*
  k_{cl} = *Thermal conductivity of cladding material, and*
  k_{fr} = *Thermal conductivity of fuel rod material.*

D. Sphere :

$$t = t_w + \frac{q_g}{6k}(R^2 - r^2) \qquad \qquad ...(i)$$

$$t_{max} = t_w + \frac{q_g}{6k} R^2 \qquad \qquad ...(ii)$$

$$\frac{t - t_w}{t_{max} - t_w} = 1 - \left(\frac{r}{R}\right)^2 \qquad \qquad ...(iii)$$

(Temperature distribution in dimensionless form)

$$t_w = t_a + \frac{q_g R}{3h} \qquad \qquad ...(iv)$$

$$\left. \begin{array}{l} t = t_a + \dfrac{q_g R}{3h} + \dfrac{q_g}{6k}(R^2 - r^2) \\[3mm] t_{max} = t_a + \dfrac{q_g}{3h}.R + \dfrac{q_g}{6k}.R^2 \end{array} \right\} \text{Considering } h \text{ and } t_a$$

12. Heat transfer from extended surfaces (Fins) :

A. Rectangular fin :

$$\theta = C_1 e^{mx} + C_2 e^{-mx} \qquad \qquad ...(i)$$

or $\qquad \qquad [(t - t_a) = C_1 e^{mx} + C_2 e^{-mx}]$

Case I. *Heat dissipation from an infinitely long fin* $(l \to \infty)$:

$$\theta = \theta_0 e^{-mx} \qquad \qquad ...(ii)$$

or $\qquad \qquad [(t - t_a) = (t_o - t_a) e^{-mx}]$

$$Q_{fin} = k A_{cs} m (t_o - t_a) \qquad \qquad ...(iii)$$

[An infinitely long fin is one for which $ml \to \infty$, and this condition may be approached when $ml > 5$]

Case II. *Heat dissipation from a fin insulated at the tip* :

$$\frac{\theta}{\theta_o} = \frac{t - t_a}{t_o - t_a} = \frac{\cosh [m \{l - x\}]}{\cosh (ml)} \qquad \qquad ...(iv)$$

$$Q_{fin} = kA_{cs} m (t_o - t_a) \tanh (ml) \qquad \qquad ...(v)$$

Case III. *Heat dissipation from a fin losing heat at the tip* :

$$\frac{\theta}{\theta_o} = \frac{t - t_a}{t_o - t_a} = \frac{\cosh \{m (l - x)\} + \dfrac{h}{km} [\sinh \{m (l - x)\}]}{\cosh (ml) + \dfrac{h}{km} [\sinh (ml)]} \qquad ...(vi)$$

$$Q_{fin} = kA_{cs} m (t_o - t_a) \left[\frac{\tanh (ml) + \dfrac{h}{km}}{1 + \dfrac{h}{km}. \tanh (ml)} \right] \qquad \qquad ...(vii)$$

where $\qquad \qquad m = \sqrt{\dfrac{hP}{kA_{cs}}}$

$[A_{cs}$ = cross-sectional area $(b \times y)$; P = perimeter of the fin $\{= 2(b + y)\}]$

$[t_o$ = temperature at the base of the fin; t_a = temperature of ambient/surrounding fluid].

Efficiency of fin : It is defined as the ratio of the actual heat transferred by the fin to the maximum heat transferable by fin, if entire fin area were at the base temperature.

Effectiveness of fin : It is the ratio of the fin heat transfer rate to the heat transfer rate that would exist without a fin.

B. Straight triangular fin :

$$Q_{fin} = b\sqrt{2hky} \cdot \theta_o \frac{I_1 (2B\sqrt{l})}{I_o (2B\sqrt{l})}$$

where,

$$B = \sqrt{\frac{2hl}{ky}}$$

THEORETICAL QUESTIONS

1. Derive general heat conduction equation in :
   - (i) Cartesian coordinates; (ii) Cylindrical coordinates; (iii) Spherical coordinates.

2. Explain briefly the terms thermal capacity and thermal diffusivity of a material.

3. Derive expressions for temperature distribution, under one dimensional steady state heat conduction, for the following systems :
   - (i) Plane wall; (ii) Composite wall;
   - (iii) Cylinder; (iv) Sphere.

4. Derive expressions for temperature distribution and heat dissipation in a straight fin of rectangular profile for the following cases :
   - (i) Infinitely long fin; (ii) Fin insulated at the tip;
   - (iii) Fin losing heat at the tip.

5. Explain the following :
   - (i) Efficiency of fin; (ii) Effectiveness of fin.

6. Derive an expression for heat dissipation in a straight triangular fin.

UNSOLVED EXAMPLES

Heat Conduction through Walls/Roofs, Cylinders and Spheres

1. The inner surface of a plane brick wall is at 50° C and the outer surface is at 30°C. Calculate the rate of heat transfer per m² of surface area of the wall, which is 250 mm thick. The thermal conductivity of the brick is 0.52 W/m°C.   [**Ans.** 41.6 W/m²]

2. The temperatures at the inner and outer surfaces of a boiler wall made of 20 mm thick steel and covered with an insulating material of 5 mm thickness are 300°C and 50°C respectively. If the thermal conductivities of steel and insulating material are 58 W/m°C and 0.116 W/m°C respectively, determine the rate of heat flow through the boiler wall.
    [**Ans.** 5.8 kW/m²]

Boiler.

3. A mild steel tank of wall thickness 10 mm contains water at 90°C. The thermal conductivity of mild steel is 50 W/m°C, and the heat transfer co-efficients for the inside and outside of the tank are 2800 and 11 W/m²°C, respectively. If the atmospheric temperature is 20°C, calculate :
   - (i) The rate of heat loss per m² of the tank surface area;
   - (ii) The temperature of the outside surface of the tank.   [**Ans.** (i) 820 W/m²; (ii) 89.6°C]

4. Calculate the rate of heat flow through the wall of a refrigerated van of 1.5 mm of steel sheet at outer surface, 100 mm plywood at the inner surface and 2 cm of glass-wool in between, if the temperatures of the inside and outside surfaces are – 15°C and 24°C respectively. Take thermal conductivities of steel, glass-wool and plywood as 23.2 W/m°C, 0.014 W/m°C and 0.052 W/m°C respectively.
    [**Ans.** 6kW/m²]

5. Calculate the temperatures at the contact surfaces of the wall of a furnace made up of 250 mm of fire brick, 120 mm of insulation brick and 200 mm of red brick. The inner and outer surface temperatures of the wall are 850°C and 65°C respectively. Neglect resistance of mortar joints :

Take $k_{fire\ brick}$ = 1.05 W/m°C; $k_{insulation\ brick}$ = 0.85 W/m°C;
                $k_{red\ brick}$ = 0.85 W/m°C.

Take $k_{fire\ brick}$ = 1.4 W/m°C; $k_{insulation\ brick}$ = 0.2 W/m°C

[Ans. 703°C, 210°C]

6. A flat wall of a furnace is made up of fire brick, insulating brick and building brick of thicknesses 25 cm, 12.5 cm and 25 cm respectively. The inside wall is at a temperature of 600°C and the atmospheric temperature is 20°C. If the heat transfer coefficient for the outside surface is 10 W/m²°C, calculate :

  (i)   That loss per m² of wall area;

  (ii)   Temperature of the outside wall surface of the furnace.   **[Ans. (i) 0.46 kW/m², (ii) 66°C]**

Take : $k_{fire\ brick}$ = 1.4 W/m°C; $k_{insulating\ brick}$ = 0.2 W/m°C.

7. A furnace wall consists of 200 mm of refractory fire clay brick, 100 mm of kaolin brick and 6 mm of steel plate. The fire side of the refractory is at 1150°C and the temperature at the outside surface of the wall is 30°C. An accurate heat balance over the furnace shows the heat loss from the wall to be 300 W/m². It is known that there may be thin layers of air between the layers of brick and steel. To how many millimeters of kaolin are these air layers equivalent? The thermal conductivities are as follows :

     $k_{refractory\ fire\ clay\ brick}$ = 1.7 W/m°C
     $k_{kaolin\ brick}$ = 0.17 W/m°C
     k_{steel} = 17 W/m°C   **[Ans. 514 mm]**

8. A furnace wall consists of 12.5 cm wide refractory brick and 12.5 cm wide insulating fire brick separated by an air gap. The outside wall is covered with 1.2 cm thick plaster. The inner surface wall is at 1100°C and room temperature is 25°C. Calculate the rate at which heat is lost per m² area of wall surface.

h_{cf}(heat transfer coefficient from outside wall surface) =17 W/m²°C

R_{air} (resistance of air gap) = 0.16 °C/W

     $k_{refractory\ brick}$ = 1.6 W/m°C
     $k_{insulation\ brick}$ = 0.3 W/m°C
     $k_{plaster}$ = 0.14 W/m°C

Also calculate the temperature of outside wall surface.   **[Ans. 1338.7 W/m², 103.7°C]**(*M.U.*)

9. A 2000 W heater element of area 0.04 m² is protected on the backside with insulation 50 mm thick of k = 1.4 W/m°C and on the front side by a plate 100 mm thick with thermal conductivity of 45 W/m°C. The backside is exposed to air at 5°C with convection coefficient of 10 W/m²°C and the front is exposed to air at 15°C with convection coefficient including radiation of 250 W/m²°C. Determine :

  (i)   The temperature of the heater element;

  (ii)   The heat flow into the room under steady state conditions   **[Ans. (i) 219.4°C; (ii)1936.8 W]**

10. Calculate the rate at which heat is being lost to the surrounding per unit length of an insulated steam pipe having the following dimensions and specifications :

d_i = 3 cm, d_o = 3.4 cm for the pipe
Thickness of insulation = 1 cm
h_i = 10 W/m²°C and h_o = 10 W/m²°C
k (pipe) = 15 W/m°C and k (insulation) = 0.5 W/m°C
t_s (steam) = 100°C and t_a (atmosphere) = 25°C   **[Ans. 41.6 W/m]**
[*M.U. Summer, 1996*]

11. A 15 cm outer diameter steam pipe is covered with 5 cm of high temperature insulation (k = 0.85 W/m°C) and 4 cm of low temperature insulation (k = 0.72 W/m°C). The steam is at 500°C and ambient air is at 40°C. Neglecting thermal resistances of steam and air sides and metal wall, calculate the heat loss from 1000 m length of the pipe.   **(Ans. 2928 kW) [*M.U. Summer 1997*]**

12. An insulated steam pipe of 160 mm inner diameter and 180 mm outer diameter is covered with insulation of 40 mm thickness and carries steam at 200°C.

    k (pipe) = 29 W/m°C and k (insulation) = 0.23 W/m°C

    h_i = 11.6 W/m²°C and h_o = 23.2 W/m²°C

    If the temperature of the air surrounding the pipe is 25°C, calculate the rate of heat loss to the surrounding from the pipe of 5 m length. Also find the interface temperatures also.

    [**Ans.** 1823 W; 137.43°C, 137.2°C, 44.3°C]

13. Heat is conducted through a tapered circular rod of 200 mm length. The ends A and B having diameters 50 mm and 25 mm are maintained at 27°C and 227°C respectively. k (rod material) = 40 W/m°C. Find :

    (i)   Heat conducted through the rod;

    (ii) The temperature at the midpoint of the rod.

    Assume there is no temperature gradient at a particular cross-section and there is no heat transfer through the peripheral surface.   [**Ans:** (i) 39.27 W, (ii) 93.7°C]

14. A steam pipe having 20 mm outer diameter is to be covered with two layers of insulation each having a thickness of 10 mm. The average thermal conductivity of one material is five times that of the other. Assuming that the inner and outer surface temperatures of the composite insulation are fixed, show that the heat transfer will be reduced by 29.9 percent when a better insulating material is next to the pipe than when it is away from the pipe.   (*M.U. 1996*)

15. A cast iron central heating pipe has an inner diameter of 100 mm and wall thickness of 5 mm. The pipe feeds a radiator with water at a temperature of 90°C and inner wall temperature of the pipe may be assumed equal to the water temperature. Calculate the outer surface temperature of the pipe and heat transfer rate per metre length of pipe in a room at 20°C.

    Take k (pipe material) = 52 W/m°C and h_o = 20 W/m²°C   (**Ans.** 89.9°C, 153.7 W/m)

16. Hot air at a temperature of 60°C is flowing through a steel pipe of 100 mm diameter. The pipe is covered with two layers of different insulating materials of thicknesses 50 mm and 30 mm, and their corresponding thermal conductivities are 0.23 and 0.37 W/m°C. The inside and outside heat transfer coefficients are 58 and 12 W/m²°C. The atmosphere is at 25°C. Find the rate of heat loss from a 50 m length of pipe. Neglect the resistance of steel pipe.   [**Ans.** 2.334 kW]

17. A steam main 250 mm in diameter and 225 m long is covered with 50 mm of high temperature insulation (k = 0.095 W/m°C) and 40 mm of low temperature insulation (k = 0.065 W/m°C). The inner and outer surface temperatures as measured are 400°C and 50°C respectively. Calculate :

    (i)   The total heat loss per hour,

    (ii)   The total heat loss per m² of outer surface,

    (iii) The heat loss per m² of the pipe surface, and

    (iv)   The temperature between the two layers of insulations.

    Neglect heat conduction through pipe material.

    [**Ans.** (i) 265514 kJ/h; (ii) 873.5 kJ/h; (iii) 1502.5 kJ/h; (iv) 215°C]

18. A steel pipe of 100 mm bore and 7 mm wall thickness, carrying steam at 260°C, is insulated with 40 mm of an insulated high temperature diatomaceous earth covering. This covering is in turn insulated with 60 mm of asbestos felt. The atmospheric temperature is 15°C. If the heat transfer coefficients for the inside and outside surfaces are 550 and 15 W/m²°C, respectively, and the thermal conductivities of steel, diatomaceous earth and asbestos felt are 50, 10.09 and 0.07 W/m°C respectively, calculate :

    (i)   The rate at which heat is lost by steam per metre length of the pipe, and

    (ii) The temperature of the outside surface.   [**Ans.** (i) 116W; (ii) 22.8°C]

19. A steam pipe of 160 mm inside diameter and 5 mm thick (k = 58 W/m°C) is covered with first layer of insulating material 30 mm thick (k = 0.17 W/m°C) and second layer of insulating material 50 mm thick (k = 0.093 W/m°C). The temperature of steam passing through the pipe is 300°C and ambient air temperature surrounding the pipe is 30°C. Taking inner and outer heat transfer coefficients 30 and 5.8 W/m²°C respectively, find the heat lost per metre length of pipe.   [**Ans.** 216W/m]

20. A spherical shaped vessel of 1.2 m diameter is 100 mm thick. Find the rate of heat leakage, if the temperature difference between the inner and outer surfaces is 200°C. Thermal conductivity of material is 0.3 kJ/mh°C. [**Ans.** 2262 kJ/h]

HEAT GENERATION

21. A voltage of 10 V is impressed on a stainless steel wire ($k = 22.5$ W/m°C), resistivity $\rho = 70 \times 10^{-6}\,\Omega\,cm$) of 3.2 mm diameter and 300 mm length. The outer surface temperature of the wire is maintained at 93°C. What is the temperature at the centre of the wire? [**Ans.** 138.4°C]

22. A current of 200 amperes is passed through a stainless steel wire ($k = 20$ W/m°C, resistivity $\rho = 70 \times 10^{-6}\,\Omega$ cm). If the wire is submerged in liquid at 110°C and the heat transfer coefficient on wire surface is 4000 W/m²°C, calculate the centre line temperature of the wire. [**Ans.** 230.7°C]

23. A plane wall ($k = 15$ W/m°C) 100 mm thick generates heat at the rate of 4×10^4 W/m³ when an electric current is passed through it. The convective heat transfer coefficient between each face of the wall and the ambient air is 50 W/m²°C. If the ambient air temperature is 20°C, determine the surface temperature and maximum temperature in the wall. [**Ans.** 60°C, 63.33°C]

24. An electric current of 34000 amperes is passed through a flat steel plate ($k = 54$ W/m°C, resistivity $\rho = 12\,\mu\Omega cm$) 12.5 mm thick and 100 mm wide. The temperature on the two surfaces of the plate are 95°C and 80°C. Determine :

    (i) The maximum temperature and its position, and

    (ii) The total amount of heat generated and flow of heat from each surface of the plate.

    [**Ans.** (i) 120°C, 5.52 mm; (ii) 111 kW, 49 kW, 62 kW]

25. The temperatures on the two surfaces of a 20 mm thick steel plate ($k = 50$ W/m°C), having a uniform volumetric heat generation of 40×10^6 W/m³, are 160°C and 100°C. Neglecting the end effects, determine the following :

    (i) The position and value of the maximum temperature, and

    (ii) The flow of heat from each surface of the plate.

    [**Ans.** (i) 6.25 mm, 175.6°C; (ii) -250×10^3 W/m², $+550 \times 10^3$ W/m²]

26. A plane wall 80 mm thick ($k = 0.15$ W/m°C) is insulated on one side while the other side is exposed to environment at 90°C. The rate of heat generation within the wall is 12×10^4 W/m³. If the convective heat transfer coefficient between the wall and the environment is 560 W/m²°C, determine the maximum temperature to which the wall will be subjected. [**Ans.** 2667°C]

27. A 60 mm thick slab of insulating material ($k = 0.407$ W/m°C) is placed between and is in contact with two parallel electrodes, and is then subjected to dielectric heating (high frequency) at a uniform rate of 40694.4 W/m³. On the attainment of steady state conditions, the coefficients of combined radiation and convection for the exposed surfaces are 12.21 W/m²°C and 13.96 W/m²°C respectively. If the ambient temperature is 25°C, determine :

    (i) Surface temperature;

    (ii) Location and magnitude of maximum temperature in the system.

    Assume the flow of heat to be unidirectional and each electrode to be at a uniform temperature equal to that of the slab with which it is in contact. [**Ans.** (i) 121°C, 115°C; (ii) 29 mm, 164°C (app.)]

28. A stainless steel rod of 2 cm diameter is carrying an electrical current of 1000 amperes. The thermal and electrical conductivities of the rod are 16 W/m°C and 1.5×10^4 (ohm cm)$^{-1}$ respectively. What is the temperature at the centre of the rod if the outer surface temperature is 400°C? [**Ans.** 400.105°C]

    (M.U.)

29. The electric cable of thermal conductivity $k = 20$ W/m°C, 3 mm in diameter and one metre long has current flow = 200 amperes, ρ (resistivity) = 70 $\mu\Omega$cm. The wire is submerged in a liquid at 100°C and the surface heat transfer coefficient (h) is 4000 W/m²°C. Calculate the centre temperature of the wire.

    [**Ans.** 372°C].

30. Two steel plates at temperatures of 200°C and 100°C are separated by a steel rod having $k = 40$ W/m°C, 40 cm long and cross-sectional area of 5 cm². Rod is welded to each plate. The space between the plates is filled with insulating material which insulates the circumference of the rod. Electric current flows through the rod dissipating energy at the rate of 20W.

    Determine :   (i)   Maximum temperature in the rod and its location, and

    (ii) Heat conducted at each end of rod.   [**Ans.** (i) 212.5°C, (ii) 15 W, 5W]

31. A fuel channel in a natural uranium reactor of 5 m length has a heat release of 0.25 MW. If the thermal conductivity of uranium is 33 W/m°C, what is the temperature difference between the surface and centre of the uranium element, assuming that the heat release is uniform along the rod?

    [**Ans.** 482.3°C]

EXTENDED SURFACES (FINS)

32. Calculate the amount of energy required to solder together two very long pieces of bare copper wire 1.625 mm in diameter with solder that melts at 195°C. The wires are positioned vertically in air at 24°C. Assume that the heat transfer coefficient on the wire surface is 17 W/m°C and thermal conductivity of wire alloy is 335 W/m°C.   [**Ans.** 2.65 W]

33. It is required to heat oil to about 350°C for frying purpose. A laddel is used in the frying. The section of the handle is 4mm × 15 mm. The surroundings are at 35°C. The conductivity of the material is 210 W/m°C. If the temperature at a distance of 400 mm from the oil should not reach 45°C, determine the convective heat transfer coefficient.   [**Ans.** 24.67 W/m²°C]

34. A temperature rise of 50°C in a circular shaft of 50 mm diameter is caused by the amount of heat generated due to friction in the bearing mounted on the crankshaft. The thermal conductivity of shaft material is 55 W/m°C and the heat transfer coefficient is 7 W/m²°C.

    (i)   Develop an expression for the temperature distribution;

    (ii) Determine the amount of heat transferred through the shaft.

    Assume that the shaft is a rod of infinite length.   [**Ans.** (i) $\theta = \theta_o\, e^{-mx}$, (ii) 17.22W]

35. One end of a long rod, 30 mm in diameter, is inserted into the furnace with the other end projecting in the outside air. After the steady state is reached, the temperature of the rod is measured at two points 150 mm apart and found to be 140°C and 100°C. The atmospheric air temperature is 30°C. If the heat transfer coefficient is 60 W/m²°C, determine the thermal conductivity of the rod.

    [**Ans.** 59.79 W/m°C]

36. The heat exchange, in a certain chemical process, is involved from metal surface to distilled water. A number of thin metal fins, each 60 mm long and 3 mm thick, are provided to increase the heat transfer rate and their ends are attached to an insulated wall. In order to prevent ionization of water, the metal fins are coated with 0.15 mm thick layer of plaster. The mean water temperature and temperature at the base of the fins are 25°C and 85°C respectively. The

Longitudinal fins.

thermal conductivities of the fin material and plastic are 210 W/m°C and 0.55 W/m°C respectively. If the heat transfer coefficient between the plastic coating and water is 260 W/m²°C, calculate :

    (i)   The temperature at the tip of the fin;

    (ii) The fin efficiency.   **[Ans.** (*i*) 45.7°C, (*ii*) 54.4%**]**

37. A motor body is 300 mm in diameter (outside) and 200 mm long. Its surface temperature should not exceed 50°C when dissipating 150 W. Longitudinal fins of 12 mm thickness and 30 mm height are proposed. The convection coefficient is 40 W/m°C. Determine the number of fins required. Atmospheric temperature is 35°C.   **[Ans.** 18**]**

38. A steel rod (k = 30 W/m°C), 10 mm in diameter and 50 mm long, with an insulated end, is to be used as a spine. It is exposed to surroundings with a temperature of 65°C and a heat coefficient of 50 W/m°C. The temperature at the base of the fin is 98°C. Determine :

    (i)   The fin efficiency,

    (ii) The temperature at the edge of the spine, and

    (iii) The heat dissipation.   **[Ans.** (*i*) 66.6; (*ii*) 81.9°C; (*iii*) 1.72W**]**

39. The temperature of the air stream in a tube is measured with the help of a thermometer placed into a protective well filled with oil. The thermometer well is made of a steel tube (k = 55.8 W/m°C), 120 mm long and 1.5 mm thick. The surface heat transfer coefficient from the air to the protective well is 23.3 W/m²°C and the temperature recorded by the thermometer is 84°C. If the temperature at the base of the well is 40°C, what is the measurement error ?   **[Ans.** 16°C**]**

40. One end of copper rod (k = 380 W/m°C) 300 mm long is connected to wall which is maintained at 300°C. The other end is firmly connected to a wall which is maintained at 100°C. Air is blown across the rod so that heat transfer coefficient of 20 W/m²°C is maintained. The diameter of the rod is 15 mm and temperature of air is 40°C. Determine the net heat transferred to the air and the heat conducted to the other end which is at 100°C.   **[Ans.** 40.9 W; 29.05 W**]**

Conduction–Steady–State Two and Three Dimensions

3

3.1. INTRODUCTION

In the previous chapter we have concentrated attention in the solution of one-dimensional problems. But in several practical situations, real heat conduction takes place along more than one dimension; this is due to *irregular boundary of system or non-uniform temperature along the boundary.* Some of the *examples of multi-dimensional heat conduction* are:

(*i*) Cooling of internal combustion engine block;

(*ii*) Air conditioning ducts;

(*iii*) Composite bodies;

(*iv*) Heat treatment of metallic parts of different shapes;

(*v*) Chimneys etc.

The following four methods, in general, are prevalent for the solution of the multi-dimensional heat conduction problems:

1. *Analytical methods :*

These methods are applied only to simple problems as these are quite cumbersome and it is difficult to get the solutions always.

2. *Graphical methods :*

These methods are also used for simple problems only. They give a rough estimate of the temperature field.

3. *Analogical methods :*

These methods can be employed for complicated geometries as these are based on certain similarities between two types of field equations.

Internal combustion engine is an innovative technology to substitute pistons and crank gear with oscillating flaps.

4. *Numerical methods* :

These methods can be applied to any mutli-dimensional problem.

An analytical approach to a multi-dimensional problems requires a prior knowledge of Fourier'series, Bessel's functions, Legendre polynomials, Laplace transform methods and complex variable theory. The other three methods do not require advanced knowledge of mathematics and are more useful for engineering calculations.

3.2. TWO DIMENSIONAL STEADY-STATE CONDUCTION

In a two-dimensional heat flow, the temperature is a function of two-coordinates; the heat flow through a corner, where two walls meet, is an *example* of such a system.

3.2.1. ANALYTICAL METHOD

3.2.1.1. Two-dimensional steady state heat conduction in rectangular plates

Refer to Fig. 3.1. Consider a thin rectangular plate ($\dfrac{\partial t}{\partial z}$ is negligible and temperature is a function of x and y) having no heat source. Assume that the three edges of this plate are maintained at a constant temperature and faces of the plate are adiabatic. Let the thermal conductivity of the plate (k) is uniform (*i.e.*, independent of both temperature and direction).

The controlling differential equation for two dimensional steady state heat conduction is given by

$$\frac{\partial^2 t}{\partial x^2} + \frac{\partial^2 t}{\partial y^2} = 0 , \text{ where } t \text{ is a function of}$$

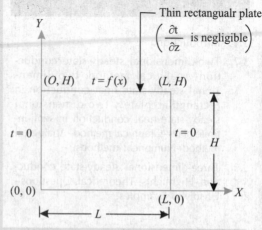

Fig. 3.1. Rectangular plate with temperature-specified boundary conditions.

$$x \text{ and } y \qquad ...(3.1)$$

Eqn. (3.1) is a linear and homogeneous partial differential equation and can be solved by assuming the following form of solution

$$t_2 = X.Y \text{ where } X = f(x) \text{ and } Y = f(y) \text{ only.} \qquad ...(3.2)$$

Substituting this solution in eqn. (3.1), we get

$$Y \frac{d^2 X}{dx^2} + X \frac{d^2 Y}{dy^2} = 0$$

Dividing both sides by XY, we have

$$-\frac{1}{X}\frac{d^2 X}{dx^2} = +\frac{1}{Y}\frac{d^2 Y}{dy^2} \qquad ...(3.3)$$

In this eqn. (3.3) since the variables are separated, each side is constant; taking this constant to be λ^2, we get the following two equations :

$$\frac{d^2 X}{dx^2} + \lambda^2 X = 0 \qquad ...(3.4)$$

$$\frac{d^2 Y}{dy^2} - \lambda^2 Y = 0 \qquad ...(3.5)$$

The general solution to Eqn. (3.4) is given by:

$$X = A \cos(\lambda x) + B \sin(\lambda x)$$

The general solution to Eqn. (3.5) is given by:

$$Y = Ce^{-\lambda y} + De^{\lambda y}$$

These solutions can be verified by substituting them into the corresponding differential equation.

The general solution of eqn. (3.1) is given by:

$$t = X.Y = [A \cos(\lambda x) + B \sin(\lambda x)][Ce^{-\lambda y} + De^{\lambda y}] \qquad ...(3.6)$$

where the values of A, B, C, D and λ are determined from the boundary conditions.

Considering the temperature distribution on the upper edge as the *sine wave*, we have the following *boundary conditions.*

(i) Along $y = 0$, $\qquad t = 0$

(ii) Along $x = 0$, $\qquad t = 0$

(iii) Along $x = L$, $\qquad t = 0$

(iv) Along $y = H$, $\qquad t = t_m \sin\left(\dfrac{\pi x}{L}\right)$

From boundary condition (ii), we get

$$0 = (A + 0)(Ce^{-\lambda y} + De^{\lambda y}) \qquad\qquad \therefore A = 0$$

From boundary conditions (ii), we get, $\qquad C + D = 0 \qquad$ or $C = -D$

$\therefore \qquad t = BD \sin(\lambda x)[e^{\lambda y} - e^{-\lambda y}]$

or, $\qquad t = 2BD \sin(\lambda x) \sin h = E \sin(\lambda x) \sin h(\lambda y)$

$$\text{(where } E = 2BD) \quad \left[\because \ \sin h(\lambda y) = \frac{e^{\lambda y} - e^{-\lambda y}}{2} \right]$$

From boundary condition (iii), we have

$$0 = E \sin(\lambda L) \sin h(\lambda y)$$

$\therefore \qquad \sin(\lambda L) = 0 \ \text{ for all } y$

$$\lambda = \frac{n\pi}{L} \qquad\qquad n = (1, 2, 3, 4,...)$$

$$\therefore \qquad t = E \sin\left(\frac{n\pi x}{L}\right) \sinh\left(\frac{n\pi y}{L}\right) \qquad\qquad ...(3.7)$$

For each integer n there exists a different solution and each solution has a separate integration constant E_n. Summing these solutions, we have

$$t = \sum_{n=1}^{\infty} E_n \sin\left(\frac{n\pi x}{L}\right)\sinh\left(\frac{n\pi y}{L}\right) \qquad\qquad ...(3.8)$$

From boundary condition (iv), we obtain

$$t_m \sin\left(\frac{\pi x}{L}\right) = \sum_{n=1}^{\infty} E_n \sin\left(\frac{n\pi x}{L}\right)\sinh\left(\frac{n\pi H}{L}\right)$$

or, $\quad t_m \sin\left(\dfrac{\pi x}{L}\right) = E_1 \sin\left(\dfrac{\pi x}{L}\right)\sinh\left(\dfrac{\pi H}{L}\right) + \displaystyle\sum_{n=2}^{\infty} E_n \sin\left(\dfrac{n\pi x}{L}\right)\sinh\left(\dfrac{n\pi H}{L}\right)$

Comparing the coefficients, we have

$$E_1 = \frac{t_m}{\sinh\left(\dfrac{\pi H}{L}\right)}; \text{ other constants are zero.}$$

The solution, therefore, becomes

$$t(x, y) = \frac{t_m \sin\left(\dfrac{\pi x}{L}\right)\sinh\left(\dfrac{\pi y}{L}\right)}{\sinh\left(\dfrac{\pi H}{L}\right)} \qquad\qquad ...(3.9)$$

If the boundary conditions are not as simple as in the preceding problem, the solution is obtained in the form of an infinite series.

Let, $\qquad t = f(x) \quad$ at $\quad y = H$. The solution is given by:

$$t = \frac{2}{L}\sum_{n=1}^{\infty} \frac{\sinh\left(\dfrac{n\pi y}{L}\right)}{\sinh\left(\dfrac{n\pi H}{L}\right)} \sin\left(\frac{n\pi x}{L}\right)\int_0^L f(x)\sin\left(\frac{n\pi x}{L}\right)dx \qquad\qquad ...(3.10)$$

3.2.1.2. Two-dimensional steady state heat conduction in semi-infinite plate

Refer to Fig. 3.2. Consider a semi-infinite plate having its length in Y-direction extremely large. Following the same procedure as given in Art. 3.2.1.1., we have, the general differential equation.

$$\frac{\partial^2 t}{\partial x^2} + \frac{\partial^2 t}{\partial y^2} = 0$$

The solution of the above equation is

$$t = X.Y = [A \cos(\lambda x) + B \sin(\lambda x)] [C e^{-\lambda y} + D e^{\lambda y}] \qquad ...(i)$$

The boundary conditions are:

(i) At $x = 0$, $t = 0$

(ii) At $x = L$, $t = 0$

(iii) At $y = \infty$, $t = 0$

(iv) At $y = 0$, $t = f(x)$

From boundary condition (i), we have

$$0 = (A + 0)(C e^{-\lambda y} + D e^{\lambda y})$$

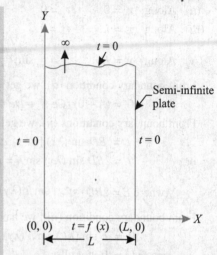

Fig. 3.2. Semi-infinite plate.

$$\therefore \qquad\qquad A = 0$$

Thus eqn. (*i*) reduces to

$$t = B \sin (\lambda x) \, [Ce^{-\lambda y} + De^{\lambda y}]$$

$$= \sin (\lambda x) \, [Ee^{-\lambda y} + Fe^{\lambda y}]$$

$$[\text{where B.C.} = E \text{ and B.D.} = F]$$

From the boundary condition (*iii*), we obtain

$$0 = \sin (\lambda x) \, [Ee^{-\lambda \infty} + Fe^{\lambda \infty}]$$

$$= \sin (\lambda x) \, [0 + Fe^{\lambda \infty}] \qquad \therefore F = 0$$

$$\therefore \qquad\qquad t = E \sin (\lambda x) \, e^{-\lambda y} \qquad\qquad\qquad …(3.11)$$

From the boundary condition (*ii*), we get

$$0 = E \sin (\lambda L) \, e^{-\lambda y}$$

$$\therefore \qquad\qquad \sin \lambda L = 0 = \sin (n\pi)$$

or, $$\qquad\qquad \lambda = \frac{n\pi}{L}$$

$$\therefore \qquad t = \sum_{n=1}^{\infty} E_n \sin \left(\frac{n\pi x}{L} \right) \exp \left(\frac{-n\pi y}{L} \right) \qquad …(3.12)$$

From boundary condition (*iv*), we get

$$f(x) = \sum_{n=1}^{\infty} E_n \sin \left(\frac{n\pi x}{L} \right)$$

$$\therefore \qquad E_n = \frac{2}{L} \int_0^L E_n \sin \left(\frac{n\pi x}{L} \right) dx \qquad\qquad …(3.13)$$

Thus, $$\qquad t = \frac{2}{L} \sum_{n=1}^{\infty} \sin \left(\frac{n\pi x}{L} \right) \exp \left(\frac{-n\pi y}{L} \right) \int_0^L f(x) \sin \left(\frac{n\pi x}{L} \right) dx \qquad …(3.14)$$

Example 3.1. *Obtain an expression for the steady state temperature distribution of a two-dimensional rectangular fin having constant thermal conductivity. The fin has a thickness L in the Y-direction and is semi-infinite in the X-direction. The base temperature of the fin and the ambient temperature are t_0 and t_∞ respectively. Assume the heat transfer coefficient to be large.*

Solution. Refer to Fig. 3.3.

Let $$\qquad \theta = t - t_\infty$$

The controlling differential equation for the given problem is given by

$$\frac{\partial^2 \theta}{\partial x^2} + \frac{\partial^2 \theta}{\partial y^2} = 0 \qquad …(i)$$

The boundary conditions are:

(*i*) At $x = \infty$, $\theta = 0$

(*ii*) At $x = 0$, $\theta = \theta_0$

(*iii*) At $y = L$, $\theta = 0$

(*iv*) At $y = 0$, $\theta = 0$

The solution of Eqn. (*i*) is

$$\theta = X(x) \, Y(y) \qquad …(ii)$$

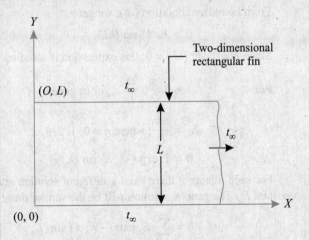

Fig. 3.3.

Substituting the solution into the controlling equation, we get

$$\frac{1}{X}\frac{d^2 X}{dx^2} = -\frac{1}{Y}\cdot\frac{d^2 Y}{dy^2} = \pm\lambda^2$$

The sign of λ^2 should be so chosen that the homogeneous Y-direction results in a characteristic value problem; a +ve value of λ^2 will satisfy all the values mentioned in the boundary conditions.

Thus the required equations are

$$\frac{d^2 X}{dx^2} - \lambda^2 X = 0 \qquad \qquad ...(iii)$$

$$\frac{d^2 Y}{dy^2} + \lambda^2 Y = 0 \qquad \qquad ...(iv)$$

The solutions of eqns. (ii) and (iii) respectively are:

$$X = A\,e^{\lambda x} + B\,e^{-\lambda x}$$

$$Y = C\cos(\lambda y) + D\sin(\lambda y)$$

$$\therefore \quad \theta = (Ae^{\lambda x} + Be^{-\lambda x})\,[C\cos(\lambda y) + D\sin(\lambda y)] \qquad \qquad ...(v)$$

From boundary condition (i), we have

$$0 = (Ae^{\lambda\infty} + Be^{-\lambda\infty})\,[C\cos(\lambda y) + D\sin(\lambda y)]$$

$$\therefore \quad A = 0,\text{ and}$$

$$\theta = Be^{-\lambda x}\,[C\cos(\lambda y) + D\sin(\lambda y)] \qquad \qquad ...(vi)$$

From boundary condition (iv), we get

$$0 = C.Be^{-\lambda x}$$

$$\therefore \quad C = 0,\text{ and eqn. }(vi)\text{ reduces to}$$

$$\theta = B\,e^{-\lambda x}\,[D\sin(\lambda y)]$$

or, $\qquad \theta = Ee^{-\lambda x}\sin(\lambda y)$

$$(\text{where } E = B.D) \qquad \qquad ...(vii)$$

From boundary condition (iii), we get

$$0 = Ee^{-\lambda x}\sin(\lambda L)$$

Since $E \neq 0$, $\sin(\lambda L) = 0$; this expression is satisfied.

For $\qquad \lambda = 0, \dfrac{\pi}{L}, \dfrac{2\pi}{L}$ ...; or in general

$$\lambda_n = \frac{n\pi}{L}; \text{ where } n = 0, 1, 2, 3, ...$$

$$\therefore \quad \theta = E\exp(-\lambda_n x)\sin(\lambda_n y) \qquad \qquad ...(viii)$$

For each integer n there exist a different solution and each solution has a separate integration constant E_n. The general solution will be the sum of these individual solutions.

$$\theta = \sum_{n=1}^{\infty} E_n \exp(-\lambda_n x)\sin(\lambda_n y) \qquad \qquad ...(ix)$$

For $n = 0$, $\lambda_n = 0$ and as such no contribution is made by the first term; eqn. (ix) can be written as

$$\theta = \sum_{n=1}^{\infty} E_n \exp\left(-\lambda_n\, x\right) \sin\left(\lambda_n y\right)$$

From boundary Eqn. (*ii*), we have

$$\theta = \sum_{n=1}^{\infty} E_n \sin\left(\lambda_n\, y\right)$$

This is an expression of θ_0 in terms of the Fourier sine series, where E_n are Fourier coefficients.

Now,

$$E_n = \frac{2}{L}\int_0^L \theta_0 \, \sin\left(\lambda_n\, y\right) dy$$

$$= \frac{2}{L}\theta_0\frac{1}{\lambda_n}\left[-\cos\lambda_n\right]_0^L = \frac{2\theta_0}{L\lambda}\left[1-(-1)^n\right]$$

$$\theta = \frac{2\theta_0}{L}\sum_{n=1}^{\infty}\frac{\left[1-(-1)^n\right]}{\lambda_n}\exp\left(-\lambda_n x\right)\sin\lambda_n y \quad \text{...Required expression.}$$

Example 3.2. *Derive an expression for the temperature distribution in a two-dimensional rectangular bar, having very long length, as shown in Fig. 3.4.*

Solution. The controlling differential equation for the given problem is

$$\frac{\partial^2 t}{\partial x^2} + \frac{\partial^2 t}{\partial y^2} = 0 \qquad \text{...(i)}$$

The boundary conditions are:

(*i*) At $x = L$, $t = 0$

(*ii*) At $x = 0$, $t = 0$

(*iii*) At $y = 0$, $t = 80$

(*iv*) At $y = H$, $t = 0$

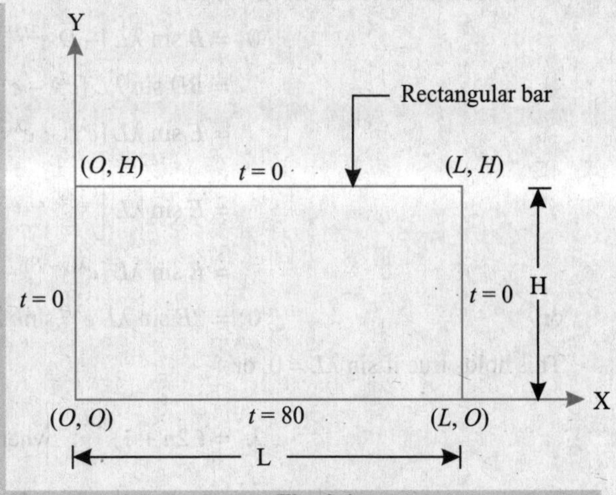

Eqn. (*i*) is a linear and homogeneous partial differential equation and can be solved by assuming the following form of solution.

$t = X.Y$ where $X = f(x)$ and $Y = f(y)$ only.

Substituting this solution in eqn. (*i*), we get

Fig. 3.4.

$$Y\frac{d^2 X}{dx^2} + X\frac{d^2 Y}{dy^2} = 0$$

Dividing both sides by XY, we have

$$-\frac{1}{X}\frac{d^2 X}{dx^2} = \frac{1}{Y}\frac{d^2 Y}{dy^2} = \lambda^2, \text{ where } \lambda^2 \text{ is constant}$$

$$\therefore \qquad \frac{d^2 X}{dx^2} + \lambda^2 x = 0 \qquad\qquad \text{...(ii)}$$

$$\frac{d^2 Y}{dy^2} - \lambda^2 y = 0 \qquad\qquad \text{...(iii)}$$

The solutions to eqns. (*ii*) and (*iii*) respectively are given by

$$X = A \cos (\lambda x) + B \sin (\lambda x)$$

$$Y = C e^{-\lambda y} + D e^{\lambda y}$$

∴ The general solution of eqn. (*i*) is

$$t = [A \cos (\lambda x) + B \sin (\lambda x)] [C e^{-\lambda y} + D e^{\lambda y}] \qquad \ldots(iv)$$

From boundary condition (*ii*), we get

$$0 = A (C e^{-\lambda y} + D e^{\lambda y}) \qquad \therefore \qquad A = 0$$

Eqn. (*iv*) thus reduces to

$$t = B \sin (\lambda x)[C e^{-\lambda y} + D e^{\lambda y}] \qquad \ldots(v)$$

From boundary condition (*iv*), we get

$$0 = B \sin \lambda x [C e^{-\lambda H} + D e^{\lambda H}]$$

Since $B \ne 0$ ∴ $C e^{-\lambda H} + D e^{\lambda H} = 0$ or $C = - D e^{2\lambda H}$

Inserting the value of C in eqn. (*v*), we get

$$t = B \sin \lambda x [- D e^{2\lambda H} . e^{-\lambda y} + D e^{\lambda y}] \qquad \ldots(vi)$$

From boundary condition (*i*), we get

$$0 = B \sin \lambda L [- D e^{2\lambda H}. e^{-\lambda y} + D e^{\lambda y}]$$

$$= BD \sin \lambda L [e^{\lambda y} - e^{\lambda(2H - y)}]$$

$$= E \sin \lambda L [e^{\lambda y} - e^{\lambda(2H - y)}] \qquad \text{(where } E = B \cdot D)$$

$$= E \sin \lambda L \left[e^{\lambda y} - e^{-\lambda y} \frac{e^{\lambda H}}{e^{-\lambda H}} \right]$$

$$= E \sin \lambda L [e^{\lambda(y - H)} - e^{-\lambda(y - H)}]e^{\lambda H}$$

or, $$0 = 2E \sin \lambda L \, e^{\lambda H} \sinh \lambda (y - H)$$

This holds true if $\sin \lambda L = 0$, or

$$\lambda = (2n + 1) \frac{\pi}{L}, \text{ where } h = 0, 1, 2, 3, \ldots.$$

∴ $$t = 2E \sin \left\{ (2n + 1)\frac{\pi x}{L} \right\} \exp \left[\frac{(2n + 1)\pi H}{L} \right] \sinh \left\{ (2n + 1)\frac{\pi}{L}(y - H) \right\}$$

or, $$t = \sum_{n=0}^{\infty} E_n \sin \left\{ (2n + 1)\frac{\pi x}{L} \right\} \sinh \left\{ (2n + 1)\frac{\pi}{L}(y - H) \right\} \exp \left[\frac{(2n + 1)\pi H}{L} \right] \ldots(vii)$$

From boundary condition (*iii*), we get

$$80 = \sum_{n=0}^{\infty} E_n \sin \left\{ (2n + 1)\frac{\pi x}{L} \right\} \sinh \left\{ (2n + 1)\frac{\pi}{L}(- H) \right\} \exp \left[\frac{(2n + 1)\pi H}{L} \right]$$

or, $$80 = \sum_{n=1}^{\infty} F_n \sin \left\{ (2n + 1)\frac{\pi x}{L} \right\}$$

where, $$F_n = E_n \sin h \left\{ (2n + 1)\left(\frac{-\pi H}{L} \right) \right\} \exp \left[\frac{(2n + 1)\pi H}{L} \right] \qquad \ldots(viii)$$

Considering the preceding equation as the Fourier sine series, we have

$$F_n = \frac{2}{L} \int_0^L 80 \sin\left\{(2n+1)\left(\frac{\pi x}{L}\right)\right\} dx$$

Let

$$\frac{(2n+1)\pi x}{L} = z$$

Then

$$(2n+1)\frac{\pi}{L} dx = dz \quad \text{or} \quad dx = \frac{L dz}{(2n+1)\pi}$$

$$\therefore \quad F_n = \frac{L}{(2n+1)\pi} \times \frac{2 \times 80}{L} \int_0^{(2n+1)\pi} \sin z . dz$$

$$= \frac{160}{(2n+1)\pi} [-\cos z]_0^{(2n+1)\pi}$$

$$= \frac{160}{(2n+1)\pi} [1 - \cos(2n+1)\pi]$$

or,

$$F_n = \frac{160}{(2n+1)\pi} [1 - (-1)] = \frac{160}{(2n+1)\pi}$$

Inserting the value of F_n in expression (viii), we get

$$\frac{160}{(2n+1)\pi} = E_n \sinh\left\{(2n+1)\left(\frac{-\pi H}{2}\right)\right\} \exp\left[\frac{(2n+1)\pi H}{L}\right]$$

$$\therefore \quad E_n = -\frac{160}{(2n+1)\pi} \operatorname{cosech}\left\{(2n+1)\frac{\pi H}{L}\right\} \times \frac{1}{\exp\left[\frac{(2n+1)\pi H}{L}\right]}$$

Substituting the value of E_n in eqn. (vii), we get

$$t = \frac{160}{\pi} \sum_{n=0}^{\infty} \frac{1}{(2n+1)} \sin\left\{(2n+1)\left(\frac{\pi x}{L}\right)\right\}$$

$$\sinh\left\{(2n+1)\frac{\pi}{L}(H-y)\right\} \operatorname{cosech}\left\{(2n+1)\frac{\pi H}{L}\right\}$$

3.2.2. GRAPHICAL METHOD

Sometimes several problems of two-dimensional heat conduction are so complex that it is extremely difficult to solve them by analytical methods. Approximate solutions of such problems are easily obtained by graphical methods (graphical method is known as *potential field plotting*). The graphical method was very popular when computing aids were rather primitive.

The graphical method consists of plotting by trial, constant temperature contours and constant heat flow paths, using the boundary conditions as the initial guide. The orthogonality of these two sets of lines help in plotting the orthogonal squares.

In order to construct the flux plot or potential field plot, the following procedures may be adopted:

1. According to some suitable scale draw the cross-section of the solid and identify all relative lines of symmetry.

2. Select the temperature intervals arbitrarily and draw, by intuition, the corresponding isotherms.

3. Draw heat flow lines in such a fashion that they intersect the isotherms at right angles everywhere, forming curvilinear squares approximately.

Any network which fulfills the following conditions gives *correct solution* of the problem:

1. *Boundary conditions :*

   (i) Isotherms must be perpendicular to insulated boundaries.

   (ii) Heat flow lines must be perpendicular to isothermal boundaries.

   (iii) Heat flow line leading to a corner of an isothermal boundary must bisect an angle between the surfaces of the boundary at the corner.

2. Heat flow lines and isotherms must cut each other at right angles at all intersection points.

3. Heat flow lines and isotherms must form a network of curvili -near squares.

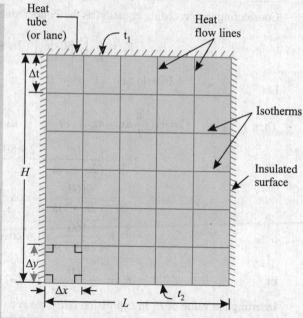

Fig. 3.5. Isotherms and heat flux lines in a parallelopiped.

4. Diagonals of the curvilinear square must bisect each other at right angles and also must bisect the corners.

Fig. 3.5 shows a parallelopiped whose two faces are maintained at constant temperatures of t_1 and t_2 respectively and other faces perfectly insulated. The face at t_1 is divided into segments of Δx each to represent heat flow tubes. Similarly lines representing isotherms can be described at intervals of Δy maintaining $\Delta y = \Delta x$ and the condition of orthogonality of isotherms and heat flow lines.

Fig. 3.6 shows another two-dimensional system whose inside and outside surfaces are maintained at temperatures t_1 and t_2 respectively. For the given system, due to symmetry, only one eight of the configuration is considered for the flux plot. In the Fig. 3.6 is also shown diagrammatically a potential fluid element for curvilinear square analysis of the two-dimensional heat flow. Assuming *unit depth* of the material, the heat flow through this curvilinear section is given by Fourier's law,

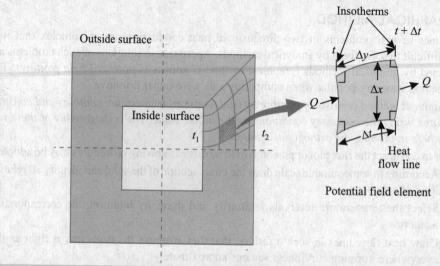

Fig. 3.6. Sketch showing potential field element for curvilinear square analysis of two-dimentional heat flow.

$$\Delta Q = -k\,(\Delta x \times 1)\,\frac{\Delta t}{\Delta y} \qquad\qquad ...(3.15)$$

This heat flow will be same through each section (or flow lane). If the sketch is drawn in such a way that $\Delta x = \Delta y$, then the rate of heat transfer is proportional to Δt across the element. Thus

$$\Delta t_{overall} = N\,\Delta t \qquad\qquad [\text{or } \Delta t = \frac{\Delta t_{overall}}{N}]$$

where, N is *the number of temperature increments* between the inner and outer surfaces.

If M is the *number of heat flow lanes/tubes*, the total heat flow

$$Q = \frac{M}{N}\,k\,\Delta t_{overall} = \frac{M}{N}\,k\,(t_1 - t_2) \qquad\qquad ...(3.16)$$

Thus in order to solve the problem graphically, we need to construct a potential field consisting of curvilinear squares and thereafter count the number of temperature increments and heat flow lanes.

The ratio, $\dfrac{M}{N}$ (*i.e.*, number of flow lanes/tubes divided by the number of temperature increments) is called the **conduction shape factor S_{fc}.**

The eqn. (3.16), therefore, reduces to

$$Q = k\,S_{fc}\,(t_1 - t_2) \qquad\qquad ...(3.17)$$

Also,

$$Q = \frac{(t_1 - t_2)}{R_{th}}$$

Therefore, the conduction shape factor (S_{fc}) and thermal resistance R_{th} are related by the following equation:

$$R_{th} = \frac{1}{k S_{fc}} \qquad\qquad ...(3.18)$$

The shape factor for any configuration may be obtained after evaluating its thermal resistance. The values of S_{fc} for some of the common geometries are tabulated in Table 3.1.

Table 3.1. "Conduction shape factors" for two-dimensional systems.

System	Schematic	Restriction or conditions	Shape factor
Plane wall (length L, area A)	*(i)*	One dimensional heat conduction	$\dfrac{A}{L}$
Edges of adjoining walls	*(ii)*	$D > \dfrac{L}{5}$	$0.54\,D$

Corners of walls	(iii)	$L <<$ length and width of wall	$0.15\,L$
Hollow cylinder (length L)	(iv)	$L >> r$	$\dfrac{2\pi L}{\ln\,(r_o/r_i)}$
Hollow sphere (length L)	(v)		$\dfrac{4\pi r_o r_i}{r_o - r_i}$
Eccentric cylinder (length L)	(vi)	$L >> r$	$\dfrac{2\pi L}{\cosh^{-1}\left[\dfrac{r_1^2 + r_2^2 - D^2}{2r_1 r_2}\right]}$
Cylinder in square (length L)	(vii)	$L >> W$	$\dfrac{2\pi L}{\ln\,(0.54\,W/r)}$
Horizontal isothermal cylinder of length L buried in semi-infinite medium having isothermal surface.	(viii)	$L >> r$ $L >> r$ $H > 3r$ $H >> r$ $L >> H$	$\dfrac{2\pi L}{\cosh^{-1}\,(H/r)}$ $\dfrac{2\pi L}{\ln\,(2H/r)}$ $\dfrac{2\pi L}{\ln\left(\dfrac{L}{r}\right)\left[1 - \dfrac{\ln\,(L/2H)}{\ln\,(L/r)}\right]}$

Isothermal sphere buried in semi-infinite medium.	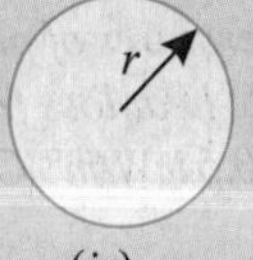 (ix)		$4\pi r$
Isothermal sphere buried in semi-infinite medium having isothermal surface.	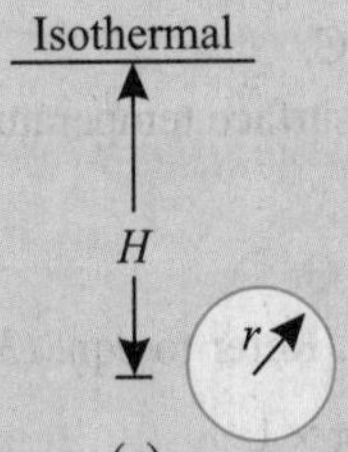 (x)	$H > r$	$\dfrac{4\pi r}{1 - (r/2H)}$
Isothermal vertical cylinder placed in semi-infinite medium having isothermal surface.	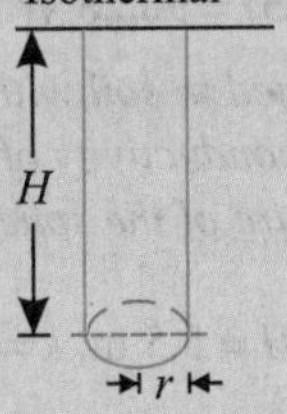 (xi)	$H \gg 2r$	$\dfrac{2\pi L}{\ln(2H/r)}$
Isothermal rectangular parallelopiped buried in semi-infinite medium having isothermal surface.	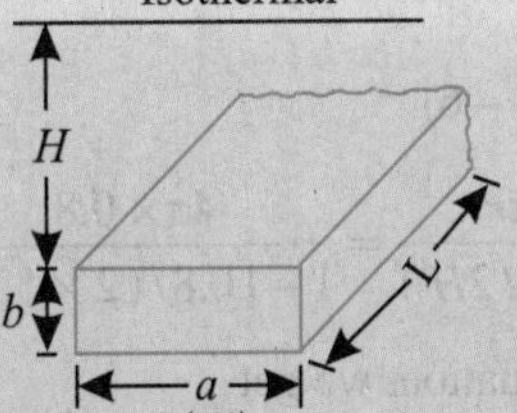 (xii)		$1.685L\left[\log\left(\dfrac{1+H}{a}\right)\right]^{-0.59}$ $\times\left(\dfrac{H}{b}\right)^{-0.078}$
Conduction between two isothermal cylinders buried in infinite medium (Length of each cylinder L)	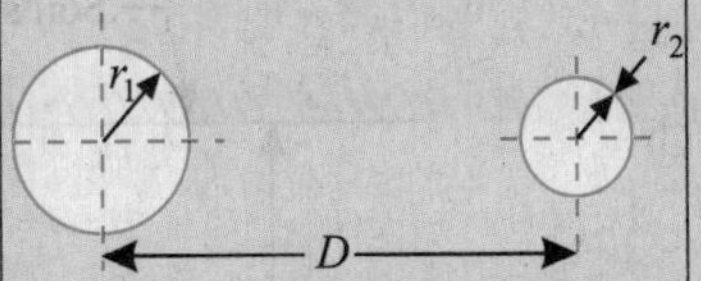 (xiii)	$L \gg r$ $L \gg D$	$\dfrac{2\pi L}{\cosh^{-1}\left[\dfrac{D^2 - r_1^2 - r_2^2}{2r_1 r_2}\right]}$
Furance wall	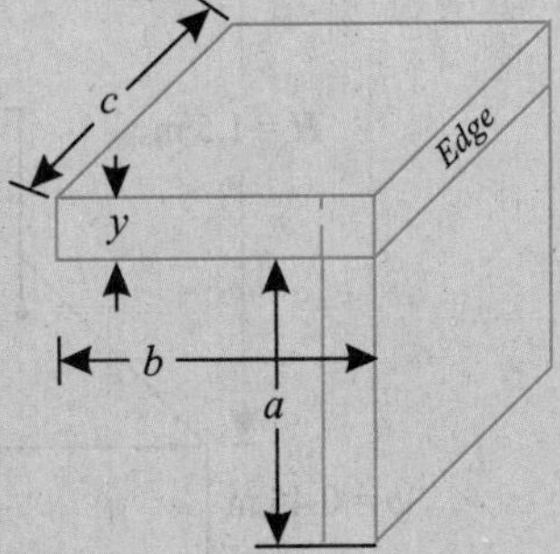 (xiv)	$(a, b, c) > \dfrac{y}{5}$	$\dfrac{2}{y}(ab + bc + ca)$ $+ 4 \times 0.54\,(a + b + c)$ $+ 8 \times 0.15\,y$

Fig. 3.7. [(i) to (xiv)]

Example 3.3. *A long pipe of 0.6 m outside diameter is buried in earth with axis at a depth of 1.8 m. The surface temperatures of pipe and earth are 95° C and 25° C respectively. Calculate the heat loss from the pipe per metre length. The conductivity of earth is 0.51 W/m° C.*

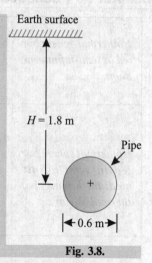

Solution. Refer to Fig. 3.8. $r = \dfrac{0.6}{2} = 0.3$ m; $L = 1$ m; $H = 1.8$ m;

$$k = 0.51 \text{ W/m° C.}$$

t_p (surface temperature of pipe) = 95°C; t_e (surface temperature of earth) = 25° C

Heat loss from the pipe per metre length, Q:

$$Q = k S_{fc} (t_p - t_e) \qquad \text{...[Refer to eqn. (3.17)]}$$

where, S_{fc} (shape factor) $= \dfrac{2\pi L}{\ln(2H/r)} = \dfrac{2\pi \times 1}{\ln[(2 \times 1.8)/0.3]} = 2.528$ m

∴ $Q = 0.51 \times 2.528 \times (95 - 25) = \mathbf{90.25}$ **W (Ans.)**

Fig. 3.8.

Example 3.4. *A 1.6 m diameter sphere is buried in soil with centre at a depth of 5.5 m. Heat is generated in the sphere at a rate of 580 W. If the conductivity of the soil is 0.51 W/m°C and the soil surface is at 6° C, calculate the surface temperature of the sphere under steady state condition.*

Solution. Refer to Fig. 3.9. $r = \dfrac{1.6}{2} = 0.8$ m; $H = 5.5$ m; $k = 0.51$ W/m°C; $Q_g = 580$ W

Temperature of soil surface = 6°C

Surface temperature of the sphere, t :

Heat generated = Heat conducted away

or, $$Q_g = k S_{fc} (t - 6)$$

where, $$S_{fc} = \dfrac{4\pi r}{1 - (r/2H)} = \dfrac{4\pi \times 0.8}{1 - [0.8/(2 \times 5.5)]} = 10.84 \text{ m}$$

Substituting the values in the above equation, we get

$$580 = 0.51 \times 10.84 \, (t - 6) \qquad \text{or} \qquad t = \mathbf{110.9°C} \textbf{ (Ans.)}$$

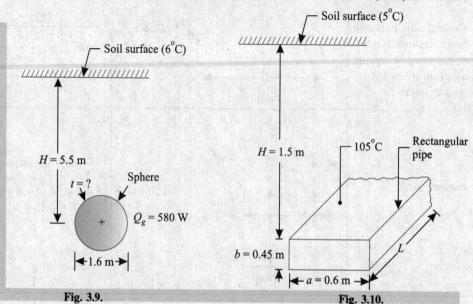

Fig. 3.9.

Fig. 3.10.

Example 3.5. *Fig. 3.10 shows a rectangular pipe with surface temperature 105°C buried in the soil. If the thermal conductivity of the soil is 0.51 W/m°C and its surface temperature is 5° C, determine the heat loss per metre length.*

Solution. Refer fig. 3.10. $a = 0.6$ m; $b = 0.45$ m, $H = 1.5$ m, $t_p = 105°C$, $t_s = 5°$ C; $k = 0.51$ W/m°C.

Heat loss per metre length, Q:

Shape factor, $S_{fc} = 1.685\ L \left[\log\left(1 + \dfrac{H}{a} \right) \right]^{-0.59} \times \left[\dfrac{H}{b} \right]^{-0.078}$

$\qquad = 1.685 \times 1 \left[\log\left(1 + \dfrac{1.5}{0.6} \right) \right]^{-0.59} \times \left[\dfrac{1.5}{0.45} \right]^{-0.078} = 2.1967\ \text{m}$

∴ $\qquad Q = k\, S_{fc}\,(t_p - t_s) = 0.51 \times 2.1967 \times 0.51\,(105 - 5) = \textbf{112.03 W/m length. (Ans.)}$

Example 3.6. *A pipe 600 mm in diameter carrying steam at a temperature of 180°C (for heating the houses in winter) and another pipe 180 mm diameter carrying water at 12°C (for supplying drinking water) are buried under the ground with centre to centre distance 1.8 m. The length of each pipe is 90 m and thermal conductivity of soil is 0.45 W/m°C. Assuming that the pipes run parallel to each other, the earth is infinite and resistance of the pipe material negligible, determine:*

(i) The net heat transfer rate between the two pipes.

(ii) The rise in water temperature due to heat transfer if the velocity of the water in the pipe is 0.05 m/s.

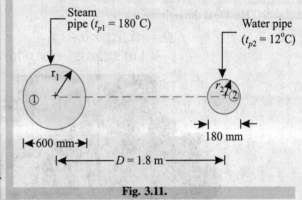

Fig. 3.11.

Solution. Refer to Fig. 3.11. $r_1 = \dfrac{600}{2} = 300$ mm $= 0.3$ m; $r_2 = \dfrac{180}{2} = 90$ mm $= 0.09$ m; $D = 1.8$ m; $L = 90$ m; $t_{p1} = 180°C$; $t_{p2} = 12°C$; $k = 0.45$ W/m°C.

(i) The net heat transfer rate between the two pipes, Q:

$\qquad Q = kS_{fc}\,(t_{p1} - t_{p2})$

where shape factor S_{fc} is given by

$$S_{fc} = \frac{2\pi L}{\cosh^{-1}\left[\dfrac{D^2 - r_1^2 - r_2^2}{2 r_1 r_2} \right]} = \frac{2\pi \times 90}{\cosh^{-1}\left[\dfrac{1.8^2 - 0.3^2 - 0.09^2}{2 \times 0.3 \times 0.09} \right]} = 118.88\ \text{m}$$

Substituting the proper values in the above equation, we get

$\qquad Q = 118.88 \times 0.45\,(180 - 12) = \textbf{8987.3 W (Ans.)}$

(ii) The rise in water temperature, Δt:

Mass of water flowing through the tube,

$\qquad m = \rho(\pi r_2^2 v) = 1000 \times \pi \times 0.09^2 \times 0.05 = 1.272$ kg/s

[where $\qquad v = $ velocity of water $= 0.05$ m/s ...(*given*)]

Also, $\qquad Q = mc_p\, \Delta t$

$$\therefore \qquad \Delta t = \frac{Q}{mc_p} = \frac{8987.3}{1.272 \times 4.18 \times 1000} = \mathbf{1.69°C \ (Ans.)}$$

Example 3.7. *The inside dimensions of a small cubical furnace constructed of fire clay bricks (k = 1.05 W/m°C) are 0.6 m × 0.6 m × 0.6 m; the walls being 0.12 m thick. The temperatures at the inside and outside surfaces are 600°C and 70°C respectively. Determine the heat lost through the walls.*

Solution. The total shape factor is computed by adding shape factor for the walls, edges, and corners.

$$(S_{fc})_{walls} = \frac{A}{L} = \frac{0.6 \times 0.6}{0.12} = 3.0 \ m$$

$$(S_{fc})_{edges} = 0.54 \ D = 0.54 \times 0.6 = 0.324 \ m$$

$$(S_{fc})_{corners} = 0.15 \ L = 0.15 \times 0.12 = 0.018 \ m$$

There are six wall sections, twelve edges, and eight corners, so that the total shape factor,

$$(S_{fc})_{total} = 6 \times 3.0 + 12 \times 0.324 + 8 \times 0.018 = 22.032 \ m$$

∴   Heat lost through the walls,

$$Q = k(S_{fc})_{total} \times (t_i - t_o)$$

$$= 1.05 \times 22.032 \times (600 - 70) = \mathbf{12260.8 \ W \ (Ans.)}$$

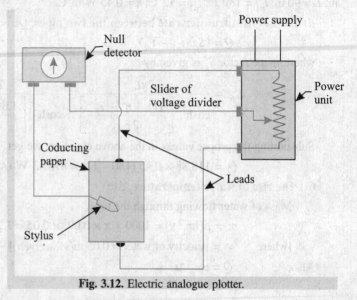

Cubical furnace.

3.2.3. ANALOGICAL METHOD

A method called 'electrical analogue' for conduction may be used for drawing curvilinear squares more precisely. This method is based upon the realisation of similarity between the governing equations of electrostatics and heat conduction. As the two-dimensional Laplace equation is used to describe a potential field for several phenomena, this distribution in the *electrostatic* and *temperature* fields is given by

$$\frac{\partial^2 E}{\partial x^2} + \frac{\partial^2 E}{\partial y^2} = 0$$

and

$$\frac{\partial^2 t}{\partial x^2} + \frac{\partial^2 t}{\partial y^2} = 0$$

Fig. 3.12. Electric analogue plotter.

Since the temperature (*t*) term can be replaced by the voltage (*E*) and *vice versa*, therefore, there exists an analogy between electrical and thermal flows. This ana- logy between the two fields is employed in practice for plotting the temperature distribution in heat conduction problems of complex nature.

In order to obtain field distribution described by the two-dimensional Laplace equation, an instrument called "**The analog field plotter**" is used; it is *faster and gives more accurate results than free hand flux plotting*. The description of this instrument is given below.

'The *analog field plotter*' (see Fig. 3.12) uses a thin sheet (0.1 mm) of electrically conducting paper (a special paper, commercially known as teledeltos paper, having a resistance of about 2000 ohms per unit square), which is cut to the shape and size of a body for which temperature distribution is desired.

– Boundary conditions corresponding to isotherms are obtained in electrical field by attaching copper wires to the paper or by painting the paper with silver paint (which is a very good conductor) and then connecting to an e.m.f source; the plain edges of the conducting paper represent the insulated surfaces in the temperature field.

– The isotherms are progressively plotted by a stylus probe and a null detector connected to a suitable bridge circuit.

– The heat flow lines are then plotted either by hand, drawing lines orthogonal to the isotherms; the heat flow lines can also be traced constant by simply reversing the conducting and insulating portions of the boundary.

3.2.4. NUMERICAL METHODS

The scope of analytical solutions is limited as only relatively simple geometric shapes can be handled. The most of the practical two-dimensional heat problems involve irregular geometries which are solved by numerical analysis techniques. The main advantage of numerical methods is that they can be applied to any two-dimensional shape irrespective of its complexity or boundary condition. *The primary difference between the analytical solution and numerical solution is that the former gives an equation from which the temperature may be obtained anywhere in the solid, whereas the latter will give values of temperatures at the chosen specific points only.* The numerical analysis, due to widespread use of digital computers these days, is the primary method of solving complex heat transfer problems.

Consider a two-dimensional body which is divided into equal increments of Δx and Δy in X and Y directions respectively as shown in Fig. 3.13. As shown

Digital computers are used in solving complex heat transfer problems.

the nodes are designated by point (m, n); m location indicates x increment and n location indicates y increment. It is required to establish the temperatures at these nodal points. Thus, instead of the continuous distribution, there will be a stepped distribution of temperature through the conduction region. It is considered that the temperature at any node represents the temperature in the region $\pm \dfrac{\Delta x}{2}$ and $\pm \dfrac{\Delta y}{2}$ around the node. In the numerical method, *finite differences* are used to approximate differential increments in temperature and are substituted in equation. *The smaller the increment we choose, the closer will be the stepped temperature distribution to actual one.*

The temperature gradients at points A, B, C and D may be written as:

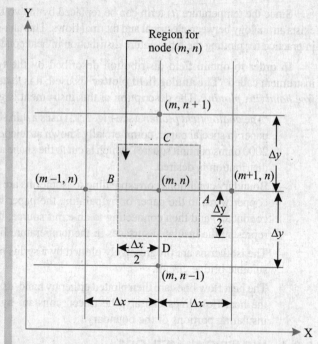

Fig. 3.13. Nodal point in conduction region.

$$\left.\frac{\partial t}{\partial x}\right|_{m+\frac{1}{2},n} \approx \frac{t_{m+1,n} - t_{m,n}}{\Delta x}$$

$$\left.\frac{\partial t}{\partial x}\right|_{m-\frac{1}{2},n} \approx \frac{t_{m,n} - t_{m-1,n}}{\Delta x}$$

$$\left.\frac{\partial t}{\partial y}\right|_{m,n+\frac{1}{2}} \approx \frac{t_{m,n+1} - t_{m,n}}{\Delta y}$$

$$\left.\frac{\partial t}{\partial y}\right|_{m,n-\frac{1}{2}} \approx \frac{t_{m,n} - t_{m,n-1}}{\Delta y} \qquad \qquad ...(3.19)$$

$$\left.\frac{\partial^2 t}{\partial x^2}\right|_{m,n} \approx \frac{\left.\frac{\partial t}{\partial x}\right|_{m+\frac{1}{2},n} - \left.\frac{\partial t}{\partial x}\right|_{m-\frac{1}{2},n}}{\Delta x} = \frac{t_{m+1,-n} + t_{m-1,n} - 2t_{m,n}}{(\Delta x)^2}$$

$$\left.\frac{\partial^2 t}{\partial y^2}\right|_{m,n} \approx \frac{\left.\frac{\partial \tau}{\partial \psi}\right|_{\mu,v+\frac{1}{2}}^{TM} \left.\frac{\partial \tau}{\partial \psi}\right|_{\mu,v^{TM}\frac{1}{2}}}{\Delta \psi} = \frac{\tau_{\mu,v+1} + \tau_{\mu,v^{TM}1}^{TM} 2\tau_{\mu,v}}{(\Delta \xi)^2}$$

Substituting the values of $\dfrac{\partial^2 t}{\partial x^2}$ and $\dfrac{\partial^2 t}{\partial y^2}$ in the two-dimensional steady state equation [Eqn. (3.1)], we get

$$\frac{t_{m+1,n} + t_{m-1,n} - 2t_{m,n}}{(\Delta x)^2} + \frac{t_{m,n+1} + t_{m,n-1} - 2t_{m,n}}{(\Delta y)^2} = 0 \qquad \qquad ...(3.20)$$

If $\Delta x = \Delta y$ (for a square mesh), the

$$t_{m+1,\,n} + t_{m-1,\,n} + t_{m,\,n+1} + t_{m,\,n-1} - 4t_{m,\,n} = 0 \qquad \text{...(3.21)}$$

If internal heat generation is to be considered, then the term $\dfrac{q_g}{k}$ may be included in the eqns. (3.1) and (3.20).

Eqn. (3.21) is the finite difference representation of the two-dimensional heat conduction equation for the node (m, n). This equation must be written for each node (within the material) and the equations may then be solved to get the temperatures at various nodes.

Relaxation Method

The numerical method was first used by Southwell and named as *relaxation method*. The *objective of the relaxation method is to establish a temperature field in the body such that each point satisfies the following equation:*

$$t_{m,\,n} = \frac{t_{m+1,n} + t_{m-1,n} + t_{m,n+1} + t_{m,n-1}}{4} \qquad \text{...(3.22)}$$

(Refer eqn. 3.21)

To do so, the right side of eqn. (3.21) is set equal to some residual $Q_{m,\,n}$ which we wish to relax to zero.

$$t_{m+1,\,n} + t_{m-1,\,n} + t_{m,\,n+1} + t_{m,\,n-1} - 4t_{m,\,n} = Q_{m,\,n} \qquad \text{...(3.23)}$$

The objective takes the form of solving eqn. (3.1) by trial and error, *viz.*, by first making an approximate assumption of these temperatures, and then adjusting the temperatures to make the residuals to zero at all nodal points.

The *relaxation process* includes the following *steps*:

(*i*) Subdivide the system into a number of small subvolumes and assign a reference number to each.

(*ii*) Assume values of temperatures at the various nodes.

(*iii*) Using the assumed temperatures, calculate the residuals at each node.

(*iv*) Relax the largest residual to zero by changing the corresponding nodal temperature by an appropriate amount.

(*v*) Change the residuals of the surrounding nodes to correspond with the temperature change in step (*iv*).

(*vi*) Continue to relax residuals until all are as close to zero as desired.

3.3. THREE-DIMENSIONAL STEADY STATE CONDUCTION

The analytical and numerical methods described in the preceding article for the two-dimensional problems can be extended to three-dimensional steady state problems by adding a third coordinate.

Analytical method. The general equation for the temperature distribution for three dimensional system is given by

$$\frac{\partial^2 t}{\partial x^2} + \frac{\partial^2 t}{\partial y^2} + \frac{\partial^2 t}{\partial z^2} = 0 \qquad \text{...(3.24)}$$

subject to boundary conditions of the problem.

As t is a function of (x, y, z), the solution would be of the form

$$t = X(x)\, Y(y)\, Z(z) \qquad \text{...(3.25)}$$

Substituting the above solution in eqn. (3.24), we get

$$\frac{1}{X}\frac{d^2X}{dx^2} = -\frac{1}{Y}\cdot\frac{d^2Y}{dy^2} = -\frac{1}{Z}\cdot\frac{d^2Z}{dz^2}$$

which can be solved for X, Y, Z subject to given boundary conditions.

Numerical method. In the numerical method of solving three-dimensional heat conduction problems a three-dimensional grid should be made. There will be six neighbouring nodes for any internal node.

Analogical method. Langmuir carried our electrical analogical studies for three-dimensional heat conduction through thick walled furnaces. He determined the conductance of a copper sulphate solution in a container of the same shape or the wall and compared it with the conductance of an equivalent plane wall with constant cross-section. He obtained empirical expression for the mean area A_m to give the same heat flow as through the given wall, so that

Alexander D. Langmuir
(1910–1993).

$$Q = \frac{kA_m\,(t_1 - t_2)}{\Delta x} \qquad\qquad ...(3.26)$$

where, Δx = Thickness of the wall.

Sometimes the eqn. (3.26) is expressed as

$$Q = k\,S_{fc}\,(t_1 - t_2),$$

where, $S_{fc} = \dfrac{A_m}{\Delta x}$ is the *conduction shape factor.*

The following values of shape factor for different configurations were suggested by Langmuir.

For one edge of length y, $S_{fc} = 0.54\,y$

For a corner, $S_{fc} = 0.15\,\Delta x$

For a cylindrical pipe of length L, $S_f = 2\pi L\,ln\,(r_2/r_1)$

For a spherical shell, $S_{fc} = \dfrac{4\pi r_1 r_2}{(r_2 - r_1)}$

Example 3.8. *The inside dimensions of a furnace are 4.5 m × 3.75 m × 3 m. The walls are 0.3 m thick and have a thermal conductivity of 1.5 W/m°C. If the temperatures of the inner and outer surfaces are 350° and 50° C, calculate rate of heat loss.*

Solution. Inside surface area, $A_i = 2\,[4.5 \times 3.75 + 3.75 \times 3 + 4.5 \times 3] = 83.25$ m^2

Length of edges $\Sigma y = 4\,(4.5 + 3.75 + 3) = 45$

Thickness, $\Delta x = 0.3$ m

Mean area, $A_m = A_i + (S_{fc})_{edge}\,\Delta x + (S_{fc})_{corner}\,\Delta x$

$$= A_i + 0.54\,\Sigma y\,\Delta x + 8\,(0.15)\,\Delta x^2$$

$$= 83.25 + 0.54 \times 45 \times 0.3 + 8 \times 0.15 \times 0.3^2$$

$$= 90.65 \text{ m}^2$$

Rate of heat loss, $Q = \dfrac{kA_m\,(t_i - t_o)}{\Delta x} = \dfrac{1.5 \times 90.65 \times (350 - 50)}{0.3} =$ **135975 W** **(Ans.)**

1. For the solution of the multi-dimensional heat conduction problems, the following methods are prevalent:

   (*i*) Analytical methods   (*ii*) Graphical methods

   (*iii*) Analogical methods   (*iv*) Numerical methods.

2. In 'graphical method', conduction shape factor (S_{fc}) is defined as the ratio of number of flow lanes/tubes divided by the number of temperature increments.

THEORETICAL QUESTIONS

1. Give four examples of multi-dimensional heat conduction.

2. Enumerate the methods prevalent for the solution of the multi-dimensional heat conduction problems.

3. Explain an analytical method for solving two dimensional steady state heat conduction problem.

4. Explain briefly graphical method for solving two-dimensional steady state heat conduction problem.

5. What is a conduction shape factor? Explain its significance in the graphical analysis of two-dimensional heat conduction problems.

6. What is an electric analogue plotter?

7. Explain the "Relaxation method" in solving two-dimensional heat conduction problems.

UNSOLVED EXAMPLES

1. A long pipe of 0.5 m outside diameter is buried in earth with axis at a depth of 1.5 m. The surface temperatures of pipe and earth are 85°C and 20°C respectively. Calculate the heat loss from the pipe per metre length. The conductivity of earth is 0.52 W/m°C.   (**Ans.** 85.48 W)

2. A 40 m long pipe of 150 mm outside diameter carrying steam is buried 3 m deep in the ground. The surface temperatures of pipe and earth are 200°C and 20°C respectively. Assuming thermal conductivity of soil 0.3 W/m°C, calculate the heat loss from the pipe.   (**Ans.** 3146.6 W)

$$\left[\textbf{Hint: } S_{fc} = \frac{2\pi L}{ln\left(\dfrac{L}{r}\right)\left[1 - \dfrac{ln\,(L/2H)}{ln\,(L/r)}\right]} \right]$$

3. A 1.5 m diameter sphere is buried in soil with centre at a depth of 6 m. Heat is generated in the sphere at a rate of 600 W. If the conductivity of soil is 0.52 W/m°C and the soil surface is at 5°C, calculate the surface temperature of the sphere under steady state condition.   (**Ans.** 119.8°C)

4. A pipe 500 mm in diameter carrying steam at a temperature of 160° C (for heating the houses in winter) and another pipe 150 mm diameter carrying water at 11°C (for supplying drinking water) are buried under the ground with centre to centre distance 1.5 m. The length of each pipe is 60 m and thermal conductivity of soil is 0.3 W/m°C. Assuming that the pipes run parallel to each other, the earth is infinite and resistance of the pipe materials is negligible, determine: (*i*) The net heat transfer rate between the two pipes; (*ii*) The rise in water temperature due to heat transfer, if the velocity of water in the pipe is 2 m/min.   [**Ans.** (*i*) 5991.5 W; (*ii*) 1.44°C]

5. The inside dimensions of a small cubical furnace constructed of fire clay bricks ($k = 1.04$ W/m°C) are 0.5 m × 0.5 m × 0.5 m; the walls being 0.1 m thick. The temperatures at the inside and outside surfaces are 500°C and 50°C respectively. Determine the heat lost through the walls.   (**Ans.** 8592 W)

6. The inside dimensions of a furnace are 3 m × 2.5 m × 2 m. The walls are 0.2 m thick and have thermal conductivity of 1.3 W/m° C. If the temperatures at the inner and outer surfaces are 300°C and 100°C respectively, calculate the rate of heat loss.   (**Ans.** 52370 W)

Conduction–
Unsteady– State
(Transient)

4.1. INTRODUCTION

If the temperature of a body does not *vary with time*, it is said to be in a *steay state*. But if there is an *abrupt change* in its surface temperature, it (body) attains an equilibrium temperature or a steady state after some period. During this period the temperature *varies with time* and the body is said to be in an *unsteady or transient state.* The term transient or unsteady designates a phenomenon which is time dependent. The steady state is thus the *limit* of transient temperature distribution for large values of time.

Conduction of heat in unsteady state refers to the transient conditions wherein the heat flow and the temperature distribution at any point of the system vary continuously with time. Transient conditions occur in:

(*i*) Cooling of I.C. engines;

(*ii*) Automobile engines;

(*iii*) Heating and cooling of metal billets;

(*iv*) Cooling and freezing of food;

(*v*) Heat treatment of metals by quenching;

(*vi*) Starting and stopping of various heat exchange units in power installation;

(*vii*) Brick burning;

(*viii*) Vulcanization of rubber etc.

The temperature field in any transient problem, in general, is given by

$$t = f(x, y, z, \tau)$$

During an unsteady state the change in temperature may follow a periodic or nonperiodic variation.

(*i*) **Non-periodic variation.** In a nonperiodic transient state, the temperature at any point within the system varies *non-linearly with time.*

Examples:

(*i*) Heating of an ingot in a furnace;

(*ii*) Cooling of bars, blanks and metal billets in steel works, etc.

(*ii*) **Periodic variation.** In a periodic transient state, *temperatures undergo periodic changes* (within the system) *which are either regular or irregular but definitely 'cyclic'.* A regular periodic variation is

Transient conditions occur in automobile engines.

characterised by a harmonic sinusoidal or nonsinusoidal function, and irregular periodic variations by any function which is cyclic but not necessarily harmonic.

Examples: The temperature variations in

(*i*) cylinder of an I.C. engine;

(*ii*) building during a period of 24 hours;

(*iii*) surface of earth during a period of 24 hours;

(*iv*) heat processing of regenerators (whose packings are heated alternately by fuel gases and cooled by air) etc.

The transient heat conduction problems may be solved by the following methods :

(*i*) Analytical;   (*ii*) Graphical;

(*iii*) Analogical;   (*iv*) Numerical.

4.2. HEAT CONDUCTION IN SOLIDS HAVING INFINITE THERMAL CONDUCTIVITY (NEGLIGIBLE INTERNAL RESISTANCE) – LUMPED PARAMETER ANALYSIS

All solids have a finite thermal conductivity and there will be always a temperature gradient inside the solid whenever heat is added or removed. However, for solids of large thermal conductivity with surface areas that are large in proportion to their volume like plates and thin metallic wires, the internal resistance $\left(\dfrac{L}{kA}\right)$ can be assumed to be small or negligible in comparison with the convective resistance $\left(\dfrac{1}{hA}\right)$ at the surface. Typical examples of this type of heat flow are:

(*i*) Heat treatment of metals;

(*ii*) Time response of thermocouples and thermometers etc.

The process in which the *internal resistance is assumed negligible in comparison with its surface resistance* is called the *Newtonian heating or cooling process.* The temperature, in this process, is considered to be uniform at a given time. Such an analysis is called *Lumped parameter analysis* because the whole solid, whose energy at any time is a *function of its temperature* and total heat capacity is treated as *one lump.*

Let us consider a body whose initial temperature is t_i throughout and which is placed suddenly in ambient air or any liquid at a constant temperature t_a as shown in Fig. 4.1.(a). The transient response of the body can be determined by *relating its rate of change of internal energy with convective exchange at the surface.* That is:

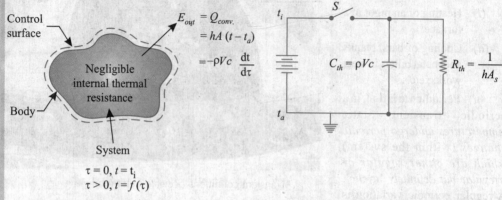

Control surface

$$E_{out} = Q_{conv.}$$
$$= hA\,(t - t_a)$$
$$= -\rho Vc\,\frac{dt}{d\tau}$$

Negligible internal thermal resistance

Body

System

$\tau = 0, t = t_i$
$\tau > 0, t = f(\tau)$

$C_{th} = \rho Vc$ $R_{th} = \dfrac{1}{hA_s}$

(a) General system for unsteady heat conduction

(b) Equivalent thermal circuit for lumped capacitance solid

Fig. 4.1. Lumped heat capacity system.

$$Q = -\rho Vc\,\frac{dt}{d\tau} = hA_s\,(t - t_a) \qquad \ldots(4.1)$$

where, ρ = Density of solid, kg/m^3,

V = Volume of the body, m^3,

c = Specific heat of body, J/kg°C,

h = Unit surface conductance, W/m^2°C,

t = Temperature of the body at any time, °C,

A_s = Surface area of the body, m^2,

t_a = Ambient temperature, °C, and

τ = Time, s.

After rearranging the eqn. (4.1), and integrating, we get

$$\int \frac{dt}{(t - t_a)} = -\frac{hA_s}{\rho Vc}\int d\tau \qquad \ldots(4.2)$$

or, $$ln\,(t - t_a) = -\frac{hA_s}{\rho Vc}\,\tau + C_1 \qquad \ldots(4.3)$$

The boundary conditions are:

At $\tau = 0$, $t = t_i$ (initial surface temperature)

$\therefore$ $C_1 = ln\,(t_i - t_a)$ [From eqn. (4.3)]

Hence $ln\,(t - t_a) = -\dfrac{hA_s}{\rho Vc}\,\tau + ln\,(t_i - t_a)$ [Substituting the values in eqn. (4.3)]

or, $$\frac{t - t_a}{t_i - t_a} = \frac{\theta}{\theta_i} = \exp\left[-\frac{hA_s}{\rho Vc}\,\tau\right] \qquad \ldots(4.4)$$

Following points are worth noting:

1. Eqn. (4.4) gives the temperature distribution in the body for *Newtonian heating or cooling* and it indicates that temperature rises *exponentially* with time as shown in Fig. 4.2.

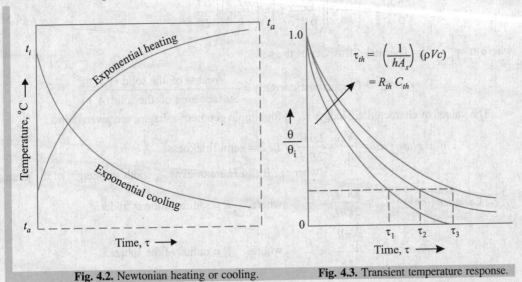

Fig. 4.2. Newtonian heating or cooling.   Fig. 4.3. Transient temperature response.

2. The quantity $\dfrac{\rho Vc}{hA_s}$ has the dimensions of time and is called **thermal time constant**, denoted by τ_{th}. Its *value is indicative of the rate of response of a system to a sudden change in its environmental temperature i.e.*, how fast a body will response to a change in the environmental temperature.

$$\tau_{th} = \left(\frac{1}{hA_s}\right)(\rho Vc) = R_{th}\, C_{th}$$

where, $$R_{th} = \left(\frac{1}{hA_s}\right) = \text{Resistance to convection heat transfer, and}$$

$$C_{th}\,(= \rho V_c) = \text{Lumped thermal capacitance of solid.}$$

Fig. 4.3 shows that any increase in R_{th} or C_{th} will cause a solid to respond *more slowly* to changes in its *thermal environmental* and will *increase* the time required to attain the thermal equilibrium ($\theta = 0$).

Fig. 4.1(*b*) shows an analogus electric network for a *lumped heat capacity system*, in which $C_{th} = \rho Vc$ represents the *thermal capacity* of the system. The value of C_{th} can be obtained from the following thermal and electrical equations, by similarity.

$$Q = (\rho Vc)t = C_{th}.t \qquad \qquad \text{...Thermal equation.}$$
$$s = C.E \qquad \qquad \text{...Electrical equation.}$$

where, $s = $ Capacitor charge,

$C = $ Capacitance of the condenser, and

$E = $ Voltage.

When the switch is *closed* [Fig. 4.1 (*b*)] the solid is charged to the temperature θ. On *opening* the switch, the thermal energy stored as C_{th} is dissipated through the thermal resistance $R_{th} = \left(\dfrac{1}{hA_s}\right)$ and the temperature of the body decays with time. From this analogy it is concluded that RC electrical circuits may be used to determine the transient behaviour of thermal systems.

The power on exponential, i.e., $\dfrac{hA_s}{\rho Vc}\tau$ can be arranged in dimensionless form as follows.

$$\frac{hA_s}{\rho Vc}\tau = \left(\frac{hV}{kA_s}\right)\left(\frac{A_s^2 k}{\rho V^2 c}\tau\right) = \left(\frac{hL_c}{k}\right)\left(\frac{\alpha\tau}{L_c^2}\right) \qquad \qquad ...(4.5)$$

where $\alpha = \left[\dfrac{k}{\rho c}\right]$ = Thermal diffusivity of the solid

$$L_c = \text{Characteristic length} = \frac{\text{Volume of the solid }(V)}{\text{Surface area of the solid}(A_s)}$$

The values of characteristic length (L_c), for simple geometric shapes, are given below:

Flat plate : $L_c = \dfrac{V}{A_s} = \dfrac{LBH}{2BH} = L/2 = \text{semi-thickness}$

where L, B and H are thickness, width and height of the plate.

Cylinder (long) : $L_c = \dfrac{\pi R^2 L}{2\pi RL} = \dfrac{R}{2}$ where, R = radius of the cylinder.

Sphere: $L_c = \dfrac{\frac{4}{3}\pi R^3}{4\pi R^2} = \dfrac{R}{3}$ where, R = radius of the sphere.

Cube: $L_c = \dfrac{L^3}{6L^2} = \dfrac{L}{6}$ where, L = Side of the cube.

Further, from eqn. (4.5):

(i) The non-dimensional factor $\dfrac{hL_c}{k}$ is called the **Biot member B_i,**

i.e. $B_i = \dfrac{hL_c}{k} = \text{Biot number.}$

It gives an indication of the *ratio of internal (conduction) resistance to surface (convection) resistance*. When the value of B_i is small, it indicates that the system has a small internal (conduction) resistance, i.e., relatively small temperature gradient or the existence of practically uniform temperature within the system. The convective resistance then predominates and the transient phenomenon is controlled by the convective heat exchange.

If $B_i < 0.1$, the lumped heat capacity approach can be used to advantage with simple shapes such as plates, cylinders, spheres and cubes. The error associated is around 5%.

(ii) The non-dimensional factor $\dfrac{\alpha\tau}{L_c^2}$ is called the **Fourier number, F_0.**

i.e. $F_0 = \dfrac{\alpha\tau}{L_c^2} = \text{Fourier number}$

It signifies the *degree of penetration of heating or cooling effect* through a solid.

Using non-dimensional terms, eqn. (4.4) takes the form of

$$\frac{\theta}{\theta_i} = \frac{t - t_a}{t_i - t_a} = e^{-BiF_0} \qquad \qquad ...(4.6)$$

The graphical representation of eqn. (4.5) for different solids (Infinite plates, infinite cylinders and infinite square rods and cubes and spheres) is shown in Fig. 4.4.

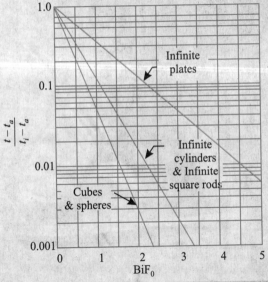

Fig. 4.4. Newtonian heating or cooling (for various solids)

Instantaneous heat flow rate and total heat transfer:

The *instantaneous rate of heat flow* (Q_i) may be found as follows:

$$Q_i = \rho Vc \frac{dt}{d\tau} = \rho Vc \frac{d}{d\tau}\left[t_a + (t_i - t_a)\exp\left\{-\frac{hA_s}{\rho Vc}\tau\right\}\right]$$

or,

$$Q_i = \rho Vc\left[(t_i - t_a)\left\{-\frac{hA_s}{\rho Vc}\right\}\exp\left\{-\frac{hA_s}{\rho Vc}\tau\right\}\right]$$

or,

$$Q_i = -hA_s (t_i - t_a)\exp\left[-\frac{hA_s}{\rho Vc}\tau\right] \qquad ...(4.7)$$

or,

$$Q_i = -hA_s (t_i - t_a) e^{-B_i F_0} \qquad ...[4.7\ (a)]$$

The *total* or *cumulative heat transfer* is

$$Q' = \int_0^\tau Q_i\, d\tau$$

$$= \int_0^\tau -hA_s (t_i - t_a)\exp\left[-\frac{hA_s}{\rho Vc}\tau\right] d\tau$$

$$= \left[-hA_s (t_i - t_a)\frac{\exp(-hA_s/\rho Vc)\tau}{-hA_s/\rho Vc}\right]_0^\tau$$

$$= \rho Vc (t_i - t_a)\left[\exp\left\{-\frac{hA_s}{\rho Vc}\tau\right\}\right]_0^\tau$$

or,

$$Q' = \rho Vc (t_i - t_a)\left[\exp\left\{-\frac{hA_s}{\rho Vc}\right\} - 1\right] \qquad ...(4.8)$$

$$Q' = \rho Vc (t_i - t_a) [e^{-B_i F_0} - 1] \qquad ...[4.8\ (a)]$$

... in terms of non-dimensional B_i and F_0 number.

Example 4.1. *A 50 cm × 50 cm copper slab 6.25 mm thick has a uniform temperature of 300°C. Its temperature is suddenly lowered to 36°C. Calculate the time required for the plate to reach the temperature of 108°C.*

Take ρ = 9000 kg/m³; c = 0.38 kJ/kg°C; k = 370 W/m°C and h = 90 W/m²°C

Burning brick oven.

Solution. Surface area of plate, $A_s = 2 \times 0.5 \times 0.5 = 0.5$ m^2 (two sides)

Volume of plate, $\qquad\qquad V = 0.5 \times 0.5 \times 0.00625 = 0.0015625$ m^3

Characteristic length, $\qquad L_c = \dfrac{V}{A_s} = \dfrac{0.0015625}{0.5} = 0.003125$ m

Biot number, $\qquad\qquad B_i = \dfrac{hL_c}{k} = \dfrac{90 \times 0.003125}{370} = 7.6 \times 10^{-4}$

Since B_i is *less than 0.1*, hence lumped capacitance method (Newtonian heating or cooling) may be applied for the solution of the problem.

The temperature distribution is given by

$$\frac{t - t_a}{t_i - t_a} = \exp\left[\frac{-hA_s}{\rho Vc}\,\tau\right] \qquad\qquad \text{...[Eqn. (4.4)]}$$

Substituting the values, we get

$$\frac{108 - 36}{300 - 36} = \exp\left[-\frac{90 \times 0.5}{9000 \times 0.0015625 \times (0.38 \times 1000)}\,\tau\right] = e^{-0.00842\tau}$$

$$0.2727 = e^{-0.00842\tau} = \frac{1}{e^{0.00842\tau}}$$

or, $\qquad\qquad e^{0.00842\tau} = \dfrac{1}{0.2727} = 3.667$

or, $\qquad\qquad 0.00842\,\tau = ln\ 3.667 = 1.2994$

or, $\qquad\qquad \tau = \dfrac{1.2994}{0.00842} = \mathbf{154.32\ s}$ **(Ans.)**

Example 4.2. *An aluminium alloy plate of 400 mm × 400 mm × 4 mm size at 200°C is suddenly quenched into liquid oxygen at − 183°C. Starting from fundamentals or deriving the necessary expression determine the time required for the plate to reach a temperature of − 70°C. Assume h = 20000 kJ/m^2-h-°C, c_p = 0.8 kJ/kg°C, and ρ = 3000 kg/m^3.*   **(AMIE Winter, 1997)**

Solution.   Surface area of the plate, $A_s = 2 \times \dfrac{400}{1000} \times \dfrac{400}{1000} = 0.32 \text{ m}^2$

Volume of the plate, $V = \dfrac{400}{1000} \times \dfrac{400}{1000} \times \dfrac{4}{1000} = 0.00064 \text{ m}^3$

Characteristic length, $L_c = \dfrac{V}{A_s} = \dfrac{0.00064}{0.32} = 0.002 \text{ m}$

k for aluminium, at low temperatures may be taken as 214 W/m°C or 770.4 kJ/mh°C.

$\therefore$ Biot number, $B_i = \dfrac{hL_c}{k} = \dfrac{20000 \times 0.002}{770.4} = 0.0519$

Since B_i is less than 0.1, hence lumper capacitance method may be applied for the solution of the problem.

The temperature distribution is given by

$$\frac{t - t_a}{t_i - t_a} = \exp\left[-\frac{hA_s}{\rho Vc}\tau\right] \qquad \text{...[Eqn. (4.4)]}$$

(For derivation of this relation please refer to Article 4.2)

$$\frac{-70-(-183)}{200-(-183)} = \exp\left[-\frac{20000 \times 0.32}{3000 \times 0.00064 \times 0.8}\cdot\tau\right]$$

or, $0.295 = e^{-4166.67\,\tau}$

$$= \frac{1}{e^{4166.67\,\tau}}$$

or, $e^{4166.67\,\tau} = \dfrac{1}{0.295} = 3.389$

or, $4166.67\,\tau = \ln 3.389 = 1.2205$

$\therefore$ $\tau = \dfrac{1.2205}{4166.67} \times 3600 = \mathbf{1.054 \text{ s}}$ **(Ans.)**

Example 4.3. *A solid copper sphere of 10 cm diameter [$\rho = 8954 \text{ kg/m}^3$, $c_p = 383 \text{ J/kg K}$, $k = 386 \text{ W/m K}$], initially at a uniform temperature $t_i = 250°C$, is suddenly immersed in a well-stirred fluid which is maintained at a uniform temperature $t_a = 50°C$. The heat transfer coefficient between the sphere and the fluid is $h = 200 \text{ W/m}^2 \text{ K}$. Determine the temperature of the copper block at $\tau = 5$ min after the immersion.*   (AMIE Winter, 1998)

Solution. *Given :* $D = 10 \text{ cm} = 0.1 \text{ m}$; $\rho = 8954 \text{ kg/m}^3$; $c_p = 383 \text{ J/kg K}$; $k = 386 \text{ W/m K}$; $t_i = 250°C$; $t_a = 50°C$; $h = 200 \text{ W/m}^2 \text{ K}$; $\tau = 5 \text{ min} = 300 \text{ s}$.

Temperature of the copper block, t :

The characteristic length of the sphere is,

$$L_c = \frac{\text{Volume } (V)}{\text{Surface area } (A_s)} = \frac{\frac{4}{3}\pi R^3}{4\pi R^2} = \frac{R}{3} = \frac{D}{6} = \frac{0.1}{6} = 0.0167 \text{ m}$$

Biot number, $B_i = \dfrac{hL_c}{k} = \dfrac{200 \times 0.01667}{386} = 8.64 \times 10^{-3}$

Since B_i is less than 0.1, hence lump capacitance method (Newtonian heating or cooling) may be applied for the solution of the problem.

The temperature distribution is given by

$$\frac{t - t_a}{t_i - t_a} = \exp\left[-\frac{hA_s}{\rho Vc}\cdot\tau\right] \qquad \text{...[Eqn. (4.4)]}$$

Substituting the value, we get

$$\frac{t - 50}{250 - 50} = \exp\left[-\frac{200}{8954 \times 0.01667 \times 383} \times 300\right] = 0.35$$

$$\left(\because \frac{A_s}{V} = \frac{L}{L_c} = \frac{1}{0.01667}\right)$$

$\therefore$ $\qquad$ $t = (250 - 50) \times 0.35 + 50 = \mathbf{120°C}$ **(Ans.)**

Example 4.4. *An average convective heat transfer coefficient for flow of 90°C air over a flat plate is measured by observing the temperature time history of a 40 mm thick copper slab ($\rho = 9000$ kg/m^3, $c = 0.38$ kJ/kg°C, $k = 370$ W/m°C) exposed to 90°C air. In one test run, the initial temperature of the plate was 200°C, and in 4.5 minutes the temperature decreased by 35°C. Find the heat transfer coefficient for this case. Neglect internal thermal resistance.*

Solution. *Given* : $t_a = 90°C$; $L = 40$ mm or 0.04 m; $\rho = 9000$ kg/m^3; $c = 0.38$ kJ/kg°C; $t_i = 200°C$; $t = 200 - 35 = 165°C$; $\tau = 4.5$ min $= 270$s

Characteristic length, $\qquad L_c = \frac{L}{2} = \frac{0.04}{2} = 0.02$ m

$$\frac{hA_s}{\rho Vc} = \frac{h}{\rho(V/A_s)c} = \frac{h}{\rho c L_c} = \frac{h}{9000 \times (0.38 \times 1000) \times 0.02} = 1.462 \times 10^{-5}\, h$$

Now, $\qquad\qquad \dfrac{t - t_a}{t_i - t_a} = \exp\left[-\dfrac{hA_s}{\rho Vc}\,\tau\right]$ $\qquad\qquad$ ...[Eqn. (4.4)]

or, $\qquad\qquad \dfrac{165 - 90}{200 - 90} = e^{-(1.462 \times 10^{-5}\, h) \times (270)} = e^{-0.003947 h} = \dfrac{1}{e^{0.003947\, h}}$

or, $\qquad\qquad 0.682 = \dfrac{1}{e^{0.003947\, h}}$ or $e^{0.003947 h} = 1.466$

or, $\qquad\qquad 0.003947\, h = ln\ 1.466 = 0.3825$

$\therefore$ $\qquad\qquad h = \dfrac{0.3825}{0.003947} = \mathbf{96.9\ W/m^2°C}$ **(Ans.)**

Example 4.5. *The heat transfer coefficients for the flow of air at 28°C over a 12.5 mm diameter sphere are measured by observing the temperature-time history of a copper ball of the same dimension. The temperature of copper ball ($c = 0.4$ kJ/kg K and $\rho = 8850$ kg/m^3) was measured by two thermocouples, one located in the centre and other near the surface. Both the thermocouples registered the same temperature at a given instant. In one test the initial temperature of the ball was 65°C and in 1.15 minute the temperature decreased by 11°C. Calculate the heat transfer coefficient for this case.* $\qquad$ **(AMIE Winter, 2001)**

Solution. *Given* : $t_a = 28°C$; R (sphere) $= \dfrac{12.5}{2} = 6.25$ mm $= 0.00625$ m; $c = 0.4$ kJ/kg°C; $\rho = 8850$ kg/m^3; $t_i = 65°C$; $t = 65 - 11 = 54°C$; $\tau = 1.15$ min $= 69$ s.

Heat transfer coefficient, h:

Biot number, $\qquad B_i = \dfrac{hL_c}{k} = \dfrac{h \cdot (R/2)}{k}$

Since *heat transfer coefficient has to be calculated, so assume that the internal resistance is negligible and B_i is less than 0.1.*

Using eqn. (4.4), we have

$$\frac{\theta}{\theta_i} = \frac{t - t_a}{t_i - t_a} = \exp\left[-\frac{hA_s}{\rho Vc}\,\tau\right] = e^{-B_i F_0}$$

or, $\quad \ln\left[\dfrac{t - t_a}{t_i - t_a}\right] = -\dfrac{hA_s}{\rho Vc} \cdot \tau$

or, $\quad h = \dfrac{\rho Vc}{A_s \tau} \ln\left[\dfrac{t_i - t_a}{t - t_a}\right]$

or, $\quad h = \left(\dfrac{\frac{4}{3}\pi R^3}{4\pi R^2}\right)\dfrac{\rho c}{\tau} \ln\left[\dfrac{t_i - t_a}{t - t_a}\right]$

or, $\quad h = \dfrac{R}{3}\dfrac{\rho c}{\tau} \ln\left[\dfrac{t_i - t_a}{t - t_a}\right]$

Substituting the proper values, we have

$h = \dfrac{0.00625}{3} \times \dfrac{8850 \times (0.4 \times 1000)}{69}$

Cooling of IC engine.

$\ln\left[\dfrac{(65 - 28)}{(54 - 28)}\right] = \mathbf{37.71\ W/m^2K}$ **(Ans.)**

Example 4.6. *A steel ball 50 mm in diameter and at 900°C is placed in still atmosphere of 30°C. Calculate the initial rate of cooling of the ball in °C/min.*

Take: $\rho = 7800\ kg/m^3$, $c = 2\ kJ/kg°C$ *(for steel);* $h = 30\ W/m^2°C$.

Neglect internal thermal resistance. **(M.U.)**

Solution. *Given:* $R = \dfrac{50}{2} = 25\ mm = 0.025\ m$; $t_i = 900°C$; $t_a = 30°C$, $\rho = 7800\ kg/m^3$;

$$C = 2\ kJ/kg°C;\ h = 30 W/m^2°C;\ \tau = 1\ min = 60\ s.$$

The temperature variation in the ball (with respect to time), neglecting internal thermal resistance, is given by:

$$\dfrac{t - t_a}{t_i - t_a} = \exp\left[-\dfrac{hA_s}{\rho Vc}\tau\right] \qquad\qquad \text{...[Eqn. (4.4)]}$$

where, $\quad \dfrac{hA_s}{\rho Vc}\cdot\tau = \dfrac{h \times 4\pi R^2}{\rho \times \frac{4}{3}\pi R^3 \times c}\ \tau = \dfrac{3h\tau}{\rho Rc} = \dfrac{3 \times 30 \times 60}{7800 \times 0.025 \times (2 \times 1000)} = 0.01385$

Substituting the values in the above equation, we get

$$\dfrac{t - 30}{900 - 30} = e^{-0.01385} = \dfrac{1}{e^{0.01385}} = 0.9862$$

or, $\quad t = 30 + 0.9862\ (900 - 30) = 888°C$

∴ $\quad$ Rate of cooling $= 900 - 888 = \mathbf{12°C/min.}$ **(Ans.)**

Example 4.7. *A cylindrical ingot 10 cm diameter and 30 cm long passes through a heat treatment furnace which is 6 m in length. The ingot must reach a temperature of 800°C before it comes out of the furnace. The furnace gas is at 1250°C and ingot initial temperature is 90°C. What is the maximum speed with which the ingot should move in the furnace to attain the required temperature? The combined radiative and convective surface heat transfer coefficient is 100 W/m² °C. Take k (steel) = 40 W/m°C and α (thermal diffusivity of steel) = 1.16 × 10⁻⁵ m²/s.*

Solution. *Given :* $D = 10\ cm = 0.1\ m$; $L = 30\ cm = 0.3\ m$; $t_i = 1250°C$; $t = 800°C$; $t_a = 90°C$; $k = 40\ W/m°C$; $h = 100\ W/m^2°C$; $\alpha = 1.16 \times 10^{-5}\ m^2/s$.

Characteristic length, $L_c = \dfrac{V \,(\text{volume})}{A_s \,(\text{surface area})} = \dfrac{\dfrac{\pi}{4}D^2 L}{\left[\pi DL + \dfrac{\pi}{4}D^2 \times 2\right]} = \dfrac{DL}{4L + 2D}$

$$= \dfrac{0.1 \times 0.3}{4 \times 0.3 + 2 \times 0.1} = 0.02143 \text{ m}$$

Biot number, $B_i = \dfrac{h\,L_c}{k} = \dfrac{100 \times 0.02143}{40} = 0.0536$

As $B_i < 0.1$, then internal thermal resistance of the ingot for conduction heat flow can be neglected.

∴ The time versus temperature relation is given as

$$\dfrac{t - t_a}{t_i - t_a} = \exp\left[-\dfrac{hA_s}{\rho Vc}\,\tau\right]$$

Now, $\dfrac{hA_s}{\rho Vc} = \dfrac{k}{k}\cdot\dfrac{hA_s}{\rho Vc} = \left(\dfrac{k}{\rho c}\right)\left(\dfrac{h}{k}\right)\left(\dfrac{A_s}{V}\right) = \alpha \cdot \dfrac{h}{k}\cdot\dfrac{A_s}{V}$

$$= 1.16 \times 10^{-5} \times \dfrac{100}{40} \times \dfrac{1}{0.02143} = 0.001353$$

Substituting the values in the above equation, we get

$$\dfrac{800 - 90}{12 - 90} = e^{-0.001353\tau} = \dfrac{1}{e^{0.001353\tau}}$$

or, $0.612 = \dfrac{1}{e^{0.001353\tau}}$ or $e^{0.001353\tau} = 1.634$

or, $0.001353\tau = ln\,(1.634) = 0.491$

∴ $\tau = \dfrac{0.491}{0.001353} = 362.9$ s

Velocity of ingot passing through the furnace,

$$v = \dfrac{\text{Furance length}}{\text{Time}} = \dfrac{6}{362.9} = \textbf{0.01653 m/s (Ans.)}$$

Example 4.8. *A 15 mm diameter mild steel sphere (k = 42 W/m°C) is exposed to cooling airflow at 20°C resulting in the convective coefficient h = 120 W/m²°C.*

Determine the following:

(i) Time required to cool the sphere from 550°C to 90°C.

(ii) Instantaneous heat transfer rate 2 minutes after the start of cooling.

(iii) Total energy transferred from the sphere during the first 2 minutes.

For mild steel take: ρ = 7850 kg/m³, c = 475 J/kg°C and α = 0.045 m²/h.

Solution: *Given :* $R = \dfrac{15}{2} = 7.5$ mm $= 0.0075$ m; $k = 42$ W/m°C; $t_a = 20°C$; $t_i = 550°C$; $t = 90°C$; $h = 120$ W/m²°C.

(i) **Time required to cool the sphere from 550°C to 90°C, τ :**

The characteristic length L_c is given by,

$$L_c = \dfrac{\dfrac{4}{3}\pi R^3}{4\pi R^2} = \dfrac{R}{3} = \dfrac{0.0075}{3} = 0.0025 \text{ m}$$

Biot number, $\qquad B_i = \dfrac{hL_c}{k} = \dfrac{120 \times 0.0025}{42} = 0.007143$

Fourier number, $\qquad F_0 = \dfrac{\alpha \tau}{L_c^2} = \dfrac{0.045 \times \tau}{(0.0025)^2} = 7200\ \tau$ (where τ is in hour)

since $B_i < 0.1$, so we can use lump theory to solve this problem.

The temperature variation with time is given by

$$\dfrac{t - t_a}{t_i - t_a} = e^{-B_i F_o}$$

Substituting the values, we get

$$\dfrac{90 - 20}{550 - 20} = e^{-0.007143 \times 7200\, \tau} = e^{-51.43\, \tau}$$

$$0.132 = e^{-51.43\,\tau} \qquad \text{or} \qquad e^{51.43\,\tau} = \dfrac{1}{0.132} = 7.576$$

or $\qquad 51.43\ \tau = 2.025 \qquad$ or $\qquad \tau = \dfrac{2.025}{51.43} = 0.03937\ h = \mathbf{141.7\ s}$ **(Ans.)**

(*ii*) **Instantaneous heat transfer rate 2 minutes (0.0333 h) after the start of cooling, Q_i:**

$$Qi = -hA_s\,(t_i - t_a)\ e^{-B_i F_o} \qquad\qquad \text{...[Eqn. 4.7(a)]}$$

Now $\qquad B_i F_o = (0.007143)\,(7200 \times 0.0333) = 1.7126$

$\therefore \qquad Q_i = -120 \times 4\,\pi \times (0.0075)^2\,(550 - 20)\ e^{-1.7126}$

$$= -\mathbf{8.1W}\ \textbf{(Ans.)}$$

The negative sign shows that *heat is given off by sphere.*

(*iii*) **Total energy transferred from the sphere during first 2 minutes (0.0333 h), Q' :**

$$Q' = \rho V c\,(t_i - t_a)\,[e^{-B_i F_o} - 1]$$

$$= 7850 \times \dfrac{4}{3}\,\pi \times (0.0075)^3\,(475)\,(550 - 20)\,[e^{-1.7126} - 1]$$

$$= (-)\ \mathbf{2862.3\ J}\ \textbf{(Ans.)}$$

Example 4.9. *The decorative plastic film on copper sphere 10 mm is diameter is cured in an oven at 75°C. After removal from oven, the sphere is exposed to an air stream at 10 m/s and 23°C. Estimate the time taken to cool the sphere to 35°C using Lump theory.*

Use correlation :

$$Nu = 2 + \left[0.4\,(Re)^{0.5} + 0.06\,(Re)^{2/3}\right]\,(Pr)^{0.4}\left(\dfrac{\mu_a}{\mu_s}\right)^{0.25}$$

for determination of correlation co-efficient h, use following properties of air and copper :

For copper : $\quad \rho = 8933\ kg/m^3,\ k = 400\ W/mK,\ c_p = 380\ J/kg°\ C$

For air at 23°C : $\quad \mu = 18.16 \times 10^{-6}\ N\text{-}s/m^{2,}\ v = 15.36 \times 10^{-6}\ m^2/s$

$\qquad\qquad k = 0.0258\ W/m\ K,\ Pr = 0.709,\ and$

$\qquad\qquad \mu_s = 19.78 \times 10^{-6}\ N\text{-}s/m^2,\ at\ 35°C.$ $\qquad$ (N.M.U., 1998)

Solution. *Given :* $D = 10\ mm = 0.01\ m;\ t_1 = 75°C;\ V = 10\ m/s;\ t_a = 23°C;\ t = 35°C$

Time taken to cool the sphere, τ :

$$Re = \dfrac{VD}{v} = \dfrac{10 \times 0.01}{15.36 \times 10^{-6}} = 6510$$

$$Nu = 2 + \left[0.4 \times (6510)^{0.5} + 0.06\,(6510)^{2/3}\right] \times (0.709)^{0.4} \times \left(\frac{18.16 \times 10^{-6}}{19.78 \times 10^{-6}}\right)^{0.25}$$

$$= 2 + [32.27 + 20.92] \times 0.87 \times 0.979 = 47.3$$

or, $\quad Nu = \dfrac{hD}{k} = 47.3$

∴ $\quad h = \dfrac{k}{D} \times 47.3 = \dfrac{0.0258}{0.01} \times 47.3 = 122 \text{ W/m}^2{}^\circ\text{C}$

The time taken to cool from 75°C to 35°C may be found from the following relation :

$$\frac{t - t_a}{t_i - t_a} = \exp\left[-\frac{hA_s}{\rho V c} \cdot \tau\right]$$

$$\frac{35 - 23}{75 - 23} = \exp\left[-\frac{122 \times 4\pi R^2}{\rho \times \dfrac{4}{3}\pi R^3 \times c} \cdot \tau\right]$$

$$0.2308 = \exp\left(-\frac{122 \times 3}{8933 \times 0.005 \times 380} \cdot \tau\right) = e^{-0.02156\tau}$$

or, $\quad e^{0.02156\,\tau} = \dfrac{1}{0.2308} = 4.333$

or, $\quad 0.2156\,\tau = 1.466$

or, $\quad \tau = \dfrac{1.466}{0.2156} = \textbf{68 s \ (Ans.)}$

Example 4.10. *An egg with mean diameter of 40 mm and initially at 20°C is placed in a boiling water pan for 4 minutes and found to be boiled to the consumer's taste. For how long should a similar egg for same consumer be boiled when taken from a refrigerator at 5°C. Take the following properties for egg:*

$k = 10$ W/m°C, $\rho = 1200$ kg/m³, $c = 2$ kJ/kg°C and h (heat transfer coefficient) = 100 W/m²°C. Use lump theory.

(N.M.U.)

Solution. *Given :* $R = \dfrac{40}{2} = 20 \text{ mm} = 0.02 \text{ m}; \ t_i = 20°\text{C}; \ \tau = 4 \times 60 = 240 \text{ s}; \ k = 10 \text{ W/m}°\text{C};$
$\rho = 1200 \text{ kg/m}^3; \ c = 2 \text{ kJ/kg}°\text{C}; \ h = 100 \text{ W/m}^2°\text{C}.$

For using the lump theory, the required condition is $B_i < 0.1$

$$B_i = \frac{h\,L_c}{k} \quad \text{where } L_c \text{ is the characteristic length which is given by,}$$

$$L_c = \frac{V \text{ (volume)}}{A_s \text{ (surface area)}} = \frac{\dfrac{4}{3}\pi R^3}{4\pi R^2} = \frac{R}{3}$$

∴ $\quad B_i = \dfrac{h}{k} \times \dfrac{R}{3} = \dfrac{100 \times 0.02}{10 \times 3} = 0.067$

As $B_i < 0.1$, we can use lump theory.

The temperature variation with time is given by :

$$\frac{t - t_a}{t_i - t_a} = \exp\left[-\frac{hA_s}{\rho V c}\tau\right] \qquad \qquad \dots(1)$$

$$\frac{hA_s}{\rho V c} = \left(\frac{h}{\rho c}\right)\left(\frac{A_s}{V}\right) = \left(\frac{100}{1200 \times 2000}\right)\left(\frac{3}{R}\right)$$

$$= \left(\frac{100}{1200 \times 2000} \right) \left(\frac{3}{0.02} \right) = 0.00625$$

Substituting the values in eqn. (1), we get

$$\frac{t - 100}{20 - 100} = e^{-0.00625 \times 240} = e^{-1.50} = \frac{1}{e^{1.50}} = \frac{1}{4.4817} = 0.223$$

or, $t = 100 + (20 - 100) \times 0.223 = 82.16°C$ say 82°C.

Now let us find 'τ' when the given data is : $t_i = 5°C$, $t_a = 100°C$ and $t = 82°C$

Again using eqn. (1), we get

$$\frac{82 - 100}{5 - 100} = e^{-0.00625 \tau} = \frac{1}{e^{0.00625 \tau}}$$

or, $0.1895 = \dfrac{1}{e^{0.00625 \tau}}$ or $e^{0.00625\tau} = 5.277$

or, $0.00625 \tau = 1.6633$ or $\tau = \dfrac{1.6633}{0.00625} = 266.13$ s $= $ **4.435 minutes (Ans.)**

Example 4.11. *A hot cylinder ingot of 50 mm diameter and 200 mm long is taken out from the furnace at 800°C and dipped in water till its temperature falls to 500°C. Then it is directly exposed to air till its temperature falls to 100°C. Find the total time required for the ingot to reach the temperature from 800 to 100°C. Take the following:*

k (thermal conductivity of ingot) = 60 W/m°C

c (specific heat of ingot) = 200 J/m°C

ρ (density of ingot material) = 800 kg/m³

h_w (heat transfer coefficient in water) = 200 W/m²°C

h_a (heat transfer coefficient in air) = 20 W/m²°C

Temperature of air or water = 30°C.   (M.U.)

Solution. *Given :* $R = \dfrac{50}{2} = 25$ mm $= 0.025$ m; $L = 200$ mm or 0.2 m

Biot number,

$$B_i = \frac{h L_c}{k} = \left(\frac{h}{k} \right) \times \left(\frac{V}{A_s} \right) = \left(\frac{h}{k} \right) \left(\frac{\pi R^2 L}{2\pi RL} \right) = \left(\frac{h}{k} \right) \left(\frac{R}{2} \right) = \left(\frac{200}{60} \right) \left(\frac{0.025}{2} \right) = 0.04166$$

As B_i is less than 0.1, internal thermal resistance can be neglected and lump theory can be used.

The total time (τ) can be calculate by calculating τ_1 (time required in water) and τ_2 (time required in air) and adding such that $\tau = \tau_1 + \tau_2$.

A_s (surface area of ingot) $= 2\pi RL = 2\pi \times$ 0.025 × 0.2 = 0.0314 m²

V (volume of ingot) $= \pi R^2 L = \pi \times 0.25^2$ × 0.2 = 3.927 × 10⁻⁴ m³

(a) The temperature variation with respect to time when cooled in **water** is given by (See Fig. 4.5)

$$\frac{t - t_w}{t_i - t_w} = \exp \left[- \frac{hA_s}{\rho Vc} \tau_1 \right]$$

where

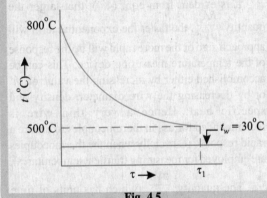

Fig. 4.5.

$$\frac{h_w A_s}{\rho V c} = \frac{200 \times 0.0314}{800 \times 3.927 \times 10^{-4} \times 200} = 0.0999$$

$$\therefore \quad \frac{500 - 30}{800 - 30} = e^{-0.0999\,\tau_1} = \frac{1}{e^{0.0999\,\tau_1}}$$

or, $0.61 = \dfrac{1}{e^{0.0999\,\tau_1}}$

or, $e^{0.0999\,\tau_1} = 1.639$

or, $0.0999\,\tau_1 = 0.494$

or, $\tau_1 = \dfrac{0.494}{0.0999} = 4.94$ s

(b) The temperature variation with respect to time when cooled in **air** is given by (See Fig. 4.6).

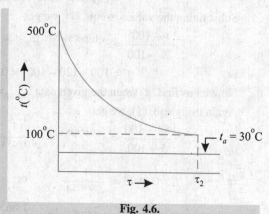

Fig. 4.6.

$$\frac{t - t_a}{t_i - t_a} = \exp.\left[-\frac{hA_s}{\rho V c}\tau_2 \right]$$

where, $\dfrac{h_a A_s}{\rho V c} = \dfrac{20 \times 0.0314}{800 \times 3.927 \times 10^{-4} \times 200} = 0.00999$

$$\frac{100 - 30}{500 - 30} = e^{-0.00999\,\tau_2} = \frac{1}{e^{0.00999\,\tau_2}}$$

$$0.1489 = \frac{1}{e^{0.00999\,\tau_2}} \quad \text{or} \quad e^{0.00999\,\tau_2} = 6.716$$

or, $0.00999\,\tau_2 = 1.9045$ or $\tau_2 = \dfrac{1.9045}{0.00999} = 190.6$ s

$\therefore$ Total time (τ) is given by

$$\tau = \tau_1 + \tau_2 = 4.94 + 190.6 = 195.54 \text{ s or } \textbf{3.259 minutes. (Ans.)}$$

4.3. TIME CONSTANT AND RESPONSE OF TEMPERATURE MEASURING INSTRUMENTS

Measurement of temperature by a thermocouple is an important application of the lumped parameter analysis. The **response of a thermocouple** is defined as the *time required for the thermocouple to attain the source temperature.*

It is evident from eqn. (4.4), that larger the quantity $\dfrac{hA_s}{\rho V c}$, the faster the exponential term will approach zero or the more rapid will be the response of the temperature measuring device. This can be accomplished either by increasing the value of '*h*' or by decreasing the wire diameter, density and specific heat. Hence a very thin wire is recommended for use in thermocouples to ensure a rapid response (especially when the thermocouples are employed for measuring transient temperatures).

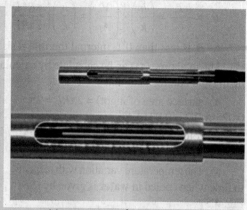

Measurement of a temperature by a thermocouple.

The quantity $\dfrac{\rho V c}{hA_s}$ (which has units of time) is called **time constant** and is denoted by the symbol τ^*. Thus

$$\tau^* = \frac{\rho Vc}{hA_s} = \frac{k}{\alpha h} \cdot \frac{V}{A_s} \qquad \qquad ...(4.9)$$

and,

$$\frac{\theta}{\theta_i} = \frac{t - t_a}{t_i - t_a} = e^{-(\tau/\tau^*)} \qquad \qquad ...(4.10)$$

At $\tau = \tau^*$ (one time constant), we have [from eqn. (4.10)]

$$\frac{\theta}{\theta_i} = \frac{t - t_a}{t_i - t_a} = e^{-1} = 0.368 \qquad \qquad ...(4.11)$$

Thus τ^* *is the time required for the temperature change to reach 36.8 percent of its final value in response to a step change in temperature.* In other words temperature difference would be reduced by 63.2 percent. *The time required by a thermocouple to reach its 63.2 percent of the value of initial temperature difference is called its* **sensitivity**.

Depending upon the type of fluid used, the response times for different sizes of thermocouple wires usually vary between 0.04 to 2.5 seconds.

Example 4.12. *A thermocouple junction of spherical form is to be used to measure the temperature of a gas stream.*

$$h = 400 \ W/m^2 °C; \ k \ (thermocouple \ junction) = 20 \ W/m°C$$
$$c = 400 \ J/kg°C \ and \ \rho = 8500 \ kg/m^3$$

Calculate the following:

(i) *Junction diameter needed for the thermocouple to have thermal time constant of one second.*

(ii) *Time required for the thermocouple junction to reach 198°C if junction is initially at 25°C and is placed in gas stream which is at 200°C.* (P.U.)

Solution. *Given* : $h = 400$ W/m²°C; $k = 20$ W/m°C; $c = 400$ J/kg°C; $\rho = 8500$ kg/m³.

(i) **Junction diameter, D:**

τ^* (Thermal time constant) = 1s ...(Given)

The time constant is given by

$$\tau^* = \frac{\rho Vc}{hA_s} = \frac{\rho \times \frac{4}{3}\pi R^3 \times c}{h \times 4\pi R^2} = \frac{\rho Rc}{3h}$$

or,

$$1 = \frac{8500 \times R \times 400}{3 \times 400} \quad \text{or} \quad R = \frac{3 \times 400}{8500 \times 400} = \frac{3}{8500} \ \text{m or } 0.353 \ \text{mm}$$

∴ $D = 2R = 2 \times 0.353 = \mathbf{0.706 \ mm}$ **(Ans.)**

(ii) **Time required for the junction to reach 198°C:**

Given : $t_i = 25°C$, $t_a = 200°C$; $t = 198°C$

$$\left[B_i = \frac{h \, L_c}{k} = \frac{h(R/3)}{k} = \frac{400 \times (0.353 \times 10^{-3}/3)}{20} = 0.00235 \right.$$
$$\left. \text{As } B_i \text{ is less than 0.1, lumped capacitance method can be used.} \right]$$

Now,

$$\frac{t - t_a}{t_i - t_a} = \exp\left(-\frac{hA_s}{\rho Vc}\tau\right)$$

$$\frac{hA_s}{\rho Vc} = \frac{h \times 4\pi R^2}{\rho \times \frac{4}{3}\pi R^3 c} = \frac{3h}{\rho Rc} = \frac{3 \times 400}{8500 \times \frac{3}{8500} \times 400} = 1$$

∴

$$\frac{198 - 200}{25 - 200} = e^{-1\tau} = \frac{1}{e^\tau}$$

or, $\quad\quad\quad 0.01143 = \dfrac{1}{e^\tau}\quad$ or $\quad e^\tau = 87.49$

$$\tau = ln\,(87.49) = \textbf{4.47s}\ \textbf{(Ans.)}$$

Example 4.13. *A thermocouple junction is in the form of 8 mm diameter sphere. Properties of material are:*

$c = 420\ J/kg°C;\ \rho = 8000\ kg/m^3;\ k = 40\ W/m°C\ and\ h = 40\ W/m^2°C.$

This junction is initially at 40°C and inserted in a stream of hot air at 300°C. Find:

(i) *Time constant of the thermocouple;*

(ii) *The thermocouple is taken out from the hot air after 10 seconds and kept in still air at 30°C. Assuming the heat transfer coefficient in air 10 W/m²°C, find the temperature attained by the junction 20 seconds after removing from hot air.* (P.U.)

Solution. Given : $R = \dfrac{8}{2} = 4$ mm $= 0.004$ m; $c = 420$ J/kg°C; $\rho = 8000$ kg/m³; $k = 40$ W/m°C; $h = 40$ W/m²°C (gas stream); $h = 10$ W/m²°C (air).

(i) **Time constant of the thermocouple, τ^*:**

$$\tau^* = \dfrac{\rho Vc}{hA_s} = \dfrac{\rho \times \left(\dfrac{4}{3}\pi R^3\right) \times c}{h \times 4\pi R^2} = \dfrac{\rho Rc}{3h}$$

$$\tau^* = \dfrac{8000 \times 0.004 \times 420}{3 \times 40} = \textbf{112 s} \text{ ...when thermocouple is in } \textit{gas stream.}\ \textbf{(Ans.)}$$

(ii) **The temperature attained by the junction, t:**

Given: $\quad\quad t_i = 40°C;\ t_a = 300°C;\ \tau = 20$ s

The temperature variation with respect to time during *heating* (when dipped in gas stream) is given by

$$\dfrac{t - t_a}{t_i - t_a} = \exp\left(-\dfrac{hA_s}{\rho Vc}\tau\right)$$

or, $\quad \dfrac{t - 300}{40 - 300} = \exp\left(-\dfrac{\tau}{\tau^*}\right) = e^{(-10/112)} = \dfrac{1}{e^{(10/112)}} = 0.9146$

or, $\quad\quad t = 300 + 0.9146\,(40 - 300) = 62.2°C$

The temperature variation with respect to time during cooling (when exposed to air) is given by

$$\dfrac{t - t_a}{t_i - t_a} = e^{\tau/\tau^*}$$

where, $\quad \tau^* = \dfrac{\rho Rc}{3h} = \dfrac{8000 \times 0.004 \times 420}{3 \times 10} = 448s$

$$\dfrac{t - 30}{62.2 - 30} = e^{(-20/448)} = \dfrac{1}{e^{(20/448)}} = 0.9563$$

or, $\quad\quad t = 30 + 0.9563\,(62.2 - 30) = \textbf{60.79°C (Ans.)}$

Example 4.14. *A very thin glass walled 3 mm diameter mercury thermometer is placed in a stream of air, where heat transfer coefficient is 55 W/m²°C, for measuring the unsteady temperature of air. Consider cylindrical thermometer bulb to consist of mercury only for which k = 8.8 W/m°C and $\alpha = 0.0166\ m^2/h$. Calculate the time required for the temperature change to reach half its final value.*

Solution. Given : $R = \dfrac{3}{2} = 1.5$ mm $= 0.0015$ m; $h = 55$ W/m²°C; $k = 8.8$ W/m°C; $\alpha = 0.0166$ m²/h.

The time constant is given by

$$\tau^* = \frac{k}{\alpha h} \times \frac{V}{A_s} \qquad\qquad ...[\text{Eqn. (4.9)}]$$

$$= \frac{k}{\alpha h} \times \frac{\pi R^2 L}{2\pi R L} = \frac{kR}{2\,\alpha\,h} = \frac{8.8 \times 0.0015}{2 \times 0.0166 \times 55} = 0.007229 \text{ h or } 26 \text{ s}$$

For temperature change to reach half its final value

$$\frac{\theta}{\theta_i} = \frac{1}{2} = e^{(-\tau/\tau^*)} = \frac{1}{e^{(\tau/\tau^*)}} \text{ or } e^{(\tau/\tau^*)} = 2$$

or,

$$\frac{\tau}{\tau^*} = \ln 2 = 0.693$$

or,

$$\tau = 26 \times 0.693 = \textbf{18.02 s (Ans.)}$$

Note. Thus, one can expect *thermometer to record the temperature trend accurately only for unsteady temperature changes which are 'slower'.*

Example 4.15. *The temperature of an air stream flowing with a velocity of 3 m/s is measured by a copper-constantan thermocouple which may be approximated as a sphere of 2.5 mm in diameter. Initially the junction and air are at a temperature of 25°C. The air temperature suddenly changes to and is maintained at 215°C.*

(i) Determine the time required for the thermocouple to indicate a temperature of 165°C. Also determine the thermal time constant and temperature inidcated by the thermocouple at that instant.

Mercury Thermometer.

(ii) Discuss the suitability of this thermocouple to measure unsteady state temperature of a fluid when the temperature variation in the fluid has a time period of 3.6 seconds.

The thermal junction properties are:

$\rho = 8750 \text{ kg/m}^3, c = 380 \text{ J/kg°C}, k(thermocouple) = 28 \text{ W/m°C and } h = 145 \text{ W/m}^2\text{°C.}$

Solution. *Given:* $R = \dfrac{2.5}{2} = 1.25 \text{ mm} = 0.00125 \text{ m}; t_i = 25°C; t_a = 215°C; t = 165°C.$

(i) **Time required to indicate temperature of 165°C; τ^*, t :**

Characteristic length

$$L_c = \frac{V}{A_s} = \frac{\frac{4}{3}\pi R^3}{4\pi R^2} = \frac{R}{3} = \frac{0.00125}{3} = 0.0004167 \text{ m}$$

Thermal diffusivity,

$$\alpha = \frac{k}{\rho c} = \frac{28}{8750 \times 380} = 8.421 \times 10^{-6} \text{ m}^2/\text{s}$$

Fourier number,

$$F_0 = \frac{\alpha \tau}{L_c^2} = \frac{8.421 \times 10^{-6}}{(0.0004167)^2} = 48.497\tau$$

Biot number, $\qquad B_i = \dfrac{h\,L_c}{k} = \dfrac{145 \times 0.0004167}{28} = 0.002158$

As $B_i < 0.1$, hence lumped capacitance method may be used for the solution of the problem.

The temperature distribution is given by

$$\frac{\theta}{\theta_i} = \frac{t - t_a}{t_i - t_a} = e^{-B_i F_o}$$

or, $\qquad \dfrac{165 - 215}{25 - 215} = e^{(-\,0.002158 \times 48.497\,\tau)} = e^{-0.1046\tau} = \dfrac{1}{e^{0.1046\tau}}$

or, $\qquad 0.263 = \dfrac{1}{e^{0.1046\tau}}$ or $e^{0.1046\tau} = 3.802$

or, $\qquad 0.1046\tau = ln\ 3.802 = 0.1335$

or, $\qquad \tau = \dfrac{1.335}{0.1046} = \mathbf{12.76\ s\ (Ans.)}$

Thus the thermocouple requires 12.76 s to indicate a temperature of 165°C. The actual time requirement will, however, be *greater* because of radiation from the probe and conduction along the thermocouple lead wires.

The *time constant* (τ^*) is defined as the *time required to yield a value of unity for the exponent term in the transient relation.*

$$B_i F_o = 1$$

or, $\qquad 0.002158 \times 48.497\ \tau^* = 1 \qquad$ or $\qquad \mathbf{\tau^* = 9.55\ s\ (Ans.)}$

At 9.55 s, the temperature indicated by the thermocouple is given by

$$\frac{t - t_a}{t_i - t_a} = e^{-1}$$

or, $\qquad \dfrac{t - 215}{25 - 215} = e^{-1}$

or, $\qquad t = 215 + (25 - 215)\ e^{-1} = \mathbf{145°C\ (Ans.)}$

(*ii*) As the thermal time constant is 9.55 s and time required to effect the temperature variation is 3.6 s which is *less* than the thermal time constant, hence the *temperature recovered* by the thermocouple *may not be reliable.*

4.4. TRANSIENT HEAT CONDUCTION IN SOLIDS WITH FINITE CONDUCTION AND CONVECTIVE RESISTANCES (O < B$_i$ < 100)

As shown in Fig. 4.7, consider the heating and cooling of a plane wall having a thickness of $2L$ and extending to infinity in Y and Z directions. Let us assume that the wall, initially, is at uniform temperature t_i and both the surfaces ($x = \pm L$) are suddenly exposed to and maintained at the ambient (surroundings) temperature t_a. The governing differential equation is

$$\frac{d^2 t}{dx^2} = \frac{1}{\alpha}\frac{dt}{d\tau} \qquad ...(4.12)$$

The boundary conditions are:

(*i*) At $\quad \tau = 0, \quad t = t_i$

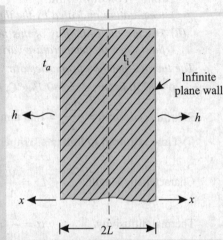

Fig. 4.7. Transient heat conduction in an infinite plane wall.

(ii) At $x = 0$, $\dfrac{dt}{dx} = 0$

(iii) At $x = \pm L$; $kA\left(\dfrac{dt}{dx}\right) = hA(t - t_a)$

...(The conduction heat transfer equals convective heat transfer at the wall surface)

The solutions obtained after rigorous mathematical analysis indicate that

$$\frac{t - t_a}{t_i - t_a} = f\left(\frac{x}{l}, \frac{hl}{k}, \frac{\alpha\tau}{l^2}\right) \qquad\qquad ...(4.13)$$

From the eqn. (4.13) it is evident that when *conduction resistance is not negligible*, the temperature history becomes a *function of Biot numbers* $\left(\dfrac{hl}{k}\right)$, *Fourier number* $\left(\dfrac{\alpha\tau}{l^2}\right)$ and the *dimensionless parameter* $\left(\dfrac{x}{l}\right)$ which indicates the location of point within the plate where temperature is to be obtained. The dimensionless parameter $\dfrac{x}{l}$ is replaced by $\dfrac{r}{R}$ in case of *cylinders* and *spheres*.

For the eqn. (4.13) *graphical charts* have been prepared in a variety of forms. In the Figs. from (4.8) to (4.10) are shown the **Heisler Charts** which depict the dimensionless temperature $\left[\dfrac{t_o - t_a}{t_i - t_a}\right]$ versus F_o (Fourier number) for various values of $\dfrac{1}{B_i}$ for solids of different geometrical shapes such as plates, cylinders and spheres. These charts provide the temperature history of the solid at its mid-planes ($x = 0$); temperatures at other locations are worked out by multiplying the midplane temperature by *correction factors* read from charts given in Figs. (4.11) to (4.13). The following relationship is used:

$$\frac{\theta}{\theta_i} = \frac{t - t_a}{t_i - t_a} = \left[\frac{t_o - t_a}{t_i - t_a}\right] \times \left[\frac{t - t_a}{t_o - t_a}\right]$$

The values B_i (Biot number) and F_o (Fourier number), as used in the Heisler charts, are evaluated on the basis of a characteristic parameter s which is the *semi-thickness in case of plates* and the *surface radius in case of cylinders and spheres*.

When *both conduction and convection resistances are almost of equal importance the Heisler charts are extensively used to determine the temperature distribution.*

Example 4.16. *A 60 mm thick large steel plate ($k = 42.6$ W/m°C, $\alpha = 0.043$ m²/h), initially at 440°C is suddenly exposed on both sides to an environment with convective heat transfer coefficient 235 W/m²°C and temperature 50°C. Determine the centre line temperature, and temperature inside the plate 15 mm from the midplane after 4.3 minutes.*

Solution. *Given:* $2L = 60$ mm $= 0.06$ m, $k = 42.6$ W/m°C, $\alpha = 0.043$ m²/h, $t_i = 440$°C, $h = 235$ W/m²°C, $t_a = 50$°C, $t = 4.3$ minutes.

Temperature at the midplane (centre line) of the plate t_o:

The characteristic length, $\qquad L_c = \dfrac{60}{2} = 30$ mm $= 0.03$ m

Fourier number, $\qquad F_o = \dfrac{\alpha\tau}{L_c^2} = \dfrac{0.043 \times (4.3/60)}{(0.03)^2} = 3.424$

Biot number, $\qquad B_i = \dfrac{h\,L_c}{k} = \dfrac{235 \times 0.03}{42.6} = 0.165$

At $B_i > 0.1$, the internal temperature gradients are not small, therefore, internal resistance *cannot*

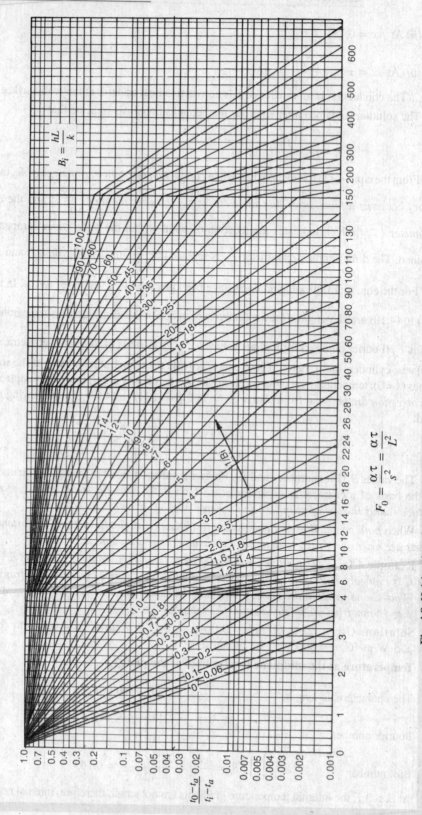

Fig. 4.8. Heisler chart for temperature history at the centre of a plate of thickness 2 L or (x/L) = 0

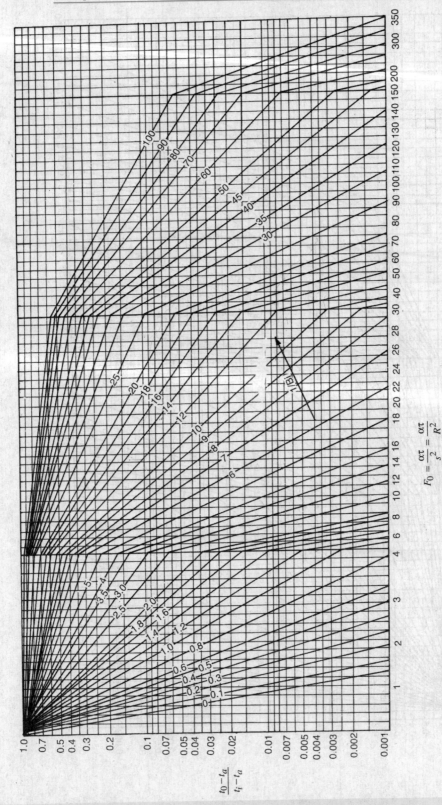

$$F_0 = \frac{\alpha \tau}{s^2} = \frac{\alpha \tau}{R^2}$$

Fig. 4.9. Heisler chart for temperature history in a cylinder.

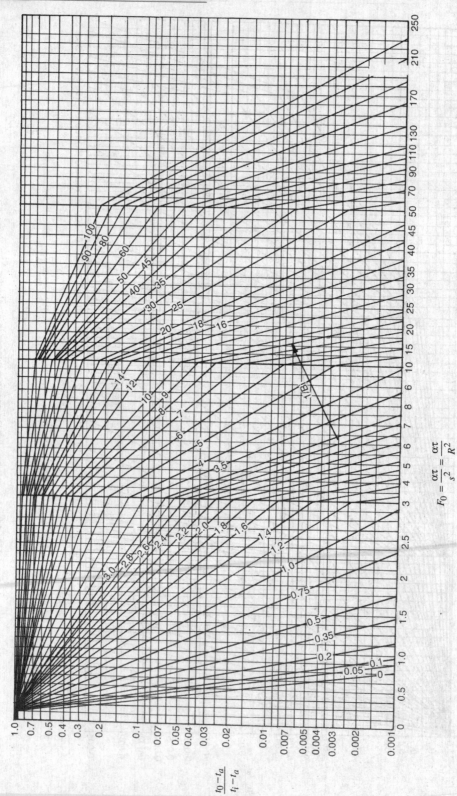

$$F_0 = \frac{\alpha\tau}{s^2} = \frac{\alpha\tau}{R^2}$$

Fig. 4.10. Heisler chart for temperature history in a sphere.

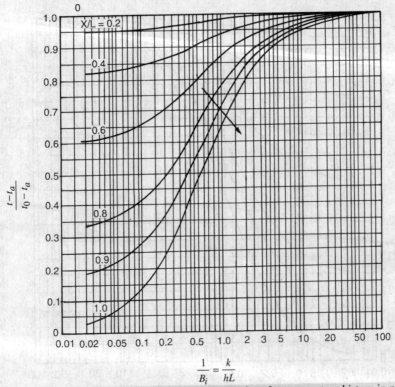

Fig. 4.11. Heisler position-correction factor chart for temperature history in plate.

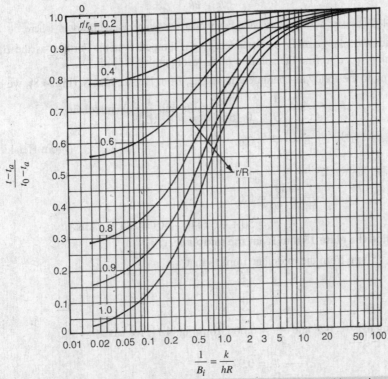

Fig. 4.12. Heisler position-correction factor chart for temperature history in cylinder.

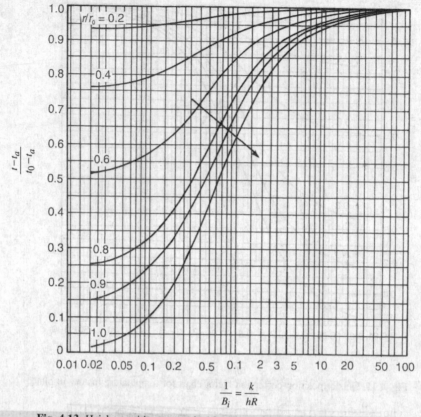

$$\frac{1}{B_i} = \frac{k}{hR}$$

Fig. 4.13. Heisler position-correction factor chart for temperature history in sphere.

be neglected. Thus the plate *cannot* be considered as a lumped system. Further, as the $B_i < 100$. *Heisler charts can be used* to find the solution of the problem.

Corresponding to the following parameteric values, from Heisler charts, (Fig. 4.8), we have

$$F_o = 3.424; \quad \frac{1}{B_i} = \frac{1}{0.165} = 6.06 \text{ and } \frac{x}{L} = 0 \text{ (midplane)}$$

$$\frac{t_o - t_a}{t_i - t_a} = 0.6 \qquad \qquad \text{(From Heisler charts)}$$

Substituting the values, we have

$$\frac{t_o - 50}{440 - 50} = 0.6$$

or, $$t_o = 50 + 0.6\,(440 - 50) = \textbf{284°C (Ans.)}$$

Temperature inside the plate 15 mm from the midplane, t:

The distance 15 mm from the midplane implies that

$$\frac{x}{L} = \frac{15}{30} = 0.5$$

Corresponding to $\dfrac{x}{L} = 0.5$ and $\dfrac{1}{B_i} = 6.06$, from Fig. 4.11, we have

$$\frac{t - t_a}{t_i - t_a} = 0.97$$

Substituting the values, we get

$$\frac{t - 50}{284 - 50} = 0.97$$

or, $t = 50 + 0.97 \,(284 - 50) = \mathbf{276.98°C} \text{ (Ans.)}$

Example 4.17. *A 6 mm thick stainless steel plate (ρ = 7800 kg/m³, c = 460 J/kg°C, k = 55 W/m°C) is used to form the nose section of missile. It is held initially at a uniform temperature of 30°C. When the missile enters the denser layers of the atmosphere at a very high velocity the effective temperature of air surrounding the nose region attains the value 2150°C; the surface convective heat transfer coefficient is estimated as 3395 W/m²°C. If the maximum metal temperature is not to exceed 1100°C, determine:*

    (i) Maximum permissible time in these surroundings.

    (ii) Inside surface temperature under these conditions.

Solution. *Given :* $2L = 6$ mm $= 0.006$ m; $\rho = 7800$ kg/m³; $c = 460$ J/kg°C; $k = 55$ W/m°C; $t_i = 30°C$; $t_a = 2150°C$; $t = 1100°C$.

(i) Maximum permissible time, τ :

Characteristic length, $\qquad L_c = \dfrac{0.006}{2} = 0.003$ m

Biot number, $\qquad B_i = \dfrac{h\,L}{k} = \dfrac{3395 \times 0.003}{55} = 0.185$

As $B_i > 0.1$, therefore, lumped analysis cannot be applied in this case. Further as $B_i < 100$, Heisler charts can be used to obtain the solution of the problem.

Corresponding to $\dfrac{1}{B_i} = 5.4$ and $\dfrac{x}{L} = 1$ (outside surface of nose section, from Fig. 4.11, we have

$$\frac{t - t_a}{t_o - t_a} = 0.93$$

Also, $\qquad \dfrac{t - t_a}{t_i - t_a} = \left[\dfrac{t_o - t_a}{t_i - t_a}\right] \times \left[\dfrac{t - t_a}{t_o - t_a}\right]$

or, $\qquad \dfrac{1100 - 2150}{30 - 2150} = \left[\dfrac{t_o - t_a}{t_i - t_a}\right] \times 0.93$

or, $\qquad \dfrac{t_o - t_a}{t_i - t_a} = \dfrac{1}{0.93}\left[\dfrac{1100 - 2150}{30 - 2150}\right] = 0.495$

Now, from Fig. 4.8, corresponding to the above dimensionless temperature and $\dfrac{1}{B_i} = 5.4$, we get the value of Fourier number, $F_o = 4.4$

$$\therefore \qquad \frac{\alpha\tau}{L_c^2} = 4.4$$

or, $\qquad \left(\dfrac{k}{\rho c}\right)\left(\dfrac{\tau}{L_c^2}\right) = 4.4$

or, $\qquad \left(\dfrac{55}{7800 \times 460}\right)\left(\dfrac{\tau}{0.003^2}\right) = 4.4$

or, $\qquad \tau = \dfrac{4.4 \times 0.003^2 \times 7800 \times 460}{55} = \mathbf{2.58s} \text{ (Ans.)}$

(ii) **Inside surface temperature, t_o :**

The temperature t_o at the inside surface $(x = 0)$ is given by

$$\frac{t_o - t_a}{t_i - t_a} = 0.495$$

or,

$$\frac{t_o - 2150}{30 - 2150} = 0.495$$

or,

$$t_o = 2150 + 0.495\,(30 - 2150) = \textbf{1100.6°C (Ans.)}$$

Example 4.18. *A long cylindrical bar ($k = 17.4$ W/m°C, $\alpha = 0.019$ m^2/h) of radius 80 mm comes out of oven at 830°C throughout and is cooled by quenching it in a large bath of 40°C coolant. The surface coefficient of heat transfer between the bar surface and the coolant is 180 W/m²°C. Determine:*

(i) The time taken by the shaft centre to reach 120°C.

(ii) The surface temperature of the shaft when its centre temperature is 120°C. Also calculate the temperature gradient at the outside surface at the same instant of time.

Solution. *Given:* $R = 80$ mm $= 0.08$ m, $t_i = 830°C$, $t_a = 40°C$, $h = 180$ W/m²°C, $t = 120°C$, $k = 17.4$ W/m°C, $\alpha = 0.019$ m^2/h.

(i) **The time taken by the shaft centre to reach 120°C, τ :**

Characteristic length,
$$L_c = \frac{\pi R^2 L}{2\pi R L} = \frac{R}{2} = \frac{0.08}{2} = 0.04 \text{ m}$$

Biot number,
$$B_i = \frac{h\,L_c}{k} = \frac{180 \times 0.04}{17.4} = 0.413$$

As $B_i > 0.1$, therefore, lumped analysis cannot be applied in this case. Further as $B_i < 100$, Heisler charts can be used to obtain the solution of the problem.

The parametric values for the cylindrical bar are:

$$\frac{1}{B_i} = \frac{1}{0.413} = 2.42$$

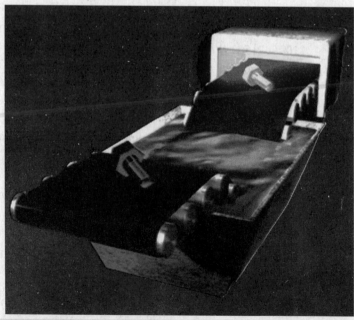

Flame arrestor functions by quenching the flame.

$$\frac{t-t_a}{t_i-t_a} = \frac{120-40}{830-40} = 0.1$$

$$\frac{r}{R} = 0 \qquad \text{(centre of the bar)}$$

Corresponding to the above values, from the chart for an infinite cylinder (Fig. 4.9), we read the Fourier number $F_o = 3.2$

$$\therefore \qquad \frac{a\,\tau}{R^2} = 3.2 \quad \text{or} \quad \frac{0.019 \times \tau}{0.04^2} = 3.2$$

or,
$$\tau = \frac{3.2 \times 0.04^2}{0.019} = 0.2695 \text{ h or } \mathbf{970.2\ s}\ (\mathbf{Ans.})$$

(ii) Temperature at the surface, t_s:

Corresponding to $\frac{r}{R} = 1$; $\frac{1}{B_i} = 2.42$, from the chart (Fig. 4.12) for an infinite cylinder, we read

$$\frac{t-t_a}{t_o-t_a} = 0.83$$

or,
$$\frac{t-40}{120-40} = 0.83 \qquad \text{or} \qquad (t-40) = 0.83\,(120-40)$$

or,
$$t\ (\text{or } t_s) = 40 + 0.83(120-40) = \mathbf{106.4^\circ C}\ (\mathbf{Ans.})$$

Temperature gradient at the outer surface, $\frac{\partial t}{\partial r}$:

$\frac{\partial t}{\partial r}$ at the outside surface is determined by the boundary condition $r = R$ at which, rate of energy conducted to the fluid-solid surface interface from within the solid = rate at which energy is convected away into the fluid.

$$kA_s \frac{\partial t}{\partial r} = h\,A_s\,(t_s - t_a)$$

or,
$$k \frac{\partial t}{\partial r} = h\,(t_s - t_a)$$

or,
$$\frac{\partial t}{\partial r} = \frac{h}{k}\,(t_s - t_a)$$

or,
$$\frac{\partial t}{\partial r} = \frac{180}{17.4}\,(106.4 - 40) = \mathbf{686.89^\circ C}\ (\mathbf{Ans.})$$

Example 4.19. *A 120 mm diameter apple ($\rho = 990$ kg/m³, $c = 4170$ J/kg°C, $k = 0.58$ W/m°C), approximately spherical in shape is taken from a 25°C environment and placed in a refrigerator where temperature is 6°C and average convective heat transfer coefficient over the apple surface is 12.8 W/m²°C. Determine the temperature at the centre of the apple after a period of 2 hours.*

Solution. *Given* : $R = \dfrac{120}{2} = 60$ mm $= 0.06$ m, $\rho = 990$ kg/m³, $c = 4170$ J/kg°C, $k = 0.58$ W/m°C, $t_i = 25°C$, $t_a = 6°C$, $h = 5.8$ W/m² °C, $\tau = 2$ hours or 7200 s.

The chracteristic length, $\quad L_c = \dfrac{\frac{4}{3}\pi R^3}{4\pi R^2} = \dfrac{R}{3} = \dfrac{0.06}{3} = 0.02$ m

Biot number, $\quad B_i = \dfrac{h\,L_c}{k} = \dfrac{12.8 \times 0.02}{0.58} = 0.441$

Since $B_i > 0.1$, a lumped capacity approach is inappropriate. Further as $B_i < 100$ Heisler charts can be used to obtain the solution of the problem.

The parametric values for the spherical apple are :

$$\frac{1}{B_i} = \frac{1}{0.441} = 2.267$$

$$F_o = \frac{\alpha \tau}{R^2} = \left(\frac{k}{\rho c}\right)\frac{\tau}{R^2} = \left(\frac{0.58}{990 \times 4170}\right) \times \left(\frac{7200}{0.06^2}\right) = 0.281$$

$$\frac{r}{R} = 0 \text{ (midplane or centre of the apple)}$$

Corresponding to the above values, from the chart for a sphere (Fig. 4.13), we read

$$\frac{t_o - t_a}{t_i - t_a} = 0.75$$

or,

$$\frac{t_o - t_a}{25 - 6} = 0.75$$

or,

$$t_o = 6 + 0.75 \, (25 - 6) = \mathbf{20.25°C} \text{ (Ans.)}$$

4.5. TRANSIENT HEAT CONDUCTION IN SEMI-INFINITE SOLIDS (H OR $B_i \to \infty$)

A solid which extends itself infinitely in all directions of space is termed as an *infinite solid*. If an infinite solid is split in the middle by a plane, each half is known as *semi-infinite solid*. In a semi-infinite body, at any instant of time, there is always a point where the effect of heating (or cooling) at one of its boundaries is not felt at all. At the *point* the temperature remains unaltered. The transient temperature change in a plane infinitely thick wall is similar to that of a semi-infinite body until enough time has passed for the surface temperature effect to penetrate through it.

As shown in the Fig. 4.14, consider a semi-infinite plate, a plate bounded by a plane $x = 0$ and extending to infinity in the +ve X-direction. The entire body is

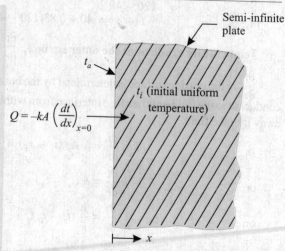

Fig. 4.14. Transient heat flow in a semi-infinite plate.

initially at uniform temperature t_i including the surface at $x = 0$. The surface temperature at $x = 0$ is suddenly raised to t_a for all times greater than $\tau = 0$. The governing equation is :

$$\frac{d^2 t}{dx^2} = \frac{1}{\alpha}\frac{dt}{d\tau}$$

The boundary conditions are :

(i) $t(x, 0) = t_i$;   (ii) $t(0, \tau) = t_a$ for $\tau > 0$;   (iii) $t(\infty, \tau) = t_i$ for $\tau > 0$.

The solution of the above differential equation, with these boundary conditions, for temperature distribution at any time τ at a plane parallel to and at a distance x from the surface is given by :

$$\frac{t(x, \tau) - t_a}{t_i - t_a} = erf(z) = erf\left(\frac{x}{2\sqrt{\alpha \tau}}\right) \qquad \qquad ...(4.14)$$

where,

$$z = \frac{x}{2\sqrt{\alpha \tau}}$$

where $erf\left(\dfrac{x}{2\sqrt{\alpha\tau}}\right)$ is known as *Gaussian error function* and is defined by

$$erf\left[\dfrac{x}{2\sqrt{\alpha\tau}}\right]erf(z) = \dfrac{2}{\sqrt{\pi}}\int_0^z e^{-\eta^2}\,d\eta \qquad\qquad ...(4.15)$$

with $erf(0) = 0$, $erf(\infty) = 1$. Table 4.1 shows a few representative values of $erf(z)$. Suitable values of error functions may also be obtained from Fig. 4.15.

Fig. 4.15. Gauss's error integral.

Table 4.1. The Error Function

$$erf(z) = \dfrac{2}{\sqrt{\pi}}\int_0^z e^{-\eta^2}\,d\eta \quad \text{where } z = \dfrac{x}{2\sqrt{\alpha\tau}}$$

z	erf (z)	z	erf (z)
0.00	0.0000	0.40	0.4284
0.02	0.0225	0.42	0.4475
0.04	0.0451	0.44	0.4662
0.06	0.0676	0.46	0.4847
0.08	0.0901	0.48	0.5027
0.10	0.1125	0.50	0.5205
0.12	0.1348	0.55	0.5633
0.14	0.1569	0.60	0.6039
0.16	0.1709	0.65	0.6420
0.18	0.2009	0.70	0.6778
0.20	0.2227	0.75	0.7112
0.22	0.2443	0.80	0.7421
0.24	0.2657	0.85	0.7707
0.26	0.2869	0.90	0.7970
0.28	0.3079	0.95	0.8270
0.30	0.3286	1.0	0.8427
0.32	0.3491	1.05	0.8614
0.34	0.3694	1.10	0.8802
0.36	0.3893	1.15	0.8952
0.38	0.4090	1.20	0.9103

1.25	0.9221	1.85	0.9909
1.30	0.9340	1.90	0.9928
1.35	0.9431	1.95	0.9940
1.40	0.9523	2.00	0.9953
1.45	0.9592	2.10	0.9967
1.50	0.9661	2.20	0.9981
1.55	0.9712	2.30	0.9987
1.60	0.9763	2.40	0.9993
1.65	0.9800	2.50	0.9995
1.70	0.9838	2.60	0.9998
1.75	0.9864	3.00	1.0000
1.80	0.9891		

By insertion of definition of error function in eqn. (4.14), we get

$$t\,(x,\tau) = t_a + (t_i - t_a)\,\frac{2}{\sqrt{\pi}}\int_o^z e^{-\eta^2}\,d\eta$$

On differentiating the above equation, we obtain

$$\frac{\partial t}{\partial x} = \frac{t_i - t_a}{\sqrt{\pi\alpha\tau}}\,e^{[-x^2/(4\alpha\tau)]}$$

∴ The instantaneous heat flow rate at a given X-location within the semi-infinite body at a specified time is given by :

$$Q_i = -\,kA(t_i - t_a)\,\frac{e^{[-x^2/(4\alpha\tau)]}}{\sqrt{\pi\alpha\tau}} \qquad \text{...(4.16)}$$

By substituting the gradient $\left(\dfrac{\partial t}{\partial x}\right)$ in Fourier's law]

The heat flow rate at the surface ($x = 0$) is given by

$$Q_{surface} = -\,\frac{kA\,(t_i - t_a)}{\sqrt{\pi\alpha\tau}} \qquad \text{...(4.17)}$$

∴ Total heat flow rate, $\quad Q' = -\,\dfrac{kA\,(t_i - t_a)}{\sqrt{\pi\alpha}}\displaystyle\int_0^\tau \frac{1}{\sqrt{\tau}}\,d\tau$

$$= -\,kA\,(t_i - t_a)\,2\,\sqrt{\frac{\tau}{\pi\alpha}}$$

or, $\qquad Q' = -\,1.13\,kA\,(t_i - t_a)\,\sqrt{\dfrac{\tau}{\alpha}} \qquad \text{...(4.18)}$

The general criterion for the infinite solution to apply to a body of finite thickness (slab) subjected to one dimensional heat transfer is

$$\frac{L}{2\sqrt{\alpha\tau}} \geq 0.5 \qquad\qquad \text{(where, } L = \text{Thickness of the body)}$$

The temperature at the centre of cylinder or sphere of radius R, under similar conditions of heating or cooling, is given as follows :

$$\frac{t - t_a}{t_i - t_a} = erf\left(\frac{\alpha\tau}{R^2}\right) \qquad \text{...(4.19)}$$

For the cylindrical and spherical surfaces the values of function $erf\left(\dfrac{\alpha\tau}{R^2}\right)$ can be obtained from Fig. 4.16.

Penetration depth and penetration time :

'*Penetration depth' refers to the location of a point where the temperature change is within 1 percent of the change in the surface temperature.*

i.e.
$$\frac{t - t_a}{t_i - t_a} = 0.9$$

This corresponds to $\dfrac{x}{2\sqrt{\alpha\tau}} = 1.8$, from the table for Gaussian error integral.

Thus, the depth (d) to which the temperature perturbation at the surface has penetrated,

$$d = 3.6\sqrt{\alpha\tau}$$

'*Penetration time' is the time τ_p taken for a surface perturbation to be felt at that depth in the range of 1 percent. It is given by*

$$\frac{d}{2\sqrt{\alpha\tau_p}} = 1.8$$

or,
$$\tau_p = \frac{d^2}{13\alpha} \qquad \qquad ...(4.20)$$

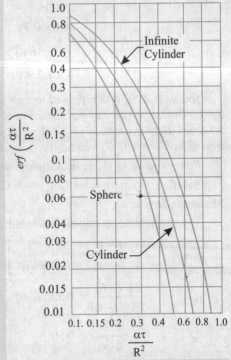

Fig. 4.16. Error integral for cylinders and spheres.

Example 4.20. *A steel ingot (large in size) heated uniformly to 745°C is hardened by quenching it in an oil bath maintained at 20°C. Determine the length of time required for the temperature to reach 595°C at a depth of 12 mm. The ingot may be approximated as a flat plate.*

For steel ingot take α (thermal diffusivity) $= 1.2 \times 10^{-5}$ m²/s

Solution. *Given :* $t_i = 745°C$, $t_a = 20°C$, $t = 595°C$, $x = 12$ mm $= 0.012$ m, $\alpha = 1.2 \times 10^{-5}$ m²/s

Time required, τ :

The temperature distribution at any time τ at a plane parallel to and at a distance x from the surface is given by :

$$\frac{t - t_a}{t_i - t_a} = erf\left[\frac{x}{2\sqrt{\alpha\tau}}\right]$$
$$...[Eqn. (4.14)]$$

or,
$$\frac{595 - 20}{745 - 20} = 0.79 = erf\left[\frac{x}{2\sqrt{\alpha\tau}}\right]$$

∴
$$\frac{x}{2\sqrt{\alpha\tau}} = 0.9 \qquad ...\text{From table}$$
4.1 or Fig. 4.15

or,
$$\frac{x^2}{4\alpha\tau} = (0.9)^2 - 0.81$$

Transient conditions occur in cooling and freezing of food.

or, $$\tau = \frac{x^2}{4\alpha \times 0.81}$$

$$= \frac{0.012^2}{4 \times 1.2 \times 10^{-5} \times 0.81} = 3.7\,s \quad \textbf{(Ans.)}$$

Example 4.21. *It is proposed to bury water pipes underground in wet soil which is initially at 5.4°C. The temperature of the surface of soil suddenly drops to – 6°C and remains at this value for 9.5 hours. Determine the minimum depth at which the pipes be laid if the surrounding soil temperature is to remain above 0°C (without water getting frozen). Assume the soil as semi-infinite solid.*

For wet soil take α (thermal diffusitivity) = 2.75 × 10⁻³ m²/h.

Solution. *Given :* $t_i = 5.4°C$, $t_a = -6°C$, $t = 0°C$, $\alpha = 2.75 \times 10^{-3}$ m²/h

Minimum Depth, x :

The temperature, at critical depth, will just reach 0°C after 9.5 hours,

Now, $$\frac{t - t_a}{t_i - t_a} = erf\left[\frac{x}{2\sqrt{\alpha\tau}}\right]$$

or, $$\frac{0 - (-6)}{5.4 - (-6)} = 0.526 = erf\left[\frac{x}{2\sqrt{\alpha\tau}}\right]$$

or, $$\frac{x}{2\sqrt{\alpha\tau}} \approx 0.50 \qquad \text{...From table 4.1 or Fig. 4.15}$$

or, $$x = 0.5 \times 2\sqrt{\alpha\tau}$$

or, $$x = 0.5 \times 2\sqrt{2.75 \times 10^{-3} \times 9.5} = \textbf{0.162 m} \quad \textbf{(Ans.)}$$

Example 4.22. *A 60 mm thick mild steel plate (α = 1.22 × 10⁻⁵ m²/s) is initially at a temperature of 30°C. It is suddenly exposed on one side to a fluid which causes the surface temperature to increase to and remain at 110°C. Determine :*

  (i)   *The maximum time that the slab be treated as a semi-infinite body;*

  (ii) *The temperature at the centre of the slab 1.5 minutes after the change in surface temperature.*

Solution. *Given :* $L = 60$ mm = 0.06 m, $\alpha = 1.22 \times 10^{-5}$ m²/s, $t_i = 30°C$, $t_a = 110°C$, $\tau = 1.5$ minutes = 90s.

(i) **The maximum time that the slab be treated as a semi-infinite body, τ_{max} :**

The general criterion for the infinite solution to apply to a body of finite thickness subjected to one-dimensional heat transfer is

$$\frac{L}{2\sqrt{\alpha\tau}} \geq 0.5 \qquad \text{(where, } L = \text{Thickness of the body)}$$

or, $$\frac{L}{2\sqrt{\alpha\tau_{max}}} = 0.5 \quad \text{or} \quad \frac{L^2}{4\alpha\tau_{max}} = 0.25$$

or, $$\tau_{max} = \frac{L^2}{4\alpha \times 0.25} = \frac{0.06^2}{4 \times 1.22 \times 10^{-5} \times 0.25} = \textbf{295.1 s} \quad \textbf{(Ans.)}$$

(ii) **The temperature at the centre of the slab, t :**

At the centre of the slab, x = 0.03 m; τ = 90s

$$\frac{t - t_a}{t_i - t_a} = erf\left[\frac{x}{2\sqrt{\alpha\tau}}\right]$$

or,
$$t = t_a + erf\left[\frac{x}{2\sqrt{\alpha\tau}}\right](t_i - t_a)$$

where,
$$erf\left[\frac{x}{2\sqrt{\alpha\tau}}\right] = erf\left[\frac{0.03}{2 \times \sqrt{1.22 \times 10^{-5} \times 90}}\right] = erf\,(0.453) \simeq 0.47$$

(From table 4.1)

∴
$$t = 110 + 0.47\,(30 - 110) = \textbf{72.4°C} \quad \textbf{(Ans.)}$$

Example 4.23. *The initial uniform temperature of a thick concrete wall ($\alpha = 1.6 \times 10^{-3}$ m²/s, $k = 0.94$ W/m°C) of a jet engine test cell is 25°C. The surface temperature of the wall suddenly rises to 340°C when the combination of exhaust gases from the turbojet and spray of cooling water occurs. Determine :*

(i) The temperature at a point 80 mm from the surface after 8 hours;

(ii) The instantaneous heat flow rate at the specified plane and at the surface itself at the instant mentioned at (i).

Use the solution for semi-infinite solid.

Solution. Given : $t_i = 25°C$, $t_a = 340°C$, $\alpha = 1.6 \times 10^{-3}$ m²/h, $k = 0.94$ W/m°C, $\tau = 8h$, $x = 80$ mm $= 0.08$ m.

(*i*) **The temperature at a point 0.08 m from the surface :**

$$\frac{t - t_a}{t_i - t_a} = erf\left[\frac{x}{2\sqrt{\alpha\tau}}\right]$$

or,
$$t = t_a + erf\left[\frac{x}{2\sqrt{\alpha\tau}}\right](t_i - t_a)$$

where,
$$erf\left[\frac{x}{2\sqrt{\alpha\tau}}\right] = erf\left[\frac{0.08}{2\sqrt{1.6 \times 10^{-3} \times 8}}\right] = erf\,(0.353) \simeq 0.37$$

∴
$$t = 340 + 0.37\,(25 - 340) = \textbf{223.45°C (Ans.)}$$

(*ii*) **The instantaneous heat flow rate, (Q_i) at the specified plane :**

$$Q_i = -kA\,(t_i - t_a)\frac{e^{[-x^2/(4\alpha\tau)]}}{\sqrt{\pi\alpha\tau}} \quad ...[Eqn.\ (4.16)]$$

$$= -0.94 \times 1 \times (25 - 340)\frac{e^{[-0.08^2/(4 \times 1.6 \times 10^{-3} \times 8)]}}{\sqrt{\pi \times 1.6 \times 10^{-3} \times 8}}$$

$$= -296.1 \times \frac{0.8825}{0.2005} = -\textbf{1303.08 W per m² of wall area (Ans.)}$$

The negative sign shows the *heat lost from the wall.*

Heat flow rate at the surface itself, $Q_{surface}$:

$$Q_{surface} = -\frac{kA\,(t_i - t_a)}{\sqrt{\pi\,\alpha\,\tau}} \quad ...[Eqn.\ (4.17)]$$

$$= -\frac{0.94 \times 1 \times (25 - 340)}{\sqrt{\pi \times 1.6 \times 10^{-3} \times 8}} = (-)\,\textbf{1476.6 W per m² of wall area (Ans.)}$$

Example 4.24. *The initial uniform temperature of a large mass of material ($\alpha = 0.42$ m²/h) is 120°C. The surface is suddenly exposed to and held permanently at 6°C. Calculate the time required for the temperature gradient at the surface to reach 400°C/m.*

Solution. $t_i = 120°C$, $t_a = 6°C$, $\alpha = 0.42$ m²/h

$\left(\dfrac{\partial t}{\partial x}\right)_{x=0}$ (temperature gradient at the surface) = 400°C/m

Time required, τ :

Heat flow rate at the surface ($x = 0$) is given by,

$$Q_{surface} = -\frac{kA(t_i - t_a)}{\sqrt{\pi \alpha \tau}} \qquad \qquad ...[Eqn.\ (4.17)]$$

or, $$-kA\left(\frac{\partial t}{\partial x}\right)_{x=0} = -\frac{kA(t_i - t_a)}{\sqrt{\pi \alpha \tau}}$$

or, $$\left(\frac{\partial t}{\partial x}\right)_{x=0} = \frac{t_i - t_a}{\sqrt{\pi \alpha \tau}}$$

Substituting the values, we obtain

$$400 = \frac{(120 - 6)}{\sqrt{\pi \times 0.42 \times \tau}}$$

or, $$\pi \times 0.42\ \tau = \left(\frac{120 - 6}{400}\right)^2 = 0.0812$$

or $$\tau = \frac{0.0812}{\pi \times 0.42} = 0.0615\ h = \mathbf{221.4\ s} \qquad \textbf{(Ans.)}$$

Example 4.25. *A motor car of mass 1600 kg travelling at 90 km/h, is brought to rest within a period of 9 seconds when the brakes are applied. The braking system consists of 4 brakes with each brake band of 360 cm² area, these press against steel drums of equivalent area. The brake lining and the drum surface ($k = 54$ W/m°C, $\alpha = 1.25 \times 10^{-5}$ m²/s) are at the same temperature and the heat generated during the stoppage action dissipates by flowing across drums. If the drum surface is treated as semi-infinite plane, calculate the maximum temperature rise.*

Solution. *Given :* $m = 1600$ kg, v (velocity) = 90 km/h, $\tau = 9$ s,

A (Area of 4 brake bands) = $4 \times 360 \times 10^{-4}$ m² or 0.144 m², $k = 54$ W/m°C, $\alpha = 1.25 \times 10^{-5}$ m²/s.

Kinetic energy is converted into heat energy after applying brakes.

Maximum temperature rise :

When the car comes to rest (after applying brakes), its knietic energy is converted into heat energy which is dissipated through the drums.

$$\text{Kinetic energy of the moving car} = \frac{1}{2}mv^2$$

$$= \frac{1}{2} \times 1600 \times \left(\frac{90 \times 1000}{60 \times 60}\right)^2$$

$$= 5 \times 10^5 \text{ J in 9 seconds}$$

∴ Heat flow rate $= \dfrac{5 \times 10^5}{9} = 0.555 \times 10^5$ J/s or W

This equals the instantaneous heat flow rate at the surface ($x = 0$), which is given by

$$(Q_i)_{surface} = \frac{-kA(t_i - t_a)}{\sqrt{\pi \alpha \tau}} = 0.5555 \times 10^5 \qquad ...[\text{Eqn. (4.17)}]$$

or, $\dfrac{54 \times 1.44 (t_i - t_a)}{\sqrt{\pi \times 1.25 \times 10^{-5} \times 9}} = 0.5555 \times 10^5$

or, $-(t_i - t_a) = \dfrac{0.5555 \times 10^5 \times \sqrt{\pi \times 1.25 \times 10^{-5} \times 9}}{54 \times 0.144} = 134.3$

or, $t_a - t_i = 134.3°C$

Hence, maximum temperature rise = **134.3°C (Ans.)**

Example 4.26. *A copper cylinder ($\alpha = 1.12 \times 10^{-4} m^2/s$), 600 mm in diameter and 750 mm in length, is initially at a uniform temperature of 20°C. When the cylinder is exposed to hot flue gases, its surface temperature suddenly increases to 480°C. Calculate :*

(i) The temperature at the centre of cylinder 3 minutes after the operation of change in surface temperature;

(ii) Time required to attain a temperature of 350°C.

Assume the cylinder as semi-infinite solid.

Solution. *Given :* $R = \dfrac{600}{2} = 300$ mm or 0.3m; $\alpha = 1.12 \times 10^{-4}$ m²/s; $t_i = 20°C$; $t_a = 480°C$; $t = 350°C$; $\tau = 3 \times 60 = 180$ s.

(i) The temperature at the centre of cylinder, t :

The temperature distribution at the centre of cylinder is expressed as

$$\frac{t - t_a}{t_i - t_a} = erf\left(\frac{\alpha \tau}{R^2}\right) \qquad ...[\text{Eqn. (4.19)}]$$

where, $erf\left(\dfrac{\alpha \tau}{R^2}\right) = erf\left(\dfrac{1.12 \times 10^{-4} \times 180}{0.3^2}\right)$

$$= erf(0.224) \approx 0.32 \qquad (\text{From Fig. 4.16})$$

Substituting the values, we obtain

$$\frac{t - 480}{20 - 480} = 0.32$$

or, $t = 480 + 0.32(20 - 480)$

$$= \textbf{332.8°C (Ans.)}$$

(*ii*) **Time required to attain a temperature of 350°C, *t*:**

Since, $t = 350°C$, hence

$$\frac{350 - 480}{20 - 480} = erf\left(\frac{\alpha\tau}{R^2}\right)$$

$$0.2826 = erf\left(\frac{\alpha\tau}{R^2}\right)$$

$\therefore$

$$\frac{\alpha\tau}{R^2} \simeq 0.23$$

or,

$$\tau = \frac{0.23 \times R^2}{\alpha}$$

$$= \frac{0.23 \times 0.3^2}{1.12 \times 10^{-4}} = 184.8 \text{ s} \quad \text{(Ans.)}$$

4.6. SYSTEMS WITH PERIODIC VARIATION OF SURFACE TEMPERATURE

The periodic type of heat flow occurs in cyclic generators, in reciprocating I.C. engines and in the earth as the result of daily cycle of the sun. These periodic changes, in general, are not simply sinusoidal but rather complex. However, these comoplex changes can be approximated by a number of sinusoidal components.

Let us consider a thick plane wall (one-dimensional case) whose surface temperature alters according to a sine function as shown in Fig. 4.17. The surface temperature oscillates about the mean temperature level t_m according to the following relation :

$$\theta_{s,\tau} = \theta_{s,a} \sin(2\pi n\tau)$$

where, $\theta_{s,\tau}$ = Excess over the mean temperature $(= t_{s,\tau} - t_m)$;

$\theta_{s,a}$ = Amplitude of temperature excess, *i.e.*, the maximum temperature excess at the surface;

n = Frequency of temperature wave.

The temperature excess at any depth x and time τ can be expressed by the relation,

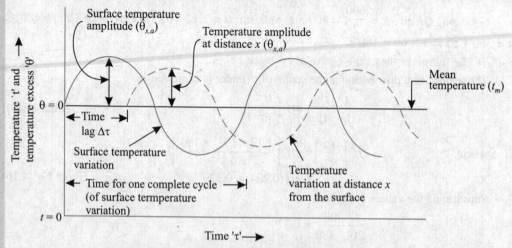

Fig. 4.17. Temperature curves for periodic variation of surface temperature.

$$\theta_{x,\tau} = \theta_{s,a} \exp\left[- x \sqrt{\pi n / \alpha}\right] \sin\left[2\pi n\tau - x\sqrt{\frac{\pi n}{\alpha}}\right] \qquad \text{...(4.21)}$$

The temperature excess, at the surface ($x = 0$), becomes zero at $\tau = 0$. But at any depth, $x > 0$, a

time $\left[\left(\dfrac{x}{2}\right)\left(\dfrac{1}{\sqrt{\alpha \pi n}}\right)\right]$ would elapse before the temperature excess $\theta_{x,\tau}$ becomes zero. The *time interval*

between the two instant is called the **time lag.**

The time lag $\quad \Delta\tau = \dfrac{x}{2}\sqrt{\dfrac{1}{\alpha \pi n}}$ ...(4.22)

At depth x, the temperature amplitude ($\theta_{x,a}$) is given by

$$\theta_{x,a} = \theta_{s,a}\, \exp\left[-x\sqrt{\dfrac{\pi n}{\alpha}}\right]$$ ...(4.23)

The above relations indicate the following facts :

1. At any depth, $x > 0$, the amplitude (maximum value) *occurs late* and is *smaller* than that at the surface ($x = 0$).

2. The amplitude of temperature oscillation *decreases* with *increasing depth*. (Therefore, the amplitude becomes negligibly small at a particular depth inside the solid and consequently a solid thicker than this particular depth is not of any importance as far as variation in temperature is concerned).

3. With *increasing value of frequency, time lag and the amplitude reduce.*

4. Increase in diffusivity α decreases the time lag but keeps the amplitude large.

5. The amplitude of temperature depends upon depth x as well as the factor $\sqrt{\dfrac{n}{\alpha}}$. Thus, if $\sqrt{\dfrac{n}{\alpha}}$ is large, eqn. (4.23) holds good for thin solid rods also.

Example 4.27. *During periodic heating and cooling of a thick brick wall, the wall temperature varies sinusoidally. The surface temperature ranges from 30°C to 80°C during a period of 24 hours. Determine the time lag of the temperature wave corresponding to a point located at 300 mm from the wall surface.*

The properties of the wall material are : $\rho = 1610\ kg/m^3$, $k = 0.65\ W/m°C$; $c = 440\ J/kg°C$.

Soltion. *Given :* $x = 300$ mm $= 0.3$ m, $\rho = 1610$ kg/m^3, $k = 0.65$ W/m°C, $c = 440$ J/kg°C,

$n = \dfrac{1}{24} = 0.04167/h$

Time lag $\Delta\tau$:

$$\Delta\tau = \dfrac{x}{2}\sqrt{\dfrac{1}{\alpha \pi n}}$$ ...[Eqn. (4.22)]

where, $\quad \alpha = \dfrac{k}{\rho c} = \dfrac{0.65}{1610 \times 440} = 9.176 \times 10^{-7}\ m^2/s$ or $0.0033\ m^2 h$

$\therefore \quad \Delta\tau = \dfrac{0.3}{2} \times \sqrt{\dfrac{1}{0.0033 \times \pi \times 0.04167}} = \textbf{7.2 h} \quad \textbf{(Ans.)}$

Example 4.28. *A single cylinder ($\alpha = 0.044\ m^2/h$ for cylinder material) two-stroke I.C. engine operates at 1400 r.p.m. Calculate the depth where the temperature wave due to variation of cylinder temperature is damped to 2% of its surface value.*

Solution. *Given :* $\alpha = 0.044$ m^2/h, $n = 1400 \times 60 = 84000/h$

The amplitude of temperature excess, at any depth x, is given by

$$\theta_{x,a} = \theta_{s,a}\, \exp\left[-x\sqrt{\dfrac{\pi n}{\alpha}}\right]$$ ...[Eqn. (4.23)]

Two stroke IC engine

or,
$$\frac{\theta_{x,a}}{\theta_{s,a}} = \exp\left[-x\sqrt{\frac{\pi n}{\alpha}}\right]$$

or,
$$\frac{2}{100} = \exp\left[-x\sqrt{\frac{\pi \times 84000}{0.044}}\right] = e^{-2449x} = \frac{1}{e^{2449x}}$$

or,
$$e^{2449x} = 50 \text{ or } 2449x = \ln 50 = 3.912$$

or,
$$x = \frac{3.912}{2449} = 0.001597 \text{ m or } \textbf{1.597 mm} \quad \textbf{(Ans.)}$$

4.7. TRANSIENT CONDUCTION WITH GIVEN TEMPERATURE DISTRIBUTION

The temperature distribution at some instant of time, in some situations, is known for the one-dimensional transient heat conduction through a solid. The known temperature distribution may be expressed in the form of polynomials : $t = a - bx + cx^2 + dx^3 - ex^4$ where a, b, c, d and e are the known coefficients. By using such distribution, the one-dimensional transient heat conduction problem can be solved.

Example 4.29. *The temperature distribution across a large concrete slab 500 mm thick heated from one side as measured by thermocouples approximates to the following relation;*

$$t = 120 - 100\,x + 24\,x^2 + 40\,x^3 - 30\,x^4$$

where t is in °C and x is in metres. Considering an area of 4 m², calculate :

(i)   The heat entering and leaving the slab in unit time;

(ii) The heat energy stored in unit time;

(iii) The rate of temperature change at both sides of the slab;

(iv) The point where the rate of heating or cooling is maximum.

The properties for concrete are : $k = 1.20$ W/m°C, $\alpha = 1.77 \times 10^{-3}$ m²/h

Solution. *Given :* $A = 4\text{m}^2$, $x = 500$ mm $= 0.5$ m, $k = 1.22$ W/m°C, $\alpha = 1.77 \times 10^{-3}$ m²/h

$t = 120 - 100x + 24x^2 + 40x^3 - 30x^4$ ...Temperature distribution polynomial

$$\frac{dt}{dx} = -100 + 48\,x + 120\,x^2 - 120\,x^3$$

$$\frac{d^2 t}{dx^2} = 48 + 240\, x - 360\, x^2$$

(*i*) The heat entering and leaving the slab in unit time :

Heat entering the slab, $\quad Q_{in} = -\, kA \left[\dfrac{dt}{dx}\right]_{x=0}$

$$= (-1.20 \times 5)\,(-100) = \mathbf{600\ W\ (Ans.)}$$

Heat leaving the slab, $\quad Q_{out} = -\, kA \left(\dfrac{dt}{dx}\right)_{x=0.5}$

$$= (-1.20 \times 5)\,(-100 + 48 \times 0.5 + 120 \times 0.5^2 - 120 \times 0.5^3)$$

$$= (-6.0)\,(-100 + 24 + 30 - 15) = \mathbf{366W\ (Ans.)}$$

(*ii*) The heat energy stored in unit time :

$$\text{Rate of heat storage} = Q_{in} - Q_{out}$$

$$= 600 - 366 = \mathbf{234\ W\ (Ans.)}$$

(*iii*) The rate of temperature change at both sides of the slab :

Rate of temperature change is given by

$$\frac{dt}{d\tau} = \alpha\, \frac{d^2 t}{dx^2}$$

$$= \alpha\,(48 + 240\, x - 360\, x^2)$$

$\therefore \qquad \left(\dfrac{dt}{d\tau}\right)_{x=0} = 1.77 \times 10^{-3}\,(48) = \mathbf{0.08496^\circ C/h\ (Ans.)}$

and, $\qquad \left(\dfrac{dt}{d\tau}\right)_{x=0.5} = 1.77 \times 10^{-3}\,(48 + 240 \times 0.5 - 360 \times 0.5^2)$

$$= \mathbf{1.3806^\circ C/h} \quad \textbf{(Ans.)}$$

(*iv*) The point where the rate of heating or cooling is maximum, *x* :

For the rate of heating or cooling to be maximum

$$\frac{d}{dx}\left(\frac{dt}{d\tau}\right) = 0$$

or, $\qquad \dfrac{d}{dx}\left[\alpha\,\dfrac{d^2 t}{dx^2}\right] = 0$

or, $\qquad \dfrac{d^3 t}{dx^3} = 0$

or, $\qquad 240 - 720\, x = 0$

$\therefore \qquad x = \dfrac{240}{720} = \mathbf{0.333\ m\ (Ans.)}$

TYPICAL EXAMPLES

Example 4.30. *A steel ball 100 mm in diameter and initially at 900°C is placed in air at 30°C.*
Find :

   (i) *Temperature of the ball after 30 seconds;*

   (ii) *The rate of cooling (°C/min) after 30 seconds.*

Take: $h = 20$ $W/m^2°C$; k *(steel)* $= 40$ $W/m°C$; ρ *(steel)* $= 7800$ kg/m^3; c *(steel)* $= 460$ $J/kg°C$.

(M.U.)

Solution: *Given* : $R = \dfrac{100}{2} = 50$ mm $= 0.05$ m; $t_i = 900°C$; $t_a = 30°C$; $h = 20W/m^2 °C$; k (steel) $= 40$ W/m°C; ρ (steel) $= 7800$ kg/m³; c (steel) $= 460$ J/kg°C; $\tau = 30$s.

(*i*) **Temperature of ball after 30 seconds, t :**

Characteristic length $\qquad L_c = \dfrac{V}{A_s} = \dfrac{\frac{4}{3}\pi R^3}{4\pi R^2} = \dfrac{R}{3} = \dfrac{0.05}{3} = 0.01667$ m

Biot number, $\qquad B_i = \dfrac{h\,L_c}{k} = \dfrac{20 \times 0.01667}{40} = 0.008335$

Since B_i is less than 0.1, hence lumped capacitance method (Newtonian heating or cooling) may be applied for the solution of the problem.

The time versus temperature distribution is given by (Eqn. 4.4)

$$\frac{t - t_a}{t_i - t_a} = \exp\left[-\frac{hA_s}{\rho Vc}\,\tau\right] \qquad\qquad ...(1)$$

Now $\qquad \dfrac{hA_s}{\rho Vc}\,\tau = \left(\dfrac{h}{\rho c}\right)\left(\dfrac{A_s}{V}\right)\tau = \left(\dfrac{20}{7800 \times 460}\right)\left(\dfrac{1}{0.01667}\right)(30) = 0.01$

$\therefore \qquad \dfrac{t - 30}{900 - 30} = e^{-0.01} = \dfrac{1}{e^{0.01}} = 0.99$

or, $\qquad\qquad\qquad t = 30 + 0.99\,(900 - 30) = \mathbf{891.3°C}$ **(Ans.)**

(*ii*) **The rate of cooling (°C/min) after 30 seconds :**

The rate of cooling means we have to find out $\dfrac{dt}{d\tau}$ at the required time.

Now differentiating eqn. (1), we get

$$\frac{1}{t_i - t_a} \times \frac{dt}{d\tau} = -\left(\frac{hA_s}{\rho Vc}\right)\exp\left[-\frac{hA_s}{\rho Vc}\,\tau\right]$$

Now substituting the proper values in the above equation, we have

$$\frac{1}{(900 - 30)} \cdot \frac{dt}{d\tau} = -\left(\frac{20}{7800 \times 460} \times \frac{1}{0.01667}\right) \times 0.99 = -3.31 \times 10^{-4}$$

$\therefore \qquad\qquad \dfrac{dt}{d\tau} = (900 - 30)\,(-3.31 \times 10^{-4}) = -0.288°C/s$

or, $\qquad\qquad \dfrac{dt}{d\tau} = -0.288 \times 60 = \mathbf{-17.28°C/min}$ **(Ans.)**

Example 4.31. *A thin copper plate 20 mm thick is initially at 150°C. One surface is in contact with water at 30°C ($h_w = 100$ $W/m^2°C$) and other surface is exposed to air at 30°C ($h_a = 20$ $W/m^2°C$). Determine the time required to cool the plate to 90°C.*

Take the following properties of the copper :

$$\rho = 8800 \text{ } kg/m^3, \quad c = 400 \text{ } J/kg°C \text{ and } k = 360 \text{ } W/m°C$$

Solution. *Given* : $L = 20$ mm $= 0.02$ m; $t_i = 150°C$; $t_a = 30°C$; $h_w = 100$ W/m² °C; $h_a = 20$ W/m² °C; $t = 90°C$; $\rho = 8800$ kg/m³; $c = 400$ J/kg°C; $k = 360$ W/m°C.

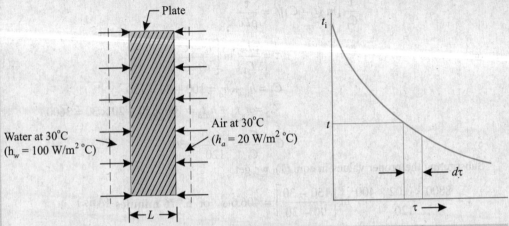

Fig. 4.18.

Time required to cool the plate, τ :

Biot number,
$$B_i = \frac{h L_c}{k} = \frac{h\left(\dfrac{L}{2}\right)}{k} = \frac{100 \times (0.02/2)}{360} = 0.00277$$

As $B_i < 0.1$, internal resistance can be neglected and lumped capacitance method may be applied for the solution of the problem.

The basic heat transfer equation can be written as,

$$dQ = -mc\, \frac{dt}{d\tau} = h_w\, A_s\, (t - t_w) + h_a\, A_s\, (t - t_a)$$

$$= A_s\, [h_w\, (t - t_w) + h_a\, (t - t_a)]$$

where, t_w and t_a are temperatures of water and air respectively and they are not changing with time.

$\therefore$
$$-(\rho)\, (A_s L)\, (c)\, \left(\frac{dt}{d\tau}\right) = A_s\, [h_w\, (t - t_w) + h_a\, (t - t_a)]$$

or,
$$-\rho L c\, \frac{dt}{d\tau} = [t\, (h_w + h_a) - (h_w\, t_w + h_a\, t_a)]$$

or,
$$\frac{dt}{t\, (h_w + h_a) - [h_w\, t_w + h_a\, t_a)]} = -\frac{d\tau}{\rho L c}$$

or,
$$\frac{dt}{C_1 t - C_2} = -\frac{d\tau}{\rho L c}$$

where
$$C_1 = h_w + h_a \text{ and } C_2 = h_w t_w + h_a t_a$$

$\therefore$
$$\frac{1}{C_1} = \int \frac{dt}{t - \dfrac{C_2}{C_1}} = -\frac{d\tau}{\rho L c}$$

or,
$$\frac{1}{C_1} = \int_{t_i}^{t} \frac{dt}{t - C} = -\int_0^{\tau} \frac{d\tau}{\rho L c} \qquad \text{where } C = \frac{C_2}{C_1}$$

or,
$$\frac{1}{C_1}\, [\ln\, (t - C)]_{t_i}^{t} = -\frac{\tau}{\rho V c}$$

$$\frac{1}{C_1} \left[\ln (t - C) \right]_t^{t_i} = \frac{\tau}{\rho L c}$$

or,

$$\tau = \frac{\rho L c}{C_1} \ln \left[\frac{t_i - C}{t - C} \right] \qquad \qquad ...(1)$$

$$C_1 = h_w + h_a = 100 + 20 = 120$$

$$C_2 = h_w t_w + h_a t_a = 100 \times 30 + 20 \times 30 = 3600$$

∴

$$C = \frac{C_2}{C_1} = \frac{3600}{120} = 30$$

Substituting the proper values in eqn. (1), we get

$$\tau = \frac{8800 \times 0.02 \times 400}{120} \ln \left[\frac{150 - 30}{90 - 30} \right] = 406.6 \ s \quad \text{or} \ \textbf{6.776 minutes} \ \textbf{(Ans.)}$$

Example 4.32. *Two infinite bodies of thermal conductivities k_1 and k_2, thermal diffusivities α_1 and α_2 are initially at temperatures t_1 and t_2 respectively. Each body has single plane surface and these surfaces are placed in contact with each other. Determine the conditions under which the contact surface remains at constant temperature t_s where $t_1 > t_s > t_2$.*

Solution. The rate of heat flow at a surface ($x = 0$) is given by

$$Q = \frac{-k A \Delta t}{\sqrt{\pi \alpha \tau}}$$

Heat received by each unit area of contact surface from the body at temperature t_1 is

$$Q_1 = \frac{-k_1 (t_1 - t_s)}{\sqrt{\pi \alpha_1 \tau}}$$

Heat lost by each unit area of contact surface to the body at temperature t_2 is

$$Q_2 = \frac{-k_2 (t_s - t_2)}{\sqrt{\pi \alpha_2 \tau}}$$

The contact surface will remain at a constant temperature if

$$\frac{-k_1 (t_1 - t_s)}{\sqrt{\pi \alpha_1 \tau}} = \frac{-k_2 (t_s - t_2)}{\sqrt{\pi \alpha_2 \tau}}$$

or,

$$\frac{k_1 (t_1 - t_s)}{\sqrt{\alpha_1}} = \frac{k_2 (t_s - t_2)}{\sqrt{\alpha_2}}$$

or,

$$k_1 (t_1 - t_s) \sqrt{\alpha_2} = k_2 (t_s - t_2) \sqrt{\alpha_1}$$

or,

$$k_1 t_1 \sqrt{\alpha_2} - k_1 t_s \sqrt{\alpha_2} = k_2 t_s \sqrt{\alpha_1} - k_2 t_2 \sqrt{\alpha_1}$$

or,

$$t_s (k_1 \sqrt{\alpha_2} + k_2 \sqrt{\alpha_1}) = k_1 t_1 \sqrt{\alpha_2} + k_2 t_2 \sqrt{\alpha_1}$$

or,

$$t_s = \frac{k_1 t_1 \sqrt{\alpha_2} + k_2 t_2 \sqrt{\alpha_1}}{k_1 \sqrt{\alpha_2} + k_2 \sqrt{\alpha_1}}$$

or,

$$t_s = \frac{(k_1 t_1 / \sqrt{\alpha_1}) + (k_2 t_2 / \sqrt{\alpha_2})}{(k_1 / \sqrt{\alpha_1}) + (k_2 / \sqrt{\alpha_2})} \qquad \textbf{(Ans.)}$$

(Dividing numerator and denomenator by $\sqrt{\alpha_1 \alpha_2}$).

HIGHLIGHTS

1. Conduction of heat in unsteady state refers to the transient conditions wherein heat flow and the temperature distribution at any point of the system vary continuously with time.

2. The process in which the internal resistance is assumed negligible in comparison with its surface resistance is called the *Newtonian* heating or cooling process.

$$\frac{t - t_a}{t_i - t_a} = \frac{\theta}{\theta_i} = \exp\left[-\frac{hA_s}{\rho Vc}\tau\right] \qquad ...(i)$$

where, ρ = Density of solid, kg/m^3

V = Volume of the body, m^3

c = Specific heat of the body, J/kg°C

h = Unit surface conductance, W/m^2 °C

A_s = Surface area of the body, m^2

t = Temperature of the body at any time, °C

t_a = Ambient temperature, °C, and

τ = Time, s.

Biot number, $\qquad B_i = \dfrac{h L_c}{k}$

Fourier number, $\qquad F_o = \dfrac{\alpha \tau}{L_c^2}$

where, $\qquad L_c$ = Characteristic length, and

$$\alpha = \left[\frac{k}{\rho c}\right] = \text{Thermal diffusivity of the solid.}$$

$$\frac{\theta}{\theta_i} = \frac{t - t_a}{t_i - t_a} = e^{-B_i F_o} \qquad ...(ii)$$

Instantaneous heat flow rate : $Q_i = -hA_s\,(t_i - t_a)\,e^{-B_i F_o}$ $\qquad ...(iii)$

Total or cumulative heat transfer : $Q' = \rho\, Vc\,(t_1 - t_a)\,[e^{-B_i F_o} - 1]$ $\qquad ...(iv)$

3. *Time constant and response of temperature measuring instruments :*

The quantity $\dfrac{\rho Vc}{hA_s}$ is called time constant (τ^*)

$$\frac{\theta}{\theta_i} = \frac{t - t_a}{t_i - t_a} = e^{-(\tau/\tau^*)}$$

The time required by a thermocouple to reach its 63.2 percent of the value of the initial temperature difference is called its *sensitivity*.

4. *Transient heat conduction in semi-infinite solids (h or $B_i \to \infty$) :*

The temperature distribution at any time τ at a plane parallel to and at a distance x from the surface is given by :

$$\frac{t - t_a}{t_i - t_a} = erf\left[\frac{x}{2\sqrt{\alpha \tau}}\right] \qquad ...(i)$$

where $erf\left[\dfrac{x}{2\sqrt{\alpha \tau}}\right]$ is known as '*Gaussian error function*'.

The instantaneous heat flow rate at a given X-location within the semi-infinite body at a specified time is given by

$$Q_i = -kA(t_i - t_a) \frac{e^{[-x^2/(4\alpha\tau)]}}{\sqrt{\pi\alpha\tau}} \qquad \text{...(ii)}$$

The heat flow rate at the surface $(x = 0)$ is given by

$$Q_{surface} = \frac{-kA(t_i - t_a)}{\sqrt{\pi\alpha\tau}} \qquad \text{...(iii)}$$

The heat flow rate (Q') is given by

$$Q' = -1.13\,kA(t_i - t_a)\sqrt{\frac{\tau}{\alpha}} \qquad \text{...(iv)}$$

THEORETICAL QUESTIONS

1. What is meant by transient heat conduction?
2. What is lumped capacity?
3. What are the assumptions for lumped capacity analysis?
4. What are Fourier and Biot numbers? What is the physical significance of these numbers?
5. Define a semi-infinite body.
6. What is an error function? Explain its significance in a semi-infinite body in transient state.
7. What are Heisler charts?
8. Explain the significance of Heisler charts in solving transient conduction problems.

UNSOLVED EXAMPLES

1. A copper slab ($\rho = 9000$ kg/m^3, $c = 380$ J/kg°C, $k = 370$ W/m°C) measuring 400 mm × 400 mm × 5 mm has a uniform temperature of 250°C. Its temperature is suddenly lowered to 30°C. Calculate the time required for the plate to reach the temperature of 90°C. Assume convective heat transfer coefficient as 90 W/m^2 °C. **(Ans.** $t = 123.75$ s)

2. An aluminium alloy plate 0.2 m^2 surface area (both sides), 4 mm thick and at 200°C is suddenly quenched into liquid oxygen which is at –183°C. Find the time required for the plate to reach the temperature of –70°C.

   Take : $\rho = 2700$ kg/m^3; $c_p = 890$ J/kg°C and $h = 500$ W/m^2 °C. **(Ans.** 23.45 s)

3. A sphere of 200 mm diameter made of cast iron initially at uniform temperature of 400°C is quenched into oil. The oil bath temperature is 40°C. If the temperature of sphere is 100°C after 5 minutes, find heat transfer coefficient on the surface of the sphere.

   Take : c_p (cast iron) = 0.32 kJ/kg°C; ρ (cast iron) = 7000 kg/m^3

   Neglect internal thermal resistance. **(Ans.** 134 kW/m^2 °C)

4. An average convective heat transfer coefficient for flow of 100°C air over a flat plate is measured by observing the temperature-time history of a 30 mm thick copper slab ($\rho = 9000$ kg/m^3, $c = 0.38$ kJ/kg°C, $k = 370$ W/m°C) exposed to 100°C air. In one test run, the initial temperature of the plate was 210°C, and in 5 minutes the temperature decreased by 40°C. Find the heat transfer coefficient for this case. Neglect internal thermal resistance. **(Ans.** 77.24 W/m^2 °C)

5. A cylindrical steel ingot 150 mm in diameter and 400 mm long passes through a heat treatment furnace which is 6 m in length. The ingot must reach a temperature of 850°C before it comes out of the furnace. The furnace gas is at 1280°C and ingot initial temperature is 100°C. What is the maximum speed with which the ingot should move in the furnace to attain the required temperature? The combined radiative and convective surface heat transfer coefficient is 100 W/m^2 °C. Take k (steel) = 45 W/m°C and α (thermal diffusivity) = 0.46 × 10^{-5} m^2/s.**(Ans.** 1.619 × 10^{-3} m/s)

6. A hot mild sphere (k = 42.5 W/m°C) having 12 mm diameter is planned to be cooled by an air flow at 27°C. The convective heat transfer coefficient is 114 W/m² °C. Determine the following :

   (*i*) Time required to cool the sphere from 540°C to 95°C;

   (*ii*) Instantaneous heat transfer rate 2 minutes after the start of cooling;

   (*iii*) Total energy transferred from the sphere during the first 2 minutes. Take mild steel properties as ρ = 7850 kg/m³; c = 475 J/kg°C; α = 0.043 m²/h.

   (**Ans.** (*i*) 2.104 min; (*ii*) 3.884 W; (*iii*) 1475.7 J)

7. The heat transfer coefficients for the flow of 30°C air over a 12.5 mm diameter sphere are measured for observing the temperature-time history of a copper ball of the same dimensions. The temperature of the copper ball (ρ = 8930 kg/m³, c = 0.375 kJ/kg°C) was measured by two thermocouples, one located at the centre and other near the surface. Both thermocouples registered within the accuracy of the recording instruments the same temperature at the given instant, on one test run, the initial temperature of the ball was 70°C and in 1.15 minutes the temperature decreased by 7°C. Calculate the convective heat transfer coefficient for this case. (**Ans.** 194.5 W/m² °C)

8. The temperature of an air stream flowing with a velocity of 3 m/s is measured by a copper-constantan thermocouple which may be approximated as a sphere of 3 mm in diameter. Initially the junction and air are at a temperature of 25°C. The air temperature suddenly changes to and is maintained at 200°C.

   (*i*) Determine the time required for the thermocouple to indicate a temperature of 150°C. Also determine the thermal time constant and temperature indicated by the thermocouple at that instant.

   (*ii*) Discuss the suitability of this thermocouple to measure unsteady state temperature of a fluid when the temperature variation in the fluid has a time period of 3 seconds.

   The thermocouple junction properties are : Density ρ = 8685 kg/m³; specific heat c = 383 J/kg°C; thermal conductivity (thermocouple) k = 29 W/m°C and convective coefficient h = 150 W/m² °C

   (**Ans.** 13.89s, 11.09s, 155.63°C)

9. A 50 mm thick large steel plate (k = 42.5 W/m°C, α = 0.043m²/h), initially at 425°C is suddenly exposed on both sides to an environment with convective heat transfer coefficient 285 W/m² °C and temperature 65°C. Determine the centre line temperature, and temperature inside the plate 12.5 mm from the midplane after 3 minutes.

10. A long cylindrical bar (k = 17.5 W/m°C, α = 0.0185 m²/h) of radius 75 mm comes out of oven at 815°C throughout and is cooled by quenching it in a large bath of 38°C coolant. The surface coefficient of heat transfer between the bar surface and the coolant is 175 W/m² °C. Determine : (*i*) The time taken by the shaft centre to reach 116°C; (*ii*) The surface temperature of the shaft when its centre temperature is 116°C. Also calculate the temperature gradient at the outside surface at the same instant of time. (**Ans.** (*i*) 2102s; (*ii*) 92.6°C, 546°C/m)

11. A concrete highway may reach a temperature of 55°C on a hot summer's day. Suppose that a stream of water is directed on the highway so that the surface temperature is suddenly lowered to 35°C. How long will it take to cool the concrete to 45°C at a depth of 50 mm from the surface? For concrete take α (thermal diffusivity) = 1.77 × 10⁻³ m²/h. (**Ans.** 1.51 h)

12. It is proposed to bury water pipes underground in wet soil which is initially at 4.5°C. The temperature of the surface of soil suddenly drops to –5°C and remains at this value for 10 hours. Determine the minimum depth at which the pipes be laid if the surrounding soil temperature is to remain above 0°C (without water getting frozen). Assume the soil as semi-infinite solid.

   For wet soil take α (thermal diffusivity) = 2.78 × 10⁻³ m²/h. (**Ans.** 0.167 m)

13. A 50 mm thick mild steel plate (α = 1.25 × 10⁻⁵ m²/s) is initially at a temperature of 40°C. It is suddenly exposed on one side to a fluid which causes the surface temperature to increase to and remain at 90°C. Determine :

   (*i*) The maximum time that the slab be treated as a semi-infinite body;

   (*ii*) The temperature at the centre of the slab one minute after the change in surface temperature.

   (**Ans.** (*i*) 200s, (*ii*) 66°C)

14. The initial uniform temperature of a thick concrete wall ($\alpha = 1.58 \times 10^{-3}$ m^2/h, $k = 0.937$ W/m°C) of a jet engine test cell is 21°C. The surface temperature of the wall suddenly rises to 315°C when the combination of exhaust gases from the turbojet and spray of cooling water occurs. Determine :

    (i) The temperature at a point 75 mm from the surface after 7.5 hours;

    (ii) The instantaneous heat flow rate at the specified plane and at the surface itself at the instant mentioned at (i).

    Use the solution for semi-infinite solid.   (**Ans.** (i) 206°C, (ii) – 1265.6 W per m^2 ; –1425 W per m^2)

15. The initial uniform temperature of a large mass of material ($\alpha = 0.41$ m^2/h) is 120°C. The surface of the material is suddenly exposed to and held permanently at 5°C. Calculate the time required for the temperature gradient at the surface to reach 350°C/m.   (**Ans.** 206s)

16. A motor car of mass 1500 kg travelling at 80 km/h is brought to rest within a period of 5 seconds when brakes are applied. The braking system consists of 4 brakes with each brake band of 350 cm^2 area; these press against steel drum of equivalent area. The brake lining and the drum surfaces ($k = 55$ W/m°C, $\alpha = 1.24 \times 0^{-5}$m^2/s) are at the same temperature and the heat generated during the stoppage action dissipates by flowing across drums. If the drum surface is treated as semi-infinite plate, calculate the maximum temperature rise.   (**Ans.** 134.11°C)

17. During periodic heating and cooling of a thick brick wall, the wall temperature varies sinusoidally. The surface temperature ranges from 25°C to 75°C during a period of 24 hours. Determine the time lag of the temperature wave corresponding to a point located at 250 mm from the wall surface. The properties of the wall material are: $\rho = 1620$ kg/m^3, $k = 0.62$ W/m°C, $c = 450$ J/kg°C.

                            (**Ans.** 6.24 h)

18. A single cylinder ($\alpha = 0.042$ m^2/h for cylinder material) two-stroke I.C. engine operates at 1500 r.p.m. Calculate the depth where the temperature wave due to variation of cylinder temperature is damped to 1% of its surface value.   (**Ans.** 1.775 mm)

19. The temperature distribution across a large concrete slab ($k = 1.2$ W/m°C, $\alpha = 1.77 \times 10^{-3}$ m^2/h) 500 mm thick heated from one side as measured by thermocouples approximates to the relation : $t = 60 - 50x + 12x^2 + 20x^3 - 15x^4$ where t is in °C and x is in metres. Considering an area of 5 m^2, compute :

    (i) The heat entering and leaving the slab in unit time. (ii) The heat energy stored in unit time, (iii) The rate of temperature change at both sides of the slab, and (iv) The point where the rate of heating or cooling is maximum.

                            (**Ans.** (i) 300 W, 183 W; (ii) 117 W; (iii) 42.48×10^{-3} °C/h, 69.03 × 10^{-3} °C/h; (iv) 0.33 m)

PART II

HEAT TRANSFER BY CONVECTION

Introduction to Hydrodynamics

5.1. INTRODUCTION

In heat transfer, the exchange of heat from a wall to a fluid or from a fluid to a wall is very important process (applicable in heat exchangers and performance of engines etc.). The rate of heat transfer by convection, between a solid boundary and a fluid, is given by

$$Q = h_a A(t_s - t_a) \qquad \ldots(5.1)$$

The Eqn. (5.1) is a definition of average unit thermal convective-conductance rather than a law of heat transfer by convection. The convective heat transfer coefficient is actually a complicated function of (i) the fluid flow, (ii) thermal properties of the fluid and (iii) geometry of the system. Its numerical value, in general, is not uniform over a surface, and depends also on the location where the fluid temperature is measured.

The relation given by Eqn. (5.1) is inadequate to explain the convective heat flow mechanism; therefore, a meaningful analysis which will eventually lead to a quantitative evaluation of the convective heat transfer coefficient must start with the study of the *dynamics of the fluid flow*.

5.2. IDEAL AND REAL FLUIDS

An **ideal fluid** is one which has *no viscosity* and *surface tension* and is *incompressible*. In true sense no such fluid exists in nature. However, fluids which have low viscosities such as water and air can be treated as ideal fluids under certain conditions. The assumption of ideal fluids helps in simplifying the mathematical analysis.

A **real practical fluid** is *one which has viscosity, surface tension and compressibility in addition to the density*. The real fluids are actually available in nature.

5.3. VISCOSITY

"*Viscosity*" may be defined as the *property of a fluid which determines its resistance to shearing stresses.* It is a measure of the internal fluid friction which causes resistance to flow. It is primarily *due to cohesion and molecular momentum exchange between fluid layers,* and as flow occurs, these effects appear as shearing stresses between the moving layers of fluid.

An *ideal fluid has no viscosity.* There is no fluid which can be classified as a perfectly ideal fluid. However, the fluids with very little viscosity are sometimes considered as ideal fluids.

Viscosity of fluids is due to *cohesion and interaction between particles.*

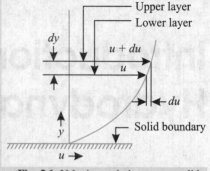

Fig. 5.1. Velocity variation near a solid boundary.

Refer to Fig. 5.1. When two layers of fluid, at a distance '*dy*' apart, move one over the other at different velocities, say *u* and *u* + *du*, the viscosity together with relative velocity causes a shear stress acting between the fluid layers. The top layer causes a shear stress on the adjacent lower layer while the lower layer causes a shear stress on the adjacent top layer. This shear stress is

Viscosity meter.

proportional to the rate of change of velocity with respect to *y*. It is denoted by τ (called Tau).

Mathematically, $$\tau \propto \frac{du}{dy}$$

or, $$\tau = \mu \cdot \frac{du}{dy} \qquad \qquad ...(5.1)$$

where, μ = Constant of proportionality and is known as *coefficient of dynamic viscosity or only viscosity,* and

$\dfrac{du}{dy}$ = Rate of shear stress or rate of shear deformation or velocity gradient.

From Fig. 5.1, we have $$\mu = \frac{\tau}{\left[\dfrac{du}{dy}\right]} \qquad \qquad ...(5.2)$$

Thus viscosity may also be defined as the *shear stress required to produce unit rate of shear strain.*

Units of viscosity :

In S.I. units N.s/m^2

In M.K.S. units kg$_f$.sec/m^2

$$\left[\because \mu = \frac{\text{force/area}}{(\text{length/time}) \times \dfrac{1}{\text{length}}} = \frac{\text{force/length}^2}{\dfrac{1}{\text{time}}} = \frac{\text{force} \times \text{time}}{(\text{length})^2} \right]$$

The unit of viscosity in C.G.S. is also called *poise* $= \dfrac{\text{dyne} - \text{sec}}{\text{cm}^2}$. One poise $= \dfrac{1}{10}$ N.s/m^2

Note: The viscosity of water at 20°C is $\dfrac{1}{100}$ poise or one centipoise.

Kinematic viscosity :

Kinematic viscosity is defined as the *ratio between the dynamic viscosity and density of fluid*. It is denoted by v (called nu).

Mathematically,
$$v = \frac{\text{Viscosity}}{\text{Density}} = \frac{\mu}{\rho} \qquad ...(5.3)$$

Units of kinematic viscosity :

In SI unit: m^2/s

In M.K.S. unit: m^2/sec.

In C.G.S. units the kinematic viscosity is also known as stoke (= cm^2/sec.)

One stoke = 10^{-4} m^2/s

Note: Centistoke means $\dfrac{1}{100}$ stoke.

Newton's law of viscosity :

This law states that the *shear stress* (τ) *on fluid element layer is directly proportional to the rate of shear strain*. The constant of proportionality is called the *coefficient of viscosity*.

Mathematically,
$$\tau = \mu \frac{du}{dy} \qquad ...(5.4)$$

The fluids which follow this law are known as *Newtonian fluids*.

5.4. CONTINUITY EQUATION IN CARTESIAN COORDINATES

Consider a fluid element (control volume) – parallelopiped with sides dx, dy and dz as shown in Fig. 5.2.

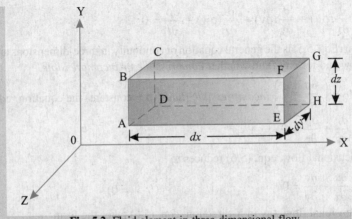

Fig. 5.2. Fluid element in three-dimensional flow.

Let, ρ = Mass density of the fluid at a particular instant, and

u, v, w = Components of velocity of flow entering the three faces of the parallelopiped.

Rate of mass of fluid entering the face ABCD (*i.e.* fluid influx).

$$= \rho \times \text{velocity in } X\text{-direction} \times \text{area of ABCD}$$

$$= \rho \, u \, dy \, dz \qquad \qquad ...(i)$$

Rate of mass of fluid leaving the face EFGH (*i.e.* fluid efflux)

$$= \rho \, u \, dy \, dz + \frac{\partial}{\partial x} (\rho \, u \, dy . dz) \, dx \qquad \qquad ...(ii)$$

The gain in mass per unit time due to flow in the X-direction is given by the difference between the fluid influx and fluid efflux.

$\therefore$ Mass accumulated per unit time due to flow in X-direction

$$= \rho u \, dy \, dz - \left[\rho u + \frac{\partial}{\partial x}(\rho u) dx \right] dy \, dz$$

$$= - \frac{\partial}{\partial x}(\rho u) \, dx \, dy \, dz \qquad \qquad ...(iii)$$

Similarly, the gain in fluid mass per unit time in the parallelopiped due to flow in Y and Z-direction

$$= - \frac{\partial}{\partial y} (\rho v) \, dy \, dz \text{ (in } Y\text{–direction)} \qquad \qquad ...(iv)$$

$$= - \frac{\partial}{\partial z} (\rho w) \, dx \, dy \, dz \text{ (in } Z\text{–direction)} \qquad \qquad ...(v)$$

The total (or net) gain in fluid mass per unit time for fluid flow along three coordinate axes

$$= - \left[\frac{\partial}{\partial x}(\rho u) + \frac{\partial}{\partial y}(\rho v) + \frac{\partial}{\partial z}(\rho w) \right] dx \, dy \, dz \qquad \qquad ...(vi)$$

Rate of change of mass of the parallelopiped (control volume)

$$= \frac{\partial}{\partial t}(\rho \, dx \, dy \, dz) \qquad \qquad ...(vii)$$

From eqns. (*vi*) and (*vii*), we get

$$= - \left[\frac{\partial}{\partial x}(\rho u) + \frac{\partial}{\partial y}(\rho v) + \frac{\partial}{\partial w}(\rho w) \right] dx \, dy \, dz = \frac{\partial}{\partial t}(\rho \, dx \, dy \, dz)$$

Simplification and rearrangement of terms would reduce the above expression to

$$\frac{\partial}{\partial x}(\rho u) + \frac{\partial}{\partial y}(\rho v) + \frac{\partial}{\partial z}(\rho w) + \frac{\partial \rho}{\partial t} = 0 \qquad \qquad ...(5.5)$$

This equation (Eqn. 5.5) is the general equation of continuity in three-dimensions and is applicable to *any type of flow* and for any fluid whether *compressible or incompressible*.

For steady flow $\left(\dfrac{\partial \rho}{dt} = 0 \right)$ *incompressible fluids* (ρ = constant) the equation reduces to

$$\frac{\partial u}{\partial x} + \frac{\partial v}{\partial y} + \frac{\partial w}{\partial z} = 0 \qquad \qquad ...(5.6)$$

For two dimensional flow, eqn. (5.6) reduces to

$$\frac{\partial u}{\partial x} + \frac{\partial v}{\partial y} = 0 \qquad \qquad (\because w = 0)$$

For one dimensional flow, say in X-direction, eqn. (5.6) takes the form

$$\frac{\partial u}{\partial x} = 0 \qquad\qquad (\because v = 0, w = 0)$$

Integrating with respect to x, we get

$$u = \text{constant} \qquad\qquad\qquad ...(5.7)$$

If the area of flow is a then the rate of flow is

$$Q = a.u = \text{constant for } steady\ flow.$$

5.5. CONTINUITY EQUATION IN POLAR COORDINATES

The equation of continuity in polar coordinates, for compressible fluids, may be written as follows:

$$\frac{1}{r}(\rho v_r) + \frac{\partial}{\partial r}(\rho v_r) + \frac{\partial}{r\partial\theta}(\rho v_\theta) = 0 \qquad\qquad ...(5.8)$$

or

$$\frac{v_r}{r} + \frac{\partial v_r}{\partial r} + \frac{\partial v_\theta}{r\partial\theta} = 0 \quad \text{(For incompressible flow)} \qquad ...(5.9)$$

where, v_r = Velocity component in radial direction, and

v_θ = Velocity component in tangential direction.

5.6. VELOCITY POTENTIAL AND STREAM FUNCTION

5.6.1. VELOCITY POTENTIAL

The **velocity potential** is *defined as a scalar function of space and time such that its negative derivative with respect to any direction gives the fluid velocity in that direction.* It is denoted by ϕ (phi). Thus, mathematically, the velocity potential is defined as:

$$\phi = f(x, y, z, t) \qquad\qquad\qquad \text{...for unsteady flow,}$$

and,

$$\phi = f(x, y, z) \qquad\qquad\qquad \text{...for steady flow; such that}$$

$$\left.\begin{aligned} u &= -\frac{\partial\phi}{\partial x} \\[4pt] v &= -\frac{\partial\phi}{\partial y} \\[4pt] w &= -\frac{\partial\phi}{\partial z} \end{aligned}\right\} \qquad\qquad ...(5.10)$$

where u, v and w are the components of velocity in the x, y and z directions respectively.

The *negative sign* signifies that ϕ *decreases with an increase in the values of x, y and z.* In other words it indicates that the flow is always in the direction of decreasing ϕ.

For *an incompressible steady* flow the continuity equation is

$$\frac{\partial u}{\partial x} + \frac{\partial v}{\partial y} + \frac{\partial w}{\partial z} = 0$$

By substituting the value of u, v and w in terms of ϕ from eqn. 5.17, we get

$$\frac{\partial}{\partial x}\left(-\frac{\partial\phi}{\partial x}\right) + \frac{\partial}{\partial y}\left(-\frac{\partial\phi}{\partial y}\right) + \frac{\partial}{\partial z}\left(-\frac{\partial\phi}{\partial z}\right) = 0$$

$$\frac{\partial^2\phi}{\partial x^2} + \frac{\partial^2\phi}{\partial y^2} + \frac{\partial^2\phi}{\partial z^2} = 0 \qquad\qquad ...(5.11)$$

This equation is known as **Laplace equation**.

Thus any function ϕ that satisfies the Laplace equation will correspond to some case of fluid flow.

The *rotational components* are given by

$$\omega_x = \frac{1}{2}\left(\frac{\partial w}{\partial y} - \frac{\partial v}{\partial z}\right)$$

$$\omega_y = \frac{1}{2}\left(\frac{\partial u}{\partial z} - \frac{\partial w}{\partial x}\right)$$

$$\omega_z = \frac{1}{2}\left(\frac{\partial v}{\partial x} - \frac{\partial u}{\partial y}\right)$$

By substituting the values of u, v and w in terms of ϕ from eqn. (5.10), we get

$$\omega_x = \frac{1}{2}\left[\frac{\partial}{\partial y}\left(-\frac{\partial\phi}{\partial z}\right) - \frac{\partial}{\partial z}\left(-\frac{\partial\phi}{\partial y}\right)\right]$$

$$= \frac{1}{2}\left[-\frac{\partial^2\phi}{\partial y\,\partial z} + \frac{\partial^2\phi}{\partial z\,\partial y}\right]$$

$$\omega_y = \frac{1}{2}\left[\frac{\partial}{\partial z}\left(-\frac{\partial\phi}{\partial x}\right) - \frac{\partial}{\partial x}\left(-\frac{\partial\phi}{\partial z}\right)\right]$$

$$= \frac{1}{2}\left[-\frac{\partial^2\phi}{\partial z\,\partial x} + \frac{\partial^2\phi}{\partial x\,\partial z}\right]$$

$$\omega_z = \frac{1}{2}\left[\frac{\partial}{\partial x}\left(-\frac{\partial\phi}{\partial y}\right) - \frac{\partial}{\partial y}\left(-\frac{\partial\phi}{\partial x}\right)\right] = \frac{1}{2}\left[-\frac{\partial^2\phi}{\partial x\,\partial y} + \frac{\partial^2\phi}{\partial y\,\partial x}\right]$$

However, if ϕ is a continuous function then

$$\frac{\partial^2\phi}{\partial y\,\partial z} = \frac{\partial^2\phi}{\partial z\,\partial y}; \frac{\partial^2\phi}{\partial z\,\partial x} = \frac{\partial^2\phi}{\partial x\,\partial z}; \text{ and } \frac{\partial^2\phi}{\partial x\,\partial y} = \frac{\partial^2\phi}{\partial y\,\partial x}$$

∴ $\omega_x = \omega_y = \omega_z = 0$ *i.e., the flow is irrotational.*

Thus *if velocity potential (ϕ) satisfies the Laplace equation, it represents the possible steady, incompressible, irrotational flow.* Often an *irrotational flow is known as* **potential flow.**

Equipotential line :

An *equipotential line is one along which velocity potential ϕ is constant.*

i.e., For equipotential line, ϕ = constant.

∴ $d\psi = 0$

But $\phi = f(x, y)$ for steady flow

∴ $d\phi = \frac{\partial\phi}{\partial x}dx + \frac{\partial\phi}{\partial y}dy$

But, $\frac{\partial\phi}{\partial x} = -u$ and $\frac{\partial\phi}{\partial y} = -v$

∴ $d\phi = -u\,dx - v\,dy = -(u\,dx + v\,dy)$

For equipotential line, $d\phi = 0$

or, $-(u\,dx + v\,dy) = 0$

or, $(u\,dx + v\,dy) = 0$

or, $\dfrac{dy}{dx} = -\dfrac{u}{v}$ ...(5.12)

where, $\dfrac{dy}{dx}$ = Slope of equipotential line.

5.6.2. STREAM FUNCTION

The **"stream function"** is defined as a scalar function of space and time, such that its partial derivative with respect to any direction gives the velocity component at right angles to this direction. It is denoted by ψ(psi).

In case of two-dimensional flow, the stream function may be defined mathematically as

$$\psi = f(x, y, t) \qquad \text{... for unsteady flow, and}$$
$$\psi = f(x, y) \qquad \text{... for steady flow; such that}$$

$$\left.\begin{array}{l} u = \dfrac{\partial\psi}{\partial y} \\[3mm] v = -\dfrac{\partial\psi}{\partial x} \end{array}\right\} \qquad\qquad ...(5.13)$$

For two dimensional flow the continuity equation is

$$\frac{\partial u}{\partial x} + \frac{\partial v}{\partial y} = 0$$

Substituting the values of u and v from eqn. (5.13), we get

$$\frac{\partial}{\partial x}\left(\frac{\partial\psi}{\partial y}\right) + \frac{\partial}{\partial y}\left(-\frac{\partial\psi}{\partial x}\right) = 0$$

$$\frac{\partial^2\psi}{\partial x\partial y} - \frac{\partial^2\psi}{\partial x\partial y} = 0$$

Hence **existence of ψ means a possible case of fluid flow.**

— The flow may be rotational or irrotational.

The rotational component ω_z is given by

$$\omega_z = \frac{1}{2}\left(\frac{\partial v}{\partial x} - \frac{\partial u}{\partial y}\right)$$

Substituting the values of u and v from eqn. (5.13), we get,

$$\omega_z = \frac{1}{2}\left[\frac{\partial}{\partial x}\left(\frac{\partial\psi}{\partial x}\right) - \frac{\partial}{\partial y}\left(-\frac{\partial\psi}{\partial y}\right)\right]$$

or,
$$\omega_z = \frac{1}{2}\left[\frac{\partial^2\psi}{\partial x^2} + \frac{\partial^2\psi}{\partial y^2}\right] \qquad\qquad ...(5.14)$$

This equation is known as **Poisson's equation.** For an irrotational flow since $\omega_z = 0$, eqn. (5.14) becomes

$$\frac{\partial^2\psi}{\partial x^2} + \frac{\partial^2\psi}{\partial y^2} = 0 \quad i.e., \ \Delta^2\psi = 0$$

which is the *Laplace equation in* ψ.

In the polar coordinates:

$$v_r = \frac{1}{r}\frac{\partial\psi}{\partial\theta}, \quad v_\theta = \frac{\partial\psi}{\partial r}$$

Let $\psi(x, y)$ represent the streamline L, Fig. 5.3. The $\psi + d\psi$ represents the adjacent streamline M. The velocity vector V perpendicular to the line AB has components u and v in the directions of X-axis and Y-axis respectively. From continuity consideration, we have,

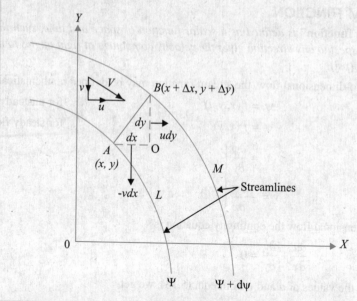

Fig. 5.3. Flow between two points and its relation to stream function.

Flow across AB = Flow across AO + flow across OB

$$Vds = -v\,dx + u\,dy$$

(The minus sign indicates that the velocity v is acting in the downward direction.)

$$Vds = \frac{\partial\psi}{\partial x}dx + \frac{\partial\psi}{\partial y}dy = d\psi \qquad \text{...(5.15)}$$

i.e.

$$dq = d\psi \qquad \text{...(5.16)}$$

Obviously, the *stream function* can also be defined as the *flux or flow rate between two streamlines.* The units of ψ are m^3/s; discharge per unit thickness of flow.

Properties of stream function :

The properties of stream function are:

1. On any streamline, ψ is constant everywhere.

   $$\begin{bmatrix} \psi = \text{constant, represents the family of streamlines} \\ \psi = \text{constant, is a streamline equation} \end{bmatrix}$$

2. If the flow is continuous, the flow around any path in the fluid is zero.
3. The rate of change of ψ with distance in arbitrary direction is proportional to the component of velocity normal to that direction.
4. The algebraic sum of stream functions for two incompressible flow patterns is the stream function for the flow resulting from the super-imposition of these patterns,

   i.e.,
   $$\frac{\partial\psi_1}{\partial s} + \frac{\partial\psi_2}{\partial s} = \frac{\partial(\psi_1 + \psi_2)}{\partial s} \qquad \text{...(5.17)}$$

Cauchy Riemann equations :

From the above discussion of velocity potential function and stream function we arrive at the following conclusions:

1. *Potential function (ϕ) exists only for irrotational flow.*
2. *Stream function (ψ) applies to both the rotational and irrotational flows* (which are steady and incompressible).
3. In case of *irrotational flow, both the stream function and velocity function satisfy Laplace*

equation and as such they are interchangeable.

For irrotational incompressible flow, the following relationship between ϕ and ψ holds good.

$$u = -\frac{\partial \phi}{\partial x} = \frac{\partial \psi}{\partial y}$$
$$v = -\frac{\partial \phi}{\partial y} = -\frac{\partial \psi}{\partial x}$$
...(5.18)

These equations, in hydrodynamics, are sometimes called *Cauchy Riemann equations*.

5.7. LAMINAR AND TURBULENT FLOWS

Reynolds Experiment

Osborne Reynolds in 1883, with the help of a simple experiment (discussed below), demonstrated the existence of the following two types of flows:

1. Laminar flow (Reynold number, $Re < 2000$)
2. Turbulent flow (Reynold number, $Re > 4000$)

(Re between 2000 and 4000 indicates transition from laminar to turbulent flow).

Apparatus

Refer Fig. 5.4, Reynolds experiment apparatus consisted essentially of the following:

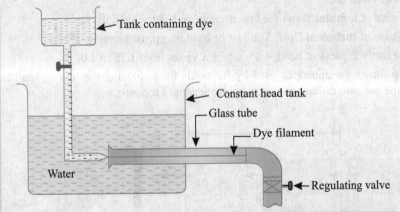

Fig. 5.4. Reynolds apparatus.

1. A constant head tank filled with water,
2. A small tank containing dye (sp. weight of dye same as that of water),
3. A horizontal glass tube provided with a bell mouthed entrance, and
4. A regulating valve.

Procedure followed :

The water was made to flow from the tank through the glass tube into the atmosphere and the velocity of flow was varied by adjusting valve. The liquid dye was introduced into the flow at the bell mouth through a small tube as shown in Fig. 5.4.

Observations made :

1. When the *velocity* of flow was *low*, the dye remained in the form of a *straight* and *stable filament* passing through

Kitchen sink has a laminar (non-turbulent) flow.

the glass tube so steadily that it scarcely seemed to be in motion. This was a case of **laminar flow** as shown in Fig. 5.5 (a).

2. With the increase of velocity a critical state was reached at which the dye filament showed irregularities and began to waver [see Fig. 5.5 (b)]. This shows that the flow is no longer a laminar one. This was a **transitional state**.

3. With further increase in velocity of flow the fluctuations in the filament of dye became more intense and ultimately the dye diffused over the entire cross-section of the tube, due to the intermingling of the particles of the flowing fluid. This was the case of a **turbulent flow** as shown in Fig. 5.5 (c).

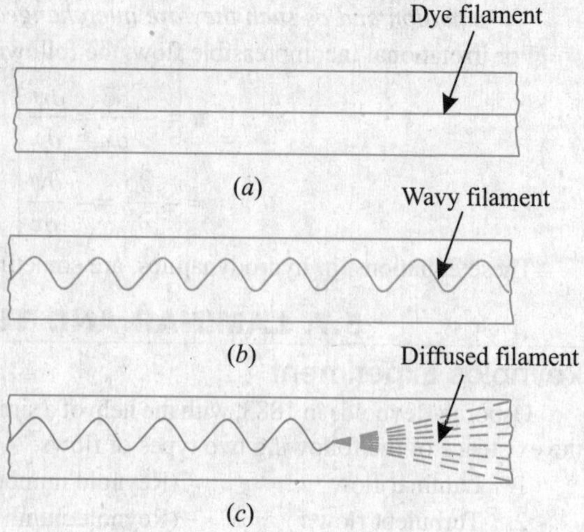

Fig. 5.5. Appearance of dye filament in (a) laminar flow, (b) transition, and (c) turbulent flows.

On the basis of his experiment Reynolds discovered that:

(i) In case of **laminar flow:** the loss of pressure head $\propto$ velocity

(ii) In case of **turbulent flow**: The loss of head is approximately $\propto V^2$

[More exactly the loss of head $\propto V^n$, where n varies from 1.75 to 2.0]

Fig. 5.6 shows the apparatus used by Reynolds for estimating the loss of head in a pipe by measuring the pressure difference over a known length of the pipe.

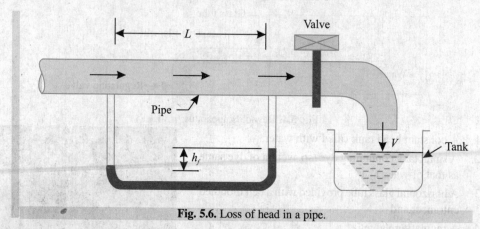

Fig. 5.6. Loss of head in a pipe.

(i) The velocity of water in the pipe was determined by measuring the volume of water (Q) collected in the tank over a known period of time

$$\left(V = \frac{Q}{A}, \text{where } A \text{ is the area of cross-section of the pipe} \right).$$

(ii) The velocity of flow (V) was changed and corresponding values of h_f (loss of head) were obtained.

(iii) A graph was plotted between V (velocity of flow) and h_f (loss of head). Such a graph is shown in Fig. 5.7. It may be seen from the graph that:

Turbulent flow.

(a) At *low velocities* the curve is a straight line, indicating that the h_f (loss of head) is directly proportional to velocity – the flow is **laminar** (or viscous).

(b) At *higher velocities* the curve is parabolic; in this range $h_f \propto V^n$, where the value of n lies between 1.75 to 2.0–the flow is **turbulent**.

(c) In the intermediate region, there is a transition zone. This is shown by *dotted line*.

Reynolds number :

Reynolds from his experiments found that the nature of flow in a *closed conduit* depends upon the following factors:

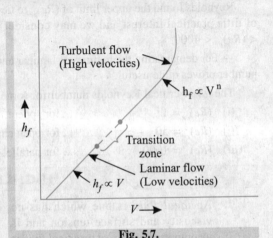

Fig. 5.7.

(i) Diameter of the pipe (D),

(ii) Density of the liquid (ρ),

(iii) Viscosity of the liquid (μ), and

(iv) Velocity of flow (V).

By combining the above variables Reynolds determined a non-dimensional quantity equal to $\dfrac{\rho V D}{\mu}$ which is known as *Reynolds number* (Re).

i.e. Reyonlds number
$$Re = \frac{\rho V D}{\mu}$$

$$\left(\text{In general case } D \text{ is replaced by } L, \text{known } as\ characteristic\ length \text{ and we have}, Re = \frac{\rho V L}{\mu} \right)$$

It may also be expressed as:

$$Re = \frac{VD}{v}$$

where,
$$v = \text{kinematic viscosity} \left(= \frac{\mu}{\rho} \right)$$

when, $Re < 2000$ ... the flow is *laminar* (or viscous)

$Re > 4000$ ... the flow is *turbulent*.

Re between 2000 and 4000   ... the flow is *unpredictable*.

Critical Reynolds number :

—All experiments agree that a lower limit of critical value of $(Re)_{cr}$ exists (though there appears to be no definite upper limit of the critical value of $(Re)_{cr}$ which characterizes full attainment of turbulence) and its value is approximately, 2000 (for circular pipe). This lower critical Reynolds number is of greater engineering importance as it defines the *limit below which all turbulence, no matter how severe, entering the flow from any source will eventually be damped out by viscous action.*

— It has been observed that the upper limit of critical Reynolds number $(Re)_{cr}$ depends upon the following factors:

(*i*)   Initial turbulence in the flow (approach),   (*ii*) Shape of the pipe entrance, and

(*iii*) Roughness of pipe.

Reynolds found the upper limit of $(Re)_{cr}$ to lie between $12000 < (Re)_{cr} < 14000$; these values are of little practical interest and we may consider the upper limit of $(Re)_{cr}$ to be defined by $2700 < (Re)_{cr} < 4000$.

— For demarcating the regimes of laminar and turbulent flows, the concept of critical Reynolds number proves quite useful.

The *lower* critical Reynolds number for some important cases are as under:

(*i*) $(Re)_{cr} = 1$ ... for sphere

(*ii*) $(Re)_{cr} = 50$ ... for open channels

(*iii*) $(Re)_{cr} = 1000$ ... for parallel plates.

HIGHLIGHTS

1. An *ideal fluid* is one which has no viscosity and surface tension and is incompressible. A *real practical fluid* is one which has viscosity, surface tension and compressibility in addition to the density

2. *Viscosity* may be defined as the property of a fluid which determines its resistance to shearing stresses. The viscosity may also be defined as the shear stress required to produce unit rate of shear strain.

3. Kinematic viscosity is defined as the ratio between the dynamic viscosity and density of fluid.

4. *Newton's law of viscosity* states that the shear stress (τ) on a fluid element layers is directly proportional to the rate of shear strain.

Mathematically, $\tau = \mu \dfrac{du}{dy}$

Viscosity tester.

5. *Continuity equation in cartesian coordinates* :

$$\frac{\partial}{\partial x}(\rho u) + \frac{\partial}{\partial x}(\rho v) + \frac{\partial}{\partial z}(\rho w) + \frac{\partial \rho}{\partial t} = 0$$

This equation is the general equation of continuity in three-dimensions and is applicable to any type of flow and for any fluid whether compressible or incompressible.

Continuity equation in polar coordinates :

$$\frac{1}{r}(\rho v_r) + \frac{\partial}{\partial r}(\rho v_r) + \frac{\partial}{r \cdot \partial \theta}(\rho v_\theta) = 0$$

where, v_r = Velocity component in radial radiation, and

v_θ = Velocity component in tangential direction.

6. The *velocity potential* (ϕ) is defined as a scalar function of space and time such that its negative derivative with respect to any direction gives the fluid velocity in that direction.

7. The *stream function* (ψ) is defined as a scalar function of space and time, such that its partial derivative with respect to any direction gives the velocity component at right angles to this direction.

8. *Reynolds experiment.*

When $Re < 2000$ ... the flow is laminar (or viscous)

$Re > 4000$ ... the flow is turbulent

Re between 2000 and 4000   ... the flow is unpredictable.

THEORETICAL QUESTIONS

1. Differentiate between an ideal fluid and a real fluid.
2. Define the term 'viscosity'. What is the relation between kinematic viscosity and dynamic viscosity?
3. What is Newton's law of viscosity?
4. Derive an expression for continuity equation in Cartesian coordinates.
5. Explain briefly the following:
   (*i*) Velocity potential   (*ii*) Stream function.
6. What is the difference between a laminar flow and a turbulent flow'?

CHAPTER

Dimensional Analysis

6

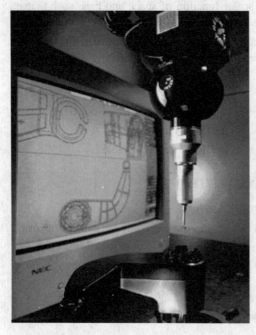

6.1. INTRODUCTION

Dimensional analysis is a mathematical technique which makes use of the study of the dimensions for solving several engineering problems. Each physical phenomenon can be expressed by an equation giving relationship between different quantities, such quantities are dimensional and non-dimensional. Dimensional analysis helps in determining a systematic arrangement of the variables in the physical relationship, combining dimensional variables to form non-dimensional parameters. It is based on the principle of *dimensional homogeneity* and uses the dimensions of relevant variables affecting the phenomenon.

Dimensional analysis has become an important tool for analysing fluid flow problems. It is specially useful in presenting experimental results in a concise form.

Uses of Dimensional Analysis:

The uses of dimensional analysis may be summarised as follows:

1. To test the dimensional homogeneity of any equation of fluid motion.

2. To derive rational formulae for a flow phenomenon.

3. To derive equations expressed in terms of non-dimensional parameters to show the relative significance of each parameter.

4. To plan model tests and present experimental results in a systematic manner; thus making it possible to analyse the complex fluid flow phenomenon.

6.2. DIMENSIONS

The various physical quantities used in fluid phenomenon can be expressed in terms of **fundamental quantities** or primary quantities. The fundamental quantities are *mass*, *length*, *time* and *temperature*, designated by the the the letters M, L, T, θ respectively. Temperature is specially useful in *compressible flow*. The quantities which are expressed in terms of the fundamental or primary quantities are called **derived** or **secondary quantities**, (*e.g.*, velocity, area, acceleration etc.). The expression for a derived quantity in terms of the primary quantities is called the **dimension** of the physical quantity.

The table 6.1 gives the dimensions of various quantities.

6.3. DIMENSIONAL HOMOGENEITY

A physical equation is the relationship between two or more physical quantities. Any *correct equation* expressing a physical relationship between quantities, *must be dimensionally homogeneous* (*according to Fourier's principle of dimensional homogeneity*) *and numerically equivalent. Dimensional homogeneity states that every term in an equation when reduced to fundamental dimensions must contain identical powers of each dimension.* A dimensionally homogeneous equation is applicable to all systems of units. In a dimensionally homogeneous equation, only quantities having the same dimensions can be added, subtracted or equated.

Applications of Dimensional Homogeneity :

The *principle of homogeneity* proves useful in the following ways:

1. It facilitates to determine the dimensions of a physical quantity.
2. It helps to check whether an equation of any physical phenomenon is dimensionally homogeneous or not.
3. It facilitates conversion of units from one system to another.
4. It provides a step towards dimensional analysis which is fruitfully employed to plan experiments and to present the results meaningfully.

Table 6.1: Quantities used in Fluid Mechanics and Heat Transfer and their Dimensions

S.No.	Quantity	Symbol	Units (SI)	Dimensions (M, L, T, θ system)
	(*a*) Fundamental Quantities			
1.	Mass	M	kg	M
2.	Length	L	m	L
3.	Time	T	s	T
4.	Temperature	θ	K	θ
	(*b*) Geometric Quantities			
5.	Area	A	m^2	L^2
6.	Volume	V	m^3	L^3
	(*c*) Kinematic Quantities			
7.	Linear velocity	u, V, U	m/s	LT^{-1}
8.	Angular velocity	ω	rad./s	T^{-1}
9.	Acceleration	a	m/s^2	LT^{-2}
10.	Angular acceleration	α	$rad./s^2$	T^{-2}

11.	Discharge	Q	m³/s	$L^3 T^{-1}$
12.	Kinematic viscosity	v	m²/s	$L^2 T^{-1}$
	(d) Dynamic Quantities			
13.	Force or resistance	F, R	N	MLT^{-2}
14.	Density	ρ	kg/m³	ML^{-3}
15.	Specific weight	w	N/m³	$ML^{-2} T^{-2}$
16.	Dynamic viscosity	μ	kg/ms	$ML^{-1} T^{-1}$
17.	Work, energy	W, E	Nm	$ML^2 T^{-2}$
18.	Power	P	Nm/s or J/s or W	$ML^2 T^{-3}$
	(e) Thermodynamic quantities			
19.	Heat	Q, H	J	$ML^2 T^{-2}$
20.	Thermal conductivity	k	W/m°C	$ML^{-3} \theta^{-1}$
21.	Specific heat	c_p, c_v	kJ/kg°C	$L^2 T^{-2} \theta^{-1}$
22.	Heat transfer coefficient	h, U	W/m²°C	$MT^{-3} \theta^{-1}$
23.	Gas constant	R	kJ/kg°C	$L^2 T^{-2} \theta^{-1}$
24.	Thermal diffusivity	α	m²/s	$L^2 T^{-1}$

6.4. METHODS OF DIMENSIONAL ANALYSIS

With the help of dimensional analysis the equation of a physical phenomenon can be developed in terms of dimensionless groups or parameters and thus reducing the number of variables. The methods of dimensional analysis are based on the Fourier's principle of homogeneity. Out of several methods of dimensional analysis, the following two methods will be discussed.

1. Rayleigh's method   2. Buckingham's π-method/theorem

6.4.1. RAYLEIGH'S METHOD

This method gives a special form of relationship among the dimensionless group, and has the *inherent drawback* that it *does not provide any information regarding the number of dimensionless groups to be obtained as a result of dimensional analysis.* Due to this reason this method has become *obsolete* and is *not favoured for use.*

Rayleigh's method is used for determining the expression for a variable which depends upon maximum three or four variables only. In case the number of independent variables become more than four, then it is very difficult to find the expression for the dependent variable.

In this method a functional relationship of some variables is expressed in the form of an exponential equation which must be dimensionally homogeneous. Thus if X is a variable which depends on $X_1, X_2, X_3, ... X_n$; the functional equation can be written as :

$$X = f(X_1, X_2, X_3, ... X_n) \qquad ...(6.1)$$

In the above equation X is a *dependent variable*, while $X_1, X_2, X_3, ... X_n$ are *independent variables*. A dependent variable is the one about which information is required while independent variables are those which govern the variation of dependent variable.

Equation (6.1) can also be written as :

$$X = C (X_1^a, X_2^b, X_3^c, ... X_b^n) \qquad ...(6.2)$$

where C is a constant and $a, b, c, ... n$ are the arbitrary powers. The values of $a, b, c, ... n$ are obtained by comparing the powers of the fundamental dimensions of both sides. Thus the expression is obtained for dependent variable.

Example 6.1. *Find an expression for the drag force on smooth sphere of diameter D, moving with a uniform velocity V in a fluid having density ρ and dynamic viscosity μ.*

Solution. The drag force F is a function of

(i) Diameter D,	(ii) Velocity V,
(iii) Fluid density ρ, and	(iv) Dynamic viscosity μ.

Mathematically, $\qquad F = f(D, V, \rho, \mu) \qquad$ or $\qquad F = C(D^a . V^b . \rho^c . \mu^d) \qquad$ ...(1)

where C is a non-dimensional constant.

Using M–L–T system the corresponding equation for dimensions is:

$$MLT^{-2} = [CL^a . (LT^{-1})^b . (ML^{-3})^c . (ML^{-1}T^{-1})^d]$$

For dimensional homogeneity the exponents of each dimension on both sides of the equation must be identical. Thus,

For	$M : 1 = c + d$	...(i)
For	$L : 1 = a + b - 3c - d$	...(ii)
For	$T : -2 = -b - d$	...(iii)

There are *four unknowns* (a, b, c, d) but *equations are three* in number. Therefore, it is not possible to find the values of a, b, c and d. However, three of them can be expressed in terms of fourth variable *which is most important*. There the role of viscosity is vital one and hence a, b, c are expressed in terms of d (*i.e.*, power to viscosity).

$$\therefore \qquad\qquad c = 1 - d \qquad\qquad\qquad \text{... from } (i)$$
$$b = 2 - d \qquad\qquad\qquad \text{... from } (iii)$$

Putting these values in (i), we get

$$a = 1 - b + 3c + d = 1 - 2 + d + 3(1 - d) + d$$
$$= 1 - 2 + d + 3 - 3d + d = 2 - d$$

Substituting these values of exponents in eqn. (1), we get

$$F = C[D^{2-d} . V^{2-d} . \rho^{1-d} . \mu^d]$$

$$= C[D^2 V^2 \rho (D^{-d} . V^{-d} . \rho^{-d} . \mu^d)] = C\left[\rho D^2 V^2 \left(\frac{\mu}{\rho VD}\right)^d\right]$$

$$= \rho D^2 V^2 \phi\left(\frac{\mu}{\rho VD}\right)$$

Example 6.2. *The efficiency η of a fan depends on the density ρ, the dynamic viscosity μ of the fluid, the angular velocity ω, diameter D of the rotor and the discharge Q. Express η in terms of dimensionless parameters.* **(AMIE)**

Solution. The efficiency η of a fan is a function of:

(i) Density ρ,	(ii) Viscosity μ,
(iii) Angular velocity ω,	(iv) Diameter D, and
(v) Discharge Q.	

Mathematically $\qquad\qquad \eta = f(\rho, \mu, \omega, D, Q)$

or $\qquad\qquad\qquad\qquad \eta = C(\rho^a, \mu^b, \omega^c, D^d, Q^e) \qquad$ ...(1)

where C is a non-dimensional constant.

Using M–L–T system, the corresponding equation for dimensions is:

$$M^{\circ}L^{\circ}T^{\circ} = C[(ML^{-3})^a (ML^{-1}T^{-1})^b (T^{-1})^c (L)^d (L^3T^{-1})^e]$$

For dimensional homogeneity the exponents of each dimension on both sides of the equation must be identical. Thus,

For $\qquad$ $M : 0 = a + b$

For $\qquad$ $L : 0 = -3a - b + d + 3e$

For $\qquad$ $T : 0 = -b - c - e$

There are *five variables* and we have only *three equations*. Experience has shown that recognized dimensionless groups appear if the exponents of D, ω and ρ are evaluated in terms of b and e (exponents of viscosity and discharge which are *more important*).

$\therefore$ $\qquad$ $a = -b; \; c = -(b + e);$

$$d = 3a + b - 3e = 3(-b) + b - 3e = -2b - 3e = -(2b + 3e)$$

Substituting these values of exponents in eqn. (1), we get

$$\eta = C(\rho^{-b} \cdot \mu^{b} \cdot \omega^{-(b+e)} \cdot D^{-(2b+3e)} \cdot Q^{e}) = C(\rho^{-b} \cdot \mu^{b} \cdot \omega^{-b} \cdot \omega^{-e} D^{-2b} \cdot D^{-3e} \cdot Q^{e})$$

$$= C\left[\left(\frac{\mu}{\rho \, \omega \, D^{2}}\right)^{b} \left(\frac{Q}{\omega \, D^{3}}\right)^{e}\right]$$

$$= \phi\left[\left(\frac{\mu}{\rho \, \omega \, D^{2}}\right), \left(\frac{Q}{\omega \, D^{3}}\right)\right]$$

6.4.2. BUCKINGHAM'S Π-METHOD/THEOREM

When a large number of physical variables are involved Rayleigh's method of dimensional analysis becomes *increasingly laborious* and *cumbersome*. Buckingham's method is an *improvement* over the Rayleigh's method. Buckingham designated the dimensionless group by the Greek capital letter π (Pi). It is, therefore, often called *Buckingham π-method*. The *advantage* of this method over Rayleigh's method is that it lets us know, in advance of the analysis, as to *how many dimensionless groups are to be expected*.

The Buckingham's π-theorem states as follows:

"If there are n variables (dependent and independent variables) in a dimensionally homogeneous equation and if these contain m fundamental dimensions (such as M, L, T, etc.), then the variables are arranged into (n-m) dimensionless terms. These dimensionless terms are called π-terms".

Mathematically, if any variable X_1, depends on independent variables, X_2, X_3, X_4, ... X_n; the functional equation may be written as

$$X_1 = f(X_2, X_3, X_4, ... X_n) \qquad\qquad ...(6.3)$$

Equation (6.3) can also be written as

$$f_1(X_1, X_2, X_3, ... X_n) = 0 \qquad\qquad ...(6.4)$$

It is a dimensionally homogeneous equation and contains n variables. If there are m fundamental dimensions, then according to Buckingham's π-theorem, it [Eqn. (6.4)] can be written in terms of number of π-terms (dimensionless groups) in which number of π-terms is equal to $(n - m)$. Hence Eqn. (6.4) becomes as

$$f_1(\pi_1, \pi_2, \pi_3, ... \pi_{n-m}) = 0 \qquad\qquad ...(6.5)$$

Each dimensionless π-term is formed by combining m variables out of the total n variables with *one of the remaining (n – m) variables i.e.*, each π-term contains $(m + 1)$ variables. These m variables which appear repeatedly in each of π-terms are consequently called *repeating variables* and are chosen from among the variables such that they together *involve all the fundamental dimensions and they themselves do not form a dimensionless parameter*. Let in the above case X_2, X_3 and X_4 are repeating variables if the fundamental dimensions m $(M, L, T) = 3$. Then each term is written as

$$\left.\begin{array}{l} \pi_1 = X_2^{a_1} \cdot X_3^{b_1} \cdot X_4^{c_1} \cdot X_1 \\[2mm] \pi_2 = X_2^{a_2} \cdot X_3^{b_2} \cdot X_4^{c_2} \cdot X_5 \\[2mm] \vdots \\ \vdots \\ \pi_{n-m} = (X_2^{a_n-m} \cdot X_3^{b_n-m} \cdot X_4^{c_n-m} \cdot X_n \end{array}\right\} \quad ...(6.6)$$

where a_1, b_1, c_1 ; a_2, b_2, c_2 etc. are the constants, which are determined, by considering dimensional homogeneity. These values are substituted in Eqn. (6.6) and values of $\pi_1, \pi_2, \pi_3, ... \pi_{n-m}$ are obtained. These values of π's are substituted in Eqn. (6.5). The final general equation for the phenomenon may then be obtained by expressing anyone of the π-terms as a function of the other as

$$\left.\begin{array}{l} \pi_1 = \phi\,(\pi_2, \pi_3, \pi_4, ... \pi_{n-m}) \\[2mm] \pi_2 = \phi\,(\pi_1, \pi_3, \pi_4, ... \pi_{n-m}) \end{array}\right\} \quad ...(6.7)$$

Selection of repeating variables :

The following points should be kept in view while selecting m repeating variables:

1. m repeating variables must contain *jointly* all the fundamental dimensions involved in the phenomenon. Usually the fundamental dimensions are M, L and T. However, if only two dimensions are involved, there will be 2 repeating variables and they must contain *together* the two dimensions involved.

2. The repeating variables *must not* form the non-dimensional parameters among themselves.

3. As far as possible, the dependent variable *should not* be selected as repeating variable.

4. No two repeating variables should have the same dimensions.

5. The repeating variables should be chosen in such a way that one variable contains **geometric property** (*e.g., length, l; diameter, d; height, H* etc.), other variable contains **flow property** (*e.g., velocity, V; acceleration* etc.) and third variable contains **fluid property** (*e.g., mass density,* ρ; *weight density, w, dynamic viscosity,* μ etc.).

The choice of repeating variables, in most of fluid mechanics problems, may be:

    (*i*) l, V, ρ (*ii*) d, V, ρ

    (*iii*) l, V, μ (*iv*) d, V, μ.

The **procedure for solving problem by Buckingham's π-theorem is out-lined in the Example 6.3 below:**

Example 6.3. *The resistance R experienced by a partially submerged body depends upon the velocity V, length of the body l, viscosity of the fluid* μ*, density of the fluid* ρ *and gravitational acceleration g. Obtain a dimensionless expression for R.*

Solution. Step 1. The resistance R is a function of:

    (*i*)   Velocity V,   (*ii*)   Length l,

    (*iii*)   Viscosity μ, and   (*iv*)   Density ρ,

    (*v*)   Gravitational acceleration g.

Mathematically, $R = f(V, l, \mu, \rho, g)$ ...(*i*)

or, $f_1\,(R, V, l, \mu, \rho, g) = 0$ ...(*ii*)

$\therefore$ Total number of variables, $n = 6$

$$\left.\begin{array}{l} m \text{ is obtained by writing dimensions of each variables as} \\[2mm] R = MLT^{-2}, V = LT^{-1}, \mu = ML^{-1}T^{-1}, \rho = ML^{-3}, g = LT^{-2}. \text{ Thus the} \\[2mm] \text{fundamental dimensions in the problem are } M, L, T \text{ and hence } m = 3. \end{array}\right\}$$

Number of dimension π-terms $= n - m = 6 - 3 = 3$

Thus three π-terms say π_1, π_2, and π_3 are formed.

The eqn. (*ii*) may be written as

$$f_1(\pi_1, \pi_2, \pi_3) = 0 \qquad \qquad ...(iii)$$

Step 2. *Selection of repeating variables*: Out of six variables R, V, l, μ, ρ, g three variables (as $m = 3$) are to be selected as *repeating variables*. R is a dependent variable and should *not* be selected as a repeating variable. Out of the remaining five variables one variable should have *geometric property*, second should have *flow property* and third one should have *fluid property*; these requirements are met by selecting l, V and ρ as *repeating variables*. The repeating variables themselves should not form a dimensionless term and must contain *jointly all fundamental dimensions equal to m i.e.*, 3 here. Dimensions of l, V and ρ are L, LT^{-1}, ML^{-3} and hence the three fundamental dimensions exist in l, V and ρ and also *no dimensionless group is formed by them*.

Step 3. Each π–term ($= m + 1$ variables) is written as given in eqn. (6.6), *i.e.*

$$\left. \begin{aligned} \pi_1 &= l^{a_1} \cdot V^{b_1} \cdot \rho^{c_1} \cdot R \\ \pi_2 &= l^{a_2} \cdot V^{b_2} \cdot \rho^{c_2} \cdot \mu \\ \pi_3 &= l^{a_3} \cdot V^{b_3} \cdot \rho^{c_3} \cdot g \end{aligned} \right\} \qquad ...(iv)$$

Step 4. Each π-term is solved by the *principle of dimensional homogeneity*, as follows:

π_1–term:

$$\pi_1 = l^{a_1} \cdot V^{b_1} \cdot \pi^{c_1} \cdot R$$

$$M^0 L^0 T^0 = L^{a_1} \cdot (LT^{-1})^{b_1} \cdot (ML^{-3})^{c_1} \cdot (MLT^{-2})$$

Equating the exponents of M, L and T respectively, we get

For M : $\qquad 0 = c_1 + 1$

For L : $\qquad 0 = a_1 + b_1 - 3c_1 + 1$

For T : $\qquad 0 = -b_1 - 2$

$\therefore \qquad c_1 = -1; b_1 = -2$

and $\qquad a_1 = -b_1 + 3c_1 - 1 = 2 - 3 - 1 = -2$

Substituting the values of a_1, b_1 and c_1 in π_1, we get

$\therefore \qquad \pi_1 = l^{-2} \cdot V^{-2} \cdot \rho^{-1} \cdot R = \dfrac{R}{l^2 V^2 \rho} \qquad ...(v)$

π_2–term:

$$\pi_2 = l^{a_2} \cdot V^{b_2} \cdot \rho^{c_2} \cdot \mu$$

$$M^0 L^0 T^0 = L^{a_2} \cdot (LT^{-1})^{b_2} \cdot (ML^{-3})^{c_2} \cdot (ML^{-1}T^{-1})$$

Equating the exponents of M, L and T respectively, we get

For M : $\qquad 0 = c_2 + 1$

For L : $\qquad 0 = a_2 + b_2 - 3c_2 - 1$

For T : $\qquad 0 = -b_2 - 1$

$\therefore \qquad c_2 = -1; b_2 = -1$

and, $\qquad a_2 = -b_2 + 3c_2 + 1 = 1 - 3 + 1 = -1$

Substituting the values of a_2, b_2 and c_2 in π_2, we get

$\therefore \qquad \pi_2 = l^{-1} \cdot V^{-1} \cdot \rho^{-1} \cdot \mu = \dfrac{\mu}{lV\rho}$

π_3–term:

$$\pi_3 = l^{a_3} \cdot V^{b_3} \cdot \rho^{c_3} \cdot g$$
$$M^0 L^0 T^0 = L^{a_3} \cdot (LT^{-1})^{b_3} \cdot (ML^{-3})^{c_3} \cdot (LT^{-2})$$

Equating the exponents of M, L and T respectively, we get

For M : $\qquad 0 = c_3$

For L : $\qquad 0 = a_3 + b_3 - 3c_3 + 1$

For T : $\qquad 0 = -b_3 - 2$

$\therefore \qquad c_3 = 0; \ b_3 = -2$

and $\qquad a_3 = -b_3 + 3c_3 - 1 = 2 + 0 - 1 = 1$

Substituting the values of a_3, b_3 and c_3 in π_3, we get

$$\therefore \qquad \pi_3 = l^1 \cdot V^{-2} \cdot \rho^0 \cdot g = \frac{lg}{V^2}$$

Step 5. Substitute the values of π_1, π_2, π_3 in eqn. (iii). The functional relationship becomes

$$f_1\left(\frac{R}{l^2 V^2 \rho}, \frac{\mu}{lV\rho}, \frac{lg}{V^2}\right) = 0$$

or, $$\frac{R}{l^2 V^2 \rho} = \phi\left(\frac{\mu}{lV\rho}, \frac{lg}{V^2}\right)$$

$$= \phi\left(\frac{\rho Vl}{\mu}, \frac{V}{\sqrt{lg}}\right)$$

The above step has been made on the postulate that *reciprocal of pi-term and its square root is non-dimensional*.

$$R = l^2 V^2 \rho \phi\left(\frac{\rho Vl}{\mu}, \frac{V}{\sqrt{lg}}\right)$$

The resistance R is thus a function of Reynolds number $\left(\dfrac{\rho Vl}{\mu}\right)$ and Froude's number $\left(\dfrac{V}{\sqrt{lg}}\right)$.

Example 6.4. (Frictional Loss in Pipes). *The pressure difference Δp in a pipe of diameter D and length l due to turbulent flow depends on the velocity V, viscosity μ, density ρ and roughness k. Using Buckingham's π-theorem, obtain an expression for Δp.*

Solution. The pressure difference Δp is a function of : D, l, V, μ, ρ, k

Mathematically, $\qquad \Delta p = f(D, l, V, \mu, \rho, k)$ ...(i)

or, $\qquad f_1(\Delta p, D, l, V, \mu, \rho, k) = 0$ ...(ii)

$\therefore \qquad$ Total number of variables, $n = 7$

Writing dimensions of each variable, we have

Δp (dimensions of pressure) $= ML^{-1}T^{-2}, D = L, l = L, V = LT^{-1},$
$$\pi = ML^{-1}T^{-1}, \rho = ML^{-3}, k = L$$

Thus, number of fundamental dimensions, $m = 3$

$\therefore \qquad$ Number of π-term $= n - m = 7 - 3 = 4$

Equation (ii) can be written as

$$f_1(\pi_1, \pi_2, \pi_3, \pi_4) = 0 \qquad \text{...(iii)}$$

Each π-term contains $(m + 1)$ variables, where $m = 3$ and is also equal to repeating variables. Choosing D, V and ρ as repeating variables, we get four π-terms as,

$$\pi_1 = D^{a_1} . V^{b_1} . \rho^{c_1} . \Delta p$$

$$\pi_2 = D^{a_2} . V^{b_2} . \rho^{c_2} . l$$

$$\pi_3 = D^{a_3} . V^{b_3} . \rho^{c_3} . \mu$$

$$\pi_4 = D^{a_4} . V^{b_4} . \rho^{c_4} . k$$

π_1-term:

$$\pi_1 = D^{a_1} . V^{b_1} . \rho^{c_1} . \Delta p$$

$$M^0 L^0 T^0 = L^{a_1} . (LT^{-1})^{b_1} . (ML^{-3})^{c_1} . (ML^{-1}T^{-2})$$

Equating the exponents of M, L and T respectively, we get

For M : $\quad\quad\quad 0 = c_1 + 1$

For L : $\quad\quad\quad 0 = a_1 + b_1 - 3c_1 - 1$

For T : $\quad\quad\quad 0 = -b_1 - 2$

$\therefore \quad\quad\quad\quad c_1 = -1; b_1 = -2$

$$a_1 = -b_1 + 3c_1 + 1 = 2 - 3 + 1 = 0$$

Substituting the values of a_1, b_1 and c_1 in π_1, we get

$$\pi_1 = D^0 . V^{-2} . \rho^{-1} . \Delta p = \frac{\Delta p}{\rho V^2}$$

π_2-term:

$$\pi_2 = D^{a_2} . V^{b_2} . \rho^{c_2} . l$$

$$M^0 L^0 T^0 = L^{a_2} . (LT^{-1})^{b_2} . (ML^{-3})^{c_2} . L$$

Equating the exponents of M, L and T respectively, we get

For M : $\quad\quad\quad 0 = c_2$

For L : $\quad\quad\quad 0 = a_2 + b_2 - 3c_2 + 1$

For T : $\quad\quad\quad 0 = -b_2$

$\therefore \quad\quad\quad\quad c_2 = 0; b_2 = 0$

and $\quad\quad\quad\quad a_2 = -b_2 + 3c_2 - 1 = -1$

Substituting the values of a_2, b_2 and c_2 in π_2, we get

$$\pi_2 = D^{-1} . V^0 . \rho^0 . l = \frac{l}{D}$$

π_3-term:

$$\pi_3 = D^{a_3} . V^{b_3} . \rho^{c_3} . \mu$$

$$M^0 L^0 T^0 = L^{a_3} . (LT^{-1})^{b_3} . (ML^{-3})^{c_3} . (ML^{-1}T^{-1})$$

Equating the exponents of M, L and T respectively, we get

For M : $\quad\quad\quad 0 = c_3 + 1$

For L : $\quad\quad\quad 0 = a_3 + b_3 - 3c_3 - 1$

For T : $\quad\quad\quad 0 = -b_3 - 1$

$\therefore \quad\quad\quad\quad c_3 = -1; b_3 = -1$

and $\quad\quad\quad\quad a_3 = -b_3 + 3c_3 + 1 = 1 - 3 + 1 = -1$

Substituting the values of a_3, b_3 and c_3 in π_3, we get

$$\pi_3 = D^{-1} . V^{-1} . \rho^{-1} . \mu = \frac{\mu}{DV\rho}$$

π_4-term:

$$\pi_4 = D^{a_4} \cdot V^{b_4} \cdot \rho^{c_4} \cdot k$$

$$M^0 L^0 T^0 = L^{a_4} \cdot (LT^{-1})^{b_4} \cdot (ML^{-3})^{c_4} \cdot L$$

(Dimension of $k = L$)

Equating the exponents of M, L and T respectively, we get

For M : $\quad 0 = c_4$

For L : $\quad 0 = a_4 + b_4 - 3c_4 + 1$

For T : $\quad 0 = -b_4$

$\therefore \qquad c_4 = 0; \, b_4 = 0$

and $\qquad a_4 = -b_4 + 3c_4 - 1 = 0 - 1 = -1$

Substituting the values of a_4, b_4 and c_4 in π_4, we get

$$\pi_4 = D^{-1} \cdot V^0 \cdot \rho^0 \cdot k = \frac{k}{D}$$

Substituting the values of π_1, π_2, π_3 and π_4 in eqn. (iii), we get

$$f_1 \left(\frac{\Delta p}{\rho V^2}, \frac{l}{D}, \frac{\mu}{DV\rho}, \frac{k}{D} \right) = 0$$

or, $$\frac{\Delta p}{\rho V^2} = \phi \left[\frac{l}{D}, \frac{\mu}{DV\rho}, \frac{k}{D} \right]$$

Expression for difference of pressure head (h_f) :

As observed from experiments, Δp is a linear function of $\frac{l}{D}$; therefore, taking this out of function, we have

$$\frac{\Delta p}{\rho V^2} = \frac{l}{D} \phi \left[\frac{\mu}{DV\rho}, \frac{k}{D} \right]$$

or, $$\frac{\Delta p}{p} = V^2 \cdot \frac{l}{D} \phi \left[\frac{\mu}{DV\rho}, \frac{k}{D} \right]$$

Dividing both sides by g, we get

$$\frac{\Delta p}{\rho g} = \frac{V^2}{g} \cdot \frac{l}{D} \phi \left[\frac{\mu}{DV\rho}, \frac{k}{D} \right]$$

Now $\phi \left[\dfrac{\mu}{DV\rho}, \dfrac{k}{D} \right]$ consists of following two terms:

(i) $\dfrac{\mu}{DV\rho}$ which is $\dfrac{1}{\text{Reynold number}}$ or $\dfrac{1}{Re}$

(ii) $\dfrac{k}{D}$ ..... called roughness factor

$\therefore \qquad \phi \left[\dfrac{1}{Re}, \dfrac{k}{D} \right]$ is put equal to f,

where, $\quad f =$ Coefficient of friction (function of Reynold number and roughness factor).

$$\therefore \qquad \frac{\Delta p}{\rho g} = \frac{4f}{2} \cdot \frac{V^2 l}{gD} \qquad \left[\because f = \phi \left(\frac{\mu}{DV\rho}, \frac{k}{D} \right) \right]$$

(Multiplying or dividing by any constant does not change the character of π-terms)

$$\therefore \qquad \frac{\Delta p}{\rho g} = h_f = \frac{4f \, l V^2}{D \times 2g}$$

6.5. DIMENSIONAL ANALYSIS APPLIED TO FORCED CONVECTION HEAT TRANSFER

Let us assume that the heat transfer coefficient in a fully developed forced convection in a tube is a function of the following variables:

$$h = f(\rho, D, V, \mu, c_p, k) \qquad \qquad ...(i)$$

or,
$$f_1(h, \rho, D, V, \mu, c_p. k) \qquad \qquad ...(ii)$$

The physical quantities with their dimensions are as under:

S.No.	Variables	Symbols	Dimensions
1	Heat transfer coefficient	h	$MT^{-3}\,\theta^{-1}$
2	Fluid density	ρ	ML^{-3}
3	Tube diameter	D	L
4	Fluid velocity	V	LT^{-1}
5	Fluid viscosity	μ	$ML^{-1}\,T^{-1}$
6	Specific heat	c_p	$L^2\,T^{-2}\,\theta^{-1}$
7	Thermal conductivity	k	$MLT^{-3}\,\theta^{-1}$

Total number of variables, $n = 7$

Fundamental dimensions in the problem are M, L, T, θ and hence $m = 4$

Number of dimensionless π-terms $= (n - m) = 7 - 4 = 3$

The eqn. (ii) may be written as:

$$f_1(\pi_1, \pi_2, \pi_3) = 0$$

We choose h, ρ, D, V as the core group (repeating variables) with unknown exponents. The groups to be formed are now represented as the following π groups.

$$\pi_1 = h^{a_1} . \rho^{b_1} . D^{c_1} . V^{d_1} . \mu$$

$$\pi_2 = h^{a_2} . \rho^{b_2} . D^{c_2} . V^{d_2} . c_p$$

$$\pi_3 = h^{a_3} . \rho^{b_3} . D^{c_3} . V^{d_3} . k$$

π_1–term:

$$M^0 L^0 T^0 = (MT^{-3}\,\theta^{-1})^{a_1} . (ML^{-3})^{b_1} . (L)^{c_1} . (LT^{-1})^{d_1} . (ML^{-1}T^{-1})$$

Equating the exponents of M, L, T and θ respectively, we get

For M : $0 = a_1 + b_1 + 1$

For L : $0 = -3b_1 + c_1 + d_1 - 1$

For T : $0 = -3a_1 - d_1 - 1$

For θ : $0 = -a_1$

Solving the above equations, we have

$$a_1 = 0, b_1 = -1, c_1 = -1, d_1 = -1$$

$$\therefore \qquad \pi_1 = \rho^{-1} . D^{-1} . V^{-1} . \mu$$

or,
$$\pi_1 = \frac{\mu}{\rho DV}$$

π_2–term:

$$M^0 L^0 T^0 = (MT^{-3}\,\theta^{-1})^{a_2} . (ML^{-3})^{b_2} . (L)^{c_2} . (LT^{-1})^{d_2} . (L^2\,T^{-2}\,\theta^{-1})$$

For M : $0 = a_2 + b_2$

For L : $0 = -3b_2 + c_2 + d_2 + 2$

For T : $\qquad 0 = -3a_2 - d_2 - 2$

For θ : $\qquad 0 = -a_2 - 1$

Solving the above equations, we have

$$a_2 = -1, b_2 = 1, c_2 = 0, d_2 = 1$$

∴ $\qquad \pi_2 = h^{-1} . \rho . V . c_p$

or $\qquad \pi_2 = \dfrac{c_p \, \rho V}{h}$

Since dimensions of h and $\dfrac{k}{D}$ are the same, hence

$$\pi_2 = \dfrac{c_p \, \rho VD}{k}$$

π_3–term:

$$\pi_3 = (MT^{-3} \theta^{-1})^{a_3} . (ML^{-3})^{b_3} . (L)^{c_3} . (LT^{-1})^{d_3} . (MLT^{-3} \theta^{-1})$$

Equating the exponents of M, L, T and θ respectively, we get

For M : $\qquad 0 = a_3 - 3b_3 + 1$

For L : $\qquad 0 = -3b_3 + c_3 + d_3 + 1$

For T : $\qquad 0 = -3a_3 - d_3 - 3$

For θ : $\qquad 0 = -a_3 - 1$

Solving the above equations, we get

$$a_3 = -1, b_3 = 0, c_3 = -1, d_3 = 0$$

∴ $\qquad \pi_3 = h^{-1} . D^{-1} . k$

or $\qquad \pi_3 = \dfrac{k}{hD}$

According to π–theorem, $\pi_3 = \phi \, (\pi_1, \pi_2)$

∴ $\qquad \dfrac{k}{hD} = C \left[\dfrac{\mu}{\rho \, DV} \right]^{m'} \left[\dfrac{c_p \, \rho \, DV}{k} \right]^{n'}$

where m' and n' are constants.

If $m' > n'$, then

$$\dfrac{k}{hD} = C \left[\dfrac{\mu}{\rho \, DV} \right]^{n'} \left[\dfrac{c_p \, \rho \, DV}{k} \right]^{n'} \left[\dfrac{\mu}{\rho \, DV} \right]^{m' - n'}$$

$$= C \left[\dfrac{\mu}{\rho \, DV} \right]^{m' - n'} \left[\dfrac{\mu}{\rho \, DV} \cdot \dfrac{c_p \, \rho \, DV}{k} \right]^{n'}$$

$$= C \left[\dfrac{\mu}{\rho \, DV} \right]^{m' - n'} \left[\dfrac{\mu c_p}{k} \right]^{n'}$$

or $\qquad \dfrac{hD}{k} = C \left[\dfrac{\rho \, DV}{\mu} \right]^{m} \left[\dfrac{\mu c_p}{k} \right]^{n}$

or $\qquad Nu = C \, (Re)^m \, (Pr)^n \qquad\qquad$ ...(6.8) where C, m and n are constants and evaluated experimentally

$$\left[\begin{array}{l} \text{where } Nu = \text{Nusselt number} = \dfrac{hD}{k} \\[3mm] Re = \text{Reynolds number} = \dfrac{\rho DV}{\mu} \\[3mm] Pr = \text{Prandtl number} = \dfrac{\mu c_p}{k} \end{array}\right]$$

It is worth noting that if V, m, ρ, c_p were chosen as the core group (repeating variables), then the analysis would have yielded the following non-dimensional groups:

$$Re = \frac{\rho VD}{\mu}; \ Pr = \frac{\mu c_p}{k}; \ St = \frac{h}{\rho V c_p}$$

(where, $St = $ Stanton number)

So, another form of correlating heat transfer data is

$$St = \phi\,(Re,\ Pr) \qquad\qquad\qquad ...(6.9)$$

6.6. DIMENSIONAL ANALYSIS APPLIED TO NATURAL OR FREE CONVECTION HEAT TRANSFER

The heat transfer coefficient in case of natural or free convection, like forced convection heat transfer coefficient, depends upon the variables V, ρ, k, μ, c_p and L or D. Since the fluid circulation in free convection is owing to difference in density between the various fluid layers due to temperature gradient and not by external agency, therefore, velocity V is no longer an independent variable but depends upon the following factors:

(i) Δt i.e., the difference of temperatures between the heated surface and the undisturbed fluid.

(ii) β i.e., coefficient of volume expansion of the fluid.

(iii) g i.e., acceleration due to gravity.

($\beta\,g\,\Delta t$ is considered as one phystical factor.)

Thus heat transfer coefficient 'h' may be expressed as follows:

$$h = f\,(\rho,\ L,\ \mu,\ c_p,\ k,\ \beta\,g\,\Delta t) \qquad\qquad ...(i)$$
$$f_1\,(\rho,\ L,\ \mu,\ k,\ h,\ c_p,\ \beta\,g\,\Delta t) \qquad\qquad ...(ii)$$

[The parameter ($\beta g\,\Delta t$) represents the buoyant force and has the dimensions of LT^{-2}.]

Total number of variables, $n = 7$

Fundamental dimensions in the problem are M, L, T, θ and hence $m = 4$

Number of dimensionless π-terms $= (n - m) = 7 - 4 = 3$

The equation (ii) may be written as:

$$f_1\,(\pi_1,\ \pi_2,\ \pi_3) = 3$$

We choose ρ, L, μ and k as the core group (repeating variables) with unknown exponents. The groups to be formed are now represented as the following π groups.

$$\pi_1 = \rho^{a_1} \cdot L^{b_1} \cdot \mu^{c_1} \cdot k^{d_1} \cdot h$$
$$\pi_2 = \rho^{a_2} \cdot L^{b_2} \cdot \mu^{c_2} \cdot k^{d_2} \cdot c_p$$
$$\pi_3 = \rho^{a_3} \cdot L^{b_3} \cdot \mu^{c_3} \cdot k^{d_3} \cdot \beta g\,\Delta t$$

π_1-term:

$$M^0 L^0 T^0\,\theta^0 = (ML^{-3})^{a_1} \cdot (L)^{b_1} \cdot (ML^{-1}T^{-1})^{c_1} \cdot (MLT^{-3}\theta^{-1})^{d_1} \cdot (ML^{-3}\theta^{-1})$$

Equating the exponents of M, L, T and θ respectively, we get

For M : $\qquad 0 = a_1 + c_1 + d_1 + 1$

For L : $\qquad 0 = -3a_1 + b_1 - c_1 + d_1$

For T : $\qquad 0 = -c_1 - 3d_1 - 3$

For θ : $\qquad 0 = -d_1 - 1$

Solving the above equations, we get

$$a_1 = 0,\ b_1 = 1,\ c_1 = 0,\ d_1 = -1$$

$\therefore \qquad \pi_1 = Lk^{-1}h$ or $\pi_1 = \dfrac{hL}{k}$

π_2-term:

$$M^0 L^0 T^0\, \theta^0 = (ML^{-3})^{a_2} \cdot (L)^{b_2} \cdot (ML^{-1}T^{-1})^{c_2} \cdot (MLT^{-3}\theta^{-1})^{d_2} \cdot (L^2 T^{-2}\theta^{-1})$$

Equating the exponents of M, L, T, θ respectively, we get

For M : $\qquad 0 = a_2 + c_2 + d_2$

For L : $\qquad 0 = -3a_2 + b_2 - c_2 + d_2 + 2$

For T : $\qquad 0 = -c_2 - 3d_2 - 2$

For θ : $\qquad 0 = -d_2 - 1$

Solving the above equations, we get

$$a_2 = 0,\ b_2 = 0,\ c_2 = 1,\ d_2 = -1$$

$\therefore \qquad \pi_2 = \mu \cdot k^{-1} \cdot c_p$ $\qquad$ or $\qquad \pi_2 = \dfrac{\mu c_p}{k}$

π_3–term:

$$M^0 L^0 T^0\, \theta^0 = (ML^{-3})^{a_3} \cdot (L)^{b_3} \cdot (ML^{-1}T^{-1})^{c_3} \cdot (MLT^{-3}\theta^{-1})^{d_3} \cdot (LT^{-2})$$

Equating the exponents of M, L, T, θ respectively, we get

For M : $\qquad 0 = a_3 + c_3 + d_3$

For L : $\qquad 0 = -3a_3 + b_3 - c_3 + d_3 + 1$

For T : $\qquad 0 = -c_3 - 3d_3 - 2$

For θ : $\qquad 0 = -d_3$

Solving the above equations, we get

$$a_3 = 2,\ b_3 = 3,\ c_3 = -2,\ d_3 = 0$$

$\therefore \qquad \pi_3 = \rho^2 \cdot L^3 \cdot \mu^{-2} \cdot (\beta\, g\, \Delta t)$

or, $\qquad \pi_3 = \dfrac{(\beta\, g\, \Delta t)\rho^2\, L^3}{\mu^2} = \dfrac{(\beta\, g\, \Delta t)L^3}{v^2}$ $\qquad$ ...(6.10)

or, $\qquad Nu = \phi\,(Pr)\,(Gr)$

or, $\qquad Nu = C\,(Pr)^n\,(Gr)^m$ (where Gr = Grashoff number) $\qquad$ ...(6.11)

Here C, n and m are constants and may be evaluated experimentally.

6.7. ADVANTAGES AND LIMITATIONS OF DIMENSIONAL ANALYSIS

Advantages :

1. It expresses the functional relationship between the variables in dimensionless terms.

2. By the proper selection of variables, the dimensionless parameters can be used to make certain logical deductions about the problem.

3. Design curves, by the use of dimensional analysis, can be developed from the experimental data or direct solution of the problem.

4. It enables getting up a theoretical solution in a simplified dimensionless form.

5. Dimensionless analysis provides partial solutions to the problems that are too complex to be dealt with mathematically.

6. Dimensional analysis is a useful tool in the analysis and correlation of experimental data, in the planning of experiments and in the formulation of empirical correlation describing a particular phenomenon.

7. The results of one series of tests can be applied, with the help of dimensional analysis, to a large number of other similar problems.

Limitations :

1. Dimensional analysis does not give any clue regarding the selection of variables. If the variables are wrongly taken, the resulting functional relationship is erroneous. It provides the information about the grouping of variables. In order to decide whether selected variables are pertinent or superfluous experiments have to be performed.

2. The complete information is not provided by dimensional analysis; it only indicates that there is some relationship between the parameters. It does not give the values of coefficients in the functional relationship. The values of coefficients and hence the nature of functions can be obtained only from experiments or from mathematical analysis.

3. No information is given about the internal mechanism of the physical phenomenon.

4. Generally it is desired to find the effect of one physical quantity upon a number of other physical quantities that are supposed to enter into a problem. It is not possible to get such information with the help of dimensional analysis.

6.8.   DIMENSIONLESS NUMBERS AND THEIR PHYSICAL SIGNIFICANCE

1. Reynolds number (Re) :

It is defined as the *ratio of the inertia force to the viscous force.*

$$Re = \frac{\text{Inertia force}}{\text{Viscous force}} = \frac{\rho V^2 L^2}{\mu VL} = \frac{\rho VL}{\mu} = \frac{VL}{v} \qquad \qquad ...(6.12)$$

• Reynolds number signifies the relative predominance of the inertia to the viscous forces occuring in the flow systems.

• The higher the value of Re the greater will be the relative contribution of inertia effect. The smaller the value of Re, the greater will be the relative magnitude of the viscous stresses.

• Reynolds number is taken as an important criterion of kinematic and dynamic similarities in forced convection heat transfer.

2. Prandtl number (Pr) :

It is the *ratio of kinematic viscosity* (v) *to thermal diffusivity* (α).

$$Pr = \frac{\mu c_p}{k} = \frac{\rho v c_p}{k} = \frac{v}{(k/\rho c_p)} = \frac{v}{\alpha} \qquad \qquad ...(6.13)$$

Kinematic viscosity indicates the impulse transport through molecular friction whereas thermal diffusivity indicates the heat energy transport by conduction process.

• Prandtl number provides a measure of the relative effectiveness of the momentum and energy transport by diffusion.

• Prandtl number is a connecting link between the velocity field and temperature field, and its value strongly influences relative growth of velocity and thermal boundary layers.

3. Nusselt number (*Nu*) :

Nusselt number can be defined in several ways:

(*i*) It is the *ratio of heat flow rate by convection process under a unit temperature gradient to the heat flow rate by conduction process under a unit temperature gradient through a stationary thickness of L metres.* Thus,

$$Nu = \frac{Q_{conv.}}{Q_{cond.}} = \frac{h}{k/L} = \frac{hL}{k} \qquad \qquad ...(6.14)$$

(*ii*) It is the *ratio of heat transfer rate, Q to the rate at which heat would be conducted within the fluid under a temperature gradient of ∆θ/L.* Thus,

$$Nu = \frac{Q}{(\Delta\theta \cdot k)/L} = \frac{Q}{\Delta\theta} \cdot \frac{L}{k} = \frac{hL}{k} \qquad \qquad ...(6.15)$$

(*iii*) It is the *ratio of characteristic length L to the thickness ∆x of a stationary fluid layer conducting the heat at the same rate under the same temperature difference as in the case of convection process.* Thus

$$Q = k \frac{\Delta t}{\Delta x} = h \cdot \Delta t$$

or,

$$\Delta x = \frac{k}{h}$$

∴

$$Nu = \frac{L}{\Delta x} = \frac{L}{k/h} = \frac{hL}{k} \qquad \qquad ...(6.16)$$

The Nusselt number is a convenient measure of the convective heat transfer coefficient. For a given value of the Nusselt number, the convective heat transfer coefficient is directly proportional to thermal conductivity of the fluid and inversely proportional to the significant length parameter. ·

4. Stanton number (*St*) :

It is the *ratio of heat transfer coefficient to the flow of heat per unit temperature rise due to the velocity of the fluid.*

$$St = \frac{h}{\rho \, Vc_p} \qquad \qquad ...(6.17)$$

or,

$$St = \frac{hL/k}{\left[\dfrac{\rho \, VL}{\mu}\right]\left[\dfrac{\mu \, c_p}{k}\right]} = \frac{Nu}{Re \times Pr} \qquad \qquad ...(6.18)$$

Thus, Stanton number may also be defined as the *ratio of Nusselt number and the product of Reynolds number and Prandtl number.*

It is worth noting that Stanton number can be *used only in correlating forced convection data* (since the expression contains the velocity *V*).

5. Peclet number (*Pe*) :

It is the *ratio of mass heat flow rate by convection to the flow rate by conduction under a unit temperature gradient and through a thickness L.*

$$Q_{conv.} = \rho \, Vc_p; \qquad \qquad Q_{cond.} = \frac{k}{1} \times \frac{1}{L} = \frac{k}{L}$$

$$\therefore \qquad Pe = \frac{Q_{conv.}}{Q_{cond.}} = \frac{\rho \, V c_p}{k / L} = \frac{\rho \, c_p}{k} \cdot \frac{LV}{1} = \frac{LV}{\alpha} \qquad \qquad ...(6.19)$$

The Peclet number can be written as

$$Pe = Re.Pr = \frac{\rho \, LV}{\mu} \times \frac{\mu \, c_p}{k} = \frac{\rho \, c_p}{k} \cdot \frac{LV}{1} = \frac{LV}{\alpha}$$

It indicates that the Peclet number can be written as a function of Re and Pr also.

6. Graetz number (G) :

It is related only for the heat flow to the fluid flowing through circular pipe. It is defined as the *ratio of heat capacity of fluid flowing through the pipe per unit length of the pipe to the conductivity of the pipe.*

$$G = \frac{\left(\dfrac{mc_p}{L}\right)}{k} = \frac{mc_p}{Lk} \qquad \qquad ...(6.20)$$

or,
$$G = \frac{\left(\dfrac{\pi}{4}D^2 . V . \rho\right)\dfrac{c_p}{L}}{k} = \frac{\pi \, \rho \, VD}{4 \, \mu} \cdot \frac{\mu \, c_p}{k} \cdot \frac{D}{L}$$

or,
$$G = \frac{\pi}{4} \, Re \, . \, Pr \, . \, \frac{D}{L} \qquad \qquad ...(6.21)$$

where D and L are the diameter and length of the pipe respectively.

This can be written in the other form as

$$G = \frac{mc_p}{Lk} = \frac{\rho \, AVc_p}{Lk} = \frac{AV}{\alpha \, L}$$

or,
$$G = \frac{\pi}{4}D^2 \times \frac{V}{\alpha \, L} = \left(\frac{VD}{\alpha}\right)\left(\frac{\pi \, D}{4L}\right)$$

or,
$$G = Pe \left(\frac{\pi \, D}{4}\right) \qquad \qquad ...(6.22)$$

This shows that Graetz number is merely a product of Peclet number and a constant.

7. Grashoff number (Gr) :

Grashoff number is related with *natural convection heat transfer*. It is defined as the *ratio of the product of inertia force and buoyancy force to the square of viscous force.* Thus

$$Gr = \frac{(\text{Inertia force}) \times (\text{Buoyancy force})}{(\text{Viscous force})^2} = \frac{(\rho' \, V^2 L^2) \times (\rho \beta \; g \, . \, \Delta t \; L^3)}{(\mu \, VL)^2}$$

or,
$$Gr = \frac{\rho^2 \beta \; g \; \Delta t \; L^3}{\mu^2} \qquad \qquad ...(6.23)$$

Grashoff number has a role in free convection similar to that played by Reynolds number in forced convection. Free convection is usually suppressed at sufficiently small Gr, begins at some critical value of Gr depending upon the arrangement and then becomes more and more effective with increasing Gr.

Example 6.5. *Show by dimensional analysis that for natural convection heat transfer, Nusselt number is a function of Grashoff number and Prandtl number.* (AMIE Summer, 2002)

Solution. Refer to Article 6.6.

Example 6.6. *It is required to estimate the heat transfer from a cylinder 50 mm diameter and of surface temperature 140°C when kept in cross-flow of air at a velocity of 4 m/s and temperature 20°C. For this purpose, scale model experiments are performed using a 1/5 scale-model with the same surface and air temperature but different velocities. The following results are obtained from experiments on the model :*

Velocity of air (m/s)	:	2.0	5.0	10.0	20.0
Heat transfer coefficient (W/m^2 K) :		39.5	71.2	106.5	165.3

Calculate : (i) *The heat transfer coefficient;*

(ii) *The rate of heat transfer per metre length of actual cylinder.*

(GATE, 1999)

Solution. Given : $D_p = 50$ mm; $D_m = 50 \times \dfrac{1}{5} = 10$ mm; $V_p = 4$ m/s; $t_1 = 140°C$; $t_2 = 20°C$.

(*i*) **The heat transfer coefficient :**

For forced convection model testing, Reynolds number of the prototype and model must be equal.

$$\therefore \qquad \left(\frac{VD}{v}\right)_m = \left(\frac{VD}{v}\right)_p$$

Since the model testing is conducted at same surface and air temperature, v can be considered to be *constant*.

$$\therefore \qquad (VD)_m = (VD)_p$$

i.e., $\qquad V_m D_m = V_p D_p$

or, $\qquad V_m = \dfrac{V_p D_p}{D_m} = \dfrac{4 \times 50}{10} = 20$ m/s

The heat transfer coefficient at 20 m/s on the model is **165.3 W/m² K. (Ans.)**

(*ii*) **The rate of heat transfer per metre length of actual cylinder, Q :**

$$Q = hA\,(t_1 - t_2)$$
$$= 165.3\,(\pi \times 0.05 \times 1) \times (140 - 20) = \textbf{3115.8 W (Ans.)}$$

6.9. CHARACTERISTIC LENGTH OR EQUIVALENT DIAMETER

In the non-dimensional number (discussed in Art. 6.8) expressions there has appeared a characteristic length L or diameter D. The pipe and flat plate are the most simple geometries for the occurrence of a flow. However, in many instances some complicated geometries are also used and then all the calculations concerning flow and convective heat transfer become much more complicated and difficult. In order to avoid such difficulties, the concept of an *equivalent circular tube is used.* This is a *tube* which would present the *same resistance against the flow* or would secure the *same heat transfer* as the duct usually used under equal or comparable conditions. The diameter of an equivalent tube is known as *equivalent diameter*, D_e or *characteristic length L_e*. The equivalent diameter is usually defined as:

$$D_e = \frac{4A_c}{P} = \frac{4 \times \left(\dfrac{\pi}{4} D^2\right)}{\pi D} = D \text{ (inner diameter of the tube)}$$

(where A_c = cross-sectional area and P = perimeter).

This primarily holds when it is *required to find the pressure drop*. However, it is also used in *problems of heat transfer by convection*, because of the existing similarity between momentum transfer and heat transfer.

The equivalent diameter or characteristic length of few geometries are given below:

1. *For rectangular duct* [Fig. 6.1 (*i*)]:

$$D_e = \frac{4A_c}{P} = \frac{4lb}{2(l+b)} = \frac{2lb}{l+b} \qquad \qquad ...(6.24)$$

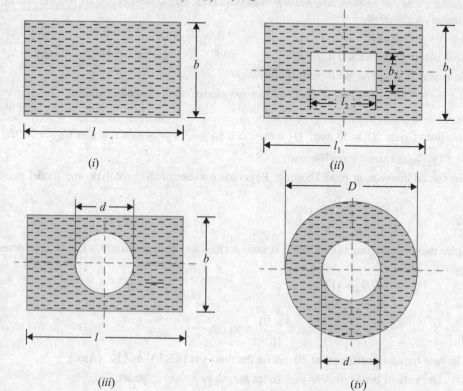

Fig. 6.1. Equivalent diameter (D_e) for various geometries.

2. *For rectangular annulus* [Fig. 6.1 (*ii*)] :

$$D_e = \frac{4A_c}{P} = \frac{4 \times (l_1 b_1 - l_2 b_2)}{2[(l_1 + b_1) + (l_2 + b_2)]} = \frac{2(l_1 b_1 - l_2 b_2)}{[(l_1 + b_1) + (l_2 + b_2)]} \qquad ...(6.25)$$

When $l_1 = b_1$ and $l_2 = b_2$,

$$D_e = \frac{2(l_1^2 - l_2^2)}{2l_1 + 2l_2} = (l_1 - l_2) \qquad \qquad ...(6.26)$$

3. *For annulus* [Fig. 6.1 (*iii*)]

$$D_e = \frac{4A_c}{P} = \frac{4lb}{[2(l+b) + \pi d]} \qquad \qquad ...(6.27)$$

4. *For annulus* [Fig. 6.1 (*iv*)]

$$D_e = \frac{4A_c}{P} = \frac{4 \times \frac{\pi}{4}(D^2 - d^2)}{\pi(D+d)} = (D-d) \qquad \qquad ...(6.28)$$

6.10. MODEL STUDIES AND SIMILITUDE

6.10.1. MODEL AND PROTOTYPE

In order to know about the performance of large machines/equipments (or structures), involving fluid flow, before actually manufacturing (or constructing) them, their models are made and tested to get the required information. The **model** is the *small scale replica of the actual machine/equipment or structure. The actual machine/equipment or structure is called* **Prototype.** The models are not always smaller than the prototype, in some cases a model may be even larger or of the same size as prototype depending upon the need and purpose (*e.g.,* the working of a wrist watch or carburettor can be studied in a large scale model).

6.10.2. SIMILITUDE

To find solutions to numerous complicated problems in fluid mechanics etc. model studies are usually conducted. In order that results obtained in the model studies represent the behaviour of prototype, the following *similarities for testing of 'heat transfer equipment'* must be ensured between the model and the prototype.

1. *Geometric similarity.* For geometric similarity to exist between the model and the proto type, the ratios of corresponding lengths in a model and in prototype must be same and the included angles between the two corresponding sides must be the same.

2. *Kinematic similarity.* Kinematic similarity is the *similarity of motion.* If at the corresponding points in the model and the prototype, the velocity or acceleration ratio are same and velocity or acceleration vectors point in the *same direction*, the two flows are said to be *kinematically similar.* The geometric similarity is a pre-requisite for kinematic similarity.

3. *Dynamic similarity.* Dynamic similarity is the *similarity of forces.* The flows in the model and in prototype are dynamically similar if at all the corresponding points, identical types of forces are parallel and bear the same ratio. In dynamic similarity, the force polygons of the two flows can be superimposed by change in force scale.

4. *Similarity of fluid entry conditions.*

5. *Similarity of boundary temperature field.*

It is not possible to meet all the above requirements. Therefore, in some cases, the dimensionless term in isothermal flow is kept the same in model and prototype (full size).

Thus,   For *forced convection*: $(Re)_{model} = (Re)_{prototype}$

For *free convection*: $(Gr.Pr)_{model} = (Gr.Pr)_{prototype}.$

HIGHLIGHTS

1. Dimensional analysis is a mathematical technique which makes use of the study of the dimensions for solving several engineering problems.

2. Dimensionless numbers:

Reynolds number, $Re = \dfrac{VL}{\nu}$

Prandtl number, $Pr = \dfrac{\mu c_p}{k} = \dfrac{\nu}{\alpha}$

Nusselt number, $Nu = \dfrac{hL}{k}$

Stanton number, $St = \dfrac{h}{\rho \, V c_p} = \dfrac{Nu}{Re \times Pr}$

Peclet number, $Pe = \dfrac{LV}{\alpha} \; (= Re.Pr)$

Graetz number, $G = Pe \left(\dfrac{\pi D}{4} \right)$

Grashoff number, $Gr = \dfrac{\rho^2 \beta g \, \Delta t \, L^3}{\mu^2}$

3. The following similarities for testing of 'heat transfer equipment' must be ensured between the model and the prototype:

    (i) Geometric similarity   (ii) Kinematic similarity

   (iii) Dynamic similarity   (iv) Similarity of fluid entry conditions

    (v) Similarity of boundary temperature field.

THEORETICAL QUESTIONS

1. What is dimensional analysis?
2. What are the uses of dimensional analysis?
3. Explain the term dimensional homogeneity.
4. Describe the Rayleigh's method for dimensional analysis.
5. Describe Buckingham's method or π-theorem to formulate a dimensionally homogeneous equation between the various physical quantities effecting a certain phenomenon.
6. What are dimensionless numbers?
7. Discuss the physical significance of the following dimensionless number Re, Nu, Pr, St, Gr.
8. Show by dimensional analysis for forced convection, $Nu = \phi \, (Re, \, Pr)$.
9. Show by dimensional analysis for free convection, $Nu = \phi \, (Pr, \, Gr)$
10. What are the advantages and limitations of 'Dimensional analysis' ?
11. What do you mean by 'Characteristic length or Equivalent diameter' ?
12. For testing of 'heat transfer equipment' which of the similarities must be ensured between the model and the prototype ?

Forced Convection

CHAPTER 7

A. LAMINAR FLOW

7.1. LAMINAR FLOW OVER A FLAT PLATE

7.1.1. INTRODUCTION TO BOUNDARY LAYER

The concept of boundary layer was first introduced by L. Prandtl in 1904 and since then it has been applied to several fluid flow problems.

When a real fluid (viscous fluid) flows past a stationary solid boundary, a layer of fluid which comes in contact with the boundary surface, adheres to it (on account of viscosity) and condition of no slip occurs (The *no-slip* condition implies that the velocity of fluid at a solid boundary must be same as that of boundary itself). Thus the layer of fluid which cannot slip away from the boundary surface undergoes retardation; this retarded layer further causes retardation for the adjacent layers of the fluid, thereby developing a small region in the immediate vicinity of the boundary surface in which the velocity of the flowing fluid increases rapidly from *zero* at the boundary surface and approaches the velocity of main stream. The *layer adjacent to the boundary is known as boundary layer. Boundary layer is formed whenever there is relative motion between the boundary and the fluid.* Since

$\tau_0 = \mu\left(\dfrac{\partial u}{\partial y}\right)_{y=0}$, the fluid exerts a shear stress on the boundary and boundary exerts an equal and opposite force on fluid known as the *shear resistance*.

According to boundary layer theory the extensive fluid medium around bodies moving in fluids can be divided into following two regions :

   (*i*) A thin layer adjoining the boundary called the *boundary layer where the viscous shear takes place.*

  (*ii*) A region outside the boundary layer where the flow behaviour is quite like that of an *ideal fluid and the potential flow theory is applicable.*

7.1.1.1 Boundary Layer Definitions and Characteristics

Consider the boundary layer formed on a flat plate kept parallel to flow of fluid of velocity U (Fig. 7.1) (Though the growth of a boundary layer depends upon the *body shape*, flow over a flat plate aligned in the direction of flow is considered, since most of the flow surface can be *approximated to a flat plate and for simplicity*).

  – The edge facing the direction of flow is called *leading edge.*

  – The rear edge is called the *trailing edge.*

  – Near the leading edge of a flat plate, the boundary layer is *wholly laminar.* For a laminar boundary layer the velocity distribution is *parabolic.*

  – The thickness of the boundary layer (δ) increases with distance from the leading edge x, as more and more fluid is slowed down by the viscous boundary, becomes unstable and breaks into turbulent boundary layer over a transition region.

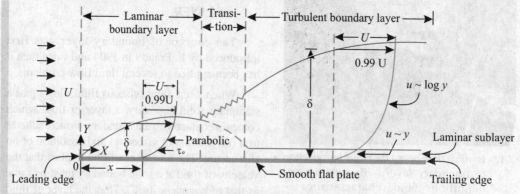

Fig. 7.1. Boundary layer on a flat plate.

For a turbulent boundary layer, if the boundary is smooth, the roughness projections are covered by a very thin layer which remains laminar, called *laminar sublayer.* The velocity distribution in the turbulent boundary layer is given *by Log law of Prandtl's one-seventh power law.*

The *characteristics* of a boundary layer may be summarised as follows :

   (*i*) δ (thickness of boundary layer) increases as distance from leading edge x increases.

  (*ii*) δ decreases as U increases.

  (*iii*) δ increases as kinematic viscosity (v) increases.

  (*iv*) $\tau_0 = \mu\left(\dfrac{U}{\delta}\right)$; hence τ_0 decreases as x increases. However, when boundary layer becomes turbulent, it shows a sudden increase and then decreases with increasing x.

  (*v*) When U decreases in the downward direction, boundary layer growth is reduced.

  (*vi*) When U decreases in the downward direction, flow near the boundary is further retarded, boundary layer growth is faster and is susceptible to separation.

 (*vii*) The various characteristics of the boundary layer on flat plate (*e.g.*, variation of δ, τ_0 or force F) are governed by inertial and viscous forces ; hence they are functions of either $\dfrac{Ux}{v}$ or $\dfrac{UL}{v}$.

(viii) If $\dfrac{Ux}{v} < 5 \times 10^5$ ... boundary layer is *laminar* (velocity distribution is *parabolic*).

If $\dfrac{Ux}{v} > 5 \times 10^5$ ... boundary layer is *turbulent on* that portion (velocity distribution follows *Log law or a power law*).

(ix) Critical value of $\dfrac{Ux}{v}$ at which boundary layer changes from laminar to turbulent depends on :

— turbulence in ambient flow,

— surface roughness,

— pressure gradient,

— plate curvature, and

Laminar flow hood.

— temperature difference between fluid and boundary.

(x) Though the velocity distribution would be a parabolic curve in the laminar sub-layer zone, but in view of the very small thickness we can reasonably assume that velocity distribution is linear and so the velocity gradient can be considered constant.

Boundary layer thickness (δ) :

The velocity within the boundary layer increases from zero at the boundary surface to the velocity of the main stream asymptotically. Therefore, the thickness of the boundary layer is arbitrarily defined as *that distance from the boundary in which the velocity reaches 99 per cent of the velocity of the free stream ($u = 0.99U$). It is denoted by the symbol δ. This definition, however, gives an approximate value* of the boundary layer thickness and hence δ is generally termed as **nominal thickness** of the boundary layer.

The boundary layer thickness for *greater accuracy* is defined in terms of certain mathematical expressions which are the measure of the boundary layer on the flow. The commonly adopted definitions of the boundary layer thickness are :

1. Displacement thickness (δ^*)
2. Momentum thickness (θ)
3. Energy thickness (δ_e).

Displacement thickness (δ^*) :

The *displacement thickness* can be defined as follws :

"It is the distance, measured perpendicular to the boundary, by which the main/free stream is displaced on account of formation of boundary layer."

Or

"It is an additional "wall thickness" that would have to be added to compensate for the reduction in flow rate on account of boundary layer formation."

The displacement thickness is denoted by δ^*.

Let fluid of density ρ flow past a stationary plate with velocity U as shown in Fig. 7.2. Consider an elementary strip of thickness dy at a distance y from the plate.

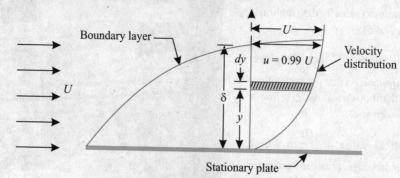

Boundary layer

Velocity distribution

$u = 0.99\ U$

Fig. 7.2. Displacement thickness.

Assuming *unit width*, the mass flow per second through the elementary strip

$$= \rho u dy \qquad \qquad ...(i)$$

Mass flow per second through the elementary strip (unit width) if the plate were not there

$$= \rho\ U.dy \qquad \qquad ...(ii)$$

Reduction of mass flow rate through the elementary strip

$$= \rho\ (U - u)dy$$

[*The difference $(U - u)$ is called* **velocity of defect**]

Total reduction of mass flow rate due to introduction of plate

$$= \int_0^\delta \rho(U - u)\,dy \qquad \qquad ...(iii)$$

(if the fluid is incompressible)

Let the plate is displaced by a distance δ^* and velocity of flow for the distance δ^* is equal to the main/free stream velocity (*i.e.*, U). Then, loss of the mass of the fluid/sec. flowing through the distance δ^*

$$= \rho U \delta^* \qquad \qquad ...(iv)$$

Equating eqns. (*iii*) and (*iv*), we get

$$\rho U \delta^* = \int_0^\delta \rho(U - u)\,dy$$

or, $$\delta^* = \int_0^\delta \left(1 - \frac{u}{U}\right)dy \qquad \qquad ...(7.1)$$

Momentum thickness (θ) :

"*Momentum thickness*" *is defined as the distance through which the total loss of momentum per second be equal to if it were passing a stationary plate.* It is denoted by θ.

It may also be defined as the *distance, measured perpendicular to the boundary of the solid body, by which the boundary should be displaced to compensate for reduction in momentum of the flowing fluid on account of boundary layer formation.*

Refer Fig. 7.2. Mass of flow per second through the elementary strip $= \rho\ u\ dy$

Momentum/sec of this fluid inside the boundary layer $= \rho\ u\ dy \times u = \rho\ u^2 dy$

Momentum/sec of the same mass of fluid before entering boundary layer $= \rho u\ Udy$

Loss of momentum/sec $= \rho u Udy - \rho u^2 dy = \rho u(U - u)\ dy$

∴ Total loss of momentum/sec.

$$= \int_0^\delta \rho u \, (U - u) \, dy \qquad \qquad ...(i)$$

Let θ = Distance by which plate is displaced when the fluid is flowing with a constant velocity U.

Then loss of momentum/sec of fluid flowing through distance θ with a velocity U

$$= \rho \, \theta \, U^2 \qquad \qquad ...(ii)$$

Equating eqns. (i) and (ii), we have

$$\rho \theta U^2 = \int_0^\delta \rho u \, (U - u) \, dy$$

or,

$$\theta = \int_0^\delta \frac{u}{U} \left(1 - \frac{u}{U} \right) dy \qquad \qquad ...(7.2)$$

The momentum thickness is useful in *kinetics*.

Energy thickness (δ_e) :

"Energy thickness" is defined as the distance, measured perpendicular to the boundary of the solid body, by which the boundary should be displaced to compensate for the reduction in K.E. of the flowing fluid on account of boundary layer formation. It is denoted by δ_e.

Refer to Fig. 7.2. Mass of flow per second through the elementary strip = $\rho u dy$

K.E. of this fluid inside the boundary layer

$$= \frac{1}{2} m u^2 = \frac{1}{2} \, (\rho u dy) \, u^2$$

K.E. of the same mass of fluid before entering the boundary layer

$$= \frac{1}{2} \, (\rho u dy) \, U^2$$

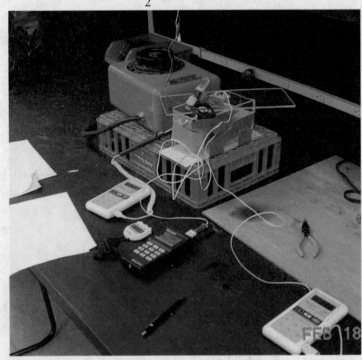

Forced convection heat transfer analysis.

Loss of K.E. through elementary strip

$$= \frac{1}{2} \, (\rho u dy) \, U^2 - \frac{1}{2} \, (\rho u dy) \, u^2 = \frac{1}{2} \rho u \, (U^2 - u^2) \, dy \qquad \qquad ...(i)$$

$\therefore$ Total loss of K.E. of fluid $= \int\limits_0^\delta \frac{1}{2} \rho u \, (U^2 - u^2) \, dy$

Let, δ_e = Distance by which the plate is displaced to compensate for the reduction in K.E.
Then loss of K.E. through δ_e of fluid flowing with velocity U

$$= \frac{1}{2} \, (\rho U \delta_e) U^2 \qquad \qquad ...(ii)$$

Equating eqns. (i) and (ii), we have

$$\frac{1}{2} \, (\rho U \delta_e) U^2 = \int\limits_0^\delta \frac{1}{2} \rho u (U^2 - u^2) \, dy$$

or, $$\delta_e = \frac{1}{U^3} \int\limits_0^\delta u (U^2 - u^2) \, dy$$

$\therefore$ $$\delta_e = \int\limits_0^\delta \frac{u}{U} \left(1 - \frac{u^2}{U^2} \right) dy \qquad \qquad ...(7.3)$$

Example 7.1. *The velocity distribution in the boundary layer is given by :* $\dfrac{u}{U} = \dfrac{y}{\delta}$, *where u is the velocity at a distance y from the plate and u = U at y = δ, δ being boundary layer thickness. Find :*

   (i)   *The displacement thickness,*   (ii)   *The momentum thickness,*

  (iii)   *The energy thickness, and*   (iv)   *The value of* $\dfrac{\delta*}{\theta}$.

Solution. Velocity distribution : $\dfrac{u}{U} = \dfrac{y}{\delta}$ ...(Given)

(i) The displacement thickness, δ* :

$$\delta* = \int\limits_0^\delta \left(1 - \frac{u}{U} \right) dy \qquad \qquad ...[Eqn.\ (7.1)]$$

$$= \int\limits_0^\delta \left(1 - \frac{y}{\delta} \right) dy \qquad \qquad \left(\because \frac{u}{U} = \frac{y}{\delta} \right)$$

$$= \left[y - \frac{y^2}{2\delta} \right]_0^\delta$$

$$\delta* = \left(\delta - \frac{\delta^2}{2\delta} \right) = \delta - \frac{\delta}{2} = \frac{\delta}{2} \text{ (Ans.)}$$

(ii) The momentum thickness, θ :

$$\theta = \int\limits_0^\delta \frac{u}{U} \left(1 - \frac{u}{U} \right) dy \qquad \qquad ...[Eqn.\ (7.2)]$$

$$= \int\limits_0^\delta \frac{y}{\delta} \left(1 - \frac{y}{\delta} \right) dy = \int\limits_0^\delta \left(\frac{y}{\delta} - \frac{y^2}{\delta^2} \right) dy$$

or, $$\theta = \left[\frac{y^2}{2\delta} - \frac{y^3}{3\delta^2} \right]_0^\delta = \frac{\delta^2}{2\delta} - \frac{\delta^3}{3\delta^2} = \frac{\delta}{2} - \frac{\delta}{3} = \frac{\delta}{6} \text{ (Ans.)}$$

(iii) The energy thickness, δ_e :

$$\delta_e = \int\limits_0^\delta \frac{u}{U} \left(1 - \frac{u^2}{U^2} \right) dy \qquad \qquad ...[Eqn.\ (7.3)]$$

$$= \int_0^\delta \frac{y}{\delta}\left(1 - \frac{y^2}{\delta^2}\right)dy = \int_0^\delta \left(\frac{y}{\delta} - \frac{y^3}{\delta^3}\right)dy$$

$$= \left[\frac{y^2}{2\delta} - \frac{y^4}{4\delta^3}\right]_0^\delta = \frac{\delta^2}{2\delta} - \frac{\delta^4}{4\delta^3} = \frac{\delta}{2} - \frac{\delta}{4} = \frac{\delta}{4}$$

i.e., $$\delta_e = \frac{\delta}{4} \quad \text{(Ans.)}$$

(iv) The value of $\dfrac{\delta^*}{\theta}$:

$$\frac{\delta^*}{\theta} = \frac{\delta/2}{\delta/6} = 3.0 \quad \text{(Ans.)}$$

Example 7.2. *The velocity distribution in the boundary layer is given by* $\dfrac{u}{U} = \dfrac{3}{2}\dfrac{y}{\delta} - \dfrac{1}{2}\dfrac{y^2}{\delta^2}$, δ *being boundary layer thickness.*

Calculate the following :

(i) *The ratio of displacement thickness to boundary layer thickness* $\left(\dfrac{\delta^*}{\delta}\right)$.

(ii) *The ratio of momentum thickness to boundary layer thickness* $\left(\dfrac{\theta}{\delta}\right)$.

Solution. Velocity distribution : $\dfrac{u}{U} = \dfrac{3}{2}\dfrac{y}{\delta} - \dfrac{1}{2}\dfrac{y^2}{\delta^2}$ ...(Given)

(i) δ^*/δ :

$$\delta^* = \int_0^\delta \left(1 - \frac{u}{U}\right)dy = \int_0^\delta \left(1 - \frac{3}{2}\frac{y}{\delta} + \frac{1}{2}\frac{y^2}{\delta^2}\right)dy$$

$$= \left[y - \frac{3}{2}\times\frac{y^2}{2\delta} + \frac{1}{2}\times\frac{y^3}{3\delta^2}\right]_0^\delta$$

$$= \left[\delta - \frac{3}{4}\cdot\frac{\delta^2}{\delta} + \frac{1}{2}\times\frac{\delta^3}{3\delta^2}\right] = \left(\delta - \frac{3}{4}\delta + \frac{\delta}{6}\right) = \frac{5}{12}\delta$$

∴ $$\frac{\delta^*}{\delta} = \frac{5}{12}$$

(ii) θ/δ :

$$\theta = \int_0^\delta \frac{u}{U}\left(1 - \frac{u}{U}\right)dy$$

$$= \int_0^\delta \left(\frac{3}{2}\frac{y}{\delta} - \frac{1}{2}\frac{y^2}{\delta^2}\right)\left(1 - \frac{3}{2}\frac{y}{\delta} + \frac{1}{2}\frac{y^2}{\delta^2}\right)dy$$

$$= \int_0^\delta \left(\frac{3}{2}\frac{y}{\delta} - \frac{9}{4}\frac{y^2}{\delta^2} + \frac{3}{4}\cdot\frac{y^3}{\delta^3} - \frac{1}{2}\frac{y^2}{\delta^2} + \frac{3}{4}\frac{y^3}{\delta^3} - \frac{1}{4}\frac{y^4}{\delta^4}\right)dy$$

$$= \int_0^\delta \left[\frac{3}{2}\frac{y}{\delta} - \left(\frac{9}{4}\frac{y^2}{\delta^2} + \frac{1}{2}\frac{y^2}{\delta^2}\right) + \left(\frac{3}{4}\frac{y^3}{\delta^3} + \frac{3}{4}\frac{y^3}{\delta^3}\right) - \frac{1}{4}\frac{y^4}{\delta^4}\right]dy$$

$$= \int_0^\delta \left[\frac{3}{2}\frac{y}{\delta} - \frac{11}{4}\frac{y^2}{\delta^2} + \frac{3}{2}\frac{y^3}{\delta^3} - \frac{1}{4}\frac{y^4}{\delta^4}\right]dy$$

$$= \left[\frac{3}{2} \times \frac{y^2}{2\delta} - \frac{11}{4} \times \frac{y^3}{3\delta^2} + \frac{3}{2} \times \frac{y^4}{4\delta^3} - \frac{1}{4} \times \frac{y^5}{5\delta^4} \right]_0^\delta$$

$$= \left[\frac{3}{2} \times \frac{\delta^2}{2\delta} - \frac{11}{4} \times \frac{\delta^3}{3\delta^2} + \frac{3}{2} \times \frac{\delta^4}{4\delta^3} - \frac{1}{4} \times \frac{\delta^5}{5\delta^4} \right]_0^\delta$$

$$= \left(\frac{3}{4}\delta - \frac{11}{12}\delta + \frac{3}{8}\delta - \frac{1}{20}\delta \right) = \frac{19}{120}\delta$$

or, $$\frac{\theta}{\delta} = \frac{19}{120} \quad \text{(Ans.)}$$

Example 7.3. *If velocity distribution in laminar boundary layer over a flat plate is assumed to be given by second order polynomial $u = a + by + cy^2$, determine its form using the necessary boundary conditions.*

Solution. Velocity distribution : $u = a + by + cy^2$

The following boundary conditions must be satisfied :

(i) At $y = 0,$ $u = 0$

∴, $u = a + by + cy^2$

      $0 = a + 0 + 0$ ∴ $a = 0$

(ii) At $y = \delta,$ $u = U$

∴ $U = b\delta + c\delta^2$ ...(i)

(iii) At $y = \delta,$ $\dfrac{du}{dy} = 0$

∴ $\left(\dfrac{du}{dy} \right)_{y=\delta} = \dfrac{d}{dy}(a + by + cy^2) = b + 2cy = b + 2c\delta = 0$ ...(ii)

Substituting the value of $b \ (= -2c\delta)$ from (ii) in (i), we get

$$U = (-2c\delta)\delta + c\delta^2 = -2c\delta^2 + c\delta^2 = -c\delta^2$$

or, $$c = -\frac{U}{\delta^2}$$

∴ $$b = -2c\delta = -2 \times \left(-\frac{U}{\delta^2} \right)\delta = \frac{2U}{\delta}$$

Hence form of the velocity distribution is

$$u = \frac{2U}{\delta}y - \frac{U}{\delta^2}y^2$$

or, $$\frac{u}{U} = 2\left(\frac{y}{\delta} \right) - \left(\frac{y}{\delta} \right)^2 \quad \text{(Ans.)}$$

7.1.2. MOMENTUM EQUATION FOR HYDRODYNAMIC BOUNDARY LAYER OVER A FLAT PLATE

Consider a fluid flowing over a stationary flat plate and the development of hydrodynamic boundary layer as shown in Fig. 7.3. (*a*). In order to derive a differential equation for the boundary layer, let us consider an elemental, two-dimensional control volume ($dx \times dy \times$ unit depth) within the boundary layer region [enlarged view shown in Fig. 7.3 (*b*)]. Following **assumptions** are made:

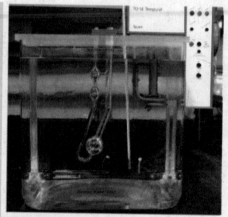

Viscosity of the fluid is constant.

1. The flow is steady and the fluid is incompressible.
2. The viscosity of the fluid is constant.
3. The pressure variations in the direction perpendicular to the plate are negligible.
4. Viscous-shear forces in the Y-direction are negligible.
5. Fluid is continuous both in space and time.

Refer Figure 7.3. (b). Let u = Velocity of fluid flow at left hand face AB.

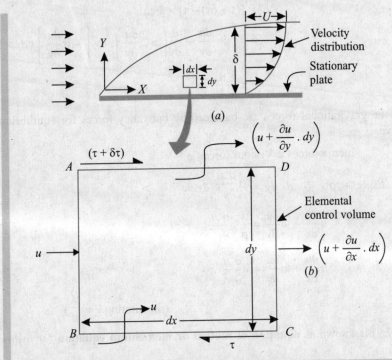

Fig. 7.3. Equation of motion for boundary layer.

Then, $u + \dfrac{\partial u}{\partial x}.dx$ = Velocity of fluid flow at the right hand face CD (since the flow velocity changes in the X-direction at the rate of change given by $\dfrac{\partial u}{\partial x}$ and the change in velocity during distance dx will be $\left(\dfrac{\partial u}{\partial x}.dx\right)$.

Similarly, let, v = Fluid velocity at the bottom face BC,

then, $v + \dfrac{\partial v}{\partial y}dy$ = fluid velocity at the top-face AD.

The mass flow rate along X-direction, $m_x = \rho u\,(dy \times 1) = \rho u\,dy$ ...(7.4)

The change of momentum of the mass m_x along X-direction is given by

$dM_x = m_x \times$ change in velocity in X-direction

$$= m_x\left[\left(u + \dfrac{\partial u}{\partial x}.dx\right) - u\right] = m_x\left(\dfrac{\partial u}{\partial x}.dx\right)$$

$$= \rho u \dfrac{\partial u}{\partial x}.dx.dy \qquad ...(7.5)$$

The mass flow rate along Y-direction, $m_y = \rho v\,(dx \times 1) = \rho v dx$ ...(7.6)

The change of momentum of the mass m_y along Y-direction is given by

$$dM_y = m_y \left[\left(u + \frac{\partial u}{\partial y} \cdot dy \right) - u \right] = m_y \left(\frac{\partial u}{\partial y} \cdot dy \right)$$

$$= \rho \upsilon \frac{\partial u}{\partial y} \cdot dx.dy \qquad \qquad ...(7.7)$$

Total viscous force along the X-direction is given by

$$F_x = [(\tau + \delta\tau) - \tau] \times \text{area}$$

$$= \left[\left\{ \mu \cdot \frac{\partial u}{\partial y} + \frac{\partial}{\partial y} \left(u \cdot \frac{\partial u}{\partial y} \right) \cdot dy \right\} - \mu \frac{\partial u}{\partial y} \right] (dx \times 1)$$

$$= \mu \frac{\partial^2 u}{\partial y^2} \cdot dx. \, dy \qquad \qquad ...(7.8)$$

Assuming the gravitational forces are balanced by buoyancy forces for equilibrium of the element, we have

$$\text{Inertia forces} = \text{Viscous forces}$$

$$\therefore \quad \rho u \frac{\partial u}{\partial x} \cdot dx.dy + \rho \upsilon \frac{\partial u}{\partial y} \cdot dx.dy = \mu \frac{\partial^2 u}{\partial y^2} \cdot dx.dy$$

$$\text{or,} \qquad u \frac{\partial u}{\partial x} + \upsilon \frac{\partial u}{\partial y} = \frac{\mu}{\rho} \cdot \frac{\partial^2 u}{\partial y^2}$$

$$\text{or,} \qquad u \frac{\partial u}{\partial x} + \upsilon \frac{\partial u}{\partial y} = v \frac{\partial^2 u}{\partial y^2} \qquad \qquad ...(7.9)$$

$$\left(\text{substituting } v = \frac{\mu}{\rho} \right)$$

Equation (7.9) is known as **equation of motion or momentum equation** *for hydrodynamic boundary layer.*

7.1.3. BLASIUS EXACT SOLUTION FOR LAMINAR BOUNDARY LAYER FLOWS

The velocity distribution in the boundary layer can be obtained by solving the equation of motion for hydrodynamic boundary layer [Eqn. (7.9)]. The following boundary conditions should be satisfied.

    (*i*)   At $y = 0$, $u = 0$ (*ii*)   At $y = 0$, $\upsilon = 0$ (*iii*)   At $y = \infty$, $u = U$

The Blasius technique for an exact solution of the hydrodynamic boundary layer lies in the conversion of the following differential equations into a single differential equation.

The hydrodynamic equation for boundary layer : $\quad u \dfrac{\partial u}{\partial x} + \upsilon \dfrac{\partial u}{\partial y} = v \dfrac{\partial^2 u}{\partial y^2}$ ...(Eqn. 7.9)

Continuity equation : $\quad \dfrac{\partial u}{\partial x} + \dfrac{\partial \upsilon}{\partial y} = 0$ ...(7.10)

Prandtl suggested that the solution of Eqn. (7.9) can be obtained by reducing the number of variables with the help of magnitude analysis of the boundary layer thickness and transforming the partial differential equation into ordinary differentials.

The *inertia forces* represented by the left terms, in the Eqn. (7.9), must be balanced by the viscous forces represented by the right terms.

As $u \geq \upsilon$, therefore, we may write as

$$\rho u \frac{\partial u}{\partial x} = \mu \frac{\partial^2 u}{\partial y^2} \qquad \left(\because \upsilon = \frac{\mu}{\rho} \right)$$

Also as $u \propto U$ and $\frac{\partial u}{\partial x} \propto \frac{U}{L}$, along a plate length L, therefore, we have

$$\frac{\rho U^2}{L} = \mu \frac{U}{\delta^2}$$

$$\therefore \qquad \delta = \sqrt{\frac{\mu L}{\rho U}} = \sqrt{\frac{\nu L}{U}} = \sqrt{\frac{\nu x}{U}} \qquad \qquad ...(7.11)$$

From experiments it has been observed that velocity profiles at different locations along the plate are geometrically similar, *i.e.*, they differ only by a **stretching factor** in the Y-direction. This implies that the dimensionless velocity $\frac{u}{U}$ can be expressed at any location x as a function of the dimensionless distance from the wall $\frac{y}{\delta}$.

$$\frac{u}{U} = f\left(\frac{y}{\delta} \right) \qquad \qquad ...(7.12)$$

Substituting the value of δ from eqn. (7.11) in eqn. (7.12), we obtain,

$$\frac{u}{U} = f\left[\frac{y}{\sqrt{x}} \sqrt{\frac{U}{\nu}} \right] = f(\eta) \qquad \qquad ...(7.13)$$

where, $\qquad \eta = y \sqrt{\dfrac{U}{\nu x}}$ denotes the *stretching factor*.

In order to account for the fact that the vertical component of velocity occurs in the boundary layer equation of motion (7.9), it is essential to define a **stream function** ψ such that,

$$\frac{\psi}{U} = \left[\sqrt{\frac{\nu x}{U}} \right] f(\eta) \qquad \qquad ...(7.14)$$

or, $\qquad \psi = \sqrt{\nu x U} \, f(\eta) \qquad \qquad ...[7.14\,(a)]$

The continuous stream function ψ is the mathematical postulation such that its partial differential with respect to x gives the velocity in the Y-direction (generally taken as negative) and its partial differential with respect to y gives the velocity in the X-direction :

$$u = \frac{\partial \psi}{\partial y} ; \qquad \qquad \upsilon = \frac{\partial \psi}{\partial x}$$

$$\therefore \qquad u = \frac{\partial \psi}{\partial y} = \frac{\partial \psi}{\partial \eta} \times \frac{\partial \eta}{\partial y} = \frac{\partial}{\partial \eta} \left[U \sqrt{\frac{\nu x}{U}} f(\eta) \right] \times \frac{\partial}{\partial y} \left[y \sqrt{\frac{U}{\nu x}} \right]$$

or, $\qquad u = U \sqrt{\dfrac{\nu x}{U}} \dfrac{df}{d\eta} \left[\sqrt{\dfrac{U}{\nu x}} \right] = U \dfrac{df}{d\eta} \qquad \qquad ...(7.15)$

Here f is abbreviated as $f(\eta)$

$$\therefore \qquad \frac{\partial u}{\partial x} = U \frac{\partial}{\partial x}\left(\frac{df}{d\eta} \right) = U \frac{\partial}{\partial \eta}\left(\frac{df}{d\eta} \right)\frac{\partial \eta}{\partial x} = -U \frac{d^2 f}{d\eta^2} \cdot \frac{1}{2x} \cdot y \sqrt{\frac{U}{\nu x}}$$

or, $\qquad \dfrac{\partial u}{\partial x} = -U \dfrac{\eta}{2x} \dfrac{d^2 f}{d\eta^2} \qquad \qquad ...(7.16)$

Now, $\dfrac{\partial u}{\partial y} = U \dfrac{\partial}{\partial y}\left(\dfrac{df}{d\eta}\right) = U \dfrac{\partial}{\partial \eta}\left(\dfrac{\partial f}{\partial \eta}\right)\dfrac{\partial \eta}{\partial y} \cdot U\sqrt{\dfrac{U}{vx}} \cdot \dfrac{d^2 f}{d\eta^2}$ ... (7.17)

Similarly, $\dfrac{\partial^2 u}{\partial y^2} = \dfrac{U^2}{vx} \cdot \dfrac{d^3 f}{d\eta^3}$ ...(7.18)

Again,
$$v = -\dfrac{\partial \psi}{\partial x} = -\dfrac{\partial}{\partial x}\left[\sqrt{\dfrac{vx}{U}}\, f(\eta)\right] = -U\sqrt{\dfrac{v}{U}} \cdot \dfrac{\partial}{\partial x}\left[\sqrt{x}\, f(\eta)\right]$$

$$= -U\sqrt{\dfrac{v}{U}} \cdot \left[\sqrt{x}\,\dfrac{\partial f}{\partial x} + f \cdot \dfrac{\partial}{\partial x}\left(\sqrt{x}\right)\right]$$

$$= -U\sqrt{\dfrac{v}{U}} \cdot \left[\sqrt{x}\,\dfrac{\partial f}{\partial \eta}\cdot\dfrac{\partial \eta}{\partial x} + \dfrac{f}{2\sqrt{x}}\right]$$

$$= -U\sqrt{\dfrac{v}{U}} \cdot \left[\sqrt{x}\,\dfrac{\partial f}{\partial \eta}\cdot\dfrac{\partial}{\partial x}\left\{y\sqrt{\dfrac{U}{vx}}\right\} + \dfrac{f}{2\sqrt{x}}\right]$$

$$= -U\sqrt{\dfrac{v}{U}} \cdot \left[\sqrt{x}\,\dfrac{\partial f}{\partial \eta}\cdot y\sqrt{\dfrac{U}{v}}\left(-\dfrac{1}{2}\right)\dfrac{1}{x\sqrt{x}} + \dfrac{f}{2\sqrt{x}}\right]$$

$$= -\sqrt{Uv}\,\dfrac{1}{2\sqrt{x}}\left[-\dfrac{df}{d\eta}\, y\sqrt{\dfrac{U}{vx}} + f\right]$$

$$= -\dfrac{1}{2}\sqrt{\dfrac{Ux}{x}}\left[-\eta\dfrac{df}{d\eta} + f\right]$$

or, $v = \dfrac{1}{2}\sqrt{\dfrac{Uv}{x}}\left[-\eta\dfrac{df}{d\eta} - f\right]$ ...(7.19)

Inserting the values of $u, \dfrac{\partial u}{\partial x}, \dfrac{\partial u}{\partial y}, \dfrac{\partial^2 u}{\partial x^2}$ and v from eqns. (7.15), (7.16), (7.17), and (7.18) in eqn. (7.9), we get

$$-U\dfrac{df}{d\eta}\cdot U\dfrac{\eta}{2x}\cdot\dfrac{d^2 f}{d\eta^2} + \dfrac{1}{2}\sqrt{\dfrac{Uv}{x}}\left[\eta\dfrac{df}{d\eta} - f\right]\cdot U\sqrt{\dfrac{U}{vx}}\dfrac{d^2 f}{d\eta^2} = v\dfrac{U^2}{vx}\cdot\dfrac{d^3 f}{d\eta^3}$$

or, $-\dfrac{1}{2x}\cdot U^2 \dfrac{df}{d\eta}\cdot\eta\dfrac{d^2 f}{d\eta^2} + \dfrac{1}{2x}U^2\dfrac{d^2 f}{d\eta^2}\left[\eta\dfrac{df}{d\eta} - f\right] = \dfrac{U^2}{x}\cdot\dfrac{d^3 f}{d\eta^3}$

or, $-\dfrac{1}{2x}U^2\dfrac{d^2 f}{d\eta^2}\left[\eta\dfrac{df}{d\eta} - \eta\dfrac{df}{d\eta} + f\right] = \dfrac{U^2}{x}\dfrac{d^3 f}{d\eta^3}$

or, $-\dfrac{1}{2x}U^2\dfrac{d^2 f}{d\eta^2}\cdot f = \dfrac{U^2}{x}\dfrac{d^3 f}{d\eta^3}$

or, $2\dfrac{d^3 f}{d\eta^3} + f\dfrac{d^2 f}{d\eta^2} = 0$

or, $2f''' + ff'' = 0$ ...(7.20)

which is an ordinary (but non-linear) differential equation for f. The number of primes on f denotes the number of successive derivatives of $f(\eta)$ with respect to y. The physical and transformed boundary conditions are :

Physical boundary conditions			Transformed boundary conditions		
(i) At	$y = 0$,	$u = 0$	At $\eta = 0$,	$\dfrac{df}{d\eta} = f' = 0$
(ii) At	$y = 0$,	$\upsilon = 0$	At $\eta = 0$,	$f = 0$
(iii) At	$y = \infty$	$u = U$	At $\eta = \infty$,	$\dfrac{df}{d\eta} = f' = 1$

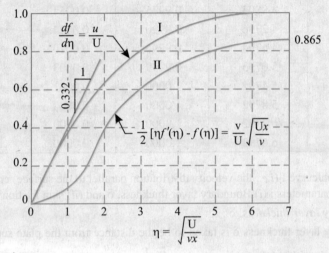

Fig. 7.4. Velocity distribution in boundary layer on flat plate by Howarth.

The numerical solution of Eqn. (7.20) with the corresponding values of u and υ are plotted in Fig. 7.4, and the results are listed in table 7.1.

The following results are of particular interest :

1. The single curve II shows the variation of normal velocity $\dfrac{v}{U}$. It is to be noted that at the outer edge of the boundary layer where $\eta \to \infty$, this does not go to zero but approaches the value

$$v = 0.865\, U\, \sqrt{\dfrac{v}{Ux}} \qquad \qquad ...(7.21)$$

Table 7.1. Laminar boundary layer solution for a flat plate

η	f	$f' = \dfrac{u}{U}$	f''	$\dfrac{1}{2}(\eta f' - f)$
0	0	0	0.3321	0
0.2	0.0664	0.0664	0.3320	0.0033
0.4	0.0266	0.1328	0.3315	0.0133
0.8	0.1061	0.2647	0.3274	0.0528
1.2	0.2379	0.3938	0.3166	0.1173
1.6	0.4203	0.5169	0.2967	0.2032
2.0	0.6500	0.6298	0.2667	0.3047
2.4	0.9223	0.7290	0. 2281	0.4136
2.8	1. 2310	0.8115	0. 1840	0.5206
3.2	1.5691	0.8761	0.1391	0.6172

3.6	1.9294	0.9233	0.0981	0.6972
4.0	2.3058	0.9555	0.0642	0.7582
4.4	2.6924	0.9759	0.0390	0.8007
4.8	3.0853	0.9878	0.0219	0.8280
5.0	3.2833	0.9915	0.0159	0.8372
5.2	3.4820	0.9942	0.0113	0.8441
5.6	3.8803	0.9975	0.0054	0.8528
6.0	4.2796	0.9990	0.0024	0.8571
6.4	4.6794	0.9996	0.0010	0.8591
6.8	5.0793	0.9999	0.0003	0.8599
7.2	5.4792	1.0000	0.0001	0.8602
7.6	5.8792	1.0000	0.0000	0.8603
8.0	6.2792	1.0000	0.0000	0.8604
8.4	6.6792	1.0000	0.0000	0.8604

2. The graph/curve I (*i.e.*, the velocity distribution parallel to the surface) enables us to calculate the parameters : (*i*) Boundary layer thickness, δ and (*ii*) skin friction coefficient, C_f.

(*i*)   *Boundary layer thickness*, δ :

The boundary layer thickness δ is taken to be the distance from the plate surface to a point at which the velocity is within 1% of the asymptotic limit, *i.e.*, $\dfrac{u}{U} = 0.99$; it occurs at $\eta = 5.0$ (Fig. 7.4). Therefore, the value of η at the edge of boundary layer ($y = \delta$) is given by

$$\eta = y\sqrt{\frac{U}{vx}} = \delta\sqrt{\frac{U}{vx}} = 5$$

or,

$$\frac{\delta}{x} = 5\sqrt{\frac{v}{Ux}} = \frac{5}{\sqrt{Re_x}} \qquad \text{...(7.22)}$$

where $Re_x = \dfrac{Ux}{v}$ is the *local* Reynolds number based on distance x from the leading edge of the plate.

(*ii*)   *Skin friction coefficient* ; C_f:

The skin friction coefficient (C_f) is defined *as the ratio of shear stress* τ_0 *at the plate to the dynamic head* $\dfrac{1}{2}\rho U^2$ *caused by free stream velocity*. Thus the local skin friction coefficient C_{fx} at any value of x is

$$C_{fx} = \frac{\tau_0}{\frac{1}{2}\rho U^2} = \frac{\mu\left(\dfrac{\partial u}{\partial y}\right)_{y=0}}{\frac{1}{2}\rho U^2} \qquad \text{...(7.23)}$$

From Fig. 7.4, the gradient at $\eta = 0$ is

$$\left[\frac{\partial(u/U)}{d\eta}\right]_{\eta=0} = 0.332$$

or,

$$\frac{1}{U}\left(\frac{\partial u}{\partial y}\right)_{y=0} = 0.332$$

But $\left(\dfrac{\partial u}{\partial y}\right)_{y=0} = \left(\dfrac{\partial u}{\partial \eta}\right)_{y=0}\left(\dfrac{\partial \eta}{\partial y}\right)$

or, $\left(\dfrac{\partial u}{\partial y}\right)_{y=0} = 0.332\, U \sqrt{\dfrac{U}{vx}}$

or, $C_{fx} = \dfrac{0.332\, U\mu \sqrt{\dfrac{U}{vx}}}{\dfrac{1}{2}\rho U^2} = 0.664 \sqrt{\dfrac{v}{Ux}}$

or, $C_{fx} = \dfrac{0.664}{\sqrt{Re_x}}$ ...(7.24)

The average value of the skin friction coefficient $\overline{C}_f$ can be determined by integrating the local skin friction coefficient Cf_x from $x=0$ to $x=L$ (where L is the plate length) and then dividing the integrated result by the plate length

Constant temperature forced convection oven

$$\overline{C}_f = \frac{1}{L}\int_0^L C_{fx}\, dx = \frac{1}{L}\int_0^L \frac{0.664}{\sqrt{Ux/v}}\, dx = \frac{0.664}{L\sqrt{Ux/v}}\int_0^L \frac{1}{\sqrt{x}}\, dx$$

$$\frac{0.664}{L\sqrt{U/v}}\left[2\sqrt{x}\right]_0^L = \frac{1.328\sqrt{L}}{L\sqrt{U/v}} = \frac{1.328}{\sqrt{UL/v}} = \frac{1.328}{\sqrt{Re_L}}$$

i.e., $$\overline{C}_f = \frac{1.328}{\sqrt{Re_L}}$$ ...(7.25)

where Re_L is the Reynolds number based upon total length L of the plate.

7.1.4. VON KARMAN INTEGRAL MOMENTUM EQUATION (APPROXIMATE HYDRODYNAMIC BOUNDARY LAYER ANALYSIS)

Since it is difficult to obtain the exact solution of hydrodynamic boundary layer [Eqn. (7.9)] even for as simple geometry as flat plate (moreover the proper similarity variable is not known or does not exist, for many practical shapes), therefore, a substitute procedure entailing adequate accuracy has been developed which is known as "*Approximate Integral Method* " and this is based upon a boundary-layer momentum equation derived by *Von Karman*.

Von Karman suggested a method based on the *momentum equation* by the use of which the growth of a boundry layer along a flat plate, the wall shear stress and the drag force could be determined (when the velocity distribution in the boundary layer is known). Starting from the beginning of the plate, the method can be used for both *laminar and turbulent boundary layers*.

Figure 7.5, shows a fluid flowing over a thin plate (placed at zero incidence) with a free stream velocity equal to U. Consider a small length dx of the plate at a distance x from the leading edge as shown in Fig. 7.5 (*a*) ; the enlarged view of the small length of the plate is shown in Fig. 7.5 (*b*). Consider *unit width* of plate perpendicular to the direction of flow.

Let *ABCD* be a small element of a boundary layer (the edge DC represents the outer edge of the boundary layer).

Mass rate of fluid entering through *AD*

$$= \int_0^\delta \rho u\, dy$$

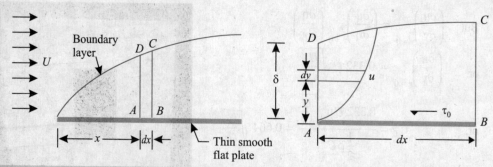

Fig. 7.5. Momentum equation for boundary layer by Von Karman.

Mass rate of fluid leaving through BC

$$= \int_0^\delta \rho u \, dy \; \frac{d}{dx} \left[\int_0^\delta \rho u \, dy \right] dx$$

∴   Mass rate of fluid entering the control volume through the surface DC = Mass rate of fluid through BC − mass rate of fluid through AD

$$= \int_0^\delta \rho u \, dy + \frac{d}{dx} \left[\int_0^\delta \rho u \, dy \right] dx - \int_0^\delta \rho u \, dy$$

$$= \frac{d}{dx} \left[\int_0^\delta \rho u \, dy \right] dx$$

The fluid is entering through DC with a uniform velocity U.

Momentum rate of fluid entering the control volume in x-direction through AD

$$= \int_0^\delta \rho u^2 \, dy$$

Momentum rate of fluid leaving the control volume in x-direction through BC

$$= \int_0^\delta \rho u^2 \, dy + \frac{d}{dx} \left[\int_0^\delta \rho u^2 \, dy \right] dx$$

Momentum rate of fluid entering the control volume through DC in x-direction

$$= \frac{d}{dx} \left[\int_0^\delta \rho u \, dy \right] dx \times U \qquad\qquad (\because \text{Velocity} = U)$$

$$= \frac{d}{dx} \left[\int_0^\delta \rho u \, U \, dy \right] dx$$

∴   Rate of change of momentum of control volume = Momentum rate of fluid through BC − momentum rate of fluid through AD − momentum rate of fluid through DC.

$$= \int_0^\delta \rho u^2 \, dy + \frac{d}{dx} \left[\int_0^\delta \rho u^2 \, dy \right] dx - \int_0^\delta \rho u^2 \, dy - \frac{d}{dx} \left[\int_0^\delta \rho u \, U \, dy \right] dx$$

$$= \frac{d}{dx} \left[\int_0^\delta \rho u^2 \, dy - \int_0^\delta \rho u \, U \, dy \right] dx$$

$$= \frac{d}{dx} \left[\int_0^\delta (\rho u^2 \, dy - \rho u \, U \, dy) \right] dx$$

$$= \frac{d}{dx} \left[\rho \int_0^\delta (u^2 - u \, U) \, dy \right] dx \qquad (\rho \text{ is constant for incompressible fluid})$$

$$= \rho \frac{d}{dx}\left[\int_0^\delta (u^2 - u\,U)\,dy\right]dx \qquad \qquad ...(7.26)$$

As per momentum principle the rate of change of momentum on the control volume *ABCD* must be equal to the total force on the control volume in the same direction. The only external force acting on the control volume is the shear force acting on the side *AB* in the direction *B* to *A* (Fig. 7.5*b*). The value of this force (*drag force*) is given by

$$\Delta F_D = \tau_0 \times dx$$

Thus the total external force in the direction of rate of change of momentum

$$= -\tau_0 \times dx \qquad \qquad ...(7.27)$$

Equating the eqns. (7.26) and (7.27), we have

$$-\tau_0 \times dx = \rho \frac{d}{dx}\left[\int_0^\delta (u^2 - u\,U)\,dy\right]dx$$

or,

$$\tau_0 = -\rho \frac{d}{dx}\left[\int_0^\delta (u^2 - u\,U)\,dy\right]$$

or,

$$= \rho \frac{d}{dx}\left[\int_0^\delta (uU - u^2)\,dy\right]$$

$$= \rho \frac{d}{dx}\left[\int_0^\delta U^2\left(\frac{u}{U} - \frac{u^2}{U^2}\right)dy\right]$$

or,

$$\tau_0 = \rho U^2 \frac{d}{dx}\left[\int_0^\delta \frac{u}{U}\left(1 - \frac{u}{U}\right)dy\right] \qquad \qquad ...(7.28)$$

or,

$$\frac{\tau_0}{\rho U^2} = \frac{d}{dx}\left[\int_0^\delta \frac{u}{U}\left(1 - \frac{u}{U}\right)dy\right] \qquad \qquad ...[7.28\ (a)]$$

But,

$$\int_0^\delta \frac{u}{U}\left(1 - \frac{u}{U}\right)dy = \text{Momentum thickness } (\theta)$$

∴

$$\frac{\tau_0}{\rho U^2} = \frac{d\theta}{dx} \qquad \qquad ...[7.28\ (b)]$$

Equation (7.28) is known as *Von Karman momentum equation for boundary layer flow*, and is *used to find out the frictional drag on smooth flat plate for both laminar and turbulent boundary layers.* Evidently, this integral equation (7.28) expresses the wall shear stress τ_0 as a function of the non-dimensional velocity distribution $\frac{u}{U}$; u is a point velocity at the boundary layer and U is the velocity at the outer edge of boundary layer.

The following boundary conditions must be satisfied for any assumed velocity distribution :

(*i*) *At the surface of the plate :* $\qquad\qquad y = 0, \qquad u = 0, \qquad \dfrac{du}{dy} = \text{finite value}$

(*ii*) *At the outer edge of boundary layer :* $\quad y = \delta, \qquad u = U$

$$y = \delta, \qquad \frac{du}{dy} = 0$$

The shear stress τ_0 for a given velocity profile in laminar, transition or turbulent zone is obtained from eqn. [7.28 (*a*)] or [7.28 (*b*)]. Then drag force on a small distance *dx* of a plate is given by

$$\Delta F_D = \text{Shear stress} \times \text{area}$$

$$= \tau_0 \times (B \times dx) = \tau_0 \times B \times dx \quad (\text{where,} \quad B = \text{Width of the plate})$$

∴   Total drag on the plate of length L one side.

$$F_D = \int \Delta F_D = \int_0^L \tau_0 \times B \times dx \qquad \qquad ...(7.29)$$

−   The ratio of the shear stress τ_0 to the quantity $\dfrac{1}{2} \rho U^2$ is known as the "*Local coefficient of drag*" (or *coefficient of skin friction*) and is denoted by C_{fx}.

i.e.,
$$C_{fx} = \frac{\tau_0}{\frac{1}{2} \rho U^2} \qquad \qquad ...(7.30)$$

−   The ratio of the total drag force to the quantity $\dfrac{1}{2} \rho A U^2$ is called '*Average coefficient of drag*' and is denote by C_D.

i.e.,
$$\bar{C}_f = \frac{F_D}{\frac{1}{2} \rho A U^2} \qquad \qquad ...(7.31)$$

where,
ρ = Mass density of fluid,
A = Area of surface/plate, and
U = Free stream velocity.

It has been observed through experiments that for laminar boundary layer, the velocity distribution is parabolic and the velocity profiles at different locations along the plate are geometrically similar. This means that the dimensionless velocity $\dfrac{u}{U}$ can be expressed at any location x as a function of the dimensionless distance from the wall, $\dfrac{y}{\delta}$:

$$\frac{u}{U} = f\left(\frac{y}{\delta}\right) = a + b\left(\frac{y}{\delta}\right) + c\left(\frac{y}{\delta}\right)^2 + d\left(\frac{y}{\delta}\right)^3 \qquad \qquad ...(7.32)$$

The constants can be evaluated by using the following boundary conditions :

(i)   At $y = 0$ (wall surface), $u = U$ and $\dfrac{\partial^2 u}{\partial y^2} = 0$

(ii)   At $y = \delta$ (outer edge of the boundary layer), $u = U$ and $\dfrac{\partial u}{\partial y} = 0$

By applying boundary conditions the constants are evaluated which gives the velocity profile as :

$$\frac{u}{U} = \frac{3}{2}\left(\frac{y}{\delta}\right) - \frac{1}{2}\left(\frac{y}{\delta}\right)^3 \qquad \qquad ...(7.33)$$

In order to determine the boundary layer thickness and average skin-friction coefficient for laminar flow over a flat plate, let us now use this above velocity profile in the Von Karman integral equation. Now putting the value of $\dfrac{u}{U}$ in eqn. (7.28), we get

$$\tau_0 = \rho U^2 \frac{d}{dx}\left[\int_0^\delta \left\{ \frac{3}{2}\left(\frac{y}{\delta}\right) - \frac{1}{2}\left(\frac{y}{\delta}\right)^3 \right\} \times \left\{ 1 - \frac{3}{2}\left(\frac{y}{\delta}\right) + \frac{1}{2}\left(\frac{y}{\delta}\right)^3 \right\} dy \right]$$

$$= \rho U^2 \frac{d}{dx}\left[\int_0^\delta \left\{ \frac{3}{2}\left(\frac{y}{\delta}\right) - \frac{9}{4}\left(\frac{y}{\delta}\right)^2 + \frac{3}{4}\left(\frac{y}{\delta}\right)^4 - \frac{1}{2}\left(\frac{y}{\delta}\right)^3 + \frac{3}{4}\left(\frac{y}{\delta}\right)^4 - \frac{1}{4}\left(\frac{y}{\delta}\right)^6 \right\} dy \right]$$

or,
$$\tau_0 = \frac{39}{280} \rho U^2 \frac{d\delta}{dx} \qquad \qquad ...(7.34)$$

Newton's law of viscosity, at solid surface, gives

$$\tau_0 = \mu \left(\frac{du}{dy} \right)_{y=0}$$

$$= \mu \left[\frac{d}{dy} \left\{ \frac{3}{2} U \left(\frac{y}{\delta} \right) - \frac{1}{2} U \left(\frac{y}{\delta} \right)^3 \right\} \right]_{y=0}$$

or, $\tau_0 = \dfrac{3\mu U}{2\delta}$ ...(7.35)

From equations (7.34) and (7.35), we have

$$\frac{39}{280} \rho U^2 \frac{d\delta}{dx} = \frac{3\mu U}{2\delta}$$

or, $\delta . d\delta = \dfrac{140}{13} . \dfrac{\mu}{\rho U} dx$

Since, δ is a function of x only, integration yields

$$\frac{\delta^2}{2} = \frac{140 \,\mu x}{13\rho U} + C$$

By using the boundary condition $\delta = 0$ at $x = 0$, we obtain the integration constant $C = 0$.

$\therefore$ $\dfrac{\delta^2}{2} = \dfrac{140 \,\mu x}{13\rho U}$ or $\delta^2 = \dfrac{140 \times 2}{13} \times \dfrac{\mu x}{\rho U}$

This can be expressed in the non-dimensional form as

$$\frac{\delta}{x} = \sqrt{\frac{140 \times 2}{13}} \sqrt{\frac{\mu}{x\rho U}} = \frac{4.64}{\sqrt{Re_x}} \qquad \qquad ...(7.36)$$

where $Re_x = \dfrac{x\rho U}{\mu}$ is the Reynolds number based on distance x from the leading edge of the plate.

Further, in order to estimate the value of τ_0, substituting the value of δ from eqn. (7.36) in eqn. (7.35), we get

$$\tau_0 = \frac{3\mu U}{2} \div \frac{4.64 \, x}{\sqrt{Re_x}} \, , \quad \text{on simplification, we get}$$

$$\tau_0 = \frac{\rho U^2}{2} \times \frac{0.646}{\sqrt{Re_x}}$$

Therefore, the local skin friction coefficient,

$$C_{fx} = \frac{\tau_0}{\frac{1}{2}\rho U^2} = \frac{0.646}{\sqrt{Re_x}} \qquad \qquad ...(7.37)$$

Average value of skin friction coefficient,

$$\overline{C}_f = \frac{1}{L} \int_0^L C_{fx} dx = \frac{1}{L} \int_0^L \frac{0.646}{\sqrt{\rho U / \mu}} \frac{dx}{\sqrt{x}}$$

or, $\overline{C}_f = 1.292 \sqrt{\dfrac{\mu}{L\rho U}} = \dfrac{1.292}{\sqrt{Re_L}}$ ...(7.38)

where $Re_L = \dfrac{L\rho U}{\mu}$ is Reynolds number based on total length L of the flate.

$\overline{C}_f$ (average skin friction coefficient) is quite often referred to as the *drag coefficient*.

Mass flow through boundary layer :

The mass flow rate per unit width through the boundary layer is calculated assuming parabolic velocity distribution in the boundary layer as,

$$m_x = \int_0^\delta \rho u \, dy = \int_0^\delta \rho \left[U \left\{ \frac{3}{2} \left(\frac{y}{\delta} \right) - \frac{1}{2} \left(\frac{y}{\delta} \right)^3 \right\} \right] dy$$

or,

$$m_x = \frac{5}{8} \rho U \delta \qquad \qquad \qquad ...(7.39)$$

The results for the boundary layer thickness and average skin friction coefficient yielded by different velocity profiles have been shown in the table 7.2.

Table 7.2. Boundary layer parameters for different velocity profiles

S. No.	Velocity profile	Boundary conditions		δ	$\overline{C}_f$
		At $y = 0$	At $y = \delta$		
1.	$\dfrac{u}{U} = \dfrac{y}{\delta}$	$u = 0$	$u = U$	$\dfrac{3.46x}{\sqrt{Re_x}}$	$\dfrac{1.155}{\sqrt{Re_L}}$
2.	$\dfrac{u}{U} = 2\left(\dfrac{y}{\delta}\right) - \left(\dfrac{y}{\delta}\right)^2$	$u = 0$	$u = U$ $\dfrac{\partial u}{\partial y} = 0$	$\dfrac{5.48x}{\sqrt{Re_x}}$	$\dfrac{1.46}{\sqrt{Re_L}}$
3.	$\dfrac{u}{U} = \dfrac{3}{2}\left(\dfrac{y}{\delta}\right) - \dfrac{1}{2}\left(\dfrac{y}{\delta}\right)^3$	$u = 0$ $\dfrac{\partial^2 u}{\partial y^2} = 0$	$u = U$ $\dfrac{\partial u}{\partial y} = 0$	$\dfrac{4.64x}{\sqrt{Re_x}}$	$\dfrac{1.292}{\sqrt{Re_L}}$
4.	$\dfrac{u}{U} = \sin\left(\dfrac{\pi}{2}\dfrac{y}{\delta}\right)$	$u = 0$	$u = U$	$\dfrac{4.795x}{\sqrt{Re_x}}$	$\dfrac{1.31}{\sqrt{Re_L}}$
5.	Blasius exact solution			$\dfrac{5x}{\sqrt{Re_x}}$	$\dfrac{1.328}{\sqrt{Re_L}}$

Example 7.4. *The velocity profile for laminar boundary is in the form given below :*

$$\frac{u}{U} = 2\left(\frac{y}{\delta}\right) - \left(\frac{y}{\delta}\right)^2$$

Find the thickness of boundary layer at the end of the plate 1.5 m long and 1 m wide when placed in water flowing with a velocity of 0.12 m/s. Calculate the value of coefficient of drag also. Take μ for water = 0.001 N-s/m²

Solution. Velocity distribution $\dfrac{u}{U} = 2\left(\dfrac{y}{\delta}\right) - \left(\dfrac{y}{\delta}\right)^2$ ...(Given)

The length of the plate, $L = 1.5$ m

The width of the plate, $B = 1$ m

Forced convection type furnace.

Free stream velocity, $U = 0.12$ m/s

μ for water $= 0.001$ Ns/m^2

Thickness of the boundary layer, δ :

Reynolds number at the end of the plate (*i.e.*, at a distance of 1.5 m from the leading edge) is given by

$$Re_L = \frac{\rho UL}{\mu} = \frac{1000 \times 0.12 \times 1.5}{0.001} = 180000$$

Since $Re_L < 5 \times 10^5$, therefore, this is case of laminar boundary layer. Thickness of boundary layer at a distance of 1.5 m is given by

$$\delta = \frac{5.48\,x}{\sqrt{Re_x}}$$

$$= \frac{5.48 \times 1.5}{\sqrt{180000}} = 0.01937\,\text{m or } 19.37\,\text{mm}$$

Coefficient of drag $\overline{C}_f$:

$$\overline{C}_f = \frac{1.46}{\overline{C}_f} = \frac{1.46}{\sqrt{180000}} = \mathbf{0.00344} \ \textbf{(Ans.)}$$

Example 7.5. *Air is flowing over a smooth flat plate with a velocity of 12 m/s. The velocity profile is in the form :*

$$\frac{u}{U} = 2\left(\frac{y}{\delta}\right) - \left(\frac{y}{\delta}\right)^2$$

The length of the plate is 1.1 m and width 0.9 m. If laminar boundary layer exists upto a value of $Re = 2 \times 10^5$ and kinematic viscosity of air is 0.15 stokes, find :

(i) *The maximum distance from the leading edge upto which laminar boundary layer exists, and*

(ii) *The maximum thickness of boundary layer.*

Solution. Velocity distribution : $\dfrac{u}{U} = 2\left(\dfrac{y}{\delta}\right) - \left(\dfrac{y}{\delta}\right)^2$

Velocity of air, $U = 12$ m/s

Length of plate, $L = 1.1$ m

Width of plate, $B = 0.9$ m

Reynolds number upto which laminar boundary exists, $Re = 2 \times 10^5$

Kinematic viscosity of air, $v = 0.15$ stokes $= 0.15 \times 10^{-4}$ m²/s

(*i*) **The maximum distance from the leading edge upto which laminar boundary layer exists, x:**

$$Re_x = \dfrac{Ux}{v} \quad \text{or} \quad 2 \times 10^5 = \dfrac{12 \times x}{0.15 \times 10^{-4}}$$

or,

$$x = \dfrac{2 \times 10^5 \times 0.15 \times 10^{-4}}{12} = 0.25\,\text{m} \ \ \textbf{(Ans.)}$$

(*ii*) **The maximum thickness of boundary layer, δ :**

For the given velocity profile, the maximum thickness of boundary layer is given by

$$\delta = \dfrac{5.48\ x}{\sqrt{Re_x}}$$

$$= \dfrac{5.48 \times 0.25}{\sqrt{2 \times 10^5}} = 0.00306\,\text{m} \ \ \text{or} \ \ \textbf{3.06mm} \ \ \textbf{(Ans.)}$$

Example 7.6. *A plate of length 750 mm and width 250 mm has been placed longitudinally in a stream of crude oil which flows with a velocity of 5 m/s. If the oil has a specific gravity of 0.8 and kinematic viscosity of 1 stoke, calculate :*

(*i*) *Boundary layer thickness at the middle of plate,*

(*ii*) *Shear stress at the middle of plate, and*

(*iii*) *Friction drag on one side of the plate.*

A cooling system shows an example of air filters used to create a laminar air flow.

Solution. Length of the plate, $L = 750$ mm $= 0.75$ m

Width of the plate, $B = 250$ mm $= 0.25$ m

Velocity of oil, U $= 5$ m/s

Specific gravity of oil $= 0.8$

Kinematic viscosity of oil, $v = 1$ stoke $= 1 \times 10^{-4}$ m²/s

(i) **Boundary layer thickness at middle of the plate δ :**

Reynold number,

$$Re_x = \frac{\rho U x}{\mu} = \frac{U x}{v} = \frac{5 \times (0.375)}{1 \times 10^{-4}} = 18750$$

(∵ At the middle of plate, $x = 0.75/2 = 0.375$ m)

Since $Re_x < 5 \times 10^5$, therefore, boundary layer is of laminar character and Blasius solution gives

$$\delta = \frac{5x}{\sqrt{Re_x}} = \frac{5 \times (0.375)}{18750} = 0.01369 \text{ m} = \textbf{13.69 mm}$$

(ii) **Shear stress at the middle of plate, τ_0 :**

According to Blasius, the local coefficient of drag (C_{fx}) is given by

$$C_{fx} = \frac{0.664}{\sqrt{Re_x}} = \frac{0.664}{\sqrt{18750}} = 4.849 \times 10^{-3}$$

By definition,

$$C_{fx} = \frac{\tau_0}{\frac{1}{2}\rho U^2}$$

$$\tau_0 = C_{fx} = \frac{1}{2}\rho U^2$$

$$= 4.849 \times 10^{-3} \times \frac{1}{2} \times (0.8 \times 1000) \times 5^2 = \textbf{48.49 N/m² (Ans.)}$$

(iii) **Friction drag on one side of the plate, F_D :**

$$Re_L = \frac{UL}{v} = \frac{5 \times 0.75}{1 \times 10^{-4}} = 37500$$

As the boundary layer is laminar even at the trailing edge, therefore, the *average drag (friction) coefficient*,

$$\overline{C}_f = \frac{1.328}{\sqrt{Re_L}} = \frac{1.328}{\sqrt{37500}} = 6.858 \times 10^{-3}$$

∴ Firction drag,

$$F_D = \overline{C}_f \times \frac{1}{2} \rho U^2 \times \text{area of plate on one side}$$

$$= 6.858 \times 10^{-3} \times \frac{1}{2} \times (0.8 \times 1000) \times 5^2 \times 0.75 \times 0.25$$

$$= \textbf{12.86 N (Ans.)}$$

(**Note :** *If velocity profile is not given in the problem, but boundary layer is laminar, then Blasius's solution is used.*).

Example 7.7. *Atmospheric air at 20°C is flowing parallel to a flat plate at a velocity of 2.8 m/s. Assuming cubic velocity profile and using exact Blasius solution, estimate the boundary layer thickness and the local coefficient of drag (or skin friction) at x = 1.2 m from the leading edge of the plate. Also find the deviation of the approximate solution from the exact solution.*

Take the kinematic viscosity of air at 20°C = 15.4 × 10⁻⁶ m²/s

Solution. Velocity of air, U $= 2.8$ m/s

Distance from the leading edge of the plate, $x = 1.2$ m

Reynolds number $Re_x = \dfrac{Ux}{v} = \dfrac{2.8 \times 1.2}{15.4 \times 10^{-6}} = 2.18 \times 10^5$

Blasius solution :

Boundary layer thickness, $\delta = \dfrac{5x}{\sqrt{Re_x}} = \dfrac{5 \times 1.2}{\sqrt{2.18 \times 10^5}} = 0.01285$ m $= $ **12.85 mm (Ans.)**

Local coefficient of drag, $C_{fx} = \dfrac{0.646}{\sqrt{Re_x}} = \dfrac{0.646}{\sqrt{2.18 \times 10^5}} = 0.001422$

Approximate solution (*with assumption of cubic velocity profile*) :

$$\delta = \dfrac{4.64\,x}{\sqrt{Re_x}} = \dfrac{4.64 \times 1.2}{\sqrt{2.18 \times 10^5}} = 0.01192 \text{ m} = 11.92 \text{ mm}$$

$$C_{fx} = \dfrac{0.646}{\sqrt{Re_x}} = \dfrac{0.646}{\sqrt{2.18 \times 10^5}} = 0.001383$$

The approximate solution deviates from the exact solution by

Deviation for δ : $\dfrac{12.85 - 11.92}{12.85} \times 100 = $ **7.24% (Ans.)**

Deviation for $\qquad C_{fx} = \dfrac{0.001422 - 0.001383}{0.001422} \times 100 = $ **2.74% (Ans.)**

Example 7.8. *Air is flowing over a flat plate 5 m long and 2.5 m wide with a velocity of 4 m/s at 15°C. If $\rho = 1.208$ kg/m³ and $v = 1.47 \times 10^{-5}$ m²/s, calculate :*

(i) *Length of plate over which the boundary layer is laminar, and thickness of the boundary layer (laminar).*

(ii) *Shear stress at the location where boundary layer ceases to be laminar, and*

(iii) *Total drag force on the both sides on that portion of plate where boundary layer is laminar.*

Solution. Length of the plate, $\qquad L = 5$ m

Width of the plate, $\qquad\qquad B = 2.5$ m

Velocity of air, $\qquad\qquad\quad U = 4$ m/s

Density of air, $\qquad\qquad\quad \rho = 1.208$ kg/m³

Kinematic viscosity of air, $\qquad v = 1.47 \times 10^{-5}$ m²/s

(i) **Length of plate over which the boundary layer is laminar :**

Reynolds number $\qquad\qquad Re_x = \dfrac{UL}{v} = \dfrac{4 \times 5}{1.47 \times 10^{-5}} = 1.361 \times 10^6$

Hence on the front portion, boundary layer is laminar and on the rear, it is turbulent.

$$Re_x = \dfrac{Ux}{v} = 5 \times 10^5$$

$\therefore \qquad\qquad \dfrac{4 \times x}{1.47 \times 10^{-5}} = 5 \times 10^5$

or, $\qquad\qquad x = \dfrac{5 \times 10^5 \times 1.47 \times 10^{-5}}{4} = 1.837$ m

Hence the boundary layer is **laminar on 1.837 m length of the plate. (Ans.)**

Thickness of the boundary layer (laminar), δ

$$= \frac{5x}{\sqrt{Re_x}} = \frac{5 \times 1.837}{\sqrt{5 \times 10^5}} = 0.01299 \text{ m or } \textbf{12.99 mm} \text{ (Ans.)}$$

(ii) **Shear stress at the location where boundary layer ceases to be laminar, τ_0 :**

Local coefficient of drag, $\quad C_{fx} = \dfrac{0.664}{\sqrt{5 \times 10^5}} = 0.000939$

$\therefore \qquad \tau_0 = C_{fx} \times \dfrac{1}{2}\rho U^2 = 0.000939 \times \dfrac{1}{2} \times 1.208 \times 4^2$

$$= \textbf{0.00907 N/m}^2 \text{ (Ans.)}$$

(iii) **Total drag force on both sides of plate, F_D :**

$$F_D = 2\overline{C}_f \times \frac{1}{2}\rho A U^2$$

where, $\overline{C}_f$ = Average coefficient of drag (or skin friction) = $\dfrac{1.328}{\sqrt{5 \times 10^5}} = 1.878 \times 10^{-3}$

and A = Area of the plate = $1.837 \times 2.5 = 4.59 \text{ m}^2$

$\therefore \qquad F_D = 2 \times 1.878 \times 10^{-3} \times \dfrac{1}{2} \times 1.208 \times 4.59 \times 4^2 = \textbf{0.167 N} \text{ (Ans.)}$

Example 7.9. *Air flows over a plate 0.5 m long and 0.6 wide with a velocity of 4 m/s. The velocity profile is in the form.*

$$\frac{u}{U} = sin\left(\frac{\pi}{2}\frac{y}{\delta}\right)$$

If $\rho = 1.24 \text{ kg/m}^3$ and $v = 0.15 \times 10^{-4} \text{ m}^2/s$, calculate :

(i) *Boundary layer thickness at the end of the plate,*

(ii) *Shear stress at 250 mm from the leading edge, and*

(iii) *Drag force on one side of the plate.*

Solution. Length of plate, $\quad L = 0.5 \text{ m}$

Width of plate, $\qquad\qquad B = 0.6 \text{ m}$

Velocity of air, $\qquad\quad U = 4 \text{ m/s}$

Density of air, $\qquad\quad \rho = 1.24 \text{ kg/m}^3$

Kinematic viscosity of air, $\quad v = 0.15 \times 10^{-4} \text{ m}^2/s$

Velocity profile, $\qquad \dfrac{u}{U} = sin\left(\dfrac{\pi}{2}\dfrac{y}{\delta}\right)$

(i) **Boundary layer thickness at the end of the plate, δ :**

Reynolds number, $\qquad Re_x = \dfrac{Ux}{v} = \dfrac{4 \times 0.5}{0.15 \times 10^{-4}} = 1.33 \times 10^5$

Since $Re_x < 5 \times 10^5$, therefore, the boundary layer is **laminar** over the entire length of the plate.

We know, $\qquad\qquad \delta = \dfrac{4.795\, x}{\sqrt{Re_x}} = \dfrac{4.795 \times 0.5}{\sqrt{1.33 \times 10^5}} \qquad (x = L = 0.5 \text{ m})$

$$= 0.00657 \text{ m} = \textbf{6.57 mm} \text{ (Ans.)}$$

(ii) **Shear stress at 250 mm from the leading edge, τ_0 :**

$$\tau_0 = C_{fx} \times \frac{\rho U^2}{2} \qquad\qquad \text{...[Eqn. (7.30)]}$$

But,

$$C_{fx} = \frac{0.654}{Re_x} = \frac{0.654}{\sqrt{\dfrac{Ux}{\nu}}} = \frac{0.654}{\sqrt{\dfrac{4 \times 0.25}{0.15 \times 10^{-4}}}} = 0.002533$$

$\therefore$

$$(\tau_0)_{x = 0.25m} = 0.002533 \times \frac{1.24 \times 4^2}{2} = \textbf{0.025 N/m}^2 \textbf{ (Ans.)}$$

(*iii*) **Drag force on one side of the plate, F_D :**

$$F_D = \overline{C}_f \times \frac{1}{2}\rho A U^2$$

where,

$$\overline{C}_f = \frac{1.31}{\sqrt{Re_L}} = \frac{1.31}{\sqrt{1.33 \times 10^5}} = 0.003592$$

and A = area of the plate = $L \times B = 0.5 \times 0.6 = 0.3 \text{ m}^2$

$\therefore$

$$F_D = 0.003592 \times \frac{1}{2} \times 1.24 \times 0.3 \times 4^2 = \textbf{0.01069 N (Ans.)}$$

7.1.5. THERMAL BOUNDARY LAYER

Whenever a flow of fluid takes place past a heated or cold surface, a temperature field is set up in the field next to the surface. If the surface of the plate is hotter than fluid, the temperature distribution will be as shown in the Fig. 7.6. *The zone or this layer wherein the temperature field exists is called the* **thermal boundary layer**. Due to the exchange of heat between the plate and the fluid, temperature gradient occurs/results.

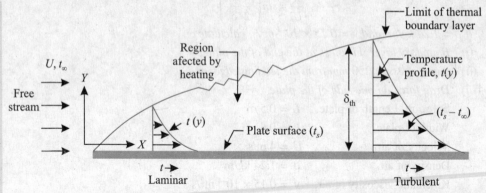

Fig. 7.6. Thermal boundary layer formed during flow of cool fluid over a warm plate.

The thermal boundary layer thickness (δ_{th}) is arbitrarily defined as the distance y from the plate surface at which

$$\frac{t_s - t}{t_s - t_\infty} = 0.99 \qquad\qquad ...(7.40)$$

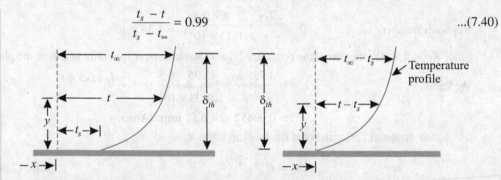

Fig. 7.7. Thermal boundary layer formed flow of warm fluid over a cool plate.

Figure 7.7. shows the shape of the thermal boundary layer when the free stream temperature t_∞ is above the plate surface temperature t_s.

The thermal boundary layer concept is analogous to hydrodynamic boundary layer; the parameters which affect their growth are however different. Whereas the velocity profile of the hydrodynamic boundary layer depends mainly on the fluid viscosity, the temperature profile of the thermal boundary layer depends upon the viscosity, velocity of flow, specific heat and thermal conducitivity of the fluid. The relative magnitude of δ and δ_{th} are affected by the thermo-physical properties of the

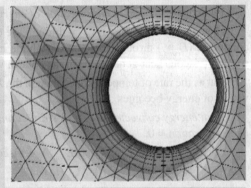

Thermal boundary layer at the coil surface.

fluid; the governing parameter, however, is the non-dimensional Prandtel number, $Pr = \dfrac{\mu c_p}{k}$.

(i) $\delta_{th} = \delta$ .... when $Pr = 1$;   (ii) $\delta_{th} < \delta$ ....when $Pr > 1$

(iii) $\delta_{th} > \delta$ .... when $Pr < 1$.

7.1.6. ENERGY EQUATION OF THERMAL BOUNDARY LAYER OVER A FLAT PLATE

Figure 7.8 (a) shows a hot fluid flowing over a cool flat plate, and development of the thermal boundary layer. In order to derive an energy equation, consider control volume ($dx \times dy \times$ unit depth) in the boundary layer so that end effects are neglected. The enlarged view of this control volume is shown in Fig. 7.8 (b) in which the quantities of energy entering and leaving have been indicated.

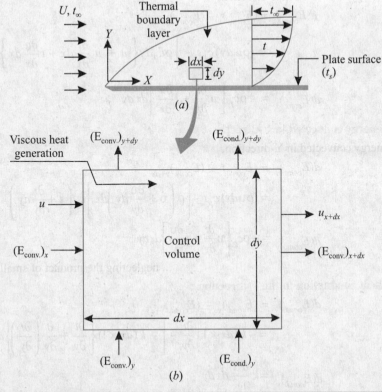

Fig. 7.8. Energies entering and leaving the control volume.

Involving *principle of conservation of energy for the steady state condition*, we have :

Heat energy convected ($E_{conv.}$) through the control volume in X and Y directions + heat energy conducted ($E_{cond.}$) through the control volume in X and Y directions + heat generated due to fluid friction (viscous heat generation) in the control volume = 0.

But as the rate of temperature change in the X-direction is small and can be neglected the conservation of energy becomes :

Heat energy convected in X and Y directions + heat energy conducted in Y-direction + viscous heat generation = 0.

or $\quad d(E_{conv.})_x + d(E_{conv.})_y + d(E_{cond.})_y + $ viscous heat generation $= 0$ ...(7.41)
$\qquad\quad (i) \qquad\qquad (ii) \qquad\quad (iii) \qquad\qquad\qquad (iv)$

(*i*) **The Energy convected in X-direction :**
$$(E_{conv.})_x = \text{Mass} \times \text{specific heat} \times \text{temperature}$$
$$= [\rho u(dy \times 1)] \, c_p t = (\rho u \, dy) \, c_p t$$

$$(E_{conv.})_{x + dx} = \left[\rho \left(u + \frac{\partial u}{\partial x} dx \right) dy \right] c_p \left(t + \frac{\partial t}{\partial x} \right) dx$$

$$= \rho c_p \, dy \left[ut + u + \frac{\partial u}{\partial x} dx + t \frac{\partial u}{\partial x} dx + \frac{\partial u}{\partial x} \frac{\partial t}{\partial x} (dx)^2 \right]$$

$$= \rho c_p \, dy \left[ut + u \frac{\partial t}{\partial x} dx + t \frac{\partial u}{\partial x} dx \right]$$

... neglecting the product of small quantities

∴   Net energy convected in X-direction,
$$d(E_{conv.})_x = (E_{conv.})_x - (E_{conv.})_{x+ dx}$$

$$= (\rho u \, dy) c_p t - \left[\rho c_p dy \left\{ ut + u \frac{\partial t}{\partial x} dx + t \frac{\partial u}{\partial x} dx \right\} \right]$$

or, $\qquad\qquad d(E_{conv.})_x = - \rho c_p \left[u \frac{\partial t}{\partial x} + t \frac{\partial u}{\partial x} \right] dx \, dy$ ...(7.42)

(*ii*) **The energy convected in Y-direction :**
The net energy convected in Y-direction,
$$d(E_{conv.})_y = (E_{conv.})_y - (E_{conv.})_{y+dy}$$

$$= (\rho v \, dx) c_p t - \left[\rho \left(v + \frac{\partial v}{\partial y} dy \right) dx \right] c_p \left(t + \frac{\partial t}{\partial y} dy \right)$$

or, $\qquad\qquad d(E_{conv.})_y = - \rho c_p \left[v \frac{\partial t}{\partial y} + t \frac{\partial v}{\partial y} \right] dx \, dy$ ...(7.43)

... neglecting the product of small quantities.

(*iii*) **The heat conduction in the Y-direction :**
$$d(E_{cond.})_y = (E_{cond.})_y - (E_{cond.})_{y+dy}$$

$$= - k (dx \times 1) \frac{\partial t}{\partial y} - \left[- k (dx \times 1) \left\{ \frac{\partial t}{\partial y} + \frac{\partial}{\partial y} \left(\frac{\partial t}{\partial y} \right) \right\} dy \right]$$

or, $\qquad\qquad d(E_{cond.})_y = k \frac{\partial^2 t}{\partial y^2} dx \, dy$ ...(7.44) *(iv)* **Viscous heat generation :**

Owing to relative motion of fluid in the boundary layer (fluid on the top face of the control volume moves faster than fluid on bottom face), there will be viscous effects which will cause generation of heat.

Viscous heat generation = Viscous force (average) × distance travelled by the viscous force (this is determined by the relative velocity of fluid flow at the upper and lower faces of the element).

= [Shear stress (τ) × area upon which it acts)]
× distance travelled

$$= \left[\mu \frac{\partial u}{\partial y}(dx \times 1) \right] \times \left(\frac{\partial u}{\partial y} dy \right)$$

or, Viscous heat generation $= \mu \left(\frac{\partial u}{\partial y} \right)^2 dx\, dy$ ...(7.45)

Substituting the values in eqn. (7.41), we get

$$- \rho c_p \left[\mu \frac{\partial t}{\partial x} + t \frac{\partial u}{\partial x} \right] dx\, dy + \left[-\rho c_p \left(\upsilon \frac{\partial t}{\partial y} + t \frac{\partial \upsilon}{\partial y} \right) \right] dx\, dy + \left[k \frac{\partial^2 t}{\partial y^2} dx\, dy \right] + \left[\mu \left(\frac{\partial u}{\partial y} \right)^2 dx\, dy \right] = 0$$

$$- \rho c_p \left[u \frac{\partial t}{\partial x} + \upsilon \frac{\partial t}{\partial y} + t \left(\frac{\partial u}{\partial x} + \frac{\partial \upsilon}{\partial y} \right) \right] dx\, dy + \left[k \frac{\partial^2 t}{\partial y^2} dx\, dy \right] + \left[\mu \left(\frac{\partial u}{\partial y} \right)^2 dx\, dy \right] = 0 \quad ...(7.46)$$

Form the continuity equation for two-dimensional flow, we have

$$\frac{\partial u}{\partial x} + \frac{\partial \upsilon}{\partial y} = 0 ; \quad \text{thus the eqn. (7.46) reduces to}$$

$$u \frac{\partial t}{\partial x} + \upsilon \frac{\partial t}{\partial y} = \frac{k}{\rho c_p} \cdot \frac{\partial^2 t}{\partial y^2} + \frac{\mu}{\rho c_p} \left(\frac{\partial u}{\partial y} \right)^2 = 0 \quad ...(7.47)$$

Equation (7.47) is the required *differential energy equation for flow past a flat plate*. If viscous heat generation is neglected [when the value of U is relatively low and difference of temperature between the free stream and the plate is small (of the order of 40°C)], the energy equation reduces to

$$u \frac{\partial t}{\partial x} + \upsilon \frac{\partial t}{\partial y} = \frac{k}{\rho c_p} \cdot \frac{\partial^2 t}{\partial y^2} = \alpha \frac{\partial^2 t}{\partial y^2} = 0 \qquad \left(\text{where } \alpha = \frac{k}{\rho c_p} \right) \quad ...(7.48)$$

It may be noted, the energy equation is similar to the momentum equation. Further the dimensions of kinematic viscosity v and thermal diffusivity α are the same.

The equation (7.48) has been derived with the following **assumptions :**

1. Steady incompressible flow.

2. The properties of the fluids evaluated at the film temperature $t_f = \dfrac{t_\infty - t_s}{2}$ are constant.

3. The body forces, viscous heating and conduction in the flow direction are negligible.

Pohlhausen solution for the 'Energy equation' :

By using the following variables the energy equation $\left[u \dfrac{\partial t}{\partial x} + \upsilon \dfrac{\partial t}{\partial x} = \alpha \dfrac{\partial^2 t}{\partial y^2} \right]$ can be recast into

an *ordinary differential equation* as follows :

η (Stretching factor) $= y \sqrt{\dfrac{U}{vx}}$, ψ (stream function) $= \sqrt{vxU}\, f(\eta)$, and

Viscous heating of fluid dampers.

$$\theta = \frac{t_s - t}{t_s - t_\infty} = f(\eta) = f\left[y\sqrt{\frac{U}{vx}} \right] \qquad \text{...(7.49)}$$

Also, the values of the velocity components u and v already calculated earlier are :

$$u = U\frac{df}{d\eta} \qquad \text{...[Eqn. (7.15)]}$$

$$v = \left[\frac{y}{2x}U\frac{df}{d\eta} - \frac{1}{2}\sqrt{\frac{Uv}{x}}\, f(\eta) \right] \qquad \text{...[Eqn. (7.19)]}$$

Further, from temperature parameter θ (non-dimensional) defined above, we have

$$t = t_s + (t_\infty - t_s)\theta$$

$$\frac{\partial t}{\partial x} = (t_\infty - t_s)\frac{\partial \theta}{\partial x} = (t_\infty - t_s)\frac{\partial \theta}{\partial \eta} \times \frac{\partial \eta}{\partial x}$$

or,

$$\frac{\partial t}{\partial x} = (t_\infty - t_s)\left[-\frac{y}{2x^{3/2}}\sqrt{\frac{U}{v}} \right]\frac{\partial \theta}{\partial \eta} \qquad \text{...(7.50)}$$

and,

$$\frac{\partial t}{\partial y} = (t_\infty - t_s)\frac{\partial \theta}{\partial y} = (t_\infty - t_s)\frac{\partial \theta}{\partial \eta} \times \frac{\partial \eta}{\partial y}$$

or,

$$\frac{\partial t}{\partial y} = (t_\infty - t_s)\sqrt{\frac{U}{vx}}\frac{d\theta}{d\eta} \qquad \text{...(7.51)}$$

Also,

$$\frac{\partial^2 t}{\partial y^2} = \frac{\partial}{\partial y}\left[(t_\infty - t_s)\sqrt{\frac{U}{vx}}\frac{d\theta}{d\eta} \right]$$

$$= (t_\infty - t_s)\sqrt{\frac{U}{vx}}\frac{d}{d\eta}\left(\frac{d\theta}{d\eta} \right)\frac{d\eta}{dy}$$

$$= (t_\infty - t_s)\sqrt{\frac{U}{vx}}\frac{d^2\theta}{d\eta^2}\sqrt{\frac{U}{vx}}$$

or, $\qquad \dfrac{\partial^2 t}{\partial y^2} = (t_\infty - t_s) \dfrac{U}{vx} \dfrac{d^2\theta}{d\eta^2}$ ...(7.52)

Inserting the above values in the energy equation, we get :

$$u \frac{\partial t}{\partial x} + v \frac{\partial t}{\partial y} = \alpha \frac{\partial^2 t}{\partial y^2}$$

$$U \frac{df}{d\eta}(t_\infty - t_s)\left[-\frac{y}{2x^{3/2}} \sqrt{\frac{U}{v}} \right] \frac{d\theta}{d\eta} + \left[\frac{y}{2x} U \frac{df}{d\eta} - \frac{1}{2}\sqrt{\frac{Uv}{x}} f(\eta) \right](t_\infty - t_s)\sqrt{\frac{U}{vx}} \frac{d\theta}{d\eta}$$

$$= \alpha(t_\infty - t_s)\frac{U}{vx}\frac{d^2\theta}{d\eta^2} \qquad\qquad ...(7.53)$$

After simplification and arrangement of the above equation, we obtain

$$\frac{d^2\theta}{d\eta^2} + \frac{1}{2}\frac{v}{\alpha} f(\eta)\frac{d\theta}{d\eta} = 0$$

or, $\qquad \dfrac{d^2\theta}{d\eta^2} + \dfrac{1}{2}Pr\, f(\eta)\dfrac{d\theta}{d\eta} = 0$ ...(7.54)

$$\left[\because pr \text{ (Prandtl number)} = \frac{v}{\alpha} \right]$$

Thus the partial differential equation (7.48) has been converted into ordinary differential equation. The boundary conditions to be satisfied are:

$$\begin{array}{lll}
\text{At } t = t_s, & y = 0 & \\
\text{At } t = t_\infty, & y = \infty & \\
\text{At } \eta = 0 & \theta(\eta) = 0 & \left.\right\} \text{ values in terms of new variable} \\
\text{At } \eta = \infty & \theta(\eta) = 1 &
\end{array} \qquad ...(7.55)$$

The solution obtained by Pohlhausen for energy equation is given by :

$$\theta(\eta) = \left(\frac{d\theta}{d\eta}\right)_{\eta=0} \int_0^\eta \exp\left[-\frac{Pr}{2}\int_0^\eta f(\eta)\,d\eta \right]d\eta \qquad ...(7.56)$$

The factor $\left(\dfrac{d\theta}{d\eta}\right)_{\eta=0}$ represents the dimensionless slope of the temperature profile at the surface where $\eta = 0$; its value can be obtained by applying the boundary condition at $\eta = \infty$, $\theta(\eta) = 1$. Thus,

$$\left(\frac{d\theta}{d\eta}\right)_{\eta=0} \int_0^\infty \exp\left[-\frac{Pr}{2}\int_0^\infty f(\eta)\,d\eta \right]d\eta \qquad ...(7.57)$$

Evidently the dimensionless slope is a function of Prandtl number and the calculations made by Prandtl gave the following result :

For $0.6 < Pr\ 15$, $\left(\dfrac{d\theta}{d\eta}\right)_{\eta=0} = 0.332\,(Pr)^{1/3}$ ...(7.58)

Figure 7.9 shows the values of θ (dimensionless temperature distribution) plotted for various values of Pr (Prandtl number).

  - The curve for $Pr = 0.7$ is typical for air and several other gases.
  - The curve for $Pr = 1$ is the same as that of curve I in Fig. 7.4.
  - These curves also enable us to determine the thickness of thermal boundary layer δ_{th} and

local average heat transfer coefficients $\bar{h}$.

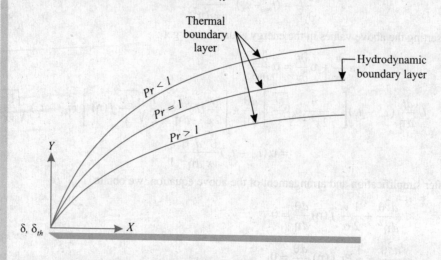

Fig. 7.9. Hydrodynamic and thermal boundary layers for different Prandtl numbers.

Thickness of thermal boundary layer, δ_{th} :

Case I.   *When Pr = 1.*

$$\eta = \left[y \sqrt{\frac{U}{vx}} \right] \simeq 5.0 \text{ at } \theta = 0.99$$

Since $y = \delta_{th}$ at the outer edge of thermal boundary layer, therefore,

$$\delta_{th} \sqrt{\frac{U}{vx}} = 5.0$$

or, $$\frac{\delta_{th}}{x} = \frac{5.0}{\sqrt{(xU)/v}} = \frac{5.0}{\sqrt{Re_x}} = \frac{\delta}{x} \qquad ...(7.59)$$

This equation shows that for $Pr = 1$, the thickness of thermal boundary layer, δ_{th} is *equal to* hydrodynamic boundary layer, δ.

Case II. *When Pr < 1.*

$$\eta \left[= y \sqrt{\frac{U}{vx}} \right] > 5.0 \text{ at } \theta = 0.99$$

$$\frac{\delta_{th}}{x} > \frac{5.0}{\sqrt{Re_x}} > \frac{\delta}{x} \qquad ...(7.60)$$

This equation shows that for $Pr < 1$, $\delta_{th} > \delta$.

Case III. *When Pr > 1.*

$$\eta \left[= y \sqrt{\frac{U}{vx}} \right] > 5.0 \text{ at } \theta = 0.99$$

$$\frac{\delta_{th}}{x} < \frac{5.0}{\sqrt{Re_x}} < \frac{\delta}{x} \qquad ...(7.61)$$

This equation shows that for $Pr > 1$, $\delta_{th} < \delta$

Pohlhausen has suggested that the following relation is general may be assumed between the thermal and hydrodynamic boundary layers :

$$\delta_{th} = \frac{\delta}{(Pr)^{1/3}} \qquad\qquad ...(7.62)$$

The local and average heat transfer coefficients :

At the surface of the plate, since there is no fluid motion and the heat transfer can occur only through conduction, the heat flux may be written as,

$$\frac{Q}{A} = h_x (t_s - t_\infty) = - k \left(\frac{\partial t}{\partial y}\right)_{y = 0} \qquad\qquad ...(7.63)$$

From the relation 7.63, we may develop $\left(\dfrac{\partial t}{\partial y}\right)_{y = 0}$ (*i.e.*, surface temperature gradient) as,

$$\left(\frac{\partial t}{\partial y}\right)_{y = 0} = - (t_s - t_\infty) \sqrt{\frac{U}{vx}} \times \left(\frac{\partial \theta}{\partial y}\right)_{\eta = 0}$$

$$= - (t_s - t_\infty) \sqrt{\frac{U}{vx}} \times 0.332 (Pr)^{1/3}$$

$$= - \frac{0.332}{x} (t_s - t_\infty) \sqrt{\frac{U}{v}} (Pr)^{1/3}$$

$$= - \frac{0.332}{x} (t_s - t_\infty) (Re_x)^{1/2} (Pr)^{1/3}$$

Substituting for $\left(\dfrac{\partial t}{\partial y}\right)_{y = 0}$ in eqn. (7.63), we obtain

$$\frac{Q}{A} = h_x (t_s - t_\infty) = 0.332 \frac{k}{x} (t_s - t_\infty)(Re_x)^{1/2}(Pr)^{1/3}$$

or,

$$h_x = 0.332 \frac{k}{x}(Re_x)^{1/2} (Pr)^{1/3} \qquad\qquad ...(7.64)$$

or,

$$Nu_x = \frac{h_x x}{k} = 0.332 (Re_x)^{1/2} (Pr)^{1/3} \qquad\qquad ...(7.65)$$

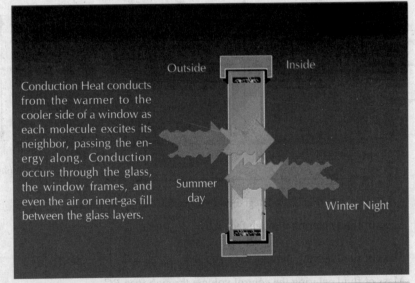

Conduction Heat conducts from the warmer to the cooler side of a window as each molecule excites its neighbor, passing the energy along. Conduction occurs through the glass, the window frames, and even the air or inert-gas fill between the glass layers.

Outside   Inside

Summer day

Winter Night

Conduction = Heat Flow through Materials

... (In non-dimensional form)

[where, h_x = Local convective heat transfer coefficient, and

Nu_x = Local value of Nusselt number (at a distance x from the leading edge of the plate,].

The *average* heat transfer coefficient is given by

$$\bar{h} = \frac{1}{L}\int_0^L h_x \cdot dx = \frac{1}{L}\int_0^L 0.332\frac{k}{x}(Re_x)^{1/2}(Pr)^{1/3}\,dx$$

$$= \frac{1}{L}\int_0^L 0.332\,k\,(Pr)^{1/3}\sqrt{\left(\frac{U}{v}\right)}x^{-1/2}\,dx$$

or, $$\bar{h} = 0.664\left(\frac{k}{L}\right)(Re_L)^{1/2}(Pr)^{1/3} \qquad\qquad ...(7.66)$$

If we compare the eqns. (7.64) and (7.66), we find that

$$\bar{h} = 2h_x \qquad\qquad ...(7.67)$$

and $\overline{Nu}$ (average value of Nusselt number) $= \dfrac{\bar{h}L}{k} = 0.664\,(Re_L)^{1/2}(Pr)^{1/3}$ ...(7.68)

All the results in eqns. (7.64), (7.65) and (7.68) are valid for $Pr > 0.5$.

7.1.7. INTEGRAL ENERGY EQUATION (APPROXIMATE SOLUTION OF ENERGY EQUATION)

Consider a control volume shown in Fig. 7.10. *Assume* that ρ, c_p and k (thermo-plastic properties) of fluid remain constant within the operating range of the temperature, and the heating of the plate commences at a distance x_0 from the leading edge of the plate (so that the boundary layer initiates at $x = x_0$ and develops and grows beyond that). For *unit width* of the plate we have :

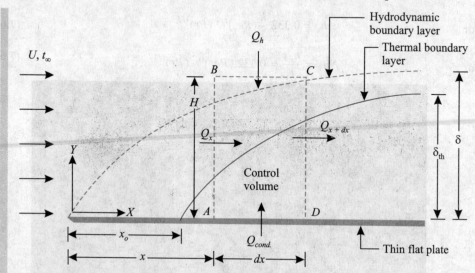

Fig. 7.10. Integral energy equation – control volume.

Mass of fluid entering through face $AB = \displaystyle\int_0^H \rho u\,dy$ ...(7.69)

Mass of fluid leaving through face $CD = \displaystyle\int_0^H \rho u\,dy + \frac{\partial}{\partial x}\left[\int_0^H \rho u\,dy\right]dx$ ...(7.70)

∴   Mass of fluid entering the control volume through face BC

$$= \left[\int_0^H \rho u \, dy + \frac{\partial}{\partial x} \left\{ \int_0^H \rho u \, dy \right\} dx \right] - \int_0^H \rho u \, dy = \frac{\partial}{\partial x} \left[\int_0^H \rho u \, dy \right] dx \qquad \text{...(7.71)}$$

Heat influx through the face AB,

$$Q_x = \text{Mass} \times \text{specific heat} \times \text{temperature}$$

or,
$$Q_x = \left(\int_0^H \rho u \, dy \right) \times cp \times t = \rho c_p \int_0^H ut \, dy \qquad \text{...(7.72)}$$

Heat efflux through the face CD,

$$Q_{x+dx} = \int_0^H ut \, dy + \frac{\partial}{\partial x} \left[\rho c_p \int_0^H ut \, dy \right] dx \qquad \text{...(7.73)}$$

Heat (energy) influx through the face BC (which is outside thermal boundary layer and there the temperature is constant at t_∞),

$$Q_h = \frac{\partial}{\partial x} \left[\int_0^H \rho u \, dy \right] dx . c_p t_\infty \qquad \text{...(7.74)}$$

Heat conducted into the control volume through face AD,

$$Q_{cond.} = -kA \left[\frac{\partial t}{\partial y} \right]_{y=0} = -k \, dx \left(\frac{\partial t}{\partial y} \right)_{y=0} \qquad \text{...(7.75)}$$

The energy balance for the element is given by

$$\rho c_p \int_0^H ut \, dy + \frac{\partial}{\partial x} \left[\rho c_p t_\infty \int_0^H u \, dy \right] dx + \left[-k \, dx \left(\frac{\partial t}{\partial y} \right)_{y=0} \right]$$

$$= \rho c_p \int_0^H ut \, dy + \frac{\partial}{\partial x} \left[\rho c_p \int_0^H ut \, dy \right] dx$$

After simplification and rearrangement, we have

$$\frac{d}{dx} \int_0^H (t_\infty - t) u \, dy = \frac{k}{\rho c_p} \left(\frac{\partial t}{\partial y} \right)_{y=0} = \alpha \left(\frac{\partial t}{\partial y} \right)_{y=0} \qquad \text{...(7.76)}$$

Equation (7.76) is the integral equation for the boundary layer for constant properties and constant free stream temperature t_∞.

If the viscous work done within the element is considered, then eqn. (7.76) becomes

$$\frac{d}{dx} \int_0^H (t_\infty - t) u \, dy = \frac{\mu}{\rho c_p} \int_0^H \frac{\partial^2 u}{\partial y^2} \, dx \, dy = \alpha \left(\frac{\partial t}{\partial y} \right)_{y=0} \qquad \text{...(7.77)}$$

[where $\dfrac{\mu}{\rho c_p} \displaystyle\int_0^H \dfrac{\partial^2 u}{\partial y^2} \, dx \, dy = $ Viscous work done within the element $\qquad$ ...Eqn. (7.8)]

Usually the viscous dissipation term is very small and is neglected (and may be considered only when velocity of flow field becomes very large).

Expression for the convective heat transfer coefficient for laminar flow over a flat plate:

In order to derive an expression for convective heat transfer coefficient for laminar flow over a flat plate (that has an unheated starting length x_0), let us use *cubic velocity and temperature distributions* in the integral boundary layer energy equation as follows :

The cubic velocity profile within the boundary layer is of the form

$$\frac{u}{U} = \frac{3}{2} \left(\frac{y}{\delta} \right) - \frac{1}{2} \left(\frac{y}{\delta} \right)^3 \qquad \text{...[Eqn. (7.33)]}$$

The conditions which are satisfied by the temperature distribution within the boundary layer are :

(i) $\qquad$ At $y = 0$, $t = t_s$ $\qquad$ (ii) At $y = 0$, $\dfrac{\partial^2 t}{\partial y^2} = 0$

(iii) At $y = \delta_{th}$, $t = t_\infty$ (iv) At $y = \delta_{th} = \dfrac{\partial t}{\partial y} = 0$

By using these boundary conditions for a cubic polynomial,

$$\frac{\theta}{\theta_\infty} = a + b\left(\frac{y}{\delta_{th}}\right) + c\left(\frac{y}{\delta_{th}}\right)^2 + d\left(\frac{y}{\delta_{th}}\right)^3 \qquad \text{...(7.78)}$$

The temperature distribution takes the following form

$$\frac{\theta}{\theta_\infty} = \frac{t - t_s}{t_\infty - t_s} = \frac{3}{2}\left(\frac{y}{\delta_{th}}\right) - \frac{1}{2}\left(\frac{y}{\delta_{th}}\right)^3 \qquad \text{...(7.79)}$$

By putting the proper values of velocity distribution and temperature distribution into the integral equation, we get

$$\alpha\left(\frac{dt}{dy}\right)_{y=0} = \frac{d}{dx}\int_0^H (t_\infty - t)u\,dy$$

$$= U(t_\infty - t_s)\frac{d}{dx}\int_0^H \frac{u}{U}\left(\frac{t_\infty - t}{t_\infty - t_s}\right)dy$$

$$= U(t_\infty - t_s)\frac{d}{dx}\int_0^H \frac{u}{U}\left[1 - \frac{t_\infty - t}{t_\infty - t_s}\right]$$

$$= U(t_\infty - t_s)\frac{d}{dx}\left[\int_0^H \left\{\frac{3}{2}\left(\frac{y}{\delta}\right) - \frac{1}{2}\left(\frac{y}{\delta}\right)^3\right\} \times \left\{1 - \frac{3}{2}\left(\frac{y}{\delta_{th}}\right) + \frac{1}{2}\left(\frac{y}{\delta_{th}}\right)^3\right\}dy\right]$$

$$= U(t_\infty - t_s)\frac{d}{dx}\left[\int_0^{\delta_{th}}\left\{\frac{3}{2\delta}y - \frac{9}{4\delta\delta_{th}}y^2 - \frac{1}{2\delta^3}y^3 + \right.\right.$$

$$\left.\left.\left(\frac{3}{4\delta\,\delta_{th}^3} + \frac{3}{4\delta^3\,\delta_{th}}\right)y^4 - \frac{1}{4\delta^3\,\delta_{th}^3}y^6\right\}dy\right] \qquad \text{...(7.80)}$$

The upper limit has been changed to δ_{th} since $\delta_{th} < \delta$ for most of the gases (for $y > \delta_{th}$ integrand would be zero).

After putting $\dfrac{\delta_{th}}{\delta} = r$ and carrying out the integration, eqn. (7.80) gets reduced to

$$\alpha\left(\frac{dt}{dy}\right)_{y=0} = U(t_\infty - t_s)\frac{d}{dx}\left[\delta\left(\frac{3}{20}r^2 - \frac{3}{280}r^4\right)\right] \qquad \text{...(7.81)}$$

Neglecting the term involving r^4 (because $\delta_{th} < \delta$, $r < 1$), we have

$$\alpha\left(\frac{dt}{dy}\right)_{y=0} = \frac{3}{20}U(t_\infty - t_s)\frac{d}{dx}(\delta r^2) \qquad \text{...(7.82)}$$

Further, from eqn. (7.77), we have

$$t = t_s + (t_\infty - t_s)\left[\frac{3}{2}\left(\frac{y}{\delta_{th}}\right) - \frac{1}{2}\left(\frac{y}{\delta_{th}}\right)^3\right]$$

or,
$$\frac{dt}{dy} = (t_\infty - t_s)\left[\frac{3}{2\delta_{th}} - \frac{3}{2\delta_{th}^3}y^2\right]$$

or,
$$\left(\frac{dt}{dy}\right)_{y=0} = \frac{3}{2}\left(\frac{t_\infty - t_s}{\delta_{th}}\right) = \frac{3}{2}\left[\frac{t_\infty - t_s}{r\delta}\right] \qquad \text{...(7.83)}$$

Upon substitution in eqn. (7.82), we get

$$\alpha \times \frac{3}{2}\left[\frac{t_\infty - t_s}{r\delta}\right] = \frac{3}{20}U(t_\infty - t_s)\frac{d}{dx}(\delta r^2)$$

or,

$$\alpha = \frac{2}{3}(r\delta) \times \frac{3}{20}U\frac{d}{dx}(\delta r^2)$$

$$= (r\delta)\frac{U}{10}\left(\delta \times 2r + \frac{dr}{dx} + r^2 \times \frac{d\delta}{dx}\right)$$

or,

$$\alpha = \frac{U}{10}\left[2\delta^2 r^2 \times \frac{dr}{dx} + \delta r^3 \times \frac{d\delta}{dx}\right] \qquad ...(7.84)$$

Also,

$$\delta\frac{d\delta}{dx} = \frac{140}{13}\cdot\frac{\mu}{\rho U} = \frac{140}{13}\cdot\frac{v}{U} \text{ and } \delta^2 = \frac{280}{13}\times\frac{ux}{\rho U} = \frac{280\,vx}{13U} \qquad ...[\text{Refer Art 7.5}]$$

Putting these values in eqn. (7.84), we obtain

$$\alpha = \frac{U}{10}\left[2r^2 \times \frac{280\,vx}{13U} \times \frac{dr}{dx} + r^3 \times \frac{140v}{13U}\right]$$

or,

$$r^3 + 4r^2 \times \frac{dr}{dx} = \frac{13\alpha}{14v} \qquad ...(7.85)$$

Using the equality $\frac{d}{dx}(r^3) = 3r^2\frac{dr}{dx}$, we can write eqn. (7.85) as

$$r^3 + 4xr^2\frac{dr}{dx} = \frac{13\alpha}{14v} \qquad ...(7.86)$$

The general solution of the equation (which is a linear differential equation of the first order in r^3) is given by

$$r^3 = Cx^{-3/4} + \frac{13\alpha}{14v}$$

The value of the constant C can be evaluated from the following boundary conditions :

At $x = x_0$,

$$r^3 = \left(\frac{\delta_{th}}{\delta}\right)^3 = 0$$

Thus,

$$0 = Cx_0^{3/4} + \frac{13\alpha}{14v} \quad \text{or} \quad C = -\frac{13\alpha}{14v}x_0^{3/4}, \text{ and}$$

$$r^3 = -\frac{13\alpha}{14v}x_0^{3/4}x^{-3/4} + \frac{13\alpha}{14v}$$

or,

$$r^3 = \frac{13\alpha}{14v}\left[1 - \left(\frac{x_0}{x}\right)^{3/4}\right] \qquad ...(7.87)$$

$$\therefore \quad r = \frac{\delta_{th}}{\delta} = \left(\frac{13}{14}\right)^{1/3}\left(\frac{\alpha}{v}\right)^{1/3}\left[1 - \left(\frac{x_0}{x}\right)^{3/4}\right]$$

$$\frac{\delta_{th}}{\delta} = \frac{0.975}{(Pr)^{1/3}}\left[1 - \left(\frac{x_0}{x}\right)^{3/4}\right]^{1/3} \qquad ...(7.88)$$

$$[\because \frac{v}{\alpha} = Pr \text{ (Prandtl number)}]$$

or,

$$\frac{\delta_{th}}{\delta} = \frac{0.975}{(Pr)^{1/3}} \qquad ...(7.89)$$

... when the plate is heated over the entire length i.e., $x_0 = 0$.

Local heat transfer coefficient h_x :

We know that,
$$\frac{Q}{A} = h_x (t_s - t_\infty) = -k\left(\frac{dt}{dy}\right)_{y=0}$$

or,
$$h_x = \frac{-k(dt/dy)_{y=0}}{t_s - t_\infty}$$

But,
$$\left(\frac{dt}{dy}\right)_{y=0} = \frac{3}{2}\left(\frac{t_s - t_\infty}{\delta_{th}}\right) \qquad ...[Eqn.\ (7.83)]$$

$\therefore$
$$h_x = \frac{-k \times \frac{3}{2}\left(\frac{t_s - t_\infty}{\delta_{th}}\right)}{(t_s - t_\infty)} = \frac{3k}{2\delta_{th}} = \frac{3k}{2} \times \frac{1}{r\delta} \qquad ...(7.90)$$

Substituting $r = \dfrac{0.975}{(Pr)^{1/3}}\left[1 - \left(\dfrac{x_0}{x}\right)^{3/4}\right]^{1/3}$ and $\delta = \dfrac{4.64\,x}{\sqrt{Re_x}}$ in eqn. (7.90), we get

$$h_x = \frac{3k}{2} \times \frac{(Pr)^{1/3}}{0.975\left[1 - \left(\dfrac{x_0}{x}\right)^{3/4}\right]^{1/3}} \times \frac{\sqrt{Re_x}}{4.64\,x}$$

or,
$$h_x = 0.332\,\frac{k}{x}(Pr)^{1/3}(Re)^{1/2} \times \frac{1}{\left[1 - \left(\dfrac{x_0}{x}\right)^{3/4}\right]^{1/3}} \qquad ...(7.91)$$

or,
$$Nu_x = \frac{h_x x}{k} = \frac{0.332\,(Pr)^{1/3}(Re_x)^{1/2}}{\left[1 - \left(\dfrac{x_0}{x}\right)^{3/4}\right]^{1/3}} \qquad ...(7.92)$$

When the plate is heated over the whole length *i.e.*, $x_0 = 0$, we have
$$h_x = 0.332\frac{k}{x}(Pr)^{1/3}(Re_x)^{1/2} \qquad ...(7.93)$$

and,
$$Nu_x = 0.332\,(Pr)^{1/3}(Re_x)^{1/2} \qquad ...(7.94)$$

The above results are applicable for *laminar conditions only*.

Example 7.10. *Air at 20°C and at a pressure of 1 bar is flowing over a flat plate at a velocity of 3 m/s. If the plate is 280 mm wide and at 56°C, calculate the following quantities at x = 280 mm,*

given that properties of air at the bulk mean temperature $\left(\dfrac{20 + 56}{2}\right) = 38°C$ *are :*

$\rho = 1.1374\ kg/m^3$; $k = 0.02732\ W/m°C$; $c_p = 1.005\ kJ/kgK$; $v = 16.768 \times 10^{-6}\ m^2/s$; $Pr = 0.7$.
  (i)   *Boundary layer thickness,*
  (ii) *Local friction coefficient,*
  (iii) *Average friction coefficient,*
  (iv) *Shearing stress due to friction,*
  (v)   *Thickness of the boundary layer,*
  (vi) *Local convective heat transfer coefficient,*
  (vii) *Average convective heat transfer coefficient,*
  (viii) *Rate of heat transfer by convection,*
  (ix) *Total drag force on the plate, and*
  (x)   *Total mass flow rate through the boundary.*

Solution. *Given* : $U = 3$ m/s, $x = 280$ mm $= 0.28$ m, $\rho = 1.1374$ kg/m^3, $k = 0.02732$ W/m°C, $c_p = 1.005$ kJ/kgK, $v = 16.768 \times 10^{-6}$ m^2/s.

Let us first ascertain the type of the flow, whether laminar or turbulent.

$$Re_x = \frac{Ux}{v} = \frac{3 \times 0.28}{16.768 \times 10^{-6}} = 5.0 \times 10^4$$

Since $Re_x < 5 \times 10^5$, hence flow in *laminar*.

(*i*) **Boundary layer thickness at $x = 0.28$ m, δ :**

$$\delta = \frac{5x}{\sqrt{Re_x}} \qquad\qquad ...[\text{Eqn. (7.22)}]$$

or,
$$\delta = \frac{5 \times 0.28}{\sqrt{5 \times 10^4}} = 0.00626 \text{ m or } \textbf{6.26 mm (Ans.)}$$

(*ii*) **Local friction coefficient, C_{fx} :**

$$C_{fx} = \frac{0.664}{\sqrt{Re_x}} \qquad\qquad ...[\text{Eqn. (7.24)}]$$

or,
$$C_{fx} = \frac{0.664}{\sqrt{5 \times 10^4}} = \textbf{0.002969 (Ans.)}$$

(*iii*) **Average friction coefficient, C_f :**

$$\overline{C}_f = \frac{1.328}{\sqrt{Re_L}} \qquad\qquad ...[\text{Eqn. (7.25)}]$$

or,
$$\overline{C}_f = \frac{1.328}{\sqrt{5 \times 10^4}} = \textbf{0.005939 (Ans.)} \qquad ...(\overline{C}_f = 2C_{fx})$$

(*iv*) **Shearing stress due to friction, τ_0 :**

$$\tau_0 = C_{fx} \times \frac{\rho U^2}{2} \qquad\qquad ...[\text{Eqn. (7.30)}]$$

$$= 0.002969 \times \frac{1.1374 \times 3^2}{2} = \textbf{0.01519 N/m}^2 \textbf{ (Ans.)}$$

(*v*) **Thickness of thermal boundary layer, δ_{th} :**

$$\delta_{th} = \frac{\delta}{(Pr)^{1/3}} \qquad\qquad ...[\text{Eqn. (7.62)}]$$

$$= \frac{0.00626}{(0.7)^{1/3}} = 0.00705 \text{ ,m or } \textbf{7.05 mm (Ans.)}$$

(*vi*) **Local convective heat transfer coefficient, h_x :**

$$h_x = 0.332 \frac{k}{x} (Re_x)^{1/2} (Pr)^{1/3} \qquad\qquad ...[\text{Eqn. (7.64)}]$$

$$= 0.332 \times \frac{0.02732}{0.28} \times (5 \times 10^4)^{1/2} \times (0.7)^{1/3}$$

$$= \textbf{6.43 W/m}^2\textbf{°C (Ans.)}$$

(*vii*) **Average convective heat transfer coefficient, $\overline{h}$:**

$$\overline{h} = 0.664 \left(\frac{k}{L}\right) (Re_L)^{1/2} (Pr)^{1/3} \qquad\qquad ...[\text{Eqn. (7.66)}]$$

$$= 0.664 \left(\frac{0.02732}{0.28} \right) (5 \times 10^4)^{1/2} (0.7)^{1/3} = 12.86 \text{ W/m}^2\text{°C (Ans.)}$$

$$\dots (\bar{h} = 2h_x)$$

(viii) **Rate of heat transfer by convection, $Q_{conv.}$:**

$$Q_{conv.} = \bar{h} A_s (t_s - t_\infty)$$
$$= 12.85 \times (0.28 \times 0.28) (56 - 20) = \mathbf{36.29 \text{ W (Ans.)}}$$

(ix) **Total drag force on the plate, F_D:**

$$F_D = \tau_0 \times \text{ area of plate on one side upto 0.28 m}$$
$$= 0.01519 \times 0.28 \times 0.28 = \mathbf{0.00119 \text{ N (Ans.)}}$$

(x) **Total mass flow rate through the boundary, m:**

$$m = \frac{5}{8} \rho U (\delta_2 - \delta_1)$$

(where $\delta_1 = 0$ at $x = 0$ and $\delta_2 = \delta$ at $x = 0.28$ m)

$$= \frac{5}{8} \times 1.1374 \times 3 (0.00626 - 0) = \mathbf{0.01335 \text{ kg/s (Ans.)}}$$

Example 7.11. *Air at atmospheric pressure and 200°C flows over a plate with a velocity of 5 m/s. The plate is 15 mm wide and is maintained at a temperature of 120°C. Calculate the thicknesses of hydrodynamic and thermal boundary layers and the local heat transfer coefficient at a distance of 0.5 m from the leading edge. Assume that flow is on one side of the plate.*

$\rho = 0.815 \text{ kg/m}^3$; $\mu = 24.5 \times 10^{-6} \text{ Ns/m}^2$; $Pr = 0.7, k = 0.0364 \text{ W/m K.}$ (AMIE Summer, 1997)

Solution. *Given*: $U = 5$ m/s; $x = 0.5$ m; $\rho = 0.815$ kg/m³; $\mu = 24.5 \times 10^{-6}$ Ns/m²;

$Pr = 0.7, k = 0.0364$ W/m K.

Let us first ascertain the type of flow, whether laminar or tubulent.

$$Re_x = \frac{Ux}{\nu} = \frac{5 \times 0.5}{\mu/\rho} = \frac{5 \times 0.5}{(24.5 \times 10^{-6} / 0.815)} = 83163$$

Since $Re_x < 5 \times 10^5$, hence flow is *laminar*.

Boundary layer thickness at $x = 0.5$ m, δ:

$$\delta = \frac{5x}{\sqrt{Re_x}} = \frac{5 \times 0.5}{\sqrt{83163}} = 8.669 \times 10^{-3} \text{ m}$$

or **8.669 mm (Ans.)**

Thickness of thermal boundary layer, at $x = 0.5$ m, δ_{th}

$$\delta_{th} = \frac{\delta}{(Pr)^{1/3}} = \frac{8.669}{(0.7)^{1/3}} = \mathbf{9.763 \text{ mm (Ans.)}}$$

Local heat transfer coefficient, h_x:

This tool can be used in a variety of heat transfer experiments, such as free convection, forced convection and fins.

$$h_x = 0.332 \times \frac{k}{x} (Re_x)^{1/2} (Pr)^{1/3} \quad \dots \text{[Eqn. (7.64)]}$$

$$= 0.332 \times \frac{0.0364}{0.5} \times (83163)^{1/2} \times (0.7)^{1/3} = \mathbf{6.189 \text{ W/m}^2\text{K (Ans.)}}$$

Example 7.12. *Air at atmospheric pressure and 40° C flows with a velocity of U = 5 m/s over a 2 m long flat plate whose surface is kept at a uniform temperature of 120°C. Determine the average heat transfer coefficient over the 2 m length of the plate. Also find out the rate of heat transfer between the plate and the air per 1 m width of the plate. [Air at 1 atm. and 80°C, $v = 2.107 \times 10^{-5}$ m²/s, k = 0.03025 W/mK ; Pr = 0.6965]*
(AMIE Winter, 1998)

Solution. Given : Given $t_\infty = 40°C$; $U = 5$m/s; $L = 2$m, $t_s = 120°C$; $B = 1$ m

The properties of air at mean bulk temperature of $\left(\dfrac{120 + 40}{2}\right) = 80°C$ are :

$$v = 2.107 \times 10^{-5} \text{ m}^2/\text{s}; \ k = 0.03025 \text{ W/m K}; \ Pr = 0.6965.$$

Average heat transfer coefficient, $\bar{h}$:

$$Re = \frac{UL}{v} = \frac{5 \times 2}{2.107 \times 10^{-5}} = 4.746 \times 10^5$$

Assuming $Re_{cr} = 5 \times 10^5$, the flow is *laminar*.

Using *exact solution*, the average Nusselt number is given by

$$\overline{Nu} = 0.664 \ (Re_L)^{1/2} \ (Pr)^{1/3} \qquad\qquad ...[\text{Eqn. (7.68)}]$$

or,

$$\frac{\bar{h}L}{k} = 0.664 \ (4.746 \times 10^5)^{1/2} \ (0.6965)^{1/3} = 405.48$$

∴

$$\bar{h} = \frac{k}{L} \times 405.48 = \frac{0.03025}{2} \times 4054.48 = \textbf{6.133 W/m}^3\textbf{K} \quad \textbf{(Ans.)}$$

Rate of heat transfer, Q :

$$Q = \bar{h} \ A_s \ (t_s - t_\infty)$$
$$= 6.133 \times (2 \times 1) (120 - 40) = \textbf{981.28 W} \quad \textbf{(Ans.)}$$

Example 7.13. *Air at 27°C and 1 bar flows over a plate at a speed of 2 m/s.*

(i) *Calculate the boundary layer thickness at 400 mm from the leading edge of the plate. Find the mass flow rate per unit width of the plate.*

For air $\mu = 19.8 \times 10^{-6}$ kg/ms at 27°C.

(ii) *If the plate is maintained at 60°C, calculate the heat transferred per hour.*

The properties of air at mean temperature of (27 + 60)/2 = 43.5° C are given below :

$$v = 17.36 \times 10^{-6} \text{ m}^2/\text{s}; \ k = 0.02749 \text{ W/m°C}$$
$$c_p = 1006 \text{ J/kg K}; \ R = 287 \text{ Nm/kg m K}; \ Pr = 0.7$$
(M.U.)

Solution. Given : $t = 27°C$; $p = 1$ bar, $U = 2$ m/s; $x = 400$ mm = 0.4 m

(i) Boundary layer thickness, δ :

$$\rho = \frac{p}{RT} = \frac{1 \times 10^5}{287 \times (27 + 273)} = 1.16 \, kg/m^3$$

$$Re_x = \frac{\rho L U}{\mu} = \frac{1.16 \times 0.4 \times 2}{19.8 \times 10^{-6}} = 46869$$

Boundary layer thickness, $\delta = \dfrac{4.64 \, x}{\sqrt{Re_x}}$ \qquad\qquad ...[Eqn.(7.36)]

or,

$$\delta = \frac{4.64 \times 0.4}{\sqrt{46869}} = 0.00857 \, m \text{ or } \textbf{8.57 mm} \quad \textbf{(Ans.)}$$

The mass flow rate per metre width is given by,

$$m_x = \int_0^\delta (dy \times 1) u \cdot \rho = \int_0^\delta \rho u \, dy$$

Now,
$$u = U \left[\frac{3}{2} \frac{y}{\delta} - \frac{1}{2} \left(\frac{y}{\delta} \right)^3 \right] \qquad \qquad ...assumed$$

$$\therefore \qquad m_x = \int_0^\delta \rho U \left[\frac{3}{2} \frac{y}{\delta} - \frac{1}{2} \left(\frac{y}{\delta} \right)^3 \right] dy$$

$$= \rho U \left[\frac{3}{4} \left(\frac{y^2}{\delta} \right) - \frac{1}{8} \left(\frac{y^4}{\delta^3} \right) \right]_0^\delta = \frac{5}{8} \rho U \delta$$

$$= \frac{5}{8} \times 1.16 \times 2 \times 0.00857 = 0.01242 \, kg/s \quad \textbf{(Ans.)}$$

Note. If the mass added in the boundary is to be calculated when the fluid moves from x_1 to x_2 along the main flow direction, then it is given by

$$\Delta m = \frac{5}{8} \rho U (\delta_2 - \delta_1)$$

where δ_1 and δ_2 are the boundary layer thicknesses at x_1 and x_2.

(ii) Heat transferred per hour, Q :

$$\overline{Nu} = \frac{\overline{h} L}{k} = 0.664 \, Re^{1/2} \, Pr^{1/3}$$

$$\overline{h} = \frac{k}{L} = 0.664 \, Re^{1/2} \, Pr^{1/3}$$

$$= \frac{0.02749}{0.4} \times 0.664 \times (46869)^{1/2} \times (0.7)^{1/3} = 8.77 \, W/m^2 \, °C$$

$$Q = \overline{h} A (t_s - t_\infty)$$
$$= 8.77 \times (0.4 \times 1)(60 - 27) = 115.76 \, J/s$$
$$= \frac{115.76 \times 3600}{1000} = \textbf{416.74 kJ/h (Ans.)}$$

Example 7.14. *Air at 1 bar and at a temperature of 30°C ($\mu = 0.06717$ kg/hm) flows at a speed of 1.2 m/s over a flat plate. Determine the boundary layer thickness at distance of 250 mm and 500 mm from the leading edge of the plate. Also, calculate the mass entrainment between these two sections. Assume the parabolic velocity distribution as :* $\frac{u}{U} = \frac{3}{2} \left(\frac{y}{\delta} \right) - \frac{1}{2} \left(\frac{y}{\delta} \right)^3$.

Solution. *Given :*　　$t_\infty = 30°C$, $\mu = 0.06717$ kg/hm, $U = 1.2$ m/s
Boundary layer thicknesses :

The density of air,
$$\rho = \frac{p}{RT} = \frac{1 \times 10^5}{287 \times (30 + 273)} = 1.15 \, kg/m^3$$

At x = 250 mm = 0.25 m

Reynolds number
$$Re_x = \frac{\rho U x}{\mu} = \frac{1.15 \times 1.2 \times 0.25 \times 3600}{0.06717} = 18490$$

$\therefore$ Boundary layer thickness,　$\delta_1 = \frac{4.64 \, x}{\sqrt{Re_x}}$　　　　...[Eqn. (7.36)]

or,
$$\delta_1 = \frac{4.64 \times 0.25}{\sqrt{18490}} = 0.00853 \, m \text{ or } \textbf{8.53 mm (Ans.)}$$

At $x = 500$ $mm = 0.5$ m

$$Re_x = \frac{1.15 \times 1.2 \times 0.5 \times 3600}{0.06717} = 36981$$

∴ Boundary layer thickness, $\delta_2 = \dfrac{4.64 \times 0.5}{\sqrt{36981}} = 0.01206$ m $= \mathbf{12.06}$ **mm** (Ans.)

Mass entrainment :

The mass flow rate at any position in the boundary layer is given by

$$m_x = \int_0^\delta \rho u \, dy = \int_0^\delta \rho \left[U \left\{ \frac{3}{2} \left(\frac{y}{\delta} \right) - \frac{1}{2} \left(\frac{y}{\delta} \right)^3 \right\} \right] dy$$

$$= \rho U \left[\frac{3}{4} \left(\frac{y}{\delta} \right)^2 - \frac{1}{8} \left(\frac{y^4}{\delta^3} \right) \right]_0^\delta = \frac{5}{8} \rho U \delta$$

∴ The mass entrainment between the two sections *i.e.*, at $x = 250$ mm and $x = 500$ mm.

$$= \frac{5}{8} \rho U (\delta_2 - \delta_1) = \frac{5}{8} \times 1.15 \times 1.2 \, (0.01206 - 0.00853)$$

$$= 3.045 \times 10^{-3} \text{ kg/s} = \mathbf{10.96 \text{ kg/h}} \quad \textbf{(Ans.)}$$

Example 7.15. *Air at 20°C is flowing over a flat plate which is 200 mm wide and 500 mm long. The plate is maintained at 100°C. Find the heat loss per hour from the plate if the air is flowing parallel to 500 mm side with 2m/s velocity. What will be the effect on heat transfer if the flow is parallel to 200 mm side.*

The properties of air at (100 + 20)/2 = 60°C are $v = 18.97 \times 10^{-6}$ m^2/s, $k = 0.025$ W/m°C and $Pr = 0.7$.

(M.U.)

Solution. *Given :* $U = 2$ m/s, $v = 18.97 \times 10^{-6}$ m²/s, $k = 0.025$ W/m°C and $Pr = 0.7$.

Heat loss per hour from the plate, Q :

Case I. *When the flow is parallel to 500 mm side :*

$$\overline{Nu} = \frac{\overline{h} L}{k} = 0.664 \, (Re_L)^{1/2} \, (Pr)^{1/3} \qquad \qquad ...[\text{Eqn. (7.68)}]$$

where, $$Re_L = \frac{UL}{v} = \frac{2 \times 0.5}{18.19 \times 10^{-6}} = 5.27 \times 10^4$$

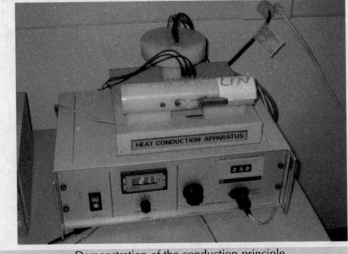

Demonstration of the conduction principle.

$$\therefore \qquad \bar{h} = \frac{k}{L} \times 0.664 \, (Re_L)^{1/2} \, (Pr)^{1/3}$$

$$= \frac{0.025}{0.5} \times 0.664 \, (5.27 \times 10^4)^{1/2} \, (0.7)^{1/3} = 6.767 \text{ W/m}^2\text{°C}$$

$$\therefore \qquad Q = \bar{h} \, A_s \, (t_s - t_\infty) = 6.767 \times (0.5 \times 0.2) \, (100 - 20) = \textbf{54.14 W} \quad \textbf{(Ans.)}$$

Case II. *When the flow is parallel to 200 mm side :*

$$Re_L = \frac{2 \times 0.2}{18.97 \times 10^{-6}} = 2.11 \times 10^4$$

$$\therefore \qquad \bar{h} = \frac{0.025}{0.2} \times 0.664 \times (2.11 \times 10^4)^{1/2} \, (0.7)^{1/3} = \textbf{10.7 W/m}^2\,\textbf{°C} \quad \textbf{(Ans.)}$$

$$\therefore \qquad Q = \bar{h} \times A_s \, (t_s - t_\infty) = 10.7 \times (0.2 \times 0.5) \times (100 - 20) = \textbf{85.6 W} \quad \textbf{(Ans.)}$$

Example 7.16. *In a certain glass making process, a square plate of glass 1 m² area and 3 mm thick heated uniformly to 90° C is cooled by air at 20°C flowing over both sides parallel to the plate at 2 m/s. Calculate the initial rate of cooling the plate.*

Neglect temperature gradient in the glass plate and consider only forced connection.

Take for glass : $\rho = 2500$ kg/m³ and $c_p = 0.67$ kJ/kg K

Take the following properties of air :

$\rho = 1.076$ kg/m²; $c_p = 1008$ J/kg K, $k = 0.0286$ W/m° C and $\mu = 19.8 \times 10^{-6}$ N-s/m².

(N.U., 1997)

Solution. *Given :* $A = 1 \text{ m}^2$; $t_s = 90°\text{C}$; $t_\infty = 20°\text{C}$, $U = 2 \text{ m/s}$.

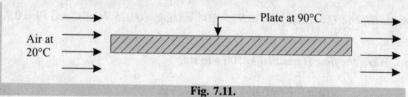

Air at 20°C   Plate at 90°C

Fig. 7.11.

Initial rate of cooling :

The average heat transfer co-efficient for the air flow parallel to the plate is given by

$$\overline{Nu} = \frac{\bar{h}L}{k} = 0.664 (Re_L)^{1/2} \, (Pr)^{1/3} \qquad \text{...[Eqn. 7.68)]}$$

(valid for $Pr > 0.5$)

$$Re_L = \frac{\rho V L}{\mu} = \frac{1.076 \times 2 \times 1}{19.8 \times 10^{-6}} = 1.087 \times 10^5$$

$$Pe = \frac{\mu c_p}{k} = \frac{19.8 \times 10^{-6} \times 1008}{0.0286} = .0698$$

Substituting the values in the above eqn. we get

$$\frac{\bar{h}L}{k} = 0.664 \times (1.087 \times 10^5)^{1/2} \times (0.698)^{1/3} = 194.19$$

or, $$\bar{h} = \frac{k}{L} \times 194.19 = \frac{0.0286}{1} \times 194.19 = 5.55 \text{ W/m}^2 \, \text{°C}$$

The heat flow (Q) from both sides of the plate is given by :

$$Q = 2\bar{h} \, A(t_s - t_\infty) = 2 \times 5.55 \times 1 \times (90 - 20) = 777 \text{ W}$$

The heat lost by the plate instantaneously is given by :

$$Q = m\, c_p\, \Delta t = 777$$

where,

$$m = (\text{ Area} \times \text{thickness }) \times \rho$$

$$= 1 \times \frac{3}{1000} \times 2500 = 7.5 \text{ kg}$$

$$\therefore \qquad 777 = 7.5 \times (0.67 \times 10^3) \times \Delta t$$

$$\therefore \qquad \Delta t = \frac{777}{7.5 \times (0.67 \times 10^3)} = 0.155°C/s \quad \text{(Ans)}$$

Example 7.17. *A flat plate, 1m wide and 1.5 m long is to be maintained at 90°C in air with a free stream temperature of 10°C. Determine the velocity with which air must flow over flat plate along 1.5 m side so that the rate of energy dissipation from the plate is 3.75 kW. Take the following properties of air at 50°C :*

$$\rho = 1.09 \text{ kg/m}^3, \ k = 0.028 W/m°C, \ c_p = 1.007 \text{ kJ/kg°C}, \ \mu = 2.03 \times 10^{-5} \text{ kg/m-s } Pr = 0.7.$$

(M.U.)

Solution. *Given :* $L = 1.5$ m, $B = 1$m, $t_s = 90°C$, $t_\infty = 10°C$, $Q = 3.75$ kW

Properties of air at $(90 + 10)/2 = 50°C$: $\rho = 1.09$ kg/m^3, $k = 0.028$ W/m°C, $c_p = 1.007$ kJ/kg°C, $\mu = 2.03 \times 10^{-5}$ kg/m^{-s}

Free stream velocity, U :

The heat flow from the plate to air is given by

$$Q = \bar{h}\, A_s\, (t_s - t_\infty)$$

where,

$$\bar{h} = \frac{k}{L} \times 0.664\, (Re_L)^{1/2}\, (Pr)^{1/3} \qquad\qquad\qquad ...[\text{Eqn. (7.68)}]$$

$$= \frac{0.028}{1.5} \times 0.664 \left(\frac{\rho LU}{\mu} \right)^{1/2} (0.7)^{1/3}$$

$$= \frac{0.028}{1.5} \times 0.664 \left(\frac{1.09 \times 1.5 \times U}{2.03 \times 10^{-5}} \right)^{1/2} (0.7)^{1/3} = 3.123\sqrt{U}$$

$$\therefore \qquad 3.75 \times 6000 = 3.123\ \sqrt{U} \times (1.5 \times 1)\,(90 - 10)$$

or,

$$\sqrt{U} = \frac{3.75 \times 1000}{3.123 \times (1.5 \times 1)\,(80)} = 10$$

or,

$$U = 100 \text{ m/s} \quad \text{(Ans.)}$$

Example 7.18. *Air at 20°C and at atmospheric pressure flows over a flat plate at a velocity of 1.8 m/s. If the length of the plate is 2.2 m and is maintained at 100°C, calculate the heat transfer rate per unit width using (i) exact and (ii) approximate methods.*

The properties of air at mean bulk temperature of $(100 + 20)/2 = 60°C$ are :

$$\rho = 1.06 \text{ kg/m}^3, \ c_p = 1.005 \text{ kJ/kg °C}, \ k = 0.02894 \text{ W/m°C}, \ Pr = 0.696$$

$$v = 18.97 \times 10^{-6} \text{ m}^2/s.$$

Solution. *Given :* $t_\infty = 20°C$, $t_s = 100°C$, $U = 1.8$ m/s, $L = 2.2$ m, $B = 1$ m

Heat transfer rate per unit width :

Reynolds number,

$$Re_L = \frac{UL}{v} = \frac{1.8 \times 2.2}{18.97 \times 10^{-6}} = 2.087 \times 10^5$$

Since Reynolds number is less than 5×10^5 hence flow is *laminar*.

(i) **Using exact solution :**

The average Nusselt number is given by

$$\overline{Nu} = 0.664 \ (Re_L)^{1/2} \ (Pr)^{1/3} \qquad \text{...[Eqn. (7.68)]}$$

or,
$$\frac{hL}{k} = 0.664 \ (2.087 \times 10^5)^{1/2} \ (0.696)^{1/3} = 268.82$$

or,
$$\overline{h} = \frac{268.82 \, k}{L} = \frac{268.82 \times 0.02894}{2.2} = 3.536 \ \text{W/m}^2\text{°C}$$

∴ Heat transfer rate from the plate,

$$Q = \overline{h} \ A_s \ (t_s - t_\infty) = 3.536 \times (2.2 \times 1) \ (100 - 20) = \textbf{622.34 W (Ans.)}$$

(ii) **Using approximate solution :**

$$\overline{Nu} = \frac{hL}{k} = 0.646 \ (\ Re_L)^{1/2} \ (Pr)^{1/3}$$

or,
$$\frac{\overline{h} \, L}{k} = 0.646 \ (2.087 \times 10^5)^{1/2} \ (0.696)^{1/3} = 261.53$$

or,
$$\overline{h} = \frac{261.53 \, k}{L} = \frac{261.53 \times 0.02894}{2.2} = 3.44 \ \text{W/m}^2 \, \text{°C}$$

∴ Heat transfer rate from the plate,

$$Q = \overline{h} \ A_s \ (t_s - t_\infty) = 3.44 \times (2.2 \times 1) \times (100 - 20) = \textbf{605.44 W} \quad \textbf{(Ans.)}$$

Example 7.19. *Air at a temperature of 30°C flows past a flat plate at a velocity of 1.8 m/s. The flat surface has a sharp leading edge and its total length equals 750 mm. Calculate :*

(i) The average skin friction or drag coefficient,

(ii) The average shear stress, and

(iii) The ratio of the average shear stress to the shear stress at the trailing edge.

Properties of air at 30°C are : $\rho = 1.165 \ kg/m^3$, $\mu = 6.717 \times 10^{-2} \ kg/hm$, $v = 16 \times 10^{-6} \ m^2/s$.

Solution. *Given :* $t_\infty = 30°C$, $U = 1.8 \ m/s$, $L = 750 \ mm = 0.75 \ m$, $\rho = 1.165 \ kg/m^3$, $\mu = 6.717 \times 10^{-2} \ kg/hm$, $v = 16 \times 10^{-6} \ m^2/s$.

(i) **The average skin friction, $\overline{C}_f$:**

Reynolds number,
$$Re_L = \frac{UL}{v} = \frac{1.8 \times 0.75}{1.6 \times 10^{-6}} = 84375$$

Since the Reynolds number is less than 5×10^5, the boundary layer over the entire plate is laminar in nature.

∴
$$\overline{C}_f = \frac{1.328}{\sqrt{Re_L}} = \frac{1.328}{\sqrt{84375}} = \textbf{0.004572 \ (Ans.)} \qquad \text{...[Eqn. (7.25)]}$$

(ii) **The average shear stress, τ_w :**

$$\tau_w = \frac{1}{2} \rho U^2 \times \overline{C}_f$$

$$= \frac{1}{2} \times 1.165 \times 1.8^2 \times 0.004572 = \textbf{0.008629 N/m}^2 \quad \textbf{(Ans.)}$$

(iii) **The ratio of average shear stress to the shear stress at the trailing edge :**

The skin friction coefficient at the trailing edge $(x = L)$

$$C_f = \frac{0.664}{\sqrt{Re_x}} \qquad \text{...[Eqn. (7.24)]}$$

or,
$$C_{fx} = \frac{0.664}{\sqrt{84375}} = 0.002286$$

$\therefore$ Shear stress at the trailing edge,

$$\tau_{wx} = \frac{1}{2} \rho U^2 C_{fx}$$

$$= \frac{1}{2} \times 1.165 \times 1.8^2 \times 0.002286 = 0.004314 \ N/m^2$$

$\therefore$ $$\frac{\tau_w}{\tau_{wx}} = \frac{0.008629}{0.004314} = 2 \quad (Ans.)$$

Example 7.20. *Air at 30°C flows with a velocity of 2.8 m/s over a plate 1000 mm (length) × 600 mm (width) × 25 mm (thickness). The top surface of the plate is maintained at 90°C. If the thermal conductivity of the plate material is 25W/m°C, calculate :*

(i) *Heat lost by the plate;*

(ii) *Bottom temperature of the plate for the steady state condition.*

The thermo-physical properties of air at mean film temperature (90 + 30)/2 = 60°C are :

$\rho = 1.06 \ kg/m^3, c_p = 1.005 \ kJ/kg \ K, k = 0.02894 \ W/m°C, v = 18.97 \times 10^{-6} \ m^2/s, Pr = 0.696.$

Solution. *Given :* $t_\infty = 30°C$, $t_s = 90°C$, $U = 2.8 \ m/s$, $k_{plate} = 25 \ W/m°C$, $L = 1000 \ mm = 1m$, $B = 600 \ mm = 0.6 \ m$, $\delta = 25 \ mm = 0.025m$.

(i)   **Heat lost by the plate :**

Reynolds number at the trailing edge,

$$Re_L = \frac{UL}{v} = \frac{2.8 \times 1.0}{18.97 \times 10^{-6}} = 1.476 \times 10^5$$

Since Reynolds number is less than 5 × 10⁵, hence flow is *laminar* throughout the length,

$$\overline{Nu} = 0.664 \ (Re_L)^{1/2} \ (Pr)^{1/3} = \frac{\overline{h}L}{k} \qquad ...[Eqn. \ (7.68)]$$

or, $\overline{h}$ (average heat transfer coefficient) $= \dfrac{\overline{Nu} \times k}{L} = \dfrac{0.664 \ (Re_L)^{1/2} \ (Pr)^{1/3} \times k}{L}$

or, $$\overline{h} = \frac{0.664 \ (1.476 \times 10^5)^{1/2} \ (0.696)^{1/3} \times 0.02894}{1.0}$$

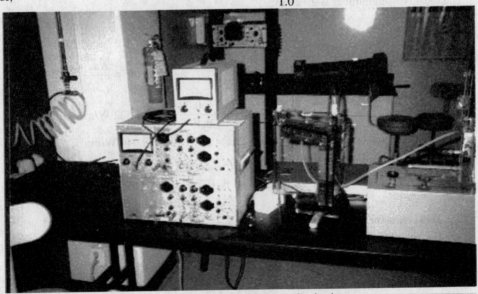

Forced convection from a heated cylinder.

$$= 6.542 \text{ W/m}^2 \text{ °C}$$

∴ Heat lost by the plate,

$$Q = \bar{h} \, A_s \, (t_s - t_\infty)$$

or,

$$Q = 6.542 \times (1.0 \times 0.6) \, (90 - 30) = \textbf{235.5 W (Ans.)}$$

(*ii*) **Bottom temperature of the plate, t_b:**

Heat lost by the plate Q (calculated above) must be conducted through the plate, hence exchange from top to bottom surface is

$$Q = -\frac{kA \, (t_s - t_\infty)}{\delta} = 235.5$$

or,

$$= \frac{25 \times (1.0 \times 0.6) \, (90 - t_b)}{0.025} = 235.5$$

or,

$$t_b = 90 + \frac{0.025 \times 235.5}{25 \, (1.0 \times 0.6)} = \textbf{90.39°C} \quad \textbf{(Ans.)}$$

Example 7.21. *Air at 30°C and at atmospheric pressure flows at a velocity of 2.2 m/s over a plate maintained at 90°C. The length and the width of the plate are 900 mm and 450 mm respectively. Using exact solution, calculate the heat transfer rate from,*

(i)   first half of the plate,   (ii)   full plate, and   (iii)   next half of the plate.

The properties of air at mean bulk temperature (90 + 30)/2 = 60°C are :

$\rho = 1.06 \text{ kg/m}^3$, $\mu = 7.211 \text{ kg/hm}$, $v = 18.97 \times 10^{-6} \text{ m}^2/s$, $Pr = 0.696$, $k = 0.02894 \text{ W/m°C}$.

Solution. Given : $t_\infty = 30°C$, $U = 2.2 \text{ m/s}$, $t_s = 90°C$, $L = 900 \text{ mm} = 0.9\text{m}$, $B = 450 \text{ mm} = 0.45 \text{ m}$.

(*i*) **Heat transfer rate from first half of the plate :**

For first half of the plate,

$$x = \frac{0.9}{2} = 0.45 \text{ m}$$

$$Re_x = \frac{Ux}{v} = \frac{2.2 \times 0.45}{18.97 \times 10^{-6}} = 52188$$

Since $Re < 5 \times 10^5$ hence the flow is *laminar*.

The local Nusselt number is given by,

$$Nu_x = 0.332 \, (Re_x)^{1/2} \, (Pr)^{1/3} \qquad \qquad \text{...[Eqn. 7.65]}$$
$$= 0.332 \, (52188)^{1/2} \, (0.696)^{1/3} = 67.21$$

But,

$$Nu_x = \frac{h_x x}{k} \qquad \text{or} \qquad h_x = \frac{Nu_x \times k}{x}$$

∴

$$h_x = \frac{67.21 \times 0.02894}{0.45} = 4.322 \text{ W/m}^2 \text{ °C}$$

Average heat transfer coefficient, $\bar{h} = 2h_x = 2 \times 4.322 = 8.644 \text{ W/m}^2 \text{ °C}$

∴ Heat transfer rate from first half of the plate,

$$Q = \bar{h} \, A_s \, (t_s - t_\infty)$$
$$= 8.644 \times (0.45 \times 0.45) \, (90 - 30) = \textbf{105 W} \quad \textbf{(Ans.)}$$

(*ii*) **Heat transfer rate from full plate :**

For full plate,

$$x = L = 0.9 \text{ m}$$

$$Re_L = \frac{2.2 \times 0.9}{18.97 \times 10^{-6}} = 104375$$

$$\bar{Nu} = 0.664 \, (Re_L)^{1/2} \, (Pr)^{1/3} = \frac{\bar{h}L}{k}$$

$$\therefore \qquad \bar{h} = 0.664 \, (Re_L)^{1/2} \, (Pr)^{1/2} \times \frac{k}{L} = 0.664 \, (104375)^{1/2} \, (0.696)^{1/3} \times \frac{0.02894}{0.9}$$

$$= 6.113 \text{ W/m}^2 \, ^\circ\text{C}$$

The heat transfer rate from entire plate,

$$Q_2 = \bar{h} \, A_s \, (t_s - t_\infty) = 6.113 \times (0.9 \times 0.45) \times (90 - 30) = \textbf{148.54 W} \quad \textbf{(Ans.)}$$

(iii) **Heat transfer rate from next half of the plate :**

Heat transfer rate from the next half of the plate

$$= Q_2 - Q_1 = 148.54 - 105 = \textbf{43.54 W} \qquad \textbf{(Ans.)}$$

Example 7.22. *Castor oil at 25°C flows at a velocity of 0.1 m/s past a flat plate, in a certain process. If the plate is 4.5 m long and is maintained at a uniform temperature of 95°C, calculate the following using exact solution :*

(i) *The hydrodynamic and thermal boundary layer thicknesses on one side of the plate,*

(ii) *The total drag force per unit width on one side of the plate,*

(iii) *The local heat transfer coefficient at the trailing edge, and*

(iv) *The heat transfer rate.*

The thermo-physical properties of oil at mean film temperature of $(95 + 25)/2 = 60°C$ *are :*

$$\rho = 956.8 \text{ kg/m}^3; \ \alpha = 7.2 \times 10^{-8} \text{ m}^2/s; \ k = 0.213 \text{ W/m}°C; \ \nu = 0.65 \times 10^{-4} \text{ m}^2/s.$$

Solution. *Given :* $t_\infty = 25°C$, $t_s = 95°C$, $L = 4.5\text{m}$, $U = 0.1$ m/s.

(i) **The hydrodynamic and thermal boundary layer thicknesses, δ, δ_{th} :**

Reynolds number at the end of the plate,

$$Re_L = \frac{UL}{\nu} = \frac{0.1 \times 4.5}{0.65 \times 10^{-4}} = 6923$$

Since Reynolds number is less than 5×10^5, hence the flow is *laminar* in nature.

The hydrodynamic boundary layer thickness,

$$\delta = \frac{5x}{\sqrt{Re_x}} = \frac{5 \times L}{\sqrt{Re_L}} = \frac{5 \times 4.5}{\sqrt{6923}}$$

$$= 0.2704 \text{ m or } \textbf{270.4 mm} \quad \textbf{(Ans.)} \qquad \qquad \text{...[Eqn. (7.22)]}$$

The thermal boundary layer thickness, according to Pohlhausen, is given by :

$$\delta_{th} = \frac{\delta}{(Pr)^{1/3}} \qquad \qquad \text{...[Eqn. (7.62)]}$$

where, $\qquad Pr \text{ (Prandtl number)} \frac{\nu}{\alpha} = \frac{(0.65 \times 10^{-4})}{7.2 \times 10^{-8}} = 902.77$

$$\therefore \qquad \delta_{th} = \frac{0.2704}{(902.77)^{1/3}} = 0.02798 \text{ m or } \textbf{27.98 mm} \quad \textbf{(Ans.)}$$

(ii) **The total drag force per unit width on one side of the plate, F_D :**

The average skin friction coefficient is given by,

$$\bar{C}_f = \frac{1.328}{\sqrt{Re_L}} \qquad \qquad \text{...[Eqn. (7.25)]}$$

or, $\qquad \bar{C}_f = \frac{1.328}{\sqrt{6923}} = 0.01596$

The drag force, $\quad F_D = \bar{C}_f \times \frac{1}{2} \rho U^2 \times$ area of plate (for one side) $\qquad \qquad \text{...[Eqn. (7.31)]}$

or, $F_D = 0.01596 \times \dfrac{1}{2} \times 956.8 \times 0.1^2 \times (4.5 \times 1) = \mathbf{0.3436}$ **N per meter width. (Ans.)**

(iii) The local heat transfer coefficient at the trailing edge, h_x (at $x = L$) :

$$Nu_x = \frac{h_x x}{k} = 0.332 \, (Re_x)^{1/2} \, (Pr)^{1/3}$$

$$= 0.332 \times (6923)^{1/2} \, (902.77)^{1/3} = 266.98 \qquad \qquad \text{...[Eqn. (7.65)]}$$

or, $h_x = \dfrac{266.98 \times k}{x} = \dfrac{266.98 \times 0.213}{4.5} = \mathbf{12.64}$ **W/m^2 °C   (Ans.)**

(iv) The heat transfer rate, Q :

$$Q = \bar{h} \, A_s \, (t_s - t_\infty)$$

where, $\bar{h} = 2h_x = 2 \times 12.64 = 25.28 \text{W/m}^2 \text{°C}$ \qquad \qquad \text{...[Eqn. (7.67)]}

∴ $Q = 25.28 \times (4.5 \times 1) \, (95 - 25) = \mathbf{7963.2}$ **W   (Ans.)**

Example 7.23. *Air at 20°C and at atmospheric pressure flows at a velocity of 4.5 m/s past a flat plate with a sharp leading edge. The entire plate surface is maintained at a temperature of 60°C. Assuming that the transition occurs at a critical Reynolds number of 5×10^5, find the distance from the leading edge at which the flow in the boundary layer changes from laminar to turbulent. At the location, calculate the following :*

(i) *Thickness of hydrodynamic layer,*

(ii) *Thickness of therml boundary layer,*

(iii) *Local and average convective heat transfer coefficients,*

(iv) *Heat transfer rate from both sides for, unit width of the plate,*

(v) *Mass entrainment in the boundary layer, and*

(vi) *The skin friction coefficient.*

Assume cubic velocity profile and approximate method.

The thermo-physical properties of air at mean film temperature $(60 + 20)/2 = 40°C$ are :
$\rho = 1.128 \text{ kg/m}^3$, $v = 16.96 \times 10^{-6} \text{ m}^2/s$, $k = 0.02755 \text{ W/m°C}$, $Pr = 0.699$.

Solution. *Given:* $t_\infty = 20 \text{ °C}$, $t_s = 60°C$, $U = 4.5$ m/s.

At the transition point, $Re_c = (Re)_{trans.} = \dfrac{U x_c}{v}$

or, $x_c = \dfrac{Re_c \times v}{U} = \dfrac{5 \times 10^5 \times 16.96 \times 10^{-6}}{4.5} = \mathbf{1.88}$ **m   (Ans.)**

(where, x_c = Distance from the leading edge at which the flow in the boundary layer changes *from laminar to turbulent*).

(i) **Thickness of hydrodynamic layer, δ :**

The thickness of hydrodynamic layer for, cubic velocity profile is given by,

$$\delta = \frac{4.64 \, x_c}{\sqrt{Re_c}} \qquad \qquad \text{...[Eqn. (7.36)]}$$

$$= \frac{4.64 \times 1.88}{\sqrt{5 \times 10^5}} = 0.01234 \text{ m or, } \mathbf{12.34 \text{ mm}}   \text{ (Ans.)}$$

(ii) **Thickness of thermal boundary layer, δ_{th} :**

The thermal boundary layer is given by,

$$\delta_{th} = \frac{0.975\,\delta}{(Pr)^{1/3}} \qquad\qquad \text{...[Eqn. (7.89)]}$$

or,

$$\delta_{th} = \frac{0.975 \times 0.01234}{(0.669)^{1/3}} = 0.01355 \text{ m or, } \mathbf{13.55 \text{ mm}} \quad \text{(Ans.)}$$

(iii) Local and average convective heat transfer coefficients:

The Nusselt number at $x = x_c$ is given by

$$Nu_c = 0.332\,(Re_c)^{1/2}\,(Pr)^{1/3} \qquad\qquad \text{...[Eqn. (7.65)]}$$

$$= 0.332\,(5 \times 10^5)^{1/2}\,(0.699)^{1/3} = 208.34$$

Put

$$Nu_x = \frac{h_x \times x_c}{k} \qquad \text{or,} \qquad h_c = \frac{Nu_c \times k}{x_c}$$

(where, h_c = Local heat transfer coefficient at $x = x_c$)

or,

$$h_c = \frac{208.34 \times 0.02755}{1.88} = 3.05 \text{ W/m}^2\,{}^\circ\text{C} \quad \text{(Ans.)}$$

Average heat transfer coefficient,

$$\bar{h} = \frac{1}{x_c} \int_0^{x_c} h_x \, dx$$

$$\bar{h} = 2h_c = 2 \times 3.05 = \mathbf{6.1 \text{ W/m}^2{}^\circ\text{C}} \quad \text{(Ans.)}$$

(iv) Heat transfer rate from both sides for, unit width of the plate; Q :

$$Q = \bar{h}\,(2A_s)\,\Delta t = 6.1\,(2 \times 1.88 \times 1)\,(60 - 20) = \mathbf{917.44 \text{ W}} \quad \text{(Ans.)}$$

(v) Mass entrainment in the boundary layer, m :

$$m = \frac{5}{8}\,\rho\,U\,(\delta_2 - \delta_1)$$

Here, $\delta_1 = 0$ at $x = 0$ and $\delta_2 = 0.01234$ m at $x = x_c = 1.88$ m

$$\therefore m = \frac{5}{8} \times 1.128 \times 4.5\,(0.01234 - 0) = \mathbf{0.039 \text{ kg/s or, } 140.4 \text{ kg/h}} \quad \text{(Ans.)}$$

(vi) The skin friction coefficient, C_{fx} :

$$C_{fx} = \frac{0.646}{\sqrt{Re_x}} \qquad\qquad \text{...[Eqn. (7.24)]}$$

or,

$$C_{fx} = \frac{0.646}{\sqrt{5 \times 10^5}} = \mathbf{9.136 \times 10^{-4}} \quad \text{(Ans.)}$$

Example 7.24. *A stream of water at 20°C ($\rho = 1.205$ kg/m³, $\mu = 0.06533$ kg/hm) flows at a velocity of 1.8 m/s over a plate 0.6 m long and placed at zero angle of incidence. Using exact solution, calculate :*

(i) The stream wise velocity component at the midpoint of the boundary layer,

(ii) The maximum boundary layer thickness, and

(iii) The maximum value of the nor,mal component of velocity at the trailing edge of the plate.

Solution. Given : $t_\infty = 20°C$, $\rho = 1.205$ kg/m³, $\mu = 0.06533$ kg/hm, $L = 0.6$ m, $U = 1.8$ m/s

(i) The stream wise velocity component at the midpoint of the boundary layer, u :

The boundary layer thickness by exact solution is given by

$$\delta = \frac{5x}{\sqrt{Re_x}} = \frac{5}{\sqrt{\dfrac{Ux}{\nu}}} = 5\sqrt{\frac{\nu x}{U}} \qquad\qquad \text{...[Eqn. 7.22]}$$

Obviously, the midpoint of the boundary layer $\left(y = \dfrac{\delta}{2} \right)$ occurs at

$$\eta = y\sqrt{\frac{U}{vx}} = 2.5$$

The stream wise velocity component is obtained for,m the Blasius solution in tabular form (Refer table 7.1).

At,
$$\eta = y\sqrt{\frac{U}{vx}} = 2.5 \text{ , we get } \frac{u}{U} = 0.736$$

or,
$$u = 0.736\, U = 0.736 \times 1.8 = \textbf{1.325 m/s}\quad\textbf{(Ans.)}$$

(ii)   The maximum boundary layer thickness, δ_L :

The maximum boundary layer thickness occurs at $x = 0.6$ m. Thus,

$$Re_L = \frac{\rho UL}{\mu} = \frac{1.205 \times 1.8 \times 0.6}{(0.06533/3600)} = 71713 \text{ , hence flow in } \textit{laminar.}$$

The boundary layer thickness at the trailing edge,

$$\delta_L = \frac{5L}{\sqrt{Re_L}} = \frac{5 \times 0.6}{\sqrt{71713}} = 0.0112\text{m} \text{ or, } \textbf{11.2 mm}\quad\textbf{(Ans.)}$$

(iii)   The maximum value of the normal component of velocity at the trailing edge, v :

The maximum value of the normal component of velocity occurs at the outer edge of the boundary layer where $u = U$. Hence for, $\dfrac{u}{U} = 1$, we have

$$\frac{v}{U}\sqrt{Re_L} = 0.86 \hspace{4cm} \text{(Refer Table 7.1)}$$

or,
$$v = \frac{0.86U}{\sqrt{Re_L}} = \frac{0.86 \times 1.8}{\sqrt{71713}} = 0.00578 \text{ m} \text{ or, } \textbf{5.78 m/s}\quad\textbf{(Ans.)}$$

7.2. LAMINAR TUBE FLOW

7.2.1. DEVELOPMENT OF BOUNDARY LAYER

In case of a pipe flow, the development of boundary layer proceeds in a fashion similar to that for, flow along a flat plate. A fluid of uniform velocity entering a tube is retarded near the walls and a boundary layer begins to develop as shown in Fig. 7.12 by dotted lines. The thickness of the boundary layer is limited to the pipe radius because of the flow being within a confined passage. Boundary layers from the pipe walls meet at the centre of the pipe and the entire flow acquires the characteristics of a boundary layer. Once the boundary layer thickness becomes equal to the radius of the tube there will not be any further change in the velocity distribution, this *invariant* velocity distribution is called *fully developed velocity profile i.e.,* **Poiseulle flow** (parabolic distribution).

According to Langhar (1942), the entrance length (L_e) is expressed as : $\dfrac{L_e}{D} = 0.0575\, Re$ where D represents the inside diameter of the pipe.

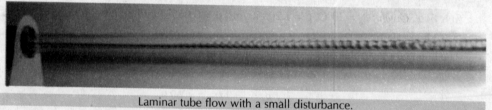

Laminar tube flow with a small disturbance.

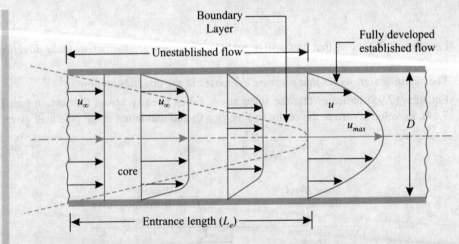

Fig. 7.12. The development of a laminar velocity profile in the intake region of a tube.

7.2.2 VELOCITY DISTRIBUTION

Fig. 7.13 shows a horizontal circular pipe of radius R, having laminar flow of fluid through it. Consider a small concentric cylinder (fluid element) of radius r and length dx as a free body.

If τ is the shear stress, the shear force F is given by

$$F = \tau \times 2\pi r \times dx$$

Let p be the intensity of pressure at left end and the intensity of pressure at the right end be

$$\left(p + \frac{\partial p}{\partial x} \cdot dx \right).$$

Thus the forces acting on the fluid element are :

1. The shear force, $\tau \times 2\pi r \times dx$ on the surface of fluid element.

2. The pressure force, $\pi \times \pi r^2$ on the left-end.

3. The pressure force, $\left(p + \dfrac{\partial p}{\partial x} \cdot dx \right)\pi r^2$ on the right end.

For steady flow, the net force on the cylinder must be *zero*.

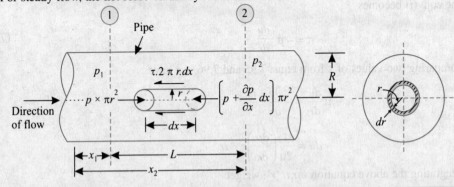

Fig. 7.13. Laminar flow through a circular pipe.

$$\left[p \times \pi r^2 - \left(p + \frac{\partial p}{\partial x} \cdot dx \right)\pi r^2 \right] - \tau \times 2\pi r \times dx = 0$$

or,

$$- \frac{\partial p}{\partial x} \cdot dx \times \pi r^2 - 2\pi r \times dx = 0$$

or,
$$\tau = -\frac{\partial p}{\partial x} \cdot \frac{r}{2} \qquad \qquad ...(7.95)$$

- Equation (7.95) shows that flow will occur only if *pressure gradient exists in the direction of flow*.

  The *negative sign shows that pressure decreases in the direction of flow*.

- Equation (7.95) indicates that the shear stress varies linearly across the section (see Fig. 7.14). Its value is zero at the centre of pipe ($r = 0$) and maximum at the pipe wall given by

$$\tau_0 = -\frac{\partial p}{\partial x}\left(\frac{R}{2}\right) \qquad \qquad ...[7.95\ (a)]$$

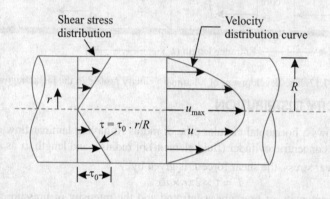

Fig. 7.14. Shear stress and velocity distribution across a section.

From Newton's law of viscosity,

$$\tau = \mu \cdot \frac{du}{dy} \qquad \qquad ...(i)$$

In this equation, the distance y is measured from the boundary. The radial distance r is related to distance y by the relation

$$y = R - r \text{ or, } dy = -\,dr$$

The eqn. (*i*) becomes

$$\tau = -\mu\,\frac{du}{dr} \qquad \qquad ...(7.96)$$

Comparing two values of τ from eqns. 7.95 and 7.96, we have

$$-\mu\frac{du}{dr} = -\frac{\partial p}{\partial x} \cdot \frac{r}{2}$$

or,
$$du = \frac{1}{2\mu}\left(\frac{\partial p}{\partial x}\right) r \cdot dr$$

Integrating the above equation w.r.t. 'r', we get

$$u = \frac{1}{4\mu} \cdot \frac{\partial p}{\partial x} r^2 + C \qquad \qquad ...(7.97)$$

where, C is the constant of integration and its value is obtained from the boundary condition :

At $r = R, u = 0$

$$\therefore \qquad 0 = \frac{1}{4\mu} \cdot \frac{\partial p}{\partial x} R^2 + C \qquad\qquad \text{or,} \qquad C = -\frac{1}{4\mu} \cdot \frac{\partial p}{\partial x} R^2$$

Substituting this value of C in eqn. (7.97), we get

$$u = \frac{1}{4\mu} \cdot \frac{\partial p}{\partial x} r^2 - \frac{1}{4\mu} \cdot \frac{\partial p}{\partial x} R^2$$

or,
$$u = -\frac{1}{4\mu} \cdot \frac{\partial p}{\partial x} (R^2 - r^2) \qquad\qquad\qquad ...(7.98)$$

Equation (7.98) shows that the velocity distribution curve is a *parabola* (see Fig. 7.14). The maximum velocity occurs at the centre and is given by

$$u_{max} = -\frac{1}{4\mu} \cdot \frac{\partial p}{\partial x} R^2 \qquad\qquad\qquad ...(7.99)$$

From eqns. (7.98) and (7.99), we have

$$u = u_{max} \left[1 - \left(\frac{r}{R} \right)^2 \right] \qquad\qquad\qquad ...(7.100)$$

Eqn. 7.100 is the *most commonly used equation for, the velocity distribution for, laminar flow through pipes.* This equation can be used to calculate the discharge as follows :

The discharge through an elementary ring of thickness dr at radial distances r is given by

$$dQ = u \times 2\pi r \times dr$$

$$= u_{max} \left[1 - \left(\frac{r}{R} \right)^2 \right] 2\pi r.dr$$

Total discharge
$$Q = \int dQ$$

$$= \int_0^R u_{max} \left[1 - \left(\frac{r}{R} \right)^2 \right] 2\pi r.dr$$

$$= 2\pi u_{max} \int_0^R \left(1 - \frac{r^3}{R^2} \right) dr$$

$$= 2\pi u_{max} \left[\frac{r^2}{2} - \frac{r^4}{4R^2} \right]_0^R = 2\pi u_{max} \left[\frac{R^2}{2} - \frac{R^4}{4R^2} \right]$$

$$= \frac{\pi}{2} u_{max} R^2$$

Average velocity of flow,
$$\bar{u} = \frac{Q}{A} = \frac{\frac{\pi}{2} u_{max} R^2}{\pi R^2} = \frac{u_{max}}{2} \qquad\qquad\qquad ...(7.101)$$

Eqn. (7.101) shows that the *average velocity is one-half the maximum velocity.* Substituting the value of u_{max} from eqn. (7.99), we have

$$\bar{u} = \frac{1}{8\mu} \left[-\frac{\partial p}{\partial x} \right] R^2 \qquad\qquad\qquad ...(7.102)$$

The pressure gradient $\dfrac{\partial p}{\partial x}$ is usually expressed in terms of a friction factor, f, defined as

$$- \frac{\partial p}{\partial x} = \frac{f}{D} \frac{\rho \bar{u}^2}{2} \qquad \qquad ...(7.103)$$

where, $\dfrac{\rho \bar{u}^2}{2}$ is dynamic pressure of the mean flow and D is the tube diameter.

From eqns. (7.102) and (7.103), we get the friction factor, as a simple function of Reynolds number,

$$f = \frac{64}{(\rho \, D\bar{u} / \mu)} = \frac{64}{Re} \qquad \qquad ...(7.104)$$

which is valid for, laminar tube flow, $Re < 2300$

Further, eqn. (7.102) can be written as,

$$- \partial p = \frac{8\mu \bar{u}}{R^2} \cdot \partial x$$

The pressure difference between two sections 1 and 2 at distances, x_1 and x_2 (see Fig. 7.13), is given by

$$- \int_{p_1}^{p_2} \partial p = \frac{8\mu \, \bar{u}}{R^2} \int_{x_1}^{x_2} \partial x$$

or, $$(p_1 - p_2) = \frac{8 \, \mu \bar{u}}{R^2} (x_2 - x_1) = \frac{8\mu \bar{u} L}{R^2} = \frac{32 \, \mu \bar{u} L}{D^2} = \frac{128 \, \mu \, Q \, L}{\pi D^4}$$

or, $$\frac{p_1 - p_2}{w} \, (= h_L) = \frac{128 \, \mu \, Q \, L}{w \pi D^4} \qquad \qquad ...(7.105)$$

Obviously the head loss h_L over a length of pipe varies directly as the first power of the rate of discharge Q and inversely as the fourth power of the pipe diameter.

7.2.3. TEMPERATURE DISTRIBUTION

In order to estimate the distribution of temperature let us consider the flow of heat through an elementary ring of thickness dr and length dx as shown in Fig. 7.15. Considering the radial conduction (neglecting axial conduction) and axial enthalpy transport in the *annular element*, we have:

Heat conducted into the annular element,

Heat exchangers combine powerful forced convection cooling with the advantages of a closed loop system for contaminated environments.

$$Q_r = - k \, (2\pi r.dx) \, \frac{\partial t}{\partial r}$$

Heat conducted out of the annular element,

$$dQ_{r+dr} = - k \left[2\pi \, (r + dr) \, dx \, \frac{\partial}{\partial x} \left(t + \frac{\partial t}{\partial r} \, dr \right) \right]$$

Net heat convected out of the annular element,

$$dQ_{conv.} = \rho \, (2\pi r dr) \, u \, c_p \, \frac{\partial t}{\partial r} \, dx$$

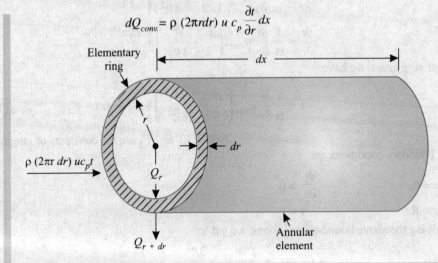

Fig. 7.15. Analysis of energy in the tube flow.

Considering energy balance on the annular element, we obtain

$$(\text{Heat conducted in})_{net} = (\text{Heat convected out})_{net}$$

$$dQ_r - dQ_{r+dr} = (dQ_{conv.})_{net}$$

$$- k \, (2\pi r.dx) \frac{\partial t}{\partial r} - \left[- k \left\{ 2\pi \, (r + dr) \, dx \, \frac{\partial}{\partial r} . \left(t + \frac{\partial t}{\partial r} . dr \right) \right\} \right] = \rho \, (2\pi r dr) u \, c_p \, \frac{\partial t}{\partial x} \, dx$$

$$- k \, (2\pi r.dx) \frac{\partial t}{\partial r} + k \left\{ 2\pi (r + dr) \right\} dx \left[\frac{\partial t}{\partial r} + \frac{\partial^2 t}{\partial r^2} \, dr \right] = \rho \, (2\pi r.dr) u \, c_p \, \frac{\partial t}{\partial x} \, dx$$

$$- k \, (2\pi r.dx) \frac{\partial t}{\partial r} + k \left(2\pi r \, dx . \frac{\partial t}{\partial r} \right) + k \left(2\pi r dx . \frac{\partial^2 t}{\partial r^2} \, dr \right) + k \, (2\pi \, dr \, dx) \frac{\partial t}{\partial r}$$

$$+ k \left(2\pi dr \, dx . \frac{\partial t^2}{\partial r^2} \, dr \right) = \rho \, (2\pi r.dr) u \, c_p \, \frac{\partial t}{\partial x} \, dx$$

Neglecting second order terms, we get

$$k \left(\frac{\partial t}{\partial r} + r \frac{\partial^2 t}{\partial r^2} \right) dx.dr = \rho r u c_p \, \frac{\partial t}{\partial x} \, dx.dr$$

$$\frac{1}{r} \frac{\partial}{\partial r} \left(r \frac{\partial t}{\partial r} \right) = u \frac{\rho c_p}{k} \frac{\partial t}{\partial x}$$

or,
$$\frac{1}{r} \frac{\partial}{\partial r} \left(r \frac{\partial t}{\partial r} \right) = \frac{u}{\alpha} \frac{\partial t}{\partial x} \qquad \qquad ...(7.106)$$

Inserting the value of u from eqn. (7.100), we get,

$$\frac{1}{r} \frac{\partial}{\partial r} \left(r \frac{\partial t}{\partial r} \right) = \frac{1}{\alpha} \frac{\partial t}{\partial x} . u_{max} \left(1 - \frac{r^2}{R^2} \right) \qquad \qquad ...(7.107)$$

or,
$$\frac{\partial}{\partial r}\left(r\frac{\partial t}{\partial r}\right) = \frac{u_{max}}{\alpha}\cdot\frac{\partial t}{\partial x}\cdot\left(r - \frac{r^3}{R^2}\right) \qquad \text{...(7.108)}$$

Let us consider the case of uniform heat flux along the wall, where we can take $\dfrac{\partial t}{\partial x}$ as a constant. Integrating eqn. (7.108) we have

$$r\frac{\partial t}{\partial r} = \frac{1}{\alpha}\frac{\partial t}{\partial x}u_{max}\cdot\left(\frac{r^2}{2} - \frac{r^4}{4R^2}\right) + C_1$$

or,
$$\frac{\partial t}{\partial r} = \frac{1}{\alpha}\frac{\partial t}{\partial x}u_{max}\cdot\left(\frac{r}{2} - \frac{r^3}{4R^2}\right) + \frac{C_1}{r}$$

Integrating again, we have

$$t = \frac{1}{\alpha}\frac{\partial t}{\partial x}u_{max}\left(\frac{r^2}{4} - \frac{r^4}{16R^2}\right) + C_1\ln(r) + C_2 \qquad \text{...(7.109)}$$

(where C_1 and C_2 are the constants of integration).

The boundary conditions are :

At $r = 0$, $\qquad\qquad\qquad \dfrac{\partial t}{\partial r} = 0$

At $r = R$, $\qquad\qquad\qquad t = t_s$

Applying the above boundary conditons, we get

$C_1 = 0$, $\qquad\qquad\qquad C_2 = t_s - \dfrac{1}{\alpha}\dfrac{\partial t}{\partial x}u_{max}\dfrac{3R^2}{16}$

Substituting the values of C_1 and C_2 in eqn. (7.109), we have

$$t = \frac{1}{\alpha}\frac{\partial t}{\partial x}u_{max}\left(\frac{r^2}{4} - \frac{r^4}{16R^2}\right) + \left[t_s - \frac{1}{\alpha}\frac{\partial t}{\partial r}u_{max}\frac{3R^2}{16}\right]$$

or,
$$t_s - t = \frac{u_{max}}{\alpha}\cdot\frac{\partial t}{\partial x}\left[\frac{3R^2}{16} - \frac{r^2}{4} + \frac{r^4}{16R^2}\right] \qquad \text{...(7.110)}$$

For determining the *heat transfer coefficient* for *fully developed pipe flow*, it is imperative to define a characteristic temperature of the fluid. It is the *bulk temperature* (t_b) or the *mixing up temperature* of the fluid which is an average taken so as to yield the total energy carried by the fluid and is defined as the *ratio of flux of enthalpy at a cross-section to the product of the mass flow rate and the specific heat of the fluid.* Thus,

$$t_b = \frac{\int_0^R \rho(2\pi r.dr)u c_p t}{\int_0^R \rho(2\pi r.dr)u c_p} \qquad \text{...(7.111)}$$

For an incompressible fluid having constant density and specific heat

$$t_b = \frac{\int_0^R u t r\, dr}{\int_0^R u r\, dr} \qquad \text{...(7.112)}$$

The average/mean velocity $(\bar{u})$ also known as the *bulk mean velocity* is calculated from the following definition :

$$\bar{u} = \frac{1}{\pi R^2}\int_0^R 2\pi r.dr.u$$

or,
$$\bar{u} = \frac{2}{R^2}\int_0^R ur.dr$$

Substituting this value of u in eqn. (7.112), we get

$$t_b = \frac{2}{\bar{u}R^2} \int_0^R u \, t \, r \, . \, dr \qquad \qquad ...(7.113)$$

Substituting the value of u from eqns. 7.100 and 7.101 and that of t from eqn. (7.110), we get

$$t_b = \frac{2}{\bar{u}R^2} \int_0^R 2\bar{u} \left[1 - \frac{r^2}{R^2} \right] \left[t_s - \frac{u_{max}}{\alpha} \cdot \frac{\partial t}{\partial x} \left\{ \frac{3R^2}{16} - \frac{r^2}{4} + \frac{r^4}{16R^2} \right\} \right] r \, dr$$

$$= \frac{4}{R^2} \int_0^R \left[t_s \left(r - \frac{r^3}{R^2} \right) - \frac{u_{max}}{\alpha} \cdot \frac{\partial t}{\partial x} \left\{ \frac{3R^2 r}{16} - \frac{7}{16} r^3 + \frac{5}{16} \frac{r^5}{R^2} - \frac{r^7}{16R^4} \right\} dr \right]$$

$$= \frac{4}{R^2} \left[t_s \left\{ \frac{r^2}{2} - \frac{r^4}{R^2} \right\} \right]_0^R - \frac{4 u_{max}}{\alpha R^2} \cdot \frac{\partial t}{\partial x}$$

$$\left[\frac{3R^2 r^2}{32} - \frac{7}{16} \times \frac{r^4}{4} + \frac{5}{16} \times \frac{r^6}{6R^2} - \frac{r^8}{8 \times 16R^4} \right]_0^R$$

$$= \frac{4}{R^2} \left[t_s \left\{ \frac{R^2}{2} - \frac{R^4}{4} \right\} \right]_0^R - \frac{4 u_{max}}{\alpha R^2} \cdot \frac{\partial t}{\partial x} \left[\frac{3R^4}{32} - \frac{7R^4}{64} + \frac{5R^4}{96} - \frac{R^4}{128} \right]$$

$$= \frac{4}{R^2} \left(t_s \times \frac{R^2}{4} \right) - \frac{4 u_{max}}{\alpha R^2} \cdot \frac{\partial t}{\partial x} \times \frac{11}{96} R^4$$

or, $$t_b = t_s - \frac{11}{96} \frac{u_{max}}{\alpha} R^2 \frac{\partial t}{\partial x} \qquad \qquad ...(7.114)$$

The *heat transfer coefficient* is calculated from the relation

$$h = \frac{Q}{A(t_s - t_b)} = \frac{kA \left(\dfrac{\partial t}{\partial r} \right)_{r=R}}{A(t_s - t_b)}$$

Patented forced convection system keeps the toaster cool and
extends the life of critical components.

From eqn. (7.110), we have

$$\left(\frac{\partial t}{\partial r}\right)_{r=R} = -\frac{u_{max}}{\alpha} \cdot \frac{\partial t}{\partial x}\left(-\frac{R}{2} + \frac{R}{4}\right)$$

$$\left(\frac{\partial t}{\partial r}\right)_{r=R} = \frac{u_{max}R}{4\alpha} \cdot \frac{\partial t}{\partial x} \qquad \qquad ...(7.115)$$

$$\therefore \qquad h = \frac{k \times \dfrac{u_{max}R}{4\alpha} \cdot \dfrac{\partial t}{\partial x}}{\dfrac{11}{96}\dfrac{u_{max}}{\alpha} \cdot R^2 \cdot \dfrac{\partial t}{\partial x}} = \frac{24k}{11R} = \frac{48k}{11D} \qquad ...(7.116)$$

where D is the diameter of the tube.

The Nusselt number is given by

$$Nu = \frac{hD}{k} = \frac{48k}{11D} \times \frac{D}{k} = \frac{48}{11} = 4.364 \qquad \qquad ...(7.117)$$

This shows that the Nusselt number for the fully developed laminar tube flow is *constant* and is *independent of the Reynolds number and Prandtl number.*

The first analytical solution for laminar flow for *constant wall temperature* was formulated by Graetz in 1885. Since $\dfrac{\partial t}{\partial x}$ is not constant, therefore, the analysis of constant wall temperature is quite cumbersome. The final result comes out to be

$$Nu = \frac{hD}{k} = 3.65 \qquad \qquad ...(7.118)$$

Example 7.25. *For laminar flow in a circular tube of 120 mm radius, the velocity and temperature distribution are given by the relations :*

$$u = (2.7r - 3.2\ r^2)\ ; \qquad\qquad t = 85\ (1 - 2.2r)°C$$

where the distance r is measured from the tube surface. Calculate the following :

(i) *The average velocity and the mean bulk temperature of the fluid;*

(ii) *The heat transfer coefficient based on the bulk mean temperature if the tube surface is maintained at a constant uniform temperature of 90°C and there occurs a heat loss of 1000 kJ/h per metre length of the tube.*

Solution. *Given :*
$$u = (2.7\ r - 3.2\ r^2) \qquad\qquad ...\text{Velocity distribution}$$
$$t = 85\ (1 - 2.2\ r)°C \qquad\qquad ...\text{Temperature distribution.}$$

(i) **Average velocity ($\bar{u}$) and mean bulk temperature (t_b) :**

The average velocity is obtained by equating the volumetric flow to the integrated flow through an elementary ring of radius r and thickness dr.

i.e.,
$$\bar{u}\ \pi R^2 = \int_0^R u\,(2\pi r)\,dr$$

$$\bar{u} = \frac{2}{R^2} \int_0^R u\,r\,dr \qquad\qquad ...(i)$$

$$= \frac{2}{R^2} \int_0^R (2.7r - 3.2r^2)\,r\,dr$$

$$= \frac{2}{R^2}\left[2.7 \times \frac{r^3}{3} - 3.2 \frac{r^4}{4}\right]_0^R$$

or, $\quad \bar{u} = \frac{2}{R^2}[0.9\, R^3 - 0.8\, R^4] = 1.8\, R - 1.6\, R^2$

Substituting $R = 0.12$ m, we have

$$\bar{u} = 1.8 \times 0.12 - 1.6 \times 0.12^2 = \textbf{0.193 m/s} \quad \textbf{(Ans.)}$$

The mean bulk temperature is given by

$$t_b = \frac{\int_0^R u\, t\, r\, dr}{\int_0^R u\, r\, dr}$$

Now, $\int_0^R u\, t\, r\, dr = \int_0^R (2.7\, r - 3.2\, r^2) \times 85\, (1 - 2.2\, r)\, r\, dr$

$$= 85 \int_0^R (2.7\, r^2 - 3.2\, r^3)(1 - 2.2\, r)\, dr$$

$$= 85 \int_0^R (2.7\, r^2 - 5.94\, r^3 - 3.2\, r^3 + 7.04\, r^4)\, dr$$

$$= 85 \left[2.7 \times \frac{r^3}{3} - 9.14 \times \frac{r^4}{4} + 7.04 \times \frac{r^5}{5}\right]_0^R$$

$$= 85\, (0.9\, R^3 - 2.285\, R^4 + 1.408\, R^5)$$

$$\therefore \qquad t_b = \frac{85\, (0.9\, R^3 - 2.285\, R^4 + 1.408\, R^5)}{(\bar{u}\, R^2 / 2)}$$

$$\left[\because \int_0^R u\, r\, dx = \frac{\bar{u}\, R^2}{2}\right] \qquad\qquad \text{...From eqn. (i)]}$$

or, $\qquad t_b = \frac{170\, (0.9\, R - 2.285\, R^2 + 1.408\, R^3)}{\bar{u}}$

Substituting, $R = 0.12$ m and $\bar{u} = 0.193$ m/s, we get

$$t_b = \frac{170\, (0.9 \times 0.12 - 2.285 \times 0.12^2 + 1.408 \times 0.12^3)}{0.193} = \textbf{68.29°C} \quad \textbf{(Ans.)}$$

(*ii*) **Heat transfer coefficient, h :**

$$Q = hA\, (t_s - t_b)$$

where, $\qquad Q = 1000$ kJ/h per metre $= \dfrac{1000 \times 1000}{3600} = 277.77$ J/s ; $t_s = 90°C$ \qquad ...Given

$$\therefore \qquad 277.77 = h \times (2\pi \times 0.12 \times 1)(90 - 68.29)$$

or, $\qquad h = \dfrac{277.77}{(2\pi \times 0.12 \times 1)(90 - 68.29)} = \textbf{16.97 W/m}^2\,\textbf{°C} \quad \textbf{(Ans.)}$

Example 7.26. *Lubricating oil at a temperature of 60°C enters 1 cm diameter tube with a velocity of 3 m/s. The tube surface is maintained at 40°C. Assuming that the oil has the following average properties calculate the tube length required to cool the oil to 45°C.*

$$\rho = 865\ kg/m^3;\ k = 0.14\ W/m\ K;\ c_p = 1.78\ kJ/kg°C.$$

Assume flow to be laminar (and fully developed)

$$\overline{Nu} = 3.657 \qquad\qquad\qquad \text{(AMIE Summer, 1997)}$$

Solution. *Given* : $t_i = 60°\ C,\ t_o = 45°C;\ D = 1\text{cm} = 0.01\text{m};\ U = 3$ m/s, $t_s = 40°C;$

$$\rho = 865\ \text{kg/m}^3;\ k = 0.14\ \text{W/m K};\ c_p = 1.78\ \text{kJ/kg°C}.$$

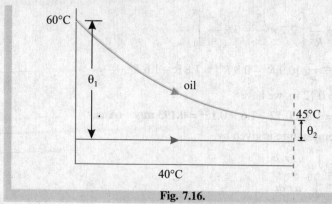

Fig. 7.16.

Length required, L :

$$Q = m c_p (t_i - t_0)$$
$$= (\rho A_f U) c_p (t_i - t_0)$$

(where U = average velocity, A_f = flow area)

$$= \left(\rho \frac{\pi}{4} D^2 U \right) c_p (t_i - t_0)$$

$$= (865 \times \frac{\pi}{4} \times 0.01^2 \times 3) \times 1.78 \times 10^3 (60 - 45) = 5441.7 \, W$$

Also,
$$Q = \bar{h} A \theta_m$$

where, A = heat transfer area = πDL, and

$$\theta_m = \frac{\theta_1 - \theta_2}{\ln(\theta_1 / \theta_2)} = \frac{(60 - 40) - (45 - 40)}{\ln\left[\dfrac{(60 - 40)}{(45 - 40)}\right]} = \frac{15}{1.386} = 10.82°C$$

$$Nu = \frac{\bar{h} D}{k} = 3.657 \qquad \qquad ...(Given)$$

$$\bar{h} = \frac{3.657 k}{D} = \frac{3.657 \times 0.140}{0.01} = 51.2 \, W/m^2 K$$

Now,
$$Q = 5441.7 = 51.2 \times \pi DL \times 10.82$$

$$\therefore \qquad L = \frac{5441.7}{51.2 \times \pi \times 0.01 \times 10.82} = \mathbf{312.7 \, m} \quad (Ans.)$$

Example 7.27. *When 0.5 kg of water per minute is passed through a tube of 20 mm diameter, it is found to be heated from 20°C to 50°C. The heating is accomplisted by condensing steam on the surface of the tube and subsequently the surface temperature of the tube is maintained at 85°C. Determine the length of the tube required for fully developed flow.*

Take the thermo-physical properties of water at 60°C as :

$\rho = 983.2 \, kg/m^3$, $c_p = 4.178 \, kJ/kgK$, $k = 0.659 \, W/m°C$, $v = 0.478 \times 10^{-6} \, m^2/s$

Solution. *Given :* $m = 0.5 \, kg/min$, $D = 20 \, mm = 0.02 \, m$, $t_i = 20°C$, $t_o = 50°C$

Length of the tube required for fully developed flow, L :

The mean film temperature, $t_f = \dfrac{1}{2}\left(85 + \dfrac{20 + 50}{2} \right) = 60°C$

Let us first determine the type of the flow.

$$m = \rho \, A \bar{u} = 983.2 \times \frac{\pi}{4} \times (0.02)^2 \times \bar{u} = \frac{0.5}{60} \, (kg/s)$$

or,
$$\bar{u} = \frac{0.5}{60} \times \frac{4}{\pi} \times \frac{1}{983.2 \times (0.02)^2} = 0.0269 \,\text{m/s}$$

Reynolds number,
$$Re = \frac{D.\bar{u}}{v} = \frac{0.02 \times 0.0269}{0.478 \times 10^{-6}} = 1125.5$$

Since $Re < 2000$, hence the flow is laminar.

With *constant wall temperature having fully developed flow,*

$$Nu = \frac{hD}{k} = 3.65 \qquad\qquad\qquad ...[\text{Eqn. (7.118)}]$$

or,
$$h = \frac{3.65 \, k}{D} = \frac{3.65 \times 0.659}{0.02} = 120.26 \,\text{W/m}^2 \,°\text{C}$$

The rate of heat transfer,

$$Q = A_s h \,(t_s - t_\infty) = m \, c_p \,(t_o - t_i)$$

Here,
$$t_\infty = \frac{20 + 50}{D} = 35°\text{C} = t_b$$

$$\therefore \; (\pi \times 0.02 \times L) \times 120.26 \times (85 - 35) = \frac{0.5}{60} \times (\,4.178 \times 10^3) \,(50 - 20)$$

or,
$$377.8 \, L = 1044.5$$

or,
$$L = \frac{1044.5}{377.5} = \textbf{2.76m (Ans.)}$$

B. TURBULENT FLOW

7.3. INTRODUCTION

The flow in the boundary layer, in majority of practical applications in the convective heat transfer, is *turbulent* rather than laminar. In a turbulent flow the irregular velocity fluctuations are mainly responsible for heat as well as momentum transfer. As the mixing in the turbulent flow is on a macroscopic scale with groups of particles transported in a zig-zig path through the fluid, the exchange mechanism is many times more effective than in laminar flow. Consequently, in turbulent flow, the rates of heat and momentum transfer and the associated friction and heat transfer coefficients are

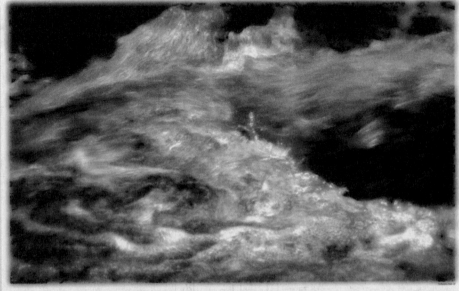

Turbulent flow.

several times larger than that in laminar. Since the nature of turbulent flow is complex, therefore, it is difficult to solve the problems relating turbulent flow analytically. The heat transfer data can best be calculated by laboratory experiments; the other method of study is the analogy between heat and momentum transfer.

A. Forced Convection-Flow over a Flat Plate

7.3.1. TURBULENT BOUNDARY LAYER

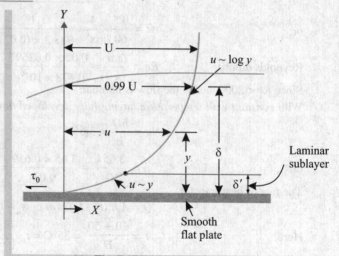

Fig. 7.17. Turbulent boundary layer.

Refer Fig. 7.17. As compared to laminar boundary layers, the turbulent boundary layers are *thicker*. Further in a turbulent boundary layer the velocity distribution is much more *uniform*, than in a laminar boundary layer, due to intermingling of fluid particles between different layers of the fluid. The velocity distribution in a turbulent boundary layer follows a logarithmic law *i.e.* $u \sim \log y$, which can also be represented by a *power law of the type*

$$\frac{u}{U} = \left(\frac{y}{\delta}\right)^{n} \qquad \qquad ...(7.119)$$

where $n = \dfrac{1}{7}$ (approx) for $Re < 10^7$ but $> 5 \times 10^5$

$$\therefore \qquad \frac{u}{U} = \left(\frac{y}{\delta}\right)^{1/7} \qquad \qquad ...(7.120)$$

This is known as **one-seventh power law.**

The Eqn. (7.120), however, cannot be applied at the boundary itself because at $y = 0$, $\left(\dfrac{\delta u}{\delta y}\right) = \dfrac{1}{7}$ $U\delta^{-1/7} y^{-6/7} = \infty$. This difficulty is circumvented by considering the *velocity in the viscous laminar sublayer to be linear and tangential to the seventh-root profile* at the point, where the laminar sublayer merges with the turbulent part of the boundary layer.

Blasius suggested the following relation for viscous shear stress :

$$\tau_0 = 0.0225 \, \rho U^2 \left(\frac{\mu}{\rho U \delta}\right)^{1/4} \qquad \qquad ...(7.121)$$

(for Re ranging from 5×10^5 to 10^7)

Let us now find the values of δ, τ_0, C_{fx}, $\bar{C}_f$ for the velocity distribution given by eqn. (7.120)

$$\left[i.e., \frac{u}{U} = \left(\frac{y}{\delta}\right)^{1/7} \right]$$

(*i*) **Boundary layer thickness, δ :**

Substituting the value of $\dfrac{u}{U}$ in Von Karman integral eqn. [7.28 (*a*)], we have

$$\frac{\tau_0}{\rho U^2} = \frac{d}{dx}\left[\int_0^{\delta} \frac{u}{U}\left(1 - \frac{u}{U}\right)dy \right]$$

$$= \frac{d}{dx}\left[\int_0^\delta \left\{\left(\frac{y}{\delta}\right)^{1/7}\left[1-\left(\frac{y}{\delta}\right)^{1/7}\right]\right\}dy\right]$$

$$= \frac{d}{dx}\left[\int_0^\delta \left\{\left(\frac{y}{\delta}\right)^{1/7}-\left(\frac{y}{\delta}\right)^{2/7}\right\}dy\right]$$

$$= \frac{d}{dx}\left[\frac{7}{8}\frac{y^{8/7}}{\delta^{1/7}}-\frac{7}{9}\frac{y^{9/7}}{\delta^{2/7}}\right]_0^\delta = \frac{d}{dx}\left[\frac{7}{8}\delta - \frac{7}{9}\delta\right] = \frac{7}{72}\frac{d\delta}{dx}$$

[In the expression, above, the limits have been taken from 0 to δ instead of δ' to δ since the laminar sublayer (δ') is *very thin*]

$\therefore$
$$\tau_0 = \frac{7}{72}\rho U^2 \frac{d\delta}{dx} \qquad \qquad ...(7.122)$$

Now equating the eqns. (7.122) and (7.121), we have

$$\frac{7}{72}\rho U^2 \frac{d\delta}{dx} = 0.0225\,\rho U^2 \left(\frac{\mu}{\rho U \delta}\right)^{1/4}$$

or,
$$\frac{7}{72}\frac{d\delta}{dx} = 0.0225\left(\frac{\mu}{\rho U}\right)^{1/4} \times \frac{1}{(\delta)^{1/4}} \qquad \text{(cancelling } \rho U^2 \text{ on both sides)}$$

or,
$$\delta^{1/4}\,d\delta = 0.0225 \times \frac{72}{7} \times \left(\frac{\mu}{\rho U}\right)^{1/4} dx$$

or,
$$\delta^{1/4}\,d\delta = 0.02314\left(\frac{\mu}{\rho U}\right)^{1/4} dx$$

Integrating both sides, we have

$$\frac{4}{5}\delta^{5/4} = 0.2314\left(\frac{\mu}{\rho U}\right)^{1/4} x + C \qquad \text{(where } C = \text{constant of integration)}$$

Let boundary layer be assumed to be turbulent over the entire length of plate.
Hence, at $\quad x = 0,\ \delta = 0 \qquad \therefore C = 0$

$\therefore$
$$\frac{4}{5}\delta^{5/4} = 0.2314\left(\frac{\mu}{\rho U}\right)^{1/4} \times x$$

or,
$$\delta^{5/4} = (5/4 \times 0.2314)\left(\frac{\mu}{\rho U}\right)^{1/4} \times x$$

or,
$$\delta = [5/4 \times 0.2314]^{4/5}\left(\frac{\mu}{\rho U}\right)^{1/5} \times x^{4/5}$$

$$= 0.371\left(\frac{\mu}{\rho U x}\right)^{1/5} x^{1/5} \times x^{4/5}$$

$$= 0.0371\left(\frac{1}{Re_x}\right)^{1/5} \times x = \frac{0.371 x}{(Re_x)^{1/5}}$$

i.e.
$$\delta = \frac{0.371 x}{(Re_x)^{1/5}} \qquad \qquad ...(7.123)$$

or,
$$\frac{\delta}{x} = \frac{0.371}{(Re_x)^{1/5}} \qquad \qquad ...[7.123\ (a)]$$

(ii) **Shear stress, τ_0 :**

$$\tau_0 = 0.0225\rho U^2 \left(\frac{\mu}{\rho U \delta} \right)^{1/4}$$

...[Eqn. (7.121)]

Substituting the value of δ from eqn. (7.123), we get

$$\tau_0 = 0.0225\rho U^2 \left(\frac{\mu}{\rho U \times \dfrac{0.371x}{(Re_x)^{1/5}}} \right)^{1/4}$$

$$= \frac{0.00225}{(0.371)^{1/4}}\rho U^2 \left[\frac{\mu}{\rho U x} \times (Re_x)^{1/5} \right]^{1/4} = 0.0288\rho U^2 \left[\frac{(Re_x)^{1/5}}{Re_x} \right]^{1/4}$$

$$\left(\because Re_x = \frac{\mu}{\rho U x} \right)$$

or, $$\tau_0 = \frac{\rho U^2}{2} \times \frac{0.0576}{(Re_x)^{1/5}} \left[= \frac{0.0288\rho U^2}{(Re_x)^{1/5}} \right]$$

...(7.124)

(iii) **Local skin friction (drag) coefficient, C_{fx} :**

We know $$\tau_0 = \frac{\rho U^2}{2} \times \frac{0.0576}{(Re_x)^{1/5}}$$

[Eqn. (7.124)]

Also $$\tau_0 = C_{fx} \times \frac{1}{2}\rho U^2$$

[Eqn. (7.30)]

Now equating the eqns. (7.124) and (7.30), we have

$$C_{fx} \times \frac{1}{2}\rho U^2 = \frac{\rho U^2}{2} \times \frac{0.0576}{(Re_x)^{1/5}}$$

or, $$C_{fx} = \frac{0.0576}{(Re_x)^{1/5}}$$ ...(7.125)

(iv) **Average value of skin friction (drag) coefficient, $\bar{C}_f$:**

$$\bar{C}_f = \frac{1}{L}\int_0^L C_{fx}\, dx$$

$$= \frac{1}{L}\int_0^L \frac{0.0576}{(Re_x)^{1/5}}\, dx$$

$$= \frac{1}{L}\int_0^L \frac{0.0576}{\left(\dfrac{\rho U x}{\mu} \right)^{1/5}}\, dx$$

$$= \frac{1}{L}\int_0^L 0.0576\left(\frac{\mu}{\rho U} \right)^{1/5} (x)^{-1/5}\, dx$$

$$= 0.0576\left(\frac{\mu}{\rho U} \right)^{1/5} \frac{1}{L}\int_0^L (x)^{-1/5}\, dx$$

$$= 0.0576\left(\frac{\mu}{\rho U} \right)^{1/5} \frac{1}{L}\left[5/4 \times x^{4/5} \right]_0^L$$

Forced air convection bottom heater provides sufficient energy for very large boards.

or, $$\bar{C}_f = 0.072 \left(\frac{\mu}{\rho UL} \right)^{1/5} = \frac{0.072}{\sqrt{(Re_x)^{1/5}}} \qquad \qquad ...(7.126)$$

This is valid for $5 \times 10^5 < Re_L < 10^7$.

For Reynolds number between 10^7 and 10^9 the following relationship suggested by Prandtl and Schlichting holds good,

$$\bar{C}_f = \frac{0.455}{(\log_{10} Re_L)^{2.58}} \qquad \qquad ...(7.127)$$

7.3.2. TOTAL DRAG DUE TO LAMINAR AND TURBULENT BOUNDARY LAYERS

When the leading edge is not very rough, the turbulent boundary layer does not begin at the leading edge, it is usually preceded by the laminar boundary layer. The *point of transition from laminar to turbulent layer depends upon the intensity of turbulence.* The distance x_c (Fig. 7.18) of the transition from the leading edge can be obtained from critical Reynolds number which normally ranges from 3×10^5 to 3×10^6.

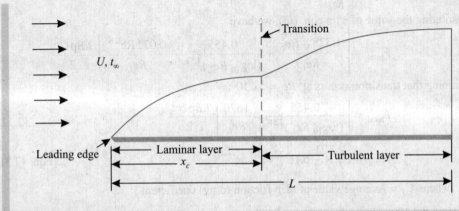

Fig. 7.18. Drag due to laminar and turbulent boundary layers.

Drag force ($F_D = F$) for the *turbulent boundary layer* can be estimated from the following relation :

$$F_{turb.} = (F_{turb.})_{total} - (F_{turb.})_{x_c}$$

where, $(F_{turb.})_{total}$ = The drag which would occur if a turbulent boundary extends along the entire length of the plate, and

       $(F_{turb.})_{x_c}$ = The drag due to fictitious turbulent bundary layer from the leading edge to a distance x_c.

Let us assume that the plate is long enough so that Reynolds number is greater than 10^7, then the turbulent drag is given by

$$F_{turb.} = \frac{0.455}{(\log_{10} Re_L)^{2.58}} \times \frac{\rho U^2}{2} \times (L \times B) - \frac{0.072}{(Re_c)^{1/5}} \times \frac{\rho U^2}{2} \times (x_c \times B) \qquad ...(i)$$

where, L = Length of the plate,

         B = Width of the plate, and

         U = Free stream velocity.

The laminar boundary layer prevails within the length x_c and its contribution to drag force is given by

$$F_{laminar} = \frac{1.328}{\sqrt{Re_c}} \times \frac{\rho U^2}{2} \times (x_c \times B) = \frac{1.328\,x_c}{\sqrt{Re_c}} \times B \times \frac{\rho U^2}{2} \qquad \text{...(ii)}$$

$\therefore$
$$F_{total} = F_{laminar} + F_{turb.}$$

$$F_{total} = \frac{1.328\,x_c}{\sqrt{Re_c}} \times B \times \frac{\rho U^2}{2} + \left[\frac{0.455\,L}{(\log_{10} Re_L)^{2.58}} \times B \times \frac{\rho U^2}{2} - \frac{0.072\,x_c}{(Re_c)^{1/5}} \times B \times \frac{\rho U^2}{2} \right]$$

$$= \left[\frac{1.328\,x_c}{\sqrt{Re_c}} \times \frac{0.455\,L}{(\log_{10} Re_L)^{2.58}} - \frac{0.072\,x_c}{(Re_c)^{1/5}} \right] \frac{B\rho U^2}{2} \qquad \text{...(iii)}$$

Also,
$$\frac{Re_c}{Re_L} = \frac{(\rho U x_c/\mu)}{(\rho U L/\mu)} = \frac{x_c}{L}$$

or,
$$x_c = \frac{Re_c \cdot L}{Re_L}$$

Substituting the value of x_c in eqn. (iii), we have

$$F_{total} = \left[\frac{1.328\sqrt{Re_c}}{Re_L} + \frac{0.455}{(\log_{10} Re_L)^{2.58}} - \frac{0.072\,Re_c^{0.8}}{Re_L} \right] \frac{L B \rho U^2}{2}$$

Assuming that transition occurs at $Re_c = 5 \times 10^5$;

$$F_{total} = \left[\frac{0.455}{(\log_{10} Re_L)^{2.58}} - \frac{1670}{Re_L} \right] \frac{L B \rho U^2}{2} \qquad \text{...(7.128)}$$

Also,
$$F_{total} = \bar{C}_f \times \frac{1}{2}\rho A U^2 = \bar{C}_f \times \frac{L B \rho U^2}{2} \qquad \text{...[Eqn. (7.31)]}$$

[where $\bar{C}_f$ = Average value of skin friction (drag) coefficient.]

Equating the above two equations, we have

$$\bar{C}_f = \frac{0.455}{(\log_{10} Re_L)^{2.58}} - \frac{1670}{Re_L} \qquad \text{...(7.129)}$$

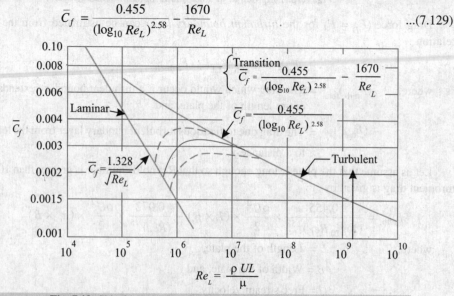

Fig. 7.19. Skin friction (drag) coefficient for smooth flat plates.

The above relation in general may be rewritten as

$$\bar{C}_f = \left[\frac{0.455}{(\log_{10} Re_L)^{2.58}} - \frac{A}{Re_L} \right] \qquad \qquad ...(7.130)$$

where the value of A depends upon the value of critical Reynolds number Re_c (at which the laminar boundary layer transforms to turbulent boundary layer).

The values of A for Re_c, 10^5, 5×10^5 and 10^6 are 360, 1670, 3300 respectively.

Fig. 7.19 shows a log-log plot of $\bar{C}_f$ versus Re_L.

Example 7.28. *A flat plate 5 m long and 0.75 m wide is kept parallel to the flow of water which is flowing at a velocity of 5 m/s. If the average drag coefficient for turbulent flow past this flat plate is expressed as* : $\bar{C}_f = \dfrac{0.455}{(\log_{10} Re_L)^{2.58}}$, *find the drag force on both sides of the plate.*

Take $v = 0.011 \times 10^{-4}$ *m²/s*

Solution: *Given* : $L = 5$ m, $B = 0.75$ m, $U = 5$ m/s, $v = 0.011 \times 10^{-4}$ m²/s

Drag force on both sides of the plate :

The Reynolds number at the end of the plate is given by

$$Re_L = \frac{UL}{v} = \frac{5 \times 5}{0.011 \times 10^{-4}} = 22.73 \times 10^6$$

This *confirms* that the nature of flow is *turbulent*.

The average drag coefficient is expressed as

$$\bar{C}_f = \frac{0.455}{\left[\log_{10} Re_L \right]^{2.58}} \qquad \qquad ...\text{Given}$$

$$= \frac{0.455}{(\log_{10} 22.73 \times 10^6)^{2.58}} = 2.642 \times 10^{-3}$$

∴   The drag force on both sides of the plate,

$$F_D = 2 \times \bar{C}_f \times \left(\frac{1}{2} \rho A U^2 \right) \qquad \qquad [\text{where } A = \text{area of one side}]$$

Crashed cylindrical submarine.

$$= 2 \times 2.642 \times 10^{-3} \times \left[\frac{1}{2} \times 1000 \times (5 \times 0.75) \times 5^2 \right] = \textbf{247.68 N} \quad \textbf{(Ans.)}$$

Example 7.29. *A submarine can be assumed to have cylindrical shape with rounded nose. Assuming its length to be 50 m and diameter 5.0 m, determine the total power required to overcome boundary friction if it cruises at 8 m/s velocity in sea water at 20°C ($\rho = 1030$ kg/m³), $v = 1 \times 10^{-6}$ m²/s.*

Solution. Length of submarine, $\qquad\qquad L = 50$ m

Diameter of submarine, $\qquad\qquad D = 50$ m

Velocity of submarine, $\qquad\qquad U = 8$ m/s

Density of sea water, $\qquad\qquad \rho = 1030$ kg/m³

Kinematic viscosity of sea water, $\quad v = 1 \times 10^{-6}$ m²/s

Total power required to overcome boundary friction, P :

Reynolds number, $\qquad\qquad R_{eL} = \dfrac{UL}{v} = \dfrac{8 \times 50}{1 \times 10^{-6}} = 4 \times 10^8$

The length over which boundary layer will be laminar is given by

$$\frac{Ux}{v} = 5 \times 10^5 \text{ or } x = \frac{5 \times 10^5 \times v}{U}$$

or, $\qquad\qquad x = \dfrac{5 \times 10^5 \times 1 \times 10^{-6}}{8} = 0.0625$ m

This being very small contribution to total drag from laminar boundary layer is negligible; hence $\overline{C}_f$ is given by

$$\overline{C}_f = \frac{0.455}{(\log_{10} Re_L)^{2.58}} = \frac{0.455}{\left[\log_{10} (4 \times 10^8)\right]^{2.58}} = 0.001765$$

Area, $\qquad\qquad A = \pi DL = \pi \times 5 \times 50 = 785.4$ m²

∴ Drag force, $\qquad F_D = \overline{C}_f \times \dfrac{1}{2} \rho A U^2 = 0.001765 \times \dfrac{1}{2} \times 1030 \times 785.4 \times 8^2$

$$= 45690.2 \text{ N}$$

Hence total power required to overcome boundary friction,

$$P = \frac{F_D U}{1000} kW = \frac{45690.2 \times 8}{1000} = \textbf{365.52 kW} \quad \textbf{(Ans.)}$$

Example 7.30. *Find the ratio of friction drag on the front half and rear half of the flat plate kept at zero incidence in a stream of uniform velocity, if the boundary layer is turbulent over the whole plate.*

Solution. The average coefficient of drag $(\overline{C}_f)$ for turbulent boundary layer is given by

$$\overline{C}_f = \frac{0.072}{(Re_L)^{1/5}} \qquad\qquad ...[\text{Eqn. (7.126)}]$$

For the entire plate, $\qquad Re_L = \dfrac{UL}{v}$

For the first half of the plate, $Re_x = \dfrac{Ux}{v} = \dfrac{UL}{2v}$

Drag force per unit width for the entire plate is,

$$F_D = \overline{C}_f \times \frac{\rho U^2}{2} \times \text{area per unit width}$$

$$= \frac{0.072}{\left(\dfrac{UL}{v}\right)^{1/5}} \times \frac{\rho U^2}{2} \times L$$

Similarly the drag force per unit width for the front *half portion* of the plate is

$$F_{D_1} = \frac{0.072}{\left(\dfrac{UL}{2v}\right)^{1/5}} \times \frac{\rho U^2}{2} \times \frac{L}{2} = \frac{0.072}{\left(\dfrac{UL}{v}\right)^{1/5}} \times \frac{\rho U^2}{2} \times \frac{L}{2} (2)^{1/5}$$

∴   Drag force for the rear half portion of the plate is

$$F_{D_2} = F_D - F_{D_1} = \frac{0.072\, L}{\left(\dfrac{UL}{v}\right)^{1/2}} \times \frac{\rho U^2}{2} \left[1 - \frac{1}{2}(2)^{1/5}\right]$$

Hence,
$$\frac{F_{D_1}}{F_{D_2}} = \frac{\dfrac{1}{2} \times (2)^{1/5}}{1 - \dfrac{1}{2}(2)^{1/5}} = \frac{0.574}{1 - 0.574} = \mathbf{1.347 \ (Ans.)}$$

Example 7.31. *A stream-lined train is 200 m long with a typical cross-section having a perimeter of 9 m above the wheels. If the kinematic viscosity of air at the prevailing temperature is 1.5×10^{-5} m²/s and density 1.24 kg/m³, determine the surface drag (friction drag) of the train when running at 90 km/h.*

Make allowance for the fact that boundary layer changes from laminar to turbulent on the train surface.

Solution. Length of the train, $L = 200$ m

Perimeter of cross-section of the train above wheels, $P = 9$ m

∴ Surface area, $A = L \times P = 200 \times 9 = 1800$ m²

Kinematic viscosity of air, $v = 1.5 \times 10^{-5}$ m²/s

Density of air, $\rho = 1.24$ kg/m³

Free stream velocity, $U = 90$ km/h $= \dfrac{90 \times 1000}{3600} = 25$ m/s

Friction drag, F_D :

The Reynolds number with length of the train as the characteristic length,

$$Re_L = \frac{UL}{v} = \frac{25 \times 200}{1.5 \times 10^{-5}} = 3.333 \times 10^8$$

Obviously the boundary layer is *turbulent*.

Assuming that the abrupt transition from laminar to turbulent flow occurs at a Reynolds number of 5×10^5, the average coefficient of drag,

$$\bar{C}_f = \frac{0.455}{(\log_{10} Re_L)^{2.58}} - \frac{1670}{Re_L} \qquad \text{[Eqn. (7.129)]}$$

$$= \frac{0.455}{[\log_{10}(3.333 \times 10^8)]^{2.58}} - \frac{1670}{3.333 \times 10^8}$$

$$= 0.001807 - 5.01 \times 10^{-6} = 0.0018$$

The approximate friction drag over the train surface,

$$F_D = \bar{C}_f \times \frac{1}{2}\, \rho A U^2 = 0.0018 \times \frac{1}{2} \times 1.24 \times 1800 \times 25^2 = \mathbf{1255.5 \ N \ (Ans.)}$$

Example 7.32. *A barge with a rectangular surface 30 m long × 10 m wide is travelling down a river with a velocity of 0.6 m/s. A laminar boundary layer exists upto a Reynolds number equivalent to 5 × 10⁵ and subsequently abrupt transition occurs to turbulent boundary layer. Calculate :*

(i) *The maximum distance from the leading edge upto which laminar boundary layer persists and the maximum boundary layer thickness at that point.*

(ii) *The total drag force on the flat bottom surface of the barge, and*

(iii) *The power required to push the bottom surface through water at the given velocity.*

For water ρ = 998 kg/m³ and v = 1 × 10⁻⁶ m²/s.

Solution. Length of the bottom surface, L = 30 m

Width of the bottom surface, $B = 10$ m

∴ Area, $A = L \times B = 30 \times 10 = 300$ m²

Velocity, $U = 0.6$ m/s

Density of water, $\rho = 998$ kg/m³

Kinematic viscosity, $v = 1 \times 10^{-6}$ m²/s

(i) The maximum distance up to which laminar boundary layer persists, x_c :

$$(Re)_{x_c} = \frac{Ux_c}{v} = 5 \times 10^5$$

∴ $$x_c = \frac{5 \times 10^5 \times v}{U} = \frac{5 \times 10^5 \times 1 \times 10^{-6}}{0.6} = 0.833 \text{ m} \quad \textbf{(Ans.)}$$

Maximum boundary layer (laminar) thickness, δ :

$$\delta = \frac{5x_c}{\sqrt{(Re)_{x_c}}} = \frac{5 \times 0.833}{\sqrt{5 \times 10^5}} = 5.89 \times 10^{-3} \text{ m} \quad \text{or,} \quad \textbf{5.89 mm (Ans.)}$$

Microgravity forced convection boiling.

(ii) **The total drag force F_D :**

$$Re_L = \frac{UL}{v} = \frac{0.6 \times 30}{1 \times 10^{-6}} = 1.8 \times 10^7$$

The average coefficient of drag,

$$\bar{C}_f = \frac{0.455}{(\log_{10} Re_L)^{2.58}} - \frac{1670}{Re_L} \qquad \text{...[Eqn. (7.129)]}$$

$$= \frac{0.455}{[\log_{10} (1.8 \times 10^7)]^{2.58}} - \frac{1670}{1.8 \times 10^7} = 0.002646$$

∴ Drag force on the bottom surface of the barge,

$$F_D = \bar{C}_f \times \frac{1}{2} \rho A U^2 = 0.002646 \times \frac{1}{2} \times 998 \times 300 \times (0.6)^2$$

$$= \textbf{142.6 N} \quad \textbf{(Ans.)}$$

(iii) **The power required, P :**

The power required to push the bottom surface through water at the given velocity,

$$P = F_D \times U = 142.6 \times 0.6 = \textbf{85.56 W} \qquad \textbf{(Ans.)}$$

Example 7.33. *Ambient air at 20°C flows at a velocity of 10 m/s parallel to a wall 5 m wide and 3 m high. Calculate the heat transfer rate if the wall is maintained at 40°C. The critical Reynolds number is equal to 5×10^5. The properties of air at the mean film temperature may be taken as :*
$k = 0.0263$ W/m K, $v = 15.89 \times 10^{-6}$ m²/s and Pr = 0.707.

If the entire boundary layer is assumed turbulent, what will be the percentage error in the computation of heat transfer rate ? Comment on the comparable values of the two results.

Appropriate correlation from the following may be used :

$$\overline{Nu} = 0.664 \, Re_L^{0.5} \, Pr^{1/3}$$

$$\overline{Nu} = 0.0375 \, Re_L^{0.8} \, Pr^{1/3}$$

$$\overline{Nu} = 0.0375 \, [Re_L^{0.8} - 23200] \, Pr^{1/3} \quad \text{(AMIE, Summer, 1999)}$$

Solution. *Given :* $\quad t_\infty = 20°C; U = 10 \text{ m/s}; L = 5 \text{ m}; B = 3 \text{ m}; t_s = 40°C; (Re)_{cr} = 5 \times 10^5$
$$k = 0.0263 \text{ W/m K}; v = 15.89 \times 10^{-6} \text{ m²/s}; Pr = 0.707.$$

Wind
$t_\infty = 20°C$
$U = 10$ m/s

Wall
$(t_s = 40°C)$

$B = 3$m

$L = 5$m

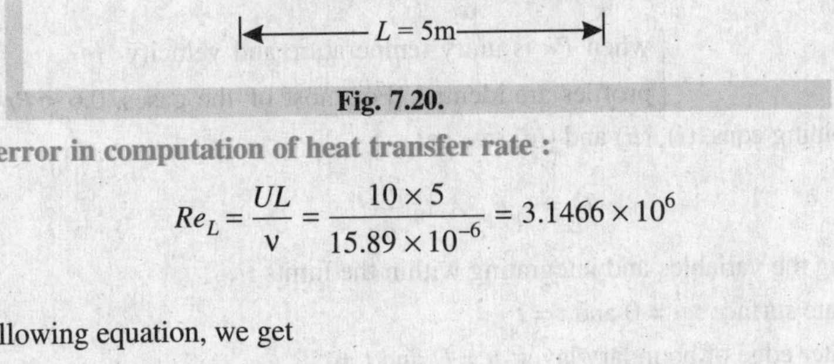

Fig. 7.20.

Percentage error in computation of heat transfer rate :

$$Re_L = \frac{UL}{v} = \frac{10 \times 5}{15.89 \times 10^{-6}} = 3.1466 \times 10^6$$

i.e., $> (Re)_{cr}$

Using the following equation, we get

$$\overline{Nu} = \frac{\overline{h}L}{k} = 0.0375 \left[Re_L^{0.8} - 23200 \right] Pr^{1/3}$$

...(*Combination of laminar and turbulent flow*)

$\therefore$

$$\overline{h} = \frac{k}{L} \times 0.0375 \left[Re_L^{0.8} - 23200 \right] Pr^{1/3}$$

$$= \frac{0.0263}{5} \times 0.0375 [(3.1466 \times 10^6)^{0.8} - 23200] \times (0.707)^{1/3}$$

$$= 0.00019725 \, (157860.4 - 23200) \times 0.8908 = 23.66 \text{ W/m}^2 \text{ °C}$$

Heat transfer rate,

$$Q = \overline{h}A \, (t_s - t_\infty) = 23.66 \times (5 \times 3) \times (40 - 20) = 7098 \text{ W}$$

If *entire boundary is assumed turbulent,*

$$\overline{Nu} = \frac{\overline{h}L}{k} = 0.0375 \, Re_L^{0.8} \, Pr^{1/3}$$

$\therefore$

$$\overline{h} = \frac{k}{L} \times 0.0375 \, Re_L^{0.8} \, Pr^{1/3}$$

$$= \frac{0.0263}{5} \times 0.0375 \times (3.1466 \times 10^6)^{0.8} \times (0.707)^{1/3}$$

$$= 0.00019725 \times 157860.4 \times 0.8908 = 27.74 \text{ W/m}^2 \text{ °C}$$

$$Q = 27.74 \times (5 \times 3) \times 20 = 8322 \text{ W}$$

$\therefore$ **Percentage error** $= \dfrac{8322 - 7098}{7098} \times 100 = \mathbf{17.24\%}$ **(Ans.)**

Comments. The difference between the two values is nearly 17%. Further the correlation for turbulent heat transfer are empirical, which may have a variation of ± 25%. Hence, the rate of heat transfer in such cases *may be calculated for all purposes, by assuming the boundary layer to be entirely turbulent.*

7.3.3. REYNOLDS ANALOGY

Reynolds analogy is the *inter-relationship between fluid friction and Newton's law of viscosity.*

We know,

$$\tau_0 = \mu \frac{du}{dy} \qquad \qquad ...(i)$$

$$Q = - kA \frac{dt}{dy} \qquad \qquad ...(ii)$$

[Heat flow along *Y*-direction ... Fourier equation]

$$\frac{\mu \, c_p}{k} = 1 \text{ or } \frac{k}{\mu} = c_p \qquad \qquad ...(iii)$$

$$\left[\begin{array}{l} \text{when } Pr \text{ is unity temperature and velocity} \\ \text{profiles are idential (For most of the gases, } 0.6 < Pr < 1.0) \end{array} \right]$$

By combining eqns. (*i*), (*ii*) and (*iii*), we get

$$Q = - c_p \, A \, \tau_0 \frac{dt}{du} \qquad \qquad ...(7.131)$$

Separating the variables and integrating within the limits :

At the plate surface : $u = 0$ and $t = t_s$

At the outer edge of boundary layer; $u = U$ and $t = t_\infty$

$$\frac{Q}{c_p\, A\, \tau_0} \int_0^U du = -\int_{t_s}^{t_\infty} dt$$

or,
$$\frac{Q}{c_p A\, \tau_0} U = (t_s - t_\infty)$$

or,
$$\frac{Q}{A\,(t_s - t_\infty)} = \frac{\tau_0\, c_p}{U} \qquad \qquad ...(7.132)$$

But,
$$\frac{Q}{A\,(t_s - t_\infty)} = h_x$$

and,
$$\tau_0 = C_{fx} \times \frac{1}{2}\, \rho U^2 \qquad \qquad ...[\text{Eqn. (7.23)}]$$

Making these substitutions in eqn. (7.132), we get

$$h_x = C_{fx} \times \frac{1}{2}\, \rho U^2 \times \frac{c_p}{U} = \frac{C_{fx}}{2}\,(\rho\, c_p\, U)$$

or,
$$\frac{h_x}{\rho\, c_p\, U} = \frac{C_{fx}}{2} \qquad \qquad ...(7.133)$$

$$...Dimensionless\ form.$$

$\dfrac{h_x}{\rho\, c_p\, U}$ is called the **Stanton number** St_x. It represents the *Nusselt number divided by the product of the Reynolds and Prandtl numbers, i.e.,*

$$\frac{Nu_x}{Re_x \cdot Pr} = St_x = \frac{C_{fx}}{2} \qquad \qquad ...(7.134)$$

Equation (7.134) is called the **Reynolds analogy**. By using this interrelationship we can infer heat transfer data from shear stress measurement.

Note: The physical significance of Stanton number is :

$$S_t = \frac{h_x\, \Delta t}{\rho\, c_p\, U\, \Delta t} = \frac{\text{Actual heat flux of the fluid}}{\text{Heat flux capacity of the fluid flow}}$$

Further in case of laminar boundary layer on a flat plate, we have

$$Nu_x = \frac{h_x\, x}{k} = 0.332\,(Re_x)^{1/2}\,(Pr)^{1/3} \qquad \qquad ...[\text{Eqn. (7.94)}]$$

Dividing both sides of the above equation by $Re_x\,(Pr)^{1/3}$, we get

$$\frac{Nu_x}{Re_x\,(Pr)^{1/3}} = \frac{0.332}{(Re_x)^{1/2}} = \frac{C_{fx}}{2} \qquad \qquad ...(7.135)$$

The L.H.S. of the equality can be rewritten as

$$\frac{Nu_x}{Re_x\,(Pr)^{1/3}} = \frac{Nu_x}{Re\ Pr} \cdot (Pr)^{2/3} = St_x\,(Pr)^{2/3} \qquad \qquad ...(7.136)$$

$$\therefore \qquad St_x\,(Pr)^{2/3} = \frac{C_{fx}}{2} \qquad \qquad ...(7.137)$$

$$...Interrelationship\ between\ heat\ and\ momentum\ transfer.$$

Equation (7.137) has been designated as **Colburn analogy**. For $Pr = 1$ the Reynolds and Colburn analogies are the same.

Heat transfer parameters for turbulent flow :

The heat transfer parameters for turbulent flow may be derived, by using Colburn analogy, as follows:

From Colburn analogy

$$St_x (Pr)^{2/3} = \frac{C_{fx}}{2} = \frac{0.0576}{2} (Re_x)^{-1/5}$$

or,

$$\frac{Nu_x}{Pr\, Re_x} (Pr)^{2/3} = 0.0288 (Re_x)^{-1/5} \qquad \left[\because C_{fx} = \frac{0.0576}{(Re_x)^{1/5}}\ \text{eqn. (7.125)} \right]$$

or,

$$Nu_x = 0.0288 (Re_x)^{4/5} (Pr)^{1/3} \qquad\qquad ...(7.138)$$

or,

$$h_x = 0.0288 \left(\frac{k}{x}\right)(Re_x)^{4/5} (Pr)^{1/3} \qquad\qquad ...(7.139)$$

The average value of heat transfer coefficient is given by,

$$\bar{h} = \frac{1}{L} \int_0^L h_x \cdot dx$$

$$= \frac{1}{L} \int_0^L 0.0288 \left(\frac{k}{x}\right)(Re_x)^{4/5} (Pr)^{1/3}\, dx$$

$$= 0.0288\, k \left(\frac{\rho U}{\mu}\right)^{4/5} (Pr)^{1/3} \times \frac{1}{L} \int_0^L (x)^{-1/5}\, dx$$

$$= 0.0288\, k \left(\frac{\rho U}{\mu}\right)^{4/5} (Pr)^{1/3} \times \frac{5}{4L} (L)^{4/5}$$

or,

$$\bar{h} = 0.036 \left(\frac{k}{L}\right)(Re_L)^{4/5} (Pr)^{1/3} \qquad ...(7.140)$$

and,

$$\bar{Nu} = \frac{\bar{h}\, L}{k} = 0.036 (Re_L)^{4/5} (Pr)^{1/3} \qquad ...(7.141)$$

Heat transfer parameters for combination of laminar and turbulent flow :

An expression for the average heat transfer coefficient over a plate of length L when both laminar and turbulent boundary layers are present can be derived by evaluating the following integral :

High temperature forced convection industrial oven.

$$\bar{h} = \frac{1}{L} \int_0^{x_c} h_x\, dx + \frac{1}{L} \int_{x_c}^L h_x\, dx$$

$$\text{(Laminar)} \qquad \text{(Turbulent)}$$

$$= \frac{1}{L}\left[\int_0^{x_c} 0.332 \left(\frac{k}{x}\right)(Re_x)^{1/2} (Pr)^{1/3}\, dx + \int_{x_c}^L 0.0288 \left(\frac{k}{x}\right)(Re_x)^{4/5} (Pr)^{1/3}\, dx \right]$$

$$= \frac{k}{L} (Pr)^{1/3} \left[0.332 \left(\frac{\rho U}{\mu}\right)^{1/2} \int_0^{x_c} (x)^{-1/2}\, dx + 0.0288 \left(\frac{\rho U}{\mu}\right)^{4/5} \int_{x_c}^L (x)^{-1/5}\, dx \right]$$

or,

$$\bar{h} = \frac{k}{L} (Pr)^{1/3} [0.664 (Re_x)^{1/2} + 0.036 \{(Re_L)^{0.8} - (Re_c)^{0.8}\}] \qquad ...(7.142)$$

Assuming that the transition occurs at critical Reynolds number, $Re_c = 5 \times 10^5$, we get

$$\bar{h} = \frac{k}{L} = (Pr)^{1/3} [0.664 (5 \times 10^5)^{1/2} + 0.036 (Re_L)^{0.8} - 0.036 (5 \times 10^5)^{0.8}]$$

$$\bar{h} = \frac{k}{L}(P_r)^{1/3}\,[0.036\,(R_{e_L})^{0.8} - 836] \qquad\qquad ...(7.143)$$

and $$\bar{Nu} = \frac{\bar{h}L}{k} = (Pr)^{1/3}\,[0.036\,(Re_L)^{0.8} - 836] \qquad\qquad ...(7.144)$$

Example 7.34. *Air flows over a heated plate at a velocity of 50 m/s. The local skin friction co-efficient at a point on a plate is 0.004. Estimate the local heat transfer coefficient at this point. The following property data for air are given :*

Density = 0.88 kg/m³; viscosity = 2.286 × 10⁻⁵ kg m/s;

specific heat, c_p = 1.001 kJ/kg K; conductivity = 0.035 W/m K.

Use $St\ Pr^{1/3} = \dfrac{C_{fx}}{2}$ **(U.P.S.C., 1993)**

Solution. *Given :* U = 50 m/s; C_{fx} = 0.004; ρ = 0.88 kg/m³; μ = 2.286 × 10⁻⁵ kg m/s;

c_p = 1.001 kJ/kg K; k = 0.035 W/m K.

Local heat transfer coefficient, h_x :

Prandtl number, $Pr = \dfrac{\mu \cdot c_p}{k} = \dfrac{2.286 \times 10^{-5} \times (1.001 \times 1000)}{0.035} = 0.654$

Stanton number, $St = \dfrac{h_x}{\rho \cdot c_p \cdot U} = \dfrac{h_x}{0.88 \times (1.001 \times 1000) \times 50} = \dfrac{h_x}{44044}$

Now, $St \cdot (Pr)^{2/3} = \dfrac{C_{fx}}{2}$ ...(Given)

$$\frac{h_x}{44044}(0.654)^{2/3} = \frac{0.004}{2}$$

or, $h_x = \dfrac{0.004}{2} \times \dfrac{44044}{(0.654)^{2/3}} = \mathbf{116.9\ W/m^2\ K}$ **(Ans.)**

Example 7.35. *The crankcase of an I.C. engine measuring 80 cm × 20 cm may be idealised as a flat plate. The engine runs at 90 km/h and the crankcase is cooled by the air flowing past it at the same speed. Calculate the heat loss from the crank surface maintained at 85°C, to the ambient air at 15°C. Due to road induced vibration, the boundary layer becomes turbulent from the leading edge itself.*

Solution. *Given :* U = 90 km/h = $\dfrac{90 \times 1000}{3600}$ = 25 m/s; t_s = 85°C; t_∞ = 15°C; L = 80 cm = 0.8 m;

B = 20 cm = 0.2m.

The properties of air at $t_f = \dfrac{85 + 15}{2}$ = 50°C are :

k = 0.02824 W/m°C, v = 17.95 × 10⁻⁶ m²/s, Pr = 0.698 ... (From tables)

Heat loss from the crankcase, Q :

The Reynolds number, $Re_L = \dfrac{UL}{v} = \dfrac{25 \times 0.8}{17.95 \times 10^{-6}} = 1.114 \times 10^6$

Since $Re_L > 5 \times 10^5$, the nature of flow is *turbulent*.

For turbulent boundary layer,

$$\bar{Nu} = \frac{\bar{h}L}{k} = 0.036\,(Re_L)^{0.8}\,(Pr)^{0.333} = 0.036\,(1.114 \times 10^6)^{0.8}\,(0.698)^{0.333} = 2196.92$$

or, $\bar{h} = \dfrac{k}{L} \times 2196.92 = \dfrac{0.02824}{0.8} \times 2196.92 = 77.55\ W/m^2\,°C$

$\therefore$ $\qquad Q = \bar{h}A\ (t_s - t_\infty) = 77.55 \times (0.8 \times 0.2)\ (85 - 15) = \textbf{868.56 W}$ **(Ans.)**

Example 7.36. *Air at 20°C and 1.013 bar flows over a flat plate at 40 m/s. The plate is 1m long and is maintained at 60°C. Assuming unit depth, calculate the heat transfer from the plate. Use the following correlation :*

(M.U.)

$$Nu_L = (Pr)^{0.33}\ [0.037\ (Re_L)^{0.8} - 850]$$

Solution. *Given :* $t_\infty = 20°C$; $U = 40$ m/s; $L = 1$m; $B = 1$ m; $t_s = 60°C$,

Properties of air at $(60 + 20)/2 = 40°C$, from the tables:

$\rho = 1.128$ kg/m³; $c_p = 1.005$ kJ/kg°C; $k = 0.0275$ W/m°C; $v = 16.96 \times 10^{-6}$ m²/s; $Pr = 0.699$.

Heat transfer from the plate, Q :

Reynolds number, $\qquad Re_L = \dfrac{UL}{v} = \dfrac{40 \times 1}{16.96 \times 10^{-6}} = 2.36 \times 10^6$

$\therefore \qquad Nu_L = \dfrac{hL}{k} = (0.699)^{0.33}\ [0.037\ (2.36 \times 10^6)^{0.8} - 850] = 3365.6$

or, $\qquad \bar{h} = \dfrac{0.0275 \times 3365.6}{1} = 92.55$ W/m²°C

$\therefore \qquad Q = \bar{h}\ A_s\ (t_s - t_\infty) = 92.55 \times (1 \times 1)\ (60 - 20)$

$\qquad\qquad = 3702$ W $\qquad$ or, $\qquad$ **3.702 kW** $\qquad$ **(Ans.)**

Example 7.37. *In a gas turbine system hot gases at 950°C flow at 70 m/s over the surface of a combustion chamber which is at a uniform temperature of 280°C. Determine the heat loss from the gases to the combustion chamber which can be idealised as a flat plate measuring 120 cm × 80 cm. The flow is parallel to the 120 cm side and transition Reynolds number is equal to 5×10^5.*

Take the properties of gas as:

$\rho = 0.494$ kg/m³, $k = 0.075$ W/m°C, $v = 95 \times 10^{-6}$ m²/s, $Pr = 0.625$.

Gas turbine generator control system.

Solution. *Given:* $L = 120$ cm $= 1.20$ m, $B = 80$ cm $= 0.8$ m, $Re_c = 5 \times 10^5$, $U = 70$ m/s.

Heat loss from the gases to the combustion chamber :

The average Nusselt number for a flow over a flat plate when both laminar and turbulent boundary layers are present is given by

$$\overline{Nu} = \left[0.664 \, (Re_L)^{0.5} + 0.036 \left\{(Re_L)^{0.8} - (Re_c)^{0.8}\right\}\right] (Pr)^{0.333}$$

If transition occurs at $Re_c = 5 \times 10^5$, then the above expression reduces to

$$\overline{Nu} = [0.036 \, (Re_L)^{0.8} - 836] \, (Pr)^{0.333}$$

The Reynolds number at the end of the plate is

$$Re_L = \frac{UL}{\nu} = \frac{70 \times 1.2}{95 \times 10^{-6}} = 8.84 \times 10^5$$

This shows that both laminar and turbulent boundary layers are present and,

Hence, $\qquad \overline{Nu} = [0.036 \, (8.84 \times 10^5)^{0.8} - 836] \, (0.625)^{0.333} = 1045$

or, $\qquad \dfrac{\overline{h}\,L}{k} = 1045 \text{ or } \overline{h} = \dfrac{k}{L} \times 1045$

or, $\qquad \overline{h} = \dfrac{0.075}{1.2} \times 1045 = 65.31 \text{ W/m}^2\,^\circ\text{C}$

Heat loss, $\qquad Q = \overline{h} A \, \Delta t$

$\qquad\qquad\qquad = 65.31 \times (1.2 \times 0.8) \times (950 - 280) = 42007.4 \text{ W} \approx \mathbf{42\ kW}$ **(Ans.)**

Example 7.38. *Air at 20°C and 1.013 bar flows over a rectangular container, with top surface 750 mm long in direction of flow and 1 m wide, at 35 m/s. Determine the heat transfer from the top surface maintained at 60°C. Use the following properties of air at average temperature of 40°C,*

$\qquad \mu = 1.906 \times 10^{-5}$ *kg/ms,* $c_p = 1.007$ *kJ/kg°C and k = 0.0272 W/m°C,*

and the following co-relations for finding average heat transfer coefficient :

$\qquad \overline{Nu} = 0.664 \, (Re_L)^{0.5} \, (Pr)^{0.33} \text{ if } Re_L \leq 5 \times 10^5$ ...(i)

$\qquad \overline{Nu} = [0.037 \, (Re_L)^{0.5} - 850] \, (Pr)^{0.33} \text{ if } Re_L > 5 \times 10^5$ ...(ii) **(P.U)**

Solution. *Given :* $p = 1.013$ bar, $L = 750$ mm $= 0.75$ m, $B = 1$ m, $U = 35$ m/s, Mean film temp.

$t_s = 60^\circ\text{C}, \ t_\infty = 20^\circ\text{C}, \ t_f = \left(\dfrac{60 + 20}{2}\right) = 40^\circ\text{C}$

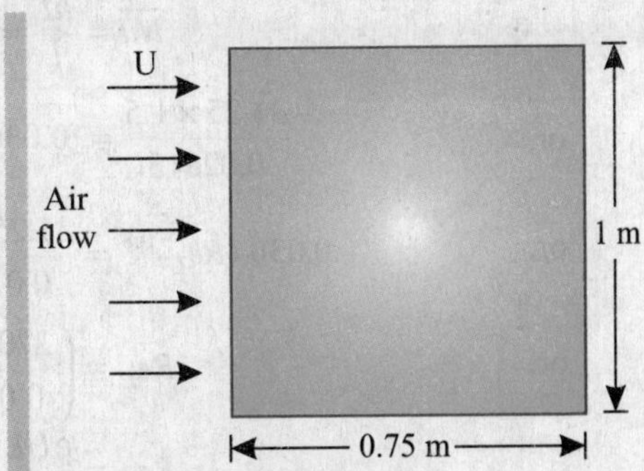

Heat transfer from the top surface, Q :

$Pr = \dfrac{\mu c_p}{k} = \dfrac{1.906 \times 10^{-5} \times (1.007 \times 10^3)}{0.0272} = 0.706$

Using the gas equation for air, we have

$p = \rho RT \qquad$ or, $\qquad \rho = \dfrac{p}{RT}$

or, $\qquad \rho = \dfrac{1.013 \times 10^5}{287 \times (20 + 273)} = 1.2 \text{ kg/m}^3$

$Re_L = \dfrac{\rho \, UL}{\mu} = \dfrac{1.2 \times 35 \times 0.75}{1.906 \times 10^{-5}} = 16.53 \times 10^5$

Since $Re > 5 \times 10^5$, we shall use eqn. *(ii)* for finding average heat transfer coefficient.

$\therefore \qquad\qquad \overline{Nu} = \dfrac{\overline{h}L}{k} = [0.037 \, (Re_L)^{0.8} - 850] \, (Pr)^{0.33}$

Fig. 7.21.

or,

$$\bar{h} = \frac{k}{L} = [0.037 \, (Re_L)^{0.8} - 850] \, (Pr)^{0.33}$$

$$= \frac{0.0272}{0.75} [0.037 \, (16.53 \times 10^5)^{0.8} - 850] \times (0.706)^{0.33}$$

$$= 0.03627 \, (3489.96 - 850) \times 0.8915 = 85.36 \text{ W/m}^2{}^{\circ}\text{C}$$

$\therefore$

$$Q = \bar{h} A_s \, (t_s - t_\infty)$$

$$= 85.36 \times (0.75 \times 1) \, (60 - 20) = \textbf{2560.8 W} \quad \textbf{(Ans.)}$$

Example 7.39. *A flat plate 1 m wide and 1.5 m long is to be maintained at 90°C in air when free stream temperature is 10°C. Determine the velocity at which air must flow over the plate so that the rate of energy dissipation from the plate is 3.75 kW.*

Use :

$$\bar{Nu} = \frac{\bar{h}L}{k} = 0.664 \, (Re_L)^{1/2} \, (Pr)^{1/3} \qquad \textit{... for laminar flow}$$

$$\bar{Nu} = \frac{\bar{h}L}{k} = [0.036 \, (Re_L)^{0.8} - 836] \, (Pr)^{1/3} \qquad \textit{... for turbulent flow}$$

Take the following air properties at 50°C :

$\rho = 1.0877 \text{ kg/m}^3, k = 0.02813 \text{ W/m}°C, c_p = 1007.3 \text{ J/kg}°C, \mu = 2.029 \times 10^{-5} \text{ kg/ms and } Pr = 0.703.$

(P.U)

Solution. *Given :* $L = 1.5$ m, $B = 1$ m, $t_s = 90°C$, $t_\infty = 10°C$, $Q = 3.75$ kW,

Mean film temperature, $t_f = (90 + 10)/2 = 50°C$

Velocity of flow, U :

$$Q = \bar{h} A_s \, (t_s - t_\infty) = \bar{h} \, (L \times B) \, (t_s - t_\infty)$$

$$3.75 \times 10^3 = \bar{h} \times (1.5 \times 1) \times (90 - 10)$$

or,

$$\bar{h} = \frac{3.75 \times 10^3}{(1.5 \times 1) \times (90 - 10)} = 31.25 \text{ W/m}^2{}^{\circ}\text{C}$$

The $\bar{h}$ value indicates that the flow must be *turbulent*. Considering the flow to be parallel to the length of the plate, we have

$$\bar{Nu} = \frac{\bar{h}L}{k} = [0.036 \, (Re_L)^{0.8} - 836] \, (Pr)^{1/3}$$

or,

$$\frac{31.25 \times 1.5}{0.02813} = [0.036 \, (Re_L)^{0.8} - 836] \, (0.703)^{0.333}$$

or,

$$0.036 \, (Re_L)^{0.8} = \frac{31.25 \times 1.5}{0.02813} \times \frac{1}{(0.703)^{0.333}} + 836 = 2709.8$$

or,

$$Re_L = \left(\frac{2709.8}{0.036} \right)^{1/0.8} = 1246790$$

$$Re_L = \frac{\rho U L}{\mu} = 1246790$$

or,

$$U = \frac{1246790 \times \mu}{\rho L} = \frac{1246790 \times 2.029 \times 10^{-5}}{1.0877 \times 1.5}$$

$$= \textbf{15.5 m/s} \quad \textbf{(Ans.)}$$

Example 7.40. *An aeroplane flies with a speed of 450 km/h at a height where the surrounding air has a temperature of 1°C and pressure of 65 cm of Hg. The aeroplane wing idealised as a flat plate 6m long, 1.2 m wide is maintained at 19°C. If the flow is made parallel to the 1.2 m width calculate :*

(i) *Heat loss from the wing;*

(ii) *Drag force on the wing.*

The properties of air at 10°C $\left(t_f = \dfrac{19+1}{2} = 10°C\right)$ *are :*

$k = 0.02511$ *W/m°C,* $v = 14.16 \times 10^{-6}$ *m²/s, Pr = 0.705.*

Solution. *Given :* $U = \dfrac{450 \times 1000}{3600} = 125$ m/s, $L = 6$ m, $B = 1.2$ m

(i) Heat loss from the wing :

The pressure of the air at flight altitude $= p = \dfrac{65}{76} \times 1.013 = 0.866$ bar

From the characteristic gas equation, we have

$$\rho = \frac{p}{RT} = \frac{0.866 \times 10^5}{287 \times (10 + 273)} = 1.066 \text{ kg/m}^3$$

The Reynolds number for the entire wing is

$$Re_L = \frac{UL}{v} = \frac{125 \times 1.2}{14.16 \times 10^{-6}} = 10.59 \times 10^6$$

Assuming that the critical Reynolds number is 5×10^5, we have

$$Re_c = 5 \times 10^5 = \frac{U x_c}{v} = \frac{125 \times x_c}{14.16 \times 10^{-6}}$$

or, $$x_c = \frac{5 \times 10^5 \times 14.16 \times 10^{-6}}{125} = 0.0566 \text{ m}$$

Propane fired heater longwave infrared, supplemented by forced convection system.

Thus we assume the flow is either a combination of laminar and turbulent or only turbulent. Considering the former, we have

$$\overline{Nu} = [\,0.036\,(Re_L)^{0.8} - 836]\,(Pr)^{0.333}$$

or,

$$\frac{\overline{h}L}{k} = [0.036\,(10.59 \times 10^6)^{0.8} - 836]\,(0.705)^{0.333} = 12611.5$$

or,

$$\overline{h} = \frac{k}{L} \times 12611.5 = \frac{0.02511}{1.2} \times 12611.5 = 263.89 \text{ W/m}^2\,^\circ\text{C}$$

$\therefore$ Heat lost, $\quad Q = \overline{h}\,A\,\Delta t = 263.89 \times (6 \times 1.2) \times (19 - 1) = 34200 \text{ W} = \textbf{34.2 kW} \quad \textbf{(Ans.)}$

(ii) **Drag force on the wing, F_D:**

The average friction coefficient is given by

$$\overline{C}_f = \left[\frac{0.072}{(Re_L)^{0.2}} - \frac{1670}{Re_L}\right] = \left[\frac{0.072}{(10.59 \times 10^6)^{0.2}} - \frac{1670}{(10.59 \times 10^6)}\right] = 2.676 \times 10^{-3}$$

Drag force on one side of the wing,

$$F_D = \overline{C}_f \times \frac{1}{2}\,\rho A U^2 \quad \text{(where } A = \text{one side area of the wing)}$$

$$= 2.676 \times 10^{-3} \times \frac{1}{2} \times 1.066 \times (6 \times 1.2) \times 125^2 = \textbf{160.46 N} \quad \textbf{(Ans.)}$$

Example 7.41. *A square plate maintained at 95°C experiences a force of 10.5 N when forced air at 25°C flows over it at a velocity of 30 m/s. Assuming the flow to be turbulent and using Colburn analogy calculate :*

(i)   The heat transfer coefficient;

(ii) The heat loss from the plate surface.

Properties of air are :

$\rho = 1.06 \text{ kg/m}^3$, $c_p = 1.005 \text{ kJ/kg K}$, $v = 18.97 \times 10^{-6} \text{ m}^2/s$, $P_r = 0.696$.

Solution. *Given :* $F_D = 10.5 \text{ N}$, $t_s = 95°C$, $t_\infty = 25°C$, $U = 30 \text{ m/s}$

(i) **The heat transfer coefficient, $\overline{h}$:**

For turbulent flow, the drag force is given by

$$F = \overline{C}_f \times \frac{1}{2}\,\rho A U^2$$

or,

$$10.5 = \frac{0.072}{(Re_L)^{0.2}} \times \frac{1}{2} \times 1.06 \times (L \times L) \times (30)^2$$

$$= 0.072 \left(\frac{v}{UL}\right)^{0.2} \times \frac{1}{2} \times 1.06 \times L^2 \times 900$$

$$= 0.072 \left(\frac{18.97 \times 10^{-6}}{25 \times L}\right)^{0.2} \times \frac{1}{2} \times 1.06 \times L^2 \times 900$$

$$= 1.424 \times \frac{L^2}{(L)^{0.2}} = 2.05\,(L)^{1.8}$$

or,

$$L = \left(\frac{10.5}{2.05}\right)^{1/1.8} = 2.478 \text{ m}$$

The Reynolds number at the end of the plate,

$$Re_L = \frac{UL}{v} = \frac{30 \times 2.478}{18.97 \times 10^{-6}} = 3.919 \times 10^6$$

Average skin friction coefficient; $\bar{C}_f = \dfrac{0.072}{(Re_L)^{0.2}}$ ...(7.26)

$$= \frac{0.072}{(3.919 \times 10^6)^{0.2}} = 3.457 \times 10^{-3}$$

From Colburn analogy, we have

$$\bar{St}\,(Pr)^{2/3} = \frac{\bar{C}_f}{2} \qquad\qquad ...[\text{Eqn. (7.137)}]$$

or, $\quad \dfrac{\bar{h}}{\rho\, c_p U}\,(Pr)^{2/3} = \dfrac{\bar{C}_f}{2}$

or, $\quad \bar{h} = \dfrac{\rho\, c_p U}{(Pr)^{2/3}} \times \dfrac{\bar{C}_f}{2}$

or, $\quad \bar{h} = \dfrac{1.06 \times (1.005 \times 10^3) \times 30}{(0.696)^{0.666}} \times \left(\dfrac{3.457 \times 10^{-3}}{2} \right)$

$$= \textbf{70.32 W/m}^2\textbf{°C} \quad \textbf{(Ans.)}$$

(*ii*) **Heat loss from the plate surface, Q :**

$$Q = \bar{h}\,A\,\Delta t = 70.32 \times (2.478 \times 2.478) \times (95 - 25) = 30226\ \text{W}$$

$$= \textbf{30.226 kW} \quad \textbf{(Ans.)}$$

Example 7.42. *Air at 20°C flows past a 800 mm long plate at a velocity of 45 m/s. If the surface of the plate is maintained at 300°C, determine :*

(i) *The heat transferred from the entire plate length to air taking into consideration both laminar and turbulent portions of the boundary layer.*

(ii) *The percentage error if the boundary layer is assumed to be of turbulent nature from the very leading edge of the plate.*

Assume unit width of the plate and critical Reynolds number to be 5×10^5.

Take the properties of air $\left(at\ \dfrac{300 + 20}{2} = 160°C \right)$ *as :*

$k = 0.03638\ W/m°C,\ v = 30.08 \times 10^{-6}\ m^2/s,\ Pr = 0.682.$

Solution. *Given:* $\quad L = 800\ \text{mm} = 0.8\ \text{m},\ U = 45\ \text{m/s},\ t_s = 300°C,\ t_\infty = 20°C.$

(*i*) **The heat transferred from the entire plate, considering both laminar and turbulent boundary layers :**

The Reynolds number for the entire plate,

$$Re_L = \frac{UL}{v} = \frac{45 \times 0.8}{30.08 \times 10^{-6}} = 1.197 \times 10^6$$

The critical distance x_c from the leading edge at which transition occurs is

$$x_c = \frac{Re_c\, v}{U} \qquad\qquad \left(\because Re_c = \frac{U\,x_c}{v} \right)$$

or, $\quad x_c = \dfrac{5 \times 10^5 \times 30.08 \times 10^{-6}}{45} = 0.3342\ \text{m}$

Laminar boundary layer region :

Average heat transfer coefficient,

$$\bar{h} = 0.664 \frac{k}{x_c} (Re_c)^{0.5} (Pr)^{0.333}$$

$$= 0.664 \times \frac{0.03638}{0.3342} \times (5 \times 10^5)^{0.5} (0.682)^{0.333} = 44.99 \text{ W/m}^2{}^\circ\text{C}$$

The heat transfer from the laminar portion,

$$Q_{lam} = \bar{h}A (t_s - t_\infty)$$

$$= 44.99 \times (0.3342 \times 1) (300 - 20) = 4209.98 \text{ W (per metre width)}$$

Turbulent boundary layer region :

Average heat transfer coefficient,

$$\bar{h} = 0.036 \frac{k}{(L - x_c)} [(Re_L)^{0.8} - (Re_c)^{0.8}] (Pr)^{0.333}$$

$$= 0.036 \times \frac{0.03638}{(0.8 - 0.3342)} [(1.197 \times 10^6)^{0.8} - (5 \times 10^5)^{0.8}] (0.682)^{0.333}$$

$$= 0.002812 \times 36618.7 \times 0.88 = 90.6 \text{ W/m}^2{}^\circ\text{C}$$

The heat transfer from the turbulent portion,

$$Q_{turb.} = \bar{h}A (t_s - t_\infty)$$

$$= 90.6 \times [(0.8 - 0.3342) \times 1] (300 - 20) = 11816.41 \text{ W}$$

Hence, total heat transferred from the plate,

$$Q_{total} = Q_{lam.} + Q_{turb.} = 4209.98 + 11816.41 \simeq \mathbf{16026 \text{ W (Ans.)}}$$

Alternatively :

Overall average heat transfer coefficient,

$$\bar{h} = \frac{k}{L} \left[0.036 (Re_L)^{0.8} - 836 \right] (Pr)^{1/3} \qquad ...(\text{Eqn. 7.143})$$

$$= \frac{0.03638}{0.8} [0.036 (1.197 \times 10^6)^{0.8} - 836] (0.682)^{0.333} = 71.54 \text{ W/m}^2{}^\circ\text{C}$$

$$\therefore \quad Q_{total} = \bar{h}A (t_s - t_\infty) = 71.54 \times (0.8 \times 1) \times (300 - 20) = 16025 \text{ W}$$

Turbulent flow along the tube.

(*ii*) **The percentage error :**

If the boundary layer is turbulent from the very beginning, then average heat transfer coefficient,

$$\bar{h} = 0.036 \left(\frac{k}{L}\right)(Re_L)^{0.8} \, (Pr)^{0.333} \qquad \qquad ...(7.140)$$

$$= 0.036 \left(\frac{0.03638}{0.8}\right)(1.197 \times 10^6)^{0.8} \, (0.682)^{0.333} = 105 \text{ W/m}^2{}^\circ\text{C}$$

$$(Q_{total})_{turb.} = \bar{h}A \, (t_s - t_\infty) = 105 \times (0.8 \times 1) \, (300 - 20) = 23520 \text{ W}$$

$$\therefore \quad \text{Percentage error} = \frac{23520 - 16026}{16026} \times 100 = \textbf{46.76 \% increase (Ans.)}$$

B.   Forced Convection - Internal Flow

7.4. TURBULENT TUBE FLOW

Some of the important relations for fully developed turbulent flow (Re > 2300) through pipes and conduits are :

(*i*)   *The velocity distribution :* $\dfrac{u}{u_{max}} = \left(\dfrac{y}{R}\right)^{1/n}$ $\qquad \qquad ...(7.145)$

where, u = Local average velocity,

$\qquad \qquad u_{max}$ = Velocity at centre line,

$\qquad \qquad R$ = Radius of the pipe, and

$\qquad \qquad y$ = Distance from the wall = $(R - r)$.

(*ii*) *The head loss :* $h_L = \dfrac{dp}{\rho} = \dfrac{f \, L \bar{u}^2}{2g}$

$\qquad$ (where, f = friction factor, and $\bar{u}$ = average flow velocity)

$\qquad \qquad \qquad \qquad \qquad \qquad \qquad$ ... *equally valid for turbulent flow.*

In case of turbulent flow through tube, it is difficult to derive simple analytical expressions for heat transfer coefficient and Nusselt number. But such expressions can be easily found out by using empirical relations.

The *friction factor* for turbulent flow, is well represented by the following empirical relations :

$$f = 0.316 \, (Re)^{-0.25} \qquad \qquad \text{for } 2 \times 10^4 < Re < 8 \times 10^4 \qquad ...(7.146)$$

$$f = 0.184 \, (Re)^{-0.2} \qquad \qquad \text{for } 10^4 < Re < 10^5 \qquad \qquad ...(7.147)$$

$$f = 0.005 + 0.396 \, (Re)^{0.3} \qquad \text{for } 2 \times 10^4 < Re < 2 \times 10^6 \qquad ..(7.148)$$

(*iii*)   *The wall shear stress,* τ_w :

$$\tau_w = \frac{f}{8} \, \rho u_{max}^2 \qquad \qquad ...(7.149)$$

(*iv*)   *From Colburn analogy* $(0.5 < P_r < 100)$

$$\bar{St} \, (Pr)^{2/3} = \frac{f}{8} \qquad \qquad ...(7.150)$$

Substituting the value of f from eqn. (7.147) in eqn. (7.150), we get following equations for heat transfer coefficients :

$$\bar{St} \, (Pr)^{2/3} = \frac{0.184}{8} \, (Re)^{-0.2}$$

$$\frac{\bar{Nu}}{Pr \, Re} \, (Pr)^{2/3} = \frac{0.184}{8} \, (Re)^{-0.2}$$

or, $$\overline{Nu} = 0.023 \ (Re)^{0.8} \ (Pr)^{1/3} \qquad\qquad ...(7.151)$$

and, $$\overline{h} = \overline{Nu} \times \frac{k}{D} = 0.023 \ \frac{k}{D} \ (Re)^{0.8} \ (Pr)^{1/3} \qquad ...(7.152)$$

The above expressions are valid for

$$1 \times 10^4 < Re < 1 \times 10^5; \ 0.5 < Pr < 100; \ \frac{L}{D} > 60.$$

The properties of fluid are evaluated *at film temperature.*

Example 7.43. *A tube 5 m long is maintained at 100°C by steam jacketing. A fluid flows through the tube at the rate of 175 kg/h at 30°C. The diameter of the tube is 2 cm. Find out average heat transfer coefficient.*

Take the following properties of the fluid :

$$\rho = 850 \ kg/m^3, \ c_p = 2000 \ J/kg°C, \ v = 5.1 \times 10^{-6} \ m^2/s \ and \ k = 0.12 \ W/m°C. \qquad \text{(M.U)}$$

Solution. *Given :* $L = 5$ m, $D = 2$ cm $= 0.02$ m

Average heat transfer coefficient $\overline{h}$:

$$\overline{Nu} = \frac{\overline{h}D}{k} = 0.023 \ (Re)^{0.8} \ (Pr)^{1/3} \ \text{if } Re > 2300 \qquad\qquad ...(i)$$

where, $$Re = \frac{\rho V D}{\mu} = \frac{VD}{v}, \ \text{where } V \text{ is the average flow velocity.}$$

The mass flow per second is given by

$$m = \frac{175}{3600} = \frac{\pi}{4} \ D^2 V = \frac{\pi}{4} \times (0.02)^2 \times V$$

or, $$V = \frac{175}{3600} \times \frac{4}{\pi \times (0.02)^2} = 154.7 \ \text{m/s}$$

$\therefore$ $$Re = \frac{154.7 \times 0.02}{5.1 \times 10^{-6}} = 0.6 \times 10^6$$

Since $Re > 2300$, the expression (i) holds good. Substituting the values, we get

$$\frac{\overline{h} \times 0.02}{0.12} = 0.023 \ (0.6 \times 10^6)^{0.8} \times (72.3)^{0.333} \simeq 4012$$

$$\left[\text{where } Pr = \frac{\mu \ c_p}{k} = \frac{\rho v \ c_p}{k} = \frac{850 \times 5.1 \times 10^{-6} \times 2000}{0.12} = 72.3 \right]$$

$\therefore$ $$\overline{h} = \frac{4012 \times 0.12}{0.02}$$

$$= 24072 \ \text{W/m}^2\text{°C} \quad \text{or} \quad \textbf{24.072 kW/m}^2\textbf{°C} \qquad \textbf{(Ans.)}$$

Example 7.44. *In a straight tube of 60 mm diameter, water is flowing at a velocity of 12 m/s. The tube surface temperature is maintained at 70°C and the flowing water is heated from the inlet temperature 15°C to an outlet temperature of 45°C. Taking the physical properties of water at its mean bulk temperature, calculate the following :*

(i)   The heat transfer coefficient from the tube surface to the water,

(ii) The heat transferred, and

(iii) The length of the tube.

Solution. *Given :* $D = 60$ mm $= 0.6$ m, $V = 12$ m/s, $t_s = 70°C$, $t_i = 15°C$, $t_o = 45°C$.

The fluid mean bulk temperature, $t_b = \dfrac{15 + 45}{2} = 30°C$

The thermo-physical properties of water at 30°C are :

ρ = 995.7 kg/m³, c_p = 4.174 kJ/kg°C, k = 61.718 × 10⁻² W/m°C, v = 0.805 × 10⁻⁶ m²/s, Pr = 5.42.

(i) **The heat transfer coefficient from the tube surface to the water :**

Reynolds number, $\qquad Re = \dfrac{VD}{v} = \dfrac{12 \times 0.06}{0.805 \times 10^{-6}} = 0.894 \times 10^6$

Since $Re > 2500$, hence nature of flow is *turbulent*. For the turbulent flow

$$\overline{Nu} = \dfrac{\overline{h}D}{k} = 0.023\ (Re)^{0.8}\ (Pr)^{0.333} \qquad\qquad ...[Eqn.\ (7.151)]$$

or, $\qquad\qquad \overline{h} = \dfrac{k}{D} \times 0.023\ (Re)^{0.8}\ (Pr)^{0.333}$

or, $\qquad\qquad \overline{h} = \dfrac{61.718 \times 10^{-2}}{0.06} \times 0.023 \times (0.894 \times 10^6)^{0.8} \times (5.42)^{0.333}$

$$= \textbf{23959.6 W/m}^2\textbf{°C \ (Ans.)}$$

(ii) **The heat transferred, Q :**

The heat transferred, $\qquad Q = m \times c_p \times (t_o - t_i) = \left(\rho \times \dfrac{\pi}{4}\ D^2 \times V\right) \times c_p \times (t_o - t_i)$

$$= (995.7 \times \dfrac{\pi}{4} \times 0.06^2 \times 12) \times (4.174 \times 10^3) \times (45 - 15)$$

$$= \textbf{4230345 W} \quad \textbf{(Ans.)}$$

(iii) **The length of the tube, L :**

$$Q = \overline{h}\ A\ (t_s - t_b)$$

or, $\qquad\qquad 4230345 = 23959.6 \times (\pi \times 0.06 \times L)\ (70 - 30)$

or, $\qquad\qquad L = \dfrac{4230345}{23959.6 \times \pi \times 0.06\ (70 - 30)} = \textbf{23.4 m} \quad \textbf{(Ans.)}$

Example 7.45. *Water is flowing at the rate of 50 kg/min through a tube of inner diameter 2.5 cm. The inner surface of the tube is maintained at 100°C. If the temperature of water increases from 25°C and 55°C, find the length of the tube required.*

The following relation may be used :

$$Nu = 0.023\ (Re)^{0.8}\ (Pr)^{0.4}.$$

The properties of water can be taken from the following table :

t (°C)	ρ (kg/m³)	c_p (J/kg-K)	$k \times 10^{-2}$ (W/m-K)	$\mu \times 10^6$ (kg/m-s)
40	992.2	4174	63.35	652
50	988.1	4178	64.74	550
60	983.2	4182	65.90	470
70	977.8	4187	66.72	405
80	971.8	4195	67.41	335

(B.U. Winter, 1998)

Solution. $\dot{m}$ = 50 kg/min = $\dfrac{50}{60}$ = 0.8333 kg/s; D_i = 2.5 cm = 0.025 m;

t_s = 100°C; t_i = 25°C; t_o = 55°C.

Length of the tube required, L :

$$Q = hA_s\, \theta_m \qquad \qquad ...(i)$$

where $A_s = \pi D_i L = \pi \times 0.025 \times L = 0.0785\ L\ \text{m}^2$

$$\theta_m = \frac{(\theta_1 - \theta_2)}{ln\ (\theta_1/\theta_2)} = \frac{(100 - 25) - (100 - 55)}{ln\left(\dfrac{100 - 25}{100 - 55}\right)} = \frac{75 - 45}{ln\left(\dfrac{75}{45}\right)} = 58.7°C$$

Also, $\qquad Q = \dot{m}\, c_p\, (t_o - t_i)$

The properties of water should be taken at

$$\frac{\left[100 + \left(\dfrac{55 + 25}{2}\right)\right]}{2} = 70°C$$

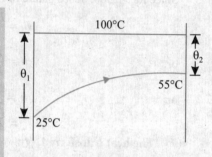

Fig. 7.22.

$\therefore \qquad Q = 0.8333 \times 4187 \times (55 - 25) = 104671\ \text{W}$

To find h we have to use the given empirical relation.

The mass flow rate is given by,

$$\dot{m} = 0.8333 = \frac{\pi}{4}\ D_i^2 \times V \times \rho = \frac{\pi}{4} \times 0.025^2 \times V \times 977.8$$

$$\therefore \qquad V = \frac{0.8333 \times 4}{\pi \times (0.025)^2 \times 977.8} = 1.74\ \text{m/s}$$

$$Re = \frac{\rho V D_i}{\mu} = \frac{977.8 \times 1.74 \times 0.025}{405 \times 10^{-6}} = 1.05 \times 10^5$$

$$Pr = \frac{\mu c_p}{k} = \frac{405 \times 10^{-6} \times 4187}{66.72 \times 10^{-2}} = 2.54$$

Now substituting the values in the given empirical formula, we get

$$Nu = \frac{hD_i}{k} = 0.023\ (Re)^{0.8}\ (Pr)^{0.4}$$

$$= \frac{h \times 0.025}{66.72 \times 10^{-2}} = 0.023\ (1.05 \times 10^5)^{0.8}\ (2.54)^{0.4} = 347.23$$

$$\therefore \qquad h = \frac{66.72 \times 10^{-2} \times 347.23}{0.025} = 9268.2\ \text{W/m}^2°C$$

Now substituting the values in (i), we get

$$104671 = 9268.2 \times 0.0785\ L \times 58.7$$

$$\therefore \qquad L = \frac{104671}{9268.2 \times 0.0785 \times 58.7} = 2.45\ \text{m} \qquad \text{(Ans.)}$$

Example 7.46. *Water at 25°C flows across a horizontal copper tube 1.5 cm OD with a velocity of 2 m/s. Calculate the heat transfer rate per unit length if the wall temperature is maintained at 75°C. Given properties of water :*

$$\rho = 988\ kg/m^3$$

$$k = 0.648\ W/m\ K$$

$$\mu = 549.2 \times 10^{-6}\ N\ s/m^2$$

$$c_p = 4.174\ kJ/kg\ K$$

$$\overline{N_{uD}} = 0.3 + \frac{0.62\ R_{eD}^{1/2}\ Pr^{1/3}}{\left[1 + \left(\dfrac{0.4}{Pr}\right)^{2/3}\right]^{1/4}} \left[1 + \left(\frac{R_{eD}}{282000}\right)^{1/2}\right]$$

(AMIE Summer, 1997)

Solution. *Given :* $\Delta t = 75 - 25 = 50°C$; $D = 1.5$ cm $= 0.015$ m, $U = 2$ m./s;

$\rho = 988$ kg/m³; $k = 0.648$ W/m K; $\mu = 549.2 \times 10^{-6}$ Ns/m²;

$c_p = 4.174$ kJ/kg K.

Heat transfer rate per unit length, $\dfrac{Q}{L}$:

Reynolds number, $Re = \dfrac{\rho UD}{\mu} = \dfrac{988 \times 2 \times 0.015}{549.2 \times 10^{-6}} = 53969.4$

Prandtl number, $Pr = \dfrac{\mu c_p}{k} = \dfrac{549.2 \times 10^{-6} \times 4.174 \times 10^3}{0.648} = 3.5376$

$$\overline{Nu} = \frac{hD}{k} = 0.3 + \frac{0.62\ (Re)^{1/2}\ (Pr)^{1/3}}{\left[1 + \left(\dfrac{0.4}{Pr}\right)^{2/3}\right]^{1/4}} \left[1 + \left(\frac{Re}{282000}\right)^{1/2}\right]$$

$$= 0.3 + \frac{0.62 \times (53969.4)^{1/2} \times (3.5376)^{1/3}}{\left[1 + \left(\dfrac{0.4}{3.5376}\right)^{2/3}\right]^{1/4}} \left[1 + \left(\frac{53969.4}{282000}\right)^{1/2}\right]$$

$$= 0.3 + \frac{219.466}{1.054} \times 1.437 = 299.5$$

Vacuum oven

or, $$\bar{h} = 299.5 \times \frac{k}{D} = 299.5 \times \frac{0.648}{0.015} = 12938.4 \ \text{W/m}^2 \ \text{K}$$

Now, $$\frac{Q}{L} = \bar{h} \times \pi D \times \Delta t$$

$$= 12938.4 \times \pi \times 0.015 \times 50 = 30485.4 \ \text{W/m or,} \ \mathbf{30.485 \ kW/m} \quad \textbf{(Ans.)}$$

Example 7.47. *Air entering at 2 bar pressure and bulk temperature of 200°C is heated as it flows through a tube with a diameter of 25.4 mm at a velocity of 10 m/s. Calculate the heat transfer per unit length of the tube if constant heat flux condition is maintained at the wall and wall temperature is 20°C above the air temperature all along the length of the tube. How much would the bulk temperature increase over 3 metres length of the tube?*

Take the properties of air as :

$\rho = 1.493 \ kg/m^3$, $\mu = 2.57 \times 10^{-5} \ Ns/m^2$, $k = 0.0386 \ W/m°C$, $c_p = 1025 \ J/kg°C$

Use the relation :

$$\overline{Nu} = 0.023 \ (Re)^{0.8} \ (Pr)^{0.4} \qquad \text{(M.U)}$$

Solution. *Given :* $D = 25.4 \ \text{mm} = 0.0254 \ \text{m}$; $U = 10 \ \text{m/s}$

Heat transfer per unit length of the tube :

$$Re = \frac{\rho \ UD}{\mu} = \frac{1.493 \times 10 \times 0.0254}{2.57 \times 10^{-5}} = 14756$$

$$Pr = \frac{\mu \ c_p}{k} = \frac{2.57 \times 10^{-5} \times 1025}{0.0386} = 0.6284$$

$\therefore \qquad \overline{Nu} = \frac{hD}{k} = 0.023 \ (Re)^{0.8} \ (Pr)^{0.4}$

or, $$\bar{h} = \frac{k}{D} [0.023 \ (Re)^{0.8} \ (Pr)^{0.4}]$$

$$= \frac{0.0386}{0.0254} [0.023 \ (14756)^{0.8} \ (0.6284)^{0.4}] = 62.8 \ \text{W/m}^2°\text{C}$$

Heat transfer *per unit length* of the tube,

$$Q = \bar{h} \ A_s \ \Delta t = \bar{h} \times (\pi D \times 1) \ \Delta t$$

$$= 62.8 \times (\pi \times 0.0254 \times 1) \times 20 = \mathbf{100.22 \ W} \quad \textbf{(Ans.)}$$

Bulk temperature increase $(\Delta t)_b$, **over a 3 m length of the tube :**

$$Q = mc_p \ (\Delta t)_b = (\rho AU) \ c_p \ (\Delta t)_b$$

$$(3 \times 100.22) = \left(1.493 \times \frac{\pi}{4} \times 0.0254^2 \times 10\right) \times 1025 \times (\Delta t)_b$$

or, $$(\Delta t)_b = \frac{3 \times 100.22 \times 4}{1.493 \times \pi \times (0.0254)^2 \times 10 \times 1025} = \mathbf{38.77°C} \quad \textbf{(Ans.)}$$

Example 7.48. *A fluid is flowing in a pipe which is 300 mm in diameter, 3.5 m long and whose surface in maintained at a constant temperature. The temperature of the wall surface at the inlet section of the pipe exceeds the fluid temperature by 40°C. What is the rise in the fluid temperature at the end section of the pipe?*

The Reynolds analogy holds good which is given by $St = \dfrac{f}{8}$ *where friction factor* $f = 0.022$.

Solution. *Given :* $D = 300 \ \text{mm} = 0.3 \ \text{m}$, $L = 3.5 \ \text{m}$, $f = 0.022$, $(t_s - t_i) = 40°\text{C}$

Rise in fluid temperature at the end section of the pipe $(t_o - t_i)$:

The energy balance yields

$$Q = \bar{h} A (t_s - t_\infty) = m c_p (t_o - t_i)$$

or,

$$h (\pi DL) \left[t_s - \frac{t_o + t_i}{2} \right] = \left[\rho \times \frac{\pi}{4} D^2 \times V \right] \times c_p (t_o - t_i)$$

Dividing throughout by $\pi \rho V c_p D$, we have

$$\frac{h L}{\rho V c_p} \left[\frac{(t_s - t_o) + (t_s - t_i)}{2} \right] = \frac{D}{4} (t_o - t_i)$$

or,

$$St \cdot \frac{L}{2} [(t_s - t_o) + (t_s - t_i)] = \frac{D}{4} [(t_s - t_i) - (t_s - t_o)]$$

or,

$$\frac{f}{8} \cdot \frac{L}{2} [(t_s - t_o) + (t_s - t_i)] = \frac{D}{4} [(t_s - t_i) - (t_s - t_o)]$$

$$...\text{substituting, } St = \frac{f}{8}$$

Inserting the values, we get

$$\frac{0.022}{8} \times \frac{3.5}{2} [(t_s - t_o) + 40] = \frac{0.3}{4} [40 - (t_s - t_o)]$$

or,

$$0.0048 [(t_s - t_o) + 40] = 0.075 [40 - (t_s - t_o)]$$

or,

$$0.0048 (t_s - t_o) + 0.192 = 3 - 0.075 (t_s - t_o)$$

or,

$$(t_s - t_o) (0.0048 + 0.075) = 2.808$$

or,

$$(t_s - t_o) = \frac{2.808}{(0.0048 + 0.075)} = 35.18°C$$

∴ The rise in the temperature of the fluid at the end,

$$(t_o - t_i) = (t_s - t_i) - (t_s - t_o)$$
$$= 40 - 35.18 = \textbf{4.82°C} \quad \textbf{(Ans.)}$$

Example 7.49. *Air at 2 bar and 40°C is heated as it flows through tube of diameter 30mm at a velocity of 10 m/s. Calculate the heat transfer per unit length of the tube when wall temperature is maintained at 100°C all along length of the tube. How much would be the bulk temperature increase over one metre length of the tube ? Use the following relation :*

$$Nu = 0.023 \ Re^{0.8} \ Pr^{0.4}$$

The properties air at $\dfrac{100 + 40}{2} = 70°C$ *are :*

$\mu = 20.6 \times 10^{-6}$ *N- s/m²; Pr = 0.694;* $c_p =$ *1.009 kJ/kg°C; k = 0.0297 kg/m°C;* (M.U., 1992)

Solution. *Given :* $p = 2$ bar $= 2 \times 10^5$ N/m²; $t_i = 40°C$, $D = 30$ mm $= 0.03$ m;

$V = 10$ m/s; $t_s = 100°C$

We know that $p = \rho RT$ or, $\rho = \dfrac{p}{RT}$

or, $\rho = \dfrac{2 \times 10^5}{287 \times (40 + 273)} = 2.226$ kg/m³

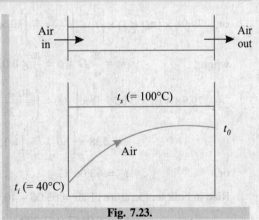

Fig. 7.23.

Refrigeration cycle machine.

$$Re = \frac{\rho V D}{\mu} = \frac{2.226 \times 10 \times 0.03}{20.6 \times 10^{-6}} = 32417$$

$$Pr = 0.696 \hspace{4cm} \text{...(Given)}$$

$$Nu = 0.023 \, (Re)^{0.8} \, (Pr)^{0.4}$$

$$= 0.023 \, (32417)^{0.8} \, (0.696)^{0.4} = 80.79$$

$$\therefore \quad \frac{hD}{k} = 80.79$$

$$\therefore \quad h = \frac{k}{D} \times 80.79 = \frac{0.0297}{0.03} \times 80.79 = 79.98 \ \text{W/m}^2 {}^\circ\text{C}$$

$$Q = hA \, (AMTD) = m \times c_p \, (t_o - t_i)$$

or, $\quad 79.98 \times (\pi D \times 1) \times \left[t_s - \left(\dfrac{t_i + t_o}{2} \right) \right] = \dot{m} \times (1.009 \times 10^3) \times (t_o - t_i)$

where, $\quad \dot{m} = \dfrac{\pi}{4} D^2 V \rho = \dfrac{\pi}{4} \times 0.03^2 \times 10 \times 2.226 = 0.0157 \ \text{kg/s}$

$$\therefore \quad 79.98 \times (\pi \times 0.03 \times 1) \times \left[100 - \left(\frac{40 + t_o}{2} \right) \right] = 0.0157 \times (1.009 \times 10^3) \times (t_o - 40)$$

$$7.538 \times \left(80 - \frac{t_o}{2} \right) = 15.84 \, (t_o - 40)$$

or, $\quad t_o = 63.06 {}^\circ\text{C}$

Rise in bulk temperature of air $= 63.06 - 40 = \textbf{23.06}{}^\circ\textbf{C}$ **(Ans.)**

$$Q = 0.0157 \times (1.009 \times 10^3) \times (63.06 - 40) = \textbf{365.3 W/m} \ \textbf{(Ans.)}$$

7.5. EMPRICAL CORRELATIONS FOR FORCED CONVECTION

The following dimensionless numbers are used for the usual forced convection problems :

(i) *Nusselt number,* $Nu = \dfrac{hL}{k}$;   (ii) *Reynolds number,* $Re = \dfrac{\rho\, LV}{\mu}$

(iii) *Prandtl number,* $Pr = \dfrac{\mu\, c_p}{k}$; (iv) *Stanton number,* $St = \dfrac{h}{\rho\, c_p V}$

In order to determine the value of convection coefficient h, the following conventional generalised basic equations are used :

$$Nu = f_1\,(Re,\ Pr) = C_1\,(Re)^m\,(Pr)^n\ ;\ St = f_2\,(Re,\ Pr) = C_2\,(Re)^a\,(Pr)^b$$

The values (numerical) of the constants and exponents are determined through experiments. The properties of the fluid are evaluated on the basis of bulk temperature (unless stated otherwise).

A. *Laminar Flow*

7.5.1. LAMINAR FLOW OVER FLAT PLATES AND WALLS

(a) The *local value of heat transfer coefficient* is given by

$$Nu_x = \frac{h_x x}{k} = 0.332\,(Re_x)^{0.5}\,(Pr)^{0.333} \qquad ...\text{Blasius equation} \qquad ..(7.153)$$

The *average value of heat transfer coefficient* is given by

$$Nu = \frac{\bar{h}L}{k} = 0.664\,(Re_L)^{0.5}\,(Pr)^{0.333} \qquad\qquad ...(7.154)$$

where, $Re_x = \dfrac{Ux}{v}$, $Re_L = \dfrac{UL}{v}$ and $Pr = \dfrac{\mu\, c_p}{k}$

The above equations are valid for the following :

(i) All fluids $(Pr \geq 0.6)$ except liquid metals

(ii) Reynolds number $Re \geq 40000$

(iii) The fluid properties are evaluated at the mean film temperature, $t_f = \dfrac{t_s + t_\infty}{2}$.

(b) For *liquid metals,* the following correlation has been proposed

$$Nu_x = 0.565\,(Pe_x) \qquad\qquad ...(7.155)$$

where $Pe_x = Re_x \cdot Pr$

The above equation is valid for the following :

(i) $Pr \leq 0.05$

(ii) The fluid properties are evaluated at the film temperature.

7.5.2. LAMINAR FLOW INSIDE TUBES

(a) For *fully developed flow* : $f = \dfrac{64}{Re}$ ..(7.156)

(b) For *uniform heat flux* : $Nu = 4.36$ ...(7.157)

(c) For *constant wall temperature* :

Slug flow : $Nu = 5.78$ ...(7.158)

Fully developed flow : $Nu = 3.66$ ...(7.159)

(d) For average Nusselt number for flow inside tubes, the following correlations, have been developed :

1. $Nu = \dfrac{hD}{k} = 3.66 + \dfrac{0.0668\,(D/L)\,Re \cdot Pr}{1 + 0.04\,[(D/L)\,Re.\,Pr]^{2/3}}$ ...(7.160)

This equation is valid

    (i)   for constant wall temperature and fully developed flow,

    (ii) when properties are evaluated at the bulk temperature,

    (iii) tube length is much greater than diameter,

    (iv) when Re and Nu are calculated on the basis of pipe diameter as the length parameter.

    (v) when $0.5 < Pr < 100$.

$$2. \quad Nu = \frac{hD}{k} = 1.86 \left[\frac{D}{L} Re \cdot Pr \right]^{1/3} \left[\frac{\mu}{\mu_s} \right]^{0.14} \qquad \text{...(7.161)}$$

This equation is valid for

    (i) short tubes $\left(\dfrac{L}{D} > 2 \right)$ (ii) $Re < 2100$

    (iii) $0.48 < Pr < 16700$ (iv) $0.0044 < (\mu/\mu_s) < 9.75$

    (v) In this equation all properties except μ_s are evaluated at bulk temperature; μ_s is evaluated at surface temperature.

B. Turbulent Flow

7.5.3. TURBULENT FLOW OVER FLAT PLATE

The local and average Nusselt numbers, from Colburn analogy, are given by :

$$Nu_x = 0.029 \, (Re_x)^{0.8} \, (Pr)^{1/3} \qquad \text{...(7.162)}$$

$$\overline{Nu} = 0.036 \, (Re_L)^{0.8} \, (Pr)^{1/3}$$

where the properties are evaluated at the mean film temperature.

When the flow lies in the *transition range*,

$$\overline{Nu} = 0.036 \, [(Re_L)^{0.8} - A] \, (Pr)^{1/3} \qquad \text{...(7.163)}$$

where $A = 18700$ when $Re_c = 4 \times 10^5$

                  $A = 23100$ when $Re_c = 5 \times 10^5$

7.5.4. TURBULENT FLOW IN TUBES

The following correlations for *fully developed turbulent flow in circular tubes* have been proposed :

    1. Mc Adams has proposed the following general correlation on the basis of $Nu = \phi \, (Re, Pr)$ for heating and cooling of all fluids with some *limitations* as given below :

$$\overline{Nu} = 0.023 \, (Re)^{0.8} \, (Pr)^n \qquad \text{...(7.164)}$$

where $n = 0.4$ ... for heating

              $n = 0.3$ ... for cooling

    (i) $\dfrac{L}{D} \geq 60$ (ii) $1 \times 10^4 < Re < 12 \times 10^4$

    (iii) $0.7 \leq Pr \leq 160$ (iv) Fluid properties are evaluated at the mean bulk temperature.

    2. Colburn suggested the following correlation :

$$Nu = 0.023 \, (Re)^{0.8} \, (Pr)^{1/3} \qquad \text{...(7.165)}$$

$$St = 0.023 \, (Re)^{-0.2} \, (Pr)^{2/3} \qquad \text{...(7.166)}$$

                                   ... in terms of staton number

It is valid for the following :

(i) St is evaluated at the mean bulk temperature.

(ii) Re and Pr are evaluated at the mean film temperature.

(iii) $\dfrac{L}{D} \geq 60$, $Re \geq 10^4$, $0.7 < Pr < 160$.

3. The Mc Adams and Colburn correlations are fairly accurate for small to moderate temperature difference (10°C in case of liquids and 50°C for gases). For larger temperature differences, Sieder and Tate proposed the following correlation :

$$\overline{Nu} = 0.023 \, (Re)^{0.8} \, (Pr)^{1/3} \left(\frac{\mu}{\mu_s}\right)^{0.14} \qquad \ldots(7.167)$$

This equation is valid for the following :

(i) $\dfrac{L}{D} > 60$, $Re \geq 10^4$, $0.7 \leq Pr \leq 16700$

(ii) All fluid properties except μ_s are evaluated at the mean bulk temperature, μ_s is evaluated at the surface temperature.

4. Desman and Sams suggested the following equation for very large temperature difference $(t_s - t_b)$ with air :

$$Nu = 0.026 \, (Re)^{0.8} \, (Pr)^{0.4} \qquad \ldots.(7.168)$$

The equation is valid for the following :

(i) $\dfrac{t_s}{t_b}$ upto 3.55

(ii) $Re \geq 10^4$

(iii) Re is evaluated at mean film temperature

(iv) Nu and Pr are evaluated at mean bulk temperature.

7.5.5. TURBULENT FLOW OVER CYLINDERS

1. The following empirical correlation is widely used for turbulent flow over cylinders :

$$\overline{Nu} = \frac{hD}{k} = C \, (Re)^n \, (Pr)^{1/3} \qquad \ldots(7.169)$$

where C and n are constants and have the values as given in the table 7.2 below :

Table 7.2. Constants for eqn. (7.169) for flow across cylinder (Hilpert, 1933; Knudsen, 1958)

S.No.	Re	C	n
1.	0.4 to 4	0.989	0.330
2.	4 to 40	0.911	0.385
3.	40 to 4×10^3	0.683	0.466
4.	4×10^3 to 4×10^4	0.193	0.618
5.	4×10^4 to 4×10^5	0.027	0.805

All properties are evaluated at the *film temperature*.

2. Churchill and Bernstein have suggested the following empirical correlation which covers the entire range of Re and wide range of Pr :

$$\overline{Nu} = 0.3 + \frac{0.62 \, (Re)^{0.5} \, (Pr)^{1/3}}{\left[1 + (0.4/Pr)^{2/3}\right]^{0.25}} \left[1 + \frac{Re}{28200}\right]^{0.8} \qquad ..(7.170)$$

This equation is valid for the following :

(i) $Re . Pr > 0.2$

(ii) All properties are to be evaluated at the film temperature.

7.5.6. TURBULENT FLOW OVER SPHERES

1. For flow of *gases* over spheres, Mc Adams suggested the following correlation :

$$\overline{Nu} = 0.37 \, (Re)^{0.6} \qquad \text{...for } 25 < Re < 1 \times 10^5 \quad \text{...(7.171)}$$

Fluid properties are to be evaluated at the film temperature.

2. Kramers proposed the following correlation for flow of *liquids* past spheres :

$$\overline{Nu} = [0.97 + 0.68 \, (Re)^{0.5}] \, (Pr)^{0.3} \quad \text{...for } 1 < Re < 2000 \quad \text{...(7.172)}$$

The fluid properties are to be evaluated at the film temperature.

3. Whitaker has proposed a single equation for flow of gases and liquids past sphere; his correlation is

$$\overline{Nu} = 2 + [0.4 \, (Re)^{1/2} + 0.06 \, (Re)^{2/3}] \, (Pr)^{0.4} \left(\frac{\mu_\infty}{\mu_s} \right)^{1/4} \qquad \text{...(7.173)}$$

for $0.71 < Pr < 300$; $3.5 < Re < 7.6 \times 10^4$; $1.0 < (\mu_\infty/\mu_s) < 3.2$

All properties except μ_s are to be evaluated at t_∞.

Example 7.50. *Air at a temperature of 15°C flows at a velocity of 6.5 m/s across a flat plate maintained at a temperature of 605°C. Calculate the amount of heat transferred per metre width from both sides of the plate over a distance of 350 mm from the leading edge. The following relation holds good in the case of large temperature difference between the plate and the fluid :*

$$Nu_x = 0.332 \, (Pr)^{1/3} \, (Re)^{1/2} \left(\frac{T_s}{T_\infty} \right)^{0.117}$$

where T_s and T_∞ are the absolute temperatures of the plate surface and free stream respectively and all fluid properties are evaluated at the mean film temperature.

Solution. Given : $T_\infty = 15 + 273 = 288$ K, $T_s = 605 + 273 = 878$ K, $x = 350$ mm = 0.35 m.

Amount of heat transferred per unit width :

The mean film temperature, $t_f = \dfrac{605 + 15}{2} = 310°C$

The thermo-physical properties, at 310°C are :

$$\rho = 0.614 \text{ kg/m}^3; \, c_p = 1.046 \text{ kJ/kg°C}$$
$$k = 0.04593 \text{ W/m°C}; \, \mu = 29.7 \times 10^{-6} \text{ kg/ms}; \, Pr = 0.675$$

Reynolds number, $Re_x = \dfrac{\rho \, Ux}{\mu} = \dfrac{0.614 \times 6.5 \times 0.35}{29.7 \times 10^{-6}} = 47032$

The Nusselt number is given by

$$Nu_x = 0.332 \, (Pr)^{1/3} \, (Re)^{1/2} \left(\frac{T_s}{T_\infty} \right)^{0.117}$$

$$= 0.332 \, (0.675)^{0.333} \, (47032)^{0.5} \left(\frac{878}{288} \right)^{0.117} = 71.96$$

or, $\dfrac{h_x \, x}{k} = 71.96$

or, $h_x = \dfrac{k}{x} \times 71.96 = \dfrac{0.04593}{0.35} \times 71.96 = 9.44 \ \text{W/m}^2\,^\circ\text{C}.$

The average heat transfer coefficient is given by

$$\bar{h} = \frac{1}{L} \int_0^L h_x \, dx = 2h_x = 2 \times 9.44 = 18.88 \ \text{W/m}^2\,^\circ\text{C}$$

Heat transfer from both sides of the plate, per metre width,

$$Q = 2\,[\,\bar{h}\, A_s \,(t_s - t_\infty)] = 2[18.88 \times (0.35 \times 1) \,(605 - 15)]$$
$$= 7797.44 \ \text{W} \quad \textbf{(Ans.)}$$

Example 7.51. *A surface condenser consists of two hundred thin walled circular tubes (each tube is 22.5 mm in diameter and 5 m long) arranged in parallel, through which water flows. If the mass flow rate of water through the tube bank is 160 kg/s and its inlet and outlet temperatures are known to be 21°C and 29°C respectively, calculate the average heat transfer coefficient associated with flow of water.*

Solution. *Given :* $D = 22.5$ mm $= 0.0225$ m, $L = 5$ m, $t_i = 21°C$, $t_o = 29°C$.

Average heat transfer coefficient, $\bar{h}$:

The mean bulk temperature, $t_b = \dfrac{t_i + t_o}{2} = \dfrac{21 + 29}{2} = 25°C$

The thermo-physical properties of water at 25°C are :

$\rho = 996.65 \ \text{kg/m}^3;$ $\mu = 0.862 \times 10^{-3} \ \text{kg/ms};$

$k = 0.6079 \ \text{W/m}°\text{C};$ $c_p = 4.178 \ \text{kJ/kg}°\text{C}$

Prandtl number, $Pr = \dfrac{\mu\, c_p}{k} = \dfrac{0.862 \times 10^{-3} \times (4.178 \times 10^3)}{0.6079} = 5.924$

The mass flow rate of water through each tube,

$$m = \frac{160}{200} = 0.8 \ \text{kg/s}$$

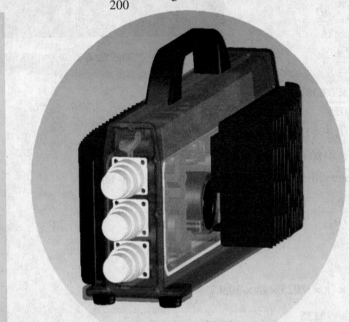

Natural convection.

Reynolds number, $Re = \dfrac{\rho\,VD}{\mu} = \dfrac{\rho\,AVD}{A\,\mu} = \dfrac{mD}{A\,\mu} = \dfrac{mD}{\dfrac{\pi}{4}\,D^2 \times \mu} = \dfrac{4m}{\pi D\mu}$

$$= \dfrac{4 \times 0.8}{\pi \times 0.0225 \times 0.862 \times 10^{-3}} = 52518.26$$

As $Re \gg 2500$, therefore, the nature of flow is *turbulent*. Since the water is being heated in condenser, hence we may use McAdams correlation

$$\overline{Nu} = 0.023\,(Re)^{0.8}\,(Pr)^{0.4} \qquad\qquad \text{...[Eqn. (7.164)]}$$

$$= 0.023\,(52518.26)^{0.8}\,(5.924)^{0.4} = 279.9$$

or, $\overline{Nu} = \dfrac{\overline{h}D}{k} = 279.9$

∴ $\overline{h} = \dfrac{k}{D} \times 279.9 = \dfrac{0.6079}{0.0225} \times 279.9 = \mathbf{7562.27\ W/m^2 °C}$ **(Ans.)**

Example 7.52. *Water at 20°C with a flow rate of 0.015 kg/s enters a 2.5 cm ID tube which is maintained at a uniform temperature of 90°C. Assuming hydrodynamically and thermally fully developed flow determine the heat transfer coefficient and the tube length required to heat the water to 70°C. [Water properties at 20°C : ρ = 1000.5 kg/m³, c_p = 4181.8 J/kg K, ν = 1.006 × 10⁻⁶ m²/s, properties at 45°C are : ρ = 992.3 kg/ m³, c_p = 4180 J/kg K, k = 0.638 W/m K, ν = 0.613 × 10⁻⁶ m²/s, the average Nusselt number for the tube Nu = 3.657]*   **(AMIE, 1998)**

Solution. *Given :* $t_i = 20°C$; $t_0 = 70°C$; $m = 0.015$ kg/s; $D = 2.5$ cm $= 0.025$ m; $t_s = 90°C$.

Considering properties of water at the fluid bulk mean temperature,

$$t_b = \dfrac{20 + 70}{2} = 45°C,$$

we have

$$\overline{Nu} = 3.657 = \dfrac{hD}{k}$$

or, $\overline{h} = \dfrac{3.657\,k}{D}$

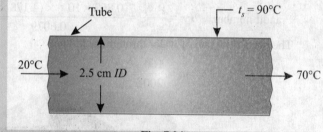

Fig. 7.24.

$$= \dfrac{3.657 \times 0.638}{0.025} = 93.33\ W/m^2\,°C$$

$$Q = \dot{m}\,c_p\,(t_o - t_i)$$

$$= 0.015 \times 4180\,(70 - 20) = 3135\ W$$

The mean temperature difference for heat transfer, (we take log- mean),

$$\theta_m = \dfrac{\theta_1 - \theta_2}{\ln\,(\theta_1/\theta_2)} = \dfrac{(90 - 20) - (90 - 70)}{\ln\left[\dfrac{90 - 20}{90 - 70}\right]} = \dfrac{50}{1.253} = 39.9°C.$$

Now, $Q = \overline{h}A\,\theta_m$

or, $3135 = 93.33 \times (\pi \times 0.025 \times L) \times 39.9$

∴ $L = \dfrac{3135}{93.33 \times \pi \times 0.025 \times 39.9} = \mathbf{10.72\ m}$ **(Ans.)**

Example 7.53. *Dry sand is heated by passing through a vertical pipe steadily downward which is heated by condensing steam on the outside surface of the pipe. The sand is passed through a mixer after coming out of the pipe for making uniform temperature.*

The sand is fed to the pipe at the rate of 0.08 m^3 per hour. The pipe is 30 mm in diameter, and 6 metres long and its inside surface temperature is maintained at 100°C.

Assuming the sand flows through the pipe with uniform velocity profile (slug flow) find the temperature of the mixed sand leaving the pipe.

Take the following properties of sand :

Density = 1500 kg/m^3; thermal conductivity = 0.3 W/m°C; c_p = 840 J/kg K.

The temperature of sand entering the pipe is 20°C.

Neglect the thermal resistance between the wall and sand.   (M.U.)

Solution.

Given : Rate of sand flow = 0.048 m^3/h; D = 30 mm = 0.03 m, L = 6 m; t_s = 100°C;

$$t_i = 20°C; \rho = 1500 \text{ kg/k}^3; k = 0.3 \text{ W/m°C}; c_p = 8405 \text{ J/kg K}.$$

Temperature of the mixed sand, t_o :

$$Q = hA\left[t_s - \left(\frac{t_i + t_o}{2}\right)\right] = m \cdot c_p \ (t_o - t_i)$$

$$= \frac{hA}{2}\ [(t_s - t_i) + (t_s - t_o)] = m \cdot c_p \ [(t_s - t_i) - (t_s - t_o)]$$

m (mass of sand flowing per second) $= 0.08 \times \dfrac{1500}{3600} = 0.0333$ kg/s

Using the relation : $Nu = \dfrac{hD}{k} = 5.78$ (slug flow)   ...[Eqn. (7.158)]

[Since the velocity profile is uniform (rod like flow) and wall temperature is constant.]

$$h = \frac{k}{D} \times 5.78 = \frac{0.3}{0.03} \times 5.78 = 57.8 \text{ W/m}^2 \text{°C}$$

$\therefore$ $\dfrac{h \ (\pi DL)}{2}\ [(t_s - t_i) + (t_s - t_o)] = m \cdot c_p \ [(t_s - t_i) - (t_s - t_o)]$

Forced convection assemblies for power modules.

Substituting the values and keeping $(t_s - t_o) = x$, we get

$$\frac{57.8}{2} (\pi \times 0.03 \times 6) [(100 - 20) + x] = 0.0333 \times 840 [(100 - 20) - x]$$

or, $16.34 (80 + x) = 27.97 (80 - x)$

or, $1307.2 + 16.34x = 2237.6 - 27.97x$

or, $x = \dfrac{(2237.6 - 1307.2)}{(27.97 + 16.34)} = 20.99°C$

∴ $x = (t_s - t_o) = 20.99$

or, $t_o = 100 - 20.99 = \mathbf{79.01°C}$ **(Ans.)**

Example 7.54. *0.06 kg/s of hot air flows through an uninsulated sheet metal duct of 180 mm diameter. The air enters the duct at a temperature of 110°C and after a distance of 4.5 m gets cooled to a temperature of 70°C. If the heat transfer coefficient between the outer surface of the duct and cold ambient air at 5°C is 6.5 W/m²°C, calculate the following :*

(i)   *The heat loss from the duct over its 4.5 m length,*

(ii) *The heat flux and the duct surface temperature at a length of 4.5 m.*

Solution. *Given :* $m = 0.06$ kg/s, $D = 180$ mm $= 0.18$ m, $h_0 = 6.5$ W/m²°C

The arrangement of the system and the electrical network for heat flow from the hot air inside the duct to the ambient air outside is shown in Fig. (7.25).

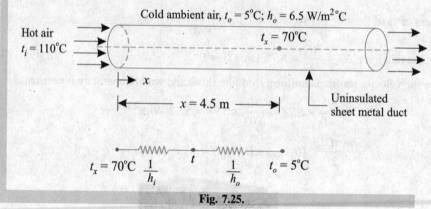

Fig. 7.25.

The mean bulk temperature, $t_b = \dfrac{110 + 70}{2} = 90°C$

The thermo-physical properties of air at 90°C are :

$$\rho = 0.972 \text{ kg/m}^3; \qquad c_p = 1.009 \text{ kJ/kg°C}$$
$$k = 0.03127 \text{ W/m°C}; \qquad v = 22.1 \times 10^{-6} \text{ m}^2/\text{s}$$
$$\mu = 22.14 \times 10^{-6} \text{ kg/ms}; \qquad Pr = 0.69$$

Reynolds number, $Re = \dfrac{\rho\, VD}{\mu} = \dfrac{\rho\, AVD}{A\,\mu} = \dfrac{mD}{\dfrac{\pi}{4} D^2 \times \mu} = \dfrac{4m}{\pi D \mu}$

$$= \dfrac{4 \times 0.06}{\pi \times 0.18 \times 22.14 \times 10^{-6}} = 19169.5$$

As $Re \gg 2500$ the flow is *turbulent*.

(i) **The heat loss from the duct over its 4.5 m length, Q :**

$$Q = m\, c_p\, \Delta t = 0.06 \times (1.009 \times 10^3)(110 - 70) = 2421.6 \text{ W} \qquad \text{(Ans.)}$$

(ii) **The heat flux and duct surface temperature at a length of 4.5 m :**

The heat flux at $x = 4.5$ m is calculated from the relation :

$$\frac{Q}{A} = \frac{\Delta t}{\Sigma R_{th}} = \frac{\Delta t}{\left[\dfrac{1}{h_i} + \dfrac{1}{h_o}\right]}$$

where, $\qquad h_o = 6.5 \text{ W/m}^2°\text{C}$ \hfill ...(Given)

h_i (inside convection coefficient) is calculated from the correlation

$$Nu = 0.023\,(Re)^{0.8}\,(Pr)^{0.333}$$
$$= 0.023\,(19169.5)^{0.8}\,(0.69)^{0.333} = 54.22$$

or, $\qquad \dfrac{h_i D}{k} = 54.22$

or, $\qquad h_i = \dfrac{k}{D} \times 54.22 = \dfrac{0.03127}{0.18} \times 54.22 = 9.42 \text{ W/m}°\text{C}$

$\therefore$ Thermal resistance, $\qquad \Sigma R_{th} = \dfrac{1}{h_i} + \dfrac{1}{h_o} = \dfrac{1}{9.42} + \dfrac{1}{6.5} = 0.26$

Hence, heat flux $\qquad \dfrac{Q}{A} = \dfrac{\Delta t}{\Sigma R_{th}} = \dfrac{(70-5)}{0.26} = 250 \text{ W/m}^2 \quad \text{(Ans.)}$

From the resistance network,

$$\frac{Q}{A} = \frac{(70-t)}{\dfrac{1}{h_i}} = h_i\,(70-t)$$

or, $\qquad 250 = 9.42\,(70 - t)$

or, $\qquad t = 70 - \dfrac{250}{9.42} = 43.46°\text{C} \quad \text{(Ans.)}$

Example 7.55. *A horizontal tubular 1-1 condenser is used to condense saturated steam at 80°C. The condenser is a shell and tube one with brass tubes (k = 110 W/m°C) of 1.59 cm OD and 1.34 cm ID. Steam is outside tubes and cooling water enters the tubes at 20°C with a velocity of 1.4 m/s and leaves at 40°C. If the rate of cooling water supply is 55000 kg/h and the latent heat of condensation of steam at 80°C is 2304 kJ/kg, calculate :*

(i) *The number of tubes,*

(ii) *The length of each tube.*

For calculating the tube side heat transfer coefficient use the Dittus-Boelter equation and for the shell side heat transfer coefficient, the average value may be taken as 10760 W/m² K.

Data : Properties of water at 30°C.

$$k = 0.659 \text{ W/m K}; \qquad \rho = 979.8 \text{ kg/m}^3$$
$$c_p = 4.180 \text{ kJ/kg K}; \qquad \mu = 0.4044 \times 10^{-3} \text{ Pa s}$$

(AMIE Summer, 1998)

Solution. *Given :* $t_{h1} = t_{h2} = t_{sat} = 80°\text{C}; \ t_{c1} = 20°\text{C}; \ t_{c2} = 40°\text{C};$

$$k_{brass} = 110 \text{ W/m°C}; \quad \dot{m}_w = \frac{55000}{60 \times 60} = 15.277 \text{ kg/s};$$

$$d_i = 1.34 \text{ cm} = 0.0134 \text{ m}; \ d_o = 1.59 \text{ cm} = 0.0159 \text{ m};$$
$$V_w = 1.4 \text{ m/s}; \ h_o = 10760 \text{ W/m}^2 \text{ K}$$

$$\begin{bmatrix} k_w = 0.659 \text{ W/m}°\text{C}; \ \rho_w = 979.8 \text{ kg/m}^3; \ c_{pw} = 4.18 \text{ kJ/kg K}; \\ \mu_w = 0.4044 \times 10^{-3} \text{ Pas} ..... \text{ at } 30°\text{C} \quad (1\text{Pas} = 1 \text{ N-s/m}^2 \end{bmatrix}$$

(i) **The number of tubes, N :**

$$Q = \dot{m}_w \, c_{pw} \, (t_{c2} - t_{c1})$$
$$= 15.277 \times 4.18 \times 10^3 \, (40 - 20) = 1277157 \text{ W}$$

Also, $\qquad \dot{m}_w = \rho_w \times \text{flow area} \times \text{velocity}$

$$\therefore \qquad 15.277 = 979.8 \times \left[N \times \frac{\pi}{4} \times (0.0134)^2 \right] \times 1.4$$

(where N = no. of tubes)

or, $\qquad N = \dfrac{15.277 \times 4}{979.8 \times \pi \times (0.0134)^2 \times 1.4} = 78.97, \ i.e., \ \mathbf{79}$ $\qquad$ **(Ans.)**

(ii) **The length of each tube, L :**

For two through tubes,

$$Re = \frac{\rho V d_i}{\mu} = \frac{979.8 \times 1.4 \times 0.0134}{0.4044 \times 10^{-3}} = 45453$$

$$Pr = \frac{\mu c_p}{k} = \frac{0.4044 \times 10^{-3} \times (4.18 \times 10^3)}{0.659} = 2.565$$

Using Dittus-Boelter equation, we have

$$Nu = \frac{h_i D_i}{k} = 0.023 \, (Re)^{0.8} \, (Pr)^{0.4}$$

or, $\qquad \bar{h} \, (h_i) = \dfrac{k}{D_i} \times 0.023 \, (Re)^{0.8} \, (Pr)^{0.4}$

$$= \frac{0.659}{0.0134} \times 0.023 \, (45453)^{0.8} \, (2.565)^{0.4} = 8774 \text{ W/m}^2 \text{ K} \qquad \textbf{(Ans.)}$$

$$U_o = \cfrac{1}{\cfrac{1}{h_o} \times \cfrac{r_o}{k} \ln (r_o / r_i) + \cfrac{r_o}{r_i} \times \cfrac{1}{h_i}}$$

$$= \cfrac{1}{\cfrac{1}{10760} \times \cfrac{(0.0159/2)}{110} \ln \left(\cfrac{0.0159/2}{0.0134/2} \right) + \cfrac{(0.0159/2)}{(0.0134/2)} \times \cfrac{1}{8774}}$$

$$= \frac{1}{9.29 \times 10^{-5} + 1.236 \times 10^{-5} + 13.52 \times 10^{-5}}$$

$$= 4158.7 \text{ W/m}^2 \text{ °C}$$

Now, $\qquad Q = U_o A_o \theta_m$

where, $\qquad \theta_m = \dfrac{\theta_1 - \theta_2}{\ln (\theta_1 / \theta_2)} = \dfrac{(80 - 20) - (80 - 40)}{\ln \left[\dfrac{80 - 20}{80 - 40} \right]} = \dfrac{20}{0.4055} = 49.32°\text{C, and}$

$$A_o = N \times \pi d_o L$$

Substituting the values in the above eqn., we get

$$1277157 = 4158.7 \times (79 \times \pi \times 0.0159 \times L) \times 49.32$$

$$\therefore \qquad L = \frac{1277157}{4158.7 \times 79 \times \pi \times 0.0159 \times 49.32} = 1.578 \text{ m (Ans.)}$$

Example 7.56. *Liquid mercury flows at a rate of 1.6 kg/s through a copper tube of 20 mm diameter. The mercury enters the tube at 15°C and after getting heated it leaves the tube at 35°C. Calculate the tube length for constant heat flux at the wall which is maintained at an average temperature of 50°C.*

For liquid metal flowing through a tube, the following empirical correlation is presumed to agree well with experimental results :

$$\overline{Nu} = 7 + 0.025 \, (Pe)^{0.8}$$

where Pe is the Peclet number; Pe = Pr . Re

Solution. *Given :* $D = 20 \text{ mm} = 0.02\text{m}$, $m = 1.6 \text{ kg/s}$, $t_i = 15°C$, $t_o = 35°C$,

Tube length, L :

The bulk temperature, $\qquad\qquad\qquad t_b = \dfrac{15 + 35}{2} = 25°C$

The thermo-physical properties of mercury at 25°C are :

$$\rho = 13582 \text{ kg/m}^3; \qquad k = 8.69 \text{ W/m°C}$$
$$c_p = 140 \text{ J/kg°C}; \qquad v = 1.5 \times 10^{-7} \text{ m}^2/\text{s}; \; Pr = 0.0248$$

The Reynolds number, $\quad Re = \dfrac{\rho V D}{\mu} = \dfrac{\rho A V D}{A \mu} = \dfrac{m D}{\dfrac{\pi}{4} D^2 \, \mu} = \dfrac{4m}{\pi D \mu} = \dfrac{4m}{\pi D (\rho v)}$

$$= \frac{4 \times 1.6}{\pi \times 0.02 \times (13582 \times 1.5 \times 10^{-7})} = 49997$$

$\therefore \qquad \overline{Nu} = 7 + 0.025 \, (Pr . Re)^{0.8}$

$$= 7 + 0.025 \, (0.0248 \times 49997)^{0.8} = 14.46$$

or, $\qquad \dfrac{\overline{h}D}{k} = 14.46 \text{ or } \overline{h} = \dfrac{k}{D} \times 14.46 = \dfrac{8.69}{0.02} \times 14.46$

$$= 6282.87 \text{ W/m}^{2}°C$$

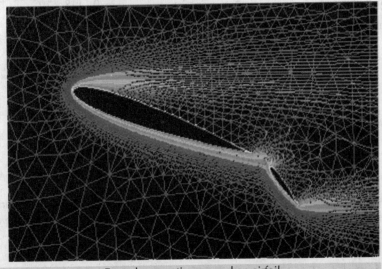

Forced convection around an airfoil.

The heat gained by mercury due to convection,

$$Q = \bar{h} \, A_s \, \Delta t = 6282.87 \times (\pi \times 0.02 \times L)(50 - 25) = 9869.11 \, L \qquad ...(i)$$

The heat gained by mercury,

$$Q = mc_p \, (t_o - t_i) = 1.6 \times 140 \, (35 - 15) = 4480 \, W \qquad ...(ii)$$

From (i) and (ii), we get

$$9869.11 \, L = 4480$$

or, $$L = \frac{4480}{9869.11} = 0.454 \, m \qquad \textbf{(Ans.)}$$

Example 7.57. *A square channel of side 20 mm and length 2.5 m, in a heat transfer problem, carries water at a velocity of 45 m/s. The mean temperature of the water along the length of the channel is found to be 30°C while the inner channel surface temperature is 70°C. Calculate the heat transfer coefficient from channel wall to the water. Use the correlation :*

$$\overline{Nu} = 0.021 \, (Re)^{0.8} \, (Pr)^{0.43} \left(\frac{Pr}{Pr_s} \right)^{0.25}$$

The thermo-physical properties are evaluated at the mean bulk temperature except Pr_s. Pr_s is evaluated at the channel surface temperature. Take equivalent diameter as the characteristic length of the channel.

The thermo-physical properties of water at 30°C are :

$$\rho = 995.7 \, kg/m^3; \; k = 0.6175 \, W/m°C; \; v = 0.805 \times 10^{-6} \, m^2/s; \; Pr = 5.42;$$

Pr_s *at 70°C = 2.55.*

Solution. *Given:* $V = 4.5$ m/s, $t_b = 30°C$, $t_s = 70°C$

Heat transfer coefficient, $\bar{h}$:

The equivalent diameter of the channel,

$$D_{eq} = \frac{4A}{P} = \frac{4 \times (0.02 \times 0.02)}{4 \times 0.02} = 0.02 \, m$$

(where A = cross-sectional area of channel, P = perimeter of the channel).

Reynolds number $\qquad Re = \dfrac{V D_{eq}}{v} = \dfrac{4.5 \times 0.02}{0.805 \times 10^{-6}} = 0.1118 \times 10^6$

Nusselt number is given by

$$\overline{Nu} = 0.021 \, (Re)^{0.8} \, (Pr)^{0.43} \left(\frac{Pr}{Pr_s} \right)^{0.25} \qquad ...\text{(Given)}$$

$$= 0.021 \, (0.1118 \times 10^6)^{0.8} \, (5.42)^{0.43} \left(\frac{5.42}{2.55} \right)^{0.25} = 573.4$$

or, $$\frac{\bar{h} \, D_{eq}}{k} = 573.4$$

or, $$\bar{h} = \frac{k}{D_{eq}} \times 573.4 = \frac{0.6175}{0.02} \times 573.4 = \textbf{17703.7 W/m}^2\textbf{°C} \qquad \textbf{(Ans.)}$$

Example 7.58. *Water is heated while flowing through a 1.5 cm $\times$ 3.5 cm rectangular tube at a velocity of 1.2 m/s. The entering water temperature is 40°C and tube wall is maintained at 85°C. Determine the length of the tube required to raise the temperature of water by 35°C.*

Use the following properties of water :

$$\rho = 985.5 \, kg/m^3; \; k = 0.653 \, W/m \, K; \; v = 0.517 \times 10^{-6} \, m^2/s; \; c_p = 4.19 \, kJ/kg \, K. \quad \text{(N.M.U., 1998)}$$

Solution. *Given :* $x = 3.5$ cm $= 0.035$ m; $y = 1.5$ cm $= 0.015$ m; $V = 1.2$ m/s;
$t_i = 40°C$; $t_o = 75°C$.

Length of tube required, L :

$$Q = hA_s\,\theta_m = \dot{m}c_p\,(t_o - t_i) \qquad\qquad ...(i)$$

where A_s is the surface area of the tube.

$$A_s = 2\,(l + b)\,L = 2\,(0.035 + 0.015) \times L = 0.1\,L\ m^2$$
$$\dot{m} = A_c\,V\rho = (l \times b)\,V\rho$$

(where A_c area of cross-section).

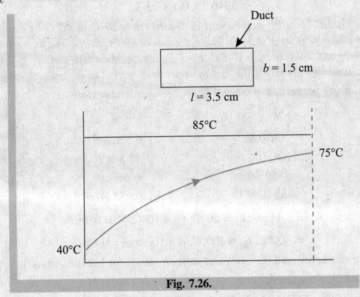

Fig. 7.26.

$$= 0.035 \times 0.015 \times 1.2 \times 985.5 = 0.621\ kg/s$$

$$\theta_m = \frac{(85 - 40) - (85 - 75)}{\ln\left[\dfrac{85 - 40}{85 - 75}\right]} = \frac{45 - 10}{\ln\left(\dfrac{45}{10}\right)} = 23.3°C$$

The heat transfer co-efficient h for the given configuration is given by :

$$Nu = \frac{hL_c}{k} = 0.023\,(Re)^{0.8}\,(Pr)^{0.33} \qquad [Eqn.\ (7.151)] \qquad\qquad ...(ii)$$

Characteristic length, $\quad L_c = \dfrac{4\,A_c}{P} = \dfrac{4\,(l \times b)}{2\,(l + b)} = \dfrac{2\,lb}{(l + b)} \qquad\qquad ...[Eqn.\ (6.24)]$

$$= \frac{2 \times 0.035 \times 0.015}{(0.035 + 0.015)} = 0.021\ m$$

$$Re = \frac{L_c V}{\nu} = \frac{0.021 \times 1.2}{0.517 \times 10^{-6}} = 0.487 \times 10^5$$

$$Pr = \frac{\mu\,c_p}{k} = \frac{\rho\nu c_p}{k} = \frac{985.5 \times 0.517 \times 10^{-6} \times (4.19 \times 10^3)}{0.653} = 3.27$$

Substituting the values in (*ii*), we get

$$\frac{h \times 0.021}{0.653} = 0.023 \, (0.487 \times 10^5)^{0.8} \, (3.27)^{0.33} = 191.23$$

$$\therefore \qquad h = \frac{0.653 \times 191.23}{0.021} = 5946.3 \text{ W/m}^2\text{°C}$$

Now substituting the values in (*i*), we get

$$5946.3 \times 0.1 \, L \times 23.3 = 0.621 \times (4.19 \times 10^3) \times (75 - 40)$$

$$\therefore \qquad L = \frac{0.621 \times (4.19 \times 10^3) \times 35}{5946.3 \times 0.1 \times 23.3} = \mathbf{6.57 \text{ m} \ (Ans.)}$$

Example 7.59. *3.8 kg of oil per second is heated from 20°C to 40°C by passing through a circular annulus with a velocity of 0.3 m/s. The hot gases at 400°C are passed through the inside tube of 100 mm diameter and are cooled to 100°C. Find the length of the pipe required for the above heat transfer process assuming the gas is flowing in opposite direction to the oil?*

Take the following properties of oil and gases at mean temperature :

		Oil	*Gases*
ρ	=	*800 kg/m³*	*0.8 kg/m³*
ν	=	*8 × 10⁻⁶ m²/s*	*32.8 × 10⁻⁶ m²/s*
c_p	=	*3350 J/kg K*	*1050 kJ/K*
k	=	*0.2 W/m°C*	*0.035 W/m°C*

(P.U.)

Solution. *Given* : $\dot{m}_c = 3.8$ kg/s; $t_{c1} = 20$°C; $t_{c2} = 40$°C; $V_c = 0.3$ m/s;

$$t_{h1} = 400\text{°C}; \ t_{h2} = 100\text{°C}; \ d = 100 \text{ mm} = 0.1 \text{ m}$$

[The suffix *c* stands for cold (*i.e.*, oil) and suffix *h* stands for hot (*i.e.*, gases)].

Length of the pipe required, L :

The diameter of the annulus is calculated as follows :

$$\frac{\pi}{4} (D^2 - d^2) \times V_c \times \rho = 3.8$$

or,

$$\frac{\pi}{4} (D^2 - 0.1^2) \times 0.3 \times 800 = 3.8$$

or,

$$D = \left[\frac{3.8 \times 4}{\pi \times 0.3 \times 800} + 0.1^2 \right]^{1/2} = 0.1737 \text{ m} \qquad \text{or,} \qquad 173.7 \text{ mm}$$

For oil :

For annulus, $\quad D_{eq.} = (D - d) \qquad \qquad \qquad \qquad \qquad \qquad \qquad \qquad \qquad \text{...[Eqn. [6.28]]}$

$$Re = \frac{V_c \, D_c}{\nu} = \frac{0.3 \, (0.1737 - 0.1)}{8 \times 10^{-6}} = 2764$$

$$Pr = \frac{\mu \, c_p}{k} = \frac{\rho \, \nu \, c_p}{k} = \frac{800 \times 8 \times 10^{-6} \times 3350}{0.2} = 107.2$$

$$Nu = 0.023 \, (Re)^{0.8} \, (Pr)^{1/3} \qquad \qquad \qquad \qquad \qquad \qquad \qquad \text{...[Eqn. [7.151]]}$$

$$= 0.023 \, (2764)^{0.8} \, (107.2)^{1/3} = 61.9$$

$$\therefore \qquad \frac{h_o \, (D - d)}{k} = 61.9 \qquad \text{or,} \qquad h_o = \frac{k \times 61.9}{(D - d)} = \frac{0.2 \times 61.9}{(0.1737 - 0.1)} = 167.98 \text{ W/m}^2 \text{ °C}$$

For gases :

Heat lost by gases = Heat gained by oil

$$\dot{m}_h \times 1050 \times (400 - 100) = 3.8 \times 3350 \times (40 - 20)$$

$$\therefore \qquad \dot{m}_h = 0.808 \text{ kg/s}$$

The velocity of hot gases (V_h) can be calculated as follows :

$$\frac{\pi}{4} (0.1)^2 \times V_h \times 0.8 = 0.808$$

$$\therefore \qquad V_h = \frac{4 \times 0.808}{\pi (0.1)^2 \times 0.8} = 128.6 \text{ m/s}$$

Forced convection cooler.

$$Re = \frac{V_h d}{\nu} = \frac{128.6 \times 0.1}{32.8 \times 10^{-6}} = 3.92 \times 10^5$$

$$Pr = \frac{\rho \nu c_p}{k} = \frac{0.8 \times 32.8 \times 10^{-6} \times 1050}{0.035} = 0.787$$

$$Nu = 0.023 \, (Re)^{0.8} \, (Pr)^{1/3}$$

$$= 0.023 \, (3.92 \times 10^5)^{0.8} \, (0.787)^{1/3} = 633.4$$

$$\therefore \quad \frac{h_i d}{k} = 633.4 \text{ or } h_i = \frac{k \times 633.4}{0.1} = \frac{0.035 \times 633.4}{0.1} = 221.69 \text{ W/m}^2 \, {}^\circ C$$

Overall heat transfer coefficient,

$$U = \frac{h_i \times h_o}{h_i + h_o} = \frac{221.69 \times 167.98}{221.69 + 167.98} = 95.57 \text{ W/m}^2 \, {}^\circ C \qquad \left[\because \frac{1}{U} = \frac{1}{h_i} + \frac{1}{h_o} \right]$$

Log-mean temperature difference,

$$\theta_m = \frac{(\theta_1 - \theta_2)}{\ln (\theta_1 / \theta_2)} = \frac{(t_{h1} - t_{c2}) - (t_{h2} - t_{c1})}{\ln \left(\dfrac{t_{h1} - t_{c2}}{t_{h2} - t_{c1}} \right)}$$

$$= \frac{(400 - 40) - (100 - 20)}{\ln \left(\dfrac{400 - 40}{100 - 20} \right)} = \frac{360 - 80}{\ln \left(\dfrac{360}{80} \right)} = 186^\circ C$$

$$\therefore \qquad Q = \dot{m}_c \times c_{pc} \times (t_{c2} - t_{c1}) = UA\theta_m$$

$$= 3.8 \times 3350 \times (40 - 20) = 95.57 \times (\pi \times 0.1 \times L) \times 186$$

or, $$\qquad L = \frac{3.8 \times 3350 \, (40 - 20)}{95.57 \times (\pi \times 0.1) \times 186} = 45.6 \text{ m} \qquad \textbf{(Ans.)}$$

Example 7.60. *Gasoline at the mean bulk temperature of 27°C flows inside a circular tube of 19 mm inside diameter. The average bulk velocity is 0.061 m/s and the tube is 1.5 m long. The flow starts at the heated tube inlet (no upstream developing section) and the tube surface temperature is constant at 38°C.*

Determine the average heat transfer co-efficient over 1.5 m length of the tube. Are the temperature and velocity profiles developing or, developed in the 1.5 m length of the tube ?

Take the following fluid properties :

$$\mu_s = 5.223 \times 10^{-4} \text{ Pa s; } \mu_b = 5.892 \times 10^{-4} \text{ Pa s; } k_b = 0.1591 \text{ W/m}^\circ C;$$

$$\rho_b = 876.6 \text{ kg/m}^3; c_{pb} = 1757 \text{ J/kg K; } P_{rb} = 6.5$$

Use the following formula :

$$Nu = 1.86 \left[\frac{Re_b \cdot Pr_b}{L/D} \right]^{0.33} \left[\frac{\mu_b}{\mu_s} \right]^{0.14}$$

x_v *(entry length for fully developed velocity profile) = 0.05 Re.D, and*

x_t *(entry length for fully developed temperature profile) = x_v . Pr_b* (M.U., 1997)

Solution. *Given :* $D = 19$ mm $= 0.019$ m; $V = 0.061$ m/s; $L = 1.5$ m

$$Re_b = \frac{\rho_b VD}{\mu_b} = \frac{874.6 \times 0.061 \times 0.019}{5.892 \times 10^{-4}} = 1720.4 \qquad \text{(1 Pa s = 1 N-s/m}^2\text{)}$$

$$Nu = 1.86 \left[\frac{Re_{eb} \cdot Pr_{rb}}{L/D} \right]^{0.33} \left[\frac{\mu_b}{\mu_s} \right]^{0.14}$$

$$= 1.86 \left[\frac{1720.4 \times 6.5}{1.5/0.019} \right]^{0.33} \left[\frac{5.892 \times 10^{-4}}{5.223 \times 10^{-4}} \right]^{0.14} = 1.86 \times 5.127 \times 1.017 = 9.698$$

$$Nu = \frac{\bar{h}D}{k} = 9.698$$

or, $$h = \frac{k}{D} \times 9.698 = \frac{0.1591}{0.019} \times 9.698 = \textbf{81.21 W/m}^2\textbf{°C} \qquad \text{(Ans.)}$$

x_v (velocity depth) $= 0.05 ReD = 0.05 \times 1720.4 \times 0.019 = \textbf{1.634 m}$

x_t (temperature depth) $= x_v \times Pr_{rb} = 1.634 \times 6.5 = \textbf{10.62 m}$

The tube length L is less than x_v as well as x_t, so *both depths are developing.* **(Ans.)**

Example 7.61. *Liquid metal flows at a rate of 270 kg/min through a 5 cm diameter stainless steel tube. It enters at 415°C and is heated to 440°C as it passes through the tube. The tube wall temperature is 20°C higher than liquid bulk temperature and a constant heat flow is maintained along the tube. Calculate the length of the tube required to effect the transfer.*

For constant wall temperature,

$$Nu = 5 + 0.025 \ (Pe)^{0.8} \qquad ...(i)$$

For constant heat flux,

$$Nu = 4.82 + 0.0185 \ (Pe)^{0.827} \qquad ...(ii)$$

Use the following fluid properties :

$\mu = 1.34 \times 10^{-3}$ *kg/m-s,* $c_p = 149$ *J/kg K, and*

$Pr = 0.013, k = 15.6$ *W/m K.*

(P.U. Winter, 1997)

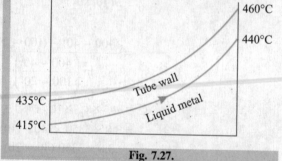

Fig. 7.27.

Solution. *Given :* $\dot{m} = \frac{270}{60} = 4.5$ kg/s; $D = 5$ cm $= 0.05$ m; $\Delta t = 440 - 415 = 25$°C

Length of the tube required, L :

The temperatures of the wall and flowing metal along the tube are shown in Fig. 7.27.

We have to use the eqn. (*ii*) as it is a constant heat flux condition to the tube.

$$Q = \dot{m}c_p \ \Delta t = 4.5 \times 149 \times 25$$

$$= 16762.5 \text{ W}$$

$$Re = \frac{4\ m}{\pi D \mu} = \frac{4 \times 4.5}{\pi \times 0.05 \times 1.34 \times 10^{-3}} = 85516$$

$$Pr = \frac{\mu c_p}{k} = \frac{1.34 \times 10^{-3} \times 149}{15.6} = 0.0128$$

$$Pe = Re \cdot Pr = 85516 \times 0.0128 = 1094.6$$

Now, $\qquad Nu = 4.82 + 0.0185\ (Pe)^{0.827}$

$$= 4.82 + 0.0185\ (1094.6)^{0.827} = 10.85$$

i.e., $\qquad \dfrac{hD}{k} = 10.85$

$\therefore \qquad h = \dfrac{k}{D} \times 10.85 = \dfrac{15.6}{0.05} \times 10.85 = 3385.2\ \text{W/m}^2\ ^\circ\text{C}$

Further, $\qquad Q = hA\ (\Delta t) = 16762.5 \qquad$ (calculated above)

i.e., $\qquad 16762.5 = 3385.2 \times (\pi \times 0.05 \times L) \times 25$

$\therefore \qquad L = \dfrac{16762.5}{3385.2 \times \pi \times 0.05 \times 25} = \mathbf{1.26\ m} \qquad \textbf{(Ans.)}$

Example 7.62. *Assuming that a man can be represented by a cylinder 350 mm in diameter and 1.65 m high with a surface temperature of 28°C. Calculate the heat he would lose while standing in a 30 km/h wind at 12°C.*

Solution. *Given :* $D = 350\ \text{mm} = 0.35\ \text{m}, L = 1.65\ \text{m}, t_s = 28°C, t_\infty = 12°C.$

$$U = 30\ \text{km/h} = \frac{30 \times 1000}{60 \times 60} = 8.33\ \text{m/s}$$

Heat lost by the man, Q :

The film temperature, $t_f = \dfrac{28 + 12}{2} = 20°C$

The properties of air at 20°C are :

$$k = 2.59 \times 10^{-2}\ \text{W/m°C}, v = 15.0 \times 10^{-6}\ \text{m}^2/\text{s}, Pr = 0.707.$$

Reynolds number, $Re = \dfrac{UD}{v} = \dfrac{8.33 \times 0.35}{15.0 \times 10^{-6}} = 1.94 \times 10^5$

Using eqn. (7.169), we have

$$\overline{Nu} = \frac{\overline{h}D}{k} = C\,(Re)^n\ (Pr)^{1/3}$$

or, $\qquad \overline{h} = \dfrac{k}{D} \cdot C\,(Re)^n\ (Pr)^{1/3}$

where $C = 0.027$ and $n = 0.805$ (From table 7.2)

Substituting the value in the above equation, we get

$$\overline{h} = \frac{2.59 \times 10^{-2}}{0.35} \times 0.027\ (1.94 \times 10^5)^{0.805} \times (0.707)^{0.333} = 32.15\ \text{W/m}^2°\text{C}$$

$\therefore$ Heat lost by the man, $\qquad Q = \overline{h}\ A_s\ (t_s - t_\infty)$

$$= 32.15 \times (\pi \times 0.35 \times 1.65)\ (28 - 12)$$

or, $\qquad Q = \mathbf{933.26\ W} \qquad \textbf{(Ans.)}$

Example 7.63. *A copper bus bar 25 mm diameter is cooled by air (in cross-flow) at 30°C and flowing past the bus bar with a velocity of 2.5 m/s. If the surface temperature of the bar is not to exceed 85°C and resistivity of copper is 0.0175 × 10⁻⁶ ohm-m³/m, calculate the following :*

(i)   *The heat transfer coefficient from the surface to the air;*

(ii)   *The permissible current intensity for the bus bar.*

The following empirical correlations may be applicable for a single cylinder placed in cross-flow :

For $10 < Re < 10^3$ $Nu = 0.44\ (Re)^{0.5}$

For $10^3 < Re < 2 \times 10^5$ $Nu = 0.22\ (Re)^{0.6}$

The thermo-physical properties are evaluated at t_∞ *(30°C) and are given as :*

$\qquad k = 0.02673\ W/m°C; \qquad v = 16 \times 10^{-6}\ m^2/s$

Solution. *Given :* $D = 25$ mm $= 0.025$ m, $t_\infty = 30°C$, $U = 2.5$ m/s,

$\qquad\qquad t_s = 85°C$, $\rho_{copper} = 0.0175 \times 10^{-6}$ ohm-m^3/m.

(i)   The heat transfer coefficient from the surface to the air :

Reynolds number $\qquad Re = \dfrac{UD}{v} = \dfrac{2.5 \times 0.025}{16 \times 10^{-6}} = 3906$

Since $Re = 3906$, so the second relation will be applicable. Thus,

$$\overline{Nu} = \frac{\overline{h}D}{k} = 0.22\ (Re)^{0.6} = 0.22\ (3906)^{0.6} = 31.44$$

or, $\qquad\qquad \overline{h} = \dfrac{k}{D} \times 31.44 = \dfrac{0.02673}{0.025} \times 31.44 = \mathbf{33.6\ W/m^2°C} \qquad \textbf{(Ans.)}$

(ii)   The permissible current intensity for the bus bar, I :

Heat dissipation to air $= \overline{h}\ A_s\ (t_s - t_\infty)$

$\qquad\qquad\qquad = 33.6 \times (\pi \times 0.025 \times 1)\ (85 - 30) = 145.14$ W/m $\qquad$ ...(1)

The heat generated in the bus bar

$$= I^2 R = I^2 \left(\frac{\rho L}{A_c} \right)$$

$$= I^2 \times \frac{(0.0175 \times 10^{-6}) \times 1}{\dfrac{\pi}{4} \times (0.025)^2} = 35.65 \times 10^{-6}\ I^2 \qquad\qquad ...(2)$$

From (1) and (2), we have

$\qquad 35.65 \times 10^{-6}\ I^2 = 145.14$

or, $\qquad\qquad I = \left[\dfrac{145.14}{35.65 \times 10^{-6}} \right]^{1/2} = \mathbf{2017.7\ amps.} \qquad \textbf{(Ans.)}$

Example 7.64. *Air stream at 24°C is flowing at 0.4 m/s across a 100 W bulb at 130°C. If the bulb is approximated by a 65 mm diameter sphere, calculate :*

(i)   *The heat transfer rate, and*

(ii)   *The percentage of power lost due to convection.*

Solution. *Given :* $t_\infty = 24°C$, $t_s = 130°C$, $D = 65$ mm $= 0.065$ m, $U = 0.4$ m/s

(i)   The heat transfer rate, Q :

The film temperature, $\qquad t_f = \dfrac{130 + 24}{2} = 77°C$

The properties of air at 77°C are :

$$k = 0.03 \text{ W/m}°C; \ v = 2.08 \times 10^{-5} \text{ m}^2/s, \ Pr = 0.697$$

Reynolds number, $\quad\quad Re = \dfrac{UD}{v} = \dfrac{0.4 \times 0.065}{2.08 \times 10^{-5}} = 1250$

Equation (7.171) gives the Nusselt number as

$$\overline{Nu} = 0.37 \ (Re)^{0.6} = \dfrac{\overline{h}D}{k}$$

or, $\quad\quad \overline{h} = \dfrac{k}{D} \times 0.37 \ (Re)^{0.6}$

$$= \dfrac{0.03}{0.065} \times 0.37 \ (1250)^{0.6} = 12.32 \text{ W/m}^2°C$$

∴ The heat transfer rate,

$$Q = \overline{h} \, A_s \, (t_s - t_\infty) = \overline{h} \times \pi D^2 \times (t_s - t_\infty)$$

$$\left(\because A_s = 4\pi R^2 = 4\pi \times \left(\dfrac{D}{2}\right)^2 = \pi D^2 \right)$$

or, $\quad\quad Q = 12.32 \times (\pi \times 0.065^2) \ (130 - 24) = \mathbf{17.33 \ W}$ **(Ans.)**

(ii) The percentage of power lost due to convection :

$$\%\text{age of power lost} = \dfrac{17.33}{100} \times 100 = \mathbf{17.33\%} \quad\quad \textbf{(Ans.)}$$

Example 7.65. *Compare the heat transfer coefficients under the following conditions, assuming that there is no change in the temperatures of the liquid and the tube wall and the flow through the tube is turbulent in character.*

(i) Two-fold increase in the diameter of the tube; the flow velocity is maintained constant by a change in the rate of liquid flow;

(ii) Two-fold increase in the flow velocity, by varying mass flow rate.

Solution. In case of turbulent tube flow, the average heat transfer coefficient is given by

$$\overline{Nu} = \dfrac{\overline{h}D}{k} = 0.023 \ (Re)^{0.8} \ (Pr)^{0.333} \quad\quad\quad ...\text{[Eqn. (7.151)]}$$

or, $\quad \overline{h} = \dfrac{k}{D} \times 0.023 \ (Re)^{0.8} \ (Pr)^{0.333}$

$$= \dfrac{k}{D} \times 0.023 \left(\dfrac{UD}{v}\right)^{0.8} (Pr)^{0.333}$$

or, $\quad \overline{h} = 0.023 \dfrac{k}{v^{0.28}} \ (Pr)^{0.333} \dfrac{(U)^{0.8}}{(D)^{0.2}}$

(i) When the flow velocity and the fluid properties remain unchanged :

$$\overline{h} \propto \dfrac{1}{D^{0.2}}$$

∴ $\quad \dfrac{\overline{h}_2}{\overline{h}_1} = \left(\dfrac{D_1}{D_2}\right)^{0.2} = \left(\dfrac{1}{2}\right)^{0.2} = \mathbf{0.87}$ **(Ans.)**

Forced convection furnace.

This *shows that the heat transfer coefficient decreases to 0.87 when there is a two-fold increase in the diameter of the tube.*

(ii) When the tube diameter and fluid properties remain the same :

$$\bar{h} \propto (U)^{0.8}$$

$$\frac{\bar{h}_2}{\bar{h}_1} = \left(\frac{U_2}{U_1}\right)^{0.8} = (2)^{0.8} = 1.74 \qquad \textbf{(Ans.)}$$

This *shows that the heat transfer is increased to 1.74 times when there is a two-fold increase in flow velocity.*

Example 7.66. *A refrigerated truck is moving on a high way at 90 km/h in a desert area where the ambient air temperature is 50°C. The body of the truck may be considered as a rectangular box measuring 10 m (length) × 4 m (width) × 3 m (height). Assume that the boundary layer on the four walls is turbulent, the heat transfer takes place only from the four surfaces and the wall surface of the truck is maintained at 10°C. Neglecting heat transfer from the front and back and assuming the flow to be parallel to 10 m long side, calculate the following :*

(i) *The heat loss from the four surfaces;*

(ii) *The tonnage of refrigeration;*

(iii) *The power required to overcome the resistance acting on the four surfaces.*

The properties of air (at $t_f = \dfrac{50 + 10}{2} = 30°C$) are :

$\rho = 1.165 \ kg/m^3, \ c_p = 1.005 \ kJ/kg°C, \ k = 0.02673 \ W/m^2°C, \ v = 16 \times 10^{-6} \ m^2/s, \ Pr = 0.701.$

Solution. *Given :* $U = 90$ km/h $= \dfrac{90 \times 1000}{3600} = 25$ m/s, $t_\infty = 50°C$, $t_s = 10°C$, $L = 10$ m, $B = 4$m, $H = 3$m.

(i) **The heat loss from the four surfaces :**

The Reynolds number at the end of the side,

$$Re_L = \frac{UL}{v} = \frac{25 \times 10}{16 \times 10^{-6}} = 15.625 \times 10^6$$

Evidently the boundary layer is *turbulent* for which

$$\bar{Nu} = \frac{\bar{h}L}{k} = 0.036 \ (Re)^{0.8} \ (Pr)^{0.333} \qquad \qquad ...[\text{Eqn. (7.141)}]$$

or,

$$\frac{\bar{h}L}{k} = 0.036 \ (15.625 \times 10^6)^{0.8} \ (0.701)^{0.333} = 18196.28$$

or,

$$\bar{h} = \frac{k}{L} \times 18196.28 = \frac{0.02673}{10} \times 18196.28 = 48.64 \ W/m^2°C$$

∴ Heat loss from the four surfaces,

$$Q = \bar{h} \ A \ \Delta t = 48.64 \ [2 \ (4 + 3) \times 10] \times (50 - 10) = 272384 \ W$$
$$= \textbf{272.384 kW} \quad \textbf{(Ans.)}$$

(ii) **The tonnage of refrigeration (TR) :**

The cooling capacity required $= \dfrac{272.384 \times 3600}{14000} = \textbf{70 TR} \qquad (\because 1 \ TR = 14000 \ kJ/h)$

(iii) **The power required to overcome the resistance, P :**

Average skin friction coefficient

$$\bar{C}_f = \frac{0.072}{(Re_L)^{0.2}} = \frac{0.072}{(15.625 \times 10^6)^{0.2}} = 2.62 \times 10^{-3}$$

Drag force, $F_D = \bar{C}_f \times \dfrac{1}{2}\rho A U^2$

$$= 2.62 \times 10^{-3} \times \dfrac{1}{2} \times 1.165 \times [2\,(4+3) \times 10] \times 25^2$$

$$= 133.54 \text{ N}$$

$\therefore$ $P = F_D \times U = 133.54 \times 25 = 3338.5$ W

$$= 3.3385 \text{ kW} \qquad \text{(Ans.)}$$

Example 7.67. *800 kg/h of cream cheese at 15°C is pumped through a tube 100 mm in diameter, 1.75 m long and maintained at 95°C. Calculate :*

(*i*)   *The temperature of cheese leaving the heated section;*

(*ii*)   *The rate of heat transfer from the tube to the cheese.*

Use the following correlation for laminar flow inside a tube :

$$\overline{Nu} = \frac{\bar{h}D}{k} = 3.65 + \frac{0.067\left[\left(\dfrac{D}{L}\right)Re\ Pr\right]}{1 + 0.04\left[\left(\dfrac{D}{L}\right)Re\ Pr\right]^{1/3}}$$

The thermo-physical properties of cheese are :

$$\rho = 1150 \text{ kg/m}^3; \qquad \mu = 22.5 \text{ kg/ms}$$
$$k = 0.42 \text{ W/m°C}; \qquad c_p = 2.75 \text{ kJ/kg°C}$$

Solution. *Given :* $m = 800$ kg/h, $D = 100$ mm $= 0.1$ m, $L = 1.75$ m, $t_s = 95°C$, $t_1 = 15°C$.

(*i*)   **The temperature of cheese leaving the heated section, t_2 :**

Velocity of cheese flowing through the tube,

$$V = \frac{m}{\rho A} = \frac{(800/3600)}{1150 \times \dfrac{\pi}{4} \times 0.1^2} = 0.0246 \text{ m/s}$$

Reynolds number $Re = \dfrac{\rho VD}{\mu} = \dfrac{1150 \times 0.0246 \times 0.1}{22.5} = 0.1257$

Obviously the nature of the flow is *laminar* and the given correlation is valid for the given flow situation.

Prandtl number, $Pr = \dfrac{\mu c_p}{k} = \dfrac{22.5 \times (2.75 \times 10^3)}{0.42} = 147321$

$$\frac{D}{L}Re\ Pr = \frac{0.1}{1.75} \times 0.1257 \times 147321 = 1058.2$$

$\therefore$ $\overline{Nu} = \dfrac{\bar{h}D}{k} = 3.65 + \dfrac{0.067 \times 1058.2}{1 + 0.04\,(1058.2)^{0.333}} = 54.05$

or, $\bar{h} = \dfrac{k}{D} \times 54.05 = \dfrac{0.42}{0.1} \times 54.05 = 227.01$ W/m²°C

Mean bulk temperature of cheese, $t_b = \dfrac{t_1 + t_2}{2} = \dfrac{15 + t_2}{2}$

Now, heat gained by cheese = convective heat flow from the tube to cheese,

$$\dot{m}c_p\,(t_2 - t_1) = \bar{h}\,A_s\,(t_s - t_b)$$

$$\frac{800}{3600} \times 2.75 \times 10^3 \times (t_2 - 15) = 227.01 \times (\pi \times 0.1 \times 1.75) \left[95 - \left(\frac{15 + t_2}{2} \right) \right]$$

$$611.11\,(t_2 - 15) = 62.4\,(175 - t_2)$$

or, $$t_2 = 29.82°C \text{ (Ans.)}$$

(ii) **The rate of heat transfer from the tube to the cheese, Q :**

$$Q = \bar{h}\,A_s\,(t_s - t_b)$$
$$= m\,c_p\,(t_2 - t_1)$$
$$= \frac{800}{3600} \times (2.75 \times 10^3)\,(29.82 - 15)$$
$$= 9056.67 \text{ W} \quad \text{(Ans.)}$$

Example 7.68. *The following data relate to a metallic cylinder of 20 mm diameter and 120 mm in length heated internally by an electric heater and subjected to cross flow of air in a low speed wind tunnel :*

Temperature of free stream = 25°C; Velocity of free stream air = 16.5 m/s;

Average temperature of cylinder surface = 130°C; Power dissipation by heater = 100 W.

If 12 percent of the power dissipation is lost through the insulated end pieces of the cylinder, calculate the experimental value of the convective heat transfer coefficient. Compare this value with that obtained by using the correlation :

$$\overline{Nu} = 0.26\,(Re)^{0.6}\,(Pr)^{0.36} \left(\frac{Pr}{Pr_s} \right)^{0.25}$$

where all thermo-physical properties except Pr_s are evaluated at the mean bulk temperature (free stream) of air. Pr_s is evaluated at the average temperature of cylinder.

The thermo-physical properties of air at 25°C are :

$$k = 0.0263 \text{ W/m°C}; \qquad v = 15.53 \times 10^{-6} \text{ m}^2/s; \qquad Pr = 0.702$$

$$Pr_s \text{ at } 130°C = 0.685.$$

Solution. Given : $t_\infty = 25°C$, $U = 16.5$ m/s,

Power dissipation by heater = 100 W, $D = 20$ mm = 0.02 m.

(a) Heat flow from the heater to the air flowing past it is given by

$$Q = \bar{h}\,A_s\,\Delta t$$

or, $$100 \left(1 - \frac{12}{100} \right) = \bar{h} \times (\pi \times 0.02 \times 0.12) \times (130 - 25)$$

or, $$\bar{h} = \frac{100 \times (1 - 0.12)}{(\pi \times 0.02 \times 0.12) \times (130 - 25)}$$
$$= 111.16 \text{ W/m}^2°C \quad \text{(Ans.)}$$

(b) Reynolds number $$Re = \frac{UD}{v} = \frac{16.5 \times 0.02}{15.53 \times 10^{-6}} = 21249$$

Using the correlation given, we have

$$\overline{Nu} = 0.26\,(Re)^{0.6}\,(Pr)^{0.36} \left(\frac{Pr}{Pr_s} \right)^{0.25}$$

$$= 0.26\,(21249)^{0.6}\,(0.702)^{0.36} \left(\frac{0.702}{0.685} \right)^{0.25} = 90.93$$

or, $$\frac{\bar{h}D}{k} = 90.93$$

or, $$\bar{h} = \frac{k}{D} \times 90.93 = \frac{0.0263}{0.02} \times 90.93 = \mathbf{119.57\ W/m^2{}^\circ C} \quad \textbf{(Ans.)}$$

HIGHLIGHTS

Important Formulae

A. Laminar Flow

I. *Flow over flat plate :*

If $\dfrac{Ux}{v} < 5 \times 10^5$ ...boundary layer is *laminar* (velocity distribution is *parabolic*)

If $\dfrac{Ux}{v} > 5 \times 10^5$ ...boundary layer is *turbulent* on that portion (velocity distribution follows *log law or, a power law*)

(i) Displacement thickness, $\qquad \delta^* = \int_0^\delta \left(1 - \frac{u}{U}\right) dy$

(ii) Momentum thickness, $\qquad \theta = \int_0^\delta \frac{u}{U}\left(1 - \frac{u}{U}\right) dy$

(iii) Energy thickenss, $\qquad \delta_e = \int_0^\delta \frac{u}{U}\left(1 - \frac{u^2}{U^2}\right) dy$

(iv) $\dfrac{\delta}{x} = \dfrac{5}{\sqrt{Re_x}}$ (Blasius)

(v) $\dfrac{\delta}{x} = \dfrac{4.64}{\sqrt{Re_x}}$ (Von-Karman)

(vi) $\dfrac{\delta_{th}}{x} = \dfrac{5}{\sqrt{Re_x}} = \dfrac{\delta}{x}$ for $Pr = 1$

(vii) $\dfrac{\delta_{th}}{\delta} = \dfrac{1}{(Pr)^{1/3}}$ (Pohlhausen)

(viii) $C_{fx} = \dfrac{0.664}{\sqrt{Re_x}}$ (Blasius)

(ix) $C_{fx} = \dfrac{0.646}{\sqrt{Re_x}}$ (Von-Karman)

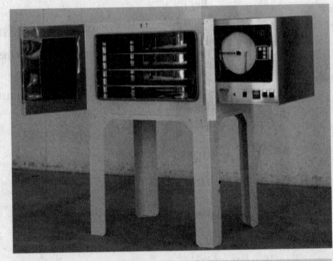

Forced convection bench oven.

(x) $\bar{C}_f = \dfrac{1.328}{\sqrt{Re_L}}$ (Blasius)

(xi) $h_x = 0.332\ \dfrac{k}{x}\ (Re_x)^{1/2}\ (Pr)^{1/3}$

(xii) $Nu_x = \dfrac{h_x x}{k} = 0.332\ (Re_x)^{1/2}\ (Pr)^{1/3}$

(xiii) $\bar{h} = 2h_x$

(xiv) $\bar{Nu} = \dfrac{\bar{h}L}{k} = 0.664 \, (Re_L)^{1/2} \, (Pr)^{1/3}$

II.   *Laminar tube flow :*

(i) $u = u_{max} \left[1 - \left(\dfrac{r}{R} \right)^2 \right]$ ... Most commonly used equation for the velocity distribution for laminar flow through pipes.

(ii) $h = \dfrac{48k}{11D}$

(iii) $Nu = 4.364$

(iv) $Nu = 3.65$ ... For constant wall temperature.

B. Turbulent Flow

I.   *For flat plate :*

(i) $\dfrac{\delta}{x} = \dfrac{0.371}{(Re_x)^{1/5}}$

(ii) $\tau_o = \dfrac{\rho U^2}{2} \times \dfrac{0.0576}{(Re_x)^{1/5}} \left[= \dfrac{0.0288 \, \rho \, U^2}{(Re_x)^{1/5}} \right]$

(iii) $C_{fx} = \dfrac{0.0576}{(Re_x)^{1/5}}$

(iv) $\bar{C_f} = \dfrac{0.072}{(Re_L)^{1/5}}$ Valid for $5 \times 10^5 < Re_L < 10^7$

$\bar{C_f} = \dfrac{0.455}{(\log_{10} Re_L)^{2.58}}$ ...Relation suggested by Prandtl and Schlichting, for Re between, 10^7 and 10^9, when the boundary layer is turbulent from the leading edge onwards.

$\bar{C_f} = \dfrac{0.455}{(\log_{10} Re_L)^{2.58}} - \dfrac{1670}{Re_L}$ ...for laminar and turbulent flow at $Re_c = 5 \times 10^5$

(v) $Nu_x = 0.0288 \, (Re_x)^{0.8} \, (Pr)^{1/3}$

$h_x = 0.0288 \left(\dfrac{k}{x} \right) (Re_x)^{0.8} \, (Pr)^{1/3}$

(vi) $\bar{Nu} = 0.036 \, (Re_L)^{0.8} \, (Pr)^{1/3}$

$\bar{h} = 0.036 \left(\dfrac{k}{L} \right) (Re_L)^{0.8} \, (Pr)^{1/3}$

(vii) $\bar{Nu} = (Pr)^{1/3} \, [0.036 \, (Re_L)^{0.8} - 836]$ ...when $Re_c = 5 \times 10^5$

II.   *For tubes :*

$\bar{Nu} = 0.023 \, (Re)^{0.8} \, (Pr)^{1/3}$

$\bar{h} = 0.023 \, \dfrac{k}{D} \, (Re)^{0.8} \, (Pr)^{1/3}$

The above expressions are valid for

$1 \times 10^4 < Re < 1 \times 10^5; \; 0.5 < Pr < 100; \; \dfrac{L}{D} > 60.$

THEORETICAL QUESTIONS

1. Define the following terms :

    (i)   Boundary layer thickness
    (ii) Displacement thickness
    (iii) Momentum thickness
    (iv) Energy thickness.

2. Derive momentum equation for hydrodynamic boundary layer over a flat plate.

3. Derive expressions for boundary layer thickness and local skin friction coefficient, following the Blasius method of solving laminar boundary layer equations, for flat plate.

4. Define Nusselt number and Prandtl number.

5. Derive an energy equation for thermal boundary layer over a flat plate.

6. Define the local and average skin friction (drag) coefficients for a flat plate at zero incidence, for laminar flow.

    Establish the follwing relations for laminar boundary layer over a flat plate :

    (i)   Local skin friction coefficient, $C_{fx} = \dfrac{0.664}{\sqrt{Re_x}}$

    (ii) Average skin friction (drag) coefficient, $\bar{C}_f = \dfrac{1.328}{\sqrt{Re_L}}$

    Take $\left(\dfrac{dt}{d\eta}\right)_{\eta=0} = 0.332$

7. Derive the Von-Karman momentum integral equation for the flow past a flat plate in the form :

    $$\tau_0 = \rho U^2 \dfrac{d}{dx}\left[\int_0^\delta \dfrac{u}{U}\left(1 - \dfrac{u}{U}\right) dy\right]$$

    Using this equation and assuming the velocity distribution $\dfrac{u}{U} = 2\left(\dfrac{y}{\delta}\right) - \left(\dfrac{y}{\delta}\right)^2$, calculate the following for laminar flow over a flat plate :

    (i)   Boundary layer thickness;
    (ii) Wall shear stress;
    (iii) Skin friction coefficient.

8. Derive the two-dimensional energy equation for thermal boundary layer on a flat plate. Mention the boundary conditions, when the plate is heated and its surface maintained at constant temperature t_s and the ambient temperature is t_∞.

9. Establish a relationship among the Nusselt number, the Reynolds number and the Prandtl number for forced convection over a flat plate, using Pohlhausen solution for temperature gradient $\left(\dfrac{d\theta}{d\eta}\right)_{\eta=0} = 0.332 \, (Pr)^{1/3}$

10. Discuss the significance of bulk temperature in case of fully developed laminar flow in a tube.

11. What is a turbulent flow ?

12. What is turbulent intensity ?

13. Can the problems relating turbulent flow be solved easily analytically, if not, why, and also state how are these solved?

14. Derive an expression for turbulent boundary layer thickness over a flat plate,

15. Define Reynolds analogy.

UNSOLVED EXAMPLES

A. Laminar Flow

1. Show that for velocity distribution,

$$\frac{u}{U} = 2\left(\frac{y}{\delta}\right) - \left(\frac{y}{\delta}\right)^2$$

the ratio of $\delta/\delta^* = 3$

2. The velocity distribution in the boundary layer over a high spillway face was found to have the following form:

$$\frac{u}{U} = \left(\frac{y}{\delta}\right)^{0.22}$$

Prove that the displacement thickness, the momentum thickness and the energy thickness in terms of δ, the boundary layer thickness, can be expressed as

$$\frac{\delta^*}{\delta} = 0.18; \quad \frac{\theta}{\delta} = 0.125; \quad \frac{\delta_e}{\delta} = 0.127$$

3. Find the ratio of displacement thickness to momentum thickness and momentum thickness to energy thickness for the velocity distribution in the boundary layer given by

$$\frac{u}{U} = 2\,(y/\delta) - (y/\delta)^2 \qquad\qquad \text{[Ans. 2.5, 7/11]}$$

4. For the velocity profile in laminar layer given as

$$\frac{u}{U} = 2\left(\frac{y}{\delta}\right) - \left(\frac{y}{\delta}\right)^2$$

find the thickness of boundary layer at the end of the plate and the drag force on the side of the plate 1 m long and 0.8 m wide when placed in water flowing with a velocity of 0.15 m/s. Calculate the value of coefficient of drag also. Take μ for water = 0.001 Ns/m².   [**Ans.** 14.15 mm, 0.0338 N, 0.00376]

5. Air flows on a smooth flat plate with a velocity of 10 m/s. The velocity profile is in the form

$$\frac{u}{U} = 2\left(\frac{y}{\delta}\right) - \left(\frac{y}{\delta}\right)^2$$

The length of the plate is 1.2 m and width 0.9 m. If laminar boundary layer exists upto a value of $R_e = 2 \times 10^5$ and kinematic viscosity of air = 0.15 stokes, find : (*i*) The maximum distance from the leading edge upto which laminar boundary layer exists, and (*ii*) The maximum thickness of boundary layer.   [**Ans.** (*i*) 0.3 m (*ii*) 3.67 mm]

6. A plate of length 500 mm and width 250 mm has been placed longitudinally in a stream of crude oil which flows with a velocity of 6 m/s. If the oil has a specific gravity of 0.9 and kinematic viscosity of 1 stoke, calculate :

   (*i*)   Boundary layer thickness at the middle of plate,

   (*ii*)   Shear stress at the middle of plate, and

   (*iii*)   Friction drag on one side of the plate.   [**Ans.** (*i*) 10.5 mm, (*ii*) 87.8 N/m², (*iii*) 12.36 N]

7. Atmospheric air at 20°C is flowing parallel to a flat plate at a velocity of 3 m/s. Assuming cubic velocity profile and using exact Blasius solution estimate the boundary layer thickness and the local coefficient of drag at $x = 1$ m from the leading edge of the plate. Also find the deviation of the approximate solution from the exact solution.   [**Ans.** 11.376 mm, 1.511 × 10⁻³; 7.2%, 2.78%]

8. Air is flowing over a plate 4 m × 2 m with a velocity of 5 m/s at 15°C. If $\rho = 1.208$ kg/m³ and $v = 1.47 \times 10^{-5}$ m²/s, calculate :

   (*i*)   Length of plate over which the boundary layer is laminar and thickness of the laminar boundary layer,

   (*ii*)   Shear stress at the location where boundary layer ceases to be laminar, and

   (*iii*)   Total force on both sides on that portion of plate where boundary layer is laminar.

               [**Ans.** (*i*) 1.47 m, 10.39 mm; (*ii*) 0.01418 N/m²; (*iii*) 0.1662 N]

9. A submarine can be assumed to have cylindrical shape with rounded nose. Assuming its length to be 55 m and diameter, 6.0 m, determine the total power required to overcome boundary friction if it cruises at 8.0 m/s velocity in water at 20°C.

   Take $\rho = 1030$ kg/m³, $v = 1 \times 10^{-6}$ m²/s [**Ans.** 476.5 kW]

10. Air at 30°C and at atmospheric pressure flows over a flat plate at a velocity of 1.5 m/s. If the length of the plate is 2 m and is maintained at 90°C, calculate the heat transfer rate per unit width using (i) exact and (ii) approximate method. [**Ans.** (i) 406.08 W, 395.04 W]

11. Air at a temperature of 30°C flows past a flat plate at a velocity of 2 m/s. The flat surface has a sharp leading edge and its total length equals 800 mm. Calculate the following :

    (i) The average skin friction or, drag coefficient,

    (ii) The average shear stress, and

    (iii) The ratio of the average shear stress to the shear stress at the trailing edge.

    Properties of air at 30°C are : $\rho = 1.165$ kg/m³, $\mu = 6.717 \times 10^{-2}$ kg/hm, $v = 16 \times 10^{-6}$ m²/s.

    [**Ans.** (i) 0.004199, (ii) 0.009783 N/m²; (iii) 2]

12. Air at 20°C flows with a velocity of 3 m/s over a plate (1000 mm) length × 500 mm (width) × 20 mm (thickness). The top surface of the plate is maintained at 100°C. If the thermal conductivity of the plate material is 23 W/m°C, calculate the following :

    (i) Heat lost by the plate, and

    (ii) Bottom temperature of the plate for the steady state condition.

    At 60°C, the thermo-physical properties of air are :

    $\rho = 1.06$ kg/m³, $c_p = 1.005$ kJ/kg°C, $k = 0.02894$ W/m°C, $v = 18.97 \times 10^{-6}$ m²/s, $Pr = 0.696$.

    [**Ans.** (i) 270.72 W, (ii) 100.47°C]

13. Air at 20°C and at atmospheric pressure flows at a velocity of 2 m/s over a plate maintained at 100°C. The length and width of the plate are 800 mm and 400 mm respectively. Using exact solution, calculate the heat transfer rate from,

    (i) first half of the plate, (ii) full plate and (iii) next half of the plate.

    Properties of air at 60°C are : $\rho = 1.06$ kg/m³, $\mu = 7.211$ kg/mh, $v = 18.97 \times 10^{-6}$ m²/s, $Pr = 0.696$

    [**Ans.** (i) 111.79 W, (ii) 158.1W, (iii) 46.31 W]

14. Castor oil at 30°C flows at a velocity of 0.08 m/s past a flat plate, in a certain process. If the plate is 5 m long and is maintained at a uniform temperature of 90°C, calculate the following using exact solution :

    (i) The hydrodynamic and thermal boundary layer thicknesses on one side of the plate,

    (ii) The total drag force per unit width on one side of the plate,

    (iii) The local heat transfer coefficient at the trailing edge, and

    (iv) The heat transfer rate.

    The thermo-physical properties of oil at mean film temperature of (30 + 90)/2 = 60°C are :

    $\rho = 956.8$ kg/m³; $\alpha = 7.2 \times 10^{-8}$ m²/s; $k = 0.213$ W/m°C; $v = 0.65 \times 10^{-4}$ m²/s

    [**Ans.** (i) 318.7 mm, 32.98 mm, (ii) 0.2591 N/m, (iii) 10.716 W/m²°C (iv) 6429.6 W]

15. Air at 30°C and at atmospheric pressure flows at a velocity of 4 m/s past a flat plate with a sharp leading edge. The entire plate surface is maintained at a temperature of 50°C. Assuming that the transition occurs at a critical Reynolds number of 5×10^5, find the distance from the leading edge at which the flow in the boundary layer changes from laminar to turbulent. At the location, calculate the following: (i) Thickness of hydrodynamic layer, (ii) Thickness of thermal boundary layer, (iii) Local and average convective heat transfer- coefficients, (iv) Heat transfer rate from both sides for unit width of the plate, (v) Mass entrainment in the boundary layer, and (vi) The skin friction coefficient.

    Assume, cubic velocity profile and approximate method.

The thermo-physical properties of air at mean film temperature $(50 + 30)/2 = 40°C$ are :

$\rho = 1.128$ kg/m^3, $v = 16.96 \times 10^{-6}$ m^2/s, $k = 0.02755$ W/m°C, $Pr = 0.699$.

[**Ans.** (*i*) 13.9 mm, (*ii*) 15.258 mm, (*iii*) 2.625 W/m^2°C, 5.250 W/m^2°C (*iv*) 445.2 W, (*v*) 140.76 kg/h, (*vi*) 0.000913]

16. A stream of water at 20°C ($\rho = 1.205$ kg/m^3, $\mu = 0.06533$ kg/hm) flows at a velocity of 1.5 m/s over a plate 0.5 m long and placed at zero angle of incidence. Using exact solution, calculate the following :

    (*i*) The stream wise velocity component at the midpoint of the boundary layer,

    (*ii*) The maximum value of the normal component of velocity at the trailing edge of the plate.

    [**Ans.** (*i*) 1.104 m/s, (*ii*) 11.2 mm, (*iii*) 0.00578 m/s]

17. Air at 25°C flows past a flat plate at 2.5 m/s. The plate measures 600 mm × 300 mm and is maintained at a uniform temperature of 95°C. Calculate the heat loss from the plate if the air flows parallel to the 600 mm side. How would this heat loss be affected if the flow of air is made parallel to the 300 mm side? [**Ans.** 100.5 W, 142.128 W]

18. Air at 1 bar and at a temperature of 30°C ($\mu = 0.06717$) flows at a speed of 1.25 m/s over a flat plate. Determine the boundary layer thicknesses at distances of 200 mm and 400 mm from the leading edge of the plate. Also calculate the mass entrainment between these two sections. Assume the parabolic velocity distribution as : $\dfrac{u}{U} = \dfrac{3}{2}\left(\dfrac{y}{\delta}\right) - \dfrac{1}{2}\left(\dfrac{y}{\delta}\right)^3$ [**Ans.** 7.478 mm, 10.5 mm, 9.77 kg/h]

B. Tubulent Flow

19. The average drag coefficient for turbulent layer flow past a thin plate is given by :

$$\bar{C}_f = \frac{0.455}{(\log_{10} Re_L)^{2.58}}$$

where Re_L is the Reynolds number based on plate length. A plate 500 mm wide and 5m long is kept parallel to the flow of water with free stream velocity 3 m/s. Calculate the drag force on both sides of the plate. Take $v = 0.01$ stoke. (**Ans.** 63.37 N)

20. The crankcase of an I.C. engine measuring 900 mm × 250 mm may be idealised as a flat plate. The engine runs at 100 km/h and the crankcase is cooled by the air flowing past it at the same speed. Calculate the heat loss from the crank surface maintained at 80°C to the ambient air at 20°C. The boundary layer becomes turbulent from the leading edge itself, due to road induced vibrations. (**Ans.** 1112.2 W)

21. In a gas turbine system hot gases at 1000°C flow at 75 m/s over the surface of a combustion chamber which is at a uniform temperature of 300°C. Determine the heat loss from the gases to the combustion chamber which can be idealised as a flat plate measuring 1 m × 0.5 m. The flow is parallel to the 1m side and transition Reynolds number is equal to 5×10^5. Take the properties of gas as :

$\rho = 0.496$ kg/m^3; $v = 93.5 \times 10^{-6}$ m^2/s; $k = 0.0744$ W/m°C; $Pr = 0.625$

(**Ans.** 23.81 kW)

Gas turbine system.

22. Air at 25°C and 215 m/s, during test-run in a wind tunnel, is made to flow past a smooth thin model air- foil which can be idealised as a flat plate. If the chord length of air foil is 150 mm, calculate the drag per unit width.

   The relevant properties of air are : $\rho = 1.82$ kg/m^3; $v = 15.53 \times 10^{-6}$ m^2/s

   (**Ans.** 25.42 N per metre width)

23. A refrigerated truck is moving on a highway at 95 km/h in a desert area where the ambient temperature is 50°C. The body of the truck may be considered as a rectangular box measuring 10 m (length) × 4 m (width) × 3 m (height). Assume that the boundary layer on the four walls is turbulent, the heat transfer takes place only from the four surfaces and the wall surface of the truck is maintained at 10°C. Ne-glecting heat transfer from the front and the back and assuming the flow to be parallel to 10 m long side, calculate the following : (*i*) The heat loss from the four surfaces; (*ii*) The tonnage of refrigera-tion; (*iii*) The power required to overcome the resistance acting on the four surfaces.

   The properties of air at 30°C are :

   $\rho = 1.165$ kg/m^3; $c_p = 1.005$ kJ/kg°C; $k = 0.02673$ W/m^2°C, $v = 16 \times 10^{-6}$ m^2/s, Pr = 0.701.

   [**Ans.** (*i*) 320.08 kW, (*ii*) 82.3 TR, (*iii*) 3.88 kW]

   (**Note.** 1 TR = 14000 kJ/h)

24. A fluid is flowing in a pipe which is 250 mm in diameter, 3 m long and whose surface is maintained at a constant temperature. The temperature of the wall surface at the inlet section of the pipe exceeds the fluid temperature by 30°C. What is the rise in the fluid temperature at the end section of the pipe?

   The Reynolds analogy holds good which is given by : $St = \dfrac{f}{8}$,

   where friction factor $f = 0.02$. (**Ans.** 3.39°C)

25. In a straight tube of 50 mm diameter, water is flowing at a velocity of 15 m/s. The tube surface temperature is maintained at 60°C and the flowing water is heated from the inlet temperature 15°C to an outlet temperature of 45°C. Calculate the following :

   (*i*) The heat transfer coefficient from the tube surface to the water, and

   (*ii*) The length of the tube. [**Ans.** (*i*) 29714.95 W/m^2°C, (*ii*) 17.479 m]

Empirical Correlations

26. Air at a temperature of 20°C flows across a flat plate maintained at a temperature of 600°C. Calculate the amount of heat transferred per metre width from both sides of the plate over a distance of 300 mm from the leading edge. The following relation holds good in the case of large temperature difference between the plate and the fluid :

$$Nu_x = 0.332 \, (Pr)^{1/3} \, (Re)^{1/2} \left(\frac{T_s}{T_\infty} \right)^{0.117}$$

   where T_s and T_∞ are the absolute temperatures of the plate surface and free stream respectively and all fluid properties are evaluated at the mean film temperature. (**Ans.** 7850.9W)

27. A surface condenser consists of two hundred thin walled circular tubes (each tube is 25 mm in diam-eter and 5 m long) arranged in parallel through which water flows. If the mass flow rate of water through the tube bank is 150 kg/s and its inlet and outlet temperatures are known to be 20°C and 30°C respectively, calculate the average heat transfer coefficient associated with flow of water.

   [**Ans.** 5941.9 W/m^2 °C]

28. 0.05 kg/s of hot air flows through an uninsulated sheet metal duct of 150 mm diameter. The air enters the duct at a temperature of 105°C and after a distance of 5m gets cooled to a temperature of 80°C. If the heat transfer coefficient between the outer surface of the duct and cold ambient air at 5°C is 6 W/m^2 °C, calculate : (*i*) the heat loss from the duct over its 5 m length; (*ii*) The heat flux and the duct surface temperature at a length of 5 m. [**Ans.** (*i*) 1261.25 W, (*ii*) 294.69 W/m^2, 54.12°C]

29. Liquid mercury flows at the rate of 1.25 kg /s through a copper tube of 20 mm diameter. The mercury enters the tube at 15°C and after getting heated it leaves the tube at 25°C. Calculate the tube length for constant heat flux at the wall which is maintained at an average temperature of 40°C.

For liquid metal flowing through a tube, the following empirical correlation is presumed to agree well with experimental results :

$$\overline{Nu} = 7 + 0.025 \, (Pe)^{0.8}$$

where Pe is the Peclet number; $Pe = Pr \cdot Re$.   **[Ans. 0.437 m]**

30. A square channel of side 15 mm and length 2.0 m, in a heat transfer problem, carries water at a velocity of 6 m/s. The mean temperature of the water along the length of the channel is found to be 30°C while the inner channel surface temperature is 70°C. Calculate the heat transfer coefficient from channel wall to the water. Use the correlation :

$$\overline{Nu} = 0.021 \, (Re)^{0.8} \, (Pr)^{0.43} \left(\frac{Pr}{Pr_s} \right)^{0.25}$$

The thermo-physical properties are evaluated at the mean bulk temperature except Pr_s; Pr_s is evaluated at the channel surface temperature. Take equivalent diameter as characteristic length of the channel.

The thermo-physical properties of water at 30°C are :

$\rho = 995.7 \text{ kg/m}^3$, $k = 0.6175 \text{ W/m°C}$; $v = 0.805 \times 10^{-6} \text{ m}^2/\text{s}$; $Pr = 5.42$; Pr_s at 70°C = 2.55 .

[Ans. 25456.6 W/m² °C]

31. A copper bus bar 20 mm diameter is cooled by air (in cross-flow) at 30°C and flowing past the bus bar with a velocity of 2 m/s. If the surface temperature of the bar is not to exceed 80°C and resistivity of copper is 0.0175×10^{-6} ohm–m³/m, calculate the following :

    (i) The heat transfer coefficient from the surface to the air; .

    (ii) The permissible current density for the bus bar.

    The following empirical correlations may be applicable for a single cylinder placed in cross-flow :

         For $10 < Re < 10^3$ $Nu = 0.44 \, (Re)^{0.5}$

         For $10^3 < Re < 2 \times 10^5$ $Nu = 0.22 \, (Re)^{0.6}$

    The thermo-physical properties are evaluated at t_∞ (30°C) and are given as :

         $k = 0.02673 \text{ W/m°C}$ $v = 16 \times 10^{-6} \text{ m}^2/\text{s}$

    [Ans. (i) 32.14 W/m² °C (ii) 1346 amps.]

Free Convection

8

8.1. INTRODUCTION

When a surface is maintained in still fluid at a temperature higher or lower than that of the fluid, a layer of fluid adjacent to the surface gets heated or cooled. A *density difference* is created between this layer and the still fluid surrounding it. The density difference introduces a *buoyant force* causing flow of fluid near the surface. Heat transfer under such conditions is known as free or natural convection. Thus "**Free or natural convection** *is the process of heat transfer which occurs due to movement of the fluid particles by density changes associated with temperature differential in a fluid.*" This mode of heat transfer occurs very commonly, some examples are given below:

(*i*) The cooling of transmission lines, electric transformers and rectifiers.

(*ii*) The heating of rooms by use of radiators.

(*iii*) The heat transfer from hot pipes and ovens surrounded by cooler air.

(*iv*) Cooling the reactor core (in nuclear power plants) and carry out the heat generated by nuclear fission etc.

– In free convection, the flow velocities encountered are *lower* compared to flow velocities in forced convection, consequently the value of convection coefficient is *lower*, generally by one order of magnitude. Hence, for a given rate of heat transfer larger area could be required. As there is no need for additional devices to force the liquid, this mode is used for heat transfer in simple devices which have to be left unattended for long periods.

- The rate of heat transfer is calculated using the general convection equation given below:

$$Q = h A (t_s - t_\infty) \qquad \qquad ...(8.1)$$

where, Q = Heat transfer, ,

h = Convection coefficient, W/m²°C,

A = Area, m², and

t_∞ = Temperature of fluid at distances well removed from the surface (here the stagnant fluid temperature).

8.2. CHARACTERISTIC PARAMETERS IN FREE CONVECTION

It has been observed that during heat transfer from a heated surface to the surrounding fluid, the fluid adjacent to the surface gets heated; this results in thermal expansion of the fluid and reduction in its density (compared to the fluid away from the surface). Subsequently a buoyancy force acts on the fluid causing it to flow up the surface, and in the neighbourhood of the plate, hydrodynamic and thermal boundary layers are set up. Since here the flow velocity is developed due to difference of temperatures, the two boundary layers are of the *same order* irrespective of Prandtl number.

- A property that comes into play in free or natural convection is the *coefficient of thermal expansion* of the fluid defined by

$$\beta = \frac{1}{\upsilon}\left(\frac{\partial \upsilon}{\partial T}\right)_p = -\frac{1}{\rho}\left(\frac{\partial p}{\partial T}\right)_p \qquad \qquad ...(8.2)$$

For an ideal gas $\upsilon = \dfrac{RT}{p}, \left(\dfrac{\partial \upsilon}{\partial T}\right)_p = \dfrac{R}{p}$

and, hence $\beta = \dfrac{1}{T}$

Since in free convection heat transfer coefficients are low and Reynolds number is not an independent parameter, a new dimensionless grouping plays the major role (in free convection) which incorporates the coefficient of thermal expansion β in the expression. This dimensionless grouping is called the **Grashoff number**, expressed as

$$Gr = \frac{L^3 g\beta\Delta t}{v^2} \qquad \qquad ...(8.3)$$

where, L = Characteristic length

$\Delta t = (t_s - t_\infty)$, where t_s and t_∞ are the surface temperature and temperature of the surrounding fluid respectively.

The role of Grashoff number is the same in free convection as that of Reynolds number in forced convection.

The *critical Grashoff number for the flow of air over a flat plate* has been observed to be 4×10^8 (approximately).

In general, $Nu = f (Gr, Pr) = C (Gr)^a (Pr)^b \qquad \qquad ...(8.4)$

In several cases, the above relation simplifies to the form

$$Nu = C (Gr. Pr)^m \qquad \qquad ...(8.5)$$

Hence, a new dimensionless group is often used called *Rayleigh number* viz.,

$$Ra = Gr . Pr$$

The product is also a criterion of laminar or turbulent character of the flow as determined by its values. Thus

$$10^4 < Gr \, Pr < 10^9 \qquad \qquad ... \text{for laminar flow}$$

$Gr\,Pr > 10^9$ *... for turbulent flow*

The values of *Gr* and *Pr* are *evaluated at the mean film temperature* $\left(t_f = \dfrac{t_w + t_\infty}{2}\right)$.

8.3. MOMENTUM AND ENERGY EQUATIONS FOR LAMINAR FREE CONVECTION HEAT TRANSFER ON A VERTICAL FLAT PLATE

Figure 8.1 shows a free convection boundary layer formed on a flat vertical plate when it is heated. Here, the velocity profile is different from that of forced convection boundary layer. At the surface/wall the velocity is zero, it increases to some maximum value and then decreases to zero again at the edge of the boundary since the free stream is at rest. Initially the boundary layer is laminar in character and at some distance from the bottom edge, it becomes turbulent. This onset of turbulence depends on the fluid properties and the temperature difference $(t_s - t_\infty)$.

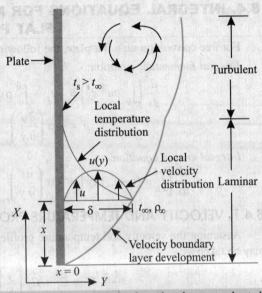

Fig. 8.1. Free-convection boundary layer over heated vertical plate.

In order to analyse the problem, let us consider the momentum equation for forced convection.

In free convection, the additional force is the body force ρg and hence the momentum equation gets modified to

$$\rho\left(u\,\frac{\partial u}{\partial x} + \upsilon\,\frac{\partial u}{\partial y}\right) = \mu\,\frac{\partial^2 u}{\partial y^2} - \rho g - \frac{\partial p}{\partial x} \qquad \text{...(8.6)}$$

In free convection, outside the boundary layer, $(y \to \infty)$ as ρ tends to ρ_∞, whereas u and υ approach zero. So eqn. (8.6) becomes

$$0 = -\frac{\partial t}{\partial x} - \rho_\infty g$$

or, $$\frac{\partial p}{\partial x} = -\rho_\infty g \qquad \text{...(8.7)}$$

(*i.e.* the change in pressure on a height dx is equal to the weight per unit area of the fluid element).

Substituting eqn. (8.7) in eqn. (8.6), we get

$$\rho\left(u\,\frac{\partial u}{dx} + \upsilon\,\frac{\partial u}{\partial y}\right) = \mu\,\frac{\partial^2 u}{\partial y^2} + g\,(\rho_\infty - \rho) \qquad \text{...(8.8)}$$

Further the density difference $(\rho_\infty - \rho)$ may be expressed in terms of the volume coefficient of expansion β

Thus, $$\beta = -\frac{1}{\rho}\left(\frac{\partial p}{\partial T}\right)_p = \frac{1}{p}\frac{(\rho_\infty - \rho)}{(t - t_\infty)} \qquad \text{...(8.9)}$$

so that eqn. (8.8) beocmes

$$\rho \left(u \frac{\partial u}{\partial x} + \upsilon \frac{\partial u}{\partial y} \right) = \mu \frac{\partial^2 y}{\partial y^2} + \rho g \beta \, (t - t_\infty) \qquad \qquad ...(8.10)$$

The energy equation for free convection boundary layer remains the same as forced convection at low velocities, *viz.*,

$$\rho c_p \left(u \frac{\partial t}{\partial x} + \upsilon \frac{\partial t}{\partial y} \right) = k \frac{\partial^2 t}{\partial y^2} \qquad \qquad ...(8.11)$$

8.4. INTEGRAL EQUATIONS FOR MOMENTUM AND ENERGY ON A FLAT PLATE

For free convection on a flat plate, the following equations can be derived.

Integral momentum equation:

$$\frac{d}{dx} \left(\int_0^\delta \rho u^2 \, dy \right) = - t_s + \int_0^\delta \rho g \beta \, (t - t_\infty) \, dy$$

$$= - \mu \left(\frac{\partial u}{\partial y} \right)_{y=0} + \int_0^\delta \rho g \beta \, (t - t_\infty) \, dy \qquad \qquad ...(8.12)$$

Integral energy equation:

$$\frac{d}{dx} \left[\int_0^\delta u \, (t - t_\infty) \, dy \right] = - \alpha \left(\frac{\partial t}{\partial y} \right)_{y=0} \qquad \qquad ...(8.13)$$

8.4.1. VELOCITY AND TEMPERATURE PROFILES ON A VERTICAL FLAT PLATE

Assuming the velocity and temperature profiles to be similar at any x, the temperature profile may be taken as

$$\frac{t - t_\infty}{t_s - t_\infty} = C_1 + C_2 \left(\frac{y}{\delta} \right) + C_3 \left(\frac{y}{\delta} \right)^2$$

The following boundary conditions apply:

(*i*) At $y = 0$ $\qquad\qquad t = t_s$

(*ii*) At $y = \delta$ $\qquad\qquad t = t_\infty$

(*iii*) At $y = \delta$ $\qquad\qquad \dfrac{\partial t}{\partial y} = 0$

The *temperature distribution* is, therefore, obtained as

$$\frac{t - t_\infty}{t_s - t_\infty} = \left(1 - \frac{y}{\delta} \right)^2 \qquad \qquad ...(8.14)$$

The velocity profile may be similarly assumed.

$$\frac{u}{u_x} = a + b \left(\frac{y}{\delta} \right) + c \left(\frac{y}{\delta} \right)^2 + d \left(\frac{y}{\delta} \right)^3$$

where u_x is any arbitrary function with the dimension of velocity.

The boundary conditions, are:

(*i*) At $y = 0,$ $\qquad\qquad u = 0$

(*ii*) At $y = \delta,$ $\qquad\qquad u = 0$

(*iii*) At $y = \delta,$ $\qquad\qquad \dfrac{\partial u}{\partial y} = 0$

(*iv*) At $y = 0,$ $\qquad\qquad \dfrac{\partial^2 u}{\partial y^2} = - g \beta \dfrac{(t_s - t_\infty)}{v}$

The velocity distribution is, therefore, found to be

$$\frac{u}{u_x} = \left[\frac{g\beta\delta^2\ (t_s - t_\infty)}{4v}\right] \frac{y}{\delta}\left(1 - \frac{y}{\delta}\right)^2 \qquad \qquad ...(8.15)$$

or,

$$u = u_1 \frac{y}{\delta}\left(1 - \frac{y}{\delta}\right)^2 \qquad \qquad ...(8.16)$$

where,

$$u_1 = \frac{u_x g\beta\delta^2\ (t_s - t_\infty)}{4v}$$

8.4.2. SOLUTION OF THE INTEGRAL EQUATIONS FOR VERTICAL FLAT PLATE

Substitution of the velocity and temperature distributions from eqns. (8.14) and (8.16) into eqn. (8.12) for momentum integral gives

$$\frac{1}{105}\frac{d}{dx}(u_1^2\ \delta) = \frac{1}{3}\ g\beta\ (t_s - t_\infty)\ \delta - \frac{v u_1}{\delta} \qquad \qquad ...(8.17)$$

and substitution into eqn. (8.13) for energy integral gives

$$\frac{1}{30}\ (t_s - t_\infty)\ \frac{d}{dx}\ (u_1\ \delta) = 2\alpha\ \frac{(t_s - t_\infty)}{\delta} \qquad \qquad ...(8.18)$$

To solve these equations, let us assume u_1 and δ as exponential functions of x

$$u_1 = C_1 x^m; \quad \delta = C_2 x^n$$

(where C_1, C_2, m and n are constants).

Substituting these values in the above equation, we get

$$\left(\frac{2m + n}{105}\right)C_1^2\ C_2\ (x)^{2m+n-1} = \frac{1}{3}\ g\beta\ (t_s - t_\infty)\ C_2 x^n - v\ \frac{C_1}{C_2}\ (x)^{m-n} \qquad ...(8.19)$$

$$\left(\frac{m + n}{30}\right)C_1\ C_2\ (x)^{m+n-1} = \frac{2\alpha}{C_2}\ (x)^{-n} \qquad \qquad ...(8.20)$$

For a similar solution to exist, both sides of these equations must be independent of x. Equating the exponents, we get

$$2m + n - 1 = m - n$$

$$m + n - 1 = - n$$

This gives $m = \dfrac{1}{2}$ and $\quad n = \dfrac{1}{4}$ (Thus $u_1 = C_1 x^{1/2}, \delta = C_2 x^{1/4}$)

Inserting these values into the above equations, we get

$$\frac{C_1^2\ C_2}{84} = g\beta\ (t_s - t_\infty)\ \frac{C_2}{3} - v\ \frac{C_1}{C_2} \qquad \qquad ...(8.21)$$

$$\frac{C_1\ C_2}{40} = \frac{2\alpha}{C_2} \qquad \qquad ...(8.22)$$

Solving these two equations for C_1 and C_2, we get

$$C_1 = 5.17\ v \left(\frac{20}{21} + \frac{v}{\alpha}\right)^{-1/2} \left[\frac{g\beta\ (t_s - t_\infty)}{v^2}\right]^{1/2} \qquad ...(8.23)$$

$$C_2 = 3.93\ v \left(\frac{20}{21} + \frac{v}{\alpha}\right)^{+1/4} \left[\frac{g\beta\ (t_s - t_\infty)}{v^2}\right]^{-1/4} \left(\frac{v}{a}\right)^{-1/2} \qquad ...(8.24)$$

From eqn. (8.16), the maximum velocity within the boundary layer is found to be

$$u_{max} = \frac{4}{27}\ u_1 = \frac{4}{27}\ C_1 x^{1/2}$$

which on substitution for C_1 from eqn. (8.23) gives

$$u_{max} = 0.766\, v \left(0.952 + \frac{v}{\alpha}\right)^{-1/2} \left[\frac{g\beta\,(t_s - t_\infty)}{v^2}\right]^{1/2} (x)^{1/2} \qquad \text{...(8.25)}$$

The resultant expression for boundary layer thickness is

$$\frac{\delta}{x} = C_2\, x^{n-1} = C_2\, x^{-3/4}$$

which on substitution for C_2 from eqn. (8.24) yields

$$\frac{\delta}{x} = 3.93 \left(0.952 + \frac{v}{x}\right)^{1/4} \left[\frac{g\beta\,(t_s - t_\infty)\, x^3}{v^2}\right]^{-1/y} \left(\frac{v}{\alpha}\right)^{-1/2} \qquad \text{...(8.26)}$$

or, $$\frac{\delta}{x} = 3.93\,(0.952 + Pr)^{1/4}\,(Gr_x)^{-1/4}\,(Pr)^{-1/2} \qquad \text{...(8.27)}$$

... in dimensionless numbers

$$\text{(where } Gr_x = \frac{g\beta\,(t_s - t_\infty)\, x^3}{v^2} \text{ and } Pr = \frac{v}{\alpha}\text{)}$$

8.4.3. FREE CONVECTION HEAT TRANSFER COEFFICIENT FOR A VERTICAL WALL

The heat transfer coefficient may be evaluated from

$$Q_s = -kA \left(\frac{dt}{dy}\right)_{y=0} = h_x A\,(t_s - t_\infty) \qquad \text{...(8.28)}$$

Using the temperature distribution of eqn. (8.14), we obtain

$$\left(\frac{dt}{dy}\right)_{y=0} = -\frac{2(t_s - t_\infty)}{\delta} \qquad \text{...(8.29)}$$

Substituting this value in eqn. (8.28), we get

$$h_x = \frac{2k}{\delta}$$

or, $$\frac{h_x x}{k} = Nu_x = \frac{2x}{\delta} \qquad \text{...(8.30)}$$

From eqns. (8.27) and (8.29) we obtain the heat transfer correlation for natural convection for a vertical flat plate as

$$Nu_x = 0.508\,(Pr)^{1/2}\,(0.952 + Pr)^{-1/4}\,(Gr_x)^{1/4} \qquad \text{...(8.31)}$$

For a given Prandtl number, Nu_x varies as $(Gr_x)^{1/4}$ or $h_x \propto x^{-1/4}$.

The local film heat transfer coefficient decreases with x. It is inversely proportional to the fourth root of x. By integration over the distance, the average heat transfer coefficient is found to be

$$\bar{h}_L = \frac{1}{L}\int_0^L h_x dx = \frac{4}{3}\,(h_x)_{x=L} \qquad \text{...(8.32)}$$

or, $$\overline{Nu_L} = \frac{\bar{h}\,L}{k} = 0.677\,(Pr)^{1/2}\,(0.952 + Pr)^{-1/4}\,(Gr_x)^{1/4} \qquad \text{...(8.33)}$$

For air with $Pr = 0.7$, eqns. (8.31) and (8.33) simplify to

$$Nu_x = 0.378\,(Gr_x)^{1/4} \qquad \text{...(8.34)}$$

$$\overline{Nu_L} = 0.504\,(Gr_L)^{1/4} \qquad \text{...(8.35)}$$

These result are only 5 per cent higher than the exact solution of the free convection problem obtained numerically by Schmidt and Beckman.

Here *all properties are evaluated at 'film temperature'*.

8.5. TRANSITION AND TURBULENCE IN FREE CONVECTION

A transition from laminar to turbulent condition in both forced and free convection is caused by thermal and hydrodynamic instabilities. It has been observed that the transition in free convection boundary layer occurs when the value of Rayleigh number approaches 10^9. Thus

$$Ra_{x,c} = Gr_{x,c} \ Pr = \frac{g\beta \ (t_s - t_\infty) \ x^3}{\nu \ \alpha} = 10^9 \qquad \qquad ...(8.36)$$

The analysis of turbulent free convection is very complex. However, the results obtained from various experiments have been used to obtain the pertinent empirical relations.

8.6. EMPIRICAL CORRELATIONS FOR FREE CONVECTION

The following dimensionless numbers apply for the usual free convection problems:

(*i*) Nusselt number $Nu = \dfrac{hL}{k}$;   (*ii*) Grashoff number $Gr = \dfrac{L^3 \beta g \Delta t}{\nu^2}$

(*iii*) Prandtl number $Pr = \dfrac{\mu \ c_p}{k}$

8.6.1. VERTICAL PLATES AND CYLINDERS

The commonly used correlations are:

Laminar flow: $\overline{Nu}_L = 0.59 \ (Gr . Pr)^{1/4}$ for $(10^4 < Gr . Pr < 10^9)$ ...(8.37)

Turbulent flow: $\overline{Nu}_L = 0.10 \ (Gr . Pr)^{1/3}$ for $(10^9 < Gr . Pr < 10^{12})$ ...(8.38)

All the fluid properties are evaluated at the mean film temperature $\left(t_f = \dfrac{t_s + t_\infty}{2}\right)$.

Churchill and Chu have recommended the following correlations:

$$\overline{Nu}_L = 0.68 + \frac{0.67 \ (Gr . Pr)^{1/4}}{\left[1 + \left(\dfrac{0.492}{Pr}\right)^{9/16}\right]^{4/9}} \qquad \text{for } (Gr . Pr < 10^9) \quad ...(8.39)$$

$$\overline{Nu}_L = \left[0.825 + \frac{0.387 \ (Gr . Pr)^{1/6}}{\left[1 + \left(\dfrac{0.492}{Pr}\right)^{9/16}\right]^{8/27}}\right]^2 \qquad \text{for } (Gr . Pr > 10^9) \quad ...(8.40)$$

8.6.2. HORIZONTAL PLATES

In case of an irregular plate, the *characteristic length* is defined as the *surface area divided by the perimeter of the plate.*

(*i*) *The upper surface heated or the lower surface cooled:*

Laminar flow: $\overline{Nu}_L = 0.54 \ (Gr . Pr)^{1/4}$ for $(10^5 < Gr . Pr \le 2 \times 10^7)$ ...(8.41)

Turbulent flow: $\overline{Nu}_L = 0.14 \ (Gr . Pr)^{1/3}$ for $(2 \times 10^7 < Gr . Pr \le 3 \times 10^{10})$ ...(8.42)

(ii) *The lower surface heated or upper surface cooled*:

$$\text{Laminar flow: } \overline{Nu}_L = 0.27 \, (Gr \cdot Pr)^{1/4} \quad \text{for } (3 \times 10^5 < Gr \cdot Pr \le 3 \times 10^{10}) \quad ...(8.43)$$

$$\text{Turbulent flow: } \overline{Nu}_L = 0.107 \, (Gr \cdot Pr)^{1/3} \quad \text{for } (7 \times 10^6 < Gr \cdot Pr \le 11 \times 10^{10}) \quad ...(8.44)$$

8.6.3. HORIZONTAL CYLINDERS

For such a case, the *outside diameter is used as the characteristic dimension.*

Mc Adams has recommended the following correlations:

$$\text{Laminar flow: } \overline{Nu} = 0.53 \, (Gr \cdot Pr)^{1/4} \quad \text{for } (10^4 \, Gr \cdot Pr < 10^9) \quad ...(8.45)$$

$$\text{Turbulent flow: } \overline{Nu} = 0.13 \, (Gr \cdot Pr)^{1/3} \quad \text{for } (10^9 < Gr \cdot Pr < 10^{12}) \quad ...(8.46)$$

The following general correlation has been suggested by Churchill and Chu for use over a wide range of $Gr \cdot Pr$.

$$\overline{Nu} = \left[0.60 + \frac{0.387 \, (Gr \cdot Pr)^{1/6}}{\left\{1 + (0.559/Pr)^{9/16}\right\}^{8/27}} \right] \quad \text{for } (10^{-5} < Gr \cdot Pr < 10^{12}) \quad ...(8.47)$$

The fluid properties, in all preceding equations, are determined at the mean film temperature

$$t_f = \left(\frac{t_s + t_\infty}{2} \right).$$

8.6.4. INCLINED PLATES

For this case multiply Grashoff number by $\cos \theta$, where θ is the angle of inclination from the vertical and use vertical plate constants.

8.6.5. SPHERES

Yuge (1959) has recommended the following correlation for free convection from a sphere of diameter D:

$$\overline{Nu} = 2 + 0.43 \, (Gr \cdot Pr)^{1/4}$$
$$\text{for } (1 < Gr \cdot Pr < 10^5) \text{ and } Pr = 1) \quad ...(8.48)$$

8.6.6. ENCLOSED SPACES

In the literature, several correlations for heat transfer between surfaces at different temperatures separated by enclosed fluids are available. In this section, some correlations are presented that are pertinent to the most common geometries.

(a) **Vertical spaces**

Jacob has suggested the following correlations for *vertical enclosed air spaces* shown in Fig. 8.2.

(i) $\dfrac{k_e}{k} = \overline{Nu} = \dfrac{\overline{h}L}{k} = 0.18 \, (Gr_L)^{1/4} \left(\dfrac{H}{L} \right)^{-1/9}$

for $(2000 \, Gr_L < 2 \times 10^4)$ ...(8.49)

(ii) $\dfrac{k_e}{k} = \overline{Nu} = \dfrac{\overline{h}L}{k} = 0.064 \, (Gr_L)^{1/3} \left(\dfrac{H}{L} \right)^{-1/9}$

for $(2 \times 10^4 < Gr_L < 11 \times 10^6)$ ...(8.50)

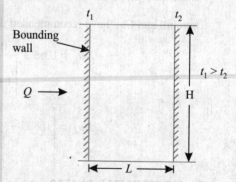

Fig. 8.2. Free convection in vertical enclosure.

where, k_e = Effective thermal conductivity, $\dfrac{Q}{h} = k_e \left(\dfrac{t_1 - t_2}{L} \right)$

H = Height of the air space, and

L = Thickness of the air space.

Gr is based on thickness of air space, L.

(b) Horizontal spaces

The following correlation has been suggested by Jacob for *horizontal enclosed air spaces*:

(i)
$$\frac{k_e}{k} = \overline{Nu} = \frac{\overline{h}L}{k} = 0.195 \, (Gr_L)^{1/4} \qquad \text{for } (10^4 < Gr_L < 4 \times 10^5) \qquad ...(8.51)$$

(ii)
$$\frac{k_e}{k} = \overline{Nu} = \frac{\overline{h}L}{k} = 0.068 \, (Gr_L)^{1/3} \qquad \text{for } (4 \times 10^5 < Gr_L) \qquad ...(8.52)$$

where
$$\overline{Nu} = \frac{q.L}{k \, (t_1 - t_2)} \qquad ...[8.52\,(a)]$$

In the case of *liquids* contained in horizontal spaces, Globe and Dropkin have proposed the following correlation:

$$\overline{Nu} = \frac{\overline{h}L}{k} = 0.069 \, (Gr_L)^{1/3} \, (Pr)^{0.407}$$

$$\text{for } (3 \times 10^5 < Gr \cdot Pr < 7 \times 10^9) \qquad ...(8.53)$$

8.6.7. CONCENTRIC CYLINDERS SPACES

Raithby and Hollands have recommended the following correlations for *long horizontal concentric cylinders*:

$$\frac{k_e}{k} = 0.386 \left(\frac{Pr}{0.861 + Pr} \right)^{1/4} (Ra_c)^{1/4}$$

$$\text{for } 10^2 \le Ra_c \le 10^7 \qquad ...(8.54)$$

where,
$$Ra_c = (Gr \cdot Pr)_c = \frac{[\ln \, (D_o / D_i)]^4}{L^3 \left[D_i^{-3/5} + D_o^{-3/5} \right]} \, Ra_L$$

and k_e is related as

$$Q = \frac{2\pi \, k_e}{\ln \, (D_o / D_i)} \, (t_i - t_o)$$

8.6.8. CONCENTRIC SPHERES SPACES

Refer Fig. 8.3. Raithby and Hollands have recommended the following correlations:

$$Q = k_e \, \pi \, (D_i \, D_o / L) \, (t_i - t_o) \qquad ...(8.55)$$

and, k_e is expressed as

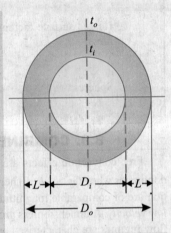

Fig. 8.3. Long concentric cylinders (or spheres).

$$\frac{k_e}{k} = 0.74 \left[\frac{Pr}{0.861 + Pr} \right]^{1/4} (Ra_s)^{1/4} \qquad ...[8.55\,(a)]$$

where,
$$Ra_s = (Gr \cdot Pr)_s = \left[\frac{L \, Ra_L}{(D_o \, D_i)^4 \, (D_i^{-7/15} + D_o^{-7/15})^5} \right]^{1/4} \qquad ...(8.56)$$

The above equations are valid for $(10^2 \le Ra_s \le 10^4)$.

8.7. SIMPLIFIED FREE CONVECTION RELATIONS FOR AIR

The simplified relation for the heat transfer coefficient from different surfaces to air at atmospheric pressure, in general, is given by

$$h = C \left(\frac{\Delta t}{L} \right)^m \qquad ...(8.57)$$

where C and m are constants depending on geometry and flow conditions; the significant length L is also a function of geometry and flow. Table 8.1 lists the values suggested by Mc Adams for various geometries, orientations and flow conditions indicated by the magnitude of product $(Gr \cdot Pr)$.

Table 8.1: Simplified free convection relations for air

S.No.	Surface and its orientation	Laminar	Turbulent
1.	Vertical plate or cylinder	$\bar{h} = 1.42 \left(\dfrac{\Delta t}{L}\right)^{1/4}$ $(10^4 < Gr \cdot Pr < 10^9)$	$\bar{h} = 1.32\,(\Delta t)^{1/3}$ $(10^9 < Gr \cdot Pr < 10^{13})$
2.	Horizontal cylinder	$\bar{h} = 1.32 \left(\dfrac{\Delta t}{D}\right)^{1/4}$ $(10^4 < Gr \cdot Pr < 10^9)$	$\bar{h} = 1.25\,(\Delta t)^{1/3}$ $(10^9 < Gr \cdot Pr < 10^{12})$
3.	Horizontal plate:		
	Heated surface facing up	$\bar{h} = 1.32 \left(\dfrac{\Delta t}{L}\right)^{1/4}$ $(10^5 < Gr \cdot Pr < 2 \times 10^7)$	$\bar{h} = 1.67\,(\Delta t)^{1/3}$ $(2 \times 10^7 < Gr \cdot Pr < 3 \times 10^{10})$
	Heated surface facing down	$\bar{h} = 0.59 \left(\dfrac{\Delta t}{L}\right)^{1/4}$ $(3 \times 10^5 < Gr \cdot Pr < 3 \times 10^{10})$	
4.	Spheres	$\bar{h} = [2 + 0.392\,(Gr)^{1/4}]\dfrac{k}{D}$ $(1 < Gr < 10^5)$	

8.8. COMBINED FREE AND FORCED CONVECTION

Free convection effects are negligible when $Gr << R_e^2$, at the other extreme, free convection dominates when $Gr >> R_e^2$. There are certain situations where the free as well as the forced convection are of comparable magnitude. One such case is *when air is flowing over a heated surface at a low velocity*. A dimensionless group (Gr/R_e^2) is used to delineate the convection regimes. The various flow regimes are characterised as follows:

$(Gr/R_e^2) \geq 1$ ... Pure free convection

$(Gr/R_e^2) \simeq 1$ ... Mixed (free and forced) convection

$(Gr/R_e^2) \leq 1$ ... Pure forced convection.

8.8.1. EXTERNAL FLOWS

The local Nusselt number Nu_x for *mixed convection on vertical plates* is given by

$$Nu_x = 0.332\,(Re_x)^{1/2}\,(Pr)^{1/3} \text{ if } (Gr_x/R_{e_x}^2) \leq A \qquad ...(8.58)$$

and,

$$Nu_x = 0.508\,(Pr)^{1/2}\,(0.952 + Pr)^{-1/4}\,(Gr_x)^{1/4} \text{ if } (Gr_x/R_{e_x}^2) > A \qquad ...(8.59)$$

where, $A \simeq 0.6$ for $Pr \leq 10$

and, $A \simeq 1.0$ for $Pr = 100$

For *horizontal plates* when $(Gr_x/Re_x^{2.5}) \leq 0.083$ the following equation for forced convection may be used

$$Nu_x = 0.332\,Re_x^{1/2}\,Pr^{1/3} \qquad ...(8.60)$$

8.8.2. INTERNAL FLOWS

(*i*) For mixed convection in laminar flow, Brown and Gauvin recommended a correlation of the form as :

$$\overline{Nu} = 1.75 \left(\frac{\mu_b}{\mu_s}\right)^{0.14} \quad [Gz + 0.012 \, (Gz \cdot Gr^{1/3})^{4/3}]^{1/3} \qquad \qquad ...(8.61)$$

where, Gz = Graetz number = $Re \, Pr \, (D/L)$

and, μ_b, μ_s = Viscosities of the fluid at the bulk mean temperature and surface temperature respectively.

(ii) For mixed convection with turbulent flow in horizontal tubes, Metais and Eckert (1966) suggest

$$\overline{Nu} = 4.69 \, (Re)^{0.27} \, (Pr)^{0.21} \, (Gr)^{0.07} \, (D/L)^{0.36} \qquad \qquad ...(8.62)$$

Example 8.1. *A vertical cylinder 1.5 m high and 180 mm in diameter is maintained at 100°C in an atmosphere environment of 20°C. Calculate heat loss by free convection from the surface of the cylinder. Assume properties of air at mean temperature as, $\rho = 1.06 \, kg/m^3$, $v = 18.97 \times 10^{-6} \, m^2/s$, $c_p = 1.004 \, kJ/kg°C$ and $k = 0.1042 \, kJ/mh°C$.* (AMIE Summer, 2000)

Solution. *Given :* $L = 1.5$ m; $D = 180$ mm $= 0.18$ m, $t_s = 100°C$;

$t_\infty = 20°C$; $\rho = 1.06 \, kg/m^3$; $v = 18.97 \times 10^{-6} \, m^2/s$;

$c_p = 1.004 \, kJ/kg°C$; $k = 0.1042 \, kJ/m \, h°C$.

Heat loss by free convection, Q :

$$\mu = \rho v = 1.06 \times (18.97 \times 10^{-6} \times 3600) = 0.07239 \, kg/mh$$

$$\beta = \frac{1}{T} = \frac{1}{273 + t_f} = \frac{1}{273 + \left(\dfrac{100 + 20}{2}\right)} = 0.003 \, K^{-1}$$

$$Gr = \frac{L^3 g \beta \Delta t}{v^2} \qquad \qquad ...[Eqn. (8.3)]$$

$$= \frac{(1.5)^3 \times 9.81 \times 0.003 \times (100 - 20)}{(18.97 \times 10^{-6})^2} = 2.208 \times 10^{10}$$

$$Pr = \frac{\mu c_p}{k} = \frac{0.07239 \times 1.004}{0.1042} = 0.6975$$

$$Gr \, Pr = 2.208 \times 10^{10} \times 0.6975 = 1.54 \times 10^{10}$$

Free convection.

For this value of $Gr\, Pr$ (tubulent range),

$$\overline{Nu_L} = \frac{\overline{h}L}{k} = 0.10\,(Gr.Pr)^{1/3} \quad \text{(for } 10^9 < Gr.Pr < 10^{12}) \quad …[\text{Eqn. (8.38)}]$$

$$= 0.10\,(1.54 \times 10^{10})^{1/3} = 248.79$$

$$\therefore \qquad \overline{h} = \frac{k}{L} \times 248.79 = \frac{0.1042}{1.5} \times 248.79 = 17.283 \text{ kJ/h m}^2\text{°C}$$

$\therefore$ Rate of heat loss, $Q = \overline{h}A\,(t_s - t_\infty)$

$$= 17.283 \times (\pi \times 0.18 \times 1.5) \times (100 - 20)$$

$$= \textbf{1172.8 kJ/h} \quad \textbf{(Ans.)}$$

Example 8.2. *A cylindrical body of 300 mm diameter and 1.6 m height is maintained at a constant temperature of 36.5°C. The surrounding temperature is 13.5°C. Find out the amount of heat to be generated by the body per hour if $\rho = 1.025$ kg/m³; $c_p = 0.96$ kJ/kg°C; $v = 15.06 \times 10^{-6}$ m²/s; $k = 0.0892$ kJ/m-h-°C and $\beta = \dfrac{1}{298}$ K^{-1}. Assume $Nu = 0.12\,(Gr\,.\,Pr)^{1/3}$ (the symbols have their usual meanings).*

(AMIE Winter, 1997)

Solution. *Given :* $D = 300$ mm $= 0.3$ m; $L = 1.6$ m; $t_s = 36.5$°C; $t_\infty = 13.5$°C;

$$\rho = 1.025 \text{ kg/m}^3; \ c_p = 0.96 \text{ kJ/kg°C}; \ v = 15.06 \times 10^{-6} \text{ m}^2\text{/s};$$

$$k = 0.0892 \text{ kJ/m-h-°C}; \ \beta = \frac{1}{298} \ K^{-1}; \ Nu = 0.12\,(Gr\,.\,Pr)^{1/3}$$

The amount of heat to be generated :

Grashoff number, $Gr = \dfrac{L^3 g\beta\,(t_s - t_\infty)}{v^2}$

$$= \frac{(1.6)^3 \times 9.81 \times \left(\dfrac{1}{298}\right) \times (36.5 - 13.5)}{(15.06 \times 10^{-6})^2} = 1.3674 \times 10^{10}$$

Prandtl number, $Pr = \dfrac{\mu c_p}{k} = \dfrac{\rho v c_p}{k} = \dfrac{1.025 \times (15.06 \times 10^{-6} \times 3600) \times 0.96}{0.0892}$ $\left(\because v = \dfrac{\mu}{\rho}\right)$

Nusselt number, $Nu = \dfrac{hL}{k} = 0.12\,(Gr.Pr)^{1/3}$

$$= 0.12\,(1.3674 \times 10^{10} \times 0.598)^{1/3} = 241.75$$

$\therefore$ $\qquad h = \dfrac{k}{L} \times 241.75 = \dfrac{0.0892}{1.6} \times 241.75 = 13.478 \text{ kJ/h m}^2\text{°C}$

Heat lost from the surface by natural convection,

$$Q = hA\,(t_s - t_\infty)$$

$$= 13.478 \times (\pi \times 0.3 \times 1.6)\,(36.5 - 13.5) = *\textbf{467.5 kJ/h} \quad \textbf{(Ans.)}$$

* This is the amount of heat to be generated.

Example 8.3. *A hot plate 1.2 m wide, 0.35 m high and at 115°C is exposed to the ambient still air at 25°C. Calculate the following:*

(i) *Maximum velocity at 180 mm from the leading edge of the plate;*

(ii) *The boundary layer thickness at 180 mm from the leading edge of the plate;*

(iii) *Local heat transfer coefficient at 180 mm from the leading edge of the plate;*

(iv) *Average heat transfer coefficient over the surface of the plate;*

(v) *Total mass flow through the boundary;*

(vi)   *Heat loss from the plate;*

(vii) *Rise in temperature of the air passing through the boundary.*

    Use the approximate solution.

Solution. Given : $t_s = 115°C$, $t_\infty = 25°C$, $x = 180$ mm $= 0.18$ m

The mean film temperature, $t_f = \dfrac{t_s + t_\infty}{2} = \dfrac{115 + 25}{2} = 70°C$

The thermo-physical properties of air at 70°C are :

$$\rho = 1.029 \text{ kg/m}^3; \ k = 0.02964 \text{ w/m°C}; \ v = 20.02 \times 10^{-6} \text{ m}^2/\text{s}$$

$$Pr = 0.694, \ \beta = \frac{1}{T} = \frac{1}{(273 + t_f)} = \frac{1}{(273 + 70)} = \frac{1}{343} = 0.002915$$

Grashoff number $Gr_x = \dfrac{x^3 \, g\beta \, (t_s - t_\infty)}{v^2}$

$$= \frac{(0.18)^3 \times 9.81 \times 0.002915 \, (115 - 25)}{(20.02 \times 10^{-6})^2} = 3.745 \times 10^7$$

and, $Gr_L = 3.745 \times 10^7 \times \left(\dfrac{0.35}{0.18}\right)^3 = 27.532 \times 10^7$

(i)   Maximum velocity at 180 mm from the leading edge of the plate, u_{max}:

$$u_{max} = 0.766 \, v \left(0.952 + \frac{v}{\alpha}\right)^{-1/2} \left[\frac{g\beta \, (t_s - t_\infty)}{v^2}\right]^{1/2} (x)^{1/2} \qquad ...[\text{Eqn. (8.25)}]$$

$$= 0.766 \times 20.02 \times 10^{-6} \, (0.952 + 0.694)^{-1/2} \times \left[\frac{9.81 \times 0.002915 \, (115 - 25)}{(20.02 \times 10^{-6})^2}\right]^{1/2} (0.18)^{1/2}$$

$\mathbf{= 0.406 \text{ m/s}}$ **(Ans.)** $\left(\because Pr = \dfrac{v}{\alpha} = 0.694 \text{ ...as given above}\right)$

(ii) The boundary layer thickness at 180 mm from the leading edge of the plate, δ:

$$\frac{\delta}{x} = 3.93 \, (0.952 + Pr)^{1/4} \, (Gr_x)^{-1/4} \, (Pr)^{-1/2} \qquad ...[\text{Eqn. (8.27)}]$$

$$= 3.93 \, (0.952 + 0.694)^{1/4} \, (3.745 \times 10^7)^{-1/4} \, (0.694)^{-1/2} = 0.0683$$

or, $\delta = 0.0683 \times 0.18 = 0.01229$ m $= \mathbf{12.29}$ **mm**   **(Ans.)**

(iii) Local heat transfer coefficient at 180 mm from the leading edge of the plate, h_x:

$$Nu_x = \frac{h_x \, x}{k} = 0.508 \, (Pr)^{1/2} \, (0.952 + Pr)^{-1/4} \, (Gr_x)^{1/4} = \frac{2x}{\delta} \qquad ...[\text{Eqn. (8.31)}]$$

$$h_x = \frac{k}{x} \times \frac{2x}{\delta} = \frac{2k}{\delta} = \frac{2 \times 0.02964}{0.01229} = \mathbf{4.823 \text{ W/m}^2°C} \qquad \textbf{(Ans.)}$$

(iv) Average heat transfer coefficient over the surface of the plate, $\overline{h}$:

$$\overline{h} = \frac{k}{L} \, [0.677 \, (Pr)^{1/2} \, (0.952 + Pr)^{-1/4} \, (Gr_L)^{1/4}] \qquad ...[\text{Eqn. (8.33)}]$$

$$= \frac{0.02964}{0.35} \, [0.677 \, (0.694)^{1/2} \, (0.952 + 0.694)^{-1/4} \, (27.532 \times 10^7)^{1/4}]$$

$$= \mathbf{5.43 \text{ W/m}^2°C} \quad \textbf{(Ans.)}$$

(v) Total mass flow through the boundary, m_t:

Total mass flow through the boundary can be calculated from the following formula :

$$m_t = 1.7 \, \rho.v \left[\frac{Gr_L}{(P_r^2)(Pr + 0.952)} \right]^{1/4}$$

$$= 1.7 \times 1.029 \times 20.02 \times 10^{-6} \left[\frac{27.532 \times 10^7}{(0.694)^2 (0.694 + 0.952)} \right]$$

or, $\qquad m_t = \textbf{0.00478 kg/s}$ **(Ans.)**

(vi) Heat loss from the plate, Q :

Heat lost from the plate will be from both the sides, hence

$$Q = 2 \, \bar{h} \, A_s \, (t_s - t_\infty)$$

$$= 2 \times 5.43 \times (0.35 \times 1.2)(115 - 25) = \textbf{410.5 W} \qquad \textbf{(Ans.)}$$

(vii) Rise in temperature of the air passing through the boundary, Δt:

Heat lost, $Q = m_t c_p \, \Delta t$

or, $\qquad 410.5 = 0.00478 \times (1.005 \times 10^3) \times \Delta t$

or, $\qquad \Delta t = \dfrac{410.5}{0.00478 \times (1.005 \times 10^3)} = \textbf{85.45°C} \qquad \textbf{(Ans.)}$

Example 8.4. *A 350 mm long glass plate is hung vertically in the air at 24°C while its temperature is maintained at 80°C. Calculate the boundary layer thickness at the trailing edge of the plate. If a similar plate is placed in a wind tunnel and air is blown over it at a velocity of 5 m/s, find the boundary layer thickness at its trailing edge.*

Also determine the average heat transfer coefficient, for natural and forced convection for the above mentioned data.

Solution. *Given:* $\quad L = 350$ mm $= 0.35$ m, $t_\infty = 24°C$, $t_s = 80°C$, $U = 5$ m/s

Film temperature, $\quad t_f = \dfrac{t_s + t_\infty}{2} = \dfrac{80 + 24}{2} = 52°C$

The properties of air at 52°C are:

$k = 28.15 \times 10^{-3}$ W/m°C; $v = 18.41 \times 10^{-6}$ m²/s; $Pr = 0.7$; $\beta = \left(\dfrac{1}{52 + 273} \right) = 3.07 \times 10^{-3}$ K⁻¹

Boundary layer thickness, δ:

Free convection:

Grashoff number, $\quad Gr_L = \dfrac{L^3 \, g\beta(t_s - t_\infty)}{v^2} = \dfrac{(0.35)^3 \times 9.81 \times 3.07 \times 10^{-3}(80-24)}{(18.41 \times 10^{-6})^2} = 2.133 \times 10^8$

$\therefore$ Rayleigh number, $Ra_L = Gr_L . Pr = 2.133 \times 10^8 \times 0.7 = 1.493 \times 10^8$

This value of the Rayleigh number, according to eqn. (8.36), indicates a laminar boundary layer. Using the eqn. (8.27), we get

$$\frac{\delta}{x} = 3.93 \, (0.952 + Pr)^{1/4} \, (Gr)^{-1/4} \, (Pr)^{-1/2}$$

or, $\qquad \delta = 0.35 \, [\, 3.93 \, (0.952 + 0.7 \,)^{1/4} \, (2.133 \times 10^8)^{-1/4} \, (0.7)^{-1/2}] = 0.0154$ m

$$= \textbf{15.4 mm} \qquad \textbf{(Ans.)}$$

Forced convection:

Reynolds number, $\quad Re = \dfrac{UL}{v} = \dfrac{5 \times 0.35}{18.41 \times 10^{-6}} = 9.505 \times 10^4$

So the boundary layer is *laminar*.

$$\delta = \frac{5L}{\sqrt{Re}} = \frac{5 \times 0.35}{\sqrt{9.505 \times 10^4}} = 0.00567 \text{ m} = \textbf{5.67 mm} \quad \textbf{(Ans.)}$$

Thus the boundary layer thickness in forced convection is *less* than that in free convection.

Heat transfer coefficient $\bar{h}$:

Free convection :

$$Nu_L = \frac{\bar{h}L}{k} = 0.677 \, (Pr)^{1/2} \, (0.952 + Pr)^{-1/4} \, (Gr)^{1/4} \qquad \text{...[Eqn. (8.33)]}$$

$$= 0.677 \, (0.7)^{1/2} \, (0.952 + 0.7)^{-1/4} \, (2.133 \times 10^8)^{1/4} = 60.378$$

or, $$\bar{h} = \frac{k}{L} \times 60.378 = \frac{28.15 \times 10^{-3}}{0.35} \times 60.378 = \textbf{4.856 W/m}^2{}^\circ\textbf{C} \quad \textbf{(Ans.)}$$

Forced convection :

$$\overline{Nu}_L = \frac{\bar{h}L}{k} = 0.664 \, (Re_L)^{1/2} \, (Pr)^{1/3}$$

$$= 0.664 \, (9.505 \times 10^4)^{1/2} \, (0.7)^{0.333} = 181.78$$

or, $$\bar{h} = \frac{k}{L} \times 181.78 = \frac{28.15 \times 10^{-3}}{0.35} \times 181.78 = \textbf{14.62 W/m}^2{}^\circ\textbf{C} \quad \textbf{(Ans.)}$$

Thus it is seen that heat transfer coefficient in forced convection is *much larger* than that in free convection.

Example 8.5. *A sheet metal air duct carries air-conditioned air at an average temperature of 10°C. The duct size is 320 mm × 200 mm and length of the duct exposed to the surrounding air at 30°C is 15 m long. Find the heat gain by the air in the duct. Assume 200 mm side is vertical and top surface of the duct is insulated. Use the following properties :*

$Nu = 0.6 \, (Gr.Pr)^{0.25}$ for vertical surface.

$Nu = 0.27 \, (Gr.Pr)^{0.25}$ for horizontal surface.

Take the properties of the air at mean temperature of $(30 + 10)/2 = 20°C$ as given below :

$c_p = 100$ J/kg K; $\rho = 1.204$ kg/m³; $\mu = 18.2 \times 10^{-6}$ N-s/m²;
$v = 15.1 \times 10^{-6}$ m²/s; $k = 0.256$ W/m K and $Pr = 0.71$.

(M.U. Winter, 1998)

Solution. Refer Fig. 8.4.

There will be two vertical surfaces and one horizontal surface from which the heat will be gained by *natural convection*. There is no heat transfer from the top surface as it is insulated.

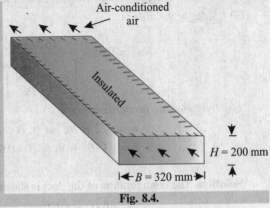

Air-conditioned air

Insulated

$H = 200$ mm

|← $B = 320$ mm →|

Fig. 8.4.

Now, $(Gr)_v = \dfrac{g\beta H^3 \, (\Delta t)}{v^2}$

$$= \frac{9.81 \times \left(\dfrac{1}{273 + 20}\right) \times 0.2^3 \times (30 - 10)}{(15.1 \times 10^{-6})^2}$$

$$= 2.35 \times 10^7$$

$$(Gr.Pr)_v = 2.35 \times 10^7 \times 0.71 = 16.68 \times 10^6$$

$$(Nu)_v = \frac{h_v \cdot H}{k} = 0.6 \ (16.68 \times 10^6)^{0.25} = 38.34$$

$$\therefore \quad h_v = \frac{k}{H} \times 38.34 = \frac{0.256}{0.2} \times 38.34 = 49.07 \ \text{W/m}^2 \, ^\circ\text{C}$$

$$Q_v = h_v \times A_v \times (\Delta t) = 49.07 \times (2 \times 15 \times 0.2) \times (30 - 10) = 5888.4 \ \text{W}$$

$$(Gr)_h = \frac{9.81 \times \dfrac{1}{(273 + 20)} \times (0.32)^3 \times (30 - 10)}{(15.1 \times 10^{-6})^2} = 9.62 \times 10^7$$

$$(Gr.Pr)_h = 9.62 \times 10^7 \times 0.71 = 6.83 \times 10^7$$

$$(Nu)_h = \frac{h_h \times B}{k} = 0.27 \ (6.83 \times 10^7)^{0.25} = 24.54$$

$$h_h = \frac{k}{B} = 24.54 = \frac{0.256}{0.32} = 24.54 = 19.63 \ \text{W/m}^2 \, ^\circ\text{C}$$

$$Q_h = h_h \times A_h \times (\Delta t) = 19.63 \times (15 \times 0.32) \times (30 - 10) = 1884.5 \ \text{W}$$

$\therefore$ Total heat gain, $Q = Q_v + Q_h = 5888.4 + 1884.5 = \textbf{7772.9 W}$ **(Ans.)**

Example 8.6. *Air flows through long rectangular heating duct of width and height of 0.75 m and 0.3 m respectively. The outer surface temperature of the duct is maintained at 45°C. If the duct is exposed to air at 15°C in a cramp-space beneath a home, what is the heat loss from the duct per metre length ?*

Use the following correlations :

(i) *Top surface :*

Take $\qquad L_c = \dfrac{B}{2} = 0.375 \, m$.

$$\overline{Nu}_L = 0.54 \ (Ra_L)^{0.25} \ \text{if} \ 10^4 \le Ra_L \le 10^7$$
$$= 0.15 \ (Ra_L)^{0.33} \ \text{if} \ 10^7 \le Ra_L \le 10^{11}$$

(ii) *Bottom surface :*

Take $\qquad L_c = \dfrac{B}{2} = 0.375 \, m$

$$\overline{Nu}_L = 0.27 \ (Ra_L)^{0.25}, \ 10^5 \le Ra_L \le 10^{10}$$

(iii) *Sides of the duct :*

$$\overline{Nu}_L = 0.68 + \frac{0.67 \ (Ra_L)^{0.25}}{\left[1 + \left(\dfrac{0.492}{Pr} \right)^{9/16} \right]^{4/9}}$$

Use the following properties of air :

$$v = 16.2 \times 10^{-6} \ m^2/s, \ \alpha = 22.9 \times 10^{-6} \ m^2/s$$
$$k = 0.0265 \ W/m \ K, \ \beta = 0.0033 \ K^{-1} \ and \ Pr = 0.71.$$

(N.M.U. Winter, 1995)

Solution. The configuration of the duct is shown in Fig. 8.5.

$$Ra_L = \frac{g\beta \ (t_s - t_a) \ L_c^3}{\alpha v} \qquad\qquad …\text{[Eqn. (8.36)]}$$

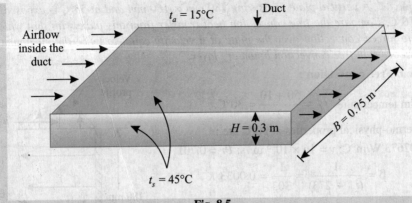

Fig. 8.5

$$= \frac{9.81 \times 0.0033 \times (45 - 15) \, L_c^3}{(22.9 \times 10^{-6}) \times (16.2 \times 10^{-6})} = 2.62 \times 10^9 \, (L_c^3)$$

For two sides :

$$L_c = H = 0.3 \text{ m}$$

$$\therefore \quad Ra_L = 2.62 \times 10^9 \, (0.3)^3 = 7.07 \times 10^7$$

$$\therefore \quad Nu_L = 0.68 + \frac{0.67 \, (7.07 \times 10^7)^{0.25}}{\left[1 + \left(\frac{0.492}{0.71}\right)^{9/16}\right]^{4/9}} = 0.68 + \frac{61.44}{1.3} = 47.94$$

$$\therefore \quad \frac{h_s \, L_c}{k} = 47.94$$

or, $$h_s = \frac{k}{L_c} \times 47.94 = \frac{0.0265 \times 47.94}{0.3} = 4.23 \text{ W/m}^2{}^\circ\text{C}$$

For top surface :

$$\overline{Nu}_L = \frac{h_t \, L_c}{k} = 0.15 \, (Ra_L)^{0.33} = 0.15 \, (7.07 \times 10^7)^{0.33} = 58.4$$

$$\therefore \quad h_t = \frac{k}{L_c} \times 58.4 = \frac{0.0265 \times 58.4}{0.375} = 4.127 \text{ W/m}^2{}^\circ\text{C}$$

$$\left(\because L_c = \frac{B}{2} = \frac{0.75}{2} = 0.375 \text{ m}\right)$$

For bottom surface :

$$\overline{Nu}_L = \frac{h_b \, L_c}{k} = 0.27 \, (Ra_L)^{0.25} = 0.27 \, (7.07 \times 10^7)^{0.25} = 24.76$$

$$\therefore \quad h_b = \frac{k}{L_c} \times 24.76 = \frac{0.0265}{0.375} \times 24.76 = 1.75 \text{ W/m}^2{}^\circ\text{C}$$

The rate of heat loss per unit length of the duct is given by,

$$Q = Q_s + Q_t + Q_b$$

$$= [2 \times h_s \times (0.3 \times 1) + h_t \times (0.75 \times 1) + h_b \times (0.75 \times 1)] \, (t_s - t_a)$$

$$= [2 \times 4.23 \times 0.3 + 4.127 \times 0.75 \times 1 + 1.75 \times 0.75 \times 1] \, (45 - 15)$$

$$= \mathbf{208.4 \ W/m} \quad \textbf{(Ans.)}$$

Example 8.7. *A vertical plate measuring 180 mm × 180 mm and at 50°C is exposed to atmosphere at 10°C. Compare the free convection heat transfer from this plate with that which would result due to forced convection over the plate at a velocity equal to twice the maximum velocity which would occur in free convection boundary layer.*

Solution. Free convection :

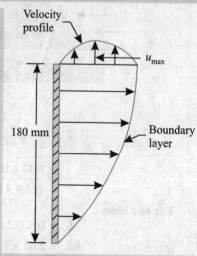

The film temperature, $t_f = \dfrac{50 + 10}{2} = 30°C.$

The thermo-physical properties at 30°C are :

$k = 0.02673$ W/m°C; $v = 16 \times 10^{-6}$ m²/s; $Pr = 0.701$

$$\beta = \frac{1}{(t_f + 273)} = \frac{1}{303} = 0.0033\ K^{-1}$$

$$Gr_L = \frac{L^3\, g\beta\, \Delta t}{v^2}$$

$$= \frac{(0.18)^3 \times 9.81 \times 0.0033 \times (50 - 10)}{(16 \times 10^{-6})^2}$$

$$= 2.95 \times 10^7$$

Since $Gr < 10^9$, hence the flow is laminar.

For laminar flow, using the following relation, we get,

Fig. 8.6.

$$\overline{Nu}_L = \frac{\overline{h}L}{k} = 0.677\ (Pr)^{1/2}\ (0.952 + Pr)^{-1/4}\ (Gr_L)^{1/4}$$

$$= 0.677\ (0.701)^{1/2}\ (0.952 + 0.701)^{-1/4}\ (2.95 \times 10^7)^{1/4} = 36.84$$

or, $\qquad \overline{h} = \dfrac{k}{L} \times 36.84 = \dfrac{0.02673}{0.18} \times 36.84 = 5.47$ W/m²°C

The heat lost from one side of the plate,

$$Q_{free} = \overline{h}\ A_s\ \Delta t = 5.47 \times (0.18 \times 0.18) \times (50 - 10) = 7.089\ W$$

Forced convection :

$$u_{max} = 0.766\ v\left(0.952 + \frac{v}{\alpha}\right)^{-1/2}\left[\frac{g\beta\ (t_s - t_\infty)}{v^2}\right]^{1/2}(x)^{1/2} \qquad ...[Eqn.\ (8.25)]$$

$$= 0.766 \times 16 \times 10^{-6}\ (0.952 + 0.701)^{-1/2}\left[\frac{9.81 \times 0.0033\ (50 - 10)}{(16 \times 10^{-6})^2}\right]^{1/2}(0.18)^{1/2}$$

$$= 0.287\ m/s \qquad\qquad\qquad\qquad \left(\because \frac{v}{\alpha} = Pr = 0.701\right)$$

The average heat transfer coefficient with forced convection if velocity is assumed equal to $2u_{max}$;

$$\overline{Nu}_L = 0.664\ (Re)^{1/2}\ (Pr)^{1/3}$$

$$Re = \frac{LU}{v} = \frac{0.18 \times (2 \times 0.287)}{16 \times 10^{-6}} = 6457.5$$

$$\overline{Nu} = \frac{\overline{h}L}{k} = 0.664\ (6457.5)^{1/2}\ (0.701)^{0.333} = 47.4$$

or, $\qquad \overline{h} = \dfrac{k}{L} \times 47.4 = \dfrac{0.02673}{0.18} \times 47.4 = 7.039$ W/m²°C

Heat lost due to forced convection,

$$Q_{forced} = \overline{h}\ A_s\ \Delta t = 7.039 \times (0.18 \times 0.18)\ (50 - 10) = 9.12\ W$$

Hence, $\dfrac{Q_{free}}{Q_{forced}} = \dfrac{7.089}{9.12} = \textbf{0.777 (Ans.)}$

Example 8.8. *Two vertical plates, each 120 mm high and at 85°C are placed in a tank of water at 15°C. Calculate the minimum spacing which will prevent interference of the free convection boundary layers.*

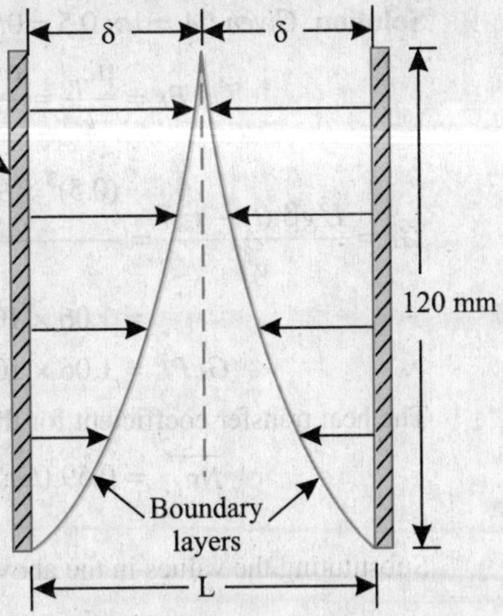

Solution. Let, δ = Boundary layer thickness at the trailing edge of the plate.

$L = 2\delta$ = The minimum spacing required.

Fig. 8.7.

The film temperature, $t_f = \dfrac{85 + 15}{2} = 50°C$

The thermo-physical properties of water at 50°C are:

$k = 0.674$ W/m°C; $v = 0.556 \times 10^{-6}$ m²/s

$Pr = 3.54$; $\beta = \dfrac{1}{(t_f + 273)} = \dfrac{1}{323}$
$= 0.003095$ K⁻¹

$Gr_x = \dfrac{x^3 \, g\beta\Delta t}{v^2} = \dfrac{(0.12)^3 \times 9.81 \times 0.003095 \times (85 - 15)}{(0.556 \times 10^{-6})^2} = 11.88 \times 10^9$

$Gr . Pr = 11.88 \times 10^9 \times 3.54 = 42.055 \times 10^9$

Since $Gr . Pr > 10^9$, hence the character of the flow is *turbulent*.

For turbulent flow, using the following relation, we get

$$\dfrac{\delta}{x} = 0.565 \, (Pr)^{-8/15} \left[\dfrac{1 + 0.494 \, (Pr)^{2/3}}{Gr_x} \right]^{0.1}$$

$$= 0.565 \, (3.54)^{-8/15} \left[\dfrac{1 + 0.494 \, (3.54)^{2/3}}{11.88 \times 10^9} \right]^{0.1} = 0.0306$$

$\delta = 0.0306 \times 0.12 = 0.003672$ m $= 3.672$ mm

$L = 2\delta = 2 \times 3.672 = \textbf{7.344 mm}$ **(Ans.)**

Example 8.9. *A hot plate 1 m × 0.5 m at 130°C is kept vertically in still air at 20°C. Find :*

(i) *Heat transfer coefficient,*

(ii) *Initial rate of cooling the plate in °C/min.*

(iii) *Time required for cooling plate from 180°C if the heat transfer is due to convection only. Mass of the plate is 20 kg and c_p = 400 J/kg K.*

Assume 0.5 m side is vertical and that the heat transfer coefficient calculated in (i) above remains constant and convection takes place from both sides of the plate.

Take properties of air at $\dfrac{130 + 20}{2} = 75°C$ as :

$c_p = 1007$ J/kg°C, $\rho = 1.07$ m²/s; $k = 0.029$ J/kg K; $v = 19.1 \times 10^{-6}$ m²/s   (N.M.U., 1998)

Solution. *Given* : $A = 1 \times 0.5 = 0.5 \text{ m}^2$; $t_p (= t_s) = 130°C$; $t_a = 20°C$; $m = 20 \text{ kg}$; $c_p = 400 \text{ J/kg K}$

$$Pr = \frac{\mu c_p}{k} = \frac{\rho v c_p}{k} = \frac{1.07 \times 19.1 \times 10^{-6} \times 1007}{0.029} = 0.709$$

$$Gr = \frac{L^3 g \beta (t_s - t_\infty)}{v^2} = \frac{(0.5)^3 \times 9.81 \times \left(\dfrac{1}{273 + 75}\right) \times (130 - 20)}{(19.1 \times 10^{-6})^2}$$

$$= 1.06 \times 10^9$$

$\therefore$ $\qquad Gr.Pr = 1.06 \times 10^9 \times 0.709 = 0.75 \times 10^9$

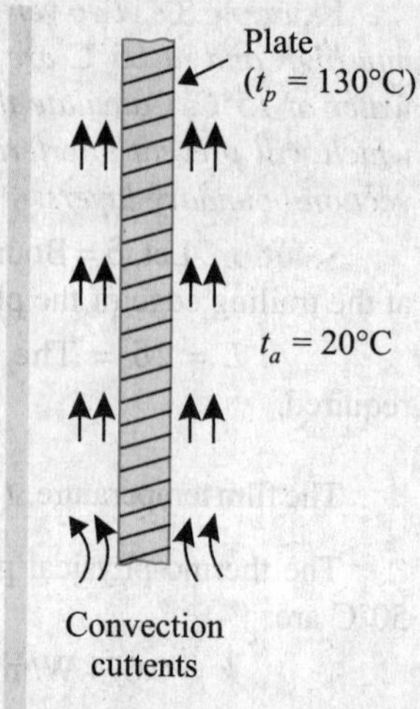

The heat transfer coefficient for the vertical plate is given by

$$\overline{Nu}_L = 0.59 \, (Gr.Pr)^{1/4} \text{ for } (10^4 < Gr.Pr < 10^9)$$

$$...\text{[Eqn. (8.37)]}$$

Substituting the values in the above eqn., we get

$$\overline{Nu}_L = \frac{\overline{h}L}{k} = 0.59 \, (0.75 \times 10^9)^{1/4}$$

or, $\qquad \overline{h} = \dfrac{k}{L} \times 0.59 \, (0.75 \times 10^9)^{1/4}$

$$= \frac{0.029}{0.5} \times 0.59 \, (0.75 \times 10^9)^{1/4} = \textbf{5.66 W/m}^2\textbf{°C} \qquad \textbf{(Ans.)}$$

Plate ($t_p = 130°C$)

$t_a = 20°C$

Convection cuttents

Fig. 8.8

(ii) Initial rate of cooling the plate in °C/min. :

Heat lost from *both sides* of the plate is given by

$$Q = 2 \, [h \times A \, (t_s - t_\infty)] = 2 \, [5.66 \times (1 \times 0.5) \times (130 - 20)] = 622.6 \text{ W}$$

Also, $\qquad Q = mc_p \, (\Delta t)$ where Δt is the rate of cooling.

$\therefore$ $\qquad \Delta t = \dfrac{622.6}{20 \times 400} = 0.0778°C/s = \textbf{4.668°C/min} \quad \textbf{(Ans.)}$

(iii) Time required for cooling plate from 180°C to 80°C, τ :

The instantaneous heat lost by the plate is given by

$$2 \times h \times A \, (t - t_\infty) = -mc_p \frac{dt}{d\tau}$$

or, $\qquad -\dfrac{mc_p}{2hA} \displaystyle\int_{t_1}^{t_2} \dfrac{dt}{(t - t_\infty)} = \int_0^\tau d\tau$

or, $\qquad -\dfrac{mc_p}{2hA} \ln\left(\dfrac{t_2 - t_\infty}{t_1 - t_\infty}\right) = \tau$

$\therefore$ $\qquad \tau = \dfrac{-20 \times 400}{2 \times 5.66 \times (1 \times 0.5)} \ln\left(\dfrac{80 - 20}{180 - 20}\right)$

$$= -1413.43 \times (-0.9808) = 1386 \text{ s or } \textbf{0.385h (Ans.)}$$

Example 8.10. *A square plate 40 cm × 40 cm maintained at 400 K is suspended vertically in atmospheric air at 300 K.*

(i) Determine the boundary layer thickness at trailing edge of the plate.

(ii) Calculate the average heat transfer coefficient using a relation,

$$Nu = 0.516 \, (Gr_L . Pr)^{0.25}$$

Take the following properties of air :

$v = 20.75 \times 10^{-6} \text{ m}^2/s$; $k = 0.03 \text{ W/m°C}$; $\beta = 2.86 \times 10^{-3} \text{ K}^{-1}$; $Pr = 0.7$ $\qquad$ (P.U.)

Solution. *Given :* $t_s = 400$ K, $t_\infty = 300$ K

(i) Boundary layer thickness, δ:

The boundary layer thickness is given by

$$\delta = x \, [3.93 \, (0.952 + Pr)^{1/4} \, (Gr)^{-1/4} \, (Pr)^{-1/2}] \qquad \text{...[Eqn. (8.27)]}$$

$$Gr_x = \frac{x^3 \, g\beta \, (\Delta t)}{\nu^2} = \frac{(0.4)^3 \times 9.81 \times (2.86 \times 10^{-3}) \times (400 - 300)}{(20.75 \times 10^{-6})^2} = 4.17 \times 10^8$$

Substituting the values in the above equation, we get

$$\delta = 0.4 \, [3.93 \, (0.952 + 0.7)^{1/4} \, (4.17 \times 10^8)^{-1/4} \, (0.7)^{-1/2}] = 0.0149 \text{ m}$$

$$= \textbf{14.9 mm} \qquad \textbf{(Ans.)}$$

(ii) Average heat transfer coefficient, $\bar{h}$:

$$Gr \, . \, Pr = (4.17 \times 10^8) \, (0.7) = 2.919 \times 10^8$$

$$\overline{Nu} = \frac{\bar{h} L}{k} = 0.516 \, (Gr \, . \, Pr)^{0.25}$$

or,
$$\bar{h} = \frac{k}{L} \times 0.516 \, (Gr \, . \, Pr)^{0.25}$$

$$= \frac{0.03}{0.4} \times 0.516 \, (2.919 \times 10^8)^{0.25} = \textbf{5.058 W/m}^2\textbf{°C} \quad \textbf{(Ans.)}$$

Example 8.11. *A nuclear reactor with its core constructed of parallel vertical plates 2.2 m high and 1.4 m wide has been designed on free convection heating of liquid bismuth. The maximum temperature of the plate surfaces is limited to 960°C while the lowest allowable temperature of bismuth is 340°C. Calculate the maximum possible heat dissipation from both sides of each plate.*

For the convection coefficient, the appropriate correlation is

$$Nu = 0.13 \, (Gr.Pr)^{0.333}$$

where different parameters are evaluated at the mean film temperature.

Solution. The mean film temperature, $t_f = \dfrac{960 + 340}{2} = 650°C$

The thermo-physical properties of bismuth are:

$\rho = 10^4 \text{ kg/m}^3$; $\quad \mu = 3.12$ kg/m-h; $c_p = 150.7$ J/kg°C; $k = 13.02$ W/m°C

$$\beta = \frac{1}{650 + 273} = 1.08 \times 10^{-3} \text{ K}^{-1}$$

$\therefore$
$$Pr = \frac{\mu c_p}{k} = \frac{(3.12/3600) \times 150.7}{13.02} = 0.01$$

$$Gr = \frac{L^3 \rho^2 g \beta \Delta t}{\mu^2} = \frac{(2.2)^3 \times (10^4)^2 \; 9.81 \times 1.08 \times 10^{-3} \times (960 - 340)}{(3.12/3600)^2}$$

$$= 9.312 \times 10^{15}$$

$$Gr.Pr = 9.312 \times 10^{15} \times 0.01 = 93.12 \times 10^{12}$$

Using the given correlation, we get

$$Nu = \frac{hL}{k} = 0.13 \, (Gr.Pr)^{0.333}$$

or,
$$h = \frac{k}{L} \times 0.13 \, (Gr.Pr)^{0.333}$$

$$= \frac{13.02}{2.2} \times 0.13 \, (93.12 \times 10^{12})^{0.33} = 34500 \text{ W/m}^2\text{°C}$$

$\therefore$ Heat dissipation from both sides of each plate,

$$Q = 2\,h\,A_s\,\Delta t$$
$$= 2 \times 34500 \times (2.2 \times 1.45) \times (960 - 340)$$
$$= 136.47 \times 10^6 \text{ W} = \mathbf{136.47 \text{ MW}} \quad \textbf{(Ans.)}$$

Example 8.12. *Find the convective heat loss from a radiator 0.6 m wide and 1.2 m high maintained at a temperature of 90°C in a room at 14°C. Consider the radiator as a vertical plate.*

Solution. *Given :* $L = 1.2$ m, $B = 0.6$ m, $t_s = 90°C$, $t_\infty = 14°C$.

Convective heat loss, Q :

Film temperature $t_f = \dfrac{t_s + t_\infty}{2} = \dfrac{90 + 14}{2} = 52°C$

The thermo-physical properties of air at 52°C are:

$k = 28.15 \times 10^{-3}$ W/m°C;$v = 18.41 \times 10^{-6}$ m²/s, $Pr = 0.7$;

$$\beta = \frac{1}{(52 + 273)} = 3.077 \times 10^{-3} \text{ K}^{-1}$$

Rayleigh number $= Ra_L = Gr_L.Pr = \dfrac{L^3 g \beta (t_s - t_\infty)}{v^2} \cdot Pr$

$$= \frac{(1.2)^3 \times 9.81 \times 3.077 \times 10^{-3} \times (90 - 14)}{(18.41 \times 10^{-6})^2} \times 0.7$$

$$= 11.69 \times 10^9$$

From eqn. (8.36) it follows that the flow becomes turbulent on the radiator plate.
Using eqn. (8.40), we have

$$\overline{Nu_L} = \left[0.825 + \frac{0.387\,(Gr.Pr)^{1/6}}{\left[1 + \left(\dfrac{0.492}{Pr} \right)^{9/16} \right]^{8/27}} \right]^2$$

$$= \left[0.825 + \frac{0.387\,(11.69 \times 10^9)^{1/6}}{\left[1 + \left(\dfrac{0.492}{0.7} \right)^{9/16} \right]^{8/27}} \right]^2 = 263.74$$

$\therefore$ $\overline{h} = \dfrac{k}{L} \times \overline{Nu_L} = \dfrac{28.15 \times 10^{-3}}{1.2} \times 263.74 = 6.187$ W/m²°C

The convective heat loss,

$$Q = h\,A_s\,\Delta t = 6.187 \times (1.2 \times 0.6)\,(90 - 14) = \mathbf{338.55 \text{ W}} \textbf{ (Ans.)}$$

Example 8.13. *A gas at 195°C is flowing through a thin walled vertical duct which is in the form of circular cross-section having diameter of 450 mm. The ambient air at 15°C, which may be considered still, surrounds the duct. Find the rate of heat transfer using the following simplified relation for air for laminar flow.*

$$\overline{h} = 1.38 \left(\frac{\Delta t}{L} \right)^{0.25}$$

where, L is the length of the duct in metres.

Solution. *Given :* $\Delta t = 195 - 15 = 180°C$, $D = 450$ mm $= 0.45$ m

$$\overline{h} = 1.38 \left(\frac{180}{1} \right)^{0.25} = 5.055 \text{ W/m}^2°C$$

$\therefore$ The rate of heat transfer,

$$Q = \overline{h}\,A_s\,\Delta t = 5.055 \times (\pi \times 0.45 \times 1) \times 180 = \mathbf{1286.34 \text{ W/m length.}} \quad \textbf{(Ans.)}$$

Example 8.14. *A horizontal heated plate measuring 1.5 m × 1.1 m and at 215°C, facing upwards, is placed in still air at 25°C. Calculated the heat loss by natural convection. The convective film coefficient for free convection is given by the following empirical relation:*

$$h = 3.05 \, (T_f)^{1/4} \, W/m^2°C$$

where, T_f is the mean film temperature in degrees kelvin.

Solution. *Given :* $A_s = 1.5 \times 1.1 = 1.65 \text{ m}^2$, $t_s = 215°C$, $t_\infty = 25°C$.

Mean film temperature,

$$T_f = 273 + \left(\frac{215 + 25}{2} \right) = 393 \text{ K}$$

∴ $$h = 3.05 \, (393)^{1/4} = 13.58 \text{ W/m}^2°C$$

Rate of heat loss, by natural convection,

$$Q = h \, A_s \, (t_s - t_\infty) = 13.58 \times 1.65 \times (215 - 25) = \textbf{4257.33 W} \qquad \textbf{(Ans.)}$$

Example 8.15. *A transformer is cooled by immersing in an oil bath which is housed in a cylindrical tank which is 0.8 m in diameter and 1.3 m long. If the electrical loss is 1.3 kW, calculate the surface temperature of the tank; the entire loss of electrical energy may be assumed to be due to free convection from the bottom of the tank. For this case the following simplified relations for the boundary layer are applicable :*

$$h = 1.35 \left(\frac{\Delta t}{L} \right)^{0.25} \qquad \text{... For a cylindrical plane;}$$

$$h = 1.45 \left(\frac{\Delta t}{L} \right)^{0.25} \qquad \text{... For a vertical plane.}$$

Assume the ambient air temperature as 20°C.

Solution. *Given :* $D = 0.8 \text{ m}$, $L = 1.3 \text{ m}$.

The total rate of heat transfer from the tank,

$$Q_{total} = Q_{side} + Q_{top} \qquad \qquad ...(i)$$

$$Q_{side} = h_{side} \times A_{side} \times \Delta t$$

$$= 1.35 \left(\frac{t - 20}{1.3} \right)^{0.25} \times (\pi \times 0.8 \times 1.3) \times (t - 20) = 4.13 \, (t - 20)^{1.25}$$

$$Q_{top} = h_{top} . \, A_{top} \, \Delta t$$

$$= 1.45 \left(\frac{t - 20}{0.8} \right)^{0.25} \times \left(\frac{\pi}{2} \times 0.8^2 \right) \times (t - 20) = 0.77 \, (t - 20)^{1.25}$$

Substituting the values in eqn. (i), we get

$$1.3 \times 10^3 = 4.13 \, (t - 20)^{1.25} + 0.77 \, (t - 20)^{1.25} = 4.9 \, (t - 20)^{1.25}$$

or, $$(t - 20) = \left[\frac{1.3 \times 10^3}{4.9} \right]^{1/1.25} = 86.89$$

or, $$t = 86.89 + 20 = \textbf{106.89°C} \quad \textbf{(Ans.)}$$

Example 8.16. *A steam pipe 7.5 cm in diameter is covered with 2.5 cm thick layer of insulation which has a surface emissivity of 0.9. The surface temperature of the insulation is 80°C and the pipe is placed in atmospheric air at 20°C. Considering heat loss both by radiation and natural convection, calculate*

(i) The heat loss from 6 m length of the pipe;

(ii) The overall heat transfer coefficient and the heat transfer coefficient due to radiation alone.

Solution. *Given* : $D = 7.5 + 2 \times 2.5 = 12.5$ cm $= 0.125$ m, $\varepsilon = 0.9$, $t_s = 80°C$, $t_\infty = 20°C$

The mean film temperature, $\quad t_f = \dfrac{80 + 20}{2} = 50°C.$

The thermo-physical properties of air at 50°C are:

$\rho = 1.092$ kg/m^3; $\quad c_p = 1007$ J/kg°C; $\mu = 19.57 \times 10^{-6}$ kg/ms; $k = 27.81 \times 10^{-3}$ W/m°C

$$\beta = \frac{1}{50 + 273} = 3.096 \times 10^{-3} \text{ K}^{-1}$$

$$Pr = \frac{\mu c_p}{k} = \frac{19.57 \times 10^{-6} \times 1007}{27.81 \times 10^{-3}} = 0.708$$

$$Gr = \frac{D^3 \rho^2 g \beta \Delta t}{\mu^2} = \frac{(0.125)^3 \times (1.092)^2 \times 9.81 \times 3.096 \times 10^{-3} \times (80 - 20)}{(19.57 \times 10^{-6})^2}$$

$$= 11.08 \times 10^6$$

Using the eqn. (8.45), we get

$$\overline{Nu} = \frac{\overline{h} D}{k} = 0.53 \, (Gr.Pr)^{1/4}$$

$$\overline{h} = h_{conv.} = \frac{k}{D} \times 0.53 \, (Gr.Pr)^{1/4}$$

$$= \frac{27.81 \times 10^{-3}}{0.125} \times 0.53 \, (11.08 \times 10^6 \times 0.708)^{0.25} = 6.24 \text{ W/m}^2°C$$

(*i*) **Heat loss from 6m length of pipe:**

Heat lost by *convection*,

$$Q_{conv.} = \overline{h} \, A_s \, \Delta t = 6.24 \times (\pi \times 0.125 \times 6) \times (80 - 20) = 882.16 \text{ W}$$

Heat lost by *radiation*,

$$Q_{rad.} = \varepsilon \, \sigma A \, (T_1^4 - T_2^4)$$

$$= 0.9 \times (5.67 \times 10^{-8}) \times (\pi \times 0.125 \times 6) \, [(80 + 273)^4 - (20 + 273)^4]$$

$$= 980.81 \text{ W}$$

Total heat loss, $\quad Q_t = Q_{conv.} + Q_{rad.} = 882.16 + 980.81 = \mathbf{1862.97 \text{ W}}$ **(Ans.)**

(*ii*) **Heat transfer coefficients, overall (h_t) and due to radiation alone ($h_{rad.}$) :**

$$Q_t = h_t . A \, \Delta t$$

or, $\qquad h_t = \dfrac{Q_1}{A.\Delta t} = \dfrac{1862.97}{(\pi \times 0.125 \times 6) \times (80 - 20)} = 13.17 \text{ W/m}^2°C$

$\therefore \qquad h_{rad.} = h_t - h_{conv.} = 13.17 - 6.24 = \mathbf{6.93 \text{ W/m}^2°C}$ **(Ans.)**

Example 8.17. *Calculate the heat transfer from a 60W incandescent bulb at 115°C to ambient air at 25°C. Assume the bulb as a sphere of 50 mm diameter. Also, find the percentage of power lost by free convection.*

The correlation is given by: $Nu = 0.60 \, (Gr.Pr)^{1/4}$

Solution. *Given* : $t_s = 110°C$, $t_\infty = 25°C$, $D = 50$ mm $= 0.05$ m.

The film temperature, $\quad t_f = \dfrac{t_s + t_\infty}{2} = \dfrac{115 + 25}{2} = 70°C$

The thermo-physical properties of air at 70°C are:

$k = 2.964 \times 10^{-2}$ W/m°C, $v = 20.02 \times 10^{-6}$, $Pr = 0.694$,

$$\beta = \frac{1}{t_f + 273} = \frac{1}{70 + 273} = 2.915 \times 10^{-3}$$

$$Gr = \frac{D^2 \, g \, \beta \Delta t}{v^2} = \frac{(0.05)^3 \times 9.81 \times 2.915 \times 10^{-3} \times (115 - 25)}{(20.20 \times 10^{-6})^2}$$

(∵ The characteristic length $L = D$ in this case)

Using given correlation, we get

$$\overline{Nu} = \frac{\overline{h} L}{k} = 0.6 \, (Gr.Pr)^{1/4}$$

$$h = \frac{k}{D} \times 0.6 \, (Gr.Pr)^{1/4}$$

$$= \frac{2.964 \times 10^{-2}}{0.05} \times 0.6 \, (8.026 \times 10^5 \times 0.694)^{1/4} = 9.72 \text{ W/m}^2 {}^\circ\text{C}$$

Heat transfer $= \overline{h} \, A_s \, \Delta t = 9.72 \times (\pi \times 0.05^2) \times (115 - 25) = \textbf{6.87 W}$ **(Ans.)**

%age of power lost by free convection $= \dfrac{6.87}{60} \times 100 = \textbf{11.45 \% (Ans.)}$

Example 8.18. *A horizontal high pressure steam pipe of 10 cm outside diameter passes through a large room whose walls and air are at 23°C. The pipe outside surface temperature is 165°C and it emissivity is 0.85. Estimate the heat loss from the pipe per unit length. Use the following correlation for the calculation of film coefficient*

$$\overline{Nu} = \left[0.6 + \frac{0.387 \, (Ra)^{1/6}}{\left\{ 1 + \left(\dfrac{0.559}{Pr} \right)^{9/16} \right\}^{8/27}} \right]^2$$

where Ra is known as Rayleigh Number and is given by

$$Ra = Gr.Pr = \frac{\beta g \, (\Delta T) \, (L_c)^3}{v \alpha}$$

Take the following properties of air :

$$k = 0.0313 \text{ W/m K}; \, v = 22.8 \times 10^{-6} \text{ m}^2/s$$
$$\alpha = 32.8 \times 10^{-6} \text{ m}^2/s, \, Pr = 0.697, \, \beta = 2.725 \times 10^{-3} \, K^{-1}.$$

(N.M.U. Winter, 1999)

Solution. *Given :* $D = 10 \text{ cm} = 0.1 \text{ m}; \, t_a = 23°C; \, t_s = 165°C; \, \varepsilon = 0.85$

Properties of air : $k = 0.0313 \text{ W/m K}; \, v = 22.8 \times 10^{-6} \text{ m}^2/s;$
$\alpha = 32.8 \times 10^{-6} \text{ m}^2/s, \, Pr = 0.697, \, \beta = 2.725 \times 10^{-3} \text{ K}^{-1}$

Heat loss from the pipe per unit length, Q :

Heat lost by convection and radiation from the sphere is given by :

$$Q = Q_{conv.} + Q_{rad.}$$

$$Q_{rad.} = \varepsilon A \sigma \, (T_s^4 - T_a^4) = \varepsilon \, (\pi DL) \, \sigma \, (T_s^4 - T_a^4)$$

$$= 0.85 \, (\pi \times 0.1 \times 1) \times 5.67 \left[\left(\frac{165 + 273}{100} \right)^4 - \left(\frac{23 + 273}{100} \right)^4 \right]$$

...(where $L = 1$ m)

$$= 1.514 \, [368.04 + 76.76] = 441 \text{ W/m}$$

$$Q_{conv.} = h \times (\pi DL) \, (t_s - t_a)$$

where h is calculated by using the given relation.

$$Ra = Gr.Pr = \frac{\beta g \, (\Delta t) \, (L_c)^3}{v \alpha} = \frac{2.725 \times 10^{-3} \times 9.81 \times (165 - 23) \times (0.1)^3}{22.8 \times 10^{-6} \times 32.8 \times 10^{-6}} = 5 \times 10^6$$

$$Nu = \frac{hD}{k} = \left[0.6 + \frac{0.387 \, (5 \times 10^6)^{1/6}}{\left\{ 1 + \left(\frac{0.559}{0.698} \right)^{9/16} \right\}^{8/27}} \right]^2 = \left(0.6 + \frac{5.06}{1.206} \right)^2 = 23$$

$$\therefore \qquad h = \frac{k}{D} \times 23 = \frac{0.0313}{0.1} \times 23 = 7.2 \text{ W/m}^2\text{°C}$$

$$\therefore \qquad Q_{conv.} = 7.2 \times (\pi \times 0.1 \times 1) \, (165 - 23) = 321.2 \text{ W, when } L = 1 \text{ m}$$

Hence, $\qquad Q = 441 + 321.2$

$$= \textbf{762.2 W/m} \qquad \textbf{(Ans.)}$$

Example 8.19. *A vertical slot of 20 mm thickness is formed by two 2 m × 2 m square plates. If the temperatures of the plates are 115°C and 25°C respectively, calculate the following:*

(i)   The effective thermal conductivity;

(ii) The rate of heat flow through the slot.

Solution. *Given:* $L = 20$ mm $= 0.02$ m; $t_1 = 115$°C; $t_2 = 25$°C

(i) **The effective thermal conductivity, k_e :**

The mean temperature between the plates $= \dfrac{115 + 25}{2} = 70$°C

The properties of air at 70°C are:

$$k = 0.0295 \text{ W/m°C}; \nu = 2.0 \times 10^{-5} \text{ m}^2/\text{s}$$

$$\beta = \frac{1}{70 + 273} = 2.915 \times 10^{-3}$$

The Grashoff number based on the gap L, is

$$Gr_L = \frac{L^3 g \beta \Delta t}{\nu^2} = \frac{(0.02)^3 \times 9.81 \times 2.915 \times 10^{-3} \times (115 - 25)}{(2.0 \times 10^{-5})^2}$$

$$= 5.147 \times 10^4$$

The effective thermal conductivity is given by

$$\frac{k_e}{k} = 0.064 \, (Gr_L)^{1/3} \left(\frac{H}{L} \right)^{-1/9} \qquad \qquad ...[\text{Eqn. (8.50)}]$$

$$k_e = 0.0295 \left[0.064 \, (5.147 \times 10^4)^{0.333} \left(\frac{2}{0.02} \right)^{-0.111} \right]$$

$$= 0.04197 \text{ W/m°C}$$

(ii) **The rate of heat flow through the slot Q :**

$$Q = k_e . A . \left(\frac{t_1 - t_2}{L} \right)$$

$$= 0.04197 \times (2 \times 2) \left[\frac{115 - 25}{0.02} \right] = \textbf{755.46 W} \qquad \textbf{(Ans.)}$$

Example 8.20. *Two horizontal panels separated by a distance of 30 mm contain air at atmospheric pressure. The temperatures of lower and upper panels are 55°C and 20.6°C respectively. Calculate the free convection heat transfer per m² of the panel surface.*

Solution. *Given.* $L = 30$ mm $= 0.03$ m, $t_1 = 55$°C, $t_2 = 20.6$°C

The mean temperature of two panels $= \dfrac{55 + 20.6}{2} = 37.8$°C

The properties of air at 37.8°C are:

$$\rho = 1.121 \text{ kg/m}^3 ; \quad v = 0.171 \times 10^{-4} \text{ m}^2/\text{s}$$
$$k = 29.2 \times 10^{-3} \text{ W/m°C}; \quad Pr = 0.70$$
$$\beta = \frac{1}{37.8 + 273} = 3.22 \times 10^{-3} \text{ K}^{-1}$$

Free convection heat transfer per m² of the panel surface, q:

$$Gr_L = \frac{L^3 g \beta \, \Delta t}{v^2} = \frac{(0.03)^3 \times 9.81 \times 3.22 \times 10^{-3} \times (55 - 20.6)}{(0.171 \times 10^{-4})^2} = 10.03 \times 10^4$$

$$\overline{Nu} = 0.195 \, (Gr_L)^{1/4} \qquad \qquad ...[\text{Eqn. (8.51)}]$$

or, $$\overline{Nu} = 0.195 \, (10.03 \times 10^4)^{1/4} = 3.47$$

Also, $$\overline{Nu} = \frac{q.L}{k \, (t_1 - t_2)} \quad (\text{where } q = Q/A) \qquad ...[\text{Eqn. 8.52 } (a)]$$

$$\therefore \quad q = \frac{\overline{Nu} \, k \, (t_1 - t_2)}{L}$$

$$= \frac{3.47 \times 29.2 \times 10^{-3} \, (55 - 20.6)}{0.03} = \textbf{116.18 W/m}^2 \quad \textbf{(Ans.)}$$

Example 8.21. (Mixed convection) *Air at 20°C and 1 atmosphere is forced through a 25 mm diameter tube 400 mm long, at an average velocity of 0.33 m/s. Calculate the rate of heat transfer if the tube wall is maintained at 180°C.*

Solution. Given: $t_b = 20°C$, $t_s = 180°C$, $V = 0.33$ m/s, $L = 400$ mm $= 0.4$ m, $D = 25$ mm $= 0.025$ m.

Rate of heat transfer :

The mean film temperature, $$t_f = \frac{180 + 20}{2} = 100°C$$

The properties of air at 100°C are:

$$k = 3.208 \times 10^{-2} \text{ W/m°C}, v = 23.13 \times 10^{-6} \text{ Ns/m}^2, Pr = 0.688$$
$$\beta = \frac{1}{100 + 273} = 2.68 \times 10^{-3}$$

For the bulk temperature of 20°C, we have

$$\mu_b = 18.15 \times 10^{-6} \text{ Ns/m}^2$$

Again, for the surface temperature of tube wall (*i.e.*, 180°C)

$$\mu_s \text{ (viscosity at the wall)} = 25.19 \times 10^{-6} \text{ Ns/m}^2$$

Reynolds number $$Re = \frac{VD}{v} = \frac{0.33 \times 0.025}{23.13 \times 10^{-6}} = 356.68$$

Thus the nature of flow is *laminar*.

Grashoff number, $$Gr = \frac{D^3 g \beta \, (t_s - t_\infty)}{v^2}$$

$$= \frac{(0.025)^3 \times 9.81 \times 2.68 \times 10^{-3} \, (180 - 20)}{(23.13 \times 10^{-6})^2}$$

$$= 1.228 \times 10^5$$

$$\therefore \quad \frac{Gr}{(Re)^2} = \frac{1.228 \times 10^5}{(356.68)^2} \simeq 0.965$$

Since $[Gr/(Re)^2] \simeq 1$, hence it is a case of *mixed* (free and forced) *convection* and the following equation may be used for calculation of $\overline{Nu}$.

$$\overline{Nu} = 1.75 \left(\frac{\mu_b}{\mu_s}\right)^{0.14} [Gz + 0.012 \, (Gz.Gr^{1/3})^{4/3}]^{1/3} \qquad \qquad ...[\text{Eqn. } (8.61)]$$

where, $\quad Gz = $ Graetz number $= Re.Pr \left(\frac{D}{L}\right) = 356.68 \times 0.688 \left(\frac{0.025}{0.4}\right) = 15.34$

$$\therefore \quad \overline{Nu} = 1.75 \left(\frac{18.15 \times 10^{-6}}{25.19 \times 10^{-6}}\right)^{0.14} [15.34 + 0.012 \, \{(15.34) \, (1.228 \times 10^5)^{0.333}\}^{1.333}]^{0.333}$$

$$= 7.7$$

$$\overline{h} = \frac{k}{D} \, \overline{Nu} = \frac{3.208 \times 10^{-2}}{0.025} \times 7.7 = 9.88 \text{ W/m}^2\,^{\circ}\text{C}$$

$$Q = \overline{h} \, A_s \, \Delta t = 9.88 \times (\pi \times 0.025 \times 0.4) \times (180 - 20) = \mathbf{49.66W} \quad \textbf{(Ans.)}$$

TYPICAL EXAMPLES

Example 8.22. *Derive a relation between Grashoff and Reynolds numbers assuming the heat transfer coefficients over vertical plates for pure forced and free convection are equal in laminar flow.*

Solution. For pure forced convection: $\overline{Nu} = 0.664 \, (Re)^{1/2} \, (Pr)^{1/3}$ $\qquad \qquad$ ...(i)

For pure natural convection: $\overline{Nu} = 0.677 \, (Pr)^{1/2} \, (0.952 + Pr)^{-1/4} \, (Gr)^{1/4}$ $\qquad$ ...(ii)

Equating equations (i) and (ii), we get

$$0.664 \, (Re)^{1/2} \, (Pr)^{1/3} = 0.677 \, (Pr)^{1/2} \, (0.952 + Pr)^{-1/4} \, (Gr)^{1/4}$$

or, $\qquad (Re)^2 \, (Pr)^{4/3} = (Pr)^2 \, (0.952 + Pr)^{-1} \, (Gr)$

or, $\qquad Gr = (Re)^2 \left[\dfrac{Pr + 0.952}{(Pr)^{2/3}}\right]$

Example 8.23. *Two horizontal steam pipes having diameters 100 mm and 300 mm are so laid in a boiler house that the mutual heat transfer may be neglected. The surface temperature of each of the steam pipes is 475°C. If the temperature of the ambient air is 35°C, calculate the ratio of heat transfer coefficients and heat losses per metre length of the pipes.*

Solution. *Given :* $D_1 = 100$ mm $= 0.1$ m, $D_2 = 300$ mm $= 0.3$ m, $t_s = 475°C$, $t_\infty = 35°C$

The steam mains are located in the boiler house where the ambient air is stationary, thus this is a case of *free convection* for which the following relation applies :

$$Nu = C \, (Gr.Pr)^{1/4} = C \left[\frac{D^3 g \beta \Delta t}{v^2} \times \frac{\mu c_p}{k}\right]^{1/4}$$

Since, the surface temperature of both pipes is the same and both are exposed to the same ambient conditions, therefore, thermo-physical properties are the same.

$$\therefore \qquad Nu \propto (D^3)^{1/4} \propto (D)^{3/4}$$

or, $\qquad \dfrac{hD}{k} \propto (D)^{3/4}$

or, $\qquad h \propto \dfrac{1}{(D)^{1/4}}$

$\therefore$ The ratio of heat transfer coefficients,

$$\frac{h_1}{h_2} = \left(\frac{D_2}{D_1}\right)^{1/4} = \left(\frac{0.3}{0.1}\right)^{1/4} = \mathbf{1.316} \qquad \textbf{(Ans.)}$$

Also, $\qquad Q = h \, A_s \, \Delta t = h \, (\pi DL) \Delta t$

∴ The ratio of heat losses, $\dfrac{Q_1}{Q_2} = \dfrac{h_1 D_1}{h_2 D_2} = 1.316 \times \left(\dfrac{0.1}{0.3}\right) = 0.438$ (Ans.)

Example 8.24. *A room is heated by initiating fire at the fireplace. The exfiltration of room air through a chimney is reduced by the use of a glass-door fire screen of height 0.8 m and width of 1.1m. If the ambient air temperature is 25°C and the surface temperature attained by the glass is 175°C, calculate the free convectin heat transfer rate from the fire place to the room. For this case the following correlation given by Churchill and Chu is valid:*

$$Nu = \left[0.825 + \dfrac{0.387 \, (Gr.Pr)^{1/6}}{[1 + (0.492/Pr)^{9/16}]^{8/27}}\right]^2$$

Solution. Given : $t_s = 175°C$, $t_\infty = 25°C$, $L = 0.8$m, $B = 1.1$ m

The film temperature, $t_f = \dfrac{t_s + t_\infty}{2} = \dfrac{175 + 25}{2} = 100°C$

The thermo-physical properties of air at 100°C are:

$$k = 3.208 \times 10^{-2} \text{ W/m}^2°C, \ v = 23.13 \times 10^{-6} \text{ m}^2/s, \ Pr = 0.688$$

$$\beta = \dfrac{1}{T_f} = \dfrac{1}{(100 + 273)} = 2.68 \times 10^{-3}$$

Grashoff number, $Gr = \dfrac{L^3 \, g \beta \Delta t}{v^2}$

$$= \dfrac{(0.8)^3 \times 9.81 \times 2.68 \times 10^{-3} \, (175 - 25)}{(23.13 \times 10^{-6})^2} = 3.77 \times 10^9$$

$$Gr.Pr = Ra = 3.77 \times 10^9 \times 0.688 = 2.594 \times 10^9$$

∴ $$Nu = \left[0.825 + \dfrac{0.387 \, (2.594 \times 10^9)^{1/6}}{\{1 + (0.492/0.688)^{9/16}\}^{8/27}}\right]^2 = 164.6$$

or, $\dfrac{\bar{h}L}{k} = Nu = 164.6$

or, $\bar{h} = \dfrac{k}{L} \times 164.6 = \dfrac{3.208 \times 10^{-2}}{0.8} \times 164.6 = 6.6 \text{ W/m}^2°C$

Free convection heat transfer rate,

$$Q = \bar{h} \, A_s \, (t_s - t_\infty) = 6.6 \, (0.8 \times 1.1) \, (175 - 25)$$

$$= \textbf{871.2W} \qquad \text{(Ans.)}$$

Example 8.25. *A 2-stroke motor cycle petrol engine cylinder consists of 15 fins. If the outside and inside diameters of each fin are 200 mm and 100 mm respectively, the average fin surface temperature is 475°C and atmospheric air temperature is 25°C, calculate the heat transfer rate from the fins for the following cases:*

(i) When the motor cycle is stationary;

(ii) When the motor cycle is running at a speed of 60 km/h.

The fin may be idealised as single horizontal flat plate of the same area.

Solution. Case (i) When the motor cycle is *stationary* the heat transfer will be due to *free convection.*

The mean film temperature, $t_f = \dfrac{475 + 25}{2} = 250°C.$

The thermo-physical properties of air at 250°C from the tables are:

$$k = 4.266 \times 10^{-2} \text{ W/m°C}; \quad v = 40.61 \times 10^{-6} \text{ m}^2/\text{s}; \quad Pr = 0.677$$

$$\beta = \frac{1}{t_f + 273} = \frac{1}{250 + 273} = 1.912 \times 10^{-3}$$

$$Gr = \frac{L^3 g \beta \Delta t}{v^2} \qquad \text{where significant length } L = 0.9 \, D$$

or,

$$Gr = \frac{(0.9 \times 0.2)^3 \times 9.81 \times 1.912 \times 10^{-3} \times (475 - 25)}{(40.61 \times 10^{-6})^2} = 2.985 \times 10^7$$

$$Gr.Pr = 2.985 \times 10^7 \times 0.677 \simeq 2 \times 10^7$$

Since $Gr.Pr < 10^9$, hence the nature of flow is *laminar*.

$$\overline{Nu} = \frac{hL}{k} = 0.54 \, (Gr.Pr)^{1/4} \qquad \qquad \text{...Eqn. (8.41)}$$

or, $\quad \overline{h} = \dfrac{k}{L} \times 0.54 \, (Gr.Pr)^{1/4} = \dfrac{4.266 \times 10^{-2}}{(0.9 \times 0.2)} \times 0.54 \times (2 \times 10^7)^{1/4} = 8.56 \text{ W/m}^2\text{°C}$

Since the heat transfer is from both sides of the fins, therefore,

$$Q = \overline{h} \, A_s \, \Delta t = 8.56 \left[2 \times 15 \times \frac{\pi}{4} \times (0.2^2 - 0.1^2) \right] [475 - 25]$$

$$= 2722.82 \text{ W} \qquad \textbf{(Ans.)}$$

Case (ii) : When the motor cycle is running the heat transfer will be due to *forced convection*.

The velocity of air on the fin = Speed of the motor cycle

$$= \frac{60 \times 1000}{3600} = 16.66 \text{ m/s}$$

Reynolds number $\quad Re = \dfrac{LU}{v} = \dfrac{(0.9 \times 0.2) \times 16.66}{40.61 \times 10^{-6}} = 7.38 \times 10^4$

Hence the flow is *turbulent*.

For turbulent flow, for cooling,

$$\overline{Nu} = \frac{hL}{k} = 0.036 \, (Re)^{0.8} \, (Pr)^{0.33}$$

or,

$$\overline{h} = \frac{k}{L} \times 0.036 \, (Re)^{0.8} \, (Pr)^{0.33}$$

$$= \frac{4.266 \times 10^{-2}}{(0.9 \times 0.2)} \times 0.036 \, (7.38 \times 10^4)^{0.8} \, (0.677)^{0.33} = 58.83 \text{ W/m}^2\text{°C}$$

∴   The heat transfer from the cylinder,

$$Q = \overline{h} \, A_s \, \Delta t = 58.83 \left[2 \times 15 \times \frac{\pi}{4} (0.2^2 - 0.1^2) \right] \times (475 - 25)$$

$$= 18713 \text{ W} \qquad \textbf{(Ans.)}$$

Example 8.26. *Gas at 350°C is conveyed through 250 mm diameter pipe laid in an atmosphere of quiescent air at 20°C. The convection heat transfer coefficient from a hot cylindrical surface freely exposed to still air is prescribed by the relation:* $h = 1.55 \left(\dfrac{\Delta t}{D} \right)^{0.25}$ *W/m²°C where Δt is the temperature difference and D is the diameter of the cylinder in metres.*

(i) *Calculate the heat loss per metre length of the bare pipe.*

(ii) *Estimate the percentage reduction in heat loss if the pipe is covered with 75 mm thick layer of material whose thermal conductivity is 0.072 W/m°C. Any temperature drop in the metal may be neglected.*

Solution. Convective heat transfer coefficient,

$$h = 1.55 \left[\frac{350 - 20}{0.25} \right]^{0.25} = 9.34 \text{ W/m}^2 {}^\circ\text{C}$$

(i) Heat loss from the bare pipe:

Convective heat loss per metre length of the bare pipe,

$$Q = h A_s \, \Delta t = 9.34 \times (\pi \times 0.25 \times 1) \times (350 - 20) = \textbf{2420.75 W} \quad \textbf{(Ans.)}$$

(ii) Percentage reduction in heat loss when pipe is lagged :

$$D_1 = 250 \text{ mm} = 0.25 \text{ m}, \qquad D_2 = 250 + (2 \times 75) = 400 \text{ mm} = 0.4 \text{ m}$$

On *attainment of steady state, the heat conducted through the lagging equals the convective heat loss from the outer surface of the lagging.* Thus

$$\frac{2\pi k L (t_1 - t)}{\ln (r_2 / r_1)} = h \times (\pi D_2 L) (t - t_\infty)$$

where t is the temperature at the outer surface of the lagging.

Substituting the appropriate values, we get

$$\frac{2\pi \times 0.072 \times 1 \times (350 - t)}{\ln (0.2/0.125)} = 1.55 \left(\frac{t - 20}{0.4} \right)^{0.25} \times (\pi \times 0.4 \times 1) (t - 20)$$

or, $\quad 0.962 (350 - t) = 2.449 (t - 20)^{1.25}$

or, $\qquad\quad 350 - t = 2.545 (t - 20)^{1.25}$

By trial and error, we get, $\qquad t \simeq 64°C$

∴ Heat loss from the lagged pipe,

$$Q = \frac{2\pi k L (t_1 - t)}{\ln (r_2 / r_1)} = \frac{2\pi \times 0.072 \times 1 \times (350 - 64)}{\ln (0.2/0.125)} = 275.28 \text{ W}$$

∴ Percentage reduction in loss $= \dfrac{2420.75 - 275.28}{2420.75} \times 100$

$$= \textbf{88.63\%} \qquad \textbf{(Ans.)}$$

HIGHLIGHTS

1. Free or natural convection is the process of heat transfer which occurs due to movement of the fluid particles by density changes associated with temperature differential in a fluid.

2. **List of formulae :**

I. *Flow over vertical plates (Laminar flow)*

   (a) *Exact solution:*

   (i) $\quad \overline{Nu}_x = 0.676 \left[\dfrac{(Gr_x /4) \, Pr^2}{0.861 + Pr^2} \right]^{1/4}$

   (ii) $\quad \overline{Nu}_x = 0.902 \left[\dfrac{(Gr_L /4) \, Pr^2}{0.861 + Pr^2} \right]^{1/4}$

(b) *Approximate solution:*

(iii) $\dfrac{u}{u_1} = \dfrac{y}{\delta}\left(1 - \dfrac{y}{\delta}\right)^2$ $\qquad \left[\text{where } u_1 = \dfrac{u_x\, g\, \beta\, \delta^2\, (t_s - t_\infty)}{4v}\right]$

(iv) $u_{max} = \dfrac{4}{27}\, u_1 = 0.766\, v\left(0.952 + \dfrac{v}{\alpha}\right)^{-1/2} \left[\dfrac{g\beta\, (t_s - t_\infty)}{v^2}\right]^{1/2} (x)^{1/2}$

(v) $\dfrac{\delta}{x} = 3.93\, (0.952 + Pr)^{1/4}\, (Gr_x)^{-1/4}\, (Pr)^{-1/2}$

$$\left(\text{where } Gr_x = \dfrac{g\beta\, (t_s - t_\infty)\, x^3}{v^2} \text{ and } Pr = \dfrac{v}{\alpha}\right)$$

(vi) $m = \dfrac{\rho}{12}\, \delta . u_x$

(vii) $\delta_m = \dfrac{\rho}{12}\left[(u_x . \delta)_{x_2} - (u_x . \delta)_{x_1}\right]$

(viii) Total mass, $m = 1.7\, \rho v\left[\dfrac{Gr_L}{(Pr)^2\, (Pr + 0.952)}\right]^{1/4}$

(ix) $Nu_x = \dfrac{h_x x}{k} = 0.508\, (Pr)^{1/2}\, (0.952 + Pr)^{-1/4}\, (Gr_x)^{1/4} = \dfrac{2x}{\delta}$

(x) $\overline{Nu_L} = \dfrac{\overline{h}\, L}{k} = \dfrac{4}{3}\, Nu_x = 0.677\, (Pr)^{1/2}\, (0.952 + Pr)^{-1/4}\, (Gr_L)^{1/4}$

II. *Flow over vertical plates (Turbulent flow):*

(xi) $\dfrac{\delta}{x} = 0.565\, (Pr)^{-8/15}\left[\dfrac{1 + 0.494\, (Pr)^{2/3}}{Gr_x}\right]^{0.1}$

(xii) $Nu_x = 0.0295\, (Pr)^{7/15}\left[\dfrac{Gr_x}{1 + 0.494\, (Pr)^{2/3}}\right]^{0.4}$

(xiii) $\overline{Nu_L} = 0.0246\, (Pr)^{7/15}\left[\dfrac{Gr_L}{1 + 0.494\, (Pr)^{2/3}}\right]^{0.4}$

UNSOLVED EXAMPLES

1. A hot plate 1.1 m wide, 300 mm high and at 120°C is exposed to the ambient still air at 20°C. Calculate: (i) Maximum velocity boundary layer thickness and local heat transfer coefficient at 150 mm from the leading edge of the plate, (ii) Total mass flow through the boundary, (iii) Heat loss from the plate and (iv) Rise in temperature of the air passing through the boundary.

   [**Ans.** (i) 0.39 m/s, 11.4 mm, 5.199 W/m²°C, (ii) 0.004372 kg/s]

2. A 300 mm long glass plate is hung vertically in the air at 27°C while its temperature is maintained at 77°C. Calculate the boundary layer thickness at the trailing edge of the plate. If a similar plate is placed in a wind tunnel and air is blown over it at a velocity of 4 m/s, find the boundary layer thickness at its trailing edge.

   Also determine the heat transfer coefficient, for natural and forced convection for the above mentioned data. [**Ans.** 15.2 mm, 5.67 mm; 4.9 W/m²°C, 14.11 W/m²°C]

3. A nuclear reactor with its core constructed of parallel vertical plates 2.25 m high and 1.5 m wide has been designed on free convection heating of liquid bismuth. The maximum temperature of the plate surfaces is limited to 975°C while the lowest allowable temperature of bismuth is 325°C. Calculate the maximum possible heat dissipation from both sides of each plate.

For the convection coefficient, the appropriate correlation is $Nu = 0.13 \, (Gr.Pr)^{0.333}$

where different parameters are evaluated at the mean film temperature. **(Ans. 153 MW)**

4. Find the convective heat loss from a radiator 0.5 m wide and 1 m high maintained at a temperature of 84°C in a room at 20°C. Consider the radiator as a vertical plate.

(Ans. 110.08 W)

5. A steam pipe 60 mm in diameter is covered with 20 mm thick layer of insulation which has a surface emissivity of 0.92. The surface temperature of the insulation is 75°C and the pipe is placed in atmospheric air at 25°C. Considering heat loss both by radiation and natural convection, calculate :

   (i) The heat loss from 5 m length of the pipe;

   (ii) The overall heat transfer coefficient and the heat transfer coefficient due to radiation alone.

   (Ans. (i) 1049.83 W, (ii) 7.07 W/m²°C)

6. Calculate the heat transfer from a 60 W incandescent bulb at 125°C to ambient air at 25°C. Assume the bulb as a sphere of 50 mm diameter. Also, find the percentage of power lost by free convection. The correlation is given by : $Nu = 0.60 \, (Gr.Pr)^{1/4}$

   (Ans. 7.71 W; 19.278%)

7. A vertical slot of 15 mm thickness is formed by two 2m × 2m square plates. If the temperature of the plates are 120°C and 20°C respectively, Calculate the following:

   (i) The effective thermal conductivity;

   (ii) The rate of heat flow through the slot.

   [Ans. (i) 0.0317 W/m°C, (ii) 845.3 W]

8. Two horizontal plates separated by a distance of 25.4 mm contain air at atmospheric pressure. The temperatures of lower and upper panels are 60°C and 15.6°C respectively. Calculate the free convection heat transfer per m² of the panel surface. **(Ans. 167.2 W/m²)**

Boiling and Condensation

9.1. INTRODUCTION

We have considered in the preceding chapter
of convective heat transfer, homogeneous single
phase systems only. However, there are specific
convection processes as *boiling* and *condensation
which are associated with change of phase*.
Whereas *boiling* involves change from liquid to
vapour phase of a fluid substance, *condensation*
refers to a change from the vapour to a liquid phase.

The mode of heat transfer with change of phase
(*i.e.* boiling and condensation processes) *finds wide
applications* as mentioned below:

(*i*) Cooling of nuclear reactors and rocket
motors;

(*ii*) Steam power plants (Boilers and
condensers);

(*iii*) Refrigerating and airconditioning
systems (Evaporators and condensers);

(*iv*) Melting of metal in furnaces;

(*v*) Refineries and sugar mills (Heat
exchangers);

(*vi*) Process heating and cooling etc.

Boiling and condensation processes entail the
following *unique features*:

(*i*) As a consequence of phase change in
these processes, the *heat transfer to or
from the fluid can occur without
influencing the fluid temperature.*

(*ii*) The *heat transfer coefficient and rates*,
due to latent heat associated with phase
change, are generally *much higher*
compared with the normal convection
process (*i.e.*, without phase change).

(*iii*)   *High rate of heat transfer* is achieved with *small temperature difference*.

The phenomena associated with boiling and condensation are much more complex (than the normal convection process) due to the following being very significant:

(*i*)   Latent heat effects;

(*ii*)   Surface tension;

(*iii*)   Surface characteristics and other properties of two phase systems.

9.2. BOILING HEAT TRANSFER

9.2.1. GENERAL ASPECTS

Boiling is *the convective heat transfer process that involves a phase change from liquid to vapour state. Boiling* is also defined as *evaporation at a solid-liquid surface*. This is possible only when the temperature of the surface (t_s) *exceeds* the saturation temperature corresponding to the liquid pressure (t_{sat}). Heat is transferred from the solid surface to the liquid according to the law

$$Q = h\, A_s(t_s - t_{sat}) = h A_s \Delta t_e \qquad\qquad ...(9.1)$$

where, $\Delta t_e = (t_s - t_{sat})$ is known as *excess temperature*.

The boiling process finds *applications* in the following cases:

(*i*)   Steam production (for generation of power and for industrial processes and space heating) in steam and nuclear power plants;

(*ii*)   Heat absorption in refrigeration and air conditioning systems;

(*iii*) Distillation and refining of liquids;

(*iv*)   Concentration, dehydration and drying of foods and materials,

(*v*)   Cooling the machines like nuclear reactors and rocket motors where the large quantities of heat are released in relatively small volume (dissipation rates are as high as 10^8 W/m²; the maximum heat transfer rate in modern boiler is about 2×10^5 W/m²).

The *boiling heat transfer phenomenon* may occur in the following forms:

1.   *Pool boiling :*

In this case the liquid above the hot surface is essentially stagnant and its motion near the surface is due to free convection and mixing induced by bubble growth and detachment.

The pool boiling occurs in steam boilers *involving natural convection*.

2.   *Forced convection boiling :*

This refers to a situation where the fluid motion is induced by external means (and also by free convection and bubble induced mixing). The liquid is pumped and forced to flow.

This type of boiling occurs in water tube boilers involving forced convection.

3.   *Sub-cooled or local boiling :*

In this case the liquid temperature is below the saturation temperature and

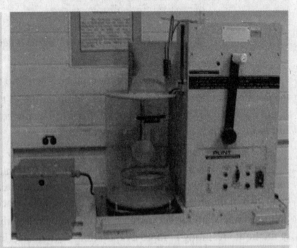

The elctrically heated copper disc is submerged into the water pool. Depending on the surface temperature of the disc and the water the heat is transferred by conduction and or convection and or radiation.

bubbles are formed in the vicinity of heat surface. These bubbles after travelling a short path get condensed in the liquid which has a temperature less than the boiling point.

4. *Saturated boiling* :

Here, the liquid temperature exceeds the saturation temperature. The vapour bubbles formed at the solid surface (liquid-solid interface) are then propelled through the liquid by buoyancy effects and eventually escape from a free surface (liquid-vapour interface).

9.2.2. BOILING REGIMES

The *process of boiling depends* upon the *nature of the surface, thermo-physical properties of the fluid and vapour bubble dynamics.* Due to involvement of large number of variables, general equations describing the boiling process are not available. Nonetheless, considerable progress has been made in arriving at a physical understanding of the boiling mechanism.

Figure 9.1 shows the temperature distribution in saturated pool boiling with a liquid-vapour interface. It is evident from the figure that although there is a sharp decline in the liquid temperature close to the solid surface, the temperature through most of the liquid remains slightly above saturation. Consequently bubbles generated at liquid-solid interface rise to and are transported across the liquid-vapour interface. Whether the boiling phenomenon corresponds to pool boiling or forced circulation boiling, there are three definite regimes of boiling (Interface evaporation, nucleate boiling and film boiling) associated with progressively increasing heat flux, as shown in Fig. 9.2. This specific curve has been obtained from an electrically heated platinum wire submerged in a pool of water (at saturation temperature) by varying its surface temperature and measuring the surface heat flux q_s.

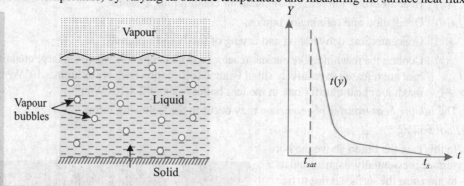

Fig. 9.1. Pool boiling with liquid-vapour interface.

1. Interface evaporation :

Interface evaporation (evaporation process with no bubble formation) exists in region *I*, called the *free convection zone.* Here the excess temperature, Δt_e, is very small and $\approx 5°C$. In this region the *liquid near the surface is superheated slightly, the convection currents circulate the liquid and evaporation takes place at the liquid surface.*

2. Nucleate boiling :

This type of boiling exists in regions *II* and *III*. With the increase in Δt_e (excess temperature) the formation of bubbles on the surface of the wire at certain localised spots commences. The bubbles condense in the liquid without reaching the liquid surface. In fact, it is the region *II* where nucleate boiling starts. With further increase in Δt_e the bubbles are formed more rapidly and rise to the surface of the liquid resulting in rapid evaporation, as indicated in the region *III*. The *nucleate boiling is thus characterised by formation of bubbles at the nucleation sites and the resulting liquid agitation. The bubble agitation induces considerable fluid mixing and that promotes substantial increase in the heat flux and the boiling heat transfer coefficient* (The equipment used for boiling should be designed to operate in this region only).

Nucleate boiling exists upto $\Delta t_e \approx 50°C$. The maximum heat flux, known as the *critical heat flux*, occurs at point A (see Fig. 9.2) and is of the order of $1MW/m^2$.

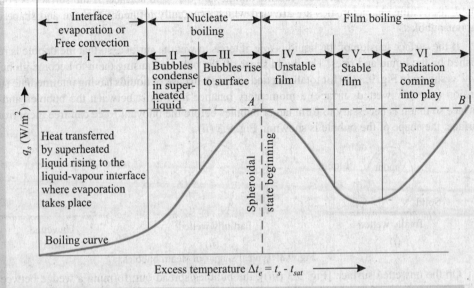

Fig. 9.2. The boiling curve for water.

3. Film boiling :

Film boiling comprises of regions *IV, V* and *VI*. The trend of increase of heat flux with increase in excess temperature observed upto region *III* is *reversed* in region *IV* (called *film boiling region*). This is due to the fact that the bubble formation is very rapid and the bubbles blanket the heating surface and prevent the incoming fresh liquid from taking their place. Eventually the bubbles coalesce and form a vapour film which covers the surface completely. Since the thermal conductivity of vapour film is *much less* than that of the liquid the heat flux *drops* with growth in Δt_e. Within the temperature range $50° C < \Delta t_e < 150°C$, conditions oscillate between nucleate and film boiling and the phase is referred to as *transition boiling, unstable film boiling or partial film boiling* (region *IV*). With further increase in Δt_e the vapour film is stabilised and the heating surface is completely covered by a vapour blanket and the *heat flux* is the lowest as shown in region *V*. The surface temperatures required to maintain a stable film are high and under these conditions a sizeable amount of heat is lost by the surface *due to radiation*, as indicated in the region *VI*. The phenomenon of stable film boiling can be observed when a drop of *water falls on a red hot stove*. The drop does not evaporate immediately but dances a few times on the stove; this is *due to the formation of a stable steam film at the interface between the hot surface and the liquid droplet.*

Critical heat flux or burnout point: The critical heat flux or burnout point (Point A in Fig. 9.2) is *the point of maximum heat flux on the boiling curve at which transition from nucleate to film boiling initiates*. This point is also called the *boiling crisis* because the boiling process beyond that point is unstable unless of course, point *B* is reached. The temperature at point *B* is extremely high and normally above the melting of the solid. So if the heating of the metallic surface is not limited to point *A*, it is possible that the metal may get damaged or it may even melt (For this reason, point *A* is often termed as *boiling crisis* or *burnout point*). Thus we may be interested to operate the equipment close to this value and not beyond it.

9.2.3. BUBBLE SHAPE AND SIZE CONSIDERATION

The heat transfer rate in nucleate boiling is *greatly influenced* by the *nature and condition of the heating surface and surface tension at the solid-liquid interface* (shape, size or inclination of bubbles, however, do not have much effect on the heat transfer rate). The surface tension signifies wetting capability of the surface with the liquid (*i.e.*, low surface tension, highly wetted surface) and that influences the angle of contact between the bubble and the solid surface. If the surface is contaminated, its wetting characteristics are affected which eventually influence the size and shape of the vapour bubbles.

If the surface tension of the liquid is *low*, it tends to wet the surface, so that the bubble is readily pushed by the liquid and rises. The liquid shear-off the bubbles causing them to become globular or oval as shown in Fig. 9.3 (*i*) (for totally wetted surface). In case of liquids having intermediate surface tension (partially wetted surface) a momentary balance may exist between the bubbles and solid surface so that it is necessary to form larger bubbles before the buoyant force can free them from the surface; the shape of the bubble is shown in Fig. 9.3 (*ii*).

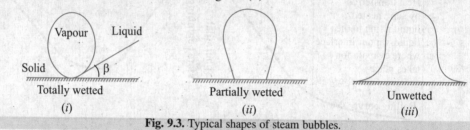

Totally wetted	Partially wetted	Unwetted
(*i*)	(*ii*)	(*iii*)

Fig. 9.3. Typical shapes of steam bubbles.

On the unwetted surface [Fig. 9.3 (*iii*)], the bubbles spread out; forming a wedge between the water and heating surface, thereby allowing hydrostatic forces to resist the action of buoyancy.

The formation of bubble as shown in Fig. 9.3 (*i*) gives high heat transfer rate compared with the bubble shapes shown in Fig. 9.3 (*ii*) and (*iii*).

Addition of agents for reducing the surface tension was found to have the same effect as providing of wettable surface and to give increased rates of heat transfer.

9.2.4. BUBBLE GROWTH AND COLLAPSE

From Experiments it has been observed that the bubbles are not always in thermodynamic equilibrium with surrounding liquid. The vapour inside the bubble is not necessarily at the same temperature as the liquid. Consider the forces acting on a spherical vapour bubble as shown in Fig. 9.4; the pressure forces on the bubble must be balanced by the surface tension at vapour-liquid interface. Thus

$$\pi r^2 (p_v - p_l) = 2\pi r.\sigma$$

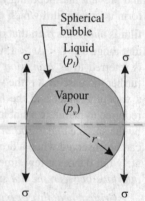

Fig. 9.4. Force balance on a spherical vapour bubble.

or, $$P_v - P_l = \frac{2\sigma}{r} \qquad ...(9.2)$$

where, p_v = Vapour pressure inside the bubble,

      p_l = Liquid pressure over the surface of bubble, and

      σ = Surface tension of vapour-liquid interface.

The vapour may be considered as a perfect gas for which the Clayperon equation may be used, which is given below:

$$\frac{dp}{p} = \frac{h_{fg}}{RT^2} dT \qquad ...(9.3)$$

where, h_{fg} = Latent heat of vaporisation.

From perfect gas law: $\dfrac{p}{RT} = \rho_v$

[where, R = Gas or vapour constant; ρ_v = Density of vapour formed]

Substituting the above equation in eqn. (9.3) and rearranging, we get

$$\frac{dp}{dT} = \frac{h_{fg} \cdot \rho_v}{T}$$

or,
$$\frac{p_v - p_t}{T_v - T_{sat}} = \frac{h_{fg} \cdot \rho_v}{T_{sat}} = \frac{p \cdot h_{fg}}{R \, T_{sat}^2} \qquad \qquad ...(9.4)$$

where, T_v = Vapour temperature inside the bubble, and

T_{sat} = Saturation temperature of vapour inside the bubble at p_v.

From eqns. (9.2) and (9.4), we get

$$T_v - T_{sat} = \frac{2\sigma}{r}\left[\frac{R}{p} \cdot \frac{T_{sat}^2}{h_{fg}}\right] \qquad \qquad ...(9.5)$$

The above equation suggests that if $(T_l - T_{sat}) > (T_v - T_{sat})$, the bubble of radius r will grow otherwise it will collapse. Here T_l is the temperature surrounding the bubble.

9.2.5. CRITICAL DIAMETER OF BUBBLE

Refer figure 9.5, the maximum diameter of the bubble formed on the heating surface depends on the following parameters:

σ_{lv} = Tension between liquid and vapour

σ_{ls} = Tension between liquid and solid surface

σ_{vs} = Tension between vapour and solid surface

β = Angle formed by the bubble as shown in Fig. 9.5

d_c = Maximum or critical diameter of bubble.

$g \, (\rho_l - \rho_v)$ = Buoyancy force.

Thus $d_c = f\left[\beta, \sigma_{lv} \, g \, (\rho_l - \rho_v), \dfrac{\sigma_{lv}}{\sigma_{ls}}\right]$

By the use of the dimensional analysis technique, we get

$$d_c = C.\beta\left(\frac{\sigma_{lv}}{\sigma_{ls}}\right)\sqrt{\frac{\sigma_{lv}}{g \, (\rho_l - \rho_v)}} \qquad ...(9.6)$$

where C is constant which is generally calculated by experimental results.

The value of $C = 0.0148$ for water bubbles.

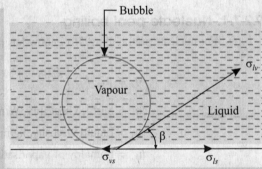

Fig. 9.5. Critical diameter of bubble.

...suggested by Fritz.

9.2.6. FACTORS AFFECTING NUCLEATE BOILING

The nucleate boiling is affected by the following factors:

1. *Material, shape and condition of the heating surface :*

   The boiling heat transfer coefficient depends greatly on the material of the heating surface; under identical conditions of pressure and temperature difference, it is different for different metals (*viz.* copper has high value than steel, zinc and chromium).

   The heat transfer rates are also influenced by the *condition of heating surface*. A *rough surface gives a better heat transmission* than when the surface is either smooth or has been coated (smoothness weakens the metal tendency to get wetted).

The shape of the heating surface also affects transmission of heat.

2. *Liquid properties* :

Through experiments it has been observed that the size of the bubble increases with the dynamic viscosity of the liquid. With increase in bubble size, frequency of bubble formation decreases which results in reduced heat transfer.

Further, high thermal conductivity of the liquid improves the rate of heat transfer.

3. *Pressure* :

The pressure influences the rate of bubble growth and in turn also affects the temperature difference $(t_s - t_\infty)$ causing heat flow. For a boiling liquid, the maximum allowable heat flux first increases with pressure until critical pressure is reached and thereafter it declines.

4. *Mechanical agitation* :

Experiments have shown that the heat transfer rate increases with the increase in degree of agitation.

9.2.7. BOILING CORRELATIONS

In boiling heat transfer, a *driving force is the excess temperature*, which is given by:

$$\Delta t_e = t_s - t_{sat}.$$

...(9.7)

For the boiling process the governing equation is

$$Q = hA\,\Delta t_e$$

where h is the *boiling film coefficient.*

Since no analytical solution is available for boiling heat transfer due to difficult fluid behaviour, empirical relations are used for engineering calculations. some of them are given in following subsections.

9.2.7.1. Nucleate pool boiling

(*i*) For nucleate pool boiling, Rosenhow has recommended the following correlation:

$$q_s = \mu_l \cdot h_{fg} \left[\frac{g\,(\rho_l - \rho_v)}{\sigma} \right]^{0.5} \left[\frac{C_{pl} \cdot \Delta t_e}{C_{sl} \cdot h_{fg} \cdot Pr_l^n} \right]^3$$

...(9.8)

where,

q_s = Surface heat flux, W/m²;

μ_l = Liquid viscosity, kg/ms;

h_{fg} = Enthalpy of vaporisation, J/kg;

ρ_l = Density of saturated liquid, kg/m³;

ρ_v = Density of the saturated vapour, kg/m³;

σ = Surface tension of the liquid-vapour interface, N/m;

c_{pl} = Specific heat of saturated liquid, J/kg K;

Δt_e = $(t_s - t_{sat})$ = excess temperature;

C_{sl} = Surface fluid constant (determined from experimental data);

n = Another constant which depends upon the liquid and the surface; for water $n = 1$, while for other liquids $n = 1.7$.

The value of C_{sl} are given in Table 9.1.

Table 9.1. Values of C_{sl} for pool boiling

S.No.	Liquid-surface	C_{sl}
1.	Water - copper	0.013
2.	Water - brass	0.060
3.	Water - platinum	0.013
4.	Water - ground and polished stainless steel	0.008
5.	Water - mechanically polished stainless steel	0.013
6.	Benzene - chromium	0.010
7.	Ethanol - chromium	0.0027
8.	n-pentane - chromiumn	0.0150
9.	n-butanol - copper	0.003
10.	Isopropyl alcohol - copper	0.00225

(ii) Jacob has proposed the following correlation for nucleate boiling at atmospheric pressure on a flat plate and with low heat fluxes :

$$Nu = 0.16 \, (Gr \, . \, Pr)^{0.33} \qquad \qquad ...(9.9)$$

(iii) For the nucleate boiling on a vertical flat plate, Jacob correlation is of the form:

$$Nu = 0.61 \, (Gr \, . \, Pr)^{0.25} \qquad \qquad ...(9.10)$$

9.2.7.2. Critical heat flux for nucleate pool boiling

On the boiling curve the critical heat flux is an important point. It is always desirable to operate a boiling process close to this point. Zuber (1958) predicted the following expression, for such a case:

$$q_{sc} = 0.18 \, (\rho_v)^{1/2} \, h_{fg} \, [g\sigma \, (\rho_l - \rho_v \,)]^{1/4} \qquad \qquad ...(9.11)$$

The expression given above is independent of fluid viscosity, conductivity and specific heat.

9.2.7.3. Film pool boiling

In *stable film boiling, the heat transfer is due to both convection and radiation.* Bromley (1950) has suggested the following correlation for film boiling from the outer surface of horizontal tubes:

$$(h)^{4/3} = (h_{conv.})^{4/3} + h_{rad} \, . \, (h)^{1/3} \qquad \qquad ...(9.12)$$

The equation (9.12) being tedious to solve, could be written within $\pm 5\%$ of error as

$$h = h_{conv.} + \frac{3}{4} \, h_{rad} \, . \qquad \qquad ...(9.13)$$

The convective coefficient, $h_{conv.}$ (in the absence of radiation), is given by

$$h_{conv.} = 0.62 \left[\frac{k_v^3 \, \rho_v \, (\rho_l - \rho_v) \, g \, (h_{fg} + 0.4 \, c_{pv} \, \Delta t_e}{\mu_v \, D \, \Delta t_e} \right]^{1/4} \qquad \qquad ...(9.14)$$

where, D is the outer diameter of the tube. The vapour properties in the above equation are evaluated at the arithmetic mean of the surface and saturation temperatures.

Radiative heat transfer coefficient

$$h_{rad} = \frac{5.67 \times 10^{-8} \, \varepsilon \, (T_s^4 - T_{sat}^{\,4})}{(T_s - T_{sat})} \qquad \qquad ...(9.15)$$

where ε is the emissivity of solid.

Example 9.1. *A wire of 1.2 mm diameter and 200 mm length is submerged horizontally in water at 7 bar. The wire carries a current of 135 A with an applied voltage of 2.18 V. If the surface of the wire is maintained at 200°C, calculate :*

(i)   *The heat flux, and*

(ii) *The boiling heat transfer coefficient.*

Solution. Given : $d = 1.2$ mm $= 0.0012$ m, $l = 200$ mm $= 0.2$ m, $I = 135$ A, $V = 2.18$ V, $t_s = 200$°C.

(i) **The heat flux, q :**

The electrical energy input to the wire is given by

$$Q = VI = 2.18 \times 135 = 294.3 \text{ W}$$

Surface area of the wire, $A = \pi dl$

$$= \pi \times 0.0012 \times 0.2 = 7.54 \times 10^{-4} \text{ m}^2$$

$$\therefore \quad q = \frac{Q}{A} = \frac{294.3}{7.54 \times 10^{-4}}$$

$$= 0.39 \times 10^6 \text{ W/m}^2 = \textbf{0.39 MW/m}^2 \text{ (Ans.)}$$

(ii) **The boiling heat transfer coefficient, h:**

Corresponding to 7 bar, $t_{sat} = 164.97$°C, and

$$q = h(t_s - t_{sat})$$

or, $$h = \frac{q}{(t_s - t_{sat})} = \frac{0.39 \times 10^6}{(200 - 164.97)}$$

$$= \textbf{11133.3 W/m}^2\textbf{°C} \quad \text{(Ans.)}$$

Film and dropwise condensation unit.

Example 9.2. *An electric wire of 1.25 mm diameter and 250 mm long is laid horizontally and submerged in water at atmospheric pressure. The wire has an applied voltage of 18 V and carries a current of 45 amperes. Calculate:*

(i)   *The heat flux, and*

(ii) *The excess temperature.*

The following correlation for water boiling on horizontal submerged surface holds good:

$$h = 1.58\left(\frac{Q}{A}\right)^{0.75} = 5.62\,(\Delta t_e)^3, \; W/m^2°C$$

Solution. *Given* : $d = 1.25$ mm $= 0.00125$ m, $l = 250$ mm $= 0.25$ m, $V = 18$ V, $I = 45$ A.

(i) **The heat flux, q :**

Electrical energy input to the wire, $Q = VI = 18 \times 45 = 810$ W

Surface area of the wire, $A_s = \pi dl = \pi \times 0.00125 \times 0.25 = 9.817 \times 10^{-4} \text{ m}^2$

$$\therefore \quad q = \frac{Q}{A} = \frac{810}{9.817 \times 10^{-4}} = 0.825 \times 10^6 \text{ W/m}^2 = \textbf{0.825 MW/m}^2 \text{ (Ans.)}$$

(ii) **The excess temperature, Δt_e :**

Using the correlation,

$$1.58\left(\frac{Q}{A}\right)^{0.75} = 5.62\,(\Delta t_e)^3 \qquad\qquad \text{...given}$$

or, $$1.58\,(0.825 \times 10^6)^{0.75} = 5.62\,(\Delta t_e)^3$$

$$\Delta t_e = \left[\frac{1.58 \ (0.825 \times 10^6)^{0.75}}{5.62} \right]^{0.333} = \mathbf{19.68°C \ (Ans.)}$$

Example 9.3. *A nickel wire of 1 mm diameter and 400 mm long, carrying current, is submerged in a water bath which is open to atmospheric pressure. Calculate the voltage at the burnout point if at this point the wire carries a current of 190 A.*

Solution. *Given :* $d = 1$ mm $= 0.001$ m; $l = 400$ mm $= 0.4$ m, $I = 190$ A

The thermo-physical properties of water and vapour at 100°C are:

$\rho_l = (\rho_f) = 958.4$ kg/m³, $\rho_v = 0.5955$ kg/m³, $h_{fg} = 2257$ kJ/kg, $\sigma = 58.9 \times 10^{-3}$ N/m.

Voltage at the burnout point, V_b:

At burnout *i.e.*, the points of critical heat flux, the correlation is

$$q_{sc} = 0.18(\rho_v)^{1/2} \ h_{fg} \ [\ g\sigma \ (\rho_l - \rho_v)]^{1/4} \qquad\qquad ...\text{[Eqn. (9.11)]}$$
$$= 0.18 \ (0.5955)^{1/2} \times 2257 \times 10^3 \ [9.81 \times 58.9 \times 10^{-3} \ (958.4 - 0.5955)]^{1/4}$$
$$= 1.52 \times 10^6 \ \text{W/m}^2 = 1.52 \ \text{MW/m}^2$$

Electric energy input to the wire,

$$Q = V_b \times I$$

or, $$q = \frac{Q}{A} = \frac{V_b \times I}{A} = q_{sc}$$

or, $$V_b = \frac{A \times q_{sc}}{I} = \frac{\pi dl \times q_{sc}}{I} = \frac{\pi \times 0.001 \times 0.4 \times (1.52 \times 10^6)}{190}$$

or, $$V_b = \mathbf{10.05 \ V}$$

Example 9.4. *Water is boiled at the rate of 25 kg/h in a polished copper pan, 280 mm in diameter, at atmospheric pressure. Assuming nucleate boiling conditions, calculate the temperature of the bottom surface of the pan.*

Solution. *Given:* $m = 25$ kg/h; $D = 280$ mm $= 0.28$ m

The properties of water at atmospheric pressure are:

$t_{sat} = 100°C$; $\rho_l = 958.4$ kg/m³; $\rho_v = 0.5955$ kg/m³; $c_{pl} = 4220$ J/kg K; $\mu_l = 279 \times 10^{-6}$; $Pr_l = 1.75$; $h_{fg} = 2257$ kJ/kg; $\sigma = 58.9 \times 10^{-3}$ N/m; $n = 1$ (for water)

The temperature of the bottom surface, t_s:

Excess temperature $\Delta t_e = t_s - t_{sat}$

For nucleate boiling (assumed), the following correlation holds good:

$$q_s = \mu_l \cdot h_{fg} \left[\frac{g \ (\rho_l - \rho_v)}{\sigma} \right]^{0.5} \left[\frac{c_{pl} \cdot \Delta t_e}{C_{sl} \cdot h_{fg} \cdot Pr_l^n} \right]^3 \qquad ...\text{[Eqn. (9.8)]}$$

For polished copper pan, $C_{sl} = 0.013$

or, $$\Delta t_e = \left[\frac{q_s}{\mu_l \cdot h_{fg}} \left\{ \frac{\sigma}{g \ (\rho_l - \rho_v)} \right\}^{0.5} \right]^{0.333} \left[\frac{C_{sl} \cdot h_{fg} \cdot Pr_l}{c_{pl}} \right]$$

Here, $$q_s = \text{Surface heat flux} = \frac{Q}{A} = \frac{m \ h_{fg}}{A}$$

(where, m = Rate of water evaporation)

or, $$q_s = \frac{25 \times (2257 \times 10^3)}{3600 \times \left(\frac{\pi}{4} \times 0.28^2 \right)} = 254544 \ \text{W/m}^2$$

$$\therefore \; \Delta t_e = \left[\frac{254544}{279 \times 10^{-6} \times 2257 \times 10^3} \left\{ \frac{58.9 \times 10^{-3}}{9.81 \,(958.4 - 0.5955)} \right\}^{0.5} \right]^{0.333} \left[\frac{0.013 \times 2257 \times 10^3 \times 1.75}{4220} \right]$$

$$= [404.23 \times 0.0025]^{0.333} \times 12.16 = 12.2$$

i.e., $\qquad \Delta t_e = t_s - t_{sat} = 12.2$

or, $\qquad t_s = 12.2 + t_{sat} = 12.2 + 100 = \textbf{112.2°C (Ans.)}$

Example 9.5. *Water at atmospheric pressure is to be boiled in polished copper pan. The diameter of the pan is 350 mm and is kept at 115°C. Calculate the following:*

   (i) Power of the burner;

   (ii) Rate of evaporation in kg/h;

   (iii) Critical heat flux for these conditions.

Solution. *Given :* $D = 350$ mm $= 0.35$ m, $t_s = 115°C$, $t_{sat} = 100°C$

The thermo-physical properties of water (from table) at 100°C are:

$$\rho_l \,(= \rho_f) = 958.4 \text{ kg/m}^3; \; \rho_v = 0.5955 \text{ kg/m}^3; \; c_{pl} \,(= c_{pf}) = 4220 \text{ J/kg K};$$
$$\mu_l = (\mu_f) = 279 \times 10^{-6} \text{ Ns/m}^2$$
$$Pr_l \,(= Pr_f) = 1.75; \; h_{fg} = 2257 \text{ kJ/kg}; \; n = 1; \; \sigma = 58.9 \times 10^{-3} \text{ N/m}$$

The excess temperature, $\Delta t_e = t_s - t_{sat} = 115 - 100 = 15°C$

(i) Power of the burner to maintain boiling:

As per boiling curve, for $\Delta t_e = 15°C$, nucleate pool boiling will occur and for this the following correlation holds good:

$$q_s = \mu_l \cdot h_{fg} \left[\frac{g \,(\rho_l - \rho_v)}{\sigma} \right]^{0.5} \left[\frac{c_{pl} \cdot \Delta t_e}{C_{sl} \cdot h_{fg} \cdot Pr_l^n} \right]^3 \qquad \text{...[Eqn (9.8)]}$$

For polished copper pan, $C_{sl} = 0.013$ $\qquad$ ...Refer table 9.1

Substituting the values in the above eqn. we get

$$q_s = 279 \times 10^{-6} \times (2257 \times 10^3) \left[\frac{9.81\,(958.4 - 0.5955)}{58.9 \times 10^{-3}} \right]^{0.5} \left[\frac{4220 \times 15}{0.013 \times 2257 \times 10^3 \times 1.75} \right]^3$$

$$= 629.7 \times 399.4 \times 1.873$$

$$= 471.06 \times 10^3 \text{ W/m}^2 = 471.06 \text{ kW/m}^2$$

The boiling heat transfer rate (power of the burner) is given by

$$Q = 471.06 \times \frac{\pi}{4} \times (0.35)^2 = \textbf{45.32 kW (Ans.)}$$

(ii) Rate of evaporation, m_w:

Under steady state conditions, all the heat added to the pan will result in evaporation of water. Thus,

$$Q = m_w \times h_{fg}$$

or, $\qquad m_w = \dfrac{Q}{h_{fg}} = \dfrac{45.32 \times 10^3}{2257 \times 10^3} = 0.02 \text{ kg/s} = \textbf{72 kg/h (Ans.)}$

(iii) Critical heat flux, q_{sc}:

$$q_{sc} = 0.18 \,(\rho_v)^{1/2} \, h_{fg} \,[\, g\sigma \,(\rho_l - \rho_v)]^{1/4} \qquad \text{...[Eqn. 9.11)]}$$

$$= 0.18 \,(0.5955)^{1/2} \times 2257 \times 10^3 \,[9.81 \times 58.9 \times 10^{-3} \,(958.4 - 0.5955)]^{1/4}$$

$$= 1.52 \times 10^6 \text{ W/m}^2 = \textbf{1.52 MW/m}^2 \textbf{ (Ans.)}$$

Example 9.6. *A metal-clad heating element of 10 mm diameter and of emissivity 0.92 is submerged in a water bath horizontally. If the surface temperature of the metal is 260°C under steady boiling conditions, calculate the power dissipation per unit length for the heater. Assume that water is exposed to atmospheric pressure and is at a uniform temperature.*

Solution. *Given :* $D = 10$ mm $= 0.01$ m, $\varepsilon = 0.92$, $t_s = 260°C$

The thermo-physical properties of water at 100°C from table are :

$$\rho_l = \rho_f = 958.4 \text{ kg/m}^3; \ h_{fg} = 2257 \text{ kJ/kg}$$

The thermo-physical properties of vapour at 260°C from table are:

$$\rho_v = 4.807 \text{ kg/m}^3, \ c_{pv} = 2.56 \text{ kJ/kg K}, \ k = 0.0331 \text{ W/mK};$$
$$\mu_v = \mu_g = 14.85 \times 10^{-6} \text{ Ns/m}^2$$

Power dissipation per unit length for the heater:

The excess temperature $\Delta t_e = t_s - t_{sat} = 260 - 100 = 160°C$

As per boiling curve, at $\Delta t_e = 160°C$, there exists a film pool boiling condition. In this case, the heat transfer is due to both convection and radiation.

The heat transfer coefficient, h (approximate) is calculated from the equation:

$$h = h_{conv} + \frac{3}{4} h_{rad} \qquad \qquad ...[Eqn. (9.13)]$$

The convective heat transfer coefficient,

$$h_{conv} = 0.62 \left[\frac{k_v^3 \, \rho_v \, (\rho_l - \rho_v) g \, (h_{fg} + 0.4 \, c_{pv} \, \Delta t_e)}{\mu_v \, D \, \Delta t_e} \right]^{1/4} \qquad ...[Eqn. (9.14)]$$

$$= 0.62 \left[\frac{(0.0331)^3 \times 4.807 \, (958.4 - 4.807) \times 9.81 \times (2257 \times 10^3 + 0.4 \times 2.56 \times 10^3 \times 160)}{14.85 \times 10^{-6} \times 0.01 \times 160} \right]^{1/4}$$

or, $\qquad h_{conv} = 395.84 \text{ W/m}^2°C$

The radiation heat transfer coefficient,

$$h_{rad} = \frac{5.67 \times 10^{-8} \, \varepsilon \, (T_s^4 - T_{sat}^4)}{(T_s - T_{sat})} \qquad \qquad ...[Eqn.(9.15)]$$

$$= \frac{5.67 \times 10^{-8} \times 0.92 \, [(260 + 273)^4 - (100 + 273)^4]}{[(260 + 273) - (100 + 273)]}$$

or, $\qquad h_{rad} = 20 \text{ W/m}^2°C$

$\therefore \qquad h = 395.84 + \frac{3}{4} \times 20 = 410.4 \text{ W/m}^2°C$

Hence the power dissipation per unit length for the heater

$$= h \times (\pi D \times 1) \times (260 - 100)$$
$$= 410.4 \times \pi \times 0.01 \times 160 = 2062.9 \text{ W/m or } \textbf{2.063 kW/m (Ans.)}$$

9.3. CONDENSATION HEAT TRANSFER

9.3.1. GENERAL ASPECTS

The **condensation process** *is the reverse of boiling process.* The condensation sets in, whenever a saturation vapour comes in contact with a surface whose temperature is *lower than the saturation temperature* corresponding to the vapour pressure. As the vapour condenses, *latent heat is liberated* and there is flow of heat to the surface. The liquid condensate may get somewhat sub-cooled by contact with the cooled surface and that may eventually cause more vapour to condense on the exposed surface or upon the previously formed condensate.

Depending upon the condition of cool surface, condensation may occur in two possible ways: *Film condensation and dropwise condensation*.

1. Film Condensation :

If the condensate tends to wet the surface and thereby forms a liquid film, then the condensation process is known as 'film condensation'. Here, the heat from the vapour to the cooling medium is transferred through the *film of the condensate* formed on the surface. The liquid flows down the cooling surface under the action of gravity and the layer continuously grows in thickness because of newly condensing vapours. *The continuous film offers thermal resistance and checks further transfer of heat between the vapour and the surface.*

Further, the heat transfer from the vapour to the cooling surface takes place through the film formed on the surface. *The heat is transferred from the vapour to the condensate formed on the surface by 'convection' and it is further transferred from the condensate film to the cooling surface by the 'conduction'.* This combined mode of heat transfer by conduction and convection reduces the rates of heat transfer considerably (compared with dropwise condensation). That is the reason that heat transfer rates of filmwise condensation are *lower* than dropwise condensation. Fig. 9.6 (*i*) shows the film condensation on a vertical plate.

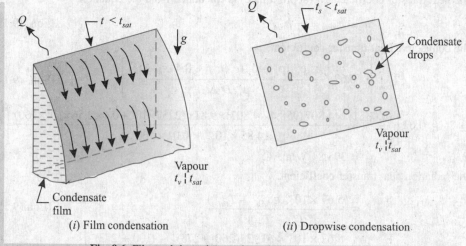

(*i*) Film condensation   (*ii*) Dropwise condensation

Fig. 9.6. Film and dropwise condensations on a vertical surface.

2. Dropwise condensation :

In 'dropwise condensation' *the vapour condenses into small liquid droplets of various sizes which fall down the surface in random fashion.* The drops form in cracks and pits on the surface, grow in size, break away from the surface, knock off other droplets and eventually run off the surface, without forming a film under the influence of gravity. Fig. 9.6 (*ii*) shows the dropwise condensation on a vertical plate.

In this type of condensation, a large portion of the area of solid surface is directly exposed to vapour without an insulating film of condensate liquid, consequently *higher heat transfer rate* (to the order of 750 kW/m^2) *are achieved*. Dropwise condensation has been observed to occur either on highly polished surfaces, or on surfaces contaminated with impurities like fatty acids and organic compounds. This type of condensation gives coefficient of heat transfer generally *5 to 10 times larger than with film condensation.* Although dropwise condensation would be preferred to filmwise condensation yet *it is extremely difficult to achieve or maintain.* This is because most surfaces become 'wetted' after being exposed to condensing vapours over a period of time. Dropwise condensation can be obtained under controlled conditions with the help of certain additives to the condensate and various surface coatings but its commercial viability has not yet been approved. For this reason the *condensing equipment in use is designed on the basis of filmwise condensation.*

9.3.2. LAMINAR FILM CONDENSATION ON A VERTICAL PLATE

An analysis for filmwise condensation on a vertical plate can be made on lines prepared by Nusselt (1916). Unless the velocity of the vapour is very high or the liquid film very thick, the motion of the condensate would be *laminar*. The thickness of the condensate film will be a function of the rate of condensation of vapour and the rate at which the condensate is removed from the surface. The film thickness on a vertical surface will increase gradually from top to bottom as shown in Fig. 9.7.

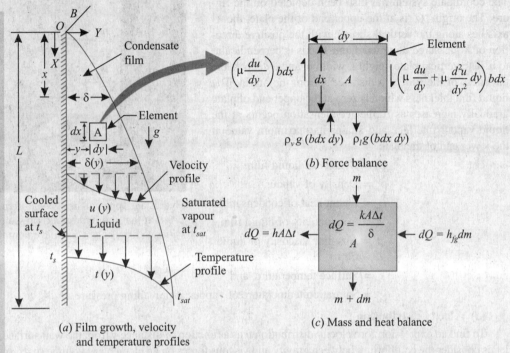

(a) Film growth, velocity and temperature profiles

(b) Force balance

(c) Mass and heat balance

Fig. 9.7. Film condensation on a flat vertical plate.

Nusselt's analysis of film condensation makes the following simplifying **assumptions.**

1. The film of the liquid formed flows under the action of gravity.

2. The condensate flow is *laminar* and the fluid properties are constant.

3. The liquid film is in good thermal contact with the cooling surface and, therefore, temperature at the inside of the film is taken equal to the surface temperature t_s. Further, the temperature at the liquid-vapour interface is equal to the saturation temperature t_{sat} at the prevailing pressure.

4. Viscous shear and gravitational forces are assumed to act on the fluid; thus normal viscous force and inertia forces are neglected.

5. The shear stress at the liquid-vapour interface is negligible. This means there is no velocity gradient at the liquid-vapour interface [*i.e.,* $\left(\dfrac{\partial u}{\partial y}\right)_{y=\delta} = 0$].

6. The heat transfer across the condensate layer is by pure conduction and temperature distribution is linear.

7. The condensing vapour is entirely clean and free from gases, air and non-condensing impurities.

8. Radiation between vapour and liquid film; horizontal component of velocity at any point in the liquid film; and curvature of the film are considered negligibly small.

Consider the process of film condensation occurring on the surface of a flat vertical plate as shown in Fig. 9.7. The coordinate system has also been depicted on the figure. The origin 'O' is at the upper end of the plate, the X-axis lies along the vertical surface with the positive direction of X measured downward and Y-axis is perpendicular to it. The vertical plate height l, width b, and δ denotes the thickness of the film at a distance x from the origin. The liquid film thickness which is zero at the upper end of plate gradually increases as further condensation occurs at the liquid-vapour interface and attains its maximum value at the lower end of the plate.

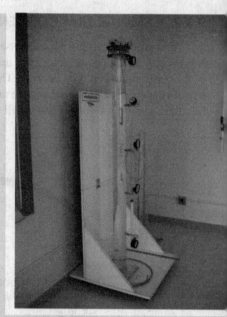

Let,

ρ_l = Density of liquid film,

ρ_v = Density of vapour,

h_{fg} = Latent heat of condensation,

k = Conductivity of liquid film,

μ = Absolute viscosity of liquid film,

Hydrostatic apparatus designed to demonstrate that the hydrostatic pressure varies with the height of liquid column.

t_s = Surface temperature, and

t_{sat} = Saturation temperature of vapour at prevailing pressure.

(a) Velocity distribution :

To find an expression for velocity distribution u as a function of distance y from the wall surface, let us consider the equilibrium between gravity and viscous forces on an elementary volume ($b\,dx\,dy$) of the liquid film.

Gravitational force on the element = $\rho_l g\,(b\,dx\,dy) - \rho_v g\,(b\,dx\,dy)$ ...(i)

Viscous shear force on the element

$$= \mu\,\frac{du}{dy}\,(b\,dx) - \left(\mu\,\frac{du}{dy} + \mu\,\frac{d^2u}{dy^2}\,dy\right)(b\,dx) \qquad ...(ii)$$

Equating (i) and (ii), we get

$$\rho_l g\,(b\,dx\,dy) - \rho_v g\,(b\,dx\,dy) = \mu\,\frac{du}{dy}\,(b\,dx) - \left(\mu\,\frac{du}{dy} + \mu\,\frac{d^2u}{dy^2}\,dy\right)(b\,dx)$$

$$\frac{d^2u}{dy^2} = -\frac{(\rho_l - \rho_v)\,g}{\mu} \qquad ...(9.16)$$

Upon integration, we have

$$\frac{du}{dy} = -\frac{(\rho_l - \rho_v)\,g}{\mu}\,y + C_1$$

Integrating again, we get

$$u = -\frac{(\rho_l - \rho_v)\,(y^2/2)\,g}{\mu} + C_1 y + C_2$$

The relevant boundary conditions are:

At $\quad y = 0, \qquad u = 0$

At $\quad y = \delta, \qquad \dfrac{du}{dy} = 0$

Using these boundary conditions, we get the following values of C_1 and C_2 :

$$C_1 = \frac{(\rho_l - \rho_v)\, g\, \delta}{\mu}, \text{ and } C_2 = 0$$

Substituting the values of C_1 and C_2 we get the velocity profile

$$u = \frac{(\rho_l - \rho_v)\, g}{\mu} \left[\delta y - \frac{y^2}{2}\right] \qquad\qquad …(9.17)$$

or, $$u = \frac{(\rho_l - \rho_v)\, g \cdot \delta^2}{\mu} \left[\frac{y}{\delta} - \frac{1}{2}\left(\frac{y}{\delta}\right)^2\right] \qquad\qquad …(9.18)$$

Equation (9.18) is the *required velocity profile*.

The mean flow velocity u_{mean} of the liquid film at a distance y is given by

$$u_m = \frac{1}{\delta} \int_0^\delta u \; dy$$

$$= \frac{1}{\delta} \int_0^\delta \frac{(\rho_l - \rho_v)\, g \cdot \delta^2}{\mu} \left[\frac{y}{\delta} - \frac{1}{2}\left(\frac{y}{\delta}\right)^2\right] dy$$

or, $$u_m = \frac{(\rho_l - \rho_v)\, g \cdot \delta^2}{3\,\mu} \qquad\qquad …(9.19)$$

(b) Mass flow rate :

The mass flow rate of condensate through any x position of the film is given by :

Mass flow rate (m) = Mean flow velocity (u_m) × flow area × density

or, $$m = \frac{(\rho_l - \rho_v)\, g \cdot \delta^2}{3\,\mu} \times b \cdot \delta \times \rho_l = \frac{\rho_l\,(\rho_l - \rho_v)\, g \cdot b \cdot \delta^3}{3\,\mu} \qquad\qquad …(9.20)$$

The mass flow is thus a function of x; this is so because the film thickness δ is essentially dependent upon x.

As the flow proceeds from x to $(x + dx)$ the film grows from δ to $(\delta + d\delta)$ because of additional condensate. The mass of condensate added between x and $(x + dx)$ can be worked out by differentiating eqn. (9.20) with respect to x (or δ).

$$dm = \frac{d}{dx}\left[\frac{\rho_l\,(\rho_l - \rho_v)\, g \cdot b \cdot \delta^3}{3\,\mu}\right] \cdot dx$$

$$= \frac{d}{d\delta}\left[\frac{\rho_l\,(\rho_l - \rho_v)\, g \cdot b \cdot \delta^3}{3\,\mu}\right] \frac{d\delta}{dx} dx$$

or, $$dm = \left[\frac{\rho_l\,(\rho_l - \rho_v)\, g \cdot b \cdot \delta^2}{\mu}\right] d\delta \qquad\qquad …(9.21)$$

(c) Heat flux :

The heat flow rate into the film (dQ) equals the rate of energy release due to condensation at the surface. Thus,

$$dQ = h_{fg} \cdot dm = h_{fg} \left[\frac{\rho_l\,(\rho_l - \rho_v)\, g \cdot b \cdot \delta^2}{\mu}\right] d\delta \qquad\qquad …(9.22)$$

According to our assumption the heat transfer across the condensate layer is by pure conduction, hence

$$dQ = \frac{k \ (b \ dx)}{\delta} (t_{sat} - t_s) \qquad \qquad ...(9.23)$$

Combining eqns. (9.22) and (9.23), we have

$$\frac{h_{fg} \ \rho_l \ (\rho_l - \rho_v) \ g \ . \ b \ \delta^2}{\mu} \cdot d\delta = \frac{k \ (b \ dx)}{\delta} (t_{sat} - t_s)$$

or, $$\delta^3 . d\delta = \frac{k\mu}{\rho_l \ (\rho_l - l_v) \ g \ h_{fg}} (t_{sat} - t_s) \ dx$$

Integrating the above equation, we get

$$\frac{\delta^4}{4} = \frac{k\mu}{\rho_l \ (\rho_l - \rho_v) \ g \ h_{fg}} (t_{sat} - t_s) x + C_1$$

Substitution of the boundary condition : $\delta = 0$ at $x = 0$ yields $C_1 = 0$. Hence

$$\delta = \left[\frac{4k\mu \ (t_{sat} - t_s)x}{\rho_l \ (\rho_l - \rho_v) \ g \ h_{fg}} \right]^{1/4} \qquad \qquad ...(9.24)$$

The equation (9.24) depicts that the heat film thickness increases as the *fourth root* of the distance down the surface; the increase is rather rapid at the upper end of the vertical surface and slows thereafter.

(d) Film heat transfer coefficient :

According to Nusselt assumption the heat flow from the vapour to the surface is by conduction through the liquid film. Thus

$$dQ = \frac{k \ (b \ dx)}{\delta} (t_{sat} - t_s) \qquad \qquad ...(i)$$

The heat flow can also be expressed as

$$dQ = h_x (b \ dx) \ (t_{sat} - t_s) \qquad \qquad ...(ii)$$

where h_x is the local heat transfer coefficient.

From (i) and (ii), we get

$$\frac{k \ (b \ dx)}{\delta} (t_{sat} - t_s) = h_x \ (b \ dx) \ (t_{sat} - t_s)$$

or, $$h_x = \frac{k}{\delta} \qquad \qquad ...(9.25)$$

Equation (9.25) depicts that at a definite point on the heat transfer surface, the film coefficient h_x is *directly* proportional to *thermal conductivity k* and *inversely* proportional to *thickness of film* δ at that point.

Substituting the value of δ from equation (9.24), we get

$$h_x = \left[\frac{\rho_l \ (\rho_l - \rho_v) \ k^3 \ g \ h_{fg}}{4 \ \mu x \ (t_{sat} - t_s)} \right]^{1/4} \qquad \qquad ...(9.26)$$

Local heat transfer coefficient at the lower end of the plate, *i.e.*, $x = L$

$$h_L = \left[\frac{k^3 \ \rho^2 \ g \ h_{fg}}{4 \ \mu \ L(t_{sat} - t_s)} \right]^{1/4} \qquad \qquad ...(9.27)$$

Evidently the *rate of condensation heat transfer is higher at the upper end of the plate than that at the lower end.*

The average value of heat transfer can be obtained by integrating the local value of coefficient [Eqn. (9.26)] as follows :

$$\bar{h} = \frac{1}{L} \int_0^L h_x \, dx$$

$$= \frac{1}{L} \int_0^L \left[\frac{\rho_l \, (\rho_l - \rho_v) \, k^3 \, g \, h_{fg}}{4 \, \mu \, x \, (t_{sat} - t_s)} \right]^{1/4} dx$$

$$= \frac{1}{L} \left[\frac{\rho_l \, (\rho_l - \rho_v) \, k^3 \, g \, h_{fg}}{4 \, \mu \, (t_{sat} - t_s)} \right]^{1/4} \int_0^L x^{-1/4} \, dx$$

$$= \frac{1}{L} \left[\frac{\rho_l \, (\rho_l - \rho_v) \, k^3 \, g \, h_{fg}}{4 \, \mu \, (t_{sat} - t_s)} \right]^{1/4} \left[\frac{x^{(-1/4 + 1)}}{-1/4 + 1} \right]_0^L$$

or, $$\bar{h} = \frac{4}{3} \left[\frac{\rho_l \, (\rho_l - \rho_v) \, k^3 \, g \, h_{fg}}{4 \, \mu \, L \, (t_{sat} - t_s)} \right]^{1/4} \qquad \qquad ...(9.28)$$

$$\bar{h} = \frac{4}{3} h_L \left(= \frac{4}{3} \times \frac{k}{\delta_L} \right)$$

where h_L is the local heat transfer coefficient *at the lower edge of the plate.*

This shows that the average heat transfer coefficient is $\dfrac{4}{3}$ times the local heat transfer coefficient at the trailing edge of plate.

Equation 9.28 is usually written in the form

$$\bar{h} = 0.943 \left[\frac{\rho_l \, (\rho_l - \rho_v) \, k^3 \, g \, h_{fg}}{\mu \, L \, (t_{sat} - t_s)} \right]^{1/4} \qquad \qquad ...(9.29)$$

The Nusselt solution derived above is an approximate one because experimental results have shown that it yields results which are approximately *20 percent* lower than the measured values. McAdams proposed to use a value of 1.13 in place of coefficient 0.943. Hence

$$\bar{h} = 1.13 \left[\frac{\rho_l \, (\rho_l - \rho_v) \, k^3 \, g \, h_{fg}}{\mu \, L \, (t_{sat} - t_s)} \right]^{1/4} \qquad \qquad ...(9.30)$$

While using above equation, it may be noted that, all liquid properties are to be evaluated at the temperature $\left(\dfrac{t_{sat} + t_s}{2} \right)$ and h_{fg} should be evaluated at t_{sat}.

The total heat transfer to the surface,

$$Q = h \, A_s \, (t_{sat} - t_s) \qquad \qquad ...(9.31)$$

The total condensation rate,

$$m = \frac{Q}{h_{fg}} = \frac{h \, A_s \, (t_{sat} - t_s)}{h_{fg}} \qquad \qquad ...(9.32)$$

Figure 9.8. shows the variation of film thickness and film coefficient with plate height [graphical representation of eqns. (9.24), (9.26) and (9.28)]. The film thickness increases with the increase of plate height. Heat transfer rate decreases with the increase of plate height since thermal resistance increases with the film thickness.

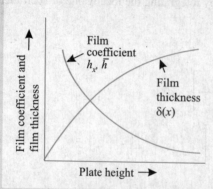

Fig. 9.8. Film thickness and film coefficient vs. plate height.

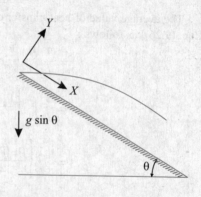

Fig. 9.9. Condensation on an inclined surface.

(e) Inclined flat plate surface

For inclined flat surfaces, the gravitational acceleration g in equation (9.30) is replaced by $g \sin \theta$ where θ is the angle between the surface and horizontal (Refer Fig. 9.9). The Eqn. (9.30) is modified as :

$$h_{inclined} = 1.13 \left[\frac{\rho_l (\rho_l - \rho_v) \, k^3 \, (g \sin \theta) \, h_{fg}}{\mu \, L \, (t_{sat} - t_s)} \right]^{1/4} \qquad ...(9.33)$$

or,
$$h_{inclined} = h_{vertical} \times (\sin \theta)^{1/4} \qquad ...(9.34)$$

Equation (9.34) is applicable only for cases where θ is *small*; is not at all applicable for horizontal plate.

9.3.3. TURBULENT FILM CONDENSATION

When the plate on which condensation occurs is *quite long* or when the *liquid film is vigorous enough*, the condensate flow may become turbulent. The *turbulent results in higher heat transfer rates because heat is now transferred not only by condensation but also by eddy diffusion*. The transition criterion may be expressed in terms of Reynolds number defined as,

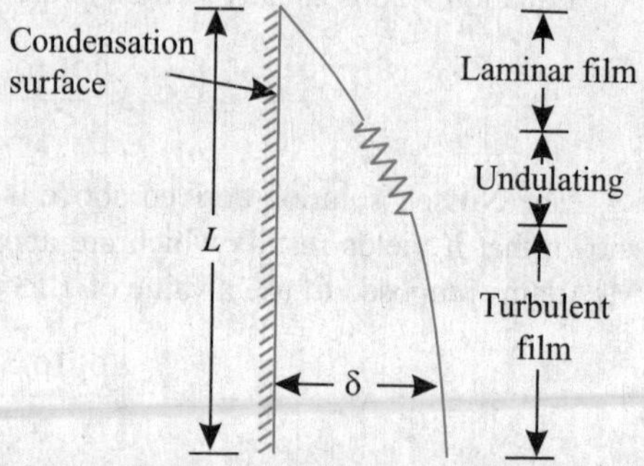

$$Re = \frac{\rho_l \, u_m \, D_h}{\mu_l}$$

where, D_h = Hydraulic diameter

$$= 4 \times \frac{\text{cross-sectional area of fluid flow}}{\text{wetted perimeter}} = \frac{4A}{P}, \text{ and}$$

u_m = Mean or average velocity of flow.

$$Re = \frac{\rho_l \mu_m \times 4 A_c}{P \times \mu_l} = \frac{4 \, m}{P \, \mu_l} \qquad ...(9.35)$$

where, $m = \rho A \, u_m$

Fig. 9.10. Regions of film condensation on a vertical surface.

For a vertical plate of unit depth, $P = 1$, the Reynolds number is sometimes expressed in terms of the mass flow rate per unit depth of plate Γ, so that

$$Re = \frac{4\Gamma}{\mu_l} \qquad ...(9.36)$$

with $\Gamma = 0$, at the top of the plate and Γ increasing with x.

The Reynolds number may also be related to heat transfer coefficient as follows:

$$Q = \bar{h} \; A_s \; (t_{sat} - t_s) = \dot{m} \; h_{fg}$$

or,

$$\dot{m} = \frac{Q}{h_{fg}} = \frac{\bar{h} \; A_s \; (t_{sat} - t_s)}{h_{fg}}$$

or,

$$Re = \frac{4\bar{h} \; A_s \; (t_{sat} - t_s)}{h_{fg} \; P\mu_l} \qquad \qquad ...(9.37)$$

For the plate, $A = L \times B$ and $P = B$, where L and B are height and width of plate, respectively.

Thus,

$$Re = \frac{4\bar{h} \; L \; (t_{sat} - t_s)}{h_{fg} \; \mu_l} \qquad \qquad ...(9.38)$$

When the value of Re exceeds 1800 (approximately), the turbulence will appear in the liquid film. For $Re > 1800$, the following correlation is used:

$$\bar{h} \; (= h_{turb}) = 0.0077 \left[\frac{\rho_l \; (\rho_l - \rho_v)k^3 \; g}{\mu_l^2} \right]^{1/3} (R_l)^{0.4} \qquad \qquad ...(9.39)$$

9.3.4. FILM CONDENSATION ON HORIZONTAL TUBES

Nusselt's analysis for laminar filmwise condensation on horizontal tubes leads to the following relations:

$$\bar{h} = 0.0725 \left[\frac{\rho_l \; (\rho_l - \rho_v)k^3 \; g \; h_{fg}}{\mu_l \; (t_{sat} - t_s) \; D} \right]^{1/4} \qquad \qquad ...(9.40)$$

... For *single horizonal tube*.

$$\bar{h} = 0.0725 \left[\frac{\rho_l \; (\rho_l - \rho_v)k^3 \; g \; h_{fg}}{N\mu_l \; (t_{sat} - t_s) \; D} \right]^{1/4} \qquad \qquad ...(9.41)$$

...For *horizontal tube bank* with N tubes placed directly over one another in the vertical direction.

where, D = Outer diameter of the tube.

9.3.5. FILM CONDENSATION INSIDE HORIZONTAL TUBES

Condensation of vapour inside the tubes finds several engineering applications such as condensers used in refrigeration and air-conditioning systems and several chemical and petrochemical industries. The phenomena insides tubes are very complicated *because the overall flow rate of vapour strongly affects the heat transfer rate and also the rate of condensation on the walls*.

Chato (1962) has recommended the following correlation for low velocities inside horizontal tubes (condensation of refrigerants):

$$\bar{h} = 0.555 \left[\frac{\rho_l \; (\rho_l - \rho_v) \; k^3 \; g \; h'_{fg}}{\mu_l \; D \; (t_{sat} - t_s)} \right]^{1/4} \qquad \qquad ...(9.42)$$

where, $h'_{fg} = h_{fg} + \frac{3}{8} \; c_{pl} \; (t_{sat} - t_s) \qquad \qquad ...(9.43)$

Equation (9.43) is restricted to low vapour Reynolds number such that

$$Re_v = \left(\frac{\rho_v \; u_{m,v} \; D}{\mu_v} \right) < 3500$$

where Re_v is evaluated at inlet conditions to the tubes.

9.3.6. INFLUENCE OF THE PRESENCE OF NON-CONDENSABLE GASES

The presence of non-condensable gas such as air in a condensing vapour produces a detrimental effect on the heat transfer coefficient. It has been observed that even with a few percent by volume of air in steam the condensation heat transfer coefficient is reduced by more than fifty percent. This is owing to the fact that when a vapour containing non-condensable gas condenses, the non-condensable gas is left at the surface. Any further condensation at the surface will occur only after incoming vapour has diffused through this non-condensable gas collected in the vicinity of the surface. *The non-condensable gas adjacent to the surface acts as a thermal resistance to the condensation process. The rate of condensation decreases greatly when the condensable vapour is contaminated with even very small amounts of noncondensable gases.*

As the presence of non-condensable gas in a condensing vapour is undesirable, the general practice in the design of a condenser should be *to vent the noncondensable gas to the maximum extent possible.*

Example 9.7. *Discuss the different types of processes for condensation of vapours on a solid surface.*

(AMIE Summer, 1998)

Solution. • *Whenever a saturated vapour comes in contact with a surface at a lower temperature condensation occurs.*

• There are two modes of condensation.

Filmwise – in which the *condensation wets the surface forming a continuous film which covers the entire surface.*

Dropwise – in which the *vapour condenses into small droplets of various sizes which fall down the surface in a random fashion.*

Filmwise condensation generally occurs on *clean uncontanimated surfaces.* In this type of condensation the film covering the entire surface grows in thickness as it moves down the surface by gravity. There exists a thermal gradient in the film and so it acts as a resistance to heat transfer.

In **dropwise condensation** a large portion of the area of the plate is *directly exposed to the vapour, making heat transfer rates much higher (5 to 10 times) than those in filmwise condensation.*

• Although dropwise condensation would be preferred to filmwise condensation yet it is *extremely difficult to achieve or maintain.* This is because most surfaces become "*wetted*" after being exposed to condensing vapours over a period of time. Dropwise condensation *can be obtained under controlled conditions with the help of certain additives to the condensate and various surface coatings, but its commercial viability has not yet been proved. For this reason the condensing equipments in use are designed on the basis of filmwise condensation.*

Example 9.8. *Saturated steam at* $t_{sat.}$ *= 90°C (p = 70.14 k Pa) condenses on the outer surface of a 1.5 m long 2.5 m OD vertical tube maintained at a uniform temperature* T_∞ *= 70°C. Assuming film condensation, calculate :*

(i) *The local transfer coefficient at the bottom of the tube, and*

(ii) *The average heat transfer coefficient over the entire length of the tube.*

Properties of water at 80° C are : ρ_l *= 974 kg/m³, k_t = 0.668 W/m K, μ_l = 0.335 × 10³ kg/ms, h_{fg} = 2309 kJ/kg, ρ_v << ρ_l*

(AMIE Winter, 1998)

Solution. Given : t_{sat} = 90°C (p = 70.14 kPa); L = 1.5 m;

$$D = 2.5 \text{ cm} = 0.025 \text{ m}; \ t_s = 70°C.$$

Properties of water at 80°C $\left(t_f = \dfrac{90 + 70}{2} = 80°C \right)$; ρ_l = 974 kg/m³;

$$k = 0.668 \text{ W/m K}; \mu = 0.335 \times 10^3 \text{ kg/ms}; h_{fg} = 2309 \text{ kJ/kg } (\rho_v << \rho_l)$$

(i) The local heat transfer coefficient, h_x :

With usual notations, the local heat transfer coefficient for film condensation is given as :

$$h_x = \left[\frac{\rho_l \,(\rho_l - \rho_v)\, k^3 \, g \, h_{fg}}{4 \, \mu x \, (t_{sat} - t_s)} \right]^{1/4} \qquad \text{...[Eqn. (9.26)]}$$

∴Local heat transfer coefficient at the bottom of the tube, $x = 1.5$ m, is

$$h_L \,(= h_{1.5}) = \left[\frac{(974)^2 \times (0.668)^3 \times 9.81 \,(2309 \times 10^3)}{4 \times 0.335 \times 10^{-3} \times 1.5 \,(90 - 70)} \right]^{1/4} \qquad (\text{as } \rho_v \ll \rho_l)$$

$$= \left[\frac{6.4053 \times 10^{15})}{40.2} \right]^{1/4} = \textbf{3552.9 W/m}^2\,\textbf{°C} \qquad \textbf{(Ans.)}$$

(ii) Average heat transfer coefficient, $\bar{h}$:

$$\bar{h} = \frac{4}{3} \, h_L = \frac{4}{3} \times 3552.9 = \textbf{4737.2 W/m}^2\,\textbf{°C} \qquad \textbf{(Ans.)}$$

Example 9.9. *Saturated steam at 120°C condenses on a 2 cm OD vertical tube which is 20 cm long. The tube wall is maintained at a temperature of 119°C. Calculate the average heat transfer coefficient and the thickness of the condensate film at the base of the tube. Assume Nusselt's solution is valid. Given :*

$$P_{sat} = 1.985 \; bar; \; \rho_w = 943 \; kg/m^3 \,; \; h_{fg} = 2202.2 \; kJ/kg;$$
$$k_w = 0.686 \; W/m \; K; \; \mu = 237.3 \times 10^{-6} \; Ns/m^2. \qquad \textbf{(AMIE Summer, 1997)}$$

Solution. From Nusselt's solution, we have

$$\delta = \left[\frac{4 k \mu \,(t_{sat.} - t_s)\, x}{\rho_l \,(\rho_l - \rho_v)\, g \, h_{fg}} \right]^{1/4} \qquad \text{...[Eqn. (9.24)]}$$

or,

$$\delta_L = \left[\frac{4 \times 0.686 \times 237.3 \times 10^{-6} \times (120 - 119) \times 0.2}{(943)^2 \times 9.81 \times 2202.2 \times 10^3} \right]^{1/4},$$

neglecting ρ_v in comparison to ρ_l (or ρ_w)

$$= \left[\frac{0.0001302}{1.92 \times 10^{13}} \right]^{1/4} = 5.1 \times 10^{-5} \text{ m} \quad \text{or} \quad \textbf{0.051 mm (Ans.)}$$

Now,

$$h_L = \frac{k}{\delta_L} = \frac{0.686}{0.051 \times 10^{-3}} \approx 13451$$

∴ Average heat transfer coefficient,

$$\bar{h} = \frac{4}{3} \, h_L = \frac{4}{3} \times 13451 = \textbf{17934.67 W/m}^2\textbf{K} \qquad \textbf{(Ans.)}$$

Example 9.10. *A vertical cooling fin approximating a flat plate 40 cm in height is exposed to saturated steam at atmospheric pressure ($t_{sat.} = 100°C$, $h_{fg} = 2257$ kJ/kg). The fin is maintained at a temperature of 90°C. Estimate the following :*

(i) Thickness of the film at the bottom of the fin;

(ii) Overall heat transfer coefficient; and

(iii) Heat transfer rate after incorporating McAdam's correction.

The relevant fluid properties are :

$$\rho_l = 965.3 \; kg/m^3$$
$$k_l = 0.68 \; W/m°C$$
$$\mu_l = 3.153 \times 10^{-4} \; N \; s/m^2$$

The following relations may be used :

$$\delta_x = \left[\frac{4k_l\mu_l \ (t_{sat.} - t_g)x}{gh_{fg} \ \rho_l \ (\rho_l - \rho_v)} \right]$$

$$\bar{h} = \frac{4}{3} \frac{k}{\delta_L}$$

(AMIE, Summer, 2001)

Solution. *Given :* $L = 60 \text{ cm} = 0.6 \text{ m}; \ t_{sat.} = 100°C; \ h_{fg} = 2257 \text{ kJ/kg};$

$t_s = 90°C; \ \rho_l = 965.3 \text{ kg/m}^3; \ k_l = 0.68 \text{ W/m°C};$

$\mu_l = 3.153 \times 10^{-4} \text{ N s/m}^2$

(i) Thickness of film at the bottom edge of the fin, δ_L :

$$\delta_x = \left[\frac{4k_l\mu_l \ (t_{sat.} - t_s)}{gh_{fg} \ \rho_l \ (\rho_l - \rho_v)} \right]^{1/4} \qquad \qquad \text{...(Given)}$$

or, $\delta_L = \left[\dfrac{4k_l\mu_l \ (t_{sat.} - t_s)L}{gh_{fg} \ \rho_l^2} \right]^{1/4}$, as $\rho_l \gg \rho_v$

$$= \left[\frac{4 \times 0.68 \times 3.153 \times 10^{-4} \ (100 - 90) \times 0.4}{9.81 \times 2257 \times 10^3 \times (965.3)^2} \right]^{1/4} = \left[\frac{34.305 \times 10^{-4}}{2.063 \times 10^{13}} \right]^{1/4}$$

$$= 0.0001136 \text{ m} = \textbf{0.1136 mm} \qquad \textbf{(Ans.)}$$

(ii) Overall heat transfer coefficient, $\bar{h}$:

$$\bar{h} = \frac{4}{3} \frac{k_l}{\delta_L} = \frac{4}{3} \times \frac{0.68}{0.0001136} = \textbf{7981.22 W/m}^2\textbf{°C} \qquad \textbf{(Ans.)}$$

(iii) Heat transfer rate with McAdam's correction :

With McAdam's correction, the value of $\bar{h}$ is 20 percent higher. Hence heat transfer rate after incorporating McAdam's correction for unit width, is :

$$Q = 1.2 \times 7981.22 \times (0.4 \times 1) \times (100 - 90)$$

$$= 38309.8 \text{ W/m} \qquad \text{or} \qquad \textbf{38.3098 kW per m width} \qquad \textbf{(Ans.)}$$

Example 9.11. *A vertical plate 500 mm high and maintained at 30°C is exposed to saturated steam at atmospheric pressure. Calculate the following:*

(i)   The rate of heat transfer, and

(ii)   The condensate rate per hour per metre of the plate width for film condensation.

The properties of water film at the mean temperature are:

$\rho = 980.3 \text{ kg/m}^3; \ k = 66.4 \times 10^{-2} \text{ W/m°C}; \ \mu = 434 \times 10^{-6} \text{ kg/ms and } h_{fg} = 2257 \text{ kJ/hg}.$

Assume vapour density is small compared to that of the condensate.

Solution. *Given:* $L = 500 \text{ mm} = 0.5 \text{ m}; \ B = 1\text{m}; \ t_s = 30°C.$

(i) The rate of heat transfer per metre width, Q:

$$\bar{h} = 0.943 \left[\frac{\rho_l \ (\rho_l - \rho_v) \ k^3 \ g \ h_{fg}}{\mu L \ (t_{sat.} - t_s)} \right]^{1/4} \qquad \text{...[Eqn. (9.29)]}$$

$$= 0.943 \left[\frac{\rho_l^2 \ k^3 \ g \ h_{fg}}{\mu L \ (t_{sat.} - t_s)} \right]^{1/4} \qquad \text{...neglecting } \rho_v [(\rho_v \ll \rho_l \text{ ...given)]}$$

or, $\bar{h} = 0.943 \left[\dfrac{(980.3)^2 \times (66.4 \times 10^{-2})^3 \times 9.81 \times (2257 \times 10^3)}{434 \times 10^{-6} \times 0.5 \ (100 - 30)} \right]^{1/4}$

$$= 0.943 \left[\frac{6.229 \times 10^{12})}{0.0152} \right]^{1/4} = 4242.8 \text{ W/m}^2\,°C$$

$$\therefore \quad Q = \bar{h}\, A\, (t_{sat} - t_s) = h \times (L \times B)\, (t_{sat} - t_s)$$
$$= 4242.8 \times (0.5 \times 1)\,(100 - 30) = 148498 \text{ W}$$
$$= \frac{148498 \times 3600}{1000} = \mathbf{534.59 \times 10^3 \text{ kJ/h}}$$

(*ii*) **The condensate rate per meter width,** *m*:

$$m = \frac{Q}{h_{fg}} = \frac{534.59 \times 10^3}{2257} = \mathbf{236.86 \text{ kg/h} \text{ (Ans.)}}$$

Example 9.12. *A vertical plate 350 mm high and 420 mm wide, at 40°C, is exposed to saturated steam at 1 atm. Calculate the following:*
  (i) *The film thickness at the bottom of the plate;*
  (ii) *The maximum velocity at the bottom of the plate;*
  (iii) *The total heat flux to the plate.*
Assume vapour density is small compared to that of the condensate.

Solution. *Given*: $t_s = 40°C$; $t_{sat} = 100°C$, $L = 350$ mm $= 0.35$ m, $B = 420$ mm $= 0.42$ m.
The properties will be evaluated at the film temperature, *i.e.*, the average of t_{sat} and t_s;

$$t_f = \frac{100 + 40}{2} = 70°C; \text{ further } h_{fg} \text{ is evaluated at } 100°C.$$

The properties at 70°C are:
$\rho_l = 977.8$ kg/m³; $\mu = 0.4 \times 10^{-3}$ kg/ms; $k = 0.667$ W/m°C and $h_{fg} = 2257$ kJ/kg.

(*i*) **The film thickness at the bottom of the plate,** δ:

$$\delta = \left[\frac{4k\,\mu\,(t_{sat} - t_s)\,x}{g\,\rho_l\,(\rho_l - \rho_v)\,h_{fg}} \right]^{1/4} \qquad \qquad ...\text{[Eqn. (9.24)]}$$

$$= \left[\frac{4k\,\mu\,(t_{sat} - t_s)\,x}{g \cdot \rho_l^2\, h_{fg}} \right]^{1/4} \qquad \text{Neglecting } \rho_v, \rho_v \ll \rho_l \qquad ...\text{(given)}$$

or, $$\delta = \left[\frac{4 \times 0.667 \times 0.4 \times 10^{-3}\,(100 - 40) \times 0.35}{9.81 \times (977.8)^2 \times 2257 \times 10^3} \right]^{1/4} = 1.8 \times 10^{-4} \text{ m} = \mathbf{0.18 \text{ mm}}$$

$$(\because x = l = 0.35 \text{ m in this case})$$

(*ii*) **The maximum velocity at the bottom of the plate,** u_{max}:

$$u = \frac{(\rho_l - \rho_v)\,g}{\mu} \left(\delta y - \frac{y^2}{2} \right) \qquad \qquad ...\text{[Eqn. (9.17)]}$$

$$= \frac{\rho_l\,g}{\mu} \left(\delta y - \frac{y^2}{2} \right) \qquad \qquad ...\text{neglecting } \rho_v$$

At $y = \delta$, $u = u_{max}$, therefore,

$$u_{max} = \frac{\rho_l\,g\,\delta^2}{2\mu} = \frac{977.8 \times 9.81 \times (1.8 \times 10^{-4})^2}{2 \times 0.4 \times 10^{-3}} = \mathbf{0.338 \text{ m/s}} \qquad \text{(Ans.)}$$

(*iii*) **The total heat flux to the plate,** *Q*:

$$\bar{h} = 0.943 \left[\frac{\rho_l\,(\rho_l - \rho_v)\,k^3\,g\,h_{fg}}{\mu\,L\,(t_{sat} - t_s)} \right]^{1/4} \qquad ...\text{[Eqn. (9.29)]}$$

$$= 0.943 \left[\frac{\rho_l^2 \, k^3 \, g \, h_{fg}}{\mu \, L \, (t_{sat} - t_s)} \right]^{1/4} \quad \text{...neglecting } \rho_v$$

or,

$$\bar{h} = 0.943 \left[\frac{(977.8)^2 \times (0.667)^3 \times 9.81 \times 2257 \times 10^3}{0.4 \times 10^{-3} \times 0.35 \, (100 - 40)} \right]^{1/4}$$

$$= 0.943 \left[\frac{6.282 \times 10^{12}}{8.4 \times 10^{-3}} \right]^{1/4} = 4931.35 \text{ W/m°C}$$

The total heat flux is given by

$$Q = \bar{h} \, A \, (t_{sat} - t_s) = \bar{h} \times (L \times B) \, (t_{sat} - t_s)$$

$$= 4931.35 \times 0.35 \times 0.42 \times (100 - 40)$$

$$= 43494 \text{ W or } \mathbf{43.494 \, kW} \quad \textbf{(Ans.)}$$

Example 9.13. *Vertical flat plate in the form of fin is 600 m in height and is exposed to steam at atmospheric pressure. If surface of the plate is maintained at 60°C, calculate the following:*

(i) *The film thickness at the trailing edge of the film,*
(ii) *The overall heat transfer coefficient,*
(iii) *The heat transfer rate, and*
(iv) *The condensate mass flow rate.*

Assume laminar flow conditions and unit width of the plate.

Solution. *Given :* $L = 600$ mm $= 0.6$ m; $t_s = 100°$C;

The properties of vapour at atmospheric pressure are:

$$t_{sat} = 100°C, \, h_{fg} = 2257 \text{ kJ/kg}; \, \rho_v = 0.596 \text{ kg/m}^3.$$

The properties of saturated vapour at the mean film temperature $t_f = \dfrac{100 + 60}{2} = 80°$C are:

$\rho_l = 971.8$ kg/m³, $k = 67.413 \times 10^{-2}$ W/m°C, $\mu = 355.3 \times 10^{-6}$ Ns/m² or kg/ms

(i) **The film thickness at the trailing edge of the plate,** δ (at $x = L = 0.6$ m):

$$\delta = \left[\frac{4 \, k \, \mu \, (t_{sat} - t_s) \, x}{\rho_l \, (\rho_l - \rho_v) \, g \, h_{fg}} \right]^{1/4} \quad \text{...[Eqn. (9.24)]}$$

$$\delta_L = \left[\frac{4 \times 67.413 \times 10^{-2} \times 355.3 \times 10^{-6} \, (100 - 60) \times 0.6}{971.8 \, (971.8 - 0.596) \times 9.81 \times (2257 \times 10^3)} \right]^{1/4}$$

or,

$$\delta_L = \frac{0.02299}{2.08972 \times 10^{13}} = 1.82 \times 10^{-4} \text{ m} = \mathbf{0.182 \, mm} \quad \textbf{(Ans.)}$$

(ii) **The overall heat transfer coefficient,** $\bar{h}$ **:**

$$\bar{h} = \frac{4}{3} h_L = \frac{4}{3} \frac{k}{\delta_L} = \frac{4}{3} \times \frac{67.413 \times 10^{-2}}{1.82 \times 10^{-4}} = 4938.68 \text{ W/m}^2 \text{°C}$$

Using McAdam's correction which is 20% higher than Nusselt's result, we have

$$\bar{h} = 4938.68 \times 1.2$$

$$= \mathbf{5926.4 \, W/m^2 °C} \quad \textbf{(Ans.)}$$

(iii) **The heat transfer rate,** Q **:**

$$Q = \bar{h} \, A_s \, (t_{sat} - t_s) = h \times (L \times B) \, (t_{sat} - t_s)$$

$$= 5926.4 \times (0.6 \times 1) \, (100 - 60) = \mathbf{142233.6 \, W}$$

(*iv*) **The condensate mass flow rate, *m* :**

$$m = \frac{Q}{h_{fg}}$$ ...[Eqn. (9.32)]

$$= \frac{142233.6}{2257 \times 10^3} = 0.063 \text{ kg/s or } \mathbf{226.8 \text{ kg/h}} \quad \text{(Ans.)}$$

Let us check whether the flow is laminar or not.

$$Re = \frac{4m}{\mu B}$$ ...[Eqn. (9.35)]

$$= \frac{4 \times 0.063}{355.3 \times 10^{-6} \times 1} = 709.26 < 1800$$

This shows that the assumption of laminar flow is correct.

Example 9.14. *A vertical tube of 60 mm outside diameter and 1.2 m long is exposed to steam at atmospheric pressure. The outer surface of the tube is maintained at a temperature of 50°C by circulating cold water through the tube. Calculate the following:*

(i) *The rate of heat transfer to the coolant, and*

(ii) *The rate of condensation of steam.*

Solution. *Given :* $D = 60$ mm $= 0.06$ m, $L = 1.2$ m, $t_s = 50°C$

Assuming the condensation film is laminar and noncondensable gases in steam are absent;

The mean film temperature $t_f = \frac{100 + 50}{2} = 75°C$

The thermo-physical properties of water at 75°C are:

$\rho_l = 975$ kg/m³, $\mu_l = 375 \times 10^{-6}$ Ns/m², $k = 0.67$ W/m°C.

The properties of saturated vapour at $t_{sat} = 100°C$ are :

$\rho_v = 0.596$ kg/m³, $h_{fg} = 2257$ kJ/kg.

(*i*) **The rate of heat transfer, *Q*:**

For laminar condensation on a vertical surface

$$\bar{h} = 1.13 \left[\frac{\rho_l (\rho_l - \rho_v) k^3 g h_{fg}}{\mu L (t_{sat} - t_s)} \right]^{1/4}$$ ...[Eqn. (9.30)]

or, $$\bar{h} = 1.13 \left[\frac{975 (975 - 0.596) \times (0.67)^3 \times 9.81 \times (2257 \times 10^3)}{375 \times 10^{-6} \times 1.2 \times (100 - 50)} \right]^{1/4}$$

$$= 4627.3 \text{ W/m}^2°C$$

$$Q = \bar{h} A_s (t_{sat} - t_s) = \bar{h} (\pi DL) (t_{sat} - t_s)$$

$$= 4627.3 \times (\pi \times 0.06 \times 1.2) (100 - 50) = 52333.5$$

$$= \mathbf{52.333 \text{ kW (Ans.)}}$$

(*ii*) **The rate of condensation of steam, *m* :**

The condensation rate is given by

$$m = \frac{Q}{h_{fg}} = \frac{52333.5}{2257 \times 10^3} = 0.0232 \text{ kg/s} = \mathbf{83.52 \text{ kg/h (Ans.)}}$$

Let us check the assumption of laminar film condensation by calculating *Re*.

$$Re = \frac{4m}{P \mu_l}$$ ...[Eqn. (9.35)]

or, $$Re = \frac{4 \times 0.0232}{\pi D \times 375 \times 10^{-6}} = \frac{4 \times 0.0232}{\pi \times 0.06 \times 375 \times 10^{-6}} = 1312.85$$

Since, $Re \; (= 1312.85) < 1800$, hence the flow is *laminar*.

Example 9.15. *A horizontal tube of outer diameter 20 mm is exposed to dry steam at 100°C. The tube surface temperature is maintained at 84°C by circulating water through it. Calculate the rate of formation of condensate per metre length of the tube.*

Solution. *Given*: $D = 20$ mm $= 0.02$ m, $t_s = 84°C$; $t_{sat} = 100°C$

The mean film temperature $t_f = \dfrac{100 + 84}{2} = 92°C$

The properties of saturated liquid at 92°C are:

$\rho_l = 963.4$ kg/m³, $\mu_l = 306 \times 10^{-6}$ Ns/m²; $k = 0.677$ W/m°C

The properties of saturated vapour at $t_{sat} = 100°C$ are:

$\rho_v = 0.596$ kg/m³, $h_{fg} = 2257$ kJ/kg

Rate of formation of condensate per metre length of the tube, m:

The average heat transfer coefficient is given by

$$\bar{h} = 0.725 \left[\frac{\rho_l \, (\rho_l - \rho_v) \, k^3 \, g \, h_{fg}}{\mu_l \, (t_{sat} - t_s) \, D} \right]^{1/4} \qquad ...[\text{Eqn. (9.40)}]$$

or, $$\bar{h} = 0.725 \left[\frac{(963.4) \, (963.4 - 0.596) \times (0.677)^3 \times 9.81 \times (2257 \times 10^3)}{306 \times 10^{-6} \, (100 - 84) \times 0.02} \right]^{1/4}$$

$$= 11579.7 \text{ W/m}^2°C$$

The heat transfer per unit length is

$$\frac{Q}{L} = \bar{h} \times \pi D \times (t_{sat} - t_s)$$

$$= 11579.7 \times \pi \times 0.02 \times (100 - 84) = 11641.2 \text{ W}$$

Rate of formation of condensate per metre length of the tube,

$$\frac{m}{L} = \frac{Q/L}{h_{fg}} = \frac{11641.2}{2257 \times 10^3} = 5.157 \times 10^{-3} \text{ kg/s} = \textbf{18.56 kg/h} \qquad \textbf{(Ans.)}$$

Example 9.16. *A steam condenser consisting of a square array of 625 horizontal tubes, each 6mm in diameter, is installed at the exhaust hood of a steam turbine. The tubes are exposed to saturated steam at a pressure of 15 kPa. If the tube surface temperature is maintained at 25°C, calculate:*

(i) The heat transfer coefficient, and

(ii) The rate at which steam is condensed per unit length of the tubes.

Assume film condensation on the tubes and absence of non-condensable gases.

Solution. *Given*: $D = 6$ mm $= 0.006$ m, $t_s = 25°C$.

Corresponding to 15 kPa pressure, the properties of vapour (from the table) are:

$$t_{sat} = 54°C, \rho_v = 0.098 \text{ kg/m}^3, h_{fg} = 2373 \text{ kJ/kg}.$$

The properties of saturated water at film temperature $t_f = \dfrac{54 + 25}{2} = 39.5°C$ are:

$$\rho_l = 992 \text{ kg/m}^3; \mu = 663 \times 10^{-6} \text{ Ns/m}^2; k = 0.631 \text{ W/m°C}$$

Since the tubes are arranged in square array, therefore, the number of horizontal tubes in vertical column is : $N = \sqrt{625} = 25$

(i) The heat transfer coefficient, $\bar{h}$:

The average heat transfer coefficient for steam condensing on bank of horizontal tubes is given by

$$\bar{h} = 0.725 \left[\frac{\rho_l \, (\rho_l - \rho_v) \, k^3 \, g \, h_{fg}}{N \, \mu_l \, (t_{sat} - t_s) \, D} \right]^{1/4} \qquad ...[\text{Eqn. (9.41)}]$$

or,

$$\bar{h} = 0.725 \left[\frac{992 \, (992 - 0.098) \times (0.631)^3 \times 9.81 \times (2373 \times 10^3)}{25 \times 663 \times 10^{-6} \, (54 - 25) \times 0.006} \right]^{1/4}$$

$$= 0.725 \left(\frac{5.7548 \times 10^{12}}{2.884 \times 10^{-3}} \right)^{1/4} = \textbf{4845.6 W/m}^2 \textbf{°C (Ans.)}$$

(ii) The rate at which steam is condensed per unit length, m :

The rate of condensation for the single tube of the array per metre length is

$$m_1 = \frac{Q}{h_{fg}} = \frac{\bar{h} \, \pi \, D \, (t_{sat} - t_s)}{h_{fg}}$$

$$= \frac{4845.6 \times \pi \times 0.006 \, (54 - 25)}{2373 \times 10^3} = 1.116 \times 10^{-3} \text{ kg/s.m}$$

The rate of condensation for the complete array is

$$m = 625 \times m_1 = 625 \times 1.116 \times 10^{-3} = \textbf{0.6975 kg/s.m (Ans.)}$$

TYPICAL EXAMPLES

Example 9.17. *A 750 mm square plate, maintained at 28°C is exposed to steam at 8.132 kPa. Calculate the following:*

(i) *The film thickness, local heat transfer coefficient and mean flow velocity of condensate at 400 mm from the top of the plate,*

(ii) *The average heat transfer coefficient and total heat transfer from the entire plate,*

(iii) *Total steam condensation rate, and*

(iv) *The heat transfer coefficient if the plate is inclined at 25° with the horizontal plane.*

Solution. *Given:* $\quad L = B = 750$ mm $= 0.75$ m, $t_s = 28°C$, $x = 400$ mm $= 0.4$ m

Assume laminar flow film condensation.

Properties of saturated vapour at 8.132 kPa (or 0.08132 bar) are:

$$t_{sat} = 42°C; \; \rho_v = 0.0561 \text{ kg/m}^3; \; h_{fg} = 2402 \text{ kJ/kg}$$

The mean film temperature $t_f = \dfrac{42 + 28}{2} = 35°C$

The properties of saturated water at 35°C are:

$$\rho_l = 993.95 \text{ kg/m}^3; \; k = 62.53 \times 10^{-2} \text{ W/m°C}, \; \mu = 728.15 \times 10^{-6} \text{ kg/ms}.$$

(i) δ_x, h_x, u_m at 400 mm from the top of the plate:

The *film thickness* at a distance x from the top edge of the plate is given by:

$$\delta = \left[\frac{4 \, k \, \mu \, (t_{sat} - t_s) \, x}{\rho_l \, (\rho_l - \rho_v) \, g \, h_{fg}} \right]^{1/4} \qquad ...[\text{Eqn. (9.24)}]$$

or, $$\delta = \left[\frac{4 \times 62.53 \times 10^{-2} \times 728.15 \times 10^{-6} \ (42 - 28) \times x}{993.95 \ (993.95 - 0.0561) \times 9.81 \times (2402 \times 10^{3})} \right]^{1/4} = 1.819 \times 10^{-4} \ (x)^{1/4}$$

At $x = 0.4$ m,

$$\delta x = 1.819 \times 10^{-4} \times (0.4)^{1/4} \simeq 1.45 \times 10^{-4} \ m \simeq \textbf{0.145 mm}   \textbf{(Ans.)}$$

At $x = L = 0.75$ m,

$$\delta_L = 1.819 \times 10^{-4} \ (0.75)^{1/4} = 1.69 \times 10^{-4} \ m = 0.169 \ mm$$

The local *heat transfer coefficient*,

$$h_x = \frac{k}{\delta_x} = \frac{62.53 \times 10^{-2}}{1.45 \times 10^{-4}} = \textbf{4312.41 W/m}^2\textbf{°C}   \textbf{(Ans.)}$$

The *mean flow velocity* of condensate,

$$u_m = \frac{(\rho_l - \rho_v) \ g \cdot \delta^2}{3 \ \mu}   ...[\text{Eqn. (9.19)}]$$

or, $$u_m = \left[\frac{(993.95 - 0.0561) \times 9.81 \times (1.45 \times 10^{-4})^2}{3 \times 728.15 \times 10^{-6}} \right] = \textbf{0.0938 m/s}$$

(ii) **Average heat transfer coefficient ($\bar{h}$):**

$$\bar{h} = h_L = \frac{4}{3} \cdot \frac{k}{\delta_L} = \frac{4}{3} \times \frac{62.53 \times 10^{-2}}{1.69 \times 10^{-4}} = 4933.33 \ W/m^2 \text{°C}$$

(where, δ_L = the film thickness at the bottom of the plate)

Using McAdams correction,

$$\bar{h} = 1.2 \times 4933.33 = \textbf{5920 W/m}^2\textbf{°C}   \textbf{(Ans.)}$$

The total heat transfer from the entire plate, Q:

$$Q = \bar{h} \ A_s \ (t_{sat} - t_s) = \bar{h} \ (L \times B) \ (t_{sat} - t_s)$$
$$= 5920 \times (0.75 \times 0.75) \ (42 - 28 \ ) = \textbf{46620 W (Ans.)}$$

(iii) **Total steam condensation rate, m:**

$$m = \frac{Q}{h_{fg}}   ...[\text{Eqn. (9.32)}]$$

or, $$m = \frac{46620}{2402 \times 10^3} = 0.0194 \ kg/s \ or \ \textbf{69.87 kg/h}   \textbf{(Ans.)}$$

(iv) **The heat transfer coefficient when the plate is inclined 25° with the horizontal, $h_{inclined}$:**
$$h_{inclined} = h_{vertical} \times (\sin \theta)^{1/4}   ...[\text{Eqn. (9.34)}]$$
$$= 5920 \times (\sin 25°)^{1/4} = \textbf{4773.2 W/m}^2\textbf{°C}   \textbf{(Ans.)}$$

Let us check the type of flow [using Eqn. (9.35)],

$$Re = \frac{4m}{\mu \ B} = \frac{4 \times 0.0194}{728.15 \times 10^{-6} \times 0.75} = 142 < 1800$$

Hence assumption is correct.

Example 9.18. *A vertical plate 3.2 m high maintained at 54°C, is exposed to saturated steam at atmospheric pressure. Calculate the heat transfer rate per unit width.*

Solution. *Given:* $L = 3.2$ m; $B = 1$ m, $t_s = 54°C$; $t_{sat} = 100°C$.

Heat transfer rate per unit width :

In order to determine whether the condensate film is laminar or turbulent; the Reynolds number must be checked.

The mean film temperature $t_f = \dfrac{100 + 54}{2} = 77°C$

The properties of the condensate at 77°C are :

$$\mu_l = 365 \times 10^{-6} \text{ Ns/m}^2; \qquad k = 668 \times 10^{-3} \text{ W/m°C};$$

$$\rho_l = \dfrac{1}{1.027 \times 10^{-3}} = 973.7 \text{ kg/m}^3.$$

The properties of saturated vapour at $t_{sat} = 100°C$

$$\rho_v = 0.596 \text{ kg/m}^3; h_{fg} = 2257 \text{ kJ/kg}.$$

Assuming the flow to be turbulent the relevant equations are :

$$Re = \dfrac{4 \bar{h} L (t_{sat} - t_s)}{h_{fg} \cdot \mu_l} \qquad\qquad \text{...[Eqn. (9.38)]}$$

and,
$$\bar{h} = 0.0077 \left[\dfrac{\rho_l (\rho_l - \rho_v) k^2 g}{\mu_l^2} \right]^{1/3} (Re)^{0.4} \qquad\qquad \text{...[Eqn. (9.39)]}$$

Eliminating $\bar{h}$ from these equations, we get the condition that the flow will be turbulent if

$$0.00296 \left[\dfrac{\rho_l (\rho_l - \rho_v) k^3 g (t_{sat} - t_s)^3 L^3}{\mu_l^5 (h_{fg})^3} \right]^{5/9} > 1800$$

Substituting the values, we get

$$0.00296 \left[\dfrac{973.7 (973.7 - 0.596) (668 \times 10^{-3})^3 \times 9.81 \times (100 - 54)^3 \times (3.2)^3}{(365 \times 10^{-6})^5 (2257 \times 10^3)^3} \right]^{5/9}$$

or,
$$0.00296 \left[\dfrac{8.837 \times 10^{12}}{74.48} \right]^{5/9} = 4144.8 > 1800$$

Thus the film is turbulent as assumed and $Re = 4144.8$

$$\therefore \quad \bar{h} = 0.007 \left[\dfrac{973.7 (973.7 - 0.596) \times (668 \times 10^{-3})^3 \times 9.81}{(365 \times 10^{-6})^2} \right]^{1/3} \times (4144.8)^{0.4}$$

$$= 0.0077 \times (2.0797 \times 10^{13})^{1/3} \times 27.99 = 5866.62 \text{ W/m}^2 \text{ °C}$$

Heat transfer rate per unit width,

$$Q = \bar{h} A_s (t_{sat} - t_s)$$

$$= 5866.62 \times (3.2 \times 1) (100 - 54) = 863566 \text{ W/m} = \textbf{863.566 kW/m (Ans.)}$$

Example 9.19. *A condenser is to be designed to condense 1800 kg/h of dry and saturated steam at a pressure of 10 kPa. A square array of 400 tubes, each of 8 mm in diameter, is to be used. If the tube surface temperature is to be maintained at 24°C, calculate the following:*

(i) The heat transfer coefficient, and

(ii) The length of each tube assuming single pass.

Solution. Given: $m = 1800$ kg/h; $D = 8$ mm $= 0.008$ m, $t_s = 24°C$.

(i) The heat transfer coefficent, $\bar{h}$:

Corresponding to 10 kPa (0.1 bar), from table, the properties of dry and saturated vapour are :

$$t_{sat} = 45.8°C; \rho_v = \left(\dfrac{1}{v_g} \right) = 0.0676 \text{ kg/m}^3; h_{fg} = 2393 \text{ kJ/kg}$$

The properties of saturated vapour at the mean film temperature,

$$t_f = \frac{45.8 + 24}{2} \approx 35°C \text{ are:}$$

$$\rho_l = 993.95 \text{ kg/m}^3; \; k = 62.53 \times 10^{-2} \text{ W/m°C}; \; \mu = 728.15 \times 10^{-6} \text{ kg/ms}.$$

As the tubes are to be arranged in an array, therefore, the number of horizontal tubes in the vertical column is, $N = \sqrt{400} = 20$.

The average heat transfer coefficient for steam condensing on bank of horizontal tubes is given by :

$$\bar{h} = 0.725 \left[\frac{\rho_l \, (\rho_l - \rho_v) \, k^3 \, g \, h_{fg}}{N \, \mu_l \, (t_{sat} - t_s) \, D} \right]^{1/4} \qquad \text{...[Eqn. (9.41)]}$$

or, $\quad h = 0.725 \left[\dfrac{993.95 \, (993.95 - 0.0676) \times (62.53 \times 10^{-2})^3 \times 9.81 \times (2393 \times 10^3)}{20 \times 728.15 \times 10^{-6} \times (45.8 - 24) \times 0.008} \right]^{1/4}$

$$= 0.725 \left(\frac{5.67 \times 10^{12}}{0.00254} \right)^{1/4} = \textbf{4983.39 W/m}^2\textbf{°C.} \quad \textbf{(Ans.)}$$

(ii) The length of each tube, assuming single pass, L :

The heat transfer rate,

$$Q = \bar{h} \, A_s \, (t_{sat} - t_s)$$

or, $\quad mh_{fg} = \bar{h} \times (400 \times \pi \, DL) \, (t_{sat} - t_s)$

$$\frac{1800}{3600} \times (2393 \times 10^3) = 4983.39 \times (400 \times \pi \times 0.008 \times L) \, (45.8 - 24)$$

$$1196500 = 1092147.3 \, L$$

or, $\quad L = \dfrac{1196500}{1092147.3} = \textbf{1.09 m} \quad \textbf{(Ans.)}$

Example 9.20. *The outer surface of a cylindrical drum 350 mm diameter is exposed to saturated steam at 2.0 bar for condensation. If the surface temperature of the drum is maintained at 80°C, calculate the following:*

(i) The length of the drum;

(ii) The thickness of the condensate layer to condense 70 kg/h of steam.

Solution. *Given :* $D = 35$ mm $= 0.35$ m; $t_s = 80°C$; $m = 70$ kg / h

Assuming film condensation and laminar flow :

Corresponding to 2.0 bar, from the table, the properties of the saturated vapour are:

$$t_{sat} = 120.2°C; \; \rho_v = \frac{1}{v_g} = \frac{1}{0.885} = 1.13 \text{ kg/m}^3, \; h_{fg} = 2201.6 \text{ kJ/kg}$$

The properties of saturated water at the mean film temperature $t_f = \dfrac{120.2 + 80}{2} \approx 100°C$

$$\rho_l = 956.4 \text{ kg/m}^3; \; k = 68.23 \times 10^{-2} \text{ W/m°C}; \; \mu = 283 \times 10^{-6} \text{ kg/ms}$$

(i) The length of the drum, L:

The film at the bottom edge of the drum is given by

$$\delta = \left[\frac{4k \, \mu \, (t_{sat} - t_s) \, x}{\rho_l \, (\rho_l - \rho_v) \, g h_{fg}} \right]^{1/4} \qquad \text{...[Eqn. (9.24)]}$$

or,
$$\delta_L = \left[\frac{4 \times 68.23 \times 10^{-2} \times 283 \times 10^{-6}\,(120.2 - 80) \times L}{958.4\,(958.4 - 1.13) \times 9.81 \times (2201.6 \times 10^3)}\right]^{1/4}$$

$$= \left(\frac{0.031L}{1.9815 \times 10^{13}}\right)^{1/4} = 1.988 \times 10^{-4} \times (L)^{1/4}$$

The average heat transfer coefficient is given by

$$\bar{h} = \frac{4}{3} \times \frac{k}{\delta_L} = \frac{4}{3} \times \frac{68.23 \times 10^{-2}}{1.988 \times 10^{-4} \times (L)^{1/4}} = 3432.09 \times (L)^{-1/4}$$

Using McAdam's correlation, we have
$$\bar{h} = 1.2 \times 3432.09 \times (L)^{-1/4} = 4118.5 \times (L)^{-1/4}$$

The heat transfer rate is given by

$$Q = \bar{h}\,A_s\,(t_{sat} - t_s) = m\,h_{fg}$$

or, $\quad 4118.5 \times (L)^{-1/4}\,(\pi \times 0.35 \times L)\,(120.2 - 80) = \dfrac{70}{3600} \times (2201.6 \times 10^3)$

or, $\quad 182046.8\,(L)^{3/4} = 42808.88$

or, $\qquad L = \left(\dfrac{42808.88}{182046.8}\right)^{4/3} = 0.1452\text{ m} = \textbf{145.2 mm} \quad \textbf{(Ans.)}$

(ii) **The thickness of condensate layer, δ :**
$$\delta = 1.988 \times 10^{-4} \times (L)^{1/4}$$
$$= 1.988 \times 10^{-4} \times (0.1452)^{1/4} = 1.227 \times 10^{-4}\text{ m}$$
$$= \textbf{0.1227 mm (Ans.)}$$

Let us check whether flow is lamniar or not.

$$Re = \frac{4m}{\mu D} = \frac{4 \times (70/3600)}{2.83 \times 10^{-6} \times (\pi \times 0.35)} = 249.9$$

As Re (= 249.9) < 1800, hence assumuption is correct.

HIGHLIGHTS

1. Boiling is the convective heat transfer process that involves a phase change from liquid to vapour state.

2. The boiling heat transfer phenomenon may occur in the following forms:

   (i) Pool boiling
   (ii) Forced convection boiling
   (iii) Sub-cooled or local boiling
   (iv) Saturated boiling.

3. The three regimes of boiling are:

   (i) Interface evaporation
   (ii) Nucleate boiling
   (iii) Film boiling.

4. The condensation process is reverse of boiling process. Condensation may occur in two possible ways:

   (i) Film condensation
   (ii) Dropwise condensation.

   If the condensate tends to wet the surface and thereby forms a liquid film, the condensation process is known as 'film condensation'.

   In 'dropwise condensation' the vapour condenses into small liquid droplets of various sizes which fall down the surface in random fashion.

SUMMARY OF FORMULAE :

A. Boiling :

1. $p_v - p_l = \dfrac{2\sigma}{r}$

2. $T_v - T_{sat} = \dfrac{2\sigma}{r}\left[\dfrac{R}{p} \cdot \dfrac{T_{sat}^2}{h_{fg}}\right]$

3. $d_c = C\beta\left(\dfrac{\sigma_{lv}}{\sigma_{ls}}\right)\sqrt{\dfrac{\sigma_{lv}}{g(\rho_l - \rho_v)}}$

4. $q_s = \mu_l \cdot h_{fg}\left[\dfrac{g(\rho_l - \rho_v)}{\sigma}\right]^{0.5}\left[\dfrac{c_{pl}\,\Delta t_e}{C_{sl}\cdot h_{fg}\cdot Pr_l^n}\right]^3$

5. $Nu = 0.16\,(Gr.Pr)^{0.33}$ ... for nucleate boiling at atmospheric pressure on a flat plate with low heat fluxes.

6. $Nu = 0.61\,(Gr.Pr)^{0.25}$ ... For the nucleate boilng on a vertical flat plate.

7. $q_{sc} = 0.18\,(\rho_v)^{1/2}\,h_{fg}\,[g\,\sigma\,(\rho_l - \rho_v)]^{1/4}$ ... critical heat flux for nucleate pool boiling

8. $(h)^{4/3} = (h_{conv.})^{4/3} + h_{rad}\cdot(h)^{1/3}$

   $h = h_{conv.} + \dfrac{3}{4}h_{rad}$ ... within ± 5% error

   $h_{conv} = 0.62\left[\dfrac{k_v^3 - \rho_v\,(\rho_l - \rho_v)\,g\,(h_{fg} + 0.4\,c_{pv}\,\Delta t_e)}{\mu_v\,D\,\Delta t_e}\right]^{1/4}$

   $h_{rad} = \dfrac{5.67 \times 10^{-8}\,\varepsilon\,(T_s^4 - T_{sat}^4)}{(T_s - T_{sat})}$

B. Condensation :

1. $u = \dfrac{(\rho_l - \rho_v)g}{\mu}\left[\delta y - \dfrac{y^2}{2}\right]$

2. $u_m = \dfrac{\rho_l\,(\rho_l - \rho_v)\,g\cdot\delta^2}{3\mu}$

3. $m = \dfrac{\rho_l\,(\rho_l - \rho_v)\,g\,b\,\delta^3}{3\mu}$

4. $\delta = \left[\dfrac{4k\,\mu\,(t_{sat} - t_s)\,x}{g\,\rho_l\,(\rho_l - \rho_v)\,h_{fg}}\right]^{1/4}$

5. $h_x = \dfrac{k}{\delta}$

6. $h_x = \left[\dfrac{\rho_l\,(\rho_l - \rho_v)\,k^3\,g\,h_{fg}}{4\mu x\,(t_{sat} - t_s)}\right]^{1/4}$

7. $\bar{h} = \dfrac{4}{3}h_L$

8. $$\bar{h} = 1.13 \left[\frac{\rho_l \, (\rho_l - \rho_v) \, k^3 \, g \, h_{fg}}{\mu \, L \, (t_{sat} - t_s)} \right]^{1/4}$$

9. $$m = \frac{Q}{h_{fg}}$$

10. $$h_{inclined} = (h)_{vertical} \times (\sin \theta)^{1/4}$$

11. $$h_{turb.} = (\bar{h}) = 0.0077 \left[\frac{\rho_l \, (\rho_l - \rho_v) \, k^3 g}{\mu^2} \right]^{1/3} (Re)^{0.4} \qquad \text{...for } R_e > 1800$$

12. $$\bar{h} = 0.725 \left[\frac{\rho_l \, (\rho_l - \rho_v) \, k^3 g \, h_{fg}}{\mu_l \, (t_{sat} - t_s) \, D} \right]^{1/4} \qquad \text{... for single horizontal tube}$$

13. $$\bar{h} = 0.725 \left[\frac{\rho_l \, (\rho_l - \rho_v) \, k^3 g \, h_{fg}}{N \, \mu_l \, (t_{sat} - t_s) \, D} \right]^{1/4} \qquad \text{... for horizontal tube bank with } N \text{ tubes placed directly over one another in the vertical direction.}$$

where, D = Outer diameter of the tube.

14. $$\bar{h} = 0.555 \left[\frac{\rho_l \, (\rho_l - \rho_v) \, k^3 \, h'_{fg}}{\mu D \, (t_{sat} - t_s)} \right]^{1/4}$$

where $h'_{fg} = h_{fg} + \dfrac{3}{8} c_{pl} \, (t_{sat} - t_s)$

THEORETICAL QUESTIONS

1. Define the term 'boiling'.
2. Enumerate the applications of boiling heat transfer.
3. Explain briefly the physical mechanism of boiling.
4. Differentiate between pool boiling and forced convection boiling.
5. Explain briefly the various regimes of saturated pool boiling.
6. What is burnout point?
7. Explain briefly the condensation mechanism.
8. Differentiate between the mechanism of filmwise and dropwise condensation.
9. Derive the Nusselt theory of laminar flow film condensation on a vertical plate.
10. Drive the following relation for laminar film condensation on vertical plate.

$$\delta = \left[\frac{4 \, k\mu \, (t_{sat} - t_s) \, x}{g \, \rho_l \, (\rho_l - \rho_v) \, h_{fg}} \right]^{1/4}$$

UNSOLVED EXAMPLES

Boiling Heat Transfer

1. Water at atmospheric pressure is to be boiled in polished copper pan. The diameter of the pan is 300 mm and is kept at 111°C. Calculate the following :

    (i) Power of the burner to maintain boiling;

    (*ii*)   Rate of evaporation in kg/h.

    Take the properties of water at 100°C as follows:

$$\rho_l = 958 \text{ kg/m}^3; \rho_v = 0.597 \text{ kg/m}^3; \mu_f = 278 \times 10^{-6} \text{ kg/ms}; c_{pf} = 4216 \text{ J/kgK};$$

$$h_{fg} = 2257 \text{ kJ/kg}; Pr = 1.723, \sigma = 58.9 \times 10^{-3} \text{ N/m} \qquad \textbf{[Ans.} (i) \text{ 13.664 kW}, (ii) \text{ 21.8 kg/h]}$$

2.   A wire of 1 mm diameter and 150 mm length is submerged horizontally in water at 7 bar. The wire carries a current of 131.5 A with an applied voltage of 2.15 V. If the surface of the wire is maintained at 180°C, calculate: (*i*) The heat flux, and (*ii*) The boiling heat transfer coefficient.

                                                         [Ans. (*i*) 0.6 MW/m², (*ii*) 39920 W/m²°C]

3.   An electric wire of 1.5 mm diameter and 200 mm long is laid horizontally and submerged in water at atmospheric pressure. The wire has an applied voltage of 16 V and carries a current of 40 amperes. Calculate: (*i*) The heat flux, and (*ii*) The excess temperature. **[Ans.** (*i*) 0.679 MW/m², (*ii*) 18.52°C]

4.   A nickel wire of 1.5 mm diameter and 500 mm long, carrynig current, is submerged in a water bath which is open to atmospheric pressure. Calculate the voltage at the burnout point if at this point the wire carries a current of 200 A.   **[Ans.** 17.9 V (appx.)]

5.   A metal-clad heating element is of 8 mm diameter and of emissivity 0.95. The element is horizontally immersed in a water bath. The surface temperature of the metal is 260°C under steady state boiling conditions. Calculate the power dissipation per unit length for the heater if water is exposed to atmospheric pressure and is at uniform temperature.   **[Ans.** 1.75 kW/m]

Condensation Heat Transfer

6.   A vertical plate 450 mm high and maintained at 30°C is exposed to staturated steam at atmospheric pressure. Calculate: (*i*) The rate of heat transfer, and (*ii*) The condensate rate per hour per metre for plate width film condensation.

    The properties of water film at the mean temperature are:

$$\rho = 980.3 \text{ kg/m}^3; k = 66.4 \times 10^{-3} \text{ W/m°C}; \mu = 434 \times 10^{-6} \text{ kg/ms}; \text{ and } h_{fg} = 2256.9 \text{ kJ/kg}$$

                                            [Ans. 439.9×10^3 kJ/h, 218.8 kg/h]

7.   A vertical plate in the form of fin is 500 mm in height and is exposed to steam at atmospheric pressure. If the surface of the plate is maintained at 60°C, calculate: (*i*) The film thickness at the trailing edge of the film, (*ii*) The overall heat transfer coefficient, (*iii*) The heat transfer rate, and (*iv*) The condensate mass flow rate. Assume laminar flow conditions and unit width of the plate.

                [Ans. (*i*) 0.1732 mm, (*ii*) 6227.52 W/m°C (McAdam's), (*iii*) 124550 W, (*iv*) 0.055 kg/s]

8.   A vertical plate 2.8 m high is maintained at 54°C in the presence of saturated steam at atmospheric pressure. Calculate the heat transfer rate per unit width.   **[Ans.** 700 kW/m)

9.   A vertical tube of 50 mm outside diameter and 2 m long is exposed to steam at atmospheric pressure. The outer surface of the tube is maintained at a temperature of 84°C by circulating cold water through the tubes. Determine: (*i*) The rate of heat transfer to the coolant, and (*ii*) the rate of condensation of steam.   **[Ans.** (*i*) 179 kW, (*ii*) 28.6 kg/h]

10.   A horizontal tube of outer diameter 25 mm is exposed to dry steam at 100°C. The tube surface temperature is maintained at 84°C by circulating water through it. Calculate the rate of formation of condensate per metre length of the tube.   **[Ans.** 21.94 kg/h]

11.   A condenser is to be deigned to condense 2250 kg/h of dry and saturated steam at a pressure of 15 kPa. A square array of 400 tubes each of 6 mm in diameter, is to be used. If the tube surface temperature is to be maintained at 26°C, calculate the heat transfer coefficient and the length of each tube, assuming single pass.   **[Ans.** 5205.3 W/m²°C; 1.35 m]

Heat Exchangers

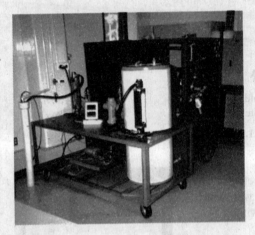

10.1. INTRODUCTION

A 'heat exchanger' *may be defined as an equipment which transfers the energy from a hot fluid to a cold fluid, with maximum rate and minimum investment and running costs.*

In heat exchangers the temperature of each fluid changes as it passes through the exchangers, and hence the temperature of the dividing wall between the fluids also changes along the length of the exchanger.

Examples of heat exchangers :

(i) Intercoolers and preheaters;

(ii) Condensers and boilers in steam plant;

(iii) Condensers and evaporators in refrigeration units;

(iv) Regenerators;

(v) Automobile radiators;

(vi) Oil coolers of heat engine;

(vii) Milk chiller of a pasteurising plant;

(viii) Several other industrial processes.

10.2. TYPES OF HEAT EXCHANGERS

In order to meet the widely varying applications, several types of heat exchangers have been developed which are classified on the basis of *nature of heat exchange process*, *relative direction of fluid motion*, *design and constructional features*, and *physical state of fluids.*

1. Nature of heat exchange process :

Heat exchangers, on the basis of nature of heat exchange process, are classified as follows :

(i) Direct contact (or open) heat exchangers.

    (*ii*) Indirect contact heat exchangers.

        (*a*) Regenerators.   (*b*) Recuperators.

  (*i*) *Direct contact heat exchangers* :

In a direct contact or open heat exchanger the exchange of heat takes place by direct mixing of hot and cold fluids and transfer of heat and mass takes place simultaneously. The use of such units is made under conditions where mixing of two fluids is either harmless or desirable. Examples : (*i*) Cooling towers; (*ii*) Jet condensers; (*iii*) Direct contact feed heaters.

Fig. 10.1 shows a direct contact heat exchanger in which steam mixes with cold water, gives its latent heat to water and gets condensed. Hot water and non-condensable gases leave the container as shown in the figure.

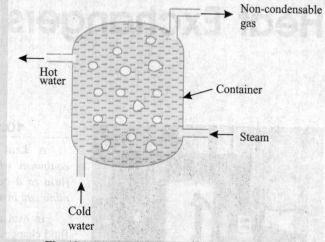

Fig. 10.1. Direct contact or open heat exchanger.

  (*ii*) *Indirect contact heat exchangers* :

In this type of heat exchanger, the heat transfer between two fluids could be carried out by transmission through wall which separates the two fluids. This type includes the following :

    (*a*) Regenerators.

    (*b*) Recuperators or surface exchangers.

(*a*) *Regenerators*: In a *regenerator* type of heat exchanger the *hot and cold fluids pass alternately through a space containing solid particles (matrix), these particles providing alternately a sink and a source for heat flow.*

Examples : (*i*) I.C. engines and gas turbines; (*ii*) Open hearth and glass melting furnaces; (*iii*) Air heaters of blast furnaces.

A regenerator generally operates periodically (the solid matrix alternately stores heat extracted from the hot fluid and then delivers it to the cold fluid). However, in some regenerators the matrix is made to rotate through the fluid passages arranged side by side which makes the heat exchange process *continuous*.

The performance of these regenerators is affected by the following *parameters* :

Oil cooler.

    (*i*) Heat capacity of regenerating material,

    (*ii*) The rate of absorption, and   (*iii*) The release of heat.

Advantages :

    1. Higher heat transfer coefficient;   2. Less weight per kW of the plant;

    3. Minimum pressure loss;   4. Quick response to load variation;

    5. Small bulk weight;   6. Efficiency quite high.

Disadvantages :

1. Costlier compared to recuperative heat exchangers.
2. Leakage is the main trouble, therefore, perfect sealing is required.

(b) *Recuperators*: 'Recuperator' is the most important type of heat exchanger in which the flowing fluids exchanging heat are on either side of *dividing wall* (in the form of pipes or tubes generally). These heat exchangers are used when two fluids cannot be allowed to mix *i.e.*, when the mixing is undesirable.

Examples : (i) Automobile radiators, (ii) Oil coolers, intercoolers, *air preheaters*, economisers, superheaters, condensers and surface feed heaters of a steam power plant, (iii) Milk chiller of pasteurising plant, (iv) Evaporator of an ice plant.

Advantages :

1. Easy construction;   2. More economical;
3. More surface area for heat transfer;   4. Much suitable for stationary plants.

Disadvantages :

1. Less heat transfer coefficient;   2. Less generating capacity;
3. Sooting problems.

The flow through *direct heat exchangers and recuperators* may be treated as *steady state* while through regenerators the *flow is essentially transient.*

2. Relative direction of fluid motion :

According to the relative directions of two fluid streams the heat exchangers are classified into the following *three* categories :

(i)   Parallel flow or unidirection flow   (ii) Counte-flow

(iii) Cross-flow.

(i) *Parallel flow heat exchangers* :

In a *parallel flow heat exchanger*, as the name suggests, the two fluid streams (hot and cold) travel in the *same direction*. The two streams enter at one end and leave at the other end. The flow arrangement and variation of temperatures of the fluid streams in case of parallel flow heat exchangers, are shown in Fig. 10.2. It is evident from the Fig.10.2 (b) that the *temperature difference* between the hot and cold fluids goes on *decreasing* from inlet to outlet. Since this type of heat exchanger needs a large area of heat transfer, therefore, it is *rarely used in practice.*

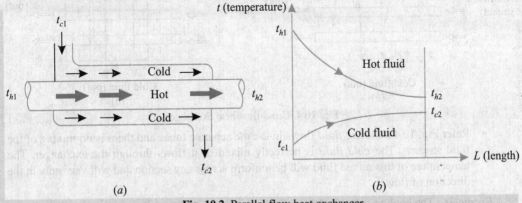

Fig. 10.2. Parallel flow heat exchanger.

Examples : Oil coolers, oil heaters, water heaters etc.

As the two fluids are separated by a wall, this type of heat exchanger may be called parallel flow recuperator or surface heat exchanger.

(ii) *Counter-flow heat exchangers* :

In a counter-flow heat exchanger, the two fluids flow in opposite directions. The hot and cold fluids enter at the opposite ends. The flow arrangement and temperature distribution for such a heat exchanger are shown schematically in Fig. 10.3. The *temperature difference* between the two fluids remains more or less *nearly constant*. This type of heat exchanger, due to counter flow, gives *maximum rate of heat transfer for a given surface area*. Hence such heat exchangers are *most favoured* for heating and cooling of fluids.

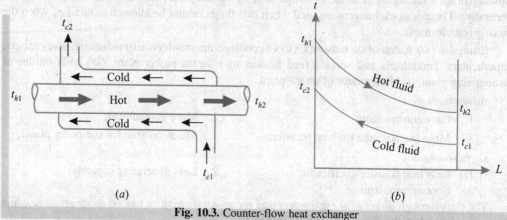

(a)   (b)

Fig. 10.3. Counter-flow heat exchanger

(*iii*)   *Cross-flow heat exchanger :*

In cross-flow heat exchangers, the *two fluids (hot and cold) cross one another in space, usually at right angles.* Fig. 10.4 shows a schematic diagram of common arrangements of cross-flow heat exchangers.

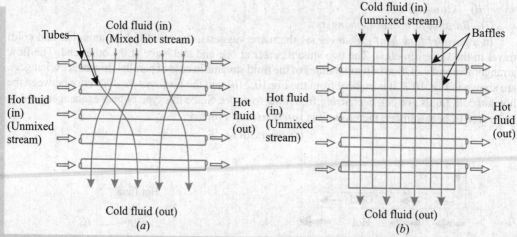

(a)   (b)

Fig. 10.4. Cross-flow heat exchangers

- Refer Fig. 10.4 (*a*) : *Hot fluid* flows in the the separate tubes and there is no mixing of the fluid streams. The *cold fluid* is perfectly mixed as it flows through the exchanger. The temperature of this mixed fluid will be uniform across any section and will vary only in the direction of flow.

Examples : The cooling unit of refrigeration system etc.

- Refer Fig. 10.4 (*b*) : In this case each of the fluids follows a prescribed path and is unmixed as it flows through heat exchanger. Hence the temperature of the fluid leaving the heater section is not uniform.

Examples : Automobile radiator etc.

- In yet another arrangement, *both the fluids are mixed* while they travel through the exchanger; consequently the temperature of both the fluids is uniform across the section and varies only in the direction in which flow takes place.

3. **Design and constructional features :**

On the basis of design and constructional features, the heat exchangers are classified as under :

(*i*) *Concentric tubes* :

In this type, two concentric tubes are used, each carrying one of the fluids. The direction of flow may be parallel or counter as depicted in Fig. 10.2 (*a*) and Fig. 10.3 (*a*). The effectiveness of the heat exchanger is increased by using swirling flow.

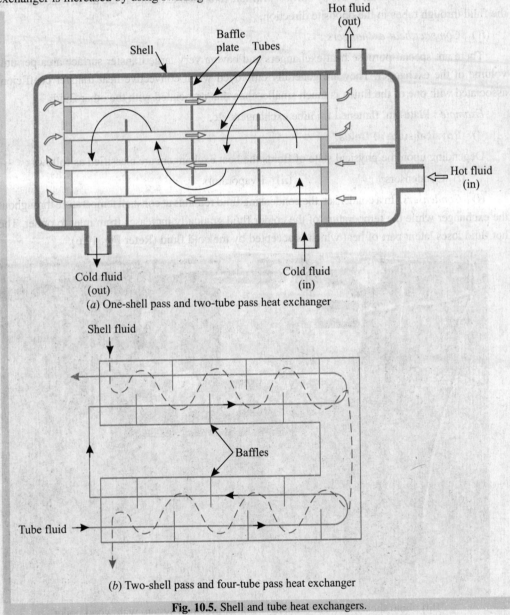

(*a*) One-shell pass and two-tube pass heat exchanger

(*b*) Two-shell pass and four-tube pass heat exchanger

Fig. 10.5. Shell and tube heat exchangers.

(*ii*) *Shell and tube* :

In this type of heat exchanger one of the fluids flows through a bundle of tubes enclosed by a shell. The other fluid is forced through the shell and it flows over the outside surface of the tubes. Such an arrangement is employed where *reliability* and *heat transfer effectiveness are important*. With the use of multiple tubes heat transfer rate is amply improved due to increased surface area.

(*iii*) *Multiple shell and tube passes* :

Multiple shell and tube passes are used for *enchancing the overall heat transfer. Multiple shell pass* is possible where the fluid flowing through the shell is re-routed. The shell side fluid is forced to flow back and forth acros the tubes by baffles. *Multiple tube pass* exchangers are those which re-route the fluid through tubes in the opposite direction.

(*iv*) *Compact heat exchangers* :

There are special purpose heat exchangers and have a very large transfer surface area per unit volume of the exchanger. They are generally employed when convective heat transfer coefficient associated with one of the fluids is much smaller than that associated with the other fluid.

Example : Plate-fin, flattened fin tube exchangers etc.

(4) Physical state of fluids

Depending upon the physical state of fluids the heat exchangers are classified as follows :

    (*i*) Condensers   (*ii*) Evaporators

(*i*) *Condensers.* In a condenser, the condensing fluid remains at constant temperature throughout the exchanger while the temperature of the colder fluid gradually increases from inlet to outlet. The hot fluid loses latent part of heat which is accepted by the cold fluid (Refer Fig. 10.6).

This photo shows the heat exchanger side of the open system with wood boiler.

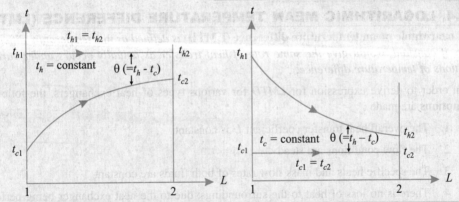

Fig. 10.6. Temperature distribution in a condenser.   Fig. 10.7. Temperature distribution in an evaporator.

(ii) *Evporators.* In this case, the boiling fluid (cold fluid) remains at constant temperature while the temperature of hot fluid gradually decreases from inlet to outlet. (Refer Fig. 10.7).

10.3. HEAT EXCHANGER ANALYSIS

For designing or predicting the performance of a heat exchanger it is necessary that the total heat transfer may be related with its governing parameters : (i) U (overall heat transfer coefficient) due to various modes of heat transfer, (ii) A total surface area of the heat transfer, and (iii) t_1, t_2 (the inlet and outlet fluid temperatures). Fig. 10.8 shows the overall energy balance in a heat exchanger.

Let, $\dot{m}$ = Mass flow rate, kg/s,

c_p = Specific heat of fluid at c nstant pressure, J/kg°C,

t = Temperature of fluid, °C, and

Δt = Temperature drop or rise of a fluid across the heat exchanger.

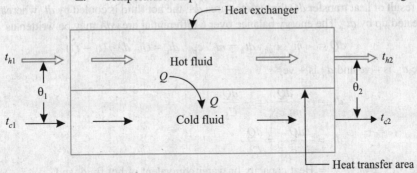

Fig. 10.8. Overall energy balance in a heat exchanger.

Subscripts h and c refer to the *hot* and *cold* fluids respectively; subscripts 1 and 2 correspond to the *inlet* and *outlet* conditions respectively.

Assuming that there is no heat loss to the surroundings and potential and kinetic energy changes are negligible, from the energy balance in a heat exchanger, we have :

Heat given up by the hot fluid, $Q = m_h c_{ph} (t_{h1} - t_{h2})$ ...(10.1)

Heat picked up by the cold fluid, $Q = m_c c_{pc} (t_{c2} - t_{c1})$ ...(10.2)

Total heat transfer rate in the heat exchanger, $Q = U A \theta_m$ ...(10.3)

where, U = Overall heat transfer coefficient between the two fluids,

A = Effective heat transfer area, and

θ_m = *Appropriate mean value of temperature difference or logarithmic mean temperature difference (LMTD).*

10.4. LOGARITHMIC MEAN TEMPERATURE DIFFERENCE (LMTD)

Logarithmic mean temperature difference (LMTD) *is defined as* that *temperature difference which, if constant, would give the same rate of heat transfer as actually occurs under variable conditions of temperature difference.*

In order to derive expression for *LMTD* for various types of heat exchangers, the following **assumptions** are made :

1. The overall heat transfer coefficient U is constant.

2. The flow conditions are steady.

3. The specific heats and mass flow rates of both fluids are constant.

4. There is no loss of heat to the surroundings, due to the heat exchanger being perfectly insulated.

5. There is no change of phase either of the fluid during the heat transfer.

6. The changes in potential and kinetic energies are negligible.

7. Axial conduction along the tubes of the heat exchanger is negligible.

10.4.1. LOGARITHMIC MEAN TEMPERATURE DIFFERENCE FOR "PARALLEL FLOW"

Refer Fig. 10.9, which shows the flow arrangement and distribution of temperature in a single-pass parallel flow heat exchanger.

Let us consider an elementary area dA of the heat exchanger. The rate of flow of heat through this elementary area is given by

$$dQ = U\, dA\, (t_h - t_c) = U \cdot dA \cdot \Delta t$$

As a result of heat transfer dQ through the area dA, the hot fluid is cooled by dt_h whereas the cold fluid is heated up by dt_c. The energy balance over a differential area dA may be written as

$$dQ = -\dot{m}_h \cdot c_{ph} \cdot dt_h = \dot{m}_c \cdot c_{pc} \cdot dt_c = U \cdot dA \cdot (t_h - t_c) \qquad \qquad ...(10.4)$$

(Here d_{th} is – ve and d_{tc} is + ve)

or, $$dt_h = -\frac{dQ}{\dot{m}_h\, c_{ph}} = -\frac{dQ}{C_h}$$

and, $$dt_c = \frac{dQ}{\dot{m}_c\, c_{pc}} = \frac{dQ}{C_c}$$

where, $C_h = \dot{m}_h\, c_{ph}$ = Heat capacity or water equivalent of hot fluid, and

$\qquad\quad\; C_c = \dot{m}_c\, c_{pc}$ = Heat capacity or water equivalent of cold fluid.

$\dot{m}_h$ and $\dot{m}_c$ are the mass flow rates of fluids and c_{ph} and c_{pc} are the respective specific heats.

$\therefore$ $$dt_h - dt_c = -dQ\left[\frac{1}{C_h} + \frac{1}{C_c}\right]$$

$$d\theta = -dQ\left[\frac{1}{C_h} + \frac{1}{C_c}\right] \qquad\qquad ...(10.5)$$

Substituting the value of dQ from eqn. (10.4) the above equation becomes

$$d\theta = -U \cdot dA\, (t_h - t_c)\left[\frac{1}{C_h} + \frac{1}{C_c}\right]$$

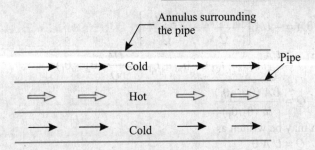

(a) Flow arrangement

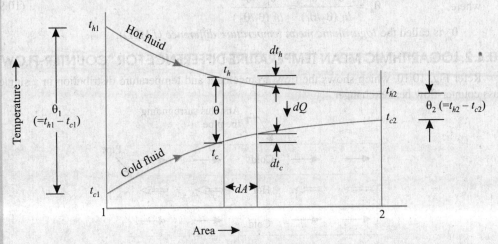

(b) Temperature distribution

Subscripts h, c refer to : *hot* and *cold* fluids
Subscript 1, 2 refer to : *inlet* and *oulet* conditions.

Fig. 10.9. Calculation of LMTD for a parallel flow heat exchanger.

or,
$$d\theta = -U \cdot dA \cdot \theta \left[\frac{1}{C_h} + \frac{1}{C_c} \right]$$

or,
$$\frac{d\theta}{\theta} = -U \cdot dA \left[\frac{1}{C_h} + \frac{1}{C_c} \right]$$

Integrating between inlet and outlet conditions (*i.e.* from $A = 0$ to $A = A$), we get

$$\int_1^2 \frac{d\theta}{\theta} = -\left[\frac{1}{C_h} + \frac{1}{C_c} \right] \int_{A=0}^{A=A} U \cdot dA$$

or,
$$ln\,(\theta_2/\theta_1) = -UA \left[\frac{1}{C_h} + \frac{1}{C_c} \right] \qquad ...(10.6)$$

Now, the total heat transfer rate between the two fluids is given by

$$Q = C_h\,(t_{h1} - t_{h2}) = C_c\,(t_{c2} - t_{c1}) \qquad ...(10.7)$$

or,
$$\frac{1}{C_h} = \frac{t_{h1} - t_{h2}}{Q} \qquad ...[10.7\,(a)]$$

$$\frac{1}{C_c} = \frac{t_{c2} - t_{c1}}{Q} \qquad ...[10.7\,(b)]$$

Substituting the values of $\dfrac{1}{C_h}$ and $\dfrac{1}{C_c}$ into eqn. (10.6), we get

$$ln\ (\theta_2/\theta_1) = -\ UA \left[\frac{t_{h1} - t_{h2}}{Q} + \frac{t_{c2} - t_{c1}}{Q} \right]$$

$$= \frac{UA}{Q}\ [(t_{h2} - t_{c2}) - (t_{h1} - t_{c1})] = \frac{UA}{Q}\ (\theta_2 - \theta_1)$$

$$Q = \frac{UA\ (\theta_2 - \theta_1)}{ln\ (\theta_2/\theta_1)}$$

The above equation may be written as

$$Q = U A\ \theta_m \qquad\qquad\qquad ...(10.8)$$

where, $$\theta_m = \frac{\theta_2 - \theta_1}{ln\ (\theta_2/\theta_1)} = \frac{\theta_1 - \theta_2}{ln\ (\theta_1/\theta_2)} \qquad\qquad ...(10.9)$$

θ_m is called the *logarithmic mean temperature difference (LMTD)*.

10.4.2. LOGARITHMIC MEAN TEMPERATURE DIFFERENCE FOR "COUNTER-FLOW"

Refer Fig. 10.10, which shows the flow arrangement and temperature distribution in a single-pass counter-flow heat exchanger.

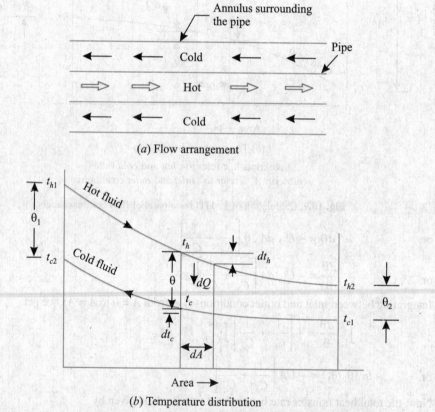

(a) Flow arrangement

(b) Temperature distribution

Fig.10.10. Calculation of LMTD for a counter-flow heat exchanger.

Let us consider an elementary area dA of the heat exchanger. The rate of flow of heat through this elementary area is given by

$$dQ = U\ .\ dA\ (t_h - t_c) = U.\ dA\ .\ \Delta t \qquad\qquad ...(10.11)$$

In this case also, due to heat transfer dQ through the area dA, the hot fluid is cooled down by dt_h whereas the cold fluid is heated by dt_c. The energy balance over a differential area dA may be written as

$$dQ = -\ \dot{m}_h\ .\ c_{ph}\ .\ dt_h = -\ \dot{m}_c\ .\ c_{pc}\ .\ dt_c \qquad\qquad ...(10.12)$$

In a counter-flow system, the temperatures of both the fluids *decrease* in the direction of heat exchanger length, hence the $-$ ve signs.

$$\therefore \qquad dt_h = -\frac{dQ}{\dot{m}_h\, c_{ph}} = -\frac{dQ}{C_h}$$

and, $$\qquad dt_c = -\frac{dQ}{\dot{m}_c\, c_{pc}} = -\frac{dQ}{C_c}$$

$$\therefore \qquad dt_h - dt_c = - dQ\left[\frac{1}{C_h} - \frac{1}{C_c}\right]$$

or, $$\qquad d\theta = - dQ\left[\frac{1}{C_h} - \frac{1}{C_c}\right] \qquad\qquad ...(10.13)$$

Inserting the value of dQ from eqn. (10.11), we get

$$d\theta = - U\, dA\, (t_h - t_c)\left[\frac{1}{C_h} - \frac{1}{C_c}\right]$$

$$= - U\, dA \,.\, \theta\left[\frac{1}{C_h} - \frac{1}{C_c}\right]$$

or, $$\qquad \frac{d\theta}{\theta} = - U\, dA \,.\,\left[\frac{1}{C_h} - \frac{1}{C_c}\right]$$

Integrating the above equation from $A = 0$ to $A = A$, we get

$$ln\,(\theta_2/\theta_1) = - U\,.\,A\left[\frac{1}{C_h} - \frac{1}{C_c}\right] \qquad\qquad ...(10.14)$$

Now, the total heat transfer rate between the two fluids is given by

$$Q = C_h\,(t_{h1} - t_{h2}) = C_c\,(t_{c2} - t_{c1}) \qquad\qquad ...(10.15)$$

or, $$\qquad \frac{1}{C_h} = \frac{t_{h1} - t_{h2}}{Q} \qquad\qquad ...[10.15\,(a)]$$

or, $$\qquad \frac{1}{C_c} = \frac{t_{c2} - t_{c1}}{Q} \qquad\qquad ...[10.15\,(b)]$$

substituting the values of $\dfrac{1}{C_h}$ and $\dfrac{1}{C_c}$ into eqn. (10.14), we get

$$ln\,(\theta_2/\theta_1) = - U\, A\left[\frac{t_{h1} - t_{h2}}{Q} - \frac{t_{c2} - t_{c1}}{Q}\right]$$

$$= -\frac{UA}{Q}[(t_{h1} - t_{c2}) - (t_{h2} - t_{c1})] = -\frac{UA}{Q}\,(\theta_1 - \theta_2) = \frac{UA}{Q}\,(\theta_2 - \theta_1)$$

or, $$\qquad Q = \frac{UA\,(\theta_2 - \theta_1)}{ln\,(\theta_2/\theta_1)}$$

Since, $$\qquad Q = UA\,\theta_m$$

$$\therefore \qquad \theta_m = \frac{\theta_2 - \theta_1}{ln\,(\theta_2/\theta_1)} = \frac{\theta_1 - \theta_2}{ln\,(\theta_1/\theta_2)} \qquad\qquad ...(10.16)$$

A special case arises when $\theta_1 = \theta_2 = \theta$ in case of a *counter-flow* heat exchanger. In such a case, we have

$$\theta_m = \frac{\theta - \theta}{ln\,(\theta/\theta)} = \frac{0}{0}$$

This value is *indeterminate*. The value of θ_m for such a case can be found by applying L' Hospital's rule :

$$\lim_{\theta_2 \to \theta_1} \frac{\theta_2 - \theta_1}{\ln (\theta_2/\theta_1)} = \lim_{(\theta_2/\theta_1) \to 1} \frac{\theta_1 \left[\dfrac{\theta_2}{\theta_1} - 1 \right]}{\ln (\theta_2/\theta_1)}$$

Let $(\theta_2/\theta_1) = R$. Therefore, the above expresion can be written as

$$\lim_{R \to 1} \frac{\theta (R - 1)}{\ln (R)}$$

Differentiating the numerator and denominator with respect to R and taking limits, we get

$$\lim_{(R \to 1)} \frac{\theta}{(1/R)} = \theta$$

Hence, when $\theta_1 = \theta_2$ eqn. (10.3) becomes

$$Q = UA\theta$$

θ_m (*LMTD*) *for a counter-flow unit is always greater than that for a parallel flow unit*; hence counter-flow heat exchanger can transfer *more* heat than parallel-flow one; in other words a counter-flow heat exchanger needs a *smaller heating surface for the same rate of heat transfer*. For this reason, the *counter-flow arrangement is usually used*.

When the temperature variations of the fluids are relatively small, then temperature variation curves are approximately straight lines and adequately accurate results are obtained by taking the *arithmatic mean temperature difference (AMTD)*.

$$AMTD = \frac{t_{h1} + t_{h2}}{2} - \frac{t_{c1} + t_{c2}}{2} = \frac{(t_{h1} - tc_1) + (t_{h2} - tc_2)}{2} = \frac{\theta_1 + \theta_2}{2} \qquad ...(10.17)$$

However, practical considerations suggest that the logarithmic mean temperature difference (θ_m) should be invariably used when $\dfrac{\theta_1}{\theta_2} > 1.7$.

10.5. OVERALL HEAT TRANSFER COEFFICIENT

In a heat exchanger in which two fluids are separated by a **plane wall** as shown in the Fig. 10.11, the overall heat transfer coefficient is given by

$$U = \frac{1}{\dfrac{1}{h_i} + \dfrac{L}{k} + \dfrac{1}{h_o}} \qquad ...(10.18)$$

If the fluids are separated by a **tubewall** as shown in Fig. 10.12 the overall heat transfer coefficient is given by,

Inner surface :

$$U_i = \frac{1}{\dfrac{1}{h_i} + \dfrac{r_i}{k} \ln (r_o/r_1) + (r_i/r_o) \times \dfrac{1}{h_o}} \qquad ...(10.19)$$

Outer surface :

$$U_0 = \frac{1}{(r_o/r_i)\dfrac{1}{h_c} + \dfrac{r_o}{k} \ln (r_o/r_i) + \dfrac{1}{h_o}} \qquad ...(10.20)$$

where,

$$U_i A_i = U_o A_o \qquad ...(10.21)$$
$$A_i = 2\pi r_i L; \qquad A_o = 2\pi r_o L$$

It may be noted that eqns. (10.20) and (10.21) are valid only for *clean and uncorroded surface.*

Consideration of fouling or scaling. In a heat exchanger, during normal operation the tube surface gets covered by deposits of ash, soot, dirt and scale etc. This *phenomenon of rust formation and deposition of fluid impurities is called* **fouling.** Due to these surface deposits the thermal resistance is increased and eventually the performance of the heat exchanger lowers. Since it is difficult to ascertain the thickness and thermal conductivity of the scale deposits, the effect of scale on heat flow is considered by specifying an equivalent *scale heat transfer coefficient h_s.* If h_{si} and h_{so} be the heat transfer coefficients for the scale deposited on the inside and outside surfaces respectively, then the thermal resistances to scale formation on the inside surface (R_{si}) and outside surface (R_{so}) are given by

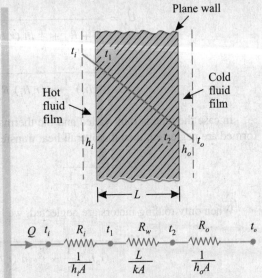

Fig. 10.11. Overall heat transfer coefficient of two fluids separated by a plane wall.

$$R_{si} = \frac{1}{A_i\, h_{si}} \qquad ...(10.22)$$

$$R_{so} = \frac{1}{A_o\, h_{so}} \qquad ...(10.23)$$

The *reciprocal of scale heat transfer coefficient, h_s is called the fouling factor, R_f.* Thus

$$R_f = \frac{1}{h_s}\ \text{m}^{2\,\circ}\text{C/W} \qquad ...(10.24)$$

Fouling factors are determined experimentally by testing the heat exchanger in both the clean and dirty conditions. The fouling factor, R_f is thus defined as :

$$R_f\left(= \frac{1}{h_s}\right) = \frac{1}{U_{dirty}} - \frac{1}{U_{clean}} \qquad ...(10.25)$$

Some typical values (approximate) of R_f are given in table 10.1. Representative values of overall heat transfer coefficient, U is given in table 10.2.

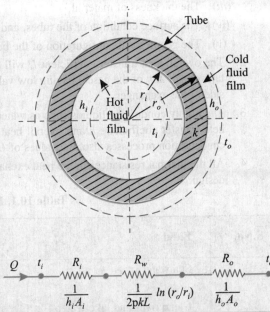

Fig. 10.12. Overall heat transfer coefficient of two fluids flowing inside and outside a tube.

The heat transfer, considering the thermal resistance due to scale formation, is given by :

$$Q = \frac{(t_i - t_o)}{\dfrac{1}{A_i\, h_i} + \dfrac{1}{A_i\, h_{si}} + \dfrac{1}{2\pi\, Lk}\, ln\,(r_o/r_i) + \dfrac{1}{A_o\, h_{so}} + \dfrac{1}{A_o\, h_o}} \qquad ...(10.26)$$

The overall heat transfer coefficients, U based on the inner and outer surfaces of the inner tube are given by,

$$U_i = \cfrac{1}{\cfrac{1}{h_i} + R_{f_i} + \cfrac{r_i}{k} \ln{(r_o/r_i)} + (r_i/r_o)\, R_{f_o} + (r_i/r_o)\cfrac{1}{h_o}} \qquad \text{...(10.27)}$$

$$U_o = \cfrac{1}{(r_o/r_i)\cfrac{1}{h_i} + (r_o/r_i)\, R_{fi} + \cfrac{r_o}{k} \ln{(r_o/r_1)} + R_{fo} + \cfrac{1}{h_o}} \qquad \text{...(10.28)}$$

In case the tube is thin walled and the thermal resistances due to tube wall thickness and scale formed are neglected, then the overall heat transfer coefficient based on outer surface is given by :

$$U_o = \cfrac{1}{\cfrac{1}{h_i} + \cfrac{1}{h_o}} \qquad \text{...(10.29)}$$

When only fouling factors are neglected, we have

$$U_o = \cfrac{1}{(r_o/r_i)\cfrac{1}{h_i} + \cfrac{r_o}{k} \ln{(r_o/r_i)} + \cfrac{1}{h_o}} \qquad \text{...(10.30)}$$

Points worth noting :

1. The overall heat transfer coefficient depends upon the following *factors* :
   - (*i*)   The flow rate,
   - (*ii*)   The properties of the fluid,
   - (*iii*)   The thickness of material,
   - (*iv*)   The surface condition of the tubes, and
   - (*v*)   The geometrical configuration of the heat exchanger.
2. The overall heat transfer coefficient U will generally decrease when any of the fluids (e.g. tars, oils or any of the gases) having low values of heat transfer coefficient, h flows on one side of the exchanger.
3. The highly conducting liquids such as water and liquid metals give much higher values of heat transfer coefficient, h and overall heat transfer coefficient, U. In case of boiling and condensation processes also, the values of U are high.
4. All the thermal resistances in the heat exchanger must be low for its efficient and effective design.

Table 10.1. Fouling factors

S.No.	Fluid	Fouling factor, $R_f = \dfrac{1}{h_s}$ (m²°C/W)
1.	Sea water	0.0001 (below 50°C)
		0.0002 (above 50°C)
2.	Clean river and lake water	0.0002 – 0.0006
3.	Well water	0.0004
4.	Distilled water	0.0001
5.	Treated boiler feed water	0.0001 – 0.0002
6.	Worst water used in heat exchangers	< 0.0002
7.	Fuel oil and crude oil	0.0009
8.	Industrial liquids	0.0002

9.	Transformer or lubricating oil	0.0002
10.	Engine exhaust and fuel gases	0.002
11.	Steam (non-oil bearing)	0.0001
12.	Refrigerant liquids brine or oil-bearing	0.0002

Table 10.2. Representative values of overall heat transfer coefficient (U)

S.No.	*Fluid combination*	$U \ (W/m^{2}{}^{\circ}C)$
1.	Water to water	850 – 1170
2.	Water to oil	110 – 350
3.	Steam condensers (water in tubes)	1000 – 6000
4.	Alcohol condensers (water in tubes)	250 – 700
5.	Feed water heaters	110 – 8500
6.	Air-condensers	350 – 780
7.	Air to various gases	60 – 550
8.	Air to heavy tars and liquids	As low as 45
9.	Air to low viscosity liquids	As high as 600
10.	Finned-tube heat echanger (water in tubes, air in cross-flow)	25 – 50

Fouling processes :

1. Precipitation or crystallization fouling.
2. Sedimentation or particulate fouling.
3. Chemical reaction fouling or polymerisation.
4. Corrosion fouling.
5. Biological fouling.
6. Freeze fouling.

Parameters affecting fouling :

- Velocity
- Temperature
- Water chemistry
- Tube material.

Prevention of fouling :

The following methods may be used to keep fouling *minimum* :

1. Design of heat exchanger.
2. Treatment of process system.
3. By using cleaning system.

Properties to be considered for selection of materials for heat exchangers :

- Physical properties
- Mechanical properties
- Climatic properties
- Chemical environment

- Quality of surface finish
- Service life
- Freedom from noise
- Reliability.

Common failures in heat exchangers :

- Chocking of tubes either expected or extraordinary.
- Excessive transfer rates in heat exchanger.
- Increasing the pump pressure to maintain throughout.
- Failure to clean tubes at regularly scheduled intervals.
- Excessive temperatures in heat exchangers.
- Lack of control of heat exchangers atmosphere to retard scaling.
- Increased product temperature over a safe design limit.
- Unexpected radiation from refractory surfaces.
- Unequal heating around the circumference or along the length of tubes.

Example 10.1. *For what value of end temperature differences ratio $\dfrac{\theta_1}{\theta_2}$, is the arithmatic mean temperature difference 5 per cent higher than the log-mean temperature difference?*

Solution. The arithmetic mean temperature difference $(\bar{\theta})$ and log-mean temperature difference (θ_m) ratio may be written as

$$\frac{\bar{\theta}}{\theta_m} = \frac{\left(\dfrac{\theta_1 + \theta_2}{2}\right)}{\left[\dfrac{\theta_1 - \theta_2}{ln\,(\theta_1/\theta_2)}\right]} = \frac{(\theta_1 + \theta_2)}{2\,(\theta_1 - \theta_2)} \times ln\,(\theta_1/\theta_2)$$

It is given that $\bar{\theta}$ is to be 5 percent higher than θ_m

$$\therefore \qquad \frac{\bar{\theta}}{\theta_m} = 1.05 = \frac{(\theta_1/\theta_2) + 1}{2\,[(\theta_1/\theta_2) - 1]}\,ln\,(\theta_1\,/\,\theta_2)$$

or, $\qquad \dfrac{(\theta_1/\theta_2) + 1}{(\theta_1/\theta_2) - 1}\,ln\,(\theta_1\,/\,\theta_2) = 2 \times 1.05 = 2.1$

By hit and trial method, we get

$$\frac{\theta_1}{\theta_2} = \mathbf{2.2} \ \ (\textbf{Ans.})$$

Thus the simple arithmetic mean temperature difference gives results to within 5 percent when end temperature differences vary by *no more than a factor of 2.2.*

Example 10.2. (a) *Derive an expression for the effectiveness of a parallel flow heat exchanger in terms of the number of transfer units, NTU, and the capacity ratio C_{min}/C_{max}.*

(b) *In a parallel flow double-pipe heat exchanger water flows through the inner pipe and is heated from $20°C$ to $70°C$. Oil flowing through the annulus is cooled from $200°C$ to $100°C$. It is desired to cool the oil to a lower exit temperature by increasing the length of the heat exchanger. Determine the minimum temperature to which the oil may be cooled.* **(U.P.S.C., 1995)**

Solution. (a) Refer Article 10.7.

(b) Using subscripts h and c for oil and water respectively, we have

$t_{h1} = 200°C; t_{h2} = 100°C;$

$t_{cl} = 20°C; t_{c2} = 70°C$ ...(Given)

Now, $Q = \dot{m}_h c_{ph} (t_{h1} - t_{h2}) = \dot{m}_c c_{pc} (t_{c2} - t_{cl})$

or, $\dot{m}_h c_{ph} (200 - 100) = \dot{m}_c c_{pc} (70 - 20)$

or, $\dfrac{\dot{m}_c c_{pc}}{\dot{m}_h c_{ph}} = \dfrac{100}{50} = 2$

Let 't' be the lowest temperature to which oil may be cooled and this will be the highest temperature of water too (Refer Fig. 10.13).

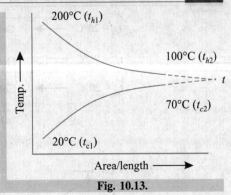

Fig. 10.13.

Hence, $\dot{m}_h c_{ph} (200 - t) = \dot{m}_c c_{pc} (t - 20)$

or, $(200 - t) = \dfrac{\dot{m}_c c_{pc}}{\dot{m}_h c_{ph}} (t - 20)$

$= 2 (t - 20)$

or, $200 - t = 2t - 40$

or, $t = \textbf{80°C}$ **(Ans.)**

Eample 10.3. *The flow rates of hot and cold water streams running through a parallel flow heat exchanger are 0.2 kg/s and 0.5 kg/s respectively. The inlet temperatures on the hot and cold sides are 75°C and 20°C respectively. The exit temperature of hot water is 45°C. If the individual heat transfer coefficients on both sides are 650 W/m²°C, calculate the area of the heat exchanger.*

Solution. Given : $\dot{m}_h = 0.2$ kg/s; $\dot{m}_c = 0.5$ kg/s; $t_{h1} = 75°$ C; $t_{h2} = 45°C$; $t_{cl} = 20°C$; $h_i = h_o = 650$ W/m²°C.

The area of heat exchanger, A :

The heat exchanger is shown diagrammatically in Fig. 10.14.

The heat transfer rate, $Q = \dot{m}_h \times c_{ph} \times (t_{h1} - t_{h2})$

$= 0.2 \times 4.187 \times (75 - 45) = 25.122$ kJ/s

Heat lost by hot water = Heat gained by cold water

$\dot{m}_h \times c_{ph} \times (t_{h1} - t_{h2}) = \dot{m}_c \times c_{pc} \times (t_{c2} - t_{cl})$

$0.2 \times 4.187 \times (75 - 45) = 0.5 \times 4.187 \times (t_{c2} - 20)$

∴ $t_{c2} = 32°C$

Logarithmic mean temperature difference (*LMTD*) is given by

$\theta_m = \dfrac{\theta_1 - \theta_2}{\ln (\theta_1/\theta_2)}$ ...[Eqn. (10.9)]

or, $\theta_m = \dfrac{(t_{h1} - t_{cl}) - (t_{h2} - t_{c2})}{\ln [(t_{h1} - t_{cl})/(t_{h2} - t_{c2})]}$

$= \dfrac{(75 - 20) - (45 - 32)}{\ln [(75 - 20)/(45 - 32)]}$

$= \dfrac{55 - 13}{\ln (55/13)} = 29.12°C$

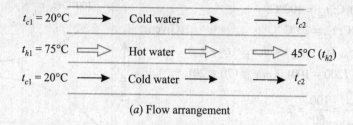

(a) Flow arrangement

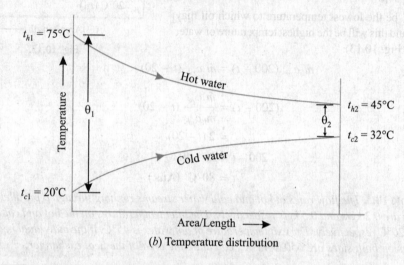

(b) Temperature distribution

Fig. 10.14. Parallel flow heat exchanger.

Overall heat transfer coefficient U is calculated from the relation,

$$\frac{1}{U} = \frac{1}{h_i} + \frac{1}{h_o}$$

$$= \frac{1}{650} + \frac{1}{650} = \frac{1}{325}$$

∴ $$U = 325 \text{ W/m}^2\text{°C}$$

Also, $$Q = U A \theta_m$$

or, $$A = \frac{Q}{U \theta_m} = \frac{25.122 \times 1000}{325 \times 29.12} = 2.66 \text{ m}^2 \qquad \textbf{(Ans.)}$$

Example 10.4. *The following data relate to a parallel flow heat exchanger in which air is heated by hot exhaust gases.*

Heat transferred per hour .....*155450 kJ*

Inside heat transfer coefficient .....*120 W/m²°C*

Outside heat transfer coefficient .....*195 W/m²°C*

Inlet and outlet temperatures of the hot fluid .....*450°C and 250°C, respectively*

Inlet and outlet temperatures of the cold fluid .....*60°C and 120°C, respectively*

Inside and outside diameters of the tube .....*50 mm and 60 mm, respectively.*

Calculate the length of the tube required for the necessary heat transfer to occur. Neglect the tube resistance.

Solution. *Given :* $Q = 155450$ kJ/h; $h_i = 120$ W/m²°C; $h_o = 195$ W/m²°C; $t_{h1} = 450$°C; $t_{h2} = 250$°C; $t_{c1} = 60$°C; $t_{c2} = 120$°C; $d_i = 50$ mm $= 0.05$ m; $d_o = 60$ mm $= 0.06$ m.

Length of each tube, L :

Logarithmic mean temperature difference ($LMTD$) is given by

$$\theta_m = \frac{\theta_1 - \theta_2}{\ln (\theta_1/\theta_2)} = \frac{(t_{h1} - t_{c1}) - (t_{h2} - t_{c2})}{\ln [(t_{h1} - t_{c1})/(t_{h2} - t_{c2})]}$$

$$= \frac{(450 - 60) - (250 - 120)}{\ln [(450 - 60)/(250 - 120)]} = \frac{390 - 130}{\ln [(390/130)]} = 236.66°C$$

The overall heat transfer coefficient, U is given by

$$\frac{1}{U} = \frac{r_o}{r_i} \frac{1}{h_i} + \frac{1}{h_o}$$

$$= \frac{0.03}{0.025} \times \frac{1}{120} + \frac{1}{195} = 0.01513$$

∴ $\quad\quad U = 66.09 \text{ W/m}^2°C$

Total heat transfer rate is given by

$$Q = U A \,\theta_m = U \times (\pi \, d_o \, L) \times \theta_m$$

or, $\quad\quad L = \dfrac{Q}{U \times \pi d_o \times \theta_m} = \dfrac{155450 \times (1000/3600)}{60.09 \times \pi \times 0.06 \times 236.66} = \mathbf{14.65 \ m \ (Ans.)}$

Example 10.5. *A hot fluid at 200°C enters a heat exchanger at a mass flow rate of 10^4 kg/h. Its specific heat is 2000 J/kg K. It is to be cooled by another fluid entering at 25°C with a mass flow rate 2500 kg/h and specific heat 400 J/kg K. The overall heat transfer coefficient based on outside area of 20 m² is 250 W/m² K. Find the exit temperature of the hot fluid when the fluids are in parallel flow.*

(GATE, 1998)

Solution. *Given :* $t_{h1} = 200°C$; $\dot{m}_h = \dfrac{10000}{3600} = 2.78$ kg/s; $c_{ph} = 2000$ J/kg K; $t_{c1} = 25°C$;

$$\dot{m}_c = \frac{2500}{3600} = 0.694 \text{ kg/s}; \ c_{pc} = 400 \text{ J/kg K}; \ U = 250 \text{ W/m}^2 \text{ K}.$$

Exit temperature of the hot fluid, t_{h2} :

Heat lost by the hot fluid, $\quad Q = \dot{m}_h c_{ph} (t_{h1} - t_{h2})$

$$= 2.78 \times 2000 \times (200 - t_{h2}) = 5560 (200 - t_{h2}) \quad\quad\quad ...(i)$$

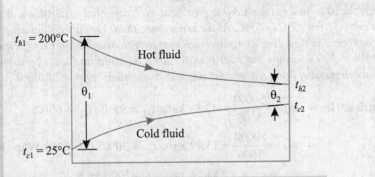

$t_{h1} = 200°C$

Hot fluid

θ_1

t_{h2}

θ_2

t_{c2}

Cold fluid

$t_{c1} = 25°C$

Fig. 10.15.

Heat gained by the cold fluid, $Q = 0.694 \times 400 \,(t_{c2} - 25)$

$$= 277.6 \,(t_{c2} - 25) \quad\quad\quad ...(ii)$$

Equating (i) and (ii), we have

$$5560 \,(200 - t_{h2}) = 277.6 \,(t_{c2} - 25)$$

or,

$$t_{c2} = \frac{5560}{277.6}(200 - t_{h2}) + 25 = 4025 - 20t_{h2} \qquad \ldots(iii)$$

Also, heat transferred is given by,

$$Q = UA\theta_m$$

where,

$$\theta_m = \frac{\theta_1 - \theta_2}{\ln(\theta_1/\theta_2)}$$

Here

$$\theta_1 = t_{h1} - t_{c1} = 200 - 25 = 175°C; \text{ and } \theta_2 = t_{h2} - t_{c2}$$

∴

$$\theta_m = \frac{175 - (t_{h2} - t_{c2})}{\ln\left[\dfrac{175}{t_{h2} - t_{c2}}\right]}$$

Substituting the values in the above equation, we get

$$Q = 250 \times 20 \left[\frac{175 - (t_{h2} - t_{c2})}{\ln\left(\dfrac{175}{t_{h2} - t_{c2}}\right)}\right] \qquad \ldots(iv)$$

Substituting the values of t_{c2} from (iii) in (iv), we get

$$Q = 250 \times 20 \left[\frac{175 - \{t_{h2} - (4025 - 20t_{h2})\}}{\ln\left\{\dfrac{175}{t_{h2} - (4025 - 20t_{h2})}\right\}}\right]$$

$$= 5000 \left[\frac{175 - (t_{h2} - 4025 + 20t_{h2})}{\ln\dfrac{175}{(t_{h2} - 4025 + 20t_{h2})}}\right] = 5000 \left[\frac{175 - (21t_{h2} - 4025)}{\ln\left\{\dfrac{175}{21t_{h2} - 4025}\right\}}\right] \qquad \ldots(v)$$

Equating (i) and (v), we get

$$5560(200 - t_{h2}) = 5000 \left[\frac{175 - (21t_{h2} - 4025)}{\ln\left\{\dfrac{175}{21t_{h2} - 4025}\right\}}\right]$$

Using hit and trial method, the value of t_{h2} may be found out.

Example 10.6. *In a certain double pipe heat exchanger hot water flows at a rate of 5000 kg/h and gets cooled from 95°C to 65°C. At the same time 50000 kg/h of cooling water at 30°C enters the heat exchanger. The flow conditions are such that overall heat transfer coefficient remains constant at 2270 W/m² K. Determine the heat transfer area required and the effectiveness, assuming two streams are in parallel flow. Assume for the both the streams $c_p = 4.2$ kJ/kg K.* **(GATE, 1997)**

Solution. *Given :* $\dot{m}_h = \dfrac{50000}{3600} = 13.89$ kg/s; $t_{h1} = 95°C$; $t_{h2} = 65°C$;

$$\dot{m}_c = \frac{50000}{3600} = 13.89 \text{ kg/s}; t_{c1} = 30°C; U = 2270 \text{ W/m}^2 \text{ K};$$

$$c_{ph} = c_{pc} = 4.2 \text{ kJ/kg or} \qquad 4200 \text{ J/kg K.}$$

$$Q = \text{Heat lost by hot water} = \text{Heat gained by cold water.}$$

$$\dot{m}_h c_{ph} \times (t_{h1} - t_{h2}) = \dot{m}_c c_{pc} \times (t_{c2} - t_{c1})$$

or, $13.89 \times 4200 \times (95 - 65) = 13.89 \times 4200 \times (t_{c2} - 30)$

∴ $t_{c2} = 60°C$

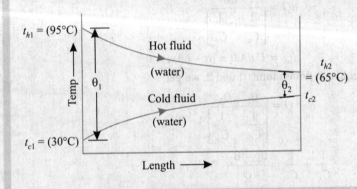

Fig. 10.16. Parallel-flow heat-exchanger.

Log mean temperature difference,

$$LMTD, \; \theta_m = \frac{(\theta_1 - \theta_2)}{\ln (\theta_1/\theta_2)}$$

$$= \frac{(t_{h1} - t_{c1}) - (t_{h2} - t_{c2})}{\ln \left(\dfrac{t_{h1} - t_{c1}}{t_{h2} - t_{c2}} \right)}$$

$$= \frac{(95 - 30) - (65 - 60)}{\ln \left(\dfrac{95 - 30}{65 - 60} \right)} = \frac{60}{0.583} = 23.4°C$$

Also, $\qquad\qquad Q = UA\theta_m$

or, $13.89 \times 4200 \times (95 - 65) = 2270 \times A \times 23.4$

Heat transfer area, $\qquad A = \mathbf{32.95 \; m^2}$ **(Ans.)**

Also, $\qquad\qquad Q_{actual} = \dot{m}_h \, c_{ph} \, (t_{h1} - t_{h2})$ and $Q_{max} = \dot{m}_c \, c_{ph} \, (t_{h1} - t_{c1})$

∴   Effectiveness of the heat exchanger,

$$\varepsilon = \frac{Q_{actual}}{Q_{max}} = \frac{\dot{m}_h c_{ph} \, (t_{h1} - t_{h2})}{\dot{m}_h c_{ph} \, (t_{h1} - t_{c1})} = \frac{95 - 65}{95 - 30} = \mathbf{0.461} \qquad \text{(Ans.)}$$

Example 10.7. *Prove that the rate of heat transfer Q for a double parallel flow heat exchanger in which the overall heat transfer coefficient varies linearly with temperature difference i.e.,* $U = a + b\theta$, *where a and b are constants, is given by*

$$Q = \frac{U_1 \, \theta_2 - U_2 \, \theta_1}{\ln \, [U_1 \, \theta_2/U_2 \, \theta_1]} A$$

Here suffix 1 and suffix 2 represent inlet and outlet of the heat exchanger respectively.

Solution. Refer Fig. 10.9, for parallel flow heat exchanger. The heat flow rate through an elementary strip of area dA is

$$dQ = - \dot{m}_h \, c_{ph} \, dt_h = \dot{m}_c \, c_{pc} \, dt_c = - C_h \, dt_h = C_c \, dt_c \qquad \text{...(i)}$$

or, $\qquad\qquad dt_h = - \frac{dQ}{C_h} \text{ and } dt_c = \frac{dQ}{C_c} \qquad\qquad \text{...(ii)}$

From eqns. (*i*) and (*ii*), we get

$$d \, (t_h - t_c) = d(\theta) = - dQ \left[\frac{1}{C_h} + \frac{1}{C_c} \right] \qquad\qquad \text{...(iii)}$$

or,
$$dQ = \frac{-d\theta}{\left[\dfrac{1}{C_h} + \dfrac{1}{C_c}\right]} \qquad \qquad ...(iv)$$

Also, $\qquad dQ = U.dA.\theta = (a + b\theta)\, dA.\theta \qquad\qquad ...(v)$

Integrating eqn. (iv) within limits 1 and 2, we get

$$Q = \frac{\theta_1 - \theta_2}{\left[\dfrac{1}{C_h} + \dfrac{1}{C_c}\right]} \qquad\qquad ...(vi)$$

or, $\qquad \dfrac{1}{C_h} + \dfrac{1}{C_c} = \dfrac{\theta_1 - \theta_2}{Q} \qquad\qquad ...(vii)$

From eqns. (iv) and (v) and using eqn. (vi), we have

$$(a + b\theta)\, dA.\theta = \frac{-d\theta}{\left[\dfrac{1}{C_h} + \dfrac{1}{C_c}\right]} = \frac{-d\theta}{\left[\dfrac{\theta_1 - \theta_2}{Q}\right]} = \frac{Q\, d\theta}{\theta_2 - \theta_1} \qquad ...(viii)$$

Integrating eqn. (viii) between limits 1 and 2, we get

$$\int_{\theta_1}^{\theta_2} \frac{d\theta}{(a + b\theta)\, \theta} = \frac{\theta_2 - \theta_1}{Q} \int_0^A dA$$

or, $\qquad \dfrac{\theta_2 - \theta_1}{Q} . A = \dfrac{1}{a} \ln\left[\dfrac{\theta}{a + b\theta}\right]_{\theta_1}^{\theta_2}$

$$= \frac{1}{a} \ln\left[\frac{\theta_2}{a + b\theta_2} - \frac{\theta_1}{a + b\theta_1}\right]$$

or, $\qquad \dfrac{\theta_2 - \theta_1}{Q} . A = \dfrac{1}{a} \ln\left[\dfrac{\theta_2\,(a + b\theta_1)}{\theta_1\,(a + b\theta_2)}\right] = \dfrac{1}{a} \ln\left[\dfrac{U_1\,\theta_2}{U_2\,\theta_1}\right] \qquad ...(ix)$

The constant a may be expressed by solving $U_1 = a + b\theta_1$ and

$$U_2 = a + b\theta_2 \text{ which results in}$$

$$a = \frac{U_1\,\theta_2 - U_2\,\theta_1}{\theta_2 - \theta_1}$$

Substituting this value of a in eqn. (ix), we get

$$\frac{\theta_2 - \theta_1}{Q} . A = \frac{\theta_2 - \theta_1}{U_1\,\theta_2 - U_2\,\theta_1} \ln\left[\frac{U_1\,\theta_2}{U_2\,\theta_1}\right]$$

or, $\qquad Q = \dfrac{U_1\,\theta_2 - U_2\,\theta_1}{\ln\left[(U_1\,\theta_2)/(U_2\,\theta_1)\right]} A \qquad\qquad$ ... **Proved.**

Example 10.8. *In a counter-flow double pipe heat exchanger, water is heated from 25°C to 65°C by an oil with a specific heat of 1.45 kJ/kg K and mass flow rate of 0.9 kg/s. The oil is cooled from 230°C to 160°C. If the overall heat transfer coefficient is 420 W/m²°C, calculate the following :*

(i) *The rate of heat transfer,*

(ii) *The mass flow rate of water, and*

(iii) *The surface area of the hat exchanger.*

Solution. *Given* : $\qquad t_{c1} = 25°C;\ t_{c2} = 65°C,\ c_{ph} = 1.45 \text{ kJ/kg K};\ \dot{m}_h = 0.9 \text{ kg/s};$

$$t_{h1} = 230°C;\ t_{h2} = 160°C,\ U = 420 \text{ W/m}^2°C.$$

(i) **The rate of heat transfer, Q :**

$$Q = \dot{m}_h \times c_{ph} \times (t_{h1} - t_{h2})$$

or, $\qquad Q = 0.9 \times (1.45) \times (230 - 160) = \mathbf{91.35\ kJ/s}$ **(Ans.)**

(ii) **The mass flow rate of water, $\dot{m}_c$:**

Heat lost by oil (hot fluid) = Heat gained by water (cold fluid)

$$\dot{m}_h \times c_{ph} \times (t_{h1} - t_{h2}) = \dot{m}_c \times c_{pc} \times (t_{c2} - t_{c1})$$

$$91.35 = \dot{m}_c \times 4.187\,(65 - 25)$$

∴ $\qquad \dot{m}_c = \dfrac{91.35}{4.187 \times (65 - 25)} = \mathbf{0.545\ kg/s}$ **(Ans.)**

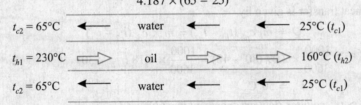

$t_{c2} = 65°C$ ← water ← ← 25°C (t_{c1})

$t_{h1} = 230°C$ ⇒ oil ⇒ ⇒ 160°C (t_{h2})

$t_{c2} = 65°C$ ← water ← ← 25°C (t_{c1})

(a) Flow arrangement

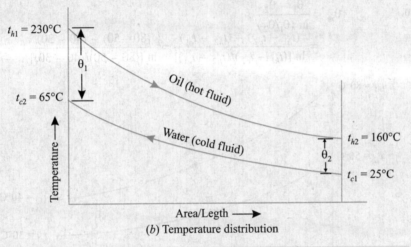

(b) Temperature distribution

Fig. 10.17. Counter-flow heat exchnager.

(iii) **The surface area of heat exchanger, A :**

Logarithmic mean temperature difference (LMTD) is given by

$$\theta_m = \frac{\theta_1 - \theta_2}{\ln\,(\theta_1/\theta_2)}$$

$$= \frac{(t_{h1} - t_{c2}) - (t_{h2} - t_{c1})}{\ln\,[(t_{h1} - t_{c2})/(t_{h2} - t_{c1})]} = \frac{(230 - 65) - (160 - 25)}{\ln\,[(230 - 65)/(160 - 25)]}$$

or, $\qquad \theta_m = \dfrac{165 - 135}{\ln\,[(165/135)]} = 149.5°C$

Also, $\qquad Q = U A\,\theta_m$

or, $\qquad A = \dfrac{Q}{U\theta_m} = \dfrac{91.35 \times 10^3}{420 \times 149.5} = \mathbf{1.45\ m^2}$ **(Ans.)**

Example 10.9. *An oil cooler for a lubrication system has to cool 1000 kg/h of oil ($c_p = 2.09$ kJ/kg°C) from 80°C to 40°C by using a cooling water flow of 1000 kg/h at 30°C. Give your choice for a parallel flow or counter-flow heat exchanger, with reasons. Calculate the surface area of the heat exchanger, if the overall heat transfer coefficient is 24 W/m²°C.*

Take c_p of water = 4.18 kJ/kg°C.

Solution. *Given* : $\dot{m}_h = \dfrac{1000}{3600}$ kg/s; $c_{ph} = 2.09$ kJ/kg°C; $c_{pc} = 4.18$ kJ/kg°C; $\dot{m}_c = \dfrac{1000}{3600}$ kg/s; $t_{h1} = 80°C$, $t_{c1} = 30°C$; $t_{h2} = 40°C$; $U = 24$ W/m²°C.

Surface area of heat exchanger, A :

Let subscripts h and c stand for hot and cold fluids respectively.

Rate of heat transfer is given by

$$Q = \dot{m}_h\, c_{ph}\,(t_{h1} - t_{h2}) = \dot{m}_c \cdot c_{pc}\,(t_{c2} - t_{c1})$$

or, $\qquad \dfrac{1000}{3600} \times 2.09\,(80 - 40) = \dfrac{1000}{3600} \times 4.18\,(t_{c2} - 30)$

or, $\qquad\qquad t_{c2} = 50°C$

Since $t_{c2} > t_{h2}$, *counter-flow arrangement must be used.*

Again, $\qquad \theta_m = \dfrac{\theta_1 - \theta_2}{\ln\,(\theta_1/\theta_2)}$

$$= \dfrac{(t_{h1} - t_{c2}) - (t_{h2} - t_{c1})}{\ln\,[(t_{h1} - t_{c2})/(t_{h2} - t_{c1})]} = \dfrac{(80 - 50) - (40 - 30)}{\ln\,[(80 - 50)/(40 - 30)]}$$

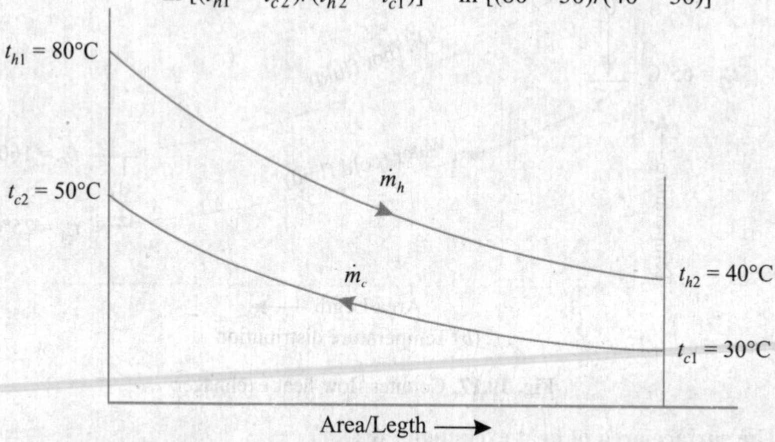

$t_{h1} = 80°C$

$t_{c2} = 50°C$

$\dot{m}_h$

$\dot{m}_c$

$t_{h2} = 40°C$

$t_{c1} = 30°C$

Area/Legth $\longrightarrow$

Fig. 10.18.

$$= \dfrac{30 - 10}{\ln\,(30/10)} = 18.2°C$$

Also, $\qquad\qquad Q = UA\,\theta_m$

$\dfrac{1000}{3600}\,(2.09 \times 10^3)\,(80 - 40) = 24 \times A \times 18.2$

or, $\qquad A = \dfrac{1000 \times (2.09 \times 10^3) \times (80 - 40)}{3600 \times 24 \times 18.2} = \textbf{53.16 m}^2$ **(Ans.)**

Example 10.10. *Show that in a double-pipe counter flow heat exchanger if $\dot{m}_h c_h = \dot{m}_c\, c_c$ the temperature profiles of the two fluids along its length are parallel straight lines.* **(GATE, 1996)**

Solution. For heat exchanger, $dQ = - \dot{m}_h\, c_h\, dt_h = \dot{m}_c\, c_c\, dt_c$

$$= - C_h\, dt_h = C_c\, dt_c$$

where, $\dot{m}_h$ = Mass flow rate of hot fluid,

and,

$\dot{m}_c$ = Mass flow rate of cold fluid.

Due to heat exchanger, temperature of hot fluid decreases by dt_h and that of cold fluid increases by dt_c

Also, C_c = Heat capacity of cold fluid,

and,

C_h = Heat capacity of hot fluid.

$$\dot{m}_h c_h = \dot{m}_c c_c \qquad ...(Given)$$

or, $C_h = C_c$

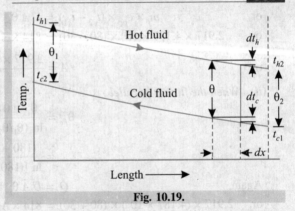

Fig. 10.19.

In counter-flow system, temperature of both the fluids decrease in the direction of heat exchanger length, therefore

$$dQ = -C_h \, dt_h = -C_c \, dt_c$$

$$\therefore \qquad dt_h = -\frac{dQ}{C_h} \text{ and } dt_c = -\frac{dQ}{C_c}$$

or, $$dt_h - dt_c = d\theta = -dQ \left[\frac{1}{C_h} - \frac{1}{C_c} \right]$$

Since constant $C_h = C_c$, $\therefore$ $d\theta = 0$ or θ = constant.

Thus, both the straight lines showing the variation of temperatures along the length are parallel lines.   ...**Proved**

Example 10.11. *A counter-flow double pipe heat exchanger using superheated steam is used to hot water at the rate of 10500 kg/h. The steam enters the heat exchanger at 180°C and leaves at 130°C. The inlet and exit temperatures of water are 30°C and 80°C respectively. If overall heat transfer coefficient from steam to water is 814 W/m²°C, calculate the heat transfer area. What would be the increase in area if the fluid flows were parallel?*

Solution. *Given :* $\dot{m}_w \, (= \dot{m}_c) = \dfrac{10500}{3600} = 2.917$ kg/s; $t_{h1} = 180°C$; $t_{h2} = 130°C$; $t_{c1} = 30°C$;

$t_{c2} = 80°C$; $U = 814$ W/m²°C.

(i)   When the flow is counter :

$$\theta_m = \frac{\theta_1 - \theta_2}{\ln (\theta_1 / \theta_2)}$$

In this $\theta_m = \theta_1 = \theta_2 = 100°C$

$t_{h1} = 180°C$

Hot fluid (steam)

$\theta_1 = 100°C$

$t_{c2} = 80°C$

Cold fluid (water) $\theta_2 = 100°C$

$t_{c1} = 30°C$

(a) Counter-flow

$t_{h1} = 180°C$

Hot fluid (steam)

$t_{h2} = 130°C$

θ_1

$t_{h2} = 130°C$

$t_{c2} = 80°C$

Cold fluid (water)

θ_2

(b) Parallel flow

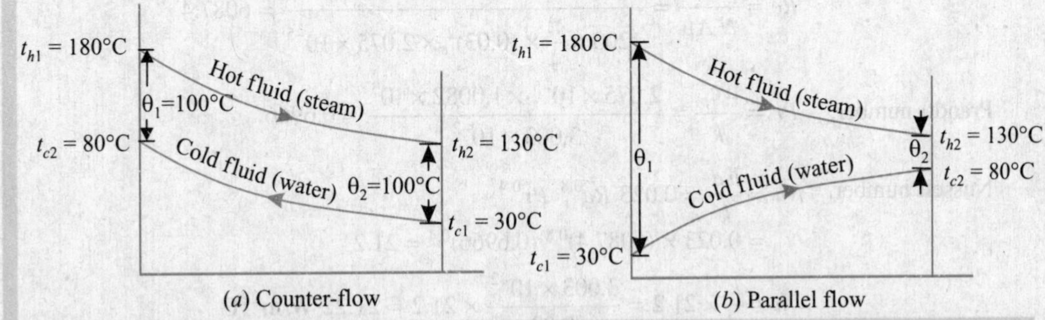

Fig. 10.20.

The heat transfer rate is given by

$$Q = U A \, \theta_m$$

or, $$\dot{m}_c \times c_{pc} \times (t_{c2} - t_{c1}) = U A \theta_m$$

or, $$2.917 \times 4.187 \times 10^3 \times (80 - 30) = 814 \times A \times 100$$

or, $$A = \frac{2.917 \times 4.187 \times 10^3 (80 - 30)}{814 \times 100} = 7.5 \ m^2 \quad \textbf{(Ans.)}$$

(ii) *When the flow is parallel :*

$$\theta_m = \frac{\theta_1 - \theta_2}{\ln (\theta_1/\theta_2)} = \frac{(t_{h1} - t_{c1}) - (t_{h2} - t_{c2})}{\ln [(t_{h1} - t_{c1})/(t_{h2} - t_{c2})]}$$

$$= \frac{(180 - 30) - (130 - 80)}{\ln [(180 - 30)/(130 - 80)]} = \frac{150 - 50}{\ln (150/50)} = 91°C$$

Again, $$Q = U A \theta_m$$

or, $$2.917 \times (4.187 \times 10^3) \times (80 - 30) = 814 \times A \times 91$$

$$A = \frac{2.917 \times (4.187 \times 10^3) \times (80 - 30)}{814 \times 91} = 8.24 \ m^2$$

∴ Increase in area $$= \frac{8.24 - 7.5}{7.5} = 0.0987 \ or \ \textbf{9.87\%} \quad \textbf{(Ans.)}$$

Example 10.12. *A counter-flow heat exchanger, through which passes 12.5 kg/s of air to be cooled from 540°C to 146°C, contains 4200 tubes, each having a diameter of 30 mm. The inlet and outlet temperatures of cooling water are 25°C and 75°C respectively. If the water side resistance to flow is negligible, calculate the tube length required for this duty.*

For turbulent flow inside tubes : $Nu = 0.023 \ Re^{0.8} \ Pr^{0.4}$

Properties of the air at the average temperature are as follows :

$\rho = 1.009 \ kg/m^3$; $c_p = 1.0082 \ kJ/kg°C$; $\mu = 2.075 \times 10^{-5} \ kg/ms \ (Ns/m^2)$ *and* $k = 3.003 \times 10^{-2} \ W/m°C.$

Solution. Given : $\dot{m}_h = 12.5$ kg/s; $t_{h1} = 540°C$; $t_{h2} = 146°C$; $t_{c1} = 25°C$; $t_{c2} = 75°C$; $N = 4200$, $d = 30$ mm $= 0.03$ m.

Tube length, L :

Reynolds number, $Re = \dfrac{\rho V d}{\mu}$

Mass flow $m = NA \, V\rho$, therefore,

$$\rho V = \frac{m}{N \, A}$$

∴ $$Re = \frac{md}{N A \mu} = \frac{12.5 \times 0.03}{4200 \times \dfrac{\pi}{4} \times (0.03)^2 \times 2.075 \times 10^{-5}} = 6087.4$$

Prandtl number, $$Pr = \frac{\mu c_p}{k} = \frac{2.075 \times 10^{-5} \times 1.0082 \times 10^3}{3.003 \times 10^{-2}} = 0.6966$$

Nusselt number, $$Nu = \frac{h d}{k} = 0.023 \ Re^{0.8} \ Pr^{0.4}$$

$$= 0.023 \times (6087.4)^{0.8} (0.6966)^{0.4} = 21.2$$

∴ $$h = \frac{k}{d} \times 21.2 = \frac{3.003 \times 10^{-2}}{0.03} \times 21.2 = 21.22 \ W/m^2°C$$

Since the water side resistance to flow is negligible

∴ $$\frac{1}{U} = \frac{1}{h} = \frac{1}{21.22} \ or \ U = 21.22 \ W/m^2°C$$

Logarithmic mean temperature difference (*LMTD*) is given by

$$\theta_m = \frac{\theta_1 - \theta_2}{\ln (\theta_1/\theta_2)}$$

$$= \frac{(t_{h1} - t_{c2}) - (t_{h2} - t_{c1})}{\ln [(t_{h1} - t_{c2})/(t_{h2} - t_{c1})]} = \frac{(540 - 75) - (146 - 25)}{\ln [(540 - 75)/(146 - 25)]}$$

$$= \frac{(465 - 121)}{\ln (465/121)} = 255.5°C$$

Further, the rate of heat transfer,

$$Q = \dot{m}_h \times c_{ph} \times (t_{h2} - t_{h1}) = U A \, \theta_m = U \times (N\pi \, d \, L) \times \theta_m$$

or, $$L = \frac{\dot{m}_h \times c_{ph} \,(t_{h2} - t_{h1})}{U \times N \pi d \times \theta_m} = \frac{12.5 \times (1.0082 \times 10^3) \times (540 - 146)}{21.22 \times 4200 \times \pi \times 0.03 \times 255.5} = \textbf{2.31 m} \quad \textbf{(Ans.)}$$

Example 10.13. *Steam enters a counter-flow heat exchanger, dry saturated at 10 bar and leaves at 350°C. The mass flow of steam is 800 kg/min. The gas enters the heat exchanger at 650°C and mass flow rate is 1350 kg/min. If the tubes are 30 mm diameter and 3 m long, determine the number of tubes required. Neglect the resistance offered by metallic tubes. Use the following data :*

For steam : $\quad t_{sat} = 180°C$ *(at 10 bar);* $c_{ps} = 2.71$ *kJ/kg°C;* $h_s = 600$ *W/m²°C*

For gas : $\quad c_{pg} = 1$ *kJ/kg°C;* $h_g = 250$ *W/m²°C.* $\qquad\qquad$ **(P.U.)**

Solution. *Given* : $\dot{m}_s = \dot{m}_c = \dfrac{800}{60} = 13.33$ kg/s; $\dot{m}_g = \dot{m}_h = \dfrac{1350}{60} = 22.5$ kg/s; $t_{h1} = 650°C$; $t_{c1} (= t_{sat}) = 180°C$; $t_{c2} = 350°C$; $d = 30$ mm $= 0.03$ m; $L = 3$ m.

Number of tubes required, N:

Heat lost by gases = Heat gained by steam

$$\dot{m}_h \times c_{ph} \times (t_{h1} - t_{h2}) = \dot{m}_c \times c_{pc} \times (t_{c2} - t_{c1})$$

$$22.5 \times 1 \times (650 - t_{h2}) = 13.33 \times 2.71 \times (350 - 180)$$

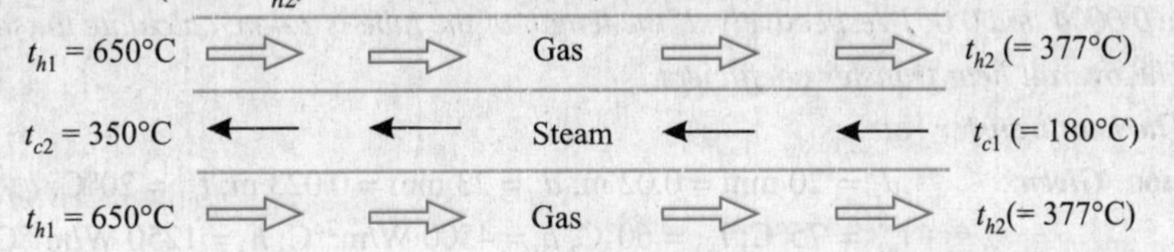

$t_{h1} = 650°C$ ⟹	⟹	Gas	⟹	⟹	$t_{h2} \, (= 377°C)$
$t_{c2} = 350°C$ ⟵	⟵	Steam	⟵	⟵	$t_{c1} \, (= 180°C)$
$t_{h1} = 650°C$ ⟹	⟹	Gas	⟹	⟹	$t_{h2} (= 377°C)$

(a) Flow arrangement

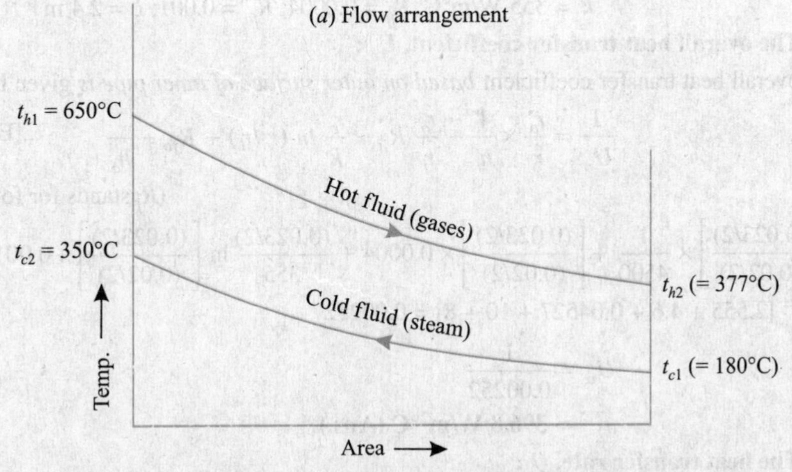

(b) Temperature distribution

Fig. 10.21. Counter-flow heat exchanger.

$$\therefore \qquad\qquad t_{h2} = 377°C$$

Overall heat transfer coefficient is given by

$$\frac{1}{U} = \frac{1}{h_g} + \frac{d_o}{d_i} \frac{1}{h_s} = \frac{1}{h_g} + \frac{1}{h_s} \qquad \text{as } d_i \approx d_o \qquad\qquad ...(\text{given})$$

or, $$U = \frac{h_g \times h_s}{h_g + h_s} = \frac{250 \times 600}{250 + 600} = 176.5 \text{ W/m}^2 °C$$

Total heat transfer rate is given by

$$Q = UA\theta_m \qquad\qquad\qquad ...(i)$$

where, $$A = N \times (\pi\, d\, L) = N \times \pi \times 0.03 \times 3 = 0.2827\, N \text{ m}^2$$

$$Q = 22.5 \times (1 \times 10^3) \times (650 - 377) = 6142.5 \times 10^3 \text{ W}$$

$$\theta_m = \frac{\theta_1 - \theta_2}{\ln(\theta_1/\theta_2)} = \frac{(t_{h1} - t_{c2}) - (t_{h2} - t_{c1})}{\ln[(t_{h1} - t_{c2})/(t_{h2} - t_{c1})]}$$

$$= \frac{(650 - 350) - (377 - 180)}{\ln[(650 - 300)/(377 - 180)]} = \frac{300 - 197}{\ln(300/197)} = 244.9°C$$

Substituting the values in eqn. (i), we get

$$6142.5 \times 10^3 = 176.5 \times 0.2827\, N \times 244.9$$

or, $$N = \frac{6142.5 \times 10^3}{176.5 \times 0.2827 \times 244.9} = \textbf{503 tubes} \ (\textbf{Ans.})$$

Example 10.14. *In a shell and tube counter-flow heat exchanger water flows through a copper tube 20 mm I.D. (internal diameter) and 23 mm O.D. (outer diameter), while oil flows through the shell. Water enters at 20°C and comes out at 30°C, while oil enters at 75°C and comes out at 60°C. The water and oil side film coefficients are 4500 and 1250 W/m²°C respectively. The thermal conductivity of the tube wall is 355 W/m°C. The fouling factors on the water and oil sides may be taken to be 0.0004 and 0.001 respectively. If the length of the tube is 2.4 m, calculate the following :*

(i) *The overall heat transfer coefficient;*

(ii) *The heat transfer rate.*

Solution. Given : $d_i = 20 \text{ mm} = 0.02 \text{ m}; d_o = 23 \text{ mm} = 0.023 \text{ m}; t_{c1} = 20°C; t_{c2} = 30°C;$
$t_{h1} = 75°C; t_{h2} = 60°C, h_i = 4500 \text{ W/m}^2°C; h_o = 1250 \text{ W/m}^2°C;$
$k = 355 \text{ W/m}°C; R_{fi} = 0.0004; R_{fo} = 0.001; L = 2.4 \text{ m}$

(i) The overall heat transfer coefficient, U_o :

The overall heat transfer coefficient *based on outer surface of inner pipe is* given by,

$$\frac{1}{U_o} = \frac{r_o}{r_i} \times \frac{1}{h_i} + \frac{r_o}{r_i} R_{fi} + \frac{r_o}{k} \ln(r_o/r_i) + R_{fo} + \frac{1}{h_o} \qquad ...[\text{Eqn. (10.28)}]$$

$$(R_f \text{ stands for fouling factor})$$

$$= \left[\frac{(0.023/2)}{(0.02/2)}\right] \times \frac{1}{4500} + \left[\frac{(0.023/2)}{(0.02/2)}\right] \times 0.0004 + \frac{(0.023/2)}{355} \ln\left[\frac{(0.023/2)}{(0.02/2)}\right] + 0.001 + \frac{1}{1250}$$

$$= 10^{-4}\,[2.555 + 4.6 + 0.04527 + 10 + 8] = 0.00252$$

$$\therefore \qquad U_o = \frac{1}{0.00252}$$

$$= \textbf{396.8 W/m}^2°\textbf{C (Ans.)}$$

(ii) The heat transfer rate, Q :

Area, $$A_o = \pi\, d_o\, L$$

$$= \pi \times 0.023 \times 2.4$$
$$= 0.1734 \text{ m}^2$$

Logarithmic mean temperature difference (*LMTD*) is given by,

$$\theta_m = \frac{\theta_1 - \theta_2}{\ln (\theta_1/\theta_2)}$$

$$= \frac{(75 - 30) - (60 - 20)}{\ln [(75 - 3)/(60 - 20)]}$$

$$= \frac{45 - 40}{\ln (45/40)} = 42.45°C$$

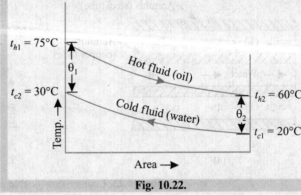

Fig. 10.22.

The heat transfer rate is given by

$$Q = U_o A_o \theta_m$$

or $= 396.8 \times 0.1734 \times 42.15 = \textbf{2900 W}$ **(Ans.)**

Example 10.15. *In a counter-flow double pipe heat exchanger water flows through a copper tube (19 mm O.D. and 16 mm I.D.), at a flow rate of 1.48 m/s. The oil flows through the annulus formed by inner copper tube and outer steel tube (30 mm O.D. and 26 mm I.D.). The steel tube is insulated from outside. The oil enters at 0.4 kg/s and is cooled from 65°C to 50°C whereas water enters at 32°C. Neglecting the copper tube wall thermal resistance, calculate the length of the tube required.*

Date given :

$Nu = 0.023 \, (Re)^{0.8} \, (Pr)^{0.4}$

Fouling factor, water side = 0.0005 m² K/W

Fouling factor, oil side = 0.0008 m² K/W

Water and oil properties :

Property	Oil	Water
ρ (kg/m³)	850	995
c_p (kJ/kg K)	1.89	4.187
k (W/m K)	0.138	0.615
ν (m²/s)	7.44×10^{-6}	4.18×10^{-7}

(U.P.S.C., 1998)

Solution. *Given* : Inner dia. of the copper tube (d_i) = 16 mm = 0.016 m;

Outer dia. of the copper tube $(d_o)_c$ = 19 mm = 0.019 m;

Inner dia. of the steel tube, $(d_i)_s$ = 26 mm = 0.026 m;

Outer dia. of the steel tube, $(d_o)_s$ = 30 mm = 0.03 m;

t_{c1} = 32°C; t_{h1} = 65°C; t_{h2} = 50°C

$\dot{m}_c = \dfrac{\pi}{4} \times (0.016)^2 \times 1.48 \times 995 = 0.296$ kg/s; $\dot{m}_h$ = 0.4 kg/s

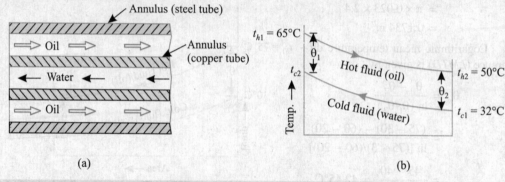

Fig. 10.23. Counter-flow double pipe heat exchanger.

Length of the tube, L :

The rate of heat transfer is given by,

$$Q = \dot{m}_h \, c_{ph} \, (t_{h1} - t_{h2}) = \dot{m}_c \, c_{pc} \, (t_{c2} - t_{c1})$$

$$0.4 \times 1.89 \, (65 - 50) = 0.296 \times 4.187 \, (t_{c2} - 32)$$

or
$$t_{c2} = \frac{0.4 \times 1.89 \, (65 - 50)}{0.296 \times 4.187} + 32 = 41°C$$

Also,
$$Q = 0.4 \times 1.89 \times (65 - 50) = 11.34 \text{ kW}$$

Reynolds number for the flow of water through copper tube,

$$Re = \frac{4 \, \dot{m}}{\pi (d_i)_c \, \mu} = \frac{4 \times 0.296}{\pi \times 0.016 \times (995 \times 418 \times 10^{-7})} = 56826 \qquad (\because \mu = \rho.v)$$

Now,
$$Nu = 0.023 \, (Re)^{0.8} \, (Pr)^{0.4} \qquad \qquad ...(Given)$$

$$= 0.023 \, (56826)^{0.8} \left(\frac{\mu c_p}{k} \right)^{0.4}$$

$$= 0.023 \, (56826)^{0.8} \left(\frac{995 \times 418 \times 10^{-7} \times 41.87}{0.615} \right)^{0.4} = 14$$

$\left(\text{Since, } Pr = \dfrac{\mu c_p}{k} \text{ and water is heated} \right)$

Also,
$$Nu = \frac{h_i \, (d_i)_c}{k} = 14$$

or,
$$h_i = \frac{14 \times 0.615}{0.016} = 538.1 \text{ W/m}^2\text{K}$$

Now oil flows through annulus diameter, therefore hydraulic diameter,

$$D_h = (d_i)_s - (d_o)_c = 0.026 - 0.019 = 0.007 \text{ m}$$

Reynolds number through the annulus,

$$Re = \frac{\rho \, u_m \, D_h}{\mu} = \frac{\rho \, [(d_i)_s - (d_o)_c]}{\mu} \times \frac{\dot{m}_h}{\frac{\pi}{4} \left[(d_i)_s^{\,2} - (d_o)_c^{\,2} \right] \rho}$$

$$= \frac{4\dot{m}_h}{\pi \, [(d_i)_s + (d_o)_c] \, \mu} = \frac{4 \times 0.4}{\pi \, [(0.026 + 0.019)] \times (850 \times 7.44 \times 10^{-6})}$$

$$\simeq 1790$$

Since Re < 2500, hence annulus flow is *laminar*.

Heat transfer coefficient at the inner surface of the annulus,

$$Nu = \frac{h_o D_h}{k} = 0.023 \, (Re)^{0.8} \, (Pr)^{0.4}$$

$$Pr = \frac{\mu c_p}{k} = \frac{(850 \times 7.44 \times 10^{-6}) \times 1.89}{0.138} = 0.0866$$

$$\therefore \quad \frac{h_o \times 0.007}{0.138} = 0.023 \, (1790)^{0.8} \times (0.0866)^{0.4} = 3.46$$

or, $$h_o = \frac{3.46 \times 0.138}{0.007} = 68.2 \text{ W/m}^2\text{K}$$

Overall heat transfer coefficient referred to outer diameter of inner tube is given by,

$$U_o = \cfrac{1}{\cfrac{(r_o)_c}{(r_i)_c} \cdot \cfrac{1}{h_i} + \cfrac{(r_o)_c}{(r_i)_c} R_{fi} + \cfrac{(r_o)_c}{k} \ln \left[\cfrac{(r_o)_c}{(r_i)_c}\right] + R_{fo} + \cfrac{1}{h_o}}$$

(R_f stands for fouling factor)

$$= \cfrac{1}{\left(\cfrac{0.019}{0.016}\right) \times \cfrac{1}{538.1} + \left(\cfrac{0.019}{0.016}\right) \times 0.0005 + \cfrac{0.019}{0.016} \ln \left[\cfrac{0.019}{0.016}\right] + 0.0008 + \cfrac{1}{68.2}}$$

$$= \frac{1}{0.002203 + 0.000594 + 0.005309 + 0.0008 + 0.01466}$$

$$= 42.43 \text{ W/m}^2 \text{ K}$$

Logarithmic mean temperature difference is given by,

$$\theta_m = \frac{\theta_1 - \theta_2}{\ln (\theta_1/\theta_2)} = \frac{(t_{h1} - t_{c2}) - (t_{h2} - t_{c1})}{\ln [(t_{h1} - t_{c2})/(t_{h2} - t_{c1})]}$$

$$= \frac{(65 - 41) - (50 - 32)}{\ln [(65 - 41)/(50 - 32)]} = \frac{24 - 18}{\ln [(24/18)]} = 20.86°C$$

The heat transfer rate is given by,

$$Q = U_o A_o \theta_m = 42.43 \times (\pi \times 0.019 \times L) = 20.86$$

or, $$L = \frac{Q}{A_o \theta_m} = \frac{11.34 \times 10^3}{42.43 \times (\pi \times 0.019) \times 20.86} = \textbf{214.6 m} \quad \textbf{(Ans.)}$$

Example 10.16. *A counter-flow, concentric tube heat exchanger is used to cool the lubricating oil for a large industrial gas turbine engine. The flow rate of cooling water through the inner tube (d_i = 20 mm) is 0.18 kg/s, while the flow rate of oil through the outer annulus (d_o = 40mm) is 0.12 kg/s. The inlet and outlet temperatures of oil are 95°C and 65°C, respectively. The water enters at 30°C to the exchanger. Neglecting tube wall thermal resistance, fouling factors and heat loss to the surroundings, calculate the length of the tube.*

Take the following properties at the bulk mean tempeature :

Engine oil at 80°C : c_p = 2131 J/kg°C; μ = 0.0325 Ns/m²; k = 0.138 W/m°C;

Water at 35°C : c_p = 4174 J/kg°C, μ = 725 × 10⁻⁶ Ns/m²; k = 0.625 W/m°C, Pr = 4.85

Solution. Given : d_i = 20 mm = 0.02 m; d_o = 40 mm = 0.04 m, $\dot{m}_w = \dot{m}_c$ = 0.18 kg/s;

$$\dot{m}_{oil} = \dot{m}_h = 0.12 \text{ kg/s}; \, t_{h1} = 95°C, \, t_{h2} = 65°C; \, t_{c1} = 30°C.$$

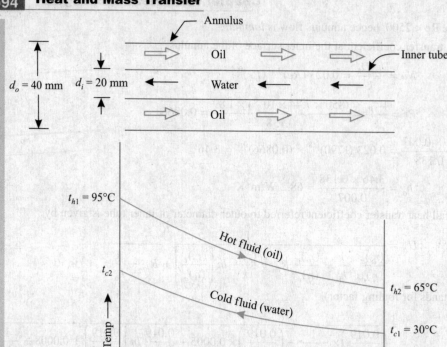

$d_o = 40$ mm $d_i = 20$ mm

Annulus

Oil

Water

Oil

Inner tube

$t_{h1} = 95°C$

Hot fluid (oil)

t_{c2}

Cold fluid (water)

$t_{h2} = 65°C$

$t_{c1} = 30°C$

Temp ⟶

Length ⟶

Fig. 10.24. The counter-flow, concentric tube heat exchanger.

Length of the tube, L :

The rate of heat transfer is given by,

$$Q = \dot{m}_h\, c_{ph}\, (t_{h1} - t_{h2}) = \dot{m}_c\, c_{pc}\, (t_{c2} - t_{c1})$$

or, $0.12 \times 2131\,(95 - 65) = 0.18 \times 4174\,(t_{c2} - 30)$

∴ $t_{c2} = 40.2°C$

LMTD is given by, $\theta_m = \dfrac{\theta_1 - \theta_2}{\ln(\theta_1/\theta_2)} = \dfrac{(t_{h1} - t_{c2}) - (t_{h2} - t_{c1})}{\ln[(t_{h1} - t_{c2})/(t_{h2} - t_{c1})]}$

or, $\theta_m = \dfrac{(95 - 40.2) - (65 - 30)}{\ln[(95 - 40.2)/(65 - 30)]} = \dfrac{54.8 - 35}{\ln(54.8/35)} = 44.2°C$

The overall heat transfer coefficient U is given by the relation

$$\frac{1}{U} = \frac{1}{h_i} + \frac{1}{h_o} \qquad\qquad ...(i)$$

Reynolds number for flow of water through the tube is

$$Re = \frac{4m}{\pi d \mu} = \frac{4 \times 0.18}{\pi \times 0.22 \times 725 \times 10^{-6}} = 1.58 \times 10^4$$

Since the flow is *turbulent*, hence

$$Nu = \frac{hd}{k} = 0.023\,(Re)^{0.8}\,(Pr)^{0.4}$$

$$= 0.023\,(1.58 \times 10^4)^{0.8}\,(4.85)^{0.4} = 98.84$$

or, $h = h_i = \dfrac{k}{d_i} \times 98.84 = \dfrac{0.625 \times 98.84}{0.02}$

$$= 3088.7 \text{ W/m}^2°C$$

The oil flows through the annulus, hence the hydraulic diameter $D_h = d_o - d_i = 0.02$ m

Reynolds number through the annulus is

$$Re \triangleq \frac{\rho \cdot u_m \, D_h}{\mu} = \frac{\rho \, (d_o - d_i)}{\mu} \times \frac{\dot{m}_h}{\frac{\pi}{4} (d_o^2 - d_i^2) \rho}$$

or, $$Re = \frac{4 \dot{m}_h}{\pi \, (d_o + d_i) \, \mu} = \frac{4 \times 0.12}{\pi \, (0.04 + 0.02) \times 0.0325} = 78.35$$

Since $Re < 2300$, hence the annular flow is *laminar*. Assuming uniform temperature along the inner surface of the annulus the heat transfer coefficient at the inner surface of the annulus, is

$$Nu = \frac{h_o \, D_h}{k} = 3.65 \qquad\qquad ...\text{[Eqn. 7.118)]}$$

or, $$h_o = \frac{k}{D_h} \times 3.65 = \frac{0.138}{0.02} \times 3.65 = 25.2 \text{ W/m}^2\text{°C}$$

Substituting the values in eqn. (*i*), we get

$$\frac{1}{U} = \frac{1}{3088.7} + \frac{1}{25.2} = 0.04$$

∴ $$U = \frac{1}{0.04} = 25 \text{ W/m}^2\text{°C}$$

Also, $$Q = \dot{m}_h \, c_{ph} \, (t_{h1} - t_{h2}) = UA \, \theta_m = U \times (\pi \, d_i \, L) \times \theta_m$$

$$0.12 \times 2131 \times (95 - 65) = 25 \times \pi \times 0.02 \times L \times 44.2$$

∴ $$L = \frac{0.12 \times 2131 \, (95 - 65)}{25 \times \pi \times 0.02 \times 44.2} = \textbf{110.49 m \ (Ans.)}$$

Example 10.17. *The following data pertain to an oil cooler of the form of tubular heat exchanger, where oil is cooled by a large pool of stagnant water.*

Temperature of stagnant water = 20°C (assumed constant),

Inlet and outlet temperatures of oil = 80°C and 30°C, respectively,

Inside diameter and length of the tube carrying oil = 20 mm and 30 m, respectively,

Specific heat and specific gravity of oil = 2.5 kJ/kg°C and 0.85 respectively,

Average velocity of oil = 0.55 m/s.

Calculate the overall heat transfer coefficient obtainable from the system.

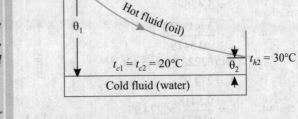

Fig. 10.25.

Solution. Given : $t_{c1} = t_{c2} = 20$°C; $t_{h1} = 80$°C; $t_{h2} = 30$°C; $d = 20$ mm $= 0.02$ m; $L = 30$ m; $c_{ph} = 2.5$ kJ/kg°C; sp.gr $= 0.85$; $V = 0.55$ m/s.

Overall heat transfer coefficient, U_i :

The mass flow rate of hot fluid (oil),

$$\dot{m}_h = A \, V \rho = \frac{\pi}{4} \times (0.02)^2 \times 0.55 \times (0.85 \times 1000) = 0.1468 \text{ kg/s}$$

Heat lost by the hot fluid,

$$Q = \dot{m}_h \, c_{ph} \, (t_{h1} - t_{h2}) = 0.1468 \times (2.5 \times 10^3) \times (80 - 30) = 18350 \text{ W}$$

LMTD is given by,

$$\theta_m = \frac{\theta_1 - \theta_2}{\ln(\theta_1/\theta_2)} = \frac{(t_{h1} - t_{c1}) - (t_{h2} - t_{c2})}{\ln[(t_{h1} - t_{c1})/(t_{h2} - t_{c2})]}$$

$$= \frac{(80 - 20) - (30 - 20)}{\ln[(80 - 20)/(30 - 20)]} = \frac{50}{\ln\left(\dfrac{60}{10}\right)} = 27.9°C$$

The heat transfer rate is given by,

$$Q = U_i A_i \theta_m = U_i (\pi d_i L) \theta_m$$
$$18350 = U_i \times \pi \times 0.02 \times 30 \times 27.9$$

$$\therefore \qquad U_i = \frac{18350}{\pi \times 0.02 \times 30 \times 27.9} = \textbf{348.9 W/m}^2\textbf{°C (Ans.)}$$

Example 10.18. *The velocity of water flowing through a tube of 22 mm diameter is 2 m/s. Steam condensing at 150°C on the outside surface of the tube heats the water from 15°C to 60°C over the length of the tube. Neglecting the tube and steam side film resistance, calculate the following :*

(i) *The heat transfer coefficient, and (ii) The length of the tube.*

Take the following properties of water at mean temperature :

$\rho = 990 \ kg/m^3$; $c_p = 4.2 \ kJ/kg°C$, $k = 0.5418 \ W/m°C$; $\mu = 700 \times 10^{-6} \ kg/ms$.   (P.U.)

Solution. *Given :* $d = 22$ mm $= 0.022$ m; $V = 2$ m/s, $t_{h1} = t_{h2} = 150°C$; $t_{c1} = 15°C$; $t_{c2} = 60°C$.

(i) **The heat transfer coefficient,** $\bar{h}$:

$$\overline{Nu} = \frac{\bar{h}d}{k} = 0.023 \, (Re)^{0.8} \, (Pr)^{0.33}$$

...[Eqn. (17.165)]

$$Re = \frac{\rho V d}{\mu} = \frac{990 \times 2 \times 0.022}{700 \times 10^{-6}}$$

$$= 62228$$

$$Pr = \frac{\mu c_p}{k} = \frac{700 \times 10^{-6} \times (4.2 \times 10^3)}{0.5418}$$

$$= 5.426$$

$$\therefore \qquad \frac{\bar{h} \times 0.022}{0.5418}$$

$$= 0.023 \times (62228)^{0.8} \times (5.426)^{0.33}$$

$$= 274.97$$

or, $$\bar{h} = \frac{0.5418}{0.022} \times 274.97$$

$$= \textbf{6771.7 W/m}^2\textbf{°C (Ans.)}$$

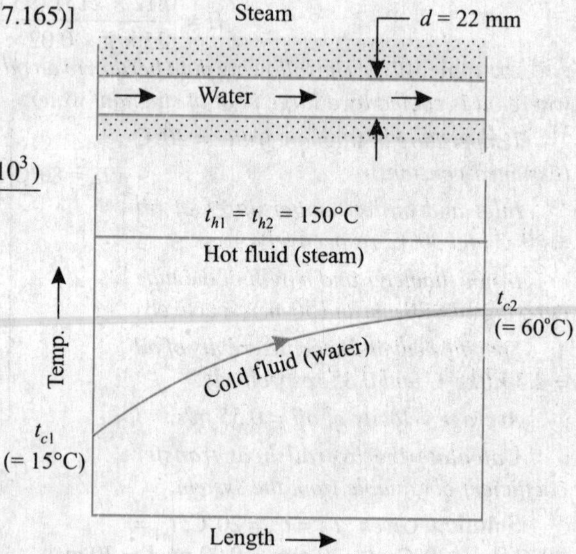

Steam $d = 22$ mm

→ Water →   →

$t_{h1} = t_{h2} = 150°C$

Hot fluid (steam)

t_{c2}
$(= 60°C)$

Temp. →

Cold fluid (water)

t_{c1}
$(= 15°C)$

Length →

Fig. 10.26.

(ii) **The length of the tube,** L :

The mass flow rate (water),

$$\dot{m}_w = \dot{m}_c = \frac{\pi}{4} d^2 \times V \times \rho = \frac{\pi}{4} \times 0.022^2 \times 2 \times 990$$

$$= 0.753 \ kg/s$$

Heat gained by water passing through the tube,

$$Q = \dot{m}_c \times c_{pc} \times (t_{c2} - t_{c1})$$

$$= 0.753 \times (4.2 \times 10^3) \times (60 - 15) = 142317 \ W$$

Q is also given by,

$$Q = UA\,\theta_m \qquad \qquad \qquad ....(i)$$

where

$$\theta_m = \frac{\theta_1 - \theta_2}{\ln(\theta_1/\theta_2)} = \frac{(t_{h1} - t_{c1}) - (t_{h2} - t_{c2})}{\ln[(t_{h1} - t_{c1})/(t_{h2} - t_{c2})]}$$

$$= \frac{(150 - 15) - (150 - 60)}{\ln[(150 - 15)/(150 - 60)]} = \frac{135 - 90}{\ln(135/90)} \approx 111^\circ C$$

Substituting the values in eqn. (*i*), we get

$$142317 = 6771.7 \times (\pi \times 0.022 \times L) \times 111 \qquad \text{(Here, } U = \bar{h}\text{)}$$

or, $\qquad \qquad L = 2.74 \text{ m (Ans.)}$

Example 10.19. *Saturated steam at 100°C is condensing on the shell side of a shell-and-tube heat exchanger. The cooling water enters the tube at 30°C and leaves at 70°C. Calculate the mean temperature difference if arrangement is (i) parallel flow, (ii) counter flow.* (**AMIE, Winter, 1997**)

Solution. The mean temperature difference will be the *same* for parallel flow or counter flow arrangements as is evident from the diagrams (Fig. 10.27) of temperature variations in both the arrangements. The mean temperature difference may be the logarithmic mean (*LMTD*), or arithmetic mean temperature difference (*AMTD*).

(*i*) $\qquad LMTD = \dfrac{(100 - 30) - (100 - 70)}{\ln\left[\dfrac{(100 - 30)}{100 - 70)}\right]} = \dfrac{40}{\ln\left(\dfrac{70}{30}\right)} = \mathbf{47.21^\circ C}$ **(Ans.)**

(*ii*) $\qquad AMTD = \dfrac{(100 - 30) + (100 - 70)}{2} = \dfrac{70 + 30}{2} = \mathbf{50^\circ C}$ **(Ans.)**

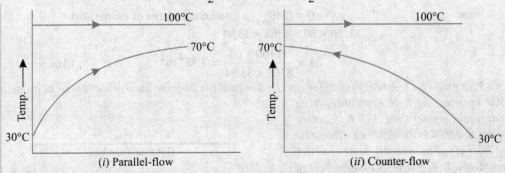

(*i*) Parallel-flow $\qquad\qquad\qquad$ (*ii*) Counter-flow

Fig. 10.27.

Example 10.20. *The amount of F_{12} used in compression refrigeration system is 4 tonnes/hour. The brine, flowing at 850 kg/min. with inlet temperature of 12°C, is cooled in the evaporator. Assuming F_{12} entering and leaving the evaporator as saturated liquid and saturated vapour respectively, determine the area of evaporator required. Take the following properties :*

For F_{12} : Saturation temperature : – 23°C; c_p = 1.17 kJ/kg°C; h_{fg} = 167.4 kJ/kg

c_p (brine) = 6.3 kJ/kg°C; U = 8368 kJ/m²h°C. (**AMIE Summer, 2000**)

Solution. Making energy balance, we have

$$- \dot{m}_h c_{ph} (t_{h2} - t_{h1}) = \dot{m}_c h_{fg}$$

or, $\qquad \dot{m}_h c_{ph} (t_{h1} - t_{h2}) = \dot{m}_c h_{fg}$

or, $\qquad 850 \times 6.3 (12 - t_{h2}) = \dfrac{4 \times 1000 \times 167.4}{60} = 11160 \text{ kJ/min}$

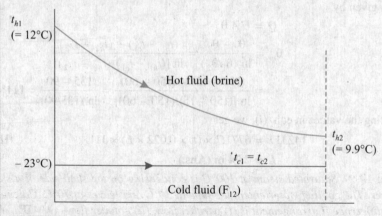

Fig. 10.28.

∴ Exit temperature of brine, $t_{h2} = 12 - \dfrac{11160}{850 \times 6.3} = 9.9°C$

Log mean temperature, $\theta_m = \dfrac{\theta_1 - \theta_2}{\ln(\theta_1/\theta_2)} = \dfrac{(t_{h1} - t_{c1}) - (t_{h2} - t_{c2})}{\ln\left[\dfrac{t_{h1} - t_{c1}}{t_{h2} - t_{c2}}\right]}$

$= \dfrac{[12 - (-23)] - [9.9 - (-23)]}{\ln\left[\dfrac{12 - (-23)}{9.9 - (-23)}\right]} = \dfrac{35 - 32.9}{\ln\left(\dfrac{35}{32.9}\right)} = 33.94°C$

Now, $Q = UA\theta_m$ (where A = area of evaporator)

$11160 \times 60 = 8368 \times 33.94$

∴ $A = \dfrac{11160 \times 60}{8368 \times 33.94} = \mathbf{2.357\,m^2}$ (Ans.)

Example 10.21. *A heat exchanger is to be designed to condense an organic vapour at a rate of 500 kg/min which is available at its saturation temperature 355 K. Cooling water at 286 K is available at a flow rate of 60 kg/s. The overall heat transfer coefficient is 475 W/m²°C. Latent heat of condensation of the organic vapour is 600 kJ/kg. Calculate :*

(i) The number of tubes required, if 25 mm outer diameter, 2mm thick and 4.87 m long tubes are available, and

(ii) The number of tube passes, if the cooling water velocity (tube side) should not exceed 2 m/s.

(M.U.)

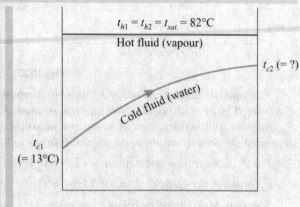

Fig. 10.29.

Solution. *Given :* $d_o = 25$ mm = 0.025 m; $d_i = 25 - 2 \times 2 = 21$ mm = 0.021 m; $L = 4.87$m; $V = 2$ m/s; $t_{c1} = 286 - 273 = 13°C$, $t_{h1} = t_{h2} = t_{sat} = 355 - 273 = 82°C$; $U = 475$ W/m°C, h_{fg} (organic vapour) = 600 kJ/kg, $\dot{m}_v = \dot{m}_h = \dfrac{500}{60} = 8.33$ kg/s; $\dot{m}_v = \dot{m}_c = 60$ kg/s.

(i) **The number of tubes required, N :**

Heat lost by vapour = Heat gained by water

$$\dot{m}_h \times h_{fg} = \dot{m}_c \times c_{pc} \times (t_{c2} - t_{c1})$$

$$8.33 \times 600 = 60 \times 4.18 \times (t_{c2} - 13)$$

$$\therefore \quad t_{c2} = \frac{8.33 \times 600}{60 \times 4.18} + 13 = 32.9°C$$

Logarithmic mean temperature difference (*LMTD*) is given by,

$$\theta_m = \frac{\theta_1 - \theta_2}{\ln (\theta_1/\theta_2)} = \frac{(82 - 13) - (82 - 32.9)}{\ln [(82 - 13)/(32.9 - 13)]}$$

$$= \frac{69 - 49.1}{\ln (69/49.1)} = 58.5°C$$

Heat transfer rate is given by,

$$Q = \dot{m}_h \times h_{fg} = U A \theta_m = U (\pi \, d_o \, L N) \times \theta_m$$

$$8.33 \times 600 \times 10^3 = 475 \times (\pi \times 0.025 \times 4.87 \times N) \times 58.5$$

$$\therefore \quad N = 470 \text{ tubes} \quad \text{(Ans.)}$$

(ii) **The number of tube passes, p :**

The cold water flow mass passing through each pass (assume p are number of passes) is given by,

$$\dot{m}_c = \left(\frac{\pi}{4} \, d_i^2 \times V \times \rho \right) \times N_p$$

where, $\quad N_p$ = Number of tubes in each pass ($N = p \times N_p$)

$$60 = \frac{\pi}{4} \times (0.021)^2 \times 2 \times 1000 \times N_p$$

$$\therefore \quad N_p = \frac{60 \times 4}{\pi \times (0.021)^2 \times 2 \times 1000} = 95.5$$

Number of passes, $\quad \boldsymbol{p} = \dfrac{N}{N_p} = \dfrac{470}{95.5} = 4.91 = \boldsymbol{5} \quad$ **(Ans.)**

Example 10.22. *(a) A steam condenser consists of 3000 brass tubes of 20 mm diameter. Cooling water enters the tubes at 20°C with a mean flow rate of 3000 kg/s. The heat transfer coefficient on the inner surface is 11270 W/m²°C and that for condensation on the outer surface is 15500 W/m²°C. The steam condenses at 50°C, and the condenser load is 230 MW. The latent heat of steam is 2380 kJ/kg. Assuming counter flow arrangement, calculate the tube length per pass if two tube passes are used.*

(b) Explain why in steam condensers the LMTD is independent of flow arrangement ?

(AMIE Summer, 2001)

Solution. *(a) Given :* N_p = 3000 per pass; d = 20 mm = 0.02 m; t_{c1} = 20°C; $\dot{m}_c$ = 3000 kg/s; h_i = 11270 W/m²°C; h_o = 15500 W/m²°C, $t_{h1} = t_{h2}$ = 50°C; condenser load = 230 MW (or 230 × 10³ kW); h_{fg} = 2380 kJ/kg; number of passes = 2.

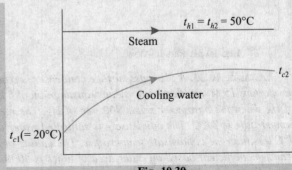

Fig. 10.30.

Tube length per pass, L :

Assuming the tubes to be thin, the overall heat transfer coefficient :

$$U_o = \frac{1}{\dfrac{1}{h_i} + \dfrac{1}{h_o}} = \frac{1}{\dfrac{1}{11270} + \dfrac{1}{15500}}$$

$$= 6525.4 \ \text{W/m}^2{}^\circ\text{C}$$

Heat exchanger load $\qquad = \dot{m}_c \, c_{pc} \, (t_{c2} - t_{c1})$

i.e., $\qquad\qquad 230 \times 10^3 = 3000 \times 4.187 \, (t_{c2} - 20)$

$\therefore$ Water outlet temperature, $t_{c2} = 38.31^\circ\text{C}$

Log-mean temperature difference,

$$\theta_m = \frac{\theta_1 - \theta_2}{\ln(\theta_1/\theta_2)} = \frac{(t_{h1} - t_{c1}) - (t_{h2} - t_{c2})}{\ln\left[\dfrac{t_{h1} - t_{c1}}{t_{h2} - t_{c2}}\right]}$$

$$= \frac{(50 - 20) - (50 - 38.31)}{\ln\left[\dfrac{50 - 20}{50 - 83.31}\right]} = \frac{18.31}{0.9425} = 19.43^\circ\text{C}$$

Now, $\qquad\qquad\qquad Q = U_o A \, \theta_m$

$$230 \times 10^6 = 6525.4 \times (\pi \, dL) \times (2N_p) \times 19.43$$

$$= 6525.4 \times (\pi \times 0.02 \times L) \times (2 \times 3000) \times 19.43$$

$\therefore \qquad\qquad\qquad L = \dfrac{230 \times 10^6}{6525.4 \times \pi \times 0.02 \times (2 \times 3000) \times 19.43} = \textbf{4.812 m} \qquad \textbf{(Ans.)}$

(b) In steam condensers, the temperature of hot fluid (steam) is the *same at inlet and exit*. Hence the terminal temperature difference *would not depend upon the arrangement*. The effectiveness of heat exchanger for all the arrangements in this case (the heat capacity ratio for condensation being *zero*) would be

$$\varepsilon = 1 - e^{-NTU}$$

The temperature variations for parallel-flow and counter-flow are as shown in Fig. 10.31 and Fig. 10.32 respectively.

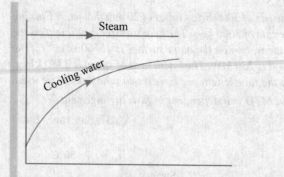

Fig. 10.31. Parallel-flow.

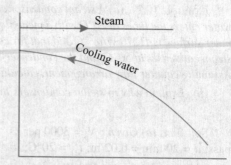

Fig. 10.32. Counter-flow.

Example 10.23. *A two-pass surface condenser is required to handle the exhaust from a turbine developing 15 MW with specific steam consumption of 5 kg/kWh. The condenser vacuum is 660 mm of Hg when the barometer reads 760 mm of Hg. The mean velocity of water is 3 m/s, water inlet temperature is 24°C. The condensate is saturated water and outlet temperature of cooling water is 4°C less than the condensate temperature. The quality of exhaust steam is 0.9 dry. The overall heat transfer coefficient based on outer area of tubes is 4000 W/m²°C. The water tubes are 38.4 mm in outer diameter and 29.6mm in inner diameter. Calculate the following :*

(i) *Mass of cooling water circulated in kg/min,*

(ii) *Condenser surface area,*

(iii) *Number of tubes required per pass, and*

(iv) *Tube length.* (P.U.)

Solution. *Given* : $d_i = 29.6$ mm $= 0.0296$ m; $d_o = 38.4$ mm $= 0.0384$ m; $U = 4000$ W/m²°C; $V = 3$ m/s; $t_{c1} = 24$°C; x (dryness fraction) $= 0.9$.

The pressure of the steam in the condenser,

$$p_s = \frac{760 - 660}{760} \times 1.0133 = 0.133 \text{ bar}$$

The properties of steam at $p_s = 0.133$ bar, from steam table, are :

$$t_{sat} = 51°C; \quad h_{fg} = 2592 \text{ kJ/kg}$$

$$\therefore \quad t_{c_2} = 51 - 4 = 47°C$$

The steam condensed per minute,

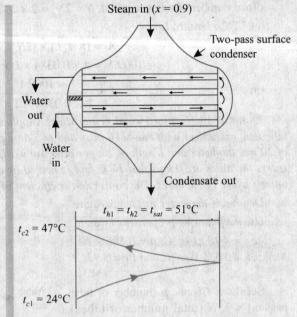

Steam in (x = 0.9)

Two-pass surface condenser

Water out

Water in

Condensate out

$t_{h1} = t_{h2} = t_{sat} = 51°C$

$t_{c2} = 47°C$

$t_{c1} = 24°C$

Fig. 10.33. A two-pass surface condenser.

$$\dot{m}_s \ (= \dot{m}_h) = \frac{(15 \times 1000) \times 5}{60} = 1250 \text{ kg/min}$$

(i) Mass of cooling water circulated per minute, $\dot{m}_w \ (= \dot{m}_c)$:

Heat lost by steam = Heat gained by water

$$\dot{m}_h \times (x \cdot h_{fg}) = \dot{m}_c \times c_{pc} \times (t_{c_2} - t_{c_1})$$

$$1250 \times (0.9 \times 2592) = \dot{m}_c \times 4.187 \ (47 - 24)$$

$$\therefore \qquad \dot{m}_c \ (= \dot{m}_w) = \textbf{30280 kg/min} \qquad \textbf{(Ans.)}$$

(ii) Condenser surface area, A :

$$Q = \frac{\dot{m}_s \times (x \cdot h_{fg})}{60} = U \, A \, \theta_m \qquad \qquad ...(i)$$

where

$$\theta_m = \frac{\theta_1 - \theta_2}{\ln(\theta_1/\theta_2)} = \frac{(t_{h1} - t_{c1}) - (t_{h2} - t_{c2})}{\ln[(t_{h1} - t_{c1})/(t_{h2} - t_{c2})]}$$

$$= \frac{(51 - 24) - (51 - 47)}{\ln[(51 - 24)/(51 - 47)]} = \frac{(27 - 4)}{\ln(27/4)} = 12.04°C$$

Substituting the values in eqn. (i), we get

$$\frac{1250}{60} \times (0.9 \times 2592 \times 10^3) = 4000 \times A \times 12.04$$

or, $$A = \textbf{1009.1 m}^2 \qquad \textbf{(Ans.)}$$

(iii) Number of tubes required per pass, N_p :

$$\dot{m}_w = \left(\frac{\pi}{4} d_i^2 \times V \times \rho\right) \times N_p$$

$$\frac{30280}{60} = \frac{\pi}{4} \times (0.0296)^2 \times 3 \times 1000 \times N_p$$

or, $$N_p = \frac{30280 \times 4}{60 \times \pi \times (0.0296)^2 \times 3 \times 1000} = 244.46 \text{ say } \textbf{245} \qquad \textbf{(Ans.)}$$

(Total number of tubes required, $N = 2N_p = 2 \times 245 = 490$)

(iv) **Tube length, L :**

$$A = (\pi \, d_o \, L) \times (2N_p)$$
$$1009.1 = \pi \times 0.0384 \times L \times (2 \times 245)$$

or, $$L = \frac{1009.1}{\pi \times 0.0384 \times 2 \times 245} \simeq \textbf{17.1 m} \quad \textbf{(Ans.)}$$

Example 10.24. *A feed water heater which supplies hot water to a boiler comprises a shell and tube heat exchanger with one-shell pass and two-tube passes. One hundred thin-walled tubes each of 20 mm diameter and length of 2m per pass are used. Under normal operating conditions, water enters the tubes at 10 kg/s and 17°C and is heated by condensing saturated steam at 1atm. on the outer surface of the tubes. The convection coefficient of the saturated steam is 10 kW/m²°C.*

Determine the water exit temperature.

Use the following properties of water:
$c_p = 4.18 \ kJ/kg°C; \ \mu = 0.596 \times 10^{-3}$
$Ns/m^2, k = 0.635 \ W/m°C \ and \ Pr = 3.93.$

(M.U.)

Solution. *Given :* p (number of tube passes) = 2, N (total number of tubes) = 200, $d = 20$ mm = 0.02 m; L (length per pass) = 2m, $\dot{m}_w = \dot{m}_c = 10$ kg/s, $t_{c1} = 17°C$;

Water exit temperature, t_{c2} :

$$\dot{m}_c = \frac{\pi}{4} \, d^2 \times V \times \rho \times N_p$$

[where V = velocity of water; N_p

= number of tubes per pass = $\dfrac{N}{2}$

$= \dfrac{200}{2} = 100$]

or, $\quad 10 = \dfrac{\pi}{4} \times 0.02^2 \times V \times 1000 \times 100$

$\therefore \quad V = \dfrac{10 \times 4}{\pi \times 10^2 \times 1000 \times 100}$

$\quad\quad = 0.318 \text{ m/s}$

Using non-dimensional heat transfer equation to water side, we get

$$Nu = \frac{h_i \, d}{k} = 0.023 \, (Re)^{0.8} \, (Pr)^{0.33}$$

or, $\quad h_i = \dfrac{k}{d} \times 0.023 \, (Re)^{0.8} \, (Pr)^{0.33}$ ...(i)

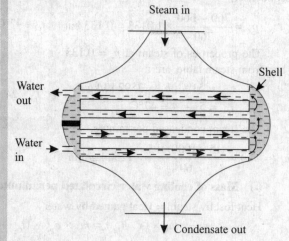

Steam in

Shell

Water out

Water in

Condensate out

Fig. 10.34. One-shell pass and two-tube passes condenser.

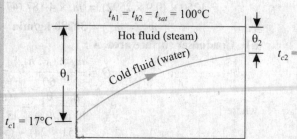

$t_{h1} = t_{h2} = t_{sat} = 100°C$

Hot fluid (steam)

θ_2

$t_{c2} = ?$

θ_1

Cold fluid (water)

$t_{c1} = 17°C$

$$Re = \frac{\rho \, V \, d}{\mu} = \frac{1000 \times 0.318 \times 0.02}{0.596 \times 10^{-3}} = 10671$$

Substituting the values in eqn. (i), we get

$$h_i = \frac{0.635}{0.02} \times 0.023 \, (10671)^{0.8} \, (3.93)^{0.33} = 1915 \text{ W/m}^2°C$$

The overall heat transfer coefficient is given by the relation,

$$\frac{1}{U} = \frac{1}{h_i} + \frac{1}{h_o}, \qquad \frac{1}{U} = \frac{1}{1915} + \frac{1}{10 \times 10^3} = 0.000622$$

$$\therefore \qquad U = \frac{1}{0.000622} = 1607.7 \text{ W/m}^2 \text{°C}$$

Further,
$$\theta_1 = t_{h1} - t_{c1} = 100 - 17 = 83°C$$
$$\theta_2 = t_{h2} - t_{c2} = 100 - t_{c2}$$

∴   Arithmatic mean temperature difference,

$$AMTD = \frac{\theta_1 + \theta_2}{2} = \frac{83 + (100 - t_{c2})}{2} = 91.5 - 0.5\, t_{c2}$$

The heat transfer rate is given by

$$Q = \dot{m}_c\, c_{pc}\, (t_{c2} - t_{c1}) = U A_s\, (AMTD) = U \times (\pi\, d\, L \times N)\, (AMTD)$$

(where A_s = surface area of *all the tubes in both passes*)

or, $10 \times (4.18 \times 10^3)\, (t_{c2} - 17) = 1607.7 \times (\pi \times 0.02 \times 2 \times 200) \times (91.5 - 0.5\, t_{c2})$

$$41800\, (t_{c2} - 17) = 40406\, (91.5 - 0.5\, t_{c2})$$

or,
$$t_{c2} - 17 = \frac{40406}{41800}\, (91.5 - 0.5\, t_{c2}) = 0.966\, (91.5 - 0.5\, t_{c2})$$
$$= 88.39 - 0.483\, t_{c2}$$

or,
$$t_{c2} = \mathbf{71°C} \ \ \textbf{(Ans.)}$$

Example 10.25. *A one ton window air-conditioner removes 3.5 kJ/s from a room and in the process rejects 4.2 kJ/s in the air-cooled condenser. The ambient temperature is 30°C whereas condensing temperature of the refrigerant is 45°C. For the condenser the product of overall heat transfer coefficient and corresponding area is 350 W/K. Calculate the temperature rise of the air as it flows over the condenser tubes.* (M.U., Winter, 2002)

Solution. Given : $t_{c1} = 30°C$; $t_{h1} = t_{h2} = 45°C$; $UA = 350$ W/K.

Temperature rise of air, t_{c2} :

The arrangement and temperature distribution are shown in Fig. 10.35.

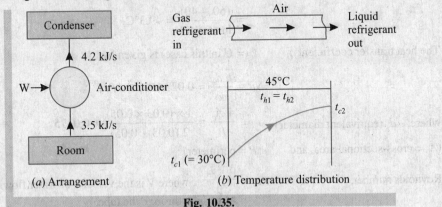

(a) Arrangement   (b) Temperature distribution

Fig. 10.35.

Heat lost by the refrigerant in condenser = Heat transferred to air

$$4.2 \times 1000 = U A \theta_m = U A\, \frac{\theta_1 - \theta_2}{ln\,(\theta_1 / \theta_2)}$$

$$= U A \times \frac{(t_{h1} - t_{c1}) - (t_{h2} - t_{c2})}{ln\left[\dfrac{t_{h1} - t_{c1}}{t_{h2} - t_{c2}}\right]} = U A\, \frac{t_{c2} - t_{c1}}{ln\left[\dfrac{t_{h1} - t_{c1}}{t_{h2} - t_{c2}}\right]} \qquad (\because\, t_{h1} = t_{h2})$$

or, $$4200 = 350 \times \frac{(t_{c2} - 30)}{\ln\left[\dfrac{45 - 30}{45 - t_{c2}}\right]}$$

$\therefore$ $$\frac{t_{c2} - 30}{\ln\left[\dfrac{15}{45 - t_{c2}}\right]} = \frac{4200}{350} = 12$$

Using trial and error method, we get, $t_{c2} = 35°C$

$\therefore$ Temperature rise of air $= 35 - 30 = \mathbf{5°C}$ **(Ans.)**

Example 10.26. *A rectangular tube, 30 mm × 50 mm, carries water at a rate of 2 kg/s. Determine the length required to heat water from 30°C to 50°C if the wall temperature is maintained at 90°C.*

Use the following properties of water at 40°C :

$\rho = 992.2 \ kg/m^3;\ k = 0.634 \ W/m°C;\ c_p = 4.174 \ kJ/kg°C;\ \mu = 6.531 \times 10^{-4} \ Ns/m^2.$ (P.U.)

Solution: *Given* : $\dot{m}_w = \dot{m}_c = 2 \ kg/s;\ t_{c1} = 30°C;$ $t_{c2} = 50°C;\ t_{h1} = t_{h2} = 90°C.$

Length required, L :

Heat gained by cold fluid (water),

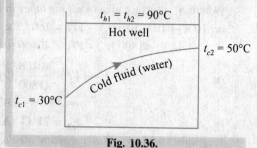

Fig. 10.36.

$$Q = \dot{m}_c \times c_{pc} \times (t_{c2} - t_{c1})$$
$$= 2 \times (4.174 \times 10^3) \times (50 - 30)$$
$$= 166960 \ W$$

The heat transfer Q is also given by

$$Q = UA\theta_m \qquad \qquad ...(1)$$

where, $$\theta_m = \frac{\theta_1 + \theta_2}{\ln(\theta_1/\theta_2)} = \frac{(90 - 30) - (90 - 50)}{\ln[(90 - 30)/(90 - 50)]}$$

$$= \frac{(60 - 40)}{\ln(60/40)} = 49.3°C$$

The heat transfer coefficient $\bar{h}$ $(= U$ in this case) is given by,

$$Nu = \frac{\bar{h} \, d_e}{k} = 0.023 \, (Re)^{0.8} \, (Pr)^{0.33} \qquad \qquad ...(2)$$

where, d_e (equivalent diameter) $= \dfrac{4 A_c}{P} = \dfrac{4 \times (0.03 \times 0.05)}{2 \, (0.03 + 0.05)} = 0.0375$

(A_c = cross-sectional area, and P = perimeter)

Reynolds number, $Re = \dfrac{\rho V L_c}{\mu}$, where V is the velocity of water flowing through the tube.

$$\dot{m}_w \, (= \dot{m}_c) = A_c . V . \rho$$
$$2 = (0.03 \times 0.05) \times V \times 992.2$$

or, $$V = \frac{2}{0.03 \times 0.05 \times 992.2} = 1.344 \ m/s$$

$\therefore$ $$Re = \frac{992.2 \times 1.344 \times 0.0375}{6.531 \times 10^{-4}} = 76568$$

$$Pr = \frac{\mu c_p}{k} = \frac{6.531 \times 10^{-4} \times (4.174 \times 10^3)}{0.634} = 4.3$$

Substituting the values in eqn. (2), we get

$$\bar{h} = \frac{k}{d_e} \times 0.023 \, (Re)^{0.8} \, (Pr)^{0.33}$$

$$= \frac{0.634}{0.0375} \times 0.023 \, (76568)^{0.8} \times (4.3)^{0.33} = 5082.4 \text{ W/m}^2\text{°C}$$

Now, putting the values in eqn. (1), we have

$$Q = UA\theta_m = \bar{h} \, A\theta_m \qquad\qquad \text{(where, } A = \text{surface area)}$$

$$166960 = 5082.4 \times [2 \, (0.03 + 0.05) \times L] \times 49.3$$

or,   **L = 4.16 m**   **(Ans.)**

Example 10.27. *Carbon dioxide (CO_2) for a gas cooled reactor is used to generate steam. A flow rate of 90000 kg/h of CO_2 at 4 bar enters the tubes of a shell and tube type steam generator at 500°C. The CO_2 leaves the generator at 330°C and steam saturation temperature is 250°C. Assume that the steam formed is dry and saturated. Using 25 mm inner diameter (I.D.) copper tubes, 2 mm wall thickness and designed for CO_2 mass flow rate of 350000 kg/m^2h, calculate the length and number of tubes to be used neglecting steam side thermal resistance.*

Take the following properties of CO_2 :

$$c_p = 1.172 \text{ kJ/kg°C}; \mu = 0.0000298 \text{ Ns/m}^2; k = 0.043 \text{ W/m°C}; \rho = 3.26 \text{ kg/m}^3.$$

Take k (for copper) = 384 W/m°C.   **(P.U.)**

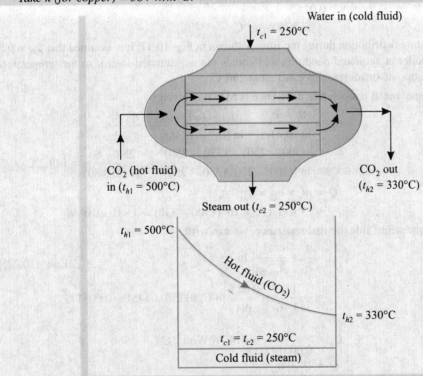

Fig. 10.37. Gas cooled reactor.

Solution. *Given :* $\dot{m}_{CO_2} = \dot{m}_h = \dfrac{90000}{3600} = 25$ kg/s; $t_{h1} = 500°C$; $t_{h2} = 330°C$, $t_{c1} = t_{c2} = 250°C$

$d_i = 25$ mm $= 0.025$ m; $d_o = 25 + 2 \times 2 = 29$ mm $= 0.029$ m.

Number of tubes (N) and length of each tube (L) :

Considering the flow of CO_2 through tubes, we have

Mass flow, $m = A.V.\rho$ (where V is the velocity of CO_2 in the tubes).

$\therefore$
$$G = \frac{m}{A} \text{ (mass flow per unit area per unit time)}$$

$$= \frac{AV\rho}{A} = V\rho$$

Reynolds number,
$$Re = \frac{\rho V d}{\mu} = \frac{G.d}{\mu}$$

(where G is in kg/m^2.s and μ in Ns/m^2)

$\therefore$
$$Re = \frac{(350000/3600) \times 0.025}{0.0000298} = 81562$$

Prandtl number
$$Pr = \frac{\mu c_p}{k} = \frac{0.0000298 \times (1.172 \times 1000)}{0.043} = 0.812$$

Nusselt number,
$$Nu = \frac{h_i\, d_i}{k} = 0.023\,(Re)^{0.8}\,(Pr)^{0.33}$$

or,
$$h_i = \frac{k}{d_i} \times 0.023\,(Re)^{0.8}\,(Pr)^{0.33}$$

$$= \frac{0.043}{0.025} \times 0.023 \times (81652)^{0.8} \times (0.812)^{0.33}$$

$$= 313.76 \text{ W/m}^2{}^\circ\text{C}$$

The temperature distribution during the flow is shown in Fig. 10.37. It is assumed that the water enters into the boiler at saturated condition and comes out as saturated steam, so the temperature during the generation of steam remains constant at 250°C.

The logarithmic mean temperature difference (LMTD) is given by

$$\theta_m = \frac{\theta_1 - \theta_2}{\ln(\theta_1/\theta_2)} = \frac{(t_{h1} - t_{c1}) - (t_{h2} - t_{c2})}{\ln[(t_{h1} - t_{c1})/(t_{h2} - t_{c2})]}$$

$$= \frac{(500 - 250) - (330 - 250)}{\ln[(500 - 250)/(330 - 250)]} = \frac{250 - 80}{\ln(250/80)} = 149.2°\text{C}$$

Further,
$$Q = \dot{m}_h \times c_{ph} \times (t_{h1} - t_{h2})$$
$$= 25 \times (1.172 \times 10^3)\,(500 - 330) = 4.981 \times 10^6 \text{ W}$$

Negletcting the steam side thermal resistance, we can write

$$\frac{1}{U_i} = \frac{1}{h_i} + \frac{r_i}{k_{copper}} \ln(r_o/r_i) \qquad \qquad \text{...[Eqn. (10.27)]}$$

$$= \frac{1}{313.76} + \frac{0.025}{384} \ln(0.0125/0.0145) = 0.003177$$

or,
$$U_i = \frac{1}{0.003177} = 314.76 \text{ W/m}^2{}^\circ\text{C}$$

Also,
$$Q = U_i A_i \theta_m$$

$\therefore$
$$4.981 \times 10^6 = 314.76 \times A_i \times 149.2$$

or,
$$A_i = \frac{4.981 \times 10^6}{314.76 \times 149.2} = 106.06 \text{ m}^2$$

Again, $\qquad G = \rho V = \dfrac{350000}{3600}$ ...(given)

$\therefore \qquad V = \dfrac{350000}{3600} \times \dfrac{1}{3.26} = 29.82$ m/s $\qquad (\because \rho = 3.26 \text{ kg/m}^3 \text{ ...given})$

The mass flow rate of CO_2 through the tubes is given by

$$m = A_i\, V \rho = \dfrac{\pi}{4}\, d_i^2 \times V \times \rho \times N$$

(where N, number of tubes)

or, $\qquad \dfrac{90000}{3600} = \dfrac{\pi}{4} \times (0.025)^2 \times 29.82 \times 3.26 \times N$

or, $\qquad N = 523.89$ say **524** (Ans.)

Now, $\qquad A_i = (\pi\, d_i\, L) \times N$

$\qquad 106.06 = \pi \times 0.025 \times L \times 524$

or, $\qquad L = \dfrac{106.06}{\pi \times 0.025 \times 524} \approx \textbf{2.58 m}$ (Ans.)

Example 10.28. *The tubes (k = 106 W/m°C) of a single pass condenser are of 30 mm outside diameter and 25 mm inside diameter. The condenser is required to handle 20000 kg/h of dry and saturated steam at 50°C. The inlet and outlet temperatures of water are 15°C and 25°C respectively. If the average velocity of water in each tube is 2.5 m/s and steam side film heat transfer coefficient is 5150 W/m²°C, calculate the outside tube area.*

The properties of water at mean temperature are given as under :

$\rho = 998.2 \text{ kg/m}^3,\ c_p = 4.182 \text{ kJ/kg K};\ \mu = 1004.5 \times 10^{-6} \text{ Ns/m}^2;\ \nu = 1.006 \times 10^{-6} \text{ m}^2/s;$ *and* $k = 0.598 \text{ W/m°C}.$

The latent heat (h_{fg}) at 50°C = 2374 kJ/kg.

For turbulent flow inside tubes, $Nu = 0.023\ Re^{0.8}\ Pr^{0.3}$.

Solution. Given : $k = 106$ W/m°C; $d_o = 30$ mm $= 0.03$ m; $d_i = 25$ mm $= 0.025$ m; $m_s = 20000$ kg/h; $h_s = 5150$ W/m²°C; $V = 2.5$ m/s.

Outside tube area, A :

Reynolds number, $\qquad Re = \dfrac{V\, d_i}{\nu} = \dfrac{2.5 \times 0.025}{1.006 \times 10^{-6}} = 62127$

Prandlt number, $\qquad Pr = \dfrac{\mu\, c_p}{k} = \dfrac{1004.5 \times 10^{-6} \times (4.182 \times 1000)}{0.598} = 7.02$

Nusselt number, $Nu = \dfrac{h_w\, d_i}{k} = 0.023\ Re^{0.8}\ Pr^{0.3} = 0.023 \times (62127)^{0.8} \times (7.02)^{0.3} = 282$

or, $\qquad h_w = \dfrac{k}{d_i} \times 282 = \dfrac{0.598}{0.025} \times 282 = 6745.4 \text{ W/m}^2\,°C$

The overall heat transfer coefficient is given by

$$\dfrac{1}{U} = \dfrac{1}{h_w} \times \dfrac{r_o}{r_i} + \dfrac{1}{h_s} + \dfrac{r_o}{k}\, ln\,(r_o/r_i)$$

where, $\qquad h_w$ = Heat transfer coefficient on the water side, and

$\qquad h_s$ = Heat transfer coefficient on the steam side.

Substituting the values, we get

$$\frac{1}{U} = \frac{1}{6745.4} \times \frac{0.015}{0.0125} + \frac{1}{5150} + \frac{0.015}{106} \, ln \, (0.015/0.0125)$$

$$= 0.0001779 + 0.0001942 + 0.0000258 = 0.0003979$$

or,

$$U = \frac{1}{0.0003979} = 2513.2 \text{ W/m}^2{}^\circ C$$

AMTD (arithmatic mean temperature difference) $= \dfrac{(50-15)+(50-25)}{2} = 30^\circ C$

Heat transfer rate is given by,

$$Q = UA \, (AMTD)$$

or,

$$m_s \, h_{fg} = UA \, (AMTD)$$

or,

$$\frac{20000}{3600} \times (2374 \times 1000) = 2513.2 \times A \times 30$$

or,

$$A = \frac{20000 \times 2374 \times 1000}{3600 \times 2513.2 \times 30} = \textbf{174.93 m}^2 \qquad \textbf{(Ans.)}$$

Example 10.29. *A single pass shell and tube heat exchanger, consisting of a bundle of 100 tubes (inner diameter = 25 mm and outer diameter = 29 mm) is used for heating 500 kg/min of water from 30°C to 70°C with the help of steam condensing at atmospheric pressure on the shell side. Calculate the overall heat transfer coefficient based on the inner area and length of the tube bundle if the condensing side heat transfer coefficient is 5000 W/m²°C. Take the fouling factor on the water side to be 0.0002 m²°C/W per tube. Neglect the effect of fouling on the shell side and thermal resistance of the tube wall.*

Take the following properties of water at the mean temperature of 50°C :

$\rho = 988.1 \text{ kg/m}^3$; $c_p = 4174 \text{ J/kg}^\circ C$; $k = 0.6474 \text{ W/m}^\circ C$; $\mu = 550 \times 10^{-6} \text{ kg/ms}$; $\nu = 0.555 \times 10^{-6} \text{ m}^2/s$, Pr = 3.54.

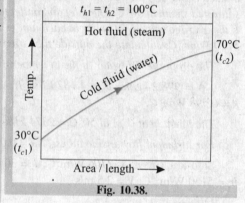

Fig. 10.38.

Solution. *Given :* $N = 100$; $d_i = 25 \text{ mm} = 0.025 \text{ m}$; $d_o = 29 \text{ mm} = 0.029 \text{ m}$; $\dot{m}_w = \dot{m}_c = 500 \text{ kg/}$ min; $t_{c1} = 30^\circ C$; $t_{c2} = 70^\circ C$; h_o (steam side) = 5000 W/m²°C; $t_{h1} = t_{h2} = 100^\circ C$. $R_{fi} = 0.0002 \text{ m}^2°C/$ W.

Overall heat transfer coefficient (U_i); tube length (L) :

Arrangement of the heat exchanger is shown in Fig. 10.38

Heat gained by water,

$$Q = \dot{m}_c \times c_{pc} \times (t_{c2} - t_{c1})$$

$$= \frac{500}{60} \times 4174 \times (70 - 30) = 1.39 \times 10^6 \text{ W}$$

The Q transferred from the steam to the water is given by

$$Q = U_i \, A_{is} \, \theta_m \qquad \qquad ...(1)$$

where, U_i = Overall heat transfer coefficient based on inner surface of the tubes,

A_{is} = Inner surface area of the tubes, and

θ_m = Logarithmic mean temperature difference (*LMTD*).

$$\theta_m = \frac{\theta_1 - \theta_2}{\ln(\theta_1/\theta_2)} = \frac{(t_{h1} - t_{c1}) - (t_{h2} - t_{c2})}{\ln[(t_{h1} - t_{c1})/(t_{h2} - t_{c2})]}$$

$$= \frac{(100 - 30) - (100 - 70)}{\ln[(100 - 30)/(100 - 70)]} = \frac{70 - 30}{\ln(70/30)} = 47.2°C$$

U_i is given by

$$\frac{1}{U} = \frac{1}{h_i} + R_{fi} + \frac{r_i}{r_o} \times \frac{1}{h_o} \qquad ...(2) \quad [Eqn. (10.27)]$$

where, h_i, h_o = Inside and outside heat transfer coefficients respectively, and

R_{fi} = Inside thermal resistance due to fouling.

In order to find out h_i we shall use the following relation :

$$Nu = \frac{h_i d_i}{k} = 0.023 (R_e)^{0.8} (Pr)^{0.33}$$

or,

$$h_i = \frac{k}{d_i} \times 0.023 (Re)^{0.8} (Pr)^{0.33} \qquad ...(3)$$

where

$$R_e = \frac{V d_i}{\nu},$$

V being the average velocity of the water flow which can be calculated by using the following equation.

$$\dot{m}_w (= \dot{m}_c) = \frac{\pi}{4} d_i^2 \times V \times \rho \times N$$

or,

$$\frac{500}{60} = \frac{\pi}{4} \times (0.025)^2 \times V \times 988.1 \times 100$$

or,

$$V = 0.172 \text{ m/s}$$

$$\therefore \qquad Re = \frac{0.172 \times 0.025}{0.555 \times 10^{-6}} = 7748$$

Substituting the values in eqn. (3), we get

$$h_i = \frac{0.6474}{0.025} \times 0.023 (7748)^{0.8} \times (3.54)^{0.33} = 1168 \text{ W/m}^2°C$$

Further, inserting the values in eqn. (2), we get

$$\frac{1}{U_i} = \frac{1}{1168} + 0.0002 + \frac{0.0125}{0.0145} \times \frac{1}{5000}$$

$$= 0.000856 + 0.0002 + 0.000172 = 0.001228$$

$$\therefore \qquad U_i = 814.3 \text{ W/m}^2°C$$

Now, substituting all the values in eqn. (1), we get

$$Q = U_i \times (N \times \pi \times d_i \times L) \times \theta_m$$

$$1.39 \times 10^6 = 814.3 \times (100 \times \pi \times 0.025 \times L) \times 47.2$$

$$\therefore \qquad L = \frac{1.39 \times 10^6}{814.3 \times 100 \times \pi \times 0.025 \times 47.2} = \textbf{4.6 m} \quad \textbf{(Ans.)}$$

Example 10.30. *A multipass heat exchanger has two passes on shell side and four passes on the tube side. The oil is passed through the tubes and cooled from 135°C to 52°C. The cooling water passing through shells enters at 13°C and leaves at 31°C. Calculate the heat transfer rate using the following data :*

h_i *(oil)* = 270 *W/m²°C, h_o (water)* = 965 *W/m²°C*

h (scale on water side) = 2840 *W/m²°C*

Number of tubes per pass = 120

Length and outer diameter of each tube are 2 m and 2.54 cm respectively.

Thickness of the tube = 1.65 *mm*

LMTD correction factor = 0.98

Neglect the tube wall resistance. (A.U. Winter, 2000)

Solution. *Given* : No. of passes two on shell side and four on tube side.

$$t_{c1} = 13°C; \ t_{c2} = 31°C; \ t_{h1} = 135°C; \ t_{h2} = 52°C; \ h_i \text{ (oil)} = 270 \text{ W/m}^2°C;$$

h_o (water) = 965 W/m²°C; h (scale on water side) = 2840 W/m²°C, N_p = 120;

$$d_o = 2.54 \text{ cm} = 0.0254 \text{ m}; \ L = 2 \text{ m}; \ d_i = 0.0254 - 2 \times 0.00165 = 0.0221 \text{ m};$$

LMTD correction factor, F = 0.98

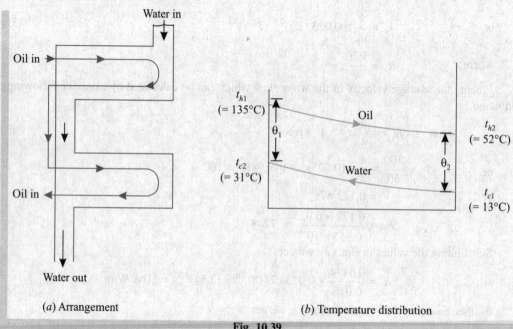

(a) Arrangement   (b) Temperature distribution

Fig. 10.39.

Rate of heat transfer, Q :

$$\text{LMTD, } \theta_m = \frac{\theta_1 - \theta_2}{\ln(\theta_1/\theta_2)} = \frac{(t_{h1} - t_{c1}) - (t_{h2} - t_{c2})}{\ln\left(\dfrac{t_{h1} - t_{c1}}{t_{h2} - t_{c2}}\right)}$$

$$= \frac{(135 - 31) - (52 - 13)}{\ln\left(\dfrac{135 - 31}{52 - 13}\right)} = \frac{65}{0.9808} = 66.3°C$$

$$(\theta_m)_{actual} = 66.3 \times F = 66.3 \times 0.98 = 65°C$$

The overall heat transfer coefficient,

$$U_o = \frac{1}{\dfrac{r_o}{r_i} \times \dfrac{1}{h_i} + \left(\dfrac{r_o}{r_i}\right) \times R_{fi} + \dfrac{1}{h_o}}$$

where, R_{fi} (inside fouling factor) $= \dfrac{1}{2840} = 0.000352$

Substituting the values, we have

$$U_o = \cfrac{1}{\left(\dfrac{0.0254}{0.0221}\right)\times\dfrac{1}{270} + \dfrac{0.0254}{0.0221}\times 0.000352 + \dfrac{1}{965}} \qquad \left(\because \dfrac{r_o}{r_i} = \dfrac{d_o}{d_i}\right)$$

$$= \cfrac{1}{0.004257 + 0.0004046 + 0.00104} = 175.4 \text{ W/m}^2\,{}^\circ\text{C}$$

$\therefore$ Rate of heat transfer, $Q = U_o A_o\,(\theta_m)_{\text{actual}}$

$$= 175.4 \times [\pi D_o L \times (N_p \times 4)] \times 65$$
$$= 175.4 \times [\pi \times 0.0254 \times 2 \times (120 \times 4)] \times 65$$
$$= 873369 \text{ W} \qquad \text{or} \qquad \textbf{873.369 kW (Ans.)}$$

10.6. CORRECTION FACTORS FOR MULTI-PASS ARRANGEMENTS

The expression $\theta_m = \dfrac{(\theta_1 - \theta_2)}{ln\,(\theta_1/\theta_2)}$ for *LMTD* is essentially valid for single-pass heat exchangers. The analytical treatment of multiple pass shell and tube heat exchangers and cross-flow heat exchangers is much more difficult than single pass cases; such cases may be analysed by using the following equation :

$$Q = UAF\,\theta_m \qquad\qquad ...(10.31)$$

where F is the *correction factor;* the correction factors have been published in the form of charts by Bonman, Mueller and Nagle and by *TEMA.*

Correction factors for several common arrangements have been given in Figs. 10.40 to 10.43. The data is presented as a function of two non-dimensional variables namely the temperature ratio P and the capacity ratio R.

Temperature ratio, P : It is defined as the *ratio of the rise in temperature of the cold fluid to the difference in the inlet temperatures of the two fluids.* Thus:

$$P = \frac{t_{c2} - t_{c1}}{t_{h1} - t_{c1}} \qquad\qquad ...(10.32)$$

where subscripts h and c denote the hot and cold fluids respectively, and the subscripts 1 and 2 refer to the inlet and outlet conditions respectively.

The temperature ratio P indicates *cooling or heating effectiveness* and it can vary from *zero* for a constant temperature of one of the fluids to *unity* for the case when inlet temperature of the hot fluid equals the outlet temperature of the cold fluid.

Capacity ratio R : *The ratio of the products of the mass flow rate times the heat capacity of the fluids is termed as capacity ratio R.* Thus :

$$R = \frac{\dot{m}_c \cdot c_{pc}}{\dot{m}_h \cdot c_{ph}} \qquad\qquad ...(10.33)$$

Since, $\quad \dot{m}_c \cdot c_{pc} \cdot (t_{c2} - t_{c1}) = \dot{m}_h \cdot c_{ph} \cdot (t_{h1} - t_{h2})$

or, $$R = \frac{\dot{m}_c \cdot c_{pc}}{\dot{m}_h \cdot c_{ph}} = \frac{t_{h1} - t_{h2}}{t_{c2} - t_{c1}}$$

$$= \left[\frac{\text{Temperature drop of the hot fluid}}{\text{Temperature rise in the cold fluid}}\right] \qquad\qquad ...(10.34)$$

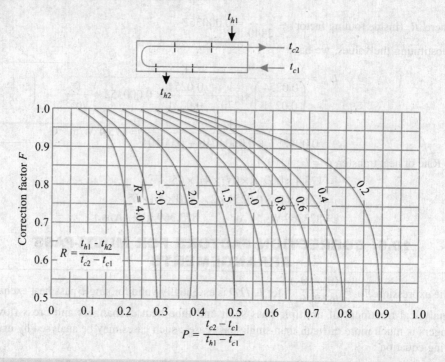

Fig. 10.40. Correction factor plot for heat exchanger with one shell pass
and two, four or any multiple of tube passes.

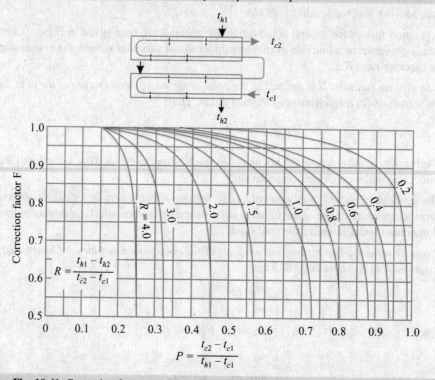

Fig. 10.41. Correction factor plot for heat exchanger with two shell passes and two, four,
eight or any multiple of tube passes.

For these correction factor plots it is immaterial whether the hot fluid flows in the shell or the tubes. The value of the correction factor indicates the *performance level of a given arrangement for the given terminal fluid temperatures. The correction factor F is always less than unity as no arrangement can be more effective than the conventional counter flow.*

Example 10.31. *Calculate for the following cases, the surface area required for a heat exchanger which is required to cool 3200 kg/h of benzene ($c_p = 1.74$ kJ/kg°C) from 72°C to 42°C. The cooling water ($c_p = 4.18$ kJ/kg°C) at 15°C has a flow rate of 2200 kg/h.*

(i) *Single pass counter-flow,*

(ii) *1-4 exchanger (one-shell pass and four-tube passes), and*

(iii) *Cross flow single pass with water mixed and benzene unmixed.*

For each configuration, the overall heat transfer coefficient may be taken as 0.28 kW/m²°C.

Solution. *Given :* $\dot{m}_h = \dfrac{3200}{3600} = 0.889$ kg/s; $c_{ph} = 1.74$ kJ/kg°C; $t_{h1} = 72°C$, $t_{h2} = 42°C$;

$\dot{m}_w = \dot{m}_c = \dfrac{2000}{3600} = 0.611$ kg/s, $c_{pc} = 4.18$ kJ/kg°C, $t_{c1} = 15°C$, $U = 280$ W/m²°C

Surface area required, A :

Using energy balance on both the fluids, we have

$$\dot{m}_h c_{ph} (t_{h1} - t_{h2}) = \dot{m}_c c_{pc} (t_{c2} - t_{c1})$$

$$0.889 \times 1.74 (72 - 42) = 0.611 \times 4.18 (t_{c2} - 15)$$

$$\therefore \quad t_{c2} = 33.2°C$$

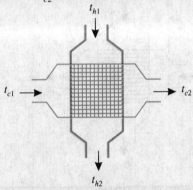

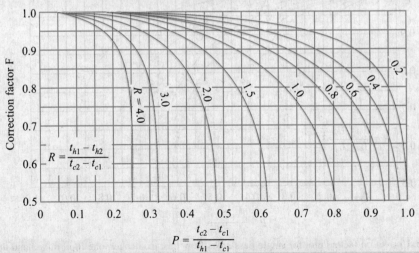

Fig. 10.42. Correction factor plot for single cross-flow heat exchanger with both fluids unmixed.

An energy balance on the hot fluid yields the total heat transfer,

$$Q = \dot{m}_h\, c_{ph}\, (t_{h1} - t_{h2}) = 0.889 \times 1.74\, (72 - 42) = 46.4 \text{ kW}$$

(i) *Single-pass counter-flow :*

$$\theta_m = \frac{\theta_1 - \theta_2}{\ln (\theta_1/\theta_2)} = \frac{(t_{h1} - t_{c2}) - (t_{h2} - t_{c1})}{\ln\,[(t_{h1} - t_{c2})/(t_{h2} - t_{c1})]}$$

$$= \frac{(72 - 33.2) - (42 - 15)}{\ln\,[(72 - 33.2)/(42 - 15)]} = \frac{38.8 - 27}{\ln\,[(38.8/27)]} = 32.5°C$$

∴ Area of the exchanger, $A = \dfrac{Q}{U\,\theta_m} = \dfrac{46.4}{0.28 \times 32.5} = \textbf{5.1 m}^2$ **(Ans.)**

(ii) *1-4 exchanger :*

Since the number of passes is more than one hence θ_m (*LMTD*) needs correction factor, *F*. To know the correction factor we have to know first *P* (temperature ratio) and (capacity ratio) *R*.

$$P = \frac{t_{c2} - t_{c1}}{t_{h1} - t_{c1}} = \frac{(33.2 - 15)}{(72 - 15)} = 0.32$$

$$R = \frac{t_{h1} - t_{h2}}{t_{c2} - t_{c1}} = \frac{(72 - 42)}{(33.2 - 15)} = 1.65$$

Using *P* = 0.32 and *R* = 1.65 the correction factor *F* from Fig. 10.40 is read as

$$F \simeq 0.9$$

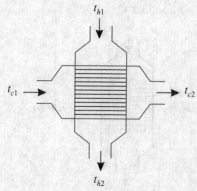

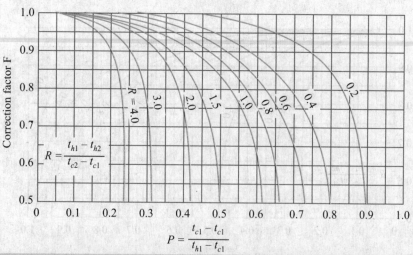

Fig. 10.43. Correction factors plot for single-pass cross-flow heat exchanger, one fluid mixed and the other unmixed.

$$\therefore \quad \text{Area of the exchanger,} \quad A = \frac{Q}{F U \theta_m} = \frac{46.4}{0.9 \times 0.28 \times 32.5} = 5.66 \text{ m}^2 \text{ (Ans.)}$$

(iii) *Cross-flow single-pass with water mixed and benzene unmixed :*

Using $P = 0.32$ and $R = 1.65$ the correction factor F from Fig. 10.43 is read as

$$F \simeq 0.92$$

$$\therefore \quad \text{Area of the exchanger,} \quad A = \frac{Q}{F U \theta_m} = \frac{46.4}{0.92 \times 0.28 \times 32.5} = 5.54 \text{ m}^2 \quad \text{(Ans.)}$$

Example 10.32. *It is required to design a shell-and-tube heat exchanger for heating 2.4 kg/s of water from 20°C to 90°C by hot engine oil (c_p = 2.4 kJ/kg°C) flowing through the shell of the heat exchanger. The oil makes a single pass entering at 145°C and leaving at 90°C with an average heat transfer coefficient of 380 W/m²°C. The water flows through 12 thin-walled tubes of 25 mm diameter with each-tube making 8-passes through the shell. The heat transfer coefficient on the water side is 2900 W/m²°C. Calculate the length of the tube required for the heat exchanger to accomplish the required water heating.*

Solution. *Given :* $\dot{m}_w = \dot{m}_c = 2.4$ kg/s, $t_{c1} = 20°C$, $t_{c2} = 90°C$; $t_{h1} = 145°C$, $t_{h2} = 90°C$,

$c_{ph} = 2.4$ kJ/kg°C, $d = 25$mm $= 0.025$ m, $N = 12$; $h_i = 2900$ W/m°C, $h_o = 380$ W/m²°C

Length of the tube L :

The overall heat transfer coefficient, neglecting thermal resistance of the tube, is given by

$$\frac{1}{U} = \frac{1}{h_i} + \frac{1}{h_o}$$

or,
$$U = \frac{h_i \times h_o}{h_i + h_o} = \frac{2900 \times 380}{2900 + 380} = 335.97 \text{ W/m}^2{}^\circ\text{C}$$

The parameters required to get the correction factors are :

$$P = \frac{t_{c2} - t_{c1}}{t_{h1} - t_{c1}} = \frac{(90 - 20)}{(145 - 20)} = 0.56$$

$$R = \frac{t_{h1} - t_{h2}}{t_{c2} - t_{c1}} = \frac{(145 - 90)}{(90 - 20)} = 0.786$$

Form Fig. 10.40, $F \simeq 0.82$

For the conventional counter-flow arrangement

$$\theta_1 = t_{h1} - t_{c2} = 145 - 90 = 55°C$$

$$\theta_2 = t_{h2} - t_{c1} = 90 - 20 = 70°C$$

$$\therefore \qquad \theta_m = \frac{(\theta_1 - \theta_2)}{\ln(\theta_1/\theta_2)} = \frac{55 - 70}{\ln(55/70)} = 103.6°C$$

The heat transfer rate is given by

$$Q = \dot{m}_c \, c_{pc} \, (t_{c2} - t_{c1})$$

$$= 2.4 \times 4.18 \times 10^3 \, (90 - 20) = 702240 \text{ W}$$

Also,
$$Q = F U A \, \theta_m, \text{ where } A = \text{heating surface}$$

$$\therefore \qquad A = \frac{Q}{F U \theta_m} = \frac{702240}{0.82 \times 335.97 \times 103.6} = 24.6 \text{ m}^2$$

But,
$$A = \pi \, d \, L \times N$$

$$\therefore \qquad L = \frac{A}{\pi d N} = \frac{24.6}{\pi \times 0.025 \times 12} \quad 26.1 \text{ m}$$

The shell length $= \dfrac{26.1}{8} = 3.26 \text{ m}$ (Ans.)

10.7. HEAT EXCHANGER EFFECTIVENESS AND NUMBER OF TRANSFER UNITS (NTU)

A heat exchanger can be designed by the *LMTD* (logarithmic mean temperature difference) when *inlet and outlet conditions are specified*. However, when the problem is to determine the inlet or exit temperatures for a particular heat exchanger, the analysis is performed more easily, by using a method based on effectiveness of the heat exchanger (concept first proposed by Nusselt) and number of transfer units (*NTU*).

The **heat exchanger effectiveness** (ε) is defined as the *ratio of actual heat transfer to the maximum possible heat transfer*. Thus

$$\varepsilon = \frac{\text{Actual heat transfer}}{\text{Maximum possible heat transfer}} = \frac{Q}{Q_{max}} \qquad ...(10.35)$$

The actual heat transfer rate Q can be determined by writing an energy balance over either side of the heat exchanger.

$$Q = \dot{m}_h\, c_{ph}\, (t_{h1} - t_{h2}) = \dot{m}_c\, c_{pc}\, (t_{c2} - t_{c1}) \qquad ...(10.36)$$

The product of mass flow rate and the specific heat, as a matter of convenience, is defined as the fluid capacity rate C :

$$\dot{m}_h\, c_{ph} = C_h = \text{Hot fluid capacity rate}$$
$$\dot{m}_c\, c_{pc} = C_c = \text{Cold fluid capcity rate}$$
$$C_{min} = \text{The minimum fluid capacity rate } (C_h \text{ or } C_c)$$
$$C_{max} = \text{The maximum fluid capacity rate } (C_h \text{ or } C_c).$$

The *maximum rate of heat transfer for parallel flow or counter-flow heat exchangers would occur if the outlet temperature of the fluid with smaller value of C_h or C_c i.e., C_{min} were to be equal to the inlet temperature of the other fluid.* The maximum possible temperature change can be achieved by *only one of fluids*, depending upon their heat capacity rates. This maximum change cannot be obtained by both the fluids except in the very special case of *equal heat capacity rates*. Thus :

$$Q_{max} = C_h\, (t_{h1} - t_{c1}) \text{ or } C_c\, (t_{h1} - t_{c1})$$

Q_{max} is the *minimum* of these two values, *i.e.,*

$$Q_{max} = C_{min}\, (t_{h1} - t_{c1}) \qquad ...(10.37)$$

$$\therefore \qquad \varepsilon = \frac{C_h\, (t_{h1} - t_{h2})}{C_{min}\, (t_{h1} - t_{c1})} = \frac{C_c\, (t_{c2} - t_{c1})}{C_{min}\, (t_{h1} - t_{c1})} \qquad ...(10.38)$$

Once the effectiveness is known, the heat transfer rate can be very easily calculated by using the equation

$$Q = \varepsilon\, C_{min}\, (t_{h1} - t_{c1}) \qquad ...(10.39)$$

Number of transfer units (NTU) method :

It is obvious from Eqn. (10.38) that effectiveness ε is a function of several variables and as such it is inconvenient to combine them in a graphical or tabular form. However, by compiling a non-dimensional grouping, ε can be expressed as a function of three non-dimensional parameters. This method is known as *NTU method*. This method/approach *facilitates the comparison between the various types of heat exchangers* which may be used for a particular application. The effectiveness expresssions for the parallel flow and counter-flow cases can be derived as follows :

(i) Effectiveness for the "Parallel-flow" heat exchanger :

Refer Fig. 10.8. The heat exchange dQ through an area dA of the heat exchanger is given by

$$dQ = U.dA\,(t_h - t_c) \qquad \qquad ...(i)$$

$$= - \dot{m}.c_{ph}.dt_h = \dot{m}_c.c_{pc}.dt_c$$

$$= - C_h.dt_h = C_c.dt_c \qquad \qquad ...(ii)$$

From expression (ii), we have

$$dt_h = \frac{-dQ}{C_h} \qquad \text{and} \qquad dt_c = \frac{dQ}{C_c}$$

$$\therefore \qquad d\,(t_h - t_c) = - dQ\left[\frac{1}{C_h} + \frac{1}{C_c}\right]$$

Substituting the value of dQ from expression (i) and rearranging, we get

$$\frac{d\,(t_h - t_c)}{(t_h - t_c)} = - U.dA\left[\frac{1}{C_h} + \frac{1}{C_c}\right]$$

Upon integration, we get

$$ln\left[\frac{(t_{h2} - t_{c2})}{(t_{h1} - t_{c1})}\right] = - UA\left[\frac{1}{C_h} + \frac{1}{C_c}\right]$$

$$ln\left[\frac{(t_{h2} - t_{c2})}{(t_{h1} - t_{c1})}\right] = - \frac{UA}{C_h}\left(1 + \frac{C_h}{C_c}\right)$$

or,

$$\left(\frac{t_{h2} - t_{c2}}{t_{h1} - t_{c1}}\right) = \exp\left[- (UA/C_h)\,\{1 + (C_h/C_c)\}\right] \qquad \qquad ...(10..40)$$

From eqn. (10.38), we have the expressions for effectiveness

$$\varepsilon = \frac{C_h\,(t_{h1} - t_{h2})}{C_{min}\,(t_{h1} - t_{c1})} = \frac{C_c\,(t_{c2} - t_{c1})}{C_{min}\,(t_{h1} - t_{c1})}$$

Hence,

$$t_{h2} = t_{h1} - \frac{\varepsilon\,C_{min}\,(t_{h1} - t_{c1})}{C_h} \qquad \qquad ...(10.41)$$

$$t_{c2} = t_{c1} + \frac{\varepsilon\,C_{min}\,(t_{h1} - t_{c1})}{C_c} \qquad \qquad ...(10.42)$$

Eliminating t_{h2} and t_{c2} from eqn. (10.40) with the help of eqns. (10.41) and (10.42), we get

$$\frac{1}{(t_{h1} - t_{c1})}\left[(t_{h1} - t_{c1}) - \varepsilon\,C_{min}\,(t_{h1} - t_{c1})\left(\frac{1}{C_h} + \frac{1}{C_c}\right)\right] = \exp\left[- (UA/C_h)\,\{1 + C_h/C_c\}\right]$$

or,

$$1 - \varepsilon\,C_{min}\left(\frac{1}{C_h} + \frac{1}{C_c}\right) = \exp\left[- (UA/C_h)\,\{1 + C_h/C_c\}\right]$$

or,

$$\varepsilon = \frac{1 - \exp\left[- (UA/C_h)\,\{1 + C_h/C_c\}\right]}{C_{min}\left(\dfrac{1}{C_h} + \dfrac{1}{C_c}\right)} \qquad \qquad ...(10.43)$$

If $C_c > C_h$ then $C_{min} = C_h$ and $C_{max} = C_c$, hence eqn. (10.43) becomes

$$\varepsilon = \frac{1 - \exp\left[- (UA/C_{min})\,\{1 + C_{min}/C_{max}\}\right]}{1 + (C_{min}/C_{max})} \qquad \qquad ..(10.44)$$

If $C_c < C_h$ then $C_{min} = C_c$ and $C_{max} = C_h$, hence eqn. (10.43) becomes

$$\varepsilon = \frac{1 - \exp\left[- (UA/C_{max})\,\{1 + C_{max}/C_{min}\}\right]}{1 + (C_{min}/C_{max})} \qquad \qquad ...(10.45)$$

By rearranging eqns. (10.44) and (10.45), we get a common equation

$$\varepsilon = \frac{1 - \exp\left[-\,(UA/C_{min})\,\{1 + C_{min}/C_{max})\}\right]}{1 + (C_{min}/C_{max})}$$

where C_{min} and C_{max} represent the smaller and larger of the two heat capacities C_c and C_h.

● The grouping of the terms $(UA)/C_{min}$ is a dimensionless expression called the number of transfer units NTU; NTU is a *measure of effectiveness of the heat exchanger*.

● C_{min}/C_{max} is the second dimensionless parameter and is called the *capacity ratio R*.

● The last dimensionless parameter is the *flow arrangement*, i.e., parallel flow, counter-flow, cross-flow and so on.

Thus the effectiveness of a parallel flow heat exchanger is given by

$$\varepsilon = \frac{1 - \exp\left[-\,NTU\,\{1 + (C_{min}/C_{max})\}\right]}{1 + (C_{min}/C_{max})} \qquad \qquad ...(10.46)$$

or,

$$\varepsilon = \frac{1 - \exp\left[-\,NTU\,(1 + R)\right]}{1 + R} \qquad \qquad ...[10.46\,(a)]$$

(ii) **"Counter-flow" heat exchanger :**

Refer Fig. 10.9. The heat exchange dQ through an area dA of the heat exchanger is given by

$$dQ = U.dA\,(t_h - t_c) \qquad \qquad ...(i)$$

$$= -\,\dot{m}\,c_{ph}\,dt_h = -\,\dot{m}\,c_{pc}\,dt_c$$

$$= -\,C_h\,dt_h = -\,C_c\,dt_c \qquad \qquad ...(ii)$$

From expression *(ii)*, we have

$$dt_h = -\,\frac{dQ}{C_h} \quad \text{and} \quad dt_c = -\,\frac{dQ}{C_c}$$

∴

$$d\,(t_h - t_c) = -\,dQ\left[\frac{1}{C_h} - \frac{1}{C_c}\right] = dQ\left[\frac{1}{C_c} - \frac{1}{C_h}\right]$$

Substituting the value of dQ from expression *(i)*, we get,

$$\frac{d\,(t_h - t_c)}{t_h - t_c} = U\,dA\left[\frac{1}{C_c} - \frac{1}{C_h}\right]$$

Upon integration, we get

$$ln\left[\frac{t_{h2} - t_{c1}}{t_{h1} - t_{c2}}\right] = UA\left[\frac{1}{C_c} - \frac{1}{C_h}\right]$$

or,

$$ln\left[\frac{t_{h2} - t_{c1}}{t_{h1} - t_{c2}}\right] = \frac{UA}{C_c}\left[1 - \frac{C_c}{C_h}\right]$$

or,

$$\frac{t_{h2} - t_{c1}}{t_{h1} - t_{c2}} = \exp\left[(UA/C_c)\,\{1 - (C_c/C_h)\}\right] \qquad \qquad ...(10.47)$$

From Eqn. (10.38), we have the expressions for effectiveness,

$$\varepsilon = \frac{C_h\,(t_{h1} - t_{h2})}{C_{min}\,(t_{h1} - t_{c1})} = \frac{C_c\,(t_{c2} - t_{c1})}{C_{min}\,(t_{h1} - t_{c1})}$$

Hence,

$$t_{h2} = t_{h1} - \frac{\varepsilon\,C_{min}\,(t_{h1} - t_{c1})}{C_h} \qquad \qquad ...(iii)$$

$$t_{c2} = t_{c1} + \frac{\varepsilon\,C_{min}\,(t_{h1} - t_{c1})}{C_c} \qquad \qquad ...(iv)$$

Substituting these values in eqn. (10.47), we get,

$$\dfrac{\left[t_{h1} - \dfrac{\varepsilon\, C_{min}\,(t_{h1} - t_{c1})}{C_h}\right] - t_{c1}}{t_{h1} - \left[t_{c1} + \dfrac{\varepsilon\, C_{min}\,(t_{h1} - t_{c1})}{C_c}\right]} = \exp\left[(UA/C_c)\,\{1 - (C_c/C_h)\}\right]$$

$$\dfrac{(t_{h1} - t_{c1})\left[1 - \dfrac{\varepsilon \cdot C_{min}}{C_h}\right]}{(t_{h1} - t_{c1})\left[1 - \dfrac{\varepsilon \cdot C_{min}}{C_c}\right]} = \exp\left[(UA/C_c)\,\{1 - (C_c/C_h)\}\right]$$

or, $\qquad \dfrac{1 - \dfrac{\varepsilon \cdot C_{min}}{C_h}}{1 - \dfrac{\varepsilon \cdot C_{min}}{C_c}} = \exp\left[(UA/C_c)\,\{1 - (C_c/C_h)\}\right]$ $\qquad$ ...(10.48)

Assume $C_c < C_h$, $C_c = C_{min}$ and $C_h = C_{max}$. Substituting these values is eqn. (10.48), we get,

$$\dfrac{1 - \dfrac{\varepsilon \cdot C_{min}}{C_{max}}}{1 - \dfrac{\varepsilon \cdot C_{min}}{C_{min}}} = \exp\left[(UA/C_{min})\,\{1 - (C_{min}/C_{max})\}\right]$$

or, $\qquad \dfrac{1 - \dfrac{\varepsilon \cdot C_{min}}{C_{max}}}{1 - \varepsilon} = \exp\left[(UA/C_{min})\,\{1 - (C_{min}/C_{max})\}\right]$

or, $\quad 1 - \dfrac{\varepsilon . C_{min}}{C_{max}} = \exp\left[(UA/C_{min})\,\{1 - (C_{min}/C_{max})\}\right] - \exp\left[(UA/C_{min})\,\{1 - (C_{min}/C_{max})\}\right]\varepsilon$

or, $\quad 1 - \exp\left[(UA/C_{min})\,\{1 - (C_{min}/C_{max})\}\right] = \varepsilon\left[\dfrac{C_{min}}{C_{max}} - \exp\left\{(UA/C_{min})\,(1 - C_{min}/C_{max})\right\}\right]$

or, $\qquad \varepsilon = \dfrac{1 - \exp\left[(UA/C_{min})\,\{1 - (C_{min}/C_{max})\}\right]}{\dfrac{C_{min}}{C_{max}} - \exp\left[(UA/C_{min})\,\{1 - (C_{min}/C_{max})\}\right]}$

$$= \dfrac{\exp\left[(UA/C_{min})\,\{1 - (C_{min}/C_{max})\}\right] - 1}{\exp\left[(UA/C_{min})\,\{1 - (C_{min}/C_{max})\}\right] - \dfrac{C_{min}}{C_{max}}}$$

or, $\qquad \varepsilon = \dfrac{1 - \exp\left[(- UA/C_{min})\,\{1 - (C_{min}/C_{max})\}\right]}{1 - \dfrac{C_{min}}{C_{max}}\exp\left[(- UA/C_{min})\,\{1 - (C_{min}/C_{max})\}\right]}$ $\qquad$ ...(10.49)

Since $C_{min}/C_{max} = R$ and $UA/C_{min} = NTU$, therefore,

$$\varepsilon = \dfrac{1 - \exp\left[- NTU\,(1 - R)\right]}{1 - R\,\exp\left[- NTU\,(1 - R)\right]} \qquad \text{...(10.50)}$$

We find that effectiveness of parallel flow and counter-flow heat exchangers is given by the following expressions :

$$(\varepsilon)_{parallel\ flow} = \dfrac{1 - \exp\left[- NTU\,(1 + R)\right]}{1 + R} \qquad \text{...(1)}$$

$$(\varepsilon)_{counter\ flow} = \dfrac{1 - \exp\left[- NTU\,(1 - R)\right]}{1 - R\,\exp\left[- NTU\,(1 - R)\right]} \qquad \text{...(2)}$$

where $R = (C_{min}/C_{max})$

Let us discuss *two limiting cases* of eqns. (1) and (2)

Case I :   When $R \simeq 0$ ...**Condensers and evaporators (boilers)**

By using the above case, we arrive at the following common expression for *parallel flow as well as counter-flow* heat exchangers

$$\varepsilon = 1 - exp\,(-\,NTU)$$ ...(10.51)

Such cases are found in *condensers and evaporators in which one fluid remains at constant temperature throughout the exchanger*. Here $C_{max} = \infty$ and thus $R = \left(\dfrac{C_{min}}{C_{max}}\right) \simeq 0$.

Obviously, no matter how large the exchanger is or how large the overall transfer coefficient is the *maximum effectiveness for parallel flow heat exchanger is 50%. For counter-flow, this limit is 100%. For this reason, a counter flow is usually more advantageous for a gas turbine heat exchangers*.

Case II :   When $R = 1$ ... **Typical regenerators**

(*i*)   In case of *parallel flow* heat exchanger using $R = 1$, we get

$$\varepsilon = \frac{1 - exp\,(-\,2NTU)}{2}$$ ...(10.52)

(*ii*)   In case of *counter-flow* heat exchanger using $R = 1$ we get an expression for effectiveness which is indeterminate. We can find the value of ε by applying L, Hospital's rule :

$$\lim_{R \to 1} = \frac{1 - exp\,[-\,NTU\,(1 - R)]}{1 - R\,exp\,[-\,NTU\,(1 - R)]}$$

$$\lim_{R \to 1} = \frac{exp\,[NTU\,(1 - R)] - 1}{exp\,[NTU\,(1 - R)] - R}$$

Differentiating the numerator and the denomenator with respect to R and taking the limit, we get,

$$\lim_{R \to 1} = \frac{exp\,[NTU\,(1 - R)\,(-\,NTU)]}{exp\,[NTU\,(1 - R)]\,(-\,NTU) - 1} = \frac{NTU}{1 + NTU}$$ ...(10.53)

The *NTU is a measure of the heat transfer size of the exchanger; the larger the value of NTU, the closer the heat exchanger approaches its thermodynamic limit.*

The effectiveness of various types of heat exchangers in the form of graphs (prepared by Kays and London) for values of $R \left(= \dfrac{C_{min}}{C_{max}}\right)$ and *NTU* are shown in Fig. 10.44 to 10.49.

10.8. PRESSURE DROP AND PUMPING POWER

An important consideration in heat exchanger design, besides the heat transfer requirements, is the *pressure drop pumping cost*. The heat exchanger size can be reduced by forcing the fluid through it at higher velocities thereby increasing the overall heat transfer coefficient. But due to higher velocities there will be larger pressure drops resulting in larger pumping costs. The smaller diameter pipe, for a given flow rate, may involve less initial capital cost but definitely higher pumping costs for the life of the exchanger.

We know that, $\Delta p \propto \dot{m}^2$ ...(*i*)

where, Δp = Pressure drop of an incompressible fluid flowing through the pipes, and

$\dot{m}$ = Mass flow rate.

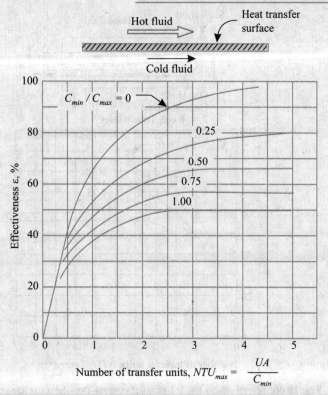

Fig. 10.44. Effectiveness for parallel flow heat exchanger.

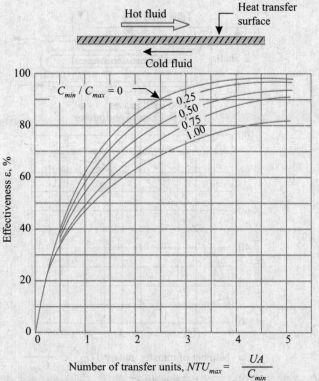

Fig. 10.45. Effectiveness for counter-flow heat exchange.

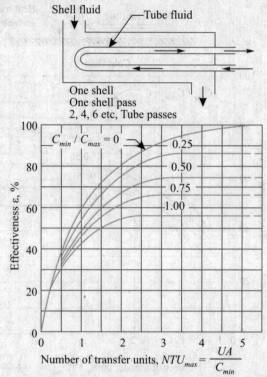

Fig. 10.46. Effectiveness for 1-2 parallel counter-flow heat exchanger.

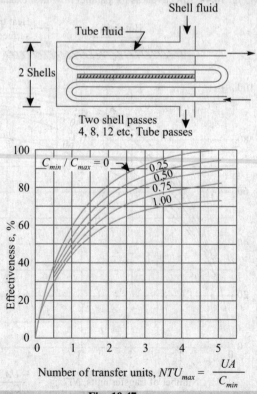

Fig. 10.47.

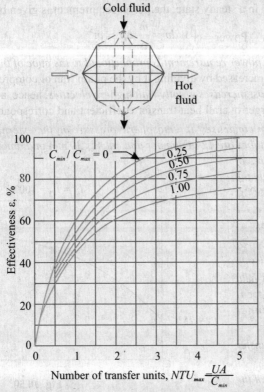

Fig. 10.48. Effectiveness for cross-flow heat exchanger with both fluids unmixed.

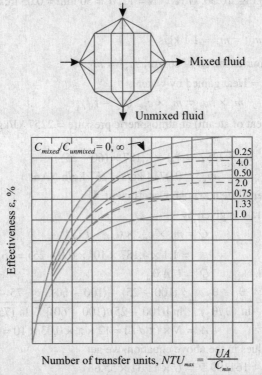

Fig. 10.49. Effectiveness for cross-flow heat exchanger with one fluid mixed and other unmixed.

In order to pump fluid in a steady state, the power requirement is given by

$$\text{Power} = \int v \, dp = \frac{\dot{m}}{\rho} \Delta p \approx \dot{m}^3 \qquad \text{...(ii)}$$

This indicates that the *power requirement is proportional to the cube of the mass flow rate of the fluid* and it may be further increased by dividing it by the pump (fan or compressor) efficiency. Thus, we find that the *pumping cost increases greatly with higher velocities*, hence, a *compromise* will have to be made between the larger overall heat transfer coefficient and corresponding velocities.

Example 10.33. *Steam condenses at atmospheric pressure on the external surface of the tubes of a steam condenser. The tubes are 12 in number and each is 30 mm in diameter and 10 m long. The inlet and outlet temperatures of cooling water flowing inside the tubes are 25°C and 60°C respectively. If the flow rate is 1.1 kg/s, calculate the following:*

(i) *The rate of condensation of steam,*

(ii) *The mean overall heat transfer coefficient based on the inner surface area,*

(iii) *The number of transfer units, and*

(iv) *The effectiveness of the condenser.*

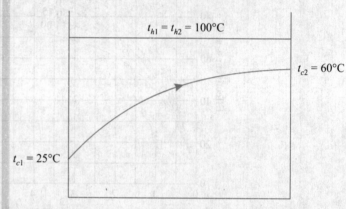

Fig. 10.50.

Solution. Refer to Fig. 10.50. *Given* : $N = 12$; $d_i = 30$ mm $= 0.03$ m; $L = 10$ m; $t_{c1} = 25°C$, $t_{c2} = 60°C$;

$t_{h1} = t_{h2} = 100°C$; $\dot{m}_w = \dot{m}_c = 1.1$ kg/s

(i) **The rate of condensation of steam, $\dot{m}_s$ ($= \dot{m}_h$)**

Heat lost by steam = Heat gained by water

$$\dot{m}_s \times h_{fg} = \dot{m}_c \times c_{pc} (t_{c2} - t_{c1})$$

where h_{fg} (latent heat of steam) at atmospheric pressure = 2257 kJ/kg. Substituting the values, we get,

$$\dot{m}_s \times 2257 = 1.1 \times 4.187 \times (60 - 25)$$

or, $\dot{m}_s = 0.0714$ kg/s $= \textbf{257 kg/h}$ **(Ans.)**

(ii) **The mean overall heat transfer coefficient, U :**

Total heat transfer rate is given by

$$Q = \dot{m}_c \times c_{pc} \times (t_{c2} - t_{c1})$$

$$= 1.1 \times 4.187 \times 10^3 \times (60 - 25) = 161199.5 \text{ J/s}$$

Also, $$Q = U A \theta_m$$

where, $$\theta_m = \frac{\theta_1 - \theta_2}{\ln (\theta_1/\theta_2)} = \frac{(100 - 25) - (100 - 60)}{\ln [(100 - 25)/(100 - 60)]} = \frac{75 - 40}{\ln (75/40)} = 55.68°C$$

and $$A = N \times (\pi \, d \, L) = 12 \times \pi \times 0.03 \times 10 = 11.31 \text{ m}^2$$

Substituting the values in the above equation, we get

$$161199.5 = U \times 11.31 \times 55.68$$

or, $\qquad U = 255.9 \text{ W/m}^2{}^\circ\text{C}$ (Ans.)

(*iii*) **The number of transfer units, *NTU* :**

In a condenser, C_{max} refers to the hot fluid which remains at constant temperature. Therefore, C_{min} refers to water;

$$C_{min} = \dot{m} \times c_{pc} = 1.1 \times (4.187 \times 10^3) = 4605.7 \text{ W/}^\circ\text{C}$$

$$\therefore \qquad NTU = \frac{UA}{C_{min}} = \frac{255.9 \times 11.31}{4605.7} = 0.628 \quad \text{(Ans.)}$$

(*iv*) **The effectiveness of the condenser, ε :**

$$\varepsilon = 1 - \exp(-NTU) \qquad\qquad\qquad\text{...[Eqn. (10.51)]}$$

or, $\qquad \varepsilon = 1 - \varepsilon^{-0.628} = 0.47$ (Ans.)

Example 10.34. *Steam at atmospheric pressure enters the shell of a surface condenser in which the water flows through a bundle of tubes of diameter 25 mm at the rate of 0.05 kg/s. The inlet and outlet temperatures of water are 15°C and 70°C, respectively. The condensation of steam takes place on the outside surface of the tube. If the overall heat transfer coefficient is 230 W/m²°C, calculate the following, using NTU method :*

(*i*) *The effectiveness of the heat exchanger,*

(*ii*) *The length of the tube, and*

(*iii*) *The rate of steam condensation.*

Take the latent heat of vaporisation at 100°C = 2257 kJ/kg

Solution. *Given :* $\qquad d = 25 \text{ mm} = 0.025 \text{ m}; \ \dot{m}_w = \dot{m}_c = 0.05 \text{ kg/s}, t_{c1} = 15°C, t_{c2} = 70°C;$

$$U = 230 \text{ W/m}^2{}^\circ\text{C} \ ; \ t_{h1} = 100°C.$$

(*i*) **The effectiveness of the heat exchanger, ε :**

Throughout the condenser the hot fluid (*i.e.*, steam), remains at constant temperature. Hence C_{max} is infinity and thus C_{min} is obviously for cold fluid (*i.e.*, water). Thus $\dfrac{C_{min}}{C_{max}} \simeq 0.$

When $C_h > C_c$, then effectiveness is given by

$$\varepsilon = \frac{Q}{Q_{max}} = \frac{t_{c2} - t_{c1}}{t_{h1} - t_{c1}} = \frac{70 - 15}{100 - 15} = 0.647 \qquad \text{(Ans.)}$$

(*ii*) **The length of the tube, L :**

$$C_{min} = \dot{m}_c \, c_{pc} = 0.05 \times 4.18 = 0.209 \text{ kJ/K}$$

For $\qquad \dfrac{C_{min}}{C_{max}} \ (= R) \simeq 0$

$$\varepsilon = 1 - \exp(-NTU) \qquad\qquad\qquad \text{...[Eqn (10.51)]}$$

or, $\qquad 0.647 = 1 - e^{-NTU}$

or, $\qquad e^{-NTU} = 1 - 0.647 = 0.353$

or, $\qquad -NTU = \ln(0.353) = -1.04$

$\therefore \qquad NTU = 1.04$

But, $\qquad NTU = \dfrac{UA}{C_{min}} = \dfrac{U \times \pi \, d \, L}{C_{min}}$

or, $\qquad L = \dfrac{NTU \times C_{min}}{U \pi d} = \dfrac{1.04 \times (0.209 \times 1000)}{230 \times \pi \times 0.025} = 12 \text{ m}$ (Ans.)

(*iii*) **The rate of steam condensation, $\dot{m}_h$:**

Using the overall energy balance, we get

$$\dot{m}_h \cdot h_{fg} = \dot{m}_c \, c_{pc} \, (t_{c2} - t_{c1})$$

$$= \dot{m}_h \times 2257 = 0.05 \times 4.18 \, (70 - 15)$$

or, $\dot{m}_h = 0.00509$ kg/s or **18.32 kg/h**   (Ans.)

Example 10.35. *A counter-flow heat exchanger is employed to cool 0.55 kg/s (cp = 2.45 kJ/kg°C) of oil from 115°C to 40°C by the use of water. The intel and outlet temperatures of cooling water are 15°C and 75°C, respectively. The overall heat transfer coefficient is expected to be 1450 W/m²°C. Using NTU method, calculate the following :*

(i)   *The mass flow rate of water;*

(ii) *The effectiveness of the heat exchanger;*

(iii) *The surface area required.*

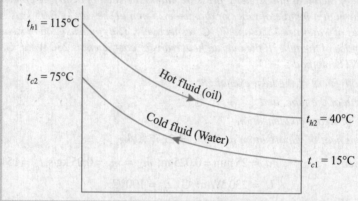

$t_{h1} = 115°C$

$t_{c2} = 75°C$

Hot fluid (oil)

Cold fluid (Water)

$t_{h2} = 40°C$

$t_{c1} = 15°C$

Fig. 10.51.

Solution. *Given :* $\dot{m}_{oil} = \dot{m}_h = 0.55$ kg/s; $c_{ph} = 2.45$ kJ/kg°C; $t_{h1} = 115°C$, $t_{h2} = 40°C$; $t_{c1} = 15°C$, $t_{c2} = 75°C$; $U = 1450$ W/m²°C.

(i)   **The mass flow rate of water,** $\dot{m}_c \, (= \dot{m}_w)$:

The mass flow rate of water can be found by using the overall energy balance

$$\dot{m}_h \, c_{ph} \, (t_{h1} - t_{h2}) = \dot{m}_c \, c_{pc} \, (t_{c2} - t_{c1})$$

$$0.55 \times 2.45 \, (115 - 40) = \dot{m}_c \times 4.18 \, (75 - 15)$$

∴ $\dot{m}_c = 0.4$ **kg/s**   (Ans.)

(ii) **The effectiveness of the heat exchanger,** ε :

The thermal capacity of cold stream (water), $C_c = \dot{m}_c \, c_{pc} = 0.4 \times 4.18 = 1.672$ kW

The thermal capacity of hot stream (oil), $C_h = \dot{m}_h \, c_{ph} = 0.55 \times 2.45 = 1.347$ kW

Since $C_c > C_h$, hence the effectiveness of the heat exchanger is given by

$$\varepsilon = \frac{\text{Actual heat transfer}}{\text{Maximum heat transfer}} = \frac{Q}{Q_{max}} = \frac{t_{h1} - t_{h2}}{t_{h1} - t_{c1}} \qquad \text{...[Eqn. (10.35)]}$$

∴ $\varepsilon = \dfrac{115 - 40}{115 - 15} = \mathbf{0.75}$ (Ans.)

(iii) **The surface area required,** A :

Here, $C_{min} = C_h = 1.347$ kW; $C_{max} = C_c = 1.672$ kW, hence

$$\frac{C_{min}}{C_{max}} = R = \frac{1.347}{1.672} = 0.806$$

For counter-flow heat exchanger,

$$\varepsilon = \frac{1 - \exp\left[- NTU\ (1 - R)\right]}{1 - R \exp\left[- NTU\ (1 - R)\right]} \qquad \text{...[Eqn. (10.50)]}$$

After rearrangement, we get

$$\frac{\varepsilon - 1}{(\varepsilon R - 1)} = \exp\left[- NTU\ (1 - R)\right]$$

or,

$$\frac{0.75 - 1}{(0.75 \times 0.806 - 1)} = \exp\left[- NTU\ (1 - 0.806)\right]$$

or, $\qquad 0.632 = \exp\left[- NTU \times 0.194\right]$

or, $\qquad \ln 0.632 = -0.194\ NTU$

or, $\qquad NTU = 2.365$

[This value of NTU may also be obtained from Fig. 10.45 for $R = \dfrac{C_{min}}{C_{max}} = 0.806$ and $\varepsilon = 0.75$]

Also, $\qquad\qquad NTU = \dfrac{UA}{C_{min}}$

or, $\qquad\qquad 2.365 = \dfrac{1450 \times A}{1.347 \times 1000}$

or, $\qquad\qquad A = \dfrac{2.365 \times 1.347 \times 1000}{1450} = \textbf{2.197 m}^2$ **(Ans.)**

Example 10.36. *16.5 kg/s of the product at 650°C (c_p = 3.55 kJ/kg°C), in a chemical plant, are to be used to heat 20.5 kg/s of the incoming fluid from 100°C (c_p = 4.2 kJ/kg°C). If the overall heat transfer coefficient is 0.95 kW/m²°C and the installed heat transfer surface is 44 m², calculate the fluid outlet temperatures for the counter-flow and parallel flow arrangements.*

Solution. *Given :* $\dot{m}_h$ = 16.5 kg/s, t_{h1} = 650°C; c_{ph} = 3.55 kJ/kg°C; $\dot{m}_c$ = 20.5 kg/s; t_{c1} = 100°C; c_{pc} = 4.2 kJ/kg°C; U = 1.2 kW/m²°C; A = 44 m².

Fluid outlet temperatures :

Case I. *Counter-flow arrangement :*

Thermal capacity of hot fluid, $\qquad C_h = \dot{m}_h \times c_{ph} = 16.5 \times 3.55 = 58.6$ kW/K

Thermal capacity of cold fluid, $\qquad C_c = \dot{m}_c \times c_{pc} = 20.5 \times 4.2 = 86.1$ kW/K

The cold fluid is the maximum fluid, whereas the hot fluid is the minimum fluid. Therefore,

$$\frac{C_{min}}{C_{max}} = R = \frac{58.6}{86.1} = 0.68$$

Number of transfer units, $\qquad NTU = \dfrac{UA}{C_{min}} = \dfrac{0.95 \times 44}{58.6} = 0.71$

The value of ε (effectiveness) for counter-flow arrangement is given by

$$\varepsilon = \frac{1 - \exp\left[- NTU\ (1 - R)\right]}{1 - R \exp\left[- NTU\ (1 - R)\right]} \qquad \text{...[Eqn. (10.50)]}$$

$$= \frac{1 - \exp[-0.71(1 - 0.68)]}{1 - 0.68 \times \exp[-0.71(1 - 0.68)]} = \frac{1 - e^{-0.2272}}{1 - 0.68 \times e^{-0.2272}}$$

$$= \frac{0.2032}{0.4582} = 0.443$$

Further, $\quad\quad\quad\quad \varepsilon = \dfrac{C_h(t_{h1} - t_{h2})}{C_{min}(t_{h1} - t_{c1})}$ ...[Eqn. (10.38)]

Because, the *hot fluid is minimum,* we have

$$\varepsilon = \frac{t_{h1} - t_{h2}}{t_{h1} - t_{c1}} = \frac{650 - t_{h2}}{650 - 100} = 0.443 \quad\quad (\because\ C_h = C_{min})$$

or, $\quad\quad\quad\quad t_{h2} = 650 - 0.443(650 - 100)$

$$= \textbf{406.35°C} \quad\quad \textbf{(Ans.)}$$

Also, $\quad\quad\quad\quad \varepsilon = \dfrac{C_c(t_{c2} - t_{c1})}{C_{min}(t_{h1} - t_{c1})}$ ...[Eqn. (10.38)]

$$0.443 = \frac{86.1(t_{c2} - 100)}{58.6(650 - 100)} = 0.002671(t_{c2} - 100)$$

$\therefore \quad\quad\quad\quad t_{c2} = \textbf{265.8°C} \quad\quad \textbf{(Ans.)}$

Case II. *Parallel flow arrangement :*

The value of ε for parallel flow arrangement is given by

$$\varepsilon = \frac{1 - \exp[-NTU(1 + R)]}{1 + R}$$ ...[Eqn. 10.46 (a)]

$$= \frac{1 - \exp[-0.71(1 + 0.68)]}{(1 + 0.68)} = \frac{1 - e^{-1.1928}}{1.68} = 0.415$$

Also, $\quad\quad\quad\quad \varepsilon = \dfrac{C_c(t_{c2} - t_{c1})}{C_{min}(t_{h1} - t_{c1})}$ ...[Eqn. (10.28)]

or, $\quad\quad\quad\quad 0.415 = \dfrac{86.1(t_{c2} - 100)}{58.6(650 - 100)} = 0.002671(t_{c2} - 100)$

or, $\quad\quad\quad\quad t_{c2} = \textbf{255.4°C} \quad\quad \textbf{(Ans.)}$

Example 10.37. *Oil ($c_p = 3.6$ kJ/kg°C) at 100°C flows at the rate of 30000 kg/h and enters into a parallel flow heat exchanger. Cooling water ($c_p = 4.2$ kJ/kg°C) enters the heat exchanger at 10°C at the rate of 50000 kg/h. The heat transfer area is 10 m^2 and $U = 1000$ W/m²°C. Calculate the following :*

(i) *The outlet temperatures of oil, and water;*

(ii) *The maximum possible outlet temperature of water.* (P.U.)

Solution. *Given :* $\dot{m}_{oil} = \dot{m}_h = \dfrac{30000}{3600} = 8.333$ kg/s; $c_{ph} = 3.6$ kJ/kg°C; $t_{h1} = 100$°C;

$\dot{m}_{water} = \dot{m}_c = \dfrac{50000}{3600} = 13.89$ kg/s, $c_{pc} = 4.2$ kJ/kg°C, $t_{c1} = 10$°C; $U = 1000$ W/m²°C; $A = 10$ m².

(i) **The outlet temperature of oil and water,** t_{h2}, t_{c2} :

$$C_h = \dot{m}_h c_{ph} = 8.333 \times (3.6 \times 1000) = 30 \times 10^3 = C_{min}$$

$$C_c = \dot{m}_c c_{pc} = 13.89 \times (4.2 \times 1000) = 58.34 \times 10^3 = C_{max}$$

$$\frac{C_{min}}{C_{max}} = \frac{30 \times 10^3}{58.34 \times 10^3} = 0.514$$

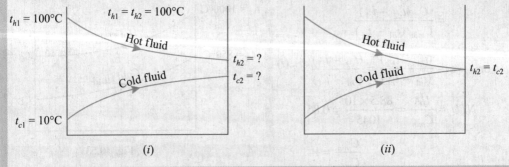

Fig. 10.52.

$$NTU = \frac{UA}{C_{min}} = \frac{1000 \times 10}{30 \times 10^3} = 0.33$$

For the calculated values of $\frac{C_{min}}{C_{max}} = 0.514$ and $NTU = 0.33$, from the Fig. 10.44, we get

$$\varepsilon = 0.32$$

Also,
$$\varepsilon = \frac{C_h \ (t_{h1} - t_{h2})}{C_{min} \ (t_{h1} - t_{c1})} = \frac{C_c \ (t_{c2} - t_{c1})}{C_{min} \ (t_{h1} - t_{c1})} \qquad \text{...[Eqn. (10.38)]}$$

or,
$$0.32 = \frac{30 \times 10^3 \ (100 - t_{h2})}{30 \times 10^3 \ (100 - 10)} = \frac{58.34 \times 10^3 \ (t_{c2} - 10)}{30 \times 10^3 \ (100 - 10)}$$

or,
$$0.32 = \left(\frac{100 - t_{h2}}{100 - 10}\right) = 1.945 \left(\frac{t_{c2} - 10}{100 - 10}\right)$$

∴
$$t_{h2} = 100 - 0.32 \ (100 - 10) = \textbf{71.2°C} \quad \textbf{(Ans.)}$$

and,
$$t_{c2} = \frac{0.32 \ (100 - 10)}{1.945} + 10 = \textbf{24.8°C} \quad \textbf{(Ans.)}$$

(ii) The maximum possible outlet temperature of water, t_{c2} :

When *maximum possible outlet temperature* of water exists then,

$$t_{h2} = t_{c2} \text{ and under this case}$$

$$\dot{m}_h \, c_{ph} \ (t_{h1} - t_{c2}) = \dot{m}_c \, c_{pc} \ (t_{c2} - t_{c1}) \qquad (\because t_{h2} = t_{c2})$$

or,
$$30 \times 10^3 \ (100 - t_{c2}) = 58.34 \times 10^3 \ (t_{c2} - 10)$$

or,
$$100 - t_{c2} = 1.945 \ (t_{c2} - 10) = 1.945 \, t_{c2} - 19.45$$

$$t_{c2} = \textbf{40.5°C} \qquad \textbf{(Ans.)}$$

Example 10.38. *The following data is given for counter-flow heat exchanger :*

$$\dot{m}_h = 1 \ kg/s; \qquad \dot{m}_c = 0.25 \ kg/s$$
$$c_{ph} = 1.045 \ kJ/kg°C; \qquad c_{pc} = 4.18 \ kJ/kg°C$$
$$t_{h1} = 1000°C \ ; \qquad t_{c2} = 850°C; \ U = 88.5 \ W/m^2°C; \ A = 10 \ m^2$$

Calculate t_{h2} and t_{c1}. (P.U.)

Solution.
$$C_h = \dot{m}_h \, c_{ph} = 1 \times (1.045 \times 10^3) = 1045$$

$$C_c = \dot{m}_c \, c_{pc} = 0.25 \times (4.18 \times 10^3) = 1045$$

∴
$$C_{min} = C_{max} = C_h = C_c = 1045$$

The effectiveness ε is given by the relation :

$$\varepsilon = \frac{C_c \cdot (t_{h1} - t_{h2})}{C_{min} \ (t_{h1} - t_{c1})}$$

$$= \frac{C_c\,(t_{c2} - t_{c1})}{C_{min}\,(t_{h1} - t_{c1})}$$

or, $\quad \varepsilon = \dfrac{(t_{h1} - t_{h2})}{(t_{h1} - t_{c1})} = \dfrac{(t_{c2} - t_{c1})}{(t_{h1} - t_{c1})}$ ...(i)

$$NTU = \frac{UA}{C_{min}} = \frac{88.5 \times 10}{1045} = 0.85$$

$$\frac{C_{min}}{C_{max}} = 1$$

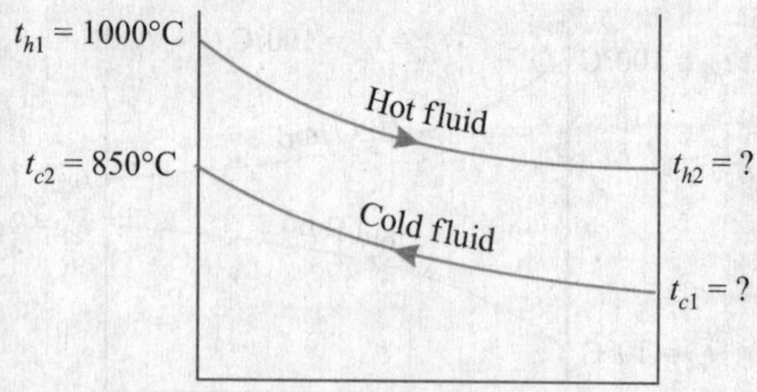

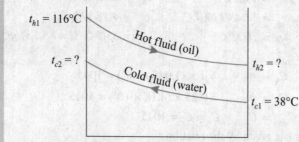

$t_{h1} = 1000°C$

$t_{c2} = 850°C$

Hot fluid

$t_{h2} = ?$

Cold fluid

$t_{c1} = ?$

Fig. 10.53.

For the known values of C_{min}/C_{max} and NTU for the counter-flow, we get from Fig. 10.45,

$$\varepsilon = 0.47$$

Substituting this value in eqn. (i), we get

$$0.47 = \frac{1000 - t_{h2}}{1000 - t_{c1}} = \frac{850 - t_{c1}}{1000 - t_{c1}}$$

or, $\qquad 0.47 = \dfrac{850 - t_{c1}}{1000 - t_{c1}}$

$0.47\,(1000 - t_{c1}) = 850 - t_{c1} \qquad$ or $\qquad 470 - 0.47\,t_{c1} = 850 - t_{c1}$

$$t_{c1} - 0.47\,t_{c1} = 850 - 470$$

$$t_{c1} = \frac{(850 - 470)}{0.53} = \mathbf{717°C} \quad \textbf{(Ans.)}$$

or, $\qquad 0.47 = \dfrac{1000 - t_{h2}}{1000 - 717}$

or, $\qquad t_{h2} = 1000 - 0.47\,(1000 - 717) \approx \mathbf{867°C} \qquad \textbf{(Ans.)}$

Example 10.39. *Water (c_{pc} = 4200 J/kg°C) enters a counter-flow double pipe heat exhanger at 38°C flowing at 0.076 kg/s. It is heated by oil (c_p = 1880 J/kg°C) flowing at the rate of 0.152 kg/s from an inlet temperature of 116°C. For an area of 1m^2 and U = 340 W/m^2°C, determine the total heat transfer rate.*

Solution. Given : $\dot{m}_w = \dot{m}_c = 0.076$ kg/s, $c_{pc} = 4200$ J/kg°C; $t_{c1} = 38°C$; $\dot{m}_{oil} = \dot{m}_h = 0.152$ kg/s, $c_{ph} = 1880$ J/kg°C; $t_{h1} = 116°C$; $U = 340$ W/m^2°C; $A = 1$ m^2.

The total heat transfer rate, Q :

As *outlet temperatures of both fluids are not known, we have to use NTU method for solving the* problem.

$t_{h1} = 116°C$

$t_{c2} = ?$

Hot fluid (oil)

Cold fluid (water)

$t_{h2} = ?$

$t_{c1} = 38°C$

Fig. 10.54. Counter-flow heat exchanger.

The effectiveness ε of heat exchanger is given by

$$\varepsilon = \frac{C_h \ (t_{h1} - t_{h2})}{C_{min} \ (t_{h1} - t_{c1})} = \frac{C_c \ (t_{c2} - t_{c1})}{C_{min} \ (t_{h1} - t_{c1})} \qquad \qquad ...(i)$$

$$C_h = \dot{m}_h \ c_{ph} = 0.152 \times 1880 = 258.8 = C_{min}$$

$$C_c = \dot{m}_c \ c_{pc} = 0.076 \times 4200 = 319.2 = C_{max}$$

$$\frac{C_{min}}{C_{max}} = \frac{285.8}{391.2} = 0.895$$

$$\text{NTU} = \frac{UA}{C_{min}} = \frac{340 \times 1}{285.8} = 1.19$$

For the calculated values of $\dfrac{C_{min}}{C_{max}} = 0.895$ and $NTU = 1.19$, from the Fig. 10.45, we get

$$\varepsilon \approx 0.53$$

Substituting the values in eqn (i), we get

$$0.53 = \frac{285.8 \ (116 - t_{h2})}{285.8 \ (116 - 38)} = \frac{319.2 \ (t_{c2} - 38)}{285.8 \ (116 - 38)}$$

or,

$$0.53 = \frac{(116 - t_{h2})}{(116 - 38)} = 1.117 \left(\frac{t_{c2} - 38}{116 - 38} \right)$$

$$\therefore \qquad t_{h2} = 116 - 0.53 \ (116 - 38) = 74.66°C \approx 75°C$$

and,

$$t_{c2} = \frac{0.53 \ (116 - 38)}{1.117} + 38 = 75°C$$

The total rate of heat transfer is given by

$$Q = U A \ \theta_m$$

where,

$$(\theta_m)_{counter} = \frac{\theta_1 - \theta_2}{\ln \ (\theta_1/\theta_2)} = \frac{(t_{h1} - t_{c2}) - (t_{h2} - t_{c1})}{\ln \ [(t_{h1} - t_{c2})/(t_{h1} - t_{c1})]}$$

$$= \frac{(116 - 75) - (75 - 38)}{\ln \ [(116 - 75)/(75 - 38)]} = \frac{41 - 37}{\ln \ (41/37)} \approx 39°C$$

$$\therefore \qquad Q = 340 \times 1 \times 39 = 13260 \ W = \mathbf{13.26 \ kW} \qquad \textbf{(Ans.)}$$

Example 10.40. *The overall temperature rise of the cold fluid in a cross-flow heat exchanger is 20°C and overall temperature drop of hot-fluid is 30°C. The effectiveness of heat exchanger is 0.6. The heat exchanger area is 1m^2 and overall heat transfer coefficient is 60 W/m^2°C. Find out the rate of heat transfer. Assume both fluids are unmixed.*

Solution. *Given* : $t_{c2} - t_{c1} = 20°C$; $t_{h1} - t_{h2} = 30°C$; $\varepsilon = 0.6$; $A = 1m^2$; $U = 60 \ W/m^2°C$.

Rate of heat transfer, Q :

Heat lost by hot fluid = Heat gained by water

$$\dot{m}_h \ c_{ph} \ (t_{h1} - t_{h2}) = \dot{m}_c \ c_{pc} \ (t_{c2} - t_{c1})$$

$$\therefore \qquad \frac{t_{h1} - t_{h2}}{t_{c2} - t_{c1}} = \frac{\dot{m}_c \ c_{pc}}{\dot{m}_h \ c_{ph}} = \frac{30}{20} = 1.5$$

$$\therefore \qquad \dot{m}_c \ c_{pc} = C_{max} \qquad \text{and} \qquad \dot{m}_h \ c_{ph} = C_{min}$$

$$\frac{C_{min}}{C_{max}} = \frac{1}{1.5} = 0.67$$

Now from the graph, for the given values of

$$\varepsilon = 0.6 \quad \text{and} \quad C_{min}/C_{max} = 0.67, \text{ we get}$$

$$NTU = 1.4 \qquad \text{(From Fig. 10.48)}$$

But,
$$NTU = \frac{UA}{C_{min}}$$

$\therefore$
$$C_{min} = \frac{UA}{NTU} = \frac{60 \times 1}{1.4} = 42.86 = C_h;$$

$$C_{max} = \frac{C_{min}}{0.67} = \frac{42.86}{0.67} = 63.97 = C_c$$

$\therefore$
$$Q = \dot{m}_h \, c_{ph} \, (t_{h1} - t_{h2}) = C_h \, (t_{h1} - t_{h2})$$
$$= 42.86 \times 30 = \textbf{1285.8 W} \textbf{ (Ans.)}$$

Example 10.41. *Define the terms NTU and effectiveness. Derive an expression for effectiveness of a counter-flow heat exchanger in terms of NTU and capacity ratio.* (U.P.S.C., 1996)

Solution. Refer Article 10.7.

Example 10.42. *Two fluids, A and B exchange heat in a counter-current heat exchanger. Fluid A enters at 420°C and has a mass flow rate of 1 kg/s. Fluid B enters at 20°C and has a mass flow rate of 1 kg/s. Effectiveness of heat exchanger is 75%.*

Determine : (i) The heat transfer rate;

(ii) The exit temperature of fluid B.

Specific heat of fluid A is 1 kJ/kg K and that of fluid B is 4 kJ/kg K. (GATE, 1999)

Solution. *Given :* $t_{A1} = t_{h1} = 420°C;$ $\dot{m}_h = 1$ kg/s; $\dot{m}_c = 1$ kg/s;

$$t_{B1} = t_{c1} = 20°C; \varepsilon = 0.75; c_{pA} = c_{ph} = 1 \text{ kJ/kg K};$$
$$c_{pB} = c_{pc} = 4 \text{ kJ/kg K}.$$

(i) **The heat transfer rate, Q :**

Effectiveness,
$$\varepsilon = \frac{C_h \, (t_{h1} - t_{h2})}{C_{min} \, (t_{h1} - t_{c1})} = \frac{t_{h1} - t_{h2}}{t_{h1} - t_{c1}} \qquad (\because C_h = \dot{m}_h \, c_{ph} = 1 \times 1 = 1 = C_{min})$$

or,
$$0.75 = \frac{420 - t_{h2}}{420 - 20}$$

or,
$$t_{h2} = 420 - 0.75 \, (420 - 20) = 120°C$$

Now,
$$Q = \varepsilon \, C_{min} \, (t_{h1} - t_{c1}) \qquad \text{...[Eqn. (10.39)]}$$
$$= 0.75 \times \dot{m}_h \, c_{ph} \times (t_{h1} - t_{c1})$$
$$= 0.75 \times 1 \times 1 \times (420 - 20) = \textbf{300 kJ} \textbf{ (Ans.)}$$

(ii) **The exit temperature of fluid B, t_{c2} :**

$$Q = \dot{m}_c \, c_{pc} \times (t_{c2} - t_{c1})$$

or,
$$300 = 1 \times 4 \, (t_{c2} - 20)$$

$\therefore$
$$t_{c2} = \frac{300}{4} + 20 = \textbf{95°C} \textbf{ (Ans.)}$$

Example 10.43. *Water at the rate of 0.5 kg/s is forced through a smooth 25 mm ID tube of 15 m length. The inlet water temperature is 10°C and the tube wall is at a constant temperature of 40°C. What is the exit water temperature ?*

Average properties of water are :
$$c_p = 4180 \text{ J/kg°C}; \mu = 0.8 \times 10^{-3} \text{ Pa s}; k = 0.57 \text{ W/m°C}. \quad \text{(AMIE Summer, 1998)}$$

Solution. *Given :* $\dot{m}_w = 0.5$ kg/s; $D = 25$ mm $= 0.025$ m; $L = 15$ m

$$t_i = 10°C; t_s = 40°C; c_p = 4180 \text{ J/kg°C}; \mu = 0.8 \times 10^{-3} \text{ Pas};$$
$$k = 0.57 \text{ W/m°C}.$$

Exit water temperature, t_o :

We know that, $\dot{m}_w = \rho V A$

$\therefore$ $V = \dfrac{\dot{m}_w}{\rho A} = \dfrac{0.5}{1000 \times \dfrac{\pi}{4} \times (0.025)^2} = 1.086$ m/s

$\therefore$ Reynolds number, $Re = \dfrac{\rho V D}{\mu} = \dfrac{1000 \times 1.086 \times 0.025}{0.8 \times 10^{-3}} = 3.183 \times 10^4$

i.e., flow is *turbulent* (since $Re > 2300$)

Using the relation,

$$\overline{Nu} = 0.023 \, (Re)^{0.8} \, (Pr)^{1/3} \qquad\qquad ...[\text{Eqn. (7.15)}]$$

$$(\text{for } t_s > t_f)$$

$$Pr = \dfrac{\mu c_p}{k} = \dfrac{0.8 \times 10^{-3} \times 4180}{0.57} = 5.867$$

Substituting the values in the above eqn., we get

$$\overline{Nu} = \dfrac{\overline{h} D}{k} = 0.023 \, (3.183 \times 10^4)^{0.8} \, (5.867)^{1/3}$$

or, $\overline{h} = \dfrac{0.57}{0.025} \times 0.023 \, (3.183 \times 10^4)^{0.8} \, (5.867)^{1/3} = 3785$ W/m^2 °C

Heat transfer area, $A = \pi DL = \pi \times 0.025 \times 15 = 1.1781$ m^2

Since the surface temperature is constant,

$$C_{min} = C_{water} = \dot{m}_w \, c_{pw} = 0.5 \times 4180 = 2090 \text{ W/°C}$$

$$NTU = \dfrac{UA}{C_{min}} = \dfrac{\overline{h} A}{C_{min}} = \dfrac{3785 \times 1.1781}{2090} = 2.133$$

Effectiveness, $\varepsilon = 1 - e^{-NTU} \qquad\qquad ...[\text{Eqn. (10.51)}]$

$$= 1 - (e)^{-2.133} = 0.8815$$

Now, $\varepsilon = \left[\dfrac{t_0 - t_i}{t_s - t_i}\right] = \dfrac{t_o - 10}{40 - 10}$

$\therefore$ $t_o = 0.8815 \, (40 - 10) + 10 = \mathbf{36.44°C}$ **(Ans.)**

Example 10.44. *A counterflow heat exchanger is to heat air entering at 400°C with a flow rate of 6 kg/s by the exhaust gas entering at 800°C with a flow rate of 4 kg/s. The overall heat transfer coefficient is 100 W/m² K and the outlet temperature of the air is 551.5°C. Specific heat at constant pressure for both air and exhaust gas can be taken as 1100 J/kg K. Calculate:*

   (i) The heat transfer area needed;

   (ii) The number of transfer units. (GATE, 1995)

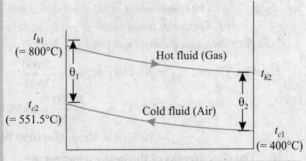

Fig. 10.55.

Solution. *Given* : $\dot{m}_c = 6$ kg/s; $t_{c1} = 400°C$; $t_{c2} = 551.5°C$; $t_{h1} = 800°C$;

$$\dot{m}_h = 4 \text{ kg/s}; U = 100 \text{ W/m}^2 \text{ K}; c_{ph} = c_{pc} = 1100 \text{ J/kg K}$$

Now, $C_c = \dot{m}_c c_{pc} = 6 \times 1100 = 6600$, and

$$C_h = \dot{m}_h c_{ph} = 4 \times 1100 = 4400$$

Hence, $C_h < C_c$

∴ $C_{min} = C_h = 4400$

Now, heat transferred to cold air = Heat transferred from hot gases

∴ $$Q = \dot{m}_c c_p (t_{c2} - t_{c1}) = \dot{m}_h c_{ph} (t_{h1} - t_{h2})$$

$$= 6600 (551.5 - 400) = 4400 (800 - t_{h2})$$

∴ $Q = 999900$ J or $t_{h2} = 800 - \dfrac{999900}{4400} = 572.75°C$

(i) **The heat transfer area needed, A :**

$$Q = U A \theta_m$$

where, $$\theta_m = \frac{(\theta_1 - \theta_2)}{\ln(\theta_1/\theta_2)} = \frac{(t_{h1} - t_{c2}) - (t_{h2} - t_{c1})}{\ln\left[\dfrac{(t_{h1} - t_{c2})}{(t_{h2} - t_{c1})}\right]}$$

$$= \frac{(800 - 551.5) - (572.75 - 400)}{\ln\left[\dfrac{(800 - 551.5)}{(572.75 - 400)}\right]} = \frac{75.75}{0.3636} = 208.33°C$$

Substituting the various values, we get

$$999900 = 100 \times A \times 208.33$$

∴ $A \approx 48$ **m²** **(Ans.)**

(ii) **The number of transfer units, (NTU) :**

$$NTU = \frac{UA}{C_{min}} = \frac{100 \times 48}{4400} = 1.09 \quad \textbf{(Ans.)}$$

Example 10.45. *A chemical having specific heat of 3.3 kJ/kg K flowing at the rate of 20000 kg/h enters a parallel flow heat exchanger at 120°C. The flow rate of cooling water is 50000 kg/h with an inlet temperature of 20°C. The heat transfer area is 10 m² and the overall heat transfer coefficient is 1050 W/m² K.*

Find : (i) *The effectiveness of the heat exchanger.*

(ii) *The outlet temperature of water and chemical.*

Take for water, specific heat = 4.186 kJ/kg K. (U.P.S.C., 1992)

Solution. *Given* : $c_{ph} = 3.3$ kJ/kg K; $\dot{m}_h = \dfrac{20000}{3600} = 5.56$ kg/s;

$$t_{h1} = 120°C; \dot{m}_c = \frac{50000}{3600} = 13.89 \text{ kg/s}; c_{pc} = 4.186 \text{ kJ/kg K};$$

$$t_{c1} = 20°C; A = 10 \text{m}^2; U = 1050 \text{ W/m}^2 \text{ K}.$$

(i) **The effectiveness of the heat exchanger, ε :**

Hot fluid capacity rate, $C_h = \dot{m}_h c_{ph}$

$$= 5.56 \times 3.3 = 18.35$$

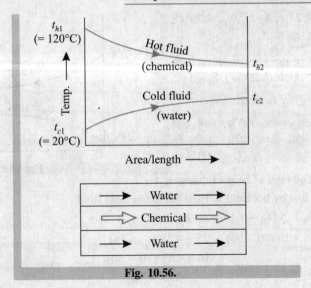

Fig. 10.56.

Cold fluid capacity rate, $\quad C_c = \dot{m}_c \, c_{pc}$

$$= 13.89 \times 4.186 = 58.14$$

We find $\qquad\qquad C_h < C_c$

Heat lost by hot fluid = Heat gained by cold fluid

$\therefore \qquad 5.56 \times 3.3 \times (120 - t_{h2}) = 13.89 \times 4.186 \times (t_{c2} - 20)$

or, $\qquad\qquad (120 - t_{h2}) = 3.17 \, (t_{c2} - 20)$ ...(i)

Now, $\qquad\qquad NTU = \dfrac{UA}{C_{\min}} = \dfrac{1050 \times 10}{18.35 \times 1000} = 0.572$

Effectiveness, $\qquad\qquad \varepsilon = \dfrac{1 - \exp[-\,NTU\,(1+R)]}{1+R}$

where R (capacity ratio) $\qquad = \dfrac{C_{\min}}{C_{\max}} = \dfrac{18.35}{58.14} = 0.316$

$\therefore \qquad\qquad \varepsilon = \dfrac{1 - \exp[-\,0.572\,(1+0.316)]}{(1+0.316)} = \dfrac{1 - 0.471}{1.316} = \mathbf{0.402}$ **(Ans.)**

(ii) The outlet temperatures of water (t_{c2}) and chemical, (t_{h2}) :

We know that, $\qquad\qquad \varepsilon = \dfrac{C_h \, (t_{h1} - t_{h2})}{C_{\min} \, (t_{h1} - t_{c1})}$ ...[Eqn. (10.38)]

or, $\qquad\qquad 0.402 = \dfrac{(120 - t_{h2})}{(120 - 20)}$ $\qquad (\because C_h = C_{\min})$

or, $\qquad\qquad t_{h2} = 120 - 0.402 \,(120 - 20) = \mathbf{79.8°C}$ **(Ans.)**

Substituting the value of $t_{h2} = 79.8°C$ in eqn. (i), we get

$$(120 - 79.8) = 3.17 \, (t_{c2} - 20)$$

$\therefore \qquad\qquad t_{c2} = \dfrac{(120 - 79.8)}{3.17} + 20 = \mathbf{32.7°C}$ **(Ans.)**

Example 10.46. *A parallel flow heat exchange has hot and cold water streams running through it and has the following data :*

$\dot{m}_h = 10$ *kg./min ;* $\dot{m}_c = 25$ *kg/min;*

$c_{ph} = c_{pc} = 4.18 \, kJ/kg \, °C; \, t_{h1} = 70°C;$
$t_{h2} = 50°C, t_{c1} = 25°C$

Individual heat transfer coefficent on both sides = 60 W/m² °C. Calculate the following :

(i)   The area of the heat exchanger;

(ii) The exit temperatures of hot and cold fluids if hot water flow rate is doubled.

(P.U.)

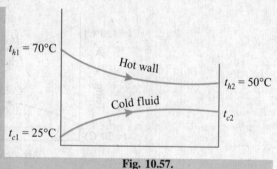

Fig. 10.57.

Solution. (i) **The area of heat exchanger, A :**

Heat lost by hot fluid = Heat gained by cold fluid

∴ $\dot{m}_h \, c_{ph} \, (t_{h1} - t_{h2}) = \dot{m}_c \, c_{pc} \, (t_{c2} - t_{c1})$

$10 \times 4.18 \, (70 - 50) = 25 \times 4.18 \, (t_{c2} - 25)$

∴ $t_{c2} = \dfrac{10 \times 4.18 \, (70 - 50)}{25 \times 4.18} + 25 = 33°C$

Log-mean temperature difference,

$$\theta_m = \frac{\theta_1 - \theta_2}{\ln (\theta_1/\theta_2)} = \frac{(t_{h1} - t_{c1}) - (t_{h2} - t_{c2})}{\ln [(t_{h1} - t_{c1})/(t_{h2} - t_{c2})]}$$

$$= \frac{(70 - 25) - (50 - 33)}{\ln [(70 - 25)/(50 - 33)]} = \frac{45 - 17}{\ln [(45/17)]} = 28.8°C$$

The overall heat transfer coefficient is given by,

$$\frac{1}{U} = \frac{1}{h_i} + \frac{1}{h_o} = \frac{h_o + h_i}{h_o \, h_i}$$

or, $U = \dfrac{h_o \, h_i}{h_o + h_i} = \dfrac{60 \times 60}{(60 + 60)} = 30 \, W/m^2 \, °C$

Also, $Q = \dot{m}_h \, c_{ph} \, (t_{h1} - t_{h2}) = UA\theta_m$

or, $\dfrac{10}{60} \times 4.18 \times (70 - 50) = 30 \times A \times 28.8$

∴ $A = \dfrac{10 \times 4.18 \, (70 - 50)}{60 \times 30 \times 28.8} = 0.0161 \, m^2$ **(Ans.)**

(ii) The exit temperatures of hot and cold fluids, t_{h2}, t_{c2} :

When $\dot{m}_h$ is increased from 10 kg/min to 20 kg/min h_i will become h_i' (considering hot fluid is inside).

$$\frac{h_i'}{h_i} = \left(\frac{20}{10}\right)^{0.8} = 1.74$$

∴ $h_i' = 60 \times 1.74 = 104.4 \, W/m^2 \, °C$

$$C_h = \dot{m}_h \, c_{ph} = \frac{20}{60} \times 4.18 = 1.39 = C_{min}$$

$$C_c = \dot{m}_c \, c_{pc} = \frac{25}{60} \times 4.18 = 1.74 = C_{max}$$

∴ $\dfrac{C_{min}}{C_{max}} = \dfrac{1.39}{1.74} = 0.799$

$$U = \frac{h_o \, h_i'}{h_o + h_i'} = \frac{60 \times 104.4}{60 + 104.4} = 38.1 \text{ W/m}^2 \, ^\circ\text{C}$$

$$NTU = \frac{UA}{C_{min}} = \frac{38.1 \times 0.0161}{1.39} = 0.44$$

For the calculated value of $\dfrac{C_{min}}{C_{max}} = 0.799$ and $NTU = 44$, from the fig. 10.44, we get

$$\varepsilon \simeq 0.31$$

Also,

$$\varepsilon = \frac{C_h \, (t_{h1} - t_{h2})}{C_{min} \, (t_{h1} - t_{c1})} = \frac{C_c \, (t_{c2} - t_{c1})}{C_{min} \, (t_{h1} - t_{c1})}$$

or

$$0.31 = \frac{1.39 \, (70 - t_{h2})}{1.39 \, (70 - 25)} = \frac{1.74 \, (t_{c2} - 25)}{1.39 \, (70 - 25)}$$

or

$$0.31 = \frac{70 - t_{h2}}{(70 - 25)} = 1.25 \left(\frac{t_{c2} - 25}{70 - 25} \right)$$

$$\therefore \qquad t_{h2} = 70 - 0.31 \, (70 - 25) = \textbf{56.05}^\circ\textbf{C (Ans.)}$$

and,

$$t_{c2} = \frac{0.31 \, (70 - 25)}{1.25} + 25 = \textbf{36.16}^\circ\textbf{C} \qquad \textbf{(Ans.)}$$

Example 10.47. *An oil is cooled to 375 K in concurrent heat exchanger by transferring its heat to the cooling water that leaves the cooler at 300 K. However, it is required that oil must be cooled down to 350 K by lengthening the cooler while the oil and water flow rates, their inlet temperatures and other dimensions of the cooler remaining unchanged. The inlet temperatures of the cooling water and oil being 288 K and 425 K respectively.*

If the length of the original cooler was 1 m, calculate the following :

(i) The outlet temperature of cooling water of the new cooler, and

(ii) The length of the new cooler. (M.U.)

Solution. *Given :* $t_{h1} = 425 - 273 = 152^\circ\text{C}$; $t_{h2} = 375 - 273 = 102^\circ\text{C}$; $t_{c1} = 288 - 273 = 15^\circ\text{C}$;

$\qquad\qquad\quad t_{c2} = 300 - 273 = 27^\circ\text{C}$; $L_1 = 1\text{m}$ \qquad ... Case I

$\qquad\qquad\quad t'_{h2} = 350 - 273 = 77^\circ\text{C}$; $t_{c2} = ?$ \qquad ... Case II

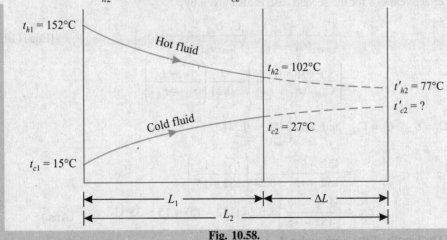

Fig. 10.58.

The outlet temperature of the cooling water of the new cooler, t'_{c2} :

Case I : *(Before increasing the length)*

$$\dot{m}_h \, c_{ph} \, (t_{h1} - t_{h2}) = \dot{m}_c \, c_{pc} \, (t_{c2} - t_{c1})$$

$$\therefore \qquad \frac{\dot{m}_h \, c_{ph}}{\dot{m}_c \, c_{pc}} = \frac{C_h}{C_c} = \frac{(t_{c2} - t_{c1})}{(t_{h1} - t_{h2})} = \frac{(27 - 15)}{(152 - 102)} = \frac{12}{50} = 0.24$$

$$\therefore \qquad C_{min} = \dot{m}_h \, c_{ph} \text{ and } \frac{C_{min}}{C_{max}} = R = 0.24$$

Heat transfer rate is given by

$$Q = \dot{m}_h \, c_{ph} \, (t_{h1} - t_{h2}) = UA_1 \left[\frac{\theta_1 - \theta_2}{\ln (\theta_1/\theta_2)} \right]$$

$$\therefore \qquad t_{h1} - t_{h2} = \frac{UA_1}{C_{min}} \left[\frac{(152 - 15) - (102 - 27)}{\ln \left[(152 - 15)/(102 - 27) \right]} \right]$$

or, $\qquad (152 - 102) = (NTU)_1 \left[\dfrac{137 - 75}{\ln (137/75)} \right] = (NTU)_1 \times 102.9$

or, $\qquad (NTU)_1 = \dfrac{(152 - 102)}{102.9} = 0.486$

$$(NTU)_1 = \frac{UA_1}{C_{min}} = \frac{UCL_1}{C_{min}}, \text{ where } C = \pi d$$

or, $\qquad 0.486 = \dfrac{UCL_1}{C_{min}}$

$$\therefore \qquad \frac{UC}{C_{min}} = \frac{0.486}{L_1} = 0.486 \qquad\qquad\qquad\qquad [\because L_1 = 1\text{m (given)}]$$

Case II : (*After increasing the length*)

The effectiveness of the parallel flow for the second case is given by

$$\varepsilon = \frac{1 - \exp \left[- (NTU)_2 \, (1 + R) \right]}{1 + R} \qquad \left[\text{where } R = \frac{C_{min}}{C_{max}} \right]$$

$$\varepsilon = \frac{1 - \exp \left[- 0.486 \, L_2 \, (1 + 0.24) \right]}{1 + 0.24} = \frac{1 - (e)^{-0.6 \, L_2}}{1.24} \qquad\qquad ...(i)$$

The effectiveness ε for the second case is also given by

$$\varepsilon = \frac{C_h \, (t_{h1} - t_{h2}')}{C_{min} \, (t_{h1} - t_{c1})} = \frac{C_c \, (t_{c2}' - t_{c1})}{C_{min} \, (t_{h1} - t_{c1})} \qquad\qquad ...[\text{Eqn. (10.38)}]$$

$$= \left(\frac{C_h \, (t_{h1} - t_{h2}')}{C_{min} \, (t_{h1} - t_{c1})} \right) = \frac{1}{0.24} \left(\frac{t_{c2}' - t_{c1}}{t_{h1} - t_{c1}} \right)$$

$$[\because C_h = C_{min}, \; C_c = C_{max} \text{ and } R = \frac{C_{min}}{C_{max}} = 0.24]$$

or, $\qquad \varepsilon = \dfrac{152 - 77}{152 - 15} = \dfrac{1}{0.24} \left(\dfrac{t_{c2}' - 15}{152 - 15} \right) \qquad\qquad ...(ii)$

or, $\qquad t_{c2}' = \left(\dfrac{152 - 77}{152 - 15} \right) \times 0.24 \, (152 - 15) + 15 = 33°C \qquad$ **(Ans.)**

(ii) The length of the new cooler, L_2 :

Equating eqns. (*i*) and (*ii*), we get.

$$\frac{1 - (e)^{-0.6 \, L_2}}{1.24} = \frac{152 - 77}{152 - 15}$$

or, $(e)^{-0.6 L_2} = 1 - 1.24\left(\dfrac{152 - 77}{152 - 15}\right) = 0.321$

or, $(e)^{0.6 L_2} = \dfrac{1}{0.321} = 3.11$

or, $0.6 L_2 = ln\,(3.11) = 1.134$

or, $L_2 = \dfrac{1.134}{0.6} = \mathbf{1.89 \ m}$ **(Ans.)**

This indicates *89% increase in length of the cooler.*

Example 10.48. *A simple counter-flow heat exchanger operates under the following conditions:*

    Fluid-A, inlet and outlet temperatures 80°C and 40°C;

    Fluid-B, inlet and outlet temperatures 20°C and 40°C.

The exchanger is cleaned, causing an increase in the overall heat transfer coefficient by 10% and inlet temperature of fluid B is changed to 30°C. What will be new outlet temperatures of fluid A and of fluid B. Assume heat transfer coefficients and capacity rates are unalered by temperature changes.

Solution. Given : $t_{h1} = 80°C,\ t_{h2} = 40°C,\ t_{c1} = 20°C,\ t_{c2} = 40°C$ ... Case I

                    $t_{h1} = 80°C,\ t_{h2} = ?,\ t_{c1} = 30°C,\ t_{c2} = ?$ ... Case II

                    $U_2 = 1.1\,U_1$

As outlet temperatures of both fluids are to be calculated, so we have to use *NTU* method to find t_{h2} and t_{c2} for the new inlet condition of the cold fluid after cleaning the exchanger.

Further the *area of heat exchanger and mass flow rates in both cases remain same.*

Case I : $\dot{m}_h\,c_{ph}\,(t_{h1} - t_{h2}) = \dot{m}_c\,c_{pc}\,(t_{c2} - t_{c1})$

$\therefore$ $\dfrac{\dot{m}_h\,c_{ph}}{\dot{m}_c\,c_{pc}} = \dfrac{(t_{c2} - t_{c1})}{(t_{h1} - t_{h2})} = \dfrac{40 - 20}{80 - 40} = 0.5 = R$ (constant)

where, $R = \text{capacity ratio} = \dfrac{C_{min}}{C_{max}}$

It is obvious that $\dot{m}_h\,c_{ph} = C_{min}$

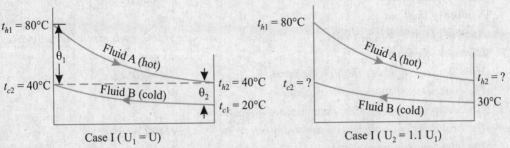

Case I ($U_1 = U$)   Case I ($U_2 = 1.1\,U_1$)

Fig. 10.59.

We can also write $Q_1 = \dot{m}_h\,c_{ph}\,(t_{h1} - t_{h2}) = U_1 A\,\dfrac{\theta_1 - \theta_2}{ln\,(\theta_1/\theta_2)}$

$\therefore$ $t_{h1} - t_{h2} = \dfrac{U_1 A}{\dot{m}_h\,c_{ph}}\left[\dfrac{(80 - 40) - (40 - 20)}{ln\,[(80 - 40)/(40 - 20)]}\right]$

                          $= (NTU)_1 \times 28.85$

$\therefore$ $(80 - 40) = (NTU)_1 \times 28.85$

or, $\qquad (NTU)_1 = 1.386$

Case II : $\qquad (NTU)_2 = \dfrac{U_2\,A}{C_{min}} = \dfrac{1.1\,U_1\,A}{C_{min}} = 1.1\,(NTU)_1 = 1.1 \times 1.386 = 1.52$

as $U_2 = 1.1\,U_1$ and A and C_{min} both the variables remain same in both cases.

The effectiveness of the counter-flow heat exchanger for the case II is given by

$$\varepsilon = \frac{1 - \exp\,[-\,(NTU)_2\,(1 - R)]}{1 - R\,\exp\,[-\,(NTU)_2\,(1 - R)]} \text{ where } R = 0.5 \text{ (calculated earlier)}$$

$$= \frac{1 - \exp\,[(-\,1.52)\,(1 - 0.5)]}{1 - 0.5\,\exp\,[(-\,1.52)\,(1 - 0.5)]} = \frac{1 - e^{-0.76}}{1 - 0.5 \times e^{-0.76}} = 0.695$$

The effectiveness ε is also given by

$$\varepsilon = \frac{C_h\,(t_{h1} - t_{h2})}{C_{min}\,(t_{h1} - t_{c1})} = \frac{C_c\,(t_{c2} - t_{c1})}{C_{min}\,(t_{h1} - t_{c1})} \qquad\qquad \text{...[Eqn. (10.38)]}$$

$\therefore \qquad\qquad \varepsilon = \dfrac{C_h\,(t_{h1} - t_{h2})}{C_{min}\,(t_{h1} - t_{c1})} = \dfrac{C_{min}\,(t_{h1} - t_{h2})}{C_{min}\,(t_{h1} - t_{c1})} = \dfrac{t_{h1} - t_{h2}}{t_{h1} - t_{c1}} \qquad (\because C_h = C_{min})$

or, $\qquad\qquad 0.696 = \dfrac{80 - t_{h2}}{80 - 30}$

or, $\qquad\qquad t_{h2} = 80 - 0.696\,(80 - 30) = \mathbf{45.2°C} \qquad \textbf{(Ans.)}$

Again, $\qquad\qquad \varepsilon = \dfrac{C_c\,(t_{c2} - t_{c1})}{C_{min}\,(t_{h1} - t_{c1})} = \dfrac{C_{max}}{C_{min}}\left[\dfrac{t_{c2} - t_{c1}}{t_{h1} - t_{c1}}\right] = 2\left[\dfrac{t_{c2} - t_{c1}}{t_{h1} - t_{c1}}\right]$

or, $\qquad\qquad 0.696 = 2\left[\dfrac{t_{c2} - 30}{80 - 30}\right] \qquad\qquad \left(\because \dfrac{C_{min}}{C_{max}} = R = 0.5\right)$

or, $\qquad\qquad t_{c2} = 30 + \dfrac{0.696}{2}\,(80 - 30)$

$$= \mathbf{47.4°C} \qquad \textbf{(Ans.)}$$

Example 10.49. *In a large steam power plant, a shell and tube type steam condenser is employed which has the following data :*

Heat exchange rate	*...2100 MW*
Number of shell passes	*...one*
Number of tubes (thin walled)	*...31500, each executing two passes*
Diameter of each tube	*...25 mm*
Mass flow rate of water through the tubes	*...3.4 × 10⁴ kg/s*
The condensation temperature of steam	*...50°C.*

(The steam condenses on the outer surface of the tubes)

The heat transfer coefficient on the steam side	*...11400 W/m²°C*
The inlet temperature of water	*...20°C*

Using LMTD correction factor method and NTU method, calculate :

(i) The outlet temperature of cooling water, and

(ii) The length of tube per pass.

Take the following properties of water (at $t_{bulk} \approx 27°C$):

$c_p = 4.18\ kJ/kg°C,\ \mu = 855 \times 10^{-6}\ Ns/m^2,\ k = 0.613\ W/m°C\ and\ Pr = 5.83$

The thermal resistance of tube material and fouling effects may be neglected.

Solution. *Given* : $Q = 2300 \times 10^6$ W; $N_p = 31500$; $d = 25$ mm $= 0.025$ m; $\dot{m}_w = \dot{m}_c = 3.4 \times 10^4$ kg/s; $t_{h1} = t_{h2} = 50°C$; $t_{c1} = 20°C$; $h_o = 11400$ W/m²°C.

(*i*) **The water outlet temperature, t_{c2} :**

In order to obtain water outlet temperature, using overall energy balance, we get

$$Q = \dot{m}_c \, c_{pc} \, (t_{c2} - t_{c1})$$

$2100 \times 10^6 = 3.4 \times 10^4 \times (4.18 \times 1000)$ $(t_{c2} - 20)$

∴ $\quad t_{c2} = \textbf{34.77°C}$ **(Ans.)**

(*ii*) **The length of the tube per pass, L :**

(1) *LMTD correction factor method* :

The total rate of heat transfer is given by,

$$Q = F U A \, \theta_m \qquad \text{...(}i\text{)}$$

where, $\quad F =$ Correction factor,

$\quad U =$ Overall heat transfer co-efficient,

$\quad A = 2N_p \pi d L$, where N_p is the number of tubes per pass,

and,

$\quad \theta_m =$ Log-mean temperature difference.

To find F we have to find P(temperature ratio) and R (capacity ratio).

$$P = \frac{t_{c2} - t_{c1}}{t_{h1} - t_{c1}} = \frac{34.77 - 20}{50 - 20} = 0.492$$

$$R = \frac{t_{h1} - t_{h2}}{t_{c2} - t_{c1}} = \frac{50 - 50}{37.44 - 20} = 0$$

With the values of $P = 0.492$ and $R = 0$, we get $F = 1$

To find the value of U, h_i has to be calculated first.

Here, mass flow rate through each tube $= \dot{m} = \dfrac{3.4 \times 10^4}{31500} = 1.079$ kg/s

∴ Reynolds number, $Re = \dfrac{\rho D V}{\mu} = \dfrac{4\dot{m}}{\pi d \mu} = \dfrac{4 \times 1.079}{\pi \times 0.025 \times 855 \times 10^{-6}} = 6.43 \times 10^4$

Since $Re > 2300$, hence the flow is *turbulent*.

∴ $\quad Nu = \dfrac{hd}{k} = 0.023 \, (R_e)^{0.8} \, (Pr)^{0.4} = 0.023 \, (6.43 \times 10^4)^{0.8} \, (5.83)^{0.4} = 327$

or, $\quad \bar{h} = \dfrac{k}{d} \times 327 = \dfrac{0.613}{0.025} \times 327 = 8018$ W/m²°C

Now, $\quad \dfrac{1}{U} = \dfrac{1}{h_o} + \dfrac{1}{h_i}$

...neglecting thermal resistance of tube material and fouling effects.

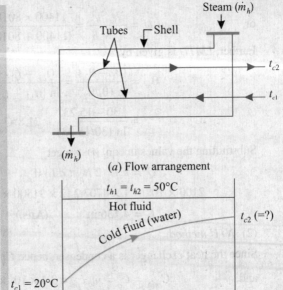

Steam ($\dot{m}_h$)

Tubes — Shell

t_{c2}

t_{c1}

($\dot{m}_h$)

(*a*) Flow arrangement

$t_{h1} = t_{h2} = 50°C$

Hot fluid

Cold fluid (water)

t_{c2} (=?)

$t_{c1} = 20°C$

(*b*) Temperature distribution

Fig. 10.60. Shell and tube type condenser.

or,
$$U = \frac{h_o\, h_i}{h_o + h_i} = \frac{11400 \times 8018}{(11400 + 8018)} = 4707.2 \text{ W/m}^2\,^\circ\text{C}$$

Further, *LMTD* is given by,

$$\theta_m = \frac{(\theta_1 - \theta_2)}{\ln(\theta_1/\theta_2)} = \frac{(t_{h1} - t_{c1}) - (t_{h2} - t_{c2})}{\ln[(t_{h1} - t_{c1})/(t_{h2} - t_{c2})]} = \frac{(50 - 20) - (50 - 34.77)}{\ln[(50 - 20)/(50 - 34.77]}$$

$$= \frac{30 - 15.23}{\ln(30/15.23)} \approx 21.8^\circ\text{C}$$

Substituting the values in eqn. (*i*), we get

$$Q = F\,U\,(2\,N_p\,\pi\,d\,L)\,\theta_m$$

$$2100 \times 10^6 = 1 \times 4707.2\,[2 \times 31500 \times \pi \times 0.025 \times L] \times 21.8$$

$$\therefore \qquad \boldsymbol{L = 4.136 \text{ m}} \qquad \textbf{(Ans.)}$$

(2) *NTU method* :

Since the heat exchanger is a condenser, hence $C_h = C_{max} = \infty$

and, $\qquad C_{min} = C_c = \dot{m}_c\, c_{pc} = 3.4 \times 10^4 \times (4.18 \times 1000) = 14212 \times 10^4$

Since, $\qquad C_h > C_c$, hence

$$\varepsilon = \frac{t_{c2} - t_{c1}}{t_{h1} - t_{c1}} = \frac{34.77 - 20}{50 - 20} = 0.492$$

Here, $\qquad \dfrac{C_{min}}{C_{max}} = 0$

$\therefore \qquad \varepsilon = 1 - exp\,(-NTU)$ \hfill ...[Eqn. (10.51)]

or, $\qquad 0.492 = 1 - e^{-NTU}$

or, $\qquad \varepsilon^{-NTU} = 1 - 0.492 = 0.508$

or, $\qquad -NTU = \ln\,(0.508) = -0.677$

or, $\qquad NTU = 0.677$

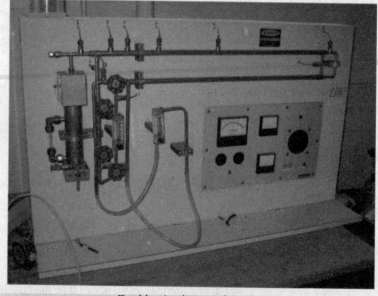

Double pipe heat exchanger.

But,
$$NTU = \frac{U\,A}{C_{min}} = \frac{U\,(2N_p\,\pi d\,L)}{C_{min}}$$

or,
$$0.677 = \frac{4707.2 \times (2 \times 31500 \times \pi \times 0.025 \times L)}{14212 \times 10^4}$$

∴
$$L = \frac{0.677 \times 14212 \times 10^4}{4707.2 \times (2 \times 31500 \times \pi \times 0.025)} = \textbf{4.131 m} \qquad \textbf{(Ans.)}$$

Example 10.50. *In a double pipe heat exchanger* $\dot{m}_h\,c_{ph} = 0.5\,\dot{m}_c\,c_{pc}$. *The inlet temperatures of hot and cold fluids are* t_{h1} *and* t_{c1}. *Deduce an expression in terms of* t_{h1}, t_{c1} *and* t_{h2} *for the ratio of the area of the counter-flow heat exchanger to that of parallel flow heat exchanger which will give the same hot fluid outlet temperature* t_{h2}. *Find this ratio if* $t_{h1} = 150°C$, $t_{c1} = 30°C$ *and* $t_{h2} = 90°C$.

(U.P.S.C., 1994)

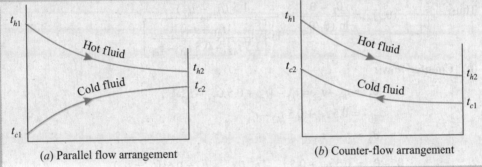

(a) Parallel flow arrangement   (b) Counter-flow arrangement

Fig. 10.61.

Solution. *Given :* $\dot{m}_h\,c_{ph}\,(C_h) = 0.5\,\dot{m}_c\,c_{pc}\,(C_c);\ (t_{h2})_{parallel} = (t_{h2})_{counter}$

The effectiveness of the heat exchanger ε is given by

∴
$$\varepsilon = \frac{C_h\,(t_{h1} - t_{h2})}{C_{min}\,(t_{h1} - t_{c1})} = \frac{C_c\,(t_{c2} - t_{c1})}{C_{min}\,(t_{h1} - t_{c1})}$$

In this case
$$C_{min} = C_h \text{ and } C_h = 0.5\,C_c \text{ and } C_c = C_{max} = 2C_h$$

∴
$$\varepsilon = \frac{C_h\,(t_{h1} - t_{h2})}{C_{min}\,(t_{h1} - t_{c1})} = \frac{2\,C_h}{C_h}\left(\frac{t_{c2} - t_{c1}}{t_{h1} - t_{c1}}\right)$$

or,
$$\varepsilon = \left(\frac{t_{h1} - t_{h2}}{t_{h1} - t_{c1}}\right) = 2\left(\frac{t_{c2} - t_{c1}}{t_{h1} - t_{c1}}\right) \qquad \qquad …(1)$$

This *equation is true for counter-flow as well as parallel flow.*

Let,
A_p = Area of parallel flow heat exchanger, and

A_c = Area of counter-flow heat exchanger.

As $(t_{h2})_p = (t_{h2})_c$ therefore, the *heat lost by hot fluid in both the cases is same.*

∴
$$Q = UA_p\,(\theta_m)_p = UA_c\,(\theta_m)_c, \text{ since } U \text{ is not dependent on the direction of flow.}$$

∴
$$\frac{A_c}{A_p} = \frac{(\theta_m)_p}{(\theta_m)_c} \qquad \qquad …(2)$$

From eqn. (1), we get t_{c2} in terms of t_{h1}, t_{h2} and t_{c1} as

$$t_{c2} = t_{c1} + 0.5\,(t_{h1} - t_{h2})$$

(a) Parallel flow :

$$\theta_1 = t_{h1} - t_{c1}$$

$$\theta_2 = t_{h2} - t_{c2} = t_{h2} - [t_{c1} + 0.5\,(t_{h1} - t_{h2})]$$

$$= t_{h2} - t_{c1} - 0.5\,t_{h1} + 0.5\,t_{h2}$$

$$= 1.5\,t_{h2} - 0.5\,t_{h1} - t_{c1}$$

$$\therefore \qquad \theta_1 - \theta_2 = t_{h1} - t_{c1} - 1.5\,t_{h2} + 0.5\,t_{h1} + t_{c1}$$

$$= 1.5\,(t_{h1} - t_{h2})$$

Thus,
$$(\theta_m)_p = \frac{\theta_1 - \theta_2}{\ln(\theta_1/\theta_2)} = \frac{1.5\,(t_{h1} - t_{h2})}{\ln\left[\dfrac{(t_{h1} - t_{c1})}{1.5\,t_{h2} - 0.5\,t_{h1} - t_{c1}}\right]} \qquad \ldots(i)$$

(b) Counter-flow :

$$\theta_1 = t_{h1} - t_{c2} = t_{h1} - [t_{c1} + 0.5\,(t_{h1} - t_{h2})]$$

$$= 0.5\,t_{h1} + 0.5\,t_{h2} - t_{c1}$$

$$\theta_2 = t_{h2} - t_{c1}$$

$$\therefore \qquad \theta_1 - \theta_2 = 0.5\,t_{h1} + 0.5\,t_{h2} - t_{c1} - t_{h2} + t_{c1} = 0.5\,(t_{h_1} - t_{h_2})$$

Thus,
$$(\theta_m)_c = \frac{\theta_1 - \theta_2}{\ln(\theta_1/\theta_2)} = \frac{0.5\,(t_{h1} - t_{h2})}{\ln\left[\dfrac{0.5\,(t_{h1} + t_{h2}) - t_{c1}}{(t_{h2} - t_{c1})}\right]} \qquad \ldots(ii)$$

Substituting the values of (i) and (ii) in eqn. (2), we get

$$\frac{A_c}{A_p} = \frac{1.5\,(t_{h1} - t_{h2})}{\ln\left[\dfrac{(t_{h1} - t_{c1})}{1.5\,t_{h2} - 0.5\,t_{h1} - t_{c1}}\right]} \times \frac{\ln\left[\dfrac{0.5\,(t_{h1} + t_{h2}) - t_{c1}}{(t_{h2} - t_{c1})}\right]}{0.5\,(t_{h1} - t_{h2})}$$

$$= 3\left[\frac{\ln\left\{\dfrac{0.5\,(t_{h1} + t_{h2}) - t_{c1}}{(t_{h2} - t_{c1})}\right\}}{\ln\left\{\dfrac{(t_{h1} - t_{c1})}{1.5\,t_{h2} - 0.5\,t_{h1} - t_{c1}}\right\}}\right]$$

The given data are : $t_{h1} = 150°C$, $t_{c1} = 30°C$ and $t_{h2} = 90°C$

$$\therefore \qquad \frac{A_c}{A_p} = 3\left[\frac{\ln\left\{\dfrac{0.5\,(150 + 90) - 30}{(90 - 30)}\right\}}{\ln\left\{\dfrac{(150 - 30)}{1.5 \times 90 - 0.5 \times 150 - 30}\right\}}\right]$$

$$= 3\left[\frac{\ln(1.5)}{\ln(4)}\right] = \mathbf{0.877} \qquad \textbf{(Ans.)}$$

Example 10.51. *8000 kg/h of air at 100°C is cooled by passing it through a single-pass cross-flow heat exchanger. To what temperature is the air cooled if water entering at 15°C flows through the tubes unmixed at the rate of 7500 kg/h?*

Take : $U = 500 \ kJ/h\text{-}m^2\text{°}C$ and $A = 20 \ m^2$

c_p (air) $= 1 \ kJ/kg\text{°}C$ and c_p (water)

$= 4.2 \ kJ/kg\text{°}C$

Treat both fluids are unmixed.

Solution. *Given* : $\dot{m}_h = \dfrac{8000}{3600} = 2.22 \ kg/s; \ c_{ph} = 1 \ kJ/kg \ \text{°}C; \ t_{h1} = 100\text{°}C;$

$$\dot{m}_c = \dfrac{7500}{3600} = 2.08 \ kg/s; \ c_{pc} = 4.2 \ kJ/kg\text{°}C$$

$$U = \dfrac{500 \times 1000}{3600} = 138.9 \ W/m^2\text{°}C; \ A = 20 \ m^2.$$

$$C_h = \dot{m}_h \ c_{ph} = 2.22 \times (1 \times 1000) = 2220 = C_{min}$$

$$C_c = \dot{m}_c \ c_{pc} = 2.08 \times (4.2 \times 1000) = 8736 = C_{max}$$

∴ $\dfrac{C_{min}}{C_{max}} = \dfrac{2220}{8736} = 0.254$

$$NTU = \dfrac{UA}{C_{min}} = \dfrac{138.9 \times 20}{2220} = 1.25$$

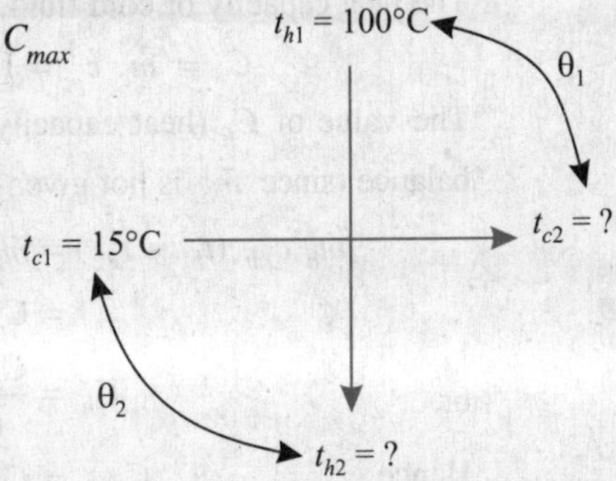

For the calculated values of $\dfrac{C_{min}}{C_{max}} = 0.254$

and $NTU = 1.25$, from the Fig. 10.48, we get

$$\varepsilon \simeq 0.63$$

The effectiveness ε is given by,

$$\varepsilon = \dfrac{C_h \ (t_{h1} - t_{h2})}{C_{min} \ (t_{h1} - t_{c1})} = \dfrac{C_c \ (t_{c2} - t_{c1})}{C_{min} \ (t_{h1} - t_{c1})}$$

or, $0.63 = \dfrac{2220 \ (100 - t_{h2})}{2220 \ (100 - 15)} = \dfrac{8736 \ (t_{c2} - 15)}{2220 \ (100 - 15)}$

or, $0.63 = \dfrac{100 - t_{h2}}{100 - 15} = 3.935 \left(\dfrac{t_{c2} - 15}{100 - 15} \right)$

∴ $t_{h2} = 100 - 0.63 \ (100 - 15) = 46.45\text{°}C$

and, $t_{c2} = \dfrac{0.63 \ (100 - 15)}{3.935} + 15 = 28.6\text{°}C$

The *air is cooled to a minimum temperature of* **46.45°C.** **(Ans.)**

Fig. 10.62.

Example 10.52. *It is required to design a finned tube, cross-flow heat exchanger to heat pressurized water by means of hot exhaust gases, which enter the exchanger at 310°C and leave it at 110°C, respectively. The water flowing at the rate of 1.4 kg/s enters the exchanger at 30°C and leaves at 130°C. The hot exhaust gases heat transfer coefficient based on the gas side is 105 W/m²°C. Using NTU method, calculate the following :*

(i) *The effectiveness, and*   (ii) *The gas side surface area.*

Take the following properties:

Exhaust gas : $c_p = 1 \ kJ/kg\text{°}C;$ *water (at* $t_{bulk} = 80\text{°}C$*) :* $c_p = 4.2 \ kJ/kg\text{°}C$

Solution. *Given :* $\dot{m}_w = \dot{m}_c = 1.4$ kg/s; $t_{c1} = 30°C$; $t_{c2} = 130°C$; $c_{pc} = 4.2$ kJ/kg°C;
$t_{h1} = 310°C$; $t_{h2} = 110°C$; $c_{ph} = 1$ kJ/kg°C; $U_h = 105$ W/m² °C.

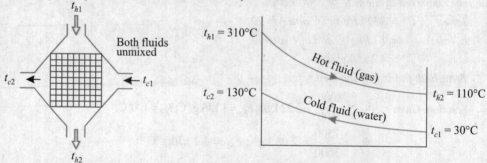

Fig. 10.63. Fixed tube, cross-flow heat exchanger.

(i) **The effectiveness, ε :**

The heat capacity of cold fluid,

$$C_c = \dot{m}_c \, c_{pc} = 1.4 \times 4.2 = 5.88 \text{ kW/°C}$$

The value of C_h (heat capacity of hot fluid) may be obtained by writing overall energy balance (since $\dot{m}_h$ is not given). Hence

$$\dot{m}_h \, c_{ph} \, (t_{h1} - t_{h2}) = \dot{m}_c \, c_{pc} \, (t_{c2} - t_{c1})$$

$$= C_c \, (t_{c2} - t_{c1})$$

or, $$C_h = \frac{C_c \, (t_{c2} - t_{c1})}{(t_{h1} - t_{h2})} = \frac{5.88 \, (130 - 30)}{(310 - 110)} = 2.94 \text{ kW/°C}$$

Hence, $$C_{max} = C_c = 5.88 \text{ kW/°C and } C_{min} = C_h = 2.94 \text{ kW/°C}$$

When $C_c > C_h$, then effectiveness ε is given by

$$\varepsilon = \frac{t_{h1} - t_{h2}}{t_{h1} - t_{c1}} = \frac{310 - 110}{310 - 30} = \mathbf{0.714} \quad \textbf{(Ans.)}$$

(ii) **The gas side surface area, A_h :**

$$\frac{C_{min}}{C_{max}} = \frac{2.94}{5.88} = 0.5$$

Corresponding to $\dfrac{C_{min}}{C_{max}} = 0.5$ and $\varepsilon = 0.714$ from Fig. 10.48, we get

$$NTU \simeq 1.8$$

But, $$NTU = \frac{U_h \, A_h}{C_{min}}$$

$$1.8 = \frac{105 \times A_h}{2.94 \times 1000}$$

$\therefore$ $$A_h = \frac{1.8 \times 2.94 \times 1000}{105} = \mathbf{50.4 \text{ m}^2} \quad \textbf{(Ans.)}$$

Example 10.53. *In a gas turbine power plant heat is being transferred in a heat exchanger from the hot gases leaving the turbine at 450°C to the air leaving the compressor at 170°C. The air flow rate is 5000 kg/h and fuel-air ratio is 0.015 kg/kg. The overall heat transfer coefficient for the heat exchanger is 52.33 W/m² °C. The surface area is 50 m² and arrangement is cross-flow (both fluids unmixed). Calculate the following :*

(i) The exit tempeatures on the air and gas sides, and

(ii) The rate of heat transfer in the exchanger.

Take $c_{ph} = c_{pc} = 1.05 \ kJ/kg \ °C$

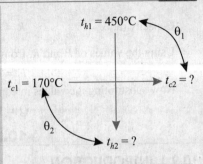

Fig. 10.64.

Solution. *Given :* $t_{h1} = 450°C$; $t_{c1} = 170°C$; $A = 50 \ m^2$.

(i) **The exit temperatures on the air and gas sides** t_{c2}, t_{h2} :

$$\dot{m}_c = \frac{5000}{3600} = 1.388$$

$$C_c = \dot{m}_c \ c_{pc}$$

$$= 1.388 \times (1.05 \times 10^3) = 1457.4$$

$$\dot{m}_h = \frac{5000 \times 1.015}{3600} = 1.41 \ kg/s \ as \ 1.015 \ kg \ of \ gases \ are \ formed \ per \ kg \ of \ air$$

$$C_h = \dot{m}_h \ c_{ph} = 1.41 \times (1.05 \times 10^3) = 1480.5$$

$$\therefore \qquad \frac{C_{min}}{C_{max}} = \frac{1457.4}{1480.5} = 0.984$$

$$NTU = \frac{UA}{C_{min}} = \frac{52.33 \times 50}{1457.4} = 1.795$$

For the calculated values of $\dfrac{C_{min}}{C_{max}} = 0.984$ and $NTU = 1.795$, From the Fig. 10.48, we get

$$\varepsilon \approx 0.52$$

The effectiveness ε is given by

$$\varepsilon = \frac{C_h \ (t_{h1} - t_{h2})}{C_{min} \ (t_{h1} - t_{c1})} = \frac{C_c \ (t_{c2} - t_{c1})}{C_{min} \ (t_{h1} - t_{c1})}$$

$$\therefore \qquad 0.52 = \frac{1480.5 \ (450 - t_{h2})}{1457.4 \ (450 - 170)}$$

or,

$$t_{h2} = 450 - \frac{0.52 \times 1457.4 \ (450 - 170)}{1480.5} = \mathbf{306.6°C \ (Ans.)}$$

and,

$$0.52 = \frac{t_{c2} - t_{c1}}{t_{h1} - t_{c1}} = \frac{t_{c2} - 170}{450 - 170} \qquad (\because \ C_c = C_{min})$$

$$\therefore \qquad t_{c2} = 0.52 \ (450 - 170) + 170 = \mathbf{315.6°C \ (Ans.)}$$

(ii) **The rate of heat transfer in exchanger, Q :**

$$Q = UA \ (\theta_m)_{counter} = FUA \ (\theta_m)_{counter} \qquad \qquad ...(i)$$

where, F = correction factor

$$(\theta_m)_{counter} = \frac{\theta_1 - \theta_2}{\ln (\theta_1/\theta_2)} = \frac{(t_{h1} - t_{c2}) - (t_{h2} - t_{c1})}{\ln [(t_{h1} - t_{c2})/(t_{h2} - t_{c1})]}$$

$$= \frac{(450 - 315.6) - (306.6 - 170)}{\ln [(450 - 315.6)/(306.6 - 170)]} = \frac{134.4 - 136.6}{\ln (134.4/136.6)}$$

$$= \frac{2.2}{\ln (136.6/134.4)} = 135.5°C$$

Temperature ratio,

$$P = \frac{t_{c2} - t_{c1}}{t_{h1} - t_{c1}} = \frac{315.6 - 170}{450 - 170} = 0.52$$

Capacity ratio,
$$R = \frac{t_{h1} - t_{h2}}{t_{c2} - t_{c1}} = \frac{450 - 306.6}{315.6 - 170} = 0.985$$

Using the values of P and R, from Fig. 10.48, we get
$$F = 0.76$$

Now substituting the values in eqn. (i), we get
$$Q = 0.76 \times 52.33 \times 50 \times 135.5 = 269447 \text{ W or } \mathbf{269.45\,kW} \quad \textbf{(Ans.)}$$

10.9. EVAPORATORS

10.9.1. INTRODUCTION

Evaporation is *a process in which the solvent is removed from a solution of a non-volatile solute and a volatile solvent.*

Examples. • Brine when heated with water (solvent) is evaporated and salt (solute) is produced.

- Other typical examples of evaporation of water are *concentration aqueous solutions of sodium hydroxide; glycerol, sugar, juices and glue.*

In certain cases where the *primary object is to get crystals by evaporation*, this special process is termed **crystallisation.**

On account of changes in concentration and properties of the solution the following special problems may creep up :

1. Concentration of liquid
2. Solubility and crystal formation
3. Foaming
4. Pressure and temperature
5. Temperature sensitivity of materials
6. Entrainment of drops
7. Scale deposition on materials of construction.

10.9.2. CLASSIFICATION OF EVAPORATORS

Evaporators may be *classified* as follows :

A. On the basis of the fluids to be evaporated :

1. *Power plant evaporators :*
   (i) *Make up evaporators for boiler feed*
   (ii) *Process evaporators*
   (iii) *Salt water evaporators*
   (iv) *Heat transfer evaporators.*

   In all above evaporators *water is the solvent.*

2. *Chemical evaporators :*

Chemical evaporators may be natural circulation type or forced circulation type. Natural circulation may fall into the following four main classes :

- *Horizontal tube*
- *Vertical tube*
- *Basket vertical tube*
- *Long tube vertical.*

B. On the basis of the method of evaporation :

1. *Single effect evaporators :*
   (i) *Batch evaporators.* Here filling, evaporating and emptying are consecutive steps.

(ii) *Semi-batch.* Here feed is continuously added to maintain a constant level until entire change reaches a final density.

(iii) *Continuous evaporators.* Here feed and discharge are continuous, and concentration of both feed and discharge remain substantially constant.

2. *Multiple effect evaporators :*

    (i) *Forward feed.* Here raw feed is introduced in the first effect, and passed from effect to effect in parallel to the steam flow. The product is withdrawn from the last feed.

    (ii) *Backward feed.* Here the raw feed enters the last (coldest) effect, the discharge from this effect becomes the feed to next to the last effect and so on, until the product is discharged from this first effect.

Pilot plant evaporator single effect.

The following characteristics are important in design and operation of evaporators :

    1. The boiling heat transfer coefficient.

    2. The boiling point.

    – The heat transfer coefficient (*i.e.,* boiling film coefficient) depends upon viscosity, and surface tension; μ (boiling coefficient) *increases with increase in viscosity and varies inversely with surface tension.*

    – h increases with increase in boiling point.

    – $h \propto \mu^n$, where n lies between 0.3 to 0.78 depending upon the solution.

Types of Evaporators :

The general types of evaporators are :

1. Open kettle or pan.
2. Horizontal tube natural circulation evaporator.
3. Vertical type natural circulation evaporator.
4. Long tube vertical type natural circulation evaporator.
5. Falling film type vertical natural circulation evaporator.
6. Forced circulation type evaporator.
7. Agitated film evaporator.

Example 10.54. (*a*) *Between counter-current and co-current heat exchangers which is more preferable, and why ?*

(*b*) *A triple effect evaporator is concentrating a liquid that has no appreciable elevation in boiling point. The temperature of the steam to the first effect is 108°C, the boiling point of the solution in the last effect is 52°C. The overall heat transfer co-efficients in W/m²°C are 2500 in the first effect, 2000 in the second effect and 1000 in the third effect. At what temperature will the liquid boil in the first and second effects ?*

                                                                    (AMIE Winter, 2000)

Solution. (*a*) *Counter-current heat exchanger is more preferable to co-current heat exchanger* because of the following *reasons* :

    1. The counter-current heat exchanger is *thermodynamically the most efficient.*

    2. For given heat flow rates, and given inlet and outlet fluid temperatures, a *counter-current heat exchanger requires the minimum heat transfer area* and a co-current heat exchanger requires the maximum heat transfer area.

    3. In co-current flow (*i.e.*, parallel flow), the lowest temperature theoretically attainable by the hot fluid is that of the outlet temperature of the cold fluid. If this temperature were attained, the *LMTD* would be zero, requiring infinite heat transfer surface. Further, inability of the hot fluid in a co-current flow to fall below the outlet temperature of the cold fluid has a marked effect upon the ability of the co-current apparatus to recover heat. Hence, *co-current heat flow heat exchanger are rarely used.*

  (*b*) Assuming that the multiple effect evaporator is *forward feed type*, the arrangement is drawn below :

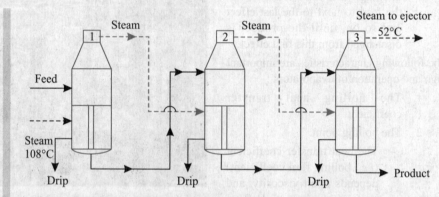

Fig. 10.65. Multiple effect evaporator (Forward feed type).

For the above arrangement, if equal surfaces are employed in each effect (as is the usual practice), the difference in pressures between the effects, Δp, will be nearly equal. From steam tables,

Corresponding to 108°C, pressure = 1.3390 bar,

Corresponding to 52°C, pressure = 0.1360 bar;

$$\text{Average pressure difference} = \frac{1.3390 - 0.1360}{3} = 0.401 \text{ bar}$$

Break-up of the total pressure difference is given in the table below :

	Pressure (bar)	*Δp (bar)*	*Steam or vapour °C*
Steam chest, first effect	1.3390	...	108
Steam chest, second effect	0.9380	0.401	98
Steam chest, third effect	0.5370	0.401	83
Vacuum to ejector	0.1360	0.401	52

So, the boiling temperatures of liquid are :

        First effect = **98°C**   **(Ans.)**

        Second effect = **83°C**   **(Ans.)**

Example 10.55. (*a*) *How are evaporators classified ? What are the characteristics of the solution which are important in design and operation of evaporators and how do these characteristics affect the evaporation process ?*

(*b*) *A single effect evaporator is used to concentrate 15000 kg/h of a 20% solution of caustic soda to 60% concentration. Heating medium is dry and saturated steam at 125°C. The vapour space pressure is 100 mm Hg (absolute). Find out the steam consumption, steam economy and the heat transfer area if the following data is available.*

$$Feed \ temperature = 37°C;$$
$$BPE = 52°C$$
$$(c_p)_{feed} = 0.92$$
$$(c_p)_{product} = 0.75$$

Overall heat transfer co-efficient, $U_o = 1200 \ W/m^2 °C.$ **(AMIE Winter, 2000)**

Solution. (*a*) Refer Article 10.9.2.

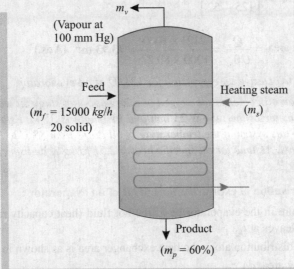

m_v

(Vapour at
100 mm Hg)

Feed
$(m_f = 15000 \ kg/h$
20 solid)

Heating steam
(m_s)

Product
$(m_p = 60\%)$

Fig. 10.66. Single effect evaporator.

(*b*) Caustic soda balance : $15000 \times 0.2 = m_p \times 0.6$

$\therefore$ Mass of product, m_p : $\dfrac{15000 \times 0.2}{0.6} = 5000$ kg/h

Total mass balance, $\qquad 1500 = m_p + m_v = 5000 + m_v$ (where m_v = mass of vapour)

$\therefore \qquad\qquad\qquad m_v = 15000 - 5000 = 10000$ kg/h

h_{fg} of heating steam (at 25°C) from steam tables = 2188 kJ/kg

Vapour pressure = 100 mm Hg

$$= (13.6 \times 1000) \times 9.81 \times \dfrac{100}{1000} \times 10^{-5} \ bar = 0.13342 \ bar$$

h_v = Enthalpy of vapour = 2595 kJ/kg (from steam tables)

Assuming that only latent heat of steam is used for heating, an energy balance of the evaporator is made as :

$$m_f \times (c_p)_{feed} \times 37 + m_s \times h_{fg} = m_v \times h_v + m_p \times (c_p)_{product} \times 52$$

$$\begin{bmatrix} where, \ m_f = mass \ of \ feed, \\ and \qquad m_s = mass \ of \ steam \end{bmatrix}$$

$$15000 \times 0.92 \times 37 + m_s \times 2188 = 10000 \times 2595 + 5000 \times 0.75 \times 52$$

∴ The steam consumption, m_s = **11716 kg/h**   **(Ans.)**

Steam economy is defined as kg of solvent evaporated per kg of steam used :

$$\text{Steam economy} = \frac{m_v}{m_s} = \frac{10000}{11716} = \mathbf{0.8535} \quad \textbf{(Ans.)}$$

$$Q = \frac{11716 \times 2188}{3600}$$

$$= 7121 \text{ kJ/s or kW}$$

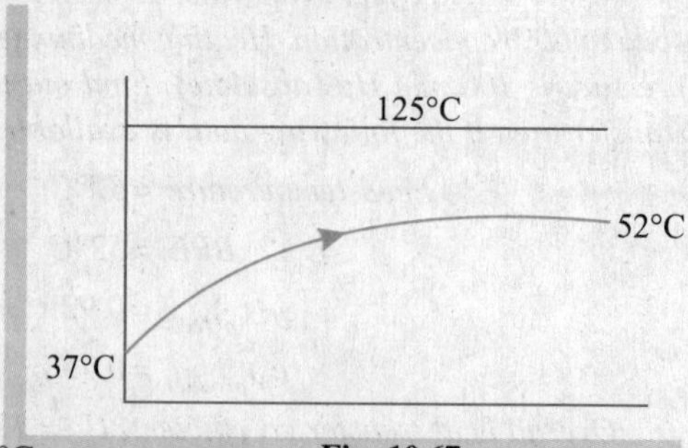

$$LMTD \ (\theta_m) = \frac{\theta_1 - \theta_2}{\ln \ (\theta_1/\theta_2)}$$

$$= \frac{(125 - 37) - (125 - 52)}{\ln \left[\dfrac{125 - 37}{125 - 52} \right]} = 80.27°C$$

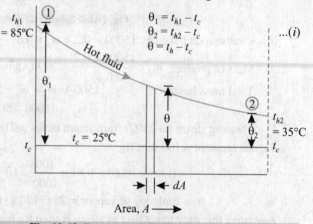

Fig. 10.67.

$$\text{Heat transfer area} = \frac{Q}{U\theta_m} = \frac{7121 \times 1000}{1200 \times 80.27} = 73.93 \text{ m}^2 \quad \textbf{(Ans.)}$$

Example 10.56. (a) Derive an expression for LMTD of an evaporator.

(b) The tube of an oil cooler is submerged in a large pool of stagnant water at temperature of 25°C. The inside diameter of the tube is 25 mm and its length is 35 m. Estimate the overall heat transfer coefficient of this system if the temperature of oil drops from 85°C to 35°C and the average velocity of oil is 0.6 m/s. Assume for oil specific heat = 2.51 kJ/kg K and specific gravity = 0.8.

(AMIE Summer, 1995)

Solution. (a) **Derivation of expression for LMTD of an evaporator :**

Let the temperature in the evaporator be t_c, the hot fluid (heat capacity rate $m_h \ c_{ph}$) enters the evaporator at t_{h1} and leaves at t_{h2}.

The temperature distribution along the heat exchanger area is as shown in Fig. 10.68.

For an elementary area, dA

$$dQ = U \cdot dA \cdot \theta = - m_h c_{ph} dt_h$$

$$dt_h = - \frac{dQ}{m_h \cdot c_{ph}} = dQ.Z$$

where, $Z = - \dfrac{1}{m_h \, c_{ph}}$ = a constant

$$\theta = t_h - t_c$$

$$d\theta = dt_h = dQ.Z \quad ...(ii)$$

On integration, we get

$$\int_1^2 d\theta = Z \int_1^2 dQ$$

or, $\theta_2 - \theta_1 = Z.Q$

or, $Z = \dfrac{\theta_2 - \theta_1}{Q}$

$$\begin{aligned} \theta_1 &= t_{h1} - t_c \\ \theta_2 &= t_{h2} - t_c \\ \theta &= t_h - t_c \end{aligned} \qquad ...(i)$$

...(iii)

Fig. 10.68. Temperature distribution of an evaporator.

$$d\theta = dQ.Z = U.dA.\theta.Z \qquad \text{...from } (ii) \text{ and } (i)$$

or,

$$\frac{d\theta}{\theta} = U.dA.Z$$

Again integrating, we get

$$\ln (\theta_2/\theta_1) = U.A.Z = UA\left(\frac{\theta_2 - \theta_1}{Q}\right) \qquad \text{...from } (iii)$$

$$\therefore \qquad Q = UA\left[\frac{\theta_2 - \theta_1}{\ln (\theta_2/\theta_1)}\right] = U A\,\theta_m = U A\,(LMTD) \qquad \textbf{(Ans.)}$$

(b) *Given* : $d = 25$ mm $= 0.025$ m; $L = 35$ m; $t_c = 25°C$; $t_{h1} = 85°C$;

$t_{h2} = 35°C$; $V = 0.6$ m/s; $c_{ph} = 2.51$ kJ/kg K; specific gravity of oil $= 0.8$

Overall heat transfer co-efficient, U :

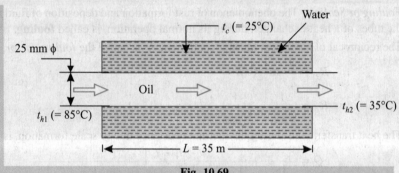

Fig. 10.69.

$$m = \rho A_f V \qquad (\text{where,} \quad A_f = \text{area of flow})$$

$$= (1000 \times 0.8) \times \frac{\pi}{4} \times \left(\frac{25}{1000}\right)^2 \times 0.6 = 0.2356 \text{ kg/s}$$

$$Q = m \cdot c_{ph} \cdot (t_{h1} - t_{h2})$$

$$= 0.2356 \times (2.51 \times 10^3) \times (85 - 35) = 29567.8 \text{ J/s}$$

$$\theta_m\ (LMTD) = \frac{(t_{h1} - t_c) - (t_{h2} - t_c)}{\ln\left[\dfrac{t_{h1} - t_c}{t_{h2} - t_c}\right]}$$

$$= \frac{(85 - 25) - (35 - 25)}{\ln\left[\dfrac{85 - 25}{35 - 25}\right]} = 27.9°C$$

$$Q = U.A.\theta_m$$

or,

$$U = \frac{Q}{A_s \cdot \theta_m} = \frac{29567.8}{\left(\pi \times \dfrac{25}{1000} \times 35\right) \times 27.9} \qquad (\because \text{Surface area, } A_s = \pi dL)$$

$$= 385.53 \text{ W/m}^{2°}\text{C} \qquad \textbf{(Ans.)}$$

HIGHLIGHTS

1. · A '*heat exchanger*' may be defined as an equipment which transfers the energy from a hot fluid to a cold fluid, with maximum rate and minimum investment and running costs.

2. Logarithmic mean temperature difference (LMTD) is defined as "*that temperature difference which, if constant, would give the same rate of heat transfer as actually occurs under variable conditions of temperature difference*".

   LMTD (θ_m) for parallel flow as well as counter-flow is given by :

   $$\theta_m = \frac{\theta_1 - \theta_2}{\ln(\theta_1/\theta_2)}$$

   θ_m for a *counter-flow unit is always greater than that for parallel flow unit*, hence counter-flow heat exchanger can transfer more heat than parallel flow one; in other words a counter-flow heat exchanger needs a *smaller heating surface* for the same rate of heat transfer. For this reason, the counter-flow arrangement is *usually used*.

3. *Fouling or Scaling* : The phenomenon of rust formation and deposition of fluid impurities in the tubes of a heat exchanger, during its normal operation, is called **fouling.**

   The reciprocal of scale heat transfer coefficient, h_s is called the *fouling factor, R_f.*

   $$R_f = \frac{1}{h_s} \ \text{m}^2{}^\circ\text{C/W} \qquad \qquad \qquad \text{...(i)}$$

   $$R_f = \frac{1}{U_{dirty}} - \frac{1}{U_{clean}} \qquad \qquad \qquad \text{...(ii)}$$

   The heat transfer, considering the thermal resistance due to scale formation, is given by

   $$Q = \frac{(t_i - t_o)}{\dfrac{1}{A_i h_i} + \dfrac{1}{A_i h_{si}} + \dfrac{1}{2\pi L k}\ln(r_o/r_i) + \dfrac{1}{A_o h_{so}} + \dfrac{1}{A_o h_o}} \qquad \text{...(iii)}$$

   The overall heat transfer coefficients, U based on the inner and outer surfaces of the inner tube are given by

   $$U_i = \frac{1}{\dfrac{1}{h_i} + R_{fi} + \dfrac{r_i}{k}\ln(r_o/r_i) + (r_i/r_o)R_{fo} + (r_i/r_o)\dfrac{1}{h_o}} \qquad \text{...(iv)}$$

   $$U_o = \frac{1}{(r_o/r_i)\dfrac{1}{h_i}(r_o/r_i)R_{fi} + \dfrac{r_o}{k}\ln(r_o/r_i) + R_{fo} + \dfrac{1}{h_o}} \qquad \text{...(v)}$$

   $$U_o = \frac{1}{(r_o/r_i)\dfrac{1}{h_i} + \dfrac{r_o}{k}\ln(r_o/r_i) + \dfrac{1}{h_o}} \quad \text{... neglecting fouling factor} \quad \text{...(vi)}$$

   $$U_o = \frac{1}{\dfrac{1}{h_i} + \dfrac{1}{h_o}} \qquad \text{...When the tube is thin walled and thermal resistance due to tube wall thickness and scale formed are neglected.}$$

4. *The heat exchanger effectiveness* (ε) is defined as the ratio of actual heat transfer to the maximum possible heat transfer. Thus

   $$\varepsilon = \frac{\text{Actual heat transfer } (Q)}{\text{Maximum possible heat transfer } (Q_{max})} \qquad \text{...(i)}$$

   $$(\varepsilon)_{parallel\ flow} = \frac{1 - \exp[-NTU(1 + R)]}{1 + R} \qquad \text{...(ii)}$$

$$(\varepsilon)_{counter-flow} = \frac{1 - \exp\left[-NTU\,(1-R)\right]}{1 - R\exp\left[-NTU\,(1-R)\right]} \qquad ...(iii)$$

where, R = (capacity ratio) = $\dfrac{C_{min}}{C_{max}}$, and

NTU = Number of transfer units.

NTU is a measure of effectiveness of the heat exchanger.

THEORETICAL QUESTIONS

1. What is a heat exchanger?
2. How are heat exchangers classified?
3. Derive an expression for logarithmic mean temperature difference (LMTD) in the case of (i) parallel flow, and (ii) counter-flow heat exchangers.
4. Define 'heat exchanger effectiveness'.
5. Derive expressions for effectiveness by NTU (number of transfer units) method for the following cases : (i) Parallel flow; (ii) Counter flow heat exchangers.
6. What do you mean by 'fouling' in heat exchangers?
7. What is 'evaporation'?
8. How are evaporators classified ?

UNSOLVED EXAMPLES

1. The flow rates of hot and cold water streams running through a heat exchanger are 600 kg/h and 1500 kg/h respectively. The inlet temperatures on the hot and cold sides are 70°C and 25°C respectively. The exit temperature of hot water is 50°C. If the individual heat transfer coefficients on both sides are 700 W/m²°C, calculate the area of the heat exchanger. **(Ans. 1.38 m²)**

2. The following data relate to a parallel flow heat exchanger in which air is heated by hot exhaust gases : Heat transferred per second = 46.52 kJ; Inside heat transfer coefficient = 116 W/m²°C; Outside heat transfer coefficient = 186 W/m²°C. Inlet and outlet temperatures of hot fluid = 400°C and 150°C, respectively. Inlet and outlet temperatures of the cold fluid = 50°C and 100°C, respectively; Inside and outside diameter of the tubes = 50 mm and 60 mm, respectively.

   Calculate the length of the tube required for necessary heat transfer to occur. Assume the tube resistance to be negligible. **(Ans. 25.2 m)**

3. Exhaust gases flowing through a tubular heat exchanger at the rate of 0.4 kg/s are cooled from 450°C to 150°C by water initially at 15°C. The specific heats of exhaust gases and water may be taken as 1.13 and 4.19 kJ/kg°C respectively, and the overall heat transfer coefficient from gases to water is 140 W/m²°C. Calculate the surface area required for the following cases, when the cooling water flow is 0.5 kg/s:

   (i) Parallel flow;   (ii) Counter-flow.   **[Ans. (i) 4.84 m²; (ii) 4.15 m²]**

4. A counter-flow heat exchanger, through which passes 11.3kg/s of air to be cooled from 538°C to 148°C, contains 4500 tubes, each having a diameter of 25.4 mm. The inlet and outlet temperatures of cooling water are 38°C and 85°C, respectively. If the water side resistance to flow is negligible, calculate the tube length required for this duty.

   For turbulent flow inside tubes : $Nu = 0.023\,Re^{0.8}\,Pr^{0.4}$

   Properties of air at the average temperature are as follows :

   ρ = 1.009 kg/m³; c_p = 1.0082 kJ/kg°C; μ = 2.075 × 10⁻⁵ kg/ms (Ns/m²) and k = 3.003 × 10⁻² W/m°C. **(Ans. 2m)**

5. 16.67 kg/s of the product at 700°C (c_p = 3.6 kJ/kg°C), in a chemical plant, are to be used to heat 20 kg/s of

the incoming fluid from 100°C (c_p = 4.2 kJ/kg°C). If the overall heat transfer coefficient is 1 kW/m²°C and the installed heat transfer surface is 42 m², calculate the fluid outlet temperatures for the counter-flow and parallel flow arrangements. **[Ans.** t_{h2} = 438.4°C, t_{c2} = 286.8°C, 274.4°C]

6. Water is heated while flowing through a 15 mm × 35 mm rectangular cross-section tube at a velocity of 1.2 m/s. The water enters at 40°C and tube wall is maintained at 85°C. Determine the length of the tube required to raise the temperature of water by 30°C.

   Take the following properties of water :

   ρ = 985.5 kg/m³; k = 0.653 W/m°C; v = 0.517 × 10⁻⁶ m²/s, c_p = 4.19 kJ/kg°C   **(Ans.** L = 4.78 m)

7. An oil cooler consists of a straight tube of 20 mm O.D. and 16 mm I.D. enclosed within a pipe and concentric with it. The external pipe is well insulated. Hot oil flows through a tube at the rate of 0.05 kg/s (c_p = 2000 J/kg°C) and cooling water flows in the annulus in opposite direction at the rate of 0.1 kg/s (c_p = 4000 J/kg°C). The oil enters the cooler at 130°C and leaves at 80°C, while the cold liquid enters at 30°C. Calculate the length of the tube required if heat transfer coefficient from oil to tube is 2000 W/m²°C and from surface to water is 4000 W/m²°C. Neglect the resistance of the tube wall. **(Ans.** 1.04 m)

8. It is desired to condense 40000 kg/h of dry and saturated steam at a pressure of 0.05 bar (saturation temperature = 32.76°C) in a single pass steam condenser. The cooling water enters the tube at 20°C and leaves at 26°C. The tubes are 25 mm I.D. and 27.5 mm O.D. and the thermal conductivity of tube material is 110 W/m²°C. The film transfer coefficients of water and steam side are 7090 and 5930 W/m²°C respectively. If the length of tube is 3 m, calculate the following :

   (i)   The surface area of the tubes;

   (ii) The heat transfer rate;

   (iii) The number of tubes.   **[Ans.** (i) 927.23 m², (ii) 26933.3 kW, (iii) 3578]

9. A surface condenser for a steam power plant is to be designed which is supposed to handle 28000 kg/h of steam at a temperature of 27°C and 0.95 dry. The cooling water enters the condenser at 15°C and leaves at 25°C. The cooling water flows through the tube at a velocity of 1.5 m/s. The inside and outside diameters of the tubes are 22 mm and 25 mm respectively. The length of tubes is limited to 6 m. The latent heat of vaporization, h_{fg} at 27°C is 2438 kJ/kg. The heat transfer coefficient on the steam side is 5000 W/m²°C. Calculate the following :

   (i)   Mass flow rate of water;

   (ii) Surface area required;

   (iii) Number of tubes;

   (iv) Number of passes.

   Assume that the condensate coming out from condenser is saturated.

10. Water and steam lose only latent heat. The heat transfer coefficient on water side is determined by the relation Nu = 0.023 $(Re)^{0.8}$ $(Pr)^{0.4}$. The physical properties of water at mean bulk temperature of 20°C are :

   ρ = 998.8 kg/m³, k = 0.59859 W/m°C, v = 1.006 × 10⁻⁶ m²/s; Pr = 7.02

   [Ans. (i) 1.551 × 10⁶ kg/h, (ii) 1301.56 m², (iii) 757, (iv) 4]

11. An oil cooler consists of straight tube of 20 mm outer diameter and 15 mm inner diameter enclosed within a pipe and concentric with it. The external pipe is well insulated. The oil flows through the tube at 0.05 kg/s (c_p = 2 kJ/kg°C) and cooling fluid flows in the annulus in opposite direction at the rate of 0.1 kg/s (c_p = 4kJ/kg°C). The oil enters the cooler at 180°C and leaves at 80°C while cooling liquid enters the cooler at 30°C.

   Calculate the length of the pipe required if heat transfer coefficient from oil to tube surface is 1720 W/m²°C and from metal surface to coolant is 3450 W/m²°C. Neglect the resistance of the tube wall. **[Ans.** 2.08 m]

12. In a shell and tube type condenser, steam condenses at 0.4 bar pressure on the external surface of the tubes. The cooling water, flowing at the rate of 3600 kg/h, enters the tubes at 25°C and leaves at 50°C. Calculate the following :

    (i)   The rate of condensation of steam in kg/h,
    (ii) The overall heat transfer coefficient based on inner surface of the condenser,
    (iii) Number of transfer units NTU, and
    (iv) The effectiveness of the condenser.

    Assume h_{fg} (latent heat of steam) = 2319 kJ/kg

    c_{pw} (specific heat of water) = 4.18 kJ/kg°C

    L (tube length) = 10 m

    d (tube diamter) = 25 mm

    N (number of tubes) = 10   [**Ans.** (*i*) 162.2 kg/h; (*ii*) 358.6 W/m²°C, (*iii*) 0.674, (*iv*) 0.49]

13. 3000 kg/h of furnace oil is heated from 10°C to 90°C in a shell and tube type heat exchanger. The oil is to flow inside the tube while the steam at 120°C is to flow through the shell.

    The tubes of *I.D.* = 1.65 cm and *O.D.* = 1.9 cm are used. The heat transfer coefficients of oil and steam sides are 85 W/m²°C and 7420 W/m²°C respectively. Find the number of passes and the number of tubes in each pass, if the length of each tube is limited to 2.85 m due to space limitations. The velocity of oil is limited to 5 cm/s. Take the following for oil: ρ = 900 kg/m³ and c_p = 1970 J/kg°C.

    [**Ans.** 87, 2 passes]

14. In a shell and tube heat counter-flow heat exchanger water flows through a copper tube 20 mm I.D. and 22 mm O.D. while oil flows through the shell. Water enters at 25°C and comes out at 35°C while oil enters at 70°C and comes out at 64°C. The water and oil side film coefficients are 4650 and 1280 W/m²°C respectively. The thermal conductivity of the tube wall is 350 W/m°C. The fouling factors on the water and oil sides may be taken to be 0.0004 and 0.001 respectively. If the length of the tube is 2.5 m, calculate the overall heat transfer coefficient and the heat transfer rate.

    [**Ans.** 401 W/m²°C, 2676.88 W]

15. The following data pertains to an oil cooler of the form of tubular heat exchanger, where oil is cooled by a large pool of stagnant water :

    Temperature of stagnant water = 25°C (assumed constant); Inlet and outlet temperatures of oil = 85°C and 35°C, respectively; inside diameter and length of the tube carrying oil = 25 mm and 35 m, respectivehy; specific heat and specific gravity of oil = 2.51 kJ/kg°C and 0.8, respectively; Average velocity of oil = 0.6 m/s.

    Calculate the overall heat transfer coefficient. [**Ans.** 385.6 W/m²°C]

16. A single pass condenser is used to condense 4000 kg of dry and saturated steam at a pressure of 0.05 bar (t_{sat} = 32.76°C). The cooling water enters the tube at 20°C and leaves at 26°C. The tubes are 25 mm I.D. and 27.5 mm O.D. and the thermal conductivity of tube material is 110 W/m²°C. The film transfer coefficients of water and steam sides are 7090 and 5930 W/m²°C respectively. Neglecting the scale resistance and assuming the length of tube 3 m, calculate the following :

    (i)   The heat transfer rate,
    (ii) The surface area of the tubes required, and
    (iii) The number of tubes.   [**Ans.** (*i*) 26933.3 kW, (*ii*) 927.3 m², (*iii*) 3578]

17. The following data relate to a single pass surface condenser :

    Quantity of steam to be handled = 5100 kg/h (dry and saturated steam at 50°C); Outer and inner diameters of the tubes = 20 mm and 17 mm respectively; Length of the tube = 3m; Inlet and outlet temperatures of water = 20°C and 30°C, respectively. Heat transfer coefficient of steam side = 11700 W/m²°C; Fouling factor of water side = 0.0002 m²°C/W; Thermal conductivity of tube material = 93 W/m°C, Fouling factor of steam side = 0.0009 m²°C/W.

    Calculate the number of tubes. [**Ans.** 1031]

18. The following data relate to a counter-flow double pipe heat exchanger with sulphuric acid flowing through inner tube and water surrounding it.

Quantity of sulphuric acid to be cooled from 80°C to 40°C = 600 kg/h; Mass flow rate of water = 500 kg/h; Water inlet temperature = 20°C; Specific heat of water = 4.18 kJ/kg°C; Specific heat of sulphuric acid = 335 kJ/kg°C; Heat transfer coefficient of water side = 580 W/m²°C; Heat transfer coefficient of sulphuric acid side = 465 W/m²°C; Inside diameter of inner tube = 25 mm; Outside diameter of inner tube = 30 mm; Thermal conductivity of tube material = 93 W/m°C; Fouling factor of water side = 0.0002 m²°C/W; Fouling factor of sulphuric acid side = 0.001 m²°C/W.

Neglecting all other losses, calculate the area of exchanger. [**Ans.** 17.684 m²]

CORRECTION FACTORS AND EFFECTIVENESS

19. Calculate for the following cases, the surface area required for a heat exchanger which is required to cool 1 kg/s of benzene (c_p = 1.74 kJ/kg°C) from 75°C to 45°C. The coolong water (c_p = 4.18 kJ/kg°C) at 15°C has a flow rate of 0.694 kg/s.

(i) Single pass counter-flow

(ii) 1-4 exchanger (one-shell pass and four-tube passes), and

(iii) Cross-flow single-pass with water mixed and benzene unmixed.

For each configuration, the overall heat transfer coefficient may be taken as 0.3 kW/m²°C.

[**Ans.** (i) 4.87 m², (ii) 5.29 m², (iii) 5.18 m²]

20. It is required to design a shell-and-tube heat exchanger for heating 2.5 kg/s of water from 15°C to 85°C by hot engine oil (c_p = 2.35 kJ/kg°C) flowing through the shell of the heat exchanger. The oil makes a single pass, entering at 150°C and leaving at 95°C with an average heat transfer coefficient of 400 W/m²°C. The water flows through 10 thin-walled tubes of 25 mm diamter with each tube making 8-passes through the shell. The heat transfer coefficient on the water side is 3000 W/m²°C. Calculate the length of the tube required for the heat exchanger to accomplish the required water heating.

[**Ans.** Tube length = 38.88 m, shell length = 4.86 m (8-passes)]

21. 8000 kg/h of air at 105°C is cooled by passing it through a counter-flow heat exchanger. Find the exit temperature of air if water enters at 15°C and flows at a rate of 7500 kg/h. The heat exchanger has heat transfer area equal to 20 m² and the overall heat transfer coefficient corresponding to this area is 145 W/m²°C.

Take c_p (air) = 1 kJ/kg°C and c_p (water) = 4.18 kJ/kg°C. [**Ans.** 76.2°C]

22. In a cross-flow heat exchanger, oil of specific heat of 3.6 kJ/kg°C flows in at the rate of 15000 kg/h at 100°C and is cooled by water which enters at 10°C and flows at the rate of 25000 kg/h. The effective heat transfer area of heat exchanger is 10 m² and the overall heat transfer coefficient is 500 W/m²°C. Calculate the outlet temperatures of oil and water. Consider both fluids are unmixed.

[**Ans.** 70.3°C, 25.3°C]

23. Steam at atmospheric pressure enters the shell of a surface condenser in which the water flows through a bundle of tubes of diameter 30 mm at the rate of 0.06 kg/s. The inlet and outlet temperatures of water are 20°C and 75°C, respectively. The condensation of steam takes place on the outside surface of the tubes. If the overall heat transfer coefficient is 250 W/m²°C, using NTU method, calculate: (i) The effectiveness of heat exchanger, (ii) The length of the tube, and (iii) The rate of steam condensation.

[**Ans.** (i) 0.6875, (ii) 12.37 m, (iii) 22.96 kg/h]

24. In a large steam power plant, a shell and tube type steam condenser is employed which effects a heat exchange rate of 2200 MW. The following data pertains to this condenser :

Number of shell passes = one; Number of tubes (thin walled) = 32000, each executing two passes; Diameter of each tube = 30 mm; Mass flow rate of water through the tubes = 3.2 × 10⁴ kg/s; The condensation temperature of steam = 50°C, the steam condenses on the outer surface of the tubes; The heat transfer coefficient on the steam side = 11500 W/m²°C; The inlet temperature of water = 20°C.

Using LMTD correction factor method and NTU method, calculate the outlet temperature of cooling water, and the length of tube per pass.

Take the following properties of water (at $t_{bulk} \simeq 27°C$) :

c_p = 4.18 kJ/kg°C, μ = 855 × 10⁻⁶ Ns/m², k = 0.613 W/m°C and Pr = 5.83.

The thermal resistance of tube material and fouling effects may be neglected.

[**Ans.** 36.44°C, 4.77 m]

PART III

HEAT TRANSFER BY RADIATION

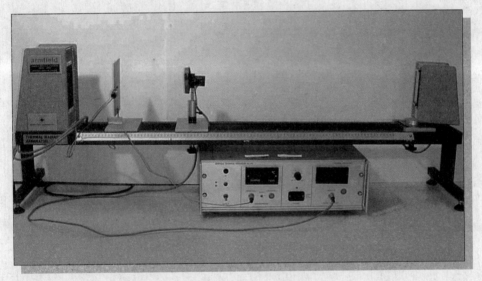

Thermal radiation apparatus.

Thermal Radiation – Basic Relations

11.1. INTRODUCTION

'**Radiation' heat transfer** is defined as "*the transfer of energy across a system boundary by means of an electromagnetic mechanism which is caused solely by a temperature difference.*" Whereas the heat transfer by conduction and convection takes place only in *the presence of medium, radiation heat transfer does not require a medium.* Radiation exchange, in fact, occurs most effectively in *vacuum.* Further, the rate of heat transfer *by conduction and convection* varies as the temperature difference to the *first power*, whereas the *radiant heat exchange* between two bodies depends on the difference between their temperature to the '*fourth power*'. Both the amount of radiation and the quality of radiation depend upon temperature. The *dissipation from the filament of a vacuum tube* or *the heat leakage through the evacuated walls of a thermos flask* are some familiar *examples* of heat transfer by radiation.

The contribution of *radiation* to heat transfer is very significant at high absolute temperature levels such as those prevailing in *furnaces, combustion chambers, nuclear explosions* and in *space applications.* The *solar energy* incident upon the earth is also governed by the *laws of radition.*

The energy which a radiating surface releases is *not continuous* but is in the form of successive and separate (discrete) packet or quanta of energy called *photons.* The photons are propagated through space as rays; the movement of swarm of photons is described as *electromagnetic waves.* The photons travel (with speed equal to that of light) in straight paths with unchanged frequency; when they approach the receiving surface, there occurs reconversion of wave motion into *thermal energy* which is partly absorbed, reflected or transmitted through the receiving surface (the magnitude of each fraction depends, upon the nature of the surface that receives the *thermal radiation*).

All types of electromagnetic waves are classified in terms of *wavelength* and are propagated at the speed of light (*c*) *i.e.*, 3×10^8 m/s. The electromagnetic spectrum is shown in Fig. 11.1. The distinction between one form of radiation and another lies only in its frequency (*f*) and wavelength (λ) which are related by

$$c = \lambda \times f \qquad \qquad ...(11.1)$$

The *emission of thermal radiation* (range lies between wavelength of 10^{-7} m and 10^{-4} m) *depends upon the nature, temperature and state of the emitting surface*; however, *with gases the dependence is also upon the thickness of the emitting layer and the gas pressure.*

Thermal radiations exhibit characteristics similar to those of *visible light*, and *follow optical laws*. These can be *reflected, refracted* and are *subject to scattering and absorption when they pass through a media*. They get *polarised* and *weakened* in strength with inverse square of radial distance from the radiating surface.

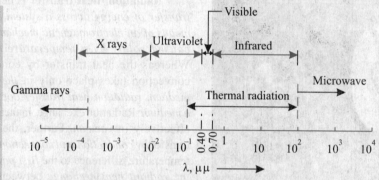

Fig. 11.1. Spectrum of electromagnetic radiation.

11.2. SURFACE EMISSION PROPERTIES

The rate of emission of radiation by a body depends upon the following factors:

(*i*) The temperature of the surface,

(*ii*) The nature of the surface, and

(*iii*) The wavelength or frequency of radiation.

The *parameters* which deal with the surface emission properties are given below :

(*i*) **Total emissive power (E).** The "*emissive power*" is defined as the *total amount of radiation emitted by a body per unit area and time*. It is expressed in W/m². The *emissive power of a black body*, according to Stefan-Boltzmann, is *proportional to absolute temperature to the fourth power.*

$$E_b = \sigma T^4 \text{ W/m}^2 \qquad \qquad ...(11.2)$$
$$E_b = \sigma A T^4 \text{ W} \qquad \qquad ...(11.2\ a)$$

where, σ = Stefan-Boltzmann constant = 5.67×10^{-8} W/m² K⁴

(*ii*) **Monochromatic (spectral) emissive power (E_λ).** It is often necessary to determine the spectral distribution of the energy radiated by a surface. At any given temperature the amount of radiation emitted per unit wavelength varies at different wavelengths. For this purpose the *monochromatic emissive power* E_λ of the surface is used. It is defined as *the rate of energy radiated per unit area of the surface per unit wavelength.*

The total emissive power is given by,

$$E = \int_0^\infty E_\lambda \, d\lambda \ \text{W/m}^2 \qquad \qquad ...(11.3)$$

(*iii*) **Emission from real surface-emissivity.** The emissive power from a real surface is given by

$$E = \varepsilon \, \sigma \, AT^4 \ \text{W} \qquad \qquad ...(11.4)$$

where, $\qquad \qquad \varepsilon$ = Emissivity of the material.

Emissivity (ε). It is defined as the *ability of the surface of a body to radiate heat*. It is also defined as the *ratio of the emissive power of any body to the emissive power of a black body of equal temperature* (*i.e.*, $\varepsilon = \dfrac{E}{E_b}$). Its values varies for different substances ranging from 0 to 1. For a black body $\varepsilon = 1$, for a white body surface $\varepsilon = 0$ and for gray bodies it lies between 0 and 1. It may vary with temperature or wavelength.

(*iv*) **Intensity of radiation.**

(*v*) **Radiation density and pressure.**

(*vi*) **Radiosity (J).** It refers to all of the radiant energy leaving a surface.

(*vii*) **Interrelationship between surface emission and irradiation properties.**

11.3. ABSORPTIVITY, REFLECTIVITY AND TRANSMISSIVITY

When incident radiation (G) also called **irradiation** (defined as the *total incident radiation on a surface from all directions per unit time and per unit area of surface; expressed in* W/m^2 *and denoted by* (G)) impinges on a surface, three things happens; a part is *reflected* back (G_r), a part is *transmitted* through (G_t) and the remainder is *absorbed* (G_a), depending upon the characteristics of the body, as shown in Fig. 11.2.

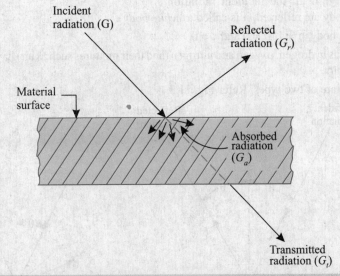

Fig. 11.2. Absorption, reflection and transmission of radiation.

By the conservation of energy principle,

$$G_a + G_r + G_t = G$$

Dividing both sides by G, we get

$$\frac{G_a}{G} + \frac{G_r}{G} + \frac{G_t}{G} = \frac{G}{G}$$

$$\alpha + \rho + \tau = 1 \qquad \qquad ...(11.5)$$

where $\qquad \alpha$ = *absorptivity* (or fraction of incident radiation absorbed),

ρ = *reflectivity* (or fraction of incident radiation reflected), and

τ = *transmittivity* (or fraction of incident radiation transmitted).

When the incident radiation is absorbed, it is converted into internal energy.

Black body: For perfectly absorbing body, α = 1, ρ = 0, τ = 0. Such a body is called a *'black body'* (i.e., a *black body is one which neither reflects nor transmits any part of the incident radiation but absorbs all of it*). In practice, a perfect black body (α = 1) does not exist. However its concept is very important.

Opaque body: When no incident radiation is transmitted through the body, it is called an *'opaque body'*.

For the opaque body τ = 0, and eqn. (11.5) reduces to

$$\alpha + \rho = 1 \qquad \qquad ...(11.6)$$

Solids generally do not transmit unless the material is of very thin section. Metals absorb radiation within a fraction of a micrometre, and insulators within a fraction of a millimetre. Glasses and liquids are, therefore, generally considered as opaque.

A black body is theoretical perfect absorber, which absorbs radiation of all wavelength falling on it.

White body: If all the incident radiation falling on the body are reflected, it is called a *'white body'*.

For a white body, ρ = 1, α = 0 and τ = 0.

Gases such as hydrogen, oxygen and nitrogen (and their mixtures such as air) have a transmissivity of practically *unity*.

Reflections are of two types: Refer Fig. 11.3.

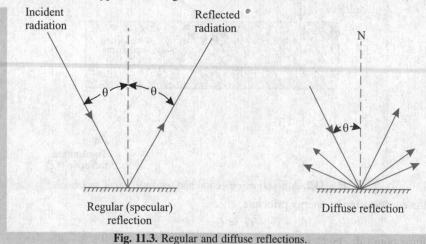

Fig. 11.3. Regular and diffuse reflections.

1. Regular (specular) reflection 2. Diffuse reflection.

Regular reflection implies that angle between the reflected beam and the normal to the *surface equals* the angle made by the incident radiation with the same normal. Reflection from highly polished and smooth surfaces approaches specular characteristics.

In a *diffused reflection*, the incident beam is reflected in *all directions*. Most of the engineering materials have rough surfaces, and these rough surfaces give diffused reflections.

Gray body: If the radiative properties, α, ρ, τ of a body are assumed to be uniform over the entire wavelength spectrum, then such a body is called *gray body*. A *gray body* is also defined as one *whose absorptivity of a surface does not vary with temperature and wavelength of the incident radiation* [$\alpha = (\alpha)_\lambda$ = constant.].

A *coloured body* is one whose absorptivity of a surface varies with the wavelength of radiation [$\alpha \neq (\alpha)_\lambda$].

11.4. CONCEPT OF A BLACK BODY

A black bdoy is an object *that absorbs all the radiant energy reaching its surface* (for a black body $\alpha = 1$, $\rho = 0$, $\tau = 0$). No actual body is perfectly black; the concept of a black body is an idealization with which the radiation characteristics of real bodies can be conveniently compared.

A *black body* has the following *properties*:

(*i*)   It absorbs all the incident radiation falling on it and does not transmit or reflect regardless of wavelength and direction.

(*ii*) It emits maximum amount of thermal radiations at all wavelengths at any specified temperature.

(*iii*) It is a *diffuse emitter* (*i.e.*, the radiation emitted by a black body is independent of direction).

Consider a hollow enclosure with a very small hole for the passage of incident radiation as shown in Fig. 11.4. Incident radiant energy passes through the small opening; some of this energy is absorbed by the inside surface and some is reflected. However, most of this energy is absorbed on a second incidence. Again, a small fraction is reflected. After a number of such reflections the amount unabsorbed is exceedingly small and very little of the original incident energy is reflected back out of the opening. A small hole leading into a cavity (Hohlraum) thus acts very nearly as a black body because all the radiant energy entering through it gets absorbed.

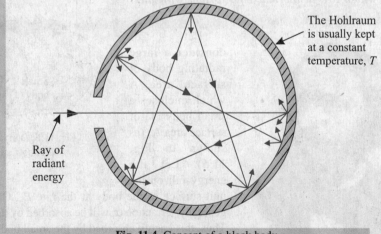

The Hohlraum is usually kept at a constant temperature, T

Ray of radiant energy

Fig. 11.4. Concept of a black body.

Isothermal furnaces, with small apertures, approximate a black body and are frequently used to *calibrate* heat flux gauges, thermometers and other radiometric devices.

11.5. THE STEFAN-BOLTZMANN LAW

The law states that *the emissive power of a black body is directly proprtional to the fourth power of its absolute temperature.*

i.e.,
$$E_b = \sigma T^4 \qquad \qquad ...(11.7)$$

where, E_b = Emissive power of a black body, and

σ = Stefan-Boltzmann constant

= 5.67×10^{-8} W/m^2 K^4.

Equation (11.7) can be rewritten as:

$$E_b = 5.67 \left(\frac{T}{100} \right)^4 \qquad \qquad ...(11.8)$$

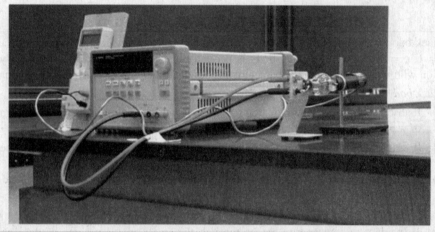

Experimental setup of Stefan-Boltzmann law

11.6. KIRCHHOFF'S LAW

The law states that *at any temperature the ratio of total emissive power E to the total absorptivity α is a constant for all substances which are in thermal equilibrium with their environment.*

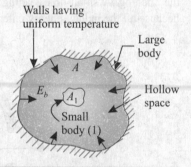

Fig. 11.5. Derivation of Kirchhoff's law.

Gustav Kirchhoff (1824-1887)

Let us consider a large radiating body of surface area A which encloses a small body (1) of surface area A_1 (as shown in Fig. 11.5). Let the energy fall on the unit surface of the body at the rate E_b. Of this energy, generally, a fraction α, will be absorbed by the small body. Thus, this energy absorbed by the small body (1) is $\alpha_1 A_1 E_b$, in which α_1 is the absorptivity of the body. When thermal equilibrium is attained, the *energy absorbed* by the body (1) must be equal to the *energy emitted*, say, E_1 per unit surface. Thus, at equilibrium, we may write

$$A_1 E_1 = \alpha_1 A_1 E_b \qquad \qquad ...(11.9)$$

Now we remove body (1) and replace it by body (2) having absorptivity α_2. The radiative energy impinging on the surface of this body is again E_b. In this case, we may write

$$A_2 E_2 = \alpha_2 A_2 E_b \qquad \qquad ...(11.10)$$

By considering generality of bodies, we obtain

$$E_b = \frac{E_1}{\alpha_1} = \frac{E_2}{\alpha_2} = \frac{E}{\alpha} \qquad \qquad ...(11.11)$$

Also, as per definition of emissivity ε, we have

$$\varepsilon = \frac{E}{E_b}$$

or, $$E_b = \frac{E}{\varepsilon} \qquad \qquad ...(11.12)$$

By comparing eqns. (11.11) and (11.12), we obtain

$$\varepsilon = \alpha \qquad \qquad ...(11.13)$$

(α is always smaller than 1. Therefore, the emissive power E is always smaller than the emissive power of a black body at equal temperature.)

Thus, Kirchhoff's law also states that *the emissivity of a body is equal to its absorptivity when the body remains in thermal equilibrium with its surroundings.*

11.7. PLANCK'S LAW

In 1900 Max Planck showed by quantum arguments that the spectral distribution of the radiation intensity of a black body is given by

$$(E_\lambda)_b = \frac{2\pi c^2 h \lambda^{-5}}{\exp\left(\dfrac{ch}{\lambda kT}\right) - 1} \qquad \text{... (Planck's law)} \qquad ...(11.14)$$

where, $(E_\lambda)_b$ = Monochromatic (single wavelength) emissive power of a black body,

c = Velocity of light in vacuum, $2.998 \times 10^8 \simeq 3 \times 10^8$ m/s

h = Planck's constant = 6.625×10^{-34} j.s

λ = Wavelength, μm

k = Boltzmann constant = 1.3805×10^{-23} J/K, and

T = Absolute temperature, K

Hence the unit of $(E_\lambda)_b$ is W/m². μm.

Quite often the Planck's law is written as

$$(E_\lambda)_b = \frac{C_1 \lambda^{-5}}{\exp\left(\dfrac{C_2}{\lambda T}\right) - 1} \qquad \qquad ...(11.15)$$

where, $C_1 = 2\pi c^2 h = 3.742 \times 10^8$ W.μm^4/m²;

$$C_2 = \frac{ch}{k} = 1.4388 \times 10^4 \ \mu mK$$

Equation (11.14) is of great importance as it provides quantitative results for the radiation from a black body.

The quantity $(E_\lambda)_b$, *monochromatic emissive power*, is defined as the *energy emitted by the black surface in all directions at a given wavelength λ per unit wavelength interval around λ*; that is, the rate of energy emission in the interval $d\lambda$ is equal to $(E_\lambda)_b \, d\lambda$. The total emissive power and monochromatic emissive power are related by the equation,

$$E_b = \int_0^\infty (E_\lambda)_b \, d\lambda \qquad\qquad ...(11.16)$$

A plot of $(E_\lambda)_b$ as a function of temperature and wavelength is given in Fig. 11.6.

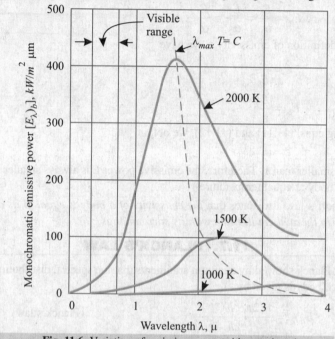

Fig. 11.6. Variation of emissive power with wavelength.

The plot shows the the following distinct characteristics of black body radiations :

1. *The energy emitted at all wavelengths increases with rise in temperature.*

2. *The peak spectral emissive power shifts towards a smaller wavelength at higher temperatures.* This shift signifies that at elevated temperature, much of the energy is emitted in a narrow band ranging on both sides of wavelength at which the monochromatic power is maximum.

3. The *area* under the monochromatic emissive power versus wavelength, at any temperature, gives *the rate of radiant energy emitted* within the wavelength interval $d\lambda$. Thus,

$$dE_b = (E_\lambda)_b \, d\lambda$$

or $$E_b = \int_{\lambda=0}^{\lambda=\infty} (E_\lambda)_b \, d\lambda \qquad\qquad ... \text{over the entire range of length.}$$

This integral represents the total emissive power per unit area radiated from a black body.

11.8. WIEN'S DISPLACEMENT LAW

In 1893 Wien established a relationship between the temperature of a black body and the wavelength at which the maximum value of monochromatic emissive power occurs. A peak monochromatic emissive power occurs at a particular wavelength. **Wien's displacement law** *states that the product of λ_{max} and T is constant, i.e.,*

$$\lambda_{max} T = \text{constant}$$

$$(E_\lambda)_b = \frac{C_1 \lambda^{-5}}{\exp\left(\dfrac{C_2}{\lambda T}\right) - 1}$$

$(E_\lambda)_b$ becomes maximum (if T remains constant) when

$$\frac{d(E_\lambda)_b}{d\lambda} = 0$$

Wilhelm Wien (1864-1928)

i.e.,

$$\frac{d(E_\lambda)_b}{d\lambda} = \frac{d}{d\lambda}\left[\frac{C_1 \lambda^{-5}}{\exp\left(\dfrac{C_2}{\lambda T}\right) - 1}\right] = 0$$

or,

$$\frac{\left[\exp\left(\dfrac{C_2}{\lambda T}\right) - 1\right](-5 C_1 \lambda^{-6}) - C_1 \lambda^{-5}\left\{\exp\left(\dfrac{C_2}{\lambda T}\right)\dfrac{C_2}{T}\left(-\dfrac{1}{\lambda^2}\right)\right\}}{\left[\exp\left(\dfrac{C_2}{\lambda T}\right) - 1\right]^2} = 0$$

or,

$$-5 C_1 \lambda^{-6}\exp\left(\frac{C_2}{\lambda T}\right) + 5 C_1 \lambda^{-6} + C_1 C_2 \lambda^{-5}\frac{1}{\lambda^2 T}\exp\left(\frac{C_2}{\lambda T}\right) = 0$$

Dividing both sides by $5 C_1 \lambda^{-6}$, we get

$$-\exp\left(\frac{C_2}{\lambda T}\right) + 1 + \frac{1}{5}C_2\frac{1}{\lambda T}\exp\left(\frac{C_2}{\lambda T}\right) = 0$$

Solving this equation by trial and error method, we get

$$\frac{C_2}{\lambda T} = \frac{C_2}{\lambda_{max}T} = 4.965$$

∴

$$\lambda_{max}T = \frac{C_2}{4.965} = \frac{1.439 \times 10^4}{4.965} \ \mu m\,K = 2898\ \mu m\,K\ (\simeq 2900 \mu m\,K)$$

i.e., $\quad\quad \lambda_{max}T = 2898\ \mu mK$ ...(11.18)

This law holds true for more *real substances*; there is however some deviation in the case of a metallic conductor where the product $(\lambda_{max}T)$ is found to vary with absolute temperature. It is used in *predicting a very high temperature through measurement of wavelength.*

A combination of Planck's law and Wien's displacement law yields the condition for the maximum monochromatic emissive power for a blackbody.

$$(E_{\lambda b})_{max} = \frac{C_1\,(\lambda_{max})^{-5}}{\exp\left[\dfrac{C_2}{\lambda_{max}T}\right] - 1} = \frac{0.374 \times 10^{-15}\left(\dfrac{2.898 \times 10^{-3}}{T}\right)^{-5}}{\exp\left[\dfrac{1.4388 \times 10^{-2}}{2.898 \times 10^{-3}}\right] - 1}$$

or, $\quad (E_{\lambda b})_{max} = 1.285 \times 10^{-5}\ T^5\ W/m^2$ per metre wavelength ...(11.19)

11.9. INTENSITY OF RADIATION AND LAMBERT'S COSINE LAW

11.9.1. INTENSITY OF RADIATION

When a surface element emits radiation, all of it will be intercepted by a hemispherical surface placed over the element. The **intensity of radiation** (I) is defined as the *rate of energy leaving a surface in a given direction per unit solid angle per unit area of the emitting surface normal to the mean direction in space. A* **solid angle** *is defined as a portion of the space inside a sphere enclosed by a conical surface with the vertex of the cone at the centre of the sphere. It is measured by the ratio of the spherical surface enclosed by the cone to the square of the radius of the sphere; its unit is* steradian (sr). The solid angle subtended by the complete hemisphere is given by: $\dfrac{2\pi r^2}{r^2} = 2\pi$.

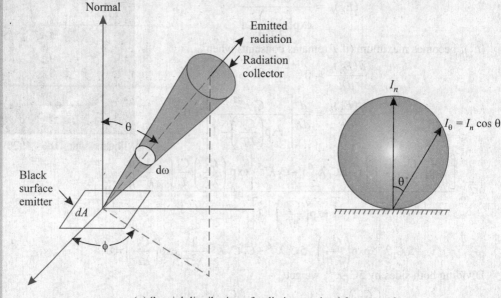

(a) Spacial distribution of radiations emitted from a surface

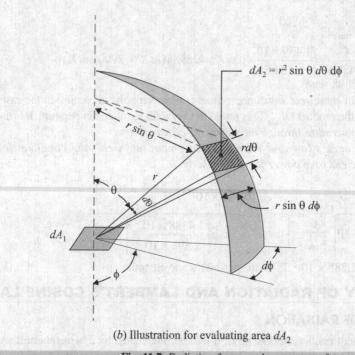

(b) Illustration for evaluating area dA_2

Fig. 11.7. Radiation from an elementary surface.

Fig. 11.7 (a) shows a small black surface of area dA (emitter) emitting radiation in different directions. A black body radiation collector through which the radiation pass is located at an angular position characterised by *zenith angle* θ towards the surface normal and angle ϕ of a spherical coordinate system. Further the collector subtends a solid angle $d\omega$ when viewed from a point on the emitter.

Let us now consider radiation from the elementary area dA_1 at the centre of a sphere as shown in Fig. 11.7(b). Suppose this radiation is absorbed by a second elemental area dA_2, a portion of the hemispherical surface.

The projected area of dA_1 on a plane perpendicular to the line joining dA_1 and $dA_2 = dA_1 \cos \theta$.

The solid angle subtended by $\qquad dA_2 = \dfrac{dA_2}{r^2}$

$\therefore$ The intensity of radiation, $\qquad I = \dfrac{dQ_{1-2}}{dA_1 \cos \theta \times \dfrac{dA_2}{r^2}}$ $\qquad$ ...(11.20)

where, dQ_{1-2} is the rate of radiation heat transfer from dA_1 to dA_2.

It is evident from the Fig. 11.7 (b) that

$$dA_2 = rd\theta \, (r \sin \theta \, d\phi)$$

or, $\qquad dA_2 = r^2 \sin \theta.d\theta.d\phi$ $\qquad$ ...(11.21)

From eqns. (11.20) and (11.21), we obtain

$$dQ_{1-2} = I \, dA_1. \sin \theta.\cos \theta. \, d\theta.d\phi$$

The total radiation through the hemisphere is given by

$$Q = IdA_1 \int_{\theta=0}^{\theta=\frac{\pi}{2}} \int_{\theta=0}^{\phi=2\pi} \sin \theta . \cos \theta \, d\theta \, d\phi$$

$$= 2\pi IdA_1 \int_{\theta=0}^{\theta=\frac{\pi}{2}} \sin \theta \cos \theta \, d\theta$$

$$= \pi IdA_1 \int_{\theta=0}^{\theta=\frac{\pi}{2}} \sin \theta \cos \theta \, d\theta$$

$$= \pi IdA_1 \int_{\theta=0}^{\theta=\frac{\pi}{2}} \sin 2\theta \, d\theta$$

or, $\qquad Q = \pi I \, dA_1$ $\qquad$ ...(11.22)

Also $\qquad Q = E.dA_1$

$\therefore \qquad EdA_1 = \pi I \, dA_1$

or, $\qquad E = \pi I$ $\qquad$ ...(11.23)

i.e., The *total emissive power of a diffuse surface is equal to* π *times its intensity of radiation.*

11.9.2. LAMBERT'S COSINE LAW

The law states that the *total emissive power* E_θ from *a radiating plane surface in any direction is directly proportional to the cosine of the angle of emission.* The angle of emission θ is the angle subtended by the normal to the radiating surface and the direction vector of emission of the receiving surface. If E_n be the total emissive power of the radiating surface in the direction of its normal, then

$$E_\theta = E_n \cos \theta \qquad \text{...(11.24)}$$

The above equation is true only for diffuse radiation surface. The radiation emanating from a point on a surface is termed diffused if the intensity, I, is constant. This law is also known as *Lambert's law of diffuse radiation.*

Example 11.1. *The effective temperature of a body having an area of 0.12 m^2 is 527°C. Calculate the following:*

(i) *The total rate of energy emission,*

(ii) *The intensity of normal radiation, and*

(iii) *The wavelength of maximum monochromatic emissive power.*

Solution. *Given:* $A = 0.12 \ m^2$; $T = 527 + 273 = 800 \ K$

(i) The total rate of energy emission, E_b:

$$E_b = \sigma A T^4 \ \text{W (watts)} \qquad \qquad \ldots[\text{Eqn. (11.2a)}]$$

$$= 5.67 \times 10^{-8} \times 0.12 \times (800)^4 = 5.67 \times 0.12 \times \left(\frac{800}{100}\right)^4 = \textbf{2786.9 W (Ans.)}$$

(ii) The intensity of normal radiation, I_{bn} :

$$I_{bn} = \frac{E_b}{\pi}, \qquad \text{where } E_b \text{ is in W/m}^2 \ K^4 \qquad \ldots(\text{Eqn. 11.23})$$

$$= \frac{\sigma T^4}{\pi} = \frac{5.67 \times \left(\dfrac{800}{100}\right)^4}{\pi} = \textbf{7392.5 W/m}^2 \textbf{.sr \ (Ans.)}$$

(iii) The wavelength of maximum monochromatic emissive power, l_{max} :

From Wien's displacement law,

$$\lambda_{max} T = 2898 \ \mu mK \qquad \qquad \ldots[\text{Eqn. (11.18)}]$$

or, $\qquad \qquad \lambda_{max} = \dfrac{2898}{T} = \dfrac{2898}{800} = \textbf{3.622} \boldsymbol{\mu} \textbf{m \ (Ans.)}$

Example 11.2. *Assuming the sun to be a black body emitting radiation with maximum intensity at* $\lambda = 0.49 \ \mu m$, *calculate the following :*

(i) *The surface temperature of the sun, and*

(ii) *The heat flux at surface of the sun.*

Solution. *Given:* $l_{max} = 0.49 \ \mu m$

(i) The surface temperature of the sun, T:

According to Wien's displacement law,

$$\lambda_{max} T = 2898 \ \mu mK$$

$\therefore \qquad \qquad T = \dfrac{2898}{\lambda_{max}} = \dfrac{2898}{0.48} = \textbf{5914 K \ (Ans.)}$

(ii) The heat flux at the surface of the sun, $(E)_{sun}$:

$$(E)_{sun} = \sigma T^4 = 5.67 \times 10^{-8} \ T^4 = 5.67 \left(\frac{T}{100}\right)^4$$

$$= 5.67 \times \left(\frac{5914}{100}\right)^4 = \textbf{6.936} \times \textbf{10}^7 \textbf{ W/m}^2 \textbf{(Ans.)}$$

Example 11.3. *Calculate the following for an industrial furnace in the form of a black body and emitting radiation at 2500°C :*

(i) *Monochromatic emissive power at 1.2 μm length,*

(ii) *Wavelength at which the emission is maximum,*

(iii) *Maximum emissive power,*

(iv) *Total emissive power, and*

(v) *Total emissive power of the furnace if it is assumed as a real surface with emissivity equal to 0.9.*

Solution. *Given* : $T = 2500 + 273 = 2773K$; $\lambda = 1.2 \ \mu m$, $\varepsilon = 0.9$

(i) Monochromatic emissive power at 1.2 μm length, $(E_\lambda)_b$:

According to Planck's law,

$$(E_\lambda)_b = \frac{C_1 \lambda^{-5}}{\exp\left(\dfrac{C_2}{\lambda T}\right) - 1} \qquad \qquad \ldots[\text{Eqn. (11.15)}]$$

where, $C_1 = 3.742 \times 10^8 \text{ W.}\mu m^4/m^2 = 0.3742 \times 10^{-15} \text{ W.m}^4/m^2$, and

$C_2 = 1.4388 \times 10^{-2} \text{ mK}$

Substituting the values, we get

$$(E_\lambda)_b = \frac{0.3742 \times 10^{-15} \times (1.2 \times 10^{-6})^{-5}}{\exp\left(\dfrac{1.4388 \times 10^{-2}}{1.2 \times 10^{-6} \times 2773}\right) - 1} = \frac{1.5 \times 10^{14}}{74.48} = 2.014 \times 10^{12} \text{ W/m}^2 \text{ (Ans.)}$$

(ii) **Wavelength at which the emission is maximum, λ_{max}:**

Accodrding to Wien's displacement law,

$$\lambda_{max} = \frac{2898}{T} = \frac{2898}{2773} = 1.045 \ \mu m \ \text{(Ans.)}$$

(iii) **Maximum emissive power, $(E_{\lambda b})$max:**

$(E_{\lambda b})_{max} = 1.285 \times 10^{-5} \ T^5 \text{ W/m}^2 \text{ per metre length}$ [Eqn. (11.19)]

$= 1.285 \times 10^{-5} \times (2773)^5 = 2.1 \times 10^{12} \text{ W/m}^2 \text{ per metre length (Ans.)}$

[**Note:** At high temperature the difference between $(E_\lambda)_b$ and $(E_{\lambda b})_{max}$ is very small].

(iv) **Total emissive power, E_b :**

$$E_b = \sigma T^4 = 5.67 \times 10^{-8} (2773)^4 = 5.67 \left(\frac{2773}{100}\right)^4 = 3.352 \times 10^6 \text{ W/m}^2. \text{ (Ans.)}$$

(v) **Total emissive power, E with emissivity (ε) = 0.9 :**

$$E = \varepsilon \ \sigma T^4 = 0.9 \times 5.67 \left(\frac{2773}{100}\right)^4 = 3.017 \times 10^6 \text{ W/m}^2. \text{ (Ans.)}$$

Example 11.4. *Assuming the sun (diameter = 1.4×10^9 m) as a black body having a surface temperature of 5750 K and at a mean distance of 15×10^{10} m from the earth (diameter = 12.8×10^6 m), estimate the following:*

(i) *The total energy emitted by the sun,*

(ii) *The emission received per m^2 just outside the atmosphere of the earth,*

(iii) *The total energy received by the earth if no radiation is blocked by the atmosphere of the earth, and*

(iv) *The energy received by a 1.6 m × 1.6 m solar collector whose normal is inclined at 50° to the sun. The energy loss through the atmosphere is 42 percent and diffuse radiation is 22 percent of direct radiation.*

Solution: Radius of the sun, $r_s = \dfrac{1.4 \times 10^9}{2} = 0.7 \times 10^9$ m

Mean distance of the sun from the earth,

$R = 15 \times 10^{10}$ m

Radius of the earth $r_e = \dfrac{12.8 \times 10^6}{2} = 6.4 \times 10^6$ m

Surface temperature of the sun, $T = 5750 \ K$

(i) **The total energy emitted by the sun, E_b:**

$$E_b = \sigma \ AT^4 = 5.67 \times 10^{-8} \times 4\pi \ r_s^2 \times (5750)^4$$

$$= 5.67 \times 4\pi \times (0.7 \times 10^9)^2 \times \left(\frac{5750}{100}\right)^4$$

$$= 3.816 \times 10^{26} \text{ W (Ans.)}$$

(ii) **The emission received per m^2:**

The sun may be regarded as a point source at a distance of 15×10^{10} m from the earth. The *mean area* just outside the earth's atmosphere over which the radiation will fall is

$$= 4\pi R^2 = 4\pi \times (15 \times 10^{10})^2 \text{ m}^2$$

∴ The emission received outside the earth's atmosphere

$$= \frac{3.816 \times 10^{26}}{4\pi \times (15 \times 10^{10})^2} = 1349.6 \text{ W/m}^2 \text{ (Ans.)}$$

(iii) **The total energy received by the earth:**

Assuming the earth a spherical body, the energy received by it will be proportional to the perpendicular projected area, *i.e.*, that of a circle ($= \pi r_e^2$).

∴   Energy received by the earth $= 1349.6 \times \pi \times (6.4 \times 10^6)^2$

$$= 1.736 \times 10^{17} \text{ W (Ans.)}$$

(iv) **The energy received by the solar collector:**

The direct energy reaching the earth $= (1 - 0.42) \times 1349.6 = 782.77 \text{ W/m}^2$

The diffuse radiation $= 0.22 \times 782.77 = 172.21 \text{ W/m}^2$

∴ Total radiation reaching the collector $= 782.77 + 172.21 \simeq 955 \text{ W/m}^2$

The projected area $= A \cos\theta = 1.6 \times 1.6 \times \cos 40° = 1.961 \text{ m}^2$

∴ Energy received by the solar collector

$$= 955 \times 1.961 = 1872.7 \text{ W (Ans.)}$$

HIGHLIGHTS

1. 'Radiation' heat transfer is defined as "the transfer of energy across a system boundary by means of an electromagnetic mechanism which is caused solely by a temperature difference.

2. The *emissive power* (E) is defined as the total amount of radiation emitted by a body per unit area per unit time; it is expressed in W/m^2.

3. *Emissivity* (ε) is defined as the ability of the surface of a body to radiate heat. It is also defined as the ratio of the emissive power of any body to the emissive power of a black body of equal temperature $\left(i.e., \ \varepsilon = \dfrac{E}{E_b} \right)$.

4. A *black body* is one which neither reflects nor transmits any part of the incident radiation but absorbs all of it.

5. A *gray body* is one whose absorptivity of a surface does not vary with temperature and wavelength of the incident radiation $[\alpha = (\alpha)_\lambda = \text{constant}]$.

6. The *Stefan-Boltzmann* law states that the emissive power of a black body is directly proportional to the fourth power of its absolute temperature.

    i.e., $E_b = \sigma T^4$

    where, E_b = Emissive power of a black body, and

    σ = Stefan-Boltzmann constant $= 5.67 \times 10^{-8} \text{ W/m}^2 \text{ K}^4$

7. *Kirchhoff's law* states that at any temperature the ratio of total emissive power E to the total absorptivity α is constant for all substances which are in thermal equilibrium with their environment.

8. *Planck's law* is given by:

    $$(E_\lambda)_b = \frac{C_1 \lambda^{-5}}{\exp\left[\dfrac{C_2}{\lambda T}\right] - 1}$$

    where, $C_1 = 2\pi c^2 h = 3.742 \times 10^8 \text{ W.μm}^4/\text{m}^2;$

$$C_2 = \frac{ch}{k} = 1.4388 \times 10^4 \ \mu mK$$

[C = velocity of light in vacuum $\simeq 3 \times 10^8$ m/s; h = Planck's constant = 6.625×10^{-34} Js; k = Boltzmann constant = 1.3805×10^{-23} J/K]

9. *Wien's displacement law* states that the product of λ_{max} and T is constant *i.e.*,
    $$\lambda_{max} \ T = \text{constant} \ (\simeq 2900 \ \mu m \ \text{K})$$
    A combination of Planck's law and Wien's displacement law yields the condition for the maximum monochromatic emissive power for a black body.
    $$(E_{\lambda b})_{max} = 1.285 \times 10^{-5} \ T^5 \ \text{W/m}^2 \text{ per metre length.}$$

10. The *intensity of radiation* (I) is defined as the rate of energy leaving a space in a given direction per unit solid angle per unit area of the emitting surface normal to the mean direction in space.

11. *Lambert's cosine law* states that the total emissive power E_θ from a radiating plane surface in any direction is directly proportional to the cosine of the angle of emission.

    or $\qquad\qquad E_\theta = E_n \cos \theta \qquad$ ... (true only for diffuse radiation surface)

    where E_n is the total emissive power of the radiating surface in the direction of its normal.

THEORETICAL QUESTIONS

1. Define 'radiation heat transfer'.
2. Enumerate the factors on which the rate of emission of radiation by a body depend.
3. Define the following terms:
    - (*i*) Total emissive power (E)
    - (*ii*) Monochromatic emissive power (E_λ),
    - (*iii*) Emissivity, and
    - (*iv*) Intensity of radiation.
4. Define the terms absorptivity, reflectivity and transmittivity of radiation.
5. What is a 'black body'? How does it differ from a gray body?
6. State and prove Kirchhoff's law of radiation.
7. State Planck's law.
8. State Stefan-Boltzmann law.
9. State and explain Wien's displacement law.
10. What is 'Intensity of radiation'?
11. Define Lambert's law of radiation.

UNSOLVED EXAMPLES

1. The effective temperature of a body having an area of 0.1 m^2 is 627°C. Calculate: (*i*) The total rate of energy emission, (*ii*) The intensity of normal radiation and (*iii*) The wavelength of maximum monochromatic emissive power. **[Ans.** (*i*) 3720 W, (*ii*) 11841.4 W/m^2.sr, (*iii*) 3.22 μm]

2. Assuming the sun to be a black body emitting radiation with maximum intensity at $\lambda = 0.5$ μm, calculate the surface temperature of the sun and the heat flux at its surface.
    [Ans. 5796 K, 6.398×10^7 W/m^2]

3. Assuming the sun (diameter = 1.4×10^9 m) as a black body having a surface temperature of 5800 K and at a mean distance of 15×10^{10} m from the earth (diameter = 12.8×10^6 m), estimate : (*i*) The total energy emitted by the sun, (*ii*) The emission received per m^2 just outside the atmosphere of the earth, (*iii*) The total energy received by the earth if no radiation is blocked by the atmosphere of the earth, and (*iv*) The energy received by a 1.5 m $\times$ 1.5 m solar collector whose normal is inclined at 45° to the sun. The energy loss through the atmosphere is 40 per cent and the diffuse radiation is 20 per cent of direct radiation. **[Ans.** (*i*) 3.95×10^{26} W, (*ii*) 1397 W, (*iii*) 1.797×10^{17} W, (*iv*) 1598.9 W]

Radiation Exchange Between Surfaces

12.1. INTRODUCTION

In chapter 11 we have dealt with basic laws for the emission and absorption of radiation by different surfaces. The actual process of relative heat exchange between different surfaces takes place in the presence of either a non-participation of medium (one where the surfaces exchanging heat are separated by vacuum or by a medium that does not interfere with the propagation of radiation) or a participating medium (one which tends to interfere with the propagation of radiation because it may absorb, emit or scatter radiation). Most of the gases meet the requirements of non-participating medium to an excellent approximation; exception are carbon dioxide and water vapours which have high absorptivities at certain wavelength of infrared radiation. In this chapter we shall deal with the radiation heat transfer between different types of surfaces both in non-participating and participating media and the following *assumptions* be made: (*i*) *All surfaces have uniform properties over their whole extent* (*ii*) *Each surface is considered to be either gray or black.* (*iii*) *The absorptivity of surface is independent of the temperature of the source of the incident radiation and equals its emissivity* and (*iv*) *Radiation and reflection processes are diffused.*

12.2. RADIATION EXCHANGE BETWEEN BLACK BODIES SEPARATED BY A NON-ABSORBING MEDIUM

Refer Fig. 12.1. Let' us consider heat exchange between elementary areas dA_1 and dA_2 of two black radiating bodies, separated by a non-absorbing medium, and having areas A_1 and A_2 and temperatures T_1 and T_2 respectively. The elementary areas are at a distance r apart and the normals to these areas make angles θ_1 and θ_2 with the line joining them. Each elemental area subtends a solid angle at the centre of the other. Let $d\omega_1$ be subtended at dA_1 by dA_2 and $d\omega_2$ subtended at dA_2 by dA_1. Then

$$d\omega_1 = \frac{dA_2 \cos \theta_2}{r^2}, \text{ and } d\omega_2 = \frac{dA_1 \cos \theta_1}{r^2}$$

$$...(12.1)$$

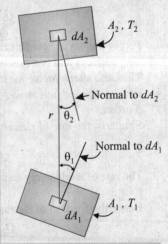

The energy leaving dA_1 in the direction given by the angle per unit solid angle $= I_{b1} dA_1 \cos \theta_1$.

where, Ib = Black body intensity, and

$dA_1 \cos \theta_1$ = Projection of dA_1 on the line between the centres.

The rate of radiant energy leaving dA_1 and striking on dA_2 is given by

$$dQ_{1-2} = I_{b1} dA_1 \cos \theta_1 . d\omega_1$$

$$= \frac{I_{b1} \cos \theta_1 \cos \theta_2 \, dA_1 \, dA_2}{r^2} \qquad ...(12.2)$$

Fig. 12.1. Radiation heat exchange between two black surface.

This energy is absorbed by the elementary area dA_2, since both the surfaces are black. The quantity of energy radiated by dA_2 and absorbed by dA_1 is given by

$$dQ_{1-2} = \frac{I_{b2} \cos \theta_2 \cos \theta_1 \, dA_2 \, dA_1}{r^2} \qquad ...(12.3)$$

The net rate of transfer of energy between dA_1 and dA_2 is

$$dQ_{12} = dQ_{1-2} - dQ_{2-1}$$

$$= \frac{dA_1 \, dA_2 \cos \theta_1 \cos \theta_2}{r^2} (I_{b1} - I_{b2})$$

But, $$I_{b1} = \frac{E_{b1}}{\pi} \text{ and } I_{b2} = \frac{E_{b2}}{\pi} \qquad ...[Eqn. (11.23)]$$

$\therefore$ $$dQ_{12} = \frac{dA_1 \, dA_2 \cos \theta_1 \cos \theta_2}{\pi \, r^2} (E_{b1} - E_{b2}) \qquad ...(12.4)$$

or, $$dQ_{12} = \frac{\sigma \, dA_1 \, dA_2 \cos \theta_1 \cos \theta_2}{\pi \, r^2} (T_1^4 - T_2^4) \qquad ...(12.5)$$

The rate of total net heat transfer for the total areas A_1 and A_2 is given by

$$Q_{12} = \int dQ_{12} = \sigma (T_1^4 - T_2^4) \int_{A_1} \int_{A_2} \frac{\cos \theta_1 \cos \theta_2 \, dA_1 \, dA_2}{r^2} \quad ...(12.6)$$

The rate of radiant energy emitted by A_1 that falls on A_2, from eqn. (12.2), is given by

$$Q_{1-2} = I_{b1} \int_{A_1} \int_{A_2} \frac{\cos \theta_1 \cos \theta_2 \, dA_1 \, dA_2}{r^2}$$

$$Q_{1-2} = \sigma T_1^4 \int_{A_1} \int_{A_2} \frac{\cos \theta_1 \cos \theta_2 \, dA_1 \, dA_2}{\pi \, r^2} \qquad ...(12.7)$$

The rate of total energy radiated by A_1 is given by

$$Q_1 = A_1 \sigma T_1^4$$

Hence the fraction of the rate of energy leaving area A_1 and impinging on area A_2 is given by

$$\frac{Q_{1-2}}{Q_1} = \frac{1}{A_1} \int_{A_1} \int_{A_2} \frac{\cos \theta_1 \cos \theta_2 \, dA_1 \, dA_2}{\pi \, r^2} \qquad ...(12.8)$$

or,

$$\frac{Q_{1-2}}{Q_1} = F_{1-2} \qquad \qquad ...(12.8\ a)$$

F_{1-2} is known as 'configuration factor' or 'surface factor' or 'view factor' between the two radiating surfaces and is a function of geometry only.

Thus, the *shape factor* may be defined as *"The fraction of radiative energy that is diffused from one surface element and strikes the other surface directly with no intervening reflections."*

Further,

$$Q_{1-2} = F_{1-2}\, A_1\, \sigma\, T_1^{\,4} \qquad \qquad ...(12.9)$$

Similarly, the rate of radiant energy by A_2 that falls on A_1, from eqn. (12.3), is given by

$$Q_{2-1} = \sigma\, T_2^{\,4} \int_{A_2} \int_{A_1} \frac{\cos\theta_1\ \cos\theta_2\ dA_1\ dA_2}{\pi\, r^2}$$

The rate of total energy radiated by A_2 is given by

$$Q_2 = A_2\, \sigma\, T_2^{\,4}$$

Hence the fraction of the rate of energy leaving area A_2 and impinging on area A_1 is given by

$$\frac{Q_{2-1}}{Q_2} = \frac{1}{A_2} \int_{A_1} \int_{A_2} \frac{\cos\theta_1\ \cos\theta_2\ dA_1\ dA_2}{\pi\, r^2} \qquad \qquad ...(12.10)$$

or,

$$\frac{Q_{2-1}}{Q_2} = F_{2-1}$$

F_{2-1} is the shape factor of A_2 with respect to A_1.

$$Q_{2-1} = F_{2-1}\, A_2\, \sigma\, T_2^{\,4} \qquad \qquad ...(12.11)$$

From eqns. (12.8) and (12.10), we get

$$A_1\, F_{1-2} = A_2\, F_{2-1} \qquad \qquad ...(12.12)$$

The above result is known as **reciprocity theorem**. It indicates that the net radiant interchange may be evaluated by computing one way configuration factor from either surface to the other. Thus the net rate of heat transfer between two surfaces A_1 and A_2 is given by

$$Q_{12} = A_1\, F_{1-2}\, \sigma\, (T_1^{\,4} - T_2^{\,4})$$
$$= A_2\, F_{2-1}\, \sigma\, (T_1^{\,4} - T_2^{\,4}) \qquad \qquad ...(12.13)$$

It may be noted that eqn. (12.13) is applicable to *black surfaces only and must not be used for surfaces having emissivities very different from unity.*

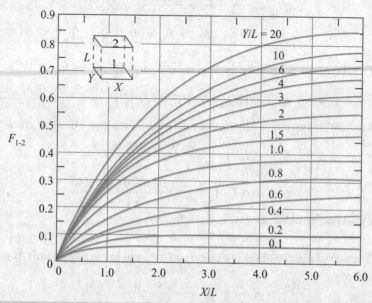

Fig. 12.2. Shape factor for aligned parallel plates.

The evaluation of the integral equation (12.8) for determining the shape factor is rather complex and cumbersome. Therefore, results have been obtained and presented in graphical form for the geometries normally encountered in engineering practice. Geometrical factors for parallel planes (discs and rectangles) directly opposed and those for radiation between perpendicular rectangles with a common edge are shown in Figs. 12.2 to 12.4.

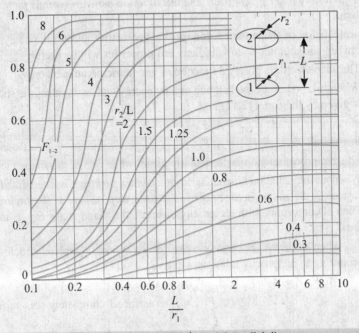

Fig. 12.3. Shape factor for coaxial parallel discs.

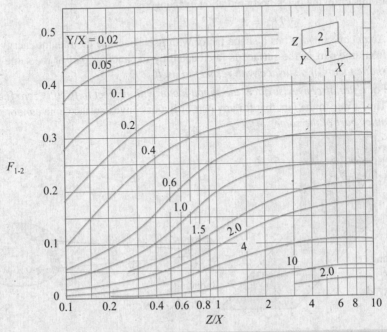

Fig. 12.4. Shape factor for perpendicular rectangles with a common edge.

12.3. SHAPE FACTOR ALGEBRA AND SALIENT FEATURES OF THE SHAPE FACTOR

In order to compute the shape factor for certain geometric arrangements for which shape factors or equations are not available, the concept of shape factor as fraction of intercepted energy, and reciprocity theorem can be used. The shape factors for these geometries can be derived in terms of *known shape factors of other geometries. The interrelation between various factors is called* **shape factor algebra.**

For the calculation of shape factors for specific geometries and for the analysis of radiant heat exchange between surfaces, the following facts and properties will be useful:

1. The shape factor is purely a function of geometric parameters only.

2. When two bodies are exchanging radiant energy with each other, the shape factor relation is given by the eqn. (12.12) *i.e.*,
$$A_1 F_{1-2} = A_2 F_{2-1}$$
    In general, $\qquad A_i F_{i-j} = A_j F_{j-i}$ ...(Reciprocity theorem)
    This reciprocal relation is particularly useful when one of the shape factors is *unity*.

3. When all the radiation emanating from a *convex surface* 1 is intercepted by the enclosing surface 2, the *shape factor of convex surface with respect to the enclosure* F_{1-2} *is unity.* Then in conformity with reciprocity theorem, the shape factor F_{2-1} is merely the ratio of areas.

> *i.e.*, when surface A_1 is *entirely convex*, say a sphere, completely enclosed by A_2, then according to reciprocity relation, we have
> $$A_1 F_{1-2} = A_2 F_{2-1} \quad \text{and} \quad A_1 = A_2 F_{2-1}$$
> $$(\because F_{1-2} = 1, \text{ as surface 1 completely sees surface 2})$$
> or $\qquad F_{2-1} = \dfrac{A_1}{A_2}$ (*i.e.*, ratio of areas), and $F_{2-1} + F_{2-2} = 1$
>
> In this case, the black body radiation exchange is
> $$Q_{12} = A_1 \sigma (T_1^4 - T_2^4)$$

4. A *concave surface* has a shape factor with itself because the radiant energy coming out from one part of the surface is intercepted by the another part of the same surface. *The shape factor of a surface with respect to itself is* F_{1-1}.

5. For *a flat or convex surface, the shape factor with respect to itself is zero* (*i.e.*, $F_{1-1} = 0$). This is due to the fact that for any part of flat or convex surface, one *cannot see/view any other part of the same surface.*

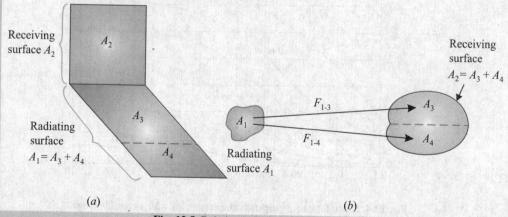

(a)   (b)

Fig. 12.5. Relation between shape factors.

6. If two surfaces A_1 and A_2 are parallel and large, radiation occurs across the gap between them so that $A_1 = A_2$ and all radiation emitted by one falls on the other; then

$$F_{1-2} = F_{2-1} = 1$$

7. If one of the two surfaces (say A_i) is divided into sub-areas $A_{i1}, A_{i2}, ... A_{in}$, then

$$A_i \, F_{i-j} = \sum A_{in} \, F_{in-j} \qquad \qquad ...(12.15)$$

Refer to Fig. 12.5 (a) : Radiating surface A_1 has been split up into areas A_3 and A_4; we have

$$A_1 \, F_{1-2} = A_3 \, F_{3-2} + A_4 \, F_{4-2}$$

Evidently, $\qquad \qquad F_{1-2} \neq F_{3-2} + F_{4-2}$

Thus if the radiant surface is subdivided, the shape factor for that surface with respect to the receiving surface is *not equal to the sum* of the individual shape factors.

Refer to Fig. 12.5 (b): Receiving surface A_2 has been divided into subareas A_3 and A_4; we have

$$A_1 \, F_{1-2} = A_1 \, F_{1-3} + A_1 \, F_{1-4}$$

or $\qquad \qquad F_{1-2} = F_{1-3} + F_{1-4}$

Obviously the shape factor from a radiating surface to a subdivided receiving surface is simply the *sum of individual shape factors*.

8. Let us now take the case of an enclosure in which one surface is exchanging radiation with all the other surfaces in the enclosure *including itself*, if it *happens to be a concave surface*; this is because a concave surface can see/view another part of it (the shape factor of a convex surface with its enclosure is *always unity* because all the heat radiated from a convex surface is intercepted by its enclosure but *not vice- versa*).

If the enclosure comprises n surfaces, then the energy radiated from one surface is always intercepted by the other $(n-1)$ surfaces, and the surface itself if it is a concave one. This is called **principle of conservation.**

Heat transfer equipment

$$F_{1-1} + F_{1-2} + F_{1-3} + ... + F_{1-n} = 1 = \sum_{i=1}^{n} F_{1-i} \qquad ...(12.16)$$

$$F_{2-1} + F_{2-2} + F_{2-3} + ... + F_{2-n} = 1$$

$$F_{n-1} + F_{n-2} + F_{n-3} + ... + F_{n-n} = 1$$

In general $\sum_{j=1}^{n} F_{i-j} = 1$ for $i = 1, 2, 3, ... n$

Example 12.1. *Assuming the sun to radiate as a black body, calculate its temperature from the data given below:*

The average radiant energy flux incident upon the earth's atmosphere (solar constant) = 1380 W/m²

Radius of the sun = 7.0 × 10⁸ m

Distance between the sun and the earth = 15 × 10¹⁰ m

Solution. *Given:* Solar constant = 1380 W/m²; r_s (radius of the sun) = 7×10^8 m

r (distance between the sun and the earth) = 15×10^{10} m

Surface temperature of the sun, T :

Refer Fig. 12.6. The heat flow from small area dA_1 (on the surface of sun) to the small area dA_2 (on the surface of the earth), is given by,

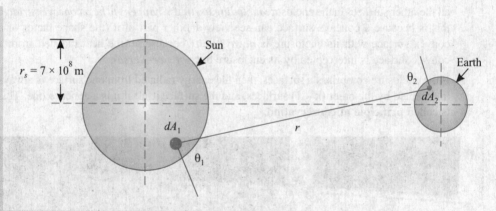

Fig. 12.6

$$dQ_{1-2} = \frac{I_{b1} \cos \theta_1 \cos \theta_2 \, dA_1 \, dA_2}{r^2} \qquad ...[\text{Eqn. (12.2)}]$$

or, $$\frac{dQ_{1-2}}{dA_2 \cos \theta_2} = \frac{E_b}{\pi \, r^2} \, dA_1 \cos \theta_1 \qquad \left(\because I_b = \frac{E_b}{\pi} \right)$$

Integrating both sides, we get

$$\int \frac{dQ_{1-2}}{dA_2 \cos \theta_2} = \frac{E_b}{\pi \, r^2} \int dA_1 \cos \theta_1$$

Also, solar constant = $\int \dfrac{dQ_{1-2}}{dA_2 \cos \theta_2}$

$\therefore$ Solar constant = $\dfrac{E_b}{\pi \, r^2} \int dA_1 \cos \theta_1$

$\int dA_1 \cos \theta_1 = A_1 = \pi \, r_s^2$, here θ_1 is taken as zero because all rays from the sun falling on the earth due to extremely long distance are considered parallel to each other; therefore, cos 0° = 1.

$$\therefore \qquad \text{Solar constant} = \frac{E_b}{\pi\, r^2} \times \pi\, r_s^2 = 1380$$

But,
$$E_b = \sigma\, T^4$$

$$\therefore \qquad \frac{\sigma\, T^4}{\pi\, r^2} \times \pi\, r_s^2 = 1380$$

or,
$$\sigma\, T^4 = 1380 \times \left(\frac{r}{r_s}\right)^2$$

or,
$$5.67 \times \left(\frac{T}{100}\right)^4 = 1380 \times \left(\frac{15 \times 10^{10}}{7 \times 10^8}\right)^2$$

or,
$$\left(\frac{T}{100}\right)^4 = 1117.58 \times 10^4 \text{ or } \frac{T}{100} = (1117.58 \times 10^4)^{1/4} = 57.82$$

or,
$$T = \textbf{5782 K (Ans.)}$$

Example 12.2. *Calculate the shape factors for the configurations shown in the Fig. 12.7.*

Solution. The shape factors can be worked out by using *summation rule*, the *reciprocity theorem* and from the *inspection of geometry*.

(*i*) *A black body inside a black enclosure:*

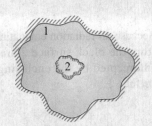
A black body inside
a black enclosure
(*i*)

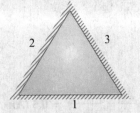
A tube with cross-section of
an equilateral triangle
(*ii*)

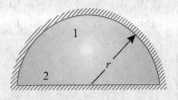
Hemispherical surface
and a plane surface
(*iii*)

Fig. 12.7

$$F_{2-1} = 1 \qquad \text{...Because all radiation emanating from the black surface is intercepted by the enclosing surface 1.}$$

$$F_{1-1} + F_{1-2} = 1 \qquad \text{... By } summation\ rule \text{ for radiation from surface 1}$$

$$A_1 F_{1-2} = A_2 F_{2-1} \qquad \text{... By } reciprocity\ theorem$$

or,
$$F_{1-2} = \frac{A_2}{A_1} F_{2-1}$$

$$\therefore \qquad F_{1-1} = 1 - F_{1-2} = 1 - \frac{A_2}{A_1} F_{2-1} = 1 - \frac{A_2}{A_1} \qquad (\because F_{2-1} = 1)$$

Hence,
$$F_{1-1} = \mathbf{1 - \frac{A_2}{A_1}} \textbf{ (Ans.)}$$

(ii) *A tube with cross-section of an equilateral triangle:*

$$F_{1-1} + F_{1-2} + F_{1-3} = 1 \qquad \text{... By summation rule}$$
$$F_{1-1} = 0 \qquad \text{... Because the flat surface 1 } cannot \text{ see itself.}$$

$\therefore$
$$F_{1-2} + F_{1-3} = 1$$
$$F_{1-2} = F_{1-3} = \textbf{0.5 (Ans.)} \qquad \text{... By symmetry}$$

Similarly, considering radiation from surface 2 :

$$F_{2-1} + F_{2-2} + F_{2-3} = 1$$
or,
$$F_{2-1} + F_{2-3} = 1 \qquad (\because F_{2-2} = 0)$$
or,
$$F_{2-3} = 1 - F_{2-1}$$
$$A_1 F_{1-2} = A_2 F_{2-1} \qquad \text{... By reciprocity theorem}$$

or,
$$F_{2-1} = \frac{A_1}{A_2} F_{1-2} = F_{1-2} \qquad (\because A_1 = A_2)$$

$\therefore$
$$F_{2-3} = 1 - F_{1-2} = 1 - 0.5 = \textbf{0.5 (Ans.)}$$

(iii) *Hemispherical surface and a plane surface:*

$$F_{1-1} + F_{1-2} = 1 \qquad \text{... By summation rule}$$
$$A_1 F_{1-2} = A_2 F_{2-1} \qquad \text{... By reciprocity theorem}$$

or,
$$F_{1-2} = \frac{A_2}{A_1} F_{2-1}$$

But,
$$F_{2-1} = 1 \qquad \text{... Because all radiation emanating from the black surface 2 are interecpted by the enclosing surface 1.}$$

$\therefore$
$$F_{1-2} = \frac{A_2}{A_1} = \frac{\pi r^2}{2 \pi r^2} = \textbf{0.5 (Ans.)}$$

Thus in case of a hemispherical surface half the radiation falls on surface 2 and the other half is intercepted by the hemisphere itself.

Example 12.3. *Explain the meaning of the term geometric factor in relation to heat exchange by radiation. Derive an expression for the geometric factor F_{11} for the inside surface of a black hemispherical cavity of radius R with respect to itself.* (U.P.S.C., 1994)

Solution. • **Geometric factor** *is defined as the fraction of radiative energy that is diffused from one surface element and strikes the other surface directly with no intervening reflection.*

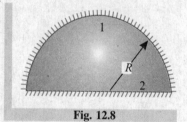

Fig. 12.8

- The *geometric factor* depends only on the *specific geometry of the emitter and the collection surfaces.*
- The geometric factor is represented by the symbol F_{i-j} which means the shape factor from a surface A_i to another surface A_j. Thus, the geometric factor F_{1-2} of surface A_1 to surface A_2 is

$$F_{1-2} = \frac{\text{Direct radiation from surface 1 incident upon surface 2}}{\text{Total radiation from emitting surface}}$$

Geometric factor F_{1-1} for the inside surface of a black hemispherical cavity of radius R with respect to itself.

$$F_{1-1} = 1 - \frac{A_2}{A_1} = 1 - \frac{\pi R^2}{2 \pi R^2} = 1 - \frac{1}{2} = \textbf{0.5 (Ans.)}$$

Example 12.4. *Derive expressions for shape factors of the cavities (each enclosed on its surface with a flat surface) shown in the Fig. 12.9. Also, calculate the net radiative heat transfer from the cavities, if h = 20 cm, d = 15 cm, temperature inside surface of each cavity = 400° C and the emissivity of each cavity surface is 0.8.*

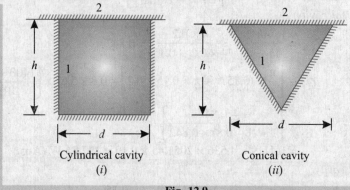

Cylindrical cavity   Conical cavity
(i)   (ii)

Fig. 12.9

Solution :

(i) Cylindrical cavity:

$$F_{1-1} + F_{1-2} = 1 \qquad \text{... By summation rule}$$

or, $\qquad F_{1-1} = 1 - F_{1-2}$

Also, $\qquad F_{2-1} + F_{2-2} = 1 \qquad$ ... By summation rule

$$F_{2-2} = 0 \qquad \text{... Being a flat surface (flat surface cannot see itself).}$$

$$F_{2-1} = 1 \qquad \text{... Because all radiation emitted by the black surface 2 is intercepted by the enclosing surface 1.}$$

$$A_1 F_{1-2} = A_2 F_{2-1} \qquad \text{... By reciprocity theorem}$$

or, $\qquad F_{1-2} = \dfrac{A_2}{A_1} F_{2-1} = \dfrac{A_2}{A_1}$

or, $\qquad F_{1-1} = 1 - F_{1-2} = 1 - \dfrac{A_2}{A_1}$

or, $\qquad F_{1-1} = 1 - \dfrac{\dfrac{\pi}{4} d^2}{\dfrac{\pi}{4} d^2 + \pi d h} = 1 - \dfrac{d}{d + 4h} = \dfrac{d + 4h - d}{4h + d} = \dfrac{4h}{4h + d}$ **(Ans.)**

(ii) Conical cavity:

$$F_{1-1} = 1 - \dfrac{A_2}{A_1} \qquad \text{... This relation (calculated above) is applicable in this case (and all such cases) also.}$$

$$= 1 - \dfrac{\dfrac{\pi}{4} d^2}{\left[\dfrac{\pi d \times \text{slant height}}{2} \right]} = 1 - \dfrac{\dfrac{\pi}{4} d^2}{\dfrac{\pi d}{2} \times \left[\sqrt{h^2 + \left(\dfrac{d}{2} \right)^2} \right]}$$

or, $\qquad F_{1-1} = 1 - \dfrac{d}{\sqrt{4h^2 + d^2}} \qquad$ **(Ans.)**

Net radiative heat transfer:

The net radiative heat transfer from a cavity can be calculated by using the following formulae:

$$Q_1 = A_1 \, \varepsilon_1 \, \sigma \, T_1^{\,4} \left[\frac{1 - F_{1-1}}{1 - (1 - \varepsilon_1) \, F_{1-1}} \right] \qquad\qquad ...(12.17)$$

(i)   *Cylindrical cavity:*

$$F_{1-1} = \frac{4h}{4h + d} = \frac{4 \times 0.2}{4 \times 0.2 + 0.15} = 0.842$$

$$Q_1 = \left[\frac{\pi}{4} \times (0.15)^2 + \pi \times 0.15 \times 0.2 \right] \times 0.8 \times 5.67 \times \left[\frac{(400 + 273)}{100} \right]^4$$

$$\left[\frac{1 - 0.842}{1 - (1 - 0.8) \times 0.842} \right]$$

$$= 0.1119 \times 4.536 \times 2051.45 \times 0.19 = \textbf{197.84 W (Ans.)}$$

(ii)   *Conical cavity:*

$$F_{1-1} = 1 - \frac{d}{\sqrt{4h^2 + d^2}} = 1 - \frac{0.15}{\sqrt{4 \times 0.2^2 + 0.15^2}} = 0.649$$

$$Q_1 = \frac{\pi \times 0.15}{2} \times \left[\sqrt{(0.2)^2 + \left(\frac{0.15}{2} \right)^2} \right] \times 0.8 \times 5.67 \times \left[\frac{400 + 273}{100} \right]^4$$

$$\left[\frac{1 - 0.649}{1 - (1 - 0.8 \times 0.649)} \right]$$

$$= 0.0503 \times 0.8 \times 5.67 \times 2051.45 \times 0.403 = \textbf{188.63 W (Ans.)}$$

Example 12.5. *A small sphere (outside diameter = 60 mm) with a surface temperature of 300° C is located at the geometric centre of a large sphere (inside diameter = 360 mm) with an inner surface temperature of 15° C. Calculate how much of emission from the inner surface of the large sphere is incident upon the outer surface of the small sphere; assume that both sides approach black body behaviour.*

What is the net interchange of heat between the two spheres?

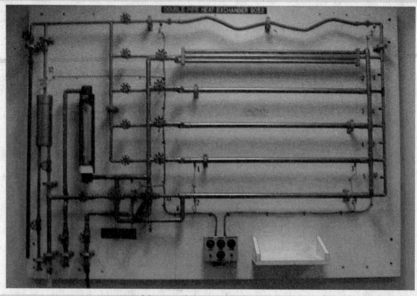

Double pipe heat exchanger (steam)

Solution. *Given:* r_1 (small sphere) $= \dfrac{60}{2} = 30$ mm $= 0.03$ m; r_2 (large sphere) $= \dfrac{360}{2} = 180$ mm $= 0.18$ m.

Since all the radiation being emitted by the small sphere is incident upon and absorbed by the inner surface of the large sphere, therefore, configuration factor between 1 and 2 is $F_{1-2} = 1$.

Now, $\qquad\qquad A_1 F_{1-2} = A_2 F_{2-1}$ $\qquad\qquad\qquad$ ... Reciprocity theorem

or, $\qquad\qquad 4\,\pi\,r_1^{\,2} \times F_{1-2} = 4\,\pi\,r_2^{\,2} \times F_{2-1}$

$\therefore \qquad\qquad F_{2-1} = F_{1-2} \times \dfrac{4\,\pi\,r_1^{\,2}}{4\,\pi\,r_2^{\,2}} = 1 \times \dfrac{r_1^{\,2}}{r_2^{\,2}} = \left(\dfrac{0.03}{0.18}\right)^2 = \textbf{0.0278 (Ans.)}$

Thus 2.78% of the emission from the inner surface of the large sphere is incident upon the small sphere and absorbed by it.

Also, $\qquad\qquad F_{2-1} + F_{2-2} = 1$ $\qquad\qquad\qquad$ ... From energy balance for the large sphere.

or, $\qquad\qquad F_{2-2} = 1 - F_{2-1} = 1 - 0.0278 = 0.9722$

Thus, 97.22% of emission from the large sphere is absorbed by the inner surface of the sphere itself.

$\therefore$ The net interchange of heat between the two spheres is,

$$Q_{net} = F_{1-2}\, A_1\, \sigma\, (T_1^{\,4} - T_2^{\,4})$$

$$= 1 \times (4\pi \times 0.03^2) \times 5.67 \left[\left(\dfrac{300 + 273}{100}\right)^4 - \left(\dfrac{15 + 273}{100}\right)^4 \right]$$

$$= 0.0113 \times 5.67 \times 1009.2 = \textbf{64.66 W (Ans.)}$$

Example 12.6. *A 70 mm thick metal plate with a circular hole of 35 mm diameter along the thickness is maintained at a uniform temperature 250° C. Find the loss of energy to the surroundings at 27° C, assuming the two ends of the hole to be as parallel discs and the metallic surfaces and surroundings have black body characteristics.*

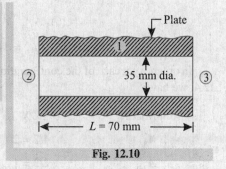

Fig. 12.10

Solution. *Given:* $r_2 = (r_3) = \dfrac{35}{2} = 17.5$ mm $= 0.0175$ m, $L = 70$ mm $= 0.07$ m, $T_1 = 250 + 273 = 523$ K

$$T_{surr.} = 27 + 273 = 300 \text{ K}.$$

Refer Fig. 12.10. Let suffix 1 designate the cavity and the suffices 2 and 3 denote the two ends of the 35 mm dia. hole which are behaving as discs. Thus,

$$\dfrac{L}{r_2} = \dfrac{0.07}{0.0175} = 4; \quad \dfrac{r_3}{L} = \dfrac{0.0175}{0.07} = 0.25$$

With reference to Fig. 12.3, the configuration factor, F_{2-3} is 0.065

Now, $\qquad F_{2-1} + F_{2-2} + F_{2-3} = 1$ $\qquad\qquad\qquad$ ... By summation rule

But, $\qquad\qquad F_{2-2} = 0$

$\therefore \qquad\qquad F_{2-1} = 1 - F_{2-3} = 1 - 0.065 = 0.935$

Also, $\qquad A_1 F_{1-2} = A_2 F_{2-1}$ $\qquad\qquad\qquad$ ... By reciprocating theorem

or,
$$F_{1-2} = \frac{A_2\, F_{2-1}}{A_1} = \frac{\pi \times (0.0175)^2 \times 0.935}{\pi \times 0.035 \times 0.07} = 0.1168$$

$$F_{1-3} = F_{1-2} = 0.1168 \qquad \text{... By symmetry}$$

The total loss of energy = Loss of heat by both ends

$$= A_1\, F_{1-2}\, \sigma\, (T_1^4 - T_{surr}^4) + A_1\, F_{1-3}\, \sigma\, (T_1^4 - T_{surr}^4)$$

$$= 2\, A_1\, F_{1-2}\, \sigma\, (T_1^4 - T_{surr}^4) \qquad\qquad (\because F_{1-2} = F_{1-3})$$

$$= 2 \times (\pi \times 0.035 \times 0.07) \times 0.1168 \times 5.6 \left[\left(\frac{523}{100}\right)^4 - \left(\frac{300}{100}\right)^4 \right] = \textbf{6.8 W (Ans.)}$$

Example 12.7. *In the Fig. 12.11 the areas A_1 and A_2 are perpendicular but do not share the common edge. Find the shape factor F_{1-2} for the arrangement shown.*

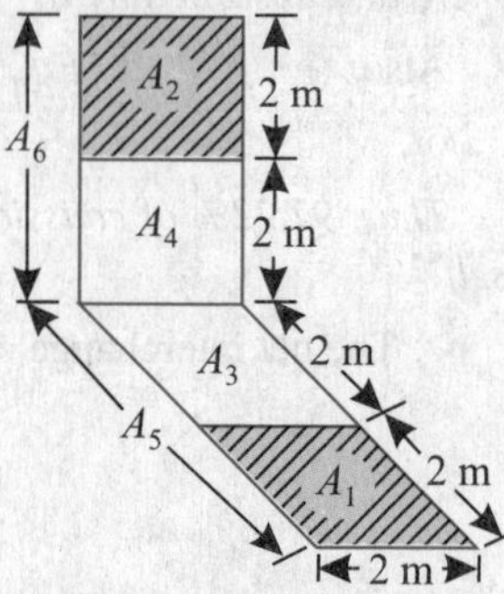

Solution. For such cases, the shape factor is evaluated by introducing hypothetical areas A_3 and A_4, so that the *arrangement of perpendicular surfaces has a common edge.*

Now, $A_5 = A_1 + A_3$, and

$$A_6 = A_2 + A_4$$

Fig. 12.11

Further, $A_5\, F_{5-6} = A_1\, F_{1-6} + A_3\, F_{3-6}$

$$= (A_1\, F_{1-4} + A_1\, F_{1-2}) + A_3\, F_{3-6}$$

$$= [(A_5\, A_{5-4} - A_3\, F_{3-4}) + A_1\, F_{1-2}] + A_3\, F_{3-6}$$

$\therefore \qquad A_1\, F_{1-2} = (A_5\, F_{5-6} + A_3\, F_{3-4}) - (A_5\, F_{5-4} + A_3\, F_{3-6})$ ...(i)

In order to get each of the configuration factor on the right hand side of the expression, using Fig. 12.4, we have:

Surfaces	Z/X	Y/X	Shape factor
A_{56}	4/2 = 2	4/2 = 2	$F_{5-6} \approx 0.15$
A_{34}	2/2 = 1	2/2 = 1	$F_{3-4} = 0.20$
A_{54}	2/2 = 1	4/2 = 2	$F_{5-4} \approx 0.11$
A_{36}	4/2 = 2	2/2 = 1	$F_{3-6} \approx 0.23$

Inserting the above values in eqn. (i), we get

$$(2 \times 2)\, F_{1-2} = [(4 \times 2) \times 0.15 + (2 \times 2) \times 0.2] - [(4 \times 2) \times 0.11 + (2 \times 2) \times 0.23]$$

$$= (1.2 + 0.8) - (0.88 + 0.92) = 0.2$$

$\therefore \qquad F_{1-2} = \dfrac{0.2}{(2 \times 2)} = \textbf{0.05 (Ans.)}$

Example 12.8. *The radiation shape factor of the circular surface of a thin hollow cylinder of 10 cm diameter and 10 cm length is 0.1716. What is the shape factor of the curved surface of the cylinder with respect to itself ?*

(M.U., 1997)

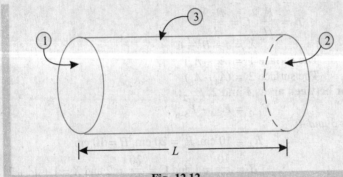

Fig. 12.12

Solution. *Given:* $\qquad r_1 = r_2 = \dfrac{10}{2} = 5$ cm; $L = 10$ cm; $F_{1-2} = 0.1716$

$$F_{1-2} = F_{2-1} = 0.1716 \text{ as } A_1 = A_2$$

The shape factor releation among three surfaces is given by

$$F_{1-1} + F_{1-2} + F_{1-3} = 1 \qquad\qquad\qquad\qquad\qquad \text{...}(i)$$

$$F_{3-3} + F_{3-2} + F_{3-1} = 1 \qquad\qquad\qquad\qquad\qquad \text{...}(ii)$$

But $\qquad\qquad\qquad F_{3-1} = F_{3-2} \qquad\qquad\qquad\qquad\qquad\qquad\qquad \text{...}(iii)$

Also $\qquad\qquad\qquad F_{1-1} = F_{2-2} = 0$

Substituting (*iii*) in (*ii*), we get

$$F_{3-3} + F_{3-1} + F_{3-1} = 1$$

$\therefore \qquad\qquad\qquad F_{3-3} = (1 - 2 \, F_{3-1}) \qquad\qquad\qquad\qquad\qquad \text{...}(iv)$

Also $\qquad\qquad\qquad A_1 \, F_{1-3} = A_3 \, F_{3-1}$

$$\therefore \qquad F_{3-1} = F_{1-3} \times \frac{A_1}{A_3} = F_{1-3} \times \frac{\pi \, r^2}{2\pi \, r \, L} = F_{1-3} \times \frac{r}{2L} \qquad \text{...}(v)$$

From eqn. (*i*), we have $\qquad F_{1-3} = 1 - F_{1-2} \qquad \text{as } F_{1-1} = 0$

$$= 1 - 0.1716 = 0.8284 \qquad\qquad\qquad\qquad \text{...}(vi)$$

Now substituting from (*vi*) in (*v*), we get

$$F_{3-1} = 0.8284 \times \frac{5}{2 \times 10} = 0.2071 \qquad\qquad\qquad \text{...}(vi)$$

Now substituting from (*vii*) in (*iv*), we obtain

$$F_{3-3} = 1 - 2 \times 0.2071 = \mathbf{0.5858}$$

(Ans.)

Example 12.9. *Find the shape factor between two areas 1 and 2 which are in the form of circular rings, coaxial and are in two parallel planes at a distance 10 cm. Area 1 has inner radius 5 cm and outer 10 cm. Area 2 has inner radius of 8 cm and outer 20 cm. Use following formula for calculating shape factor between two circular areas located coaxially in two parallel planes :*

$$F_{1-2} = \frac{1}{2B^2} \left[X - \sqrt{X^2 - 4B^2 \, C^2} \right]$$

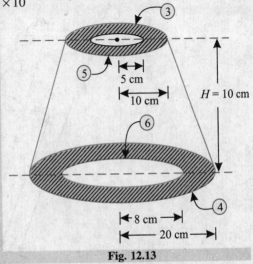

Fig. 12.13

where, $B = \dfrac{R_1}{H}, C = \dfrac{R_2}{H}$

and, $X = 1 + B^2 + C^2.$ (P.U., 1998)

Solution.   The surface $1 = (A_3 - A_5)$

The surface $2 = (A_4 - A_6)$

Shape factor between areas 1 and 2, F_{1-2}:

$$F_{1-2} = F_{3-4} - F_{5-6}$$

For surfaces 3 and 4:

$$R_3 = 10 \text{ cm}, R_4 = 20 \text{ cm}, H = 10 \text{ cm}$$

$\therefore$ $B = \dfrac{10}{10} = 1$ and $C = \dfrac{20}{10} = 2$ and $X = 1 + 1^2 + 2^2 = 6$

$\therefore$ $F_{3-4} = \dfrac{1}{2 \times 1^2} [6 - \sqrt{6^2 - 4 \times 1^2 \times 2^2}] = \dfrac{1}{2} (6 - 4.47) = 0.765$

For surfaces 5 and 6:

$$R_5 = 5 \text{ cm}, R_6 = 8 \text{ cm}, H = 10 \text{ cm}$$

$\therefore$ $B = \dfrac{5}{10} = 0.5$ and $C = \dfrac{8}{10} = 0.8$ and $X = 1 + 0.5^2 + 0.8^2 = 1.89$

$\therefore$ $F_{5-6} = \dfrac{1}{2 \times 0.5^2} [1.89 - \sqrt{1.89^2 - 4 \times 0.5^2 \times 0.8^2}]$

$$= \dfrac{1}{0.5} (1.89 - 1.71) = 0.36$$

$\therefore$ $F_{1-2} = F_{3-4} - F_{5-6} = 0.765 - 0.36 = \mathbf{0.405}$ **(Ans.)**

Example 12.10. *A truncated cone has top and bottom diamters of 20 cm and 10 cm respectively and a height of 10 cm. Calculate the shape factor between the top surface and side (conical surface) and also the shape factor between the side and itself. The fraction of radiation leaving the top surface which is intercepted by the bottom surface is 0.12.*   (M.U., 1997)

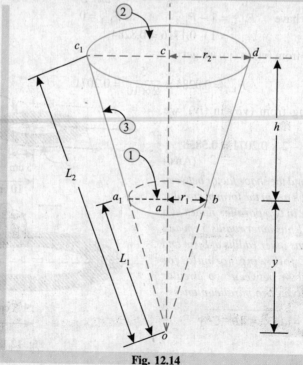

Fig. 12.14

Solution. First we have to find the area of the curved surface of the frustrum in terms of r_1, r_2 and h.

Refer to Fig. 12.14. From the symmetrical triangles Δoab and ∇ocd, we can write $\dfrac{r_1}{y} = \dfrac{r_2}{y + h}$

$$\therefore \qquad y = \frac{r_1\, h}{r_2 - r_1} \qquad\qquad ...(i)$$

Area (A) of the curved surface of the frustrum $a_1 bdc_1$, is given by

$$A = \text{Area of cone } oc_1 d - \text{Area of cone } oa_1 b$$

$$= \pi\, r_2\, L_2 - \pi\, r_1\, L_1$$

$$= \pi \left[r_2 \left\{ \sqrt{(h+y)^2 + r_2^2} \right\} - r_1 \left\{ \sqrt{y^2 + r_1^2} \right\} \right] \qquad\qquad ...(ii)$$

Now substituting the value of y from (i) in (ii), we get

$$A = \pi \left[r_2 \left\{ \sqrt{\left(h + \frac{r_1\, h}{r_2 - r_1}\right)^2 + r_2^2} \right\} - r_1 \left\{ \sqrt{\left(\frac{r_1\, h}{r_2 - r_1}\right)^2 + r_1^2} \right\} \right]$$

Simplifying the above equation, we get

$$A = \pi\, (r_2 + r_1)\, \sqrt{(r_2 - r_1)^2 + h^2} \qquad\qquad ...(iii)$$

The surfaces 1, 2 and 3 are indicated as shown in Fig. 12.14

The given data is:

$$r_1 = \frac{10}{2} = 5 \text{ cm}, \; r_2 = \frac{20}{2} = 10 \text{ cm and } h = 10 \text{ cm}$$

The area of the inclined plane A_3 is given by

$$A_3 = \pi\, (r_1 + r_2)\, \sqrt{(r_2 - r_1)^2 + h^2}$$

$$= \pi\, (5 + 10)\, \sqrt{(10 - 5)^2 + 10^2} = 15\, \pi\, \sqrt{125} = 526.86 \text{ cm}^2$$

The fraction of radiation leaving the top surface and intercepted by the bottom surface is 0.12.

$$\therefore \qquad F_{2-1} = 0.12$$

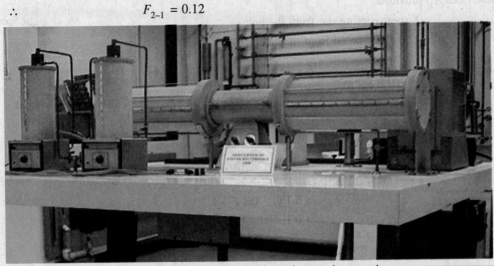

Heat conduction through straight and tapered copper bars.

Also, $\qquad\qquad\qquad A_1 F_{1-2} = A_2 F_{2-1}$ ... By reciprocity theorem

$\therefore \qquad\qquad\qquad F_{1-2} = \dfrac{A_2}{A_1} \cdot F_{2-1} = \dfrac{\pi (10)^2}{\pi (5)^2} \times 0.12 = 0.48$

Also, $\qquad\qquad F_{1-1} + F_{1-2} + F_{1-3} = 1$

$\therefore \qquad\qquad\qquad F_{1-2} + F_{1-3} = 1 \qquad\qquad\qquad\qquad$ as $F_{1-1} = 0$

or, $\qquad\qquad\qquad F_{1-3} = 1 - F_{1-2} = 1 - 0.48 = 0.52$

Similarly,

$\qquad\qquad\qquad F_{2-1} + F_{2-2} + F_{2-3} = 1$

$\therefore \qquad\qquad\qquad F_{2-1} + F_{2-3} = 1 \qquad\qquad\qquad\qquad$ as $F_{2-2} = 0$

or, $\qquad\qquad\qquad F_{2-3} = 1 - F_{2-1} = 1 - 0.12 = \mathbf{0.88}$ **(Ans.)**

Also, $\qquad\qquad\qquad A_2 F_{2-3} = A_3 F_{3-2}$

$\therefore \qquad\qquad\qquad F_{3-2} = \dfrac{A_2}{A_3} \cdot F_{2-3} = \dfrac{\pi \times 10^2}{526.86} \times 0.88 = 0.525$

Similarly,

$\qquad\qquad\qquad A_1 F_{1-3} = A_3 F_{3-1}$

or, $\qquad\qquad\qquad F_{3-1} = \dfrac{A_1}{A_3} F_{1-3} = \dfrac{\pi \times 5^2}{526.86} \times 0.52 = 0.078$

Now, $\qquad\qquad F_{3-1} + F_{3-2} + F_{3-3} = 1$

$\therefore \qquad\qquad\qquad F_{3-3} = 1 - F_{3-1} - F_{3-2} = 1 - 0.078 - 0.525 = \mathbf{0.397}$ **(Ans.)**

Example 12.11. *A thin copper sphere with its internal surface highly oxidised, has a diameter of 20 cm. How small a hole must be made in the sphere to make an opening that will have an absorptivity of 0.9?*

                                                                (M.U. 1996)

Soluton. *Given :* $r = \dfrac{20}{2} = 10$ cm $= 0.1$ m; $\alpha = 0.9$

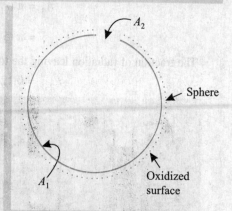

The sphere absorbs 90% of the energy (as given) and the remaining 10% is lost to the surrounding through the hole (area A_2) provided.

Fig. 12.15

$$\dfrac{Q' \text{ (heat coming out from the hole)}}{Q \text{ (heat radiated from the cavity)}}$$

$$= \dfrac{1 - F_{1-1}}{1 - (1 - \varepsilon_1) F_{1-1}} = 0.1 \text{ } (Given)$$

Assuming $\alpha = \varepsilon = 0.9$

$$\dfrac{1 - F_{1-1}}{1 - (1 - 0.9) F_{1-1}} = 0.1$$

or $\qquad\qquad \dfrac{1 - F_{1-1}}{1 - 0.1 F_{1-1}} = 0.1$

or $\qquad\qquad 1 - F_{1-1} = 0.1 (1 - 0.1 F_{1-1})$

$\qquad\qquad\qquad\qquad = 0.1 - 0.01 F_{1-1}$

or $\qquad\qquad 0.99 F_{1-1} = 0.90$ or $F_{1-1} = \dfrac{0.90}{0.99} = \dfrac{10}{11}$

Also, $$F_{1-1} = 1 - \frac{A_2}{A_1} = \frac{10}{11}$$

or, $$\frac{A_2}{A_1} = 1 - \frac{10}{11} = \frac{1}{11}$$

or, $$\frac{A_2}{A_s - A_2} = \frac{1}{11}, \text{ where } A_s \text{ is complete surface area.}$$

or, $$11 A_2 = A_s - A_2$$

or, $$12 A_2 = A_s$$

or, $$A_2 = \frac{A_s}{12} = \frac{4\pi r^2}{12} = \frac{4\pi \times (10)^2}{12} = 104.72 \text{ cm}^2 \quad \textbf{(Ans.)}$$

Example 12.12. *Show that the radiation shape factor between a disc of radius r located at a distance h from the centre of a small sphere is given by*

$$F_{sphere-disc} = \frac{1}{2}\left[1 - \frac{h}{\sqrt{r^2 + h^2}}\right].$$ (P.U. 1997)

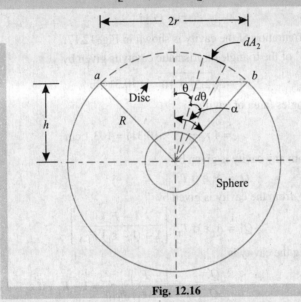

Fig. 12.16

Solution. Draw an imaginary circle of radius R as shown in Fig. 12.16.

Let us first find out the area of the surface of the sector ab of the sphere. For this, consider an elemental area dA_2 of included angle $d\theta$ at an angle θ, as shown in the Fig. 12.16.

Now, the total surface area of the sector ab is given by

$$A_2 = \int_o^\alpha (2\pi R \sin \theta) . R . d\theta$$

$$= 2\pi R^2 \int_o^\alpha \sin \theta . d\theta = 2\pi R^2 (1 - \cos \alpha)$$

$$F_{sphere-disc} = \frac{A_2}{\text{Area of the sphere of radius } R}$$

$$= \frac{2\pi R^2 (1 - \cos \alpha)}{4\pi R^2} = \frac{1}{2} (1 - \cos \alpha)$$

$$= \frac{1}{2}\left[1 - \frac{h}{R}\right] = \frac{1}{2}\left[1 - \frac{h}{\sqrt{r^2 + h^2}}\right] \quad \textbf{... Proved.}$$

Example 12.13. *A prismatic cavity exists in a very large flat surface. The depth of cavity is 10 cm and its base is square of 5 cm side. What portion of energy radiated by the surface of the cavity is leaving from the opening of the cavity?*

(M.U. 1999)

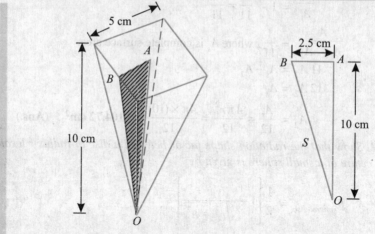

Fig. 12.17

Solution. The configuration of the cavity is shown in Fig. 12.17.

The slant height 'S' of the triangle of prismatic cavity is given by

$$S = \sqrt{2.5^2 + 10^2} = 10.31 \text{ cm}$$

∴ Area of 4-triangles (area of cavity)

$$= 4 \times \frac{1}{2} (5 \times 10.31) = 103.1 \text{ cm}^2$$

Heat radiated Q from any cavity is given by

$$Q = A_1 \varepsilon \sigma T_1^4$$

Heat coming out Q' from the cavity is given by

$$Q' = A_1 \varepsilon \sigma T_1^4 \left[\frac{1 - F_{1-1}}{1 - (1 - \varepsilon_1) F_{1-1}} \right]$$

Portion of Q leaving the cavity is

$$= \frac{Q'}{Q} = \frac{1 - F_{1-1}}{1 - (1 - \varepsilon_1) F_{1-1}} = 1 - F_{1-1} \text{ if } \varepsilon_1 = 1 \text{ (assumed)}$$

$$F_{1-1} = 1 - \frac{A_2}{A_1}$$

where, $A_1 = 103.1 \text{ cm}^2$ (surface area of the cavity)

$$A_2 = 5 \times 5 = 25 \text{ cm}^2 \text{ (top surface area of the cavity)}$$

∴

$$F_{1-1} = 1 - \frac{25}{103.1} = 0.7575$$

∴ Percentage of heat lost by the cavity to the surroundings

$$= 1 - F_{1-1} = 1 - 0.7575$$

$$= 0.2425 \text{ or } \mathbf{24.25\%} \text{ (Ans.)}$$

Example 12.14. *Fig. 12.18 shows a cavity having surface temperature as 900° C and emissivity as 0.6. Find the rate of emission from the cavity to surroundings.*

(P.U. 1999)

Solution. The heat flow from the cavity to the surroundings is given by

$$Q = A_1 \varepsilon_1 \sigma T_1^4 \left[\frac{1 - F_{1-1}}{1 - (1 - \varepsilon_1) F_{1-1}} \right] \quad ...(i)$$

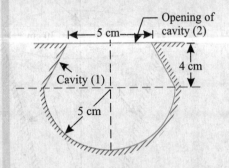

Opening of cavity (2)

Fig. 12.18

where, A_1 = Area of cavity, and

A_2 = Area of the opening of cavity

$$= \frac{\pi}{4} d_2^2 = \frac{\pi}{4} \times \left(\frac{5}{100} \right)^2$$

$$= 0.001963 \text{ m}^2$$

$$A_1 = A_f + A_{hs}$$

where, A_f = Area of frustrum, and

A_{hs} = Area of half sphere

$$A_f = \pi (r_1 + r_2) \sqrt{(r_2 - r_1)^2 + h^2}$$

where, r_1 = 2.5 cm, r_2 = 5 cm and h = 4 cm

∴ $$A_f = \pi (2.5 + 5) \sqrt{(5 - 2.5)^2 + 4^2}$$

$$= 7.5 \, \pi \times 4.717 = 111.14 \text{ cm}^2 = 0.01111 \text{ m}^2$$

$$A_{hs} = \frac{1}{2} \times 4\pi r^2 = 2 \, \pi r^2 = 2 \, \pi \times 5^2 = 157 \text{ cm}^2 = 0.0157 \text{ m}^2$$

∴ $$A_1 = 0.01111 + 0.0157 = 0.0268 \text{ m}^2$$

∴ $$F_{1-1} = 1 - \frac{A_2}{A_1} = 1 - \frac{0.001963}{0.0268} = 0.926$$

Now substituting the values in eqn. (i), we get

$$Q = 0.0268 \times 0.6 \times 5.67 \left(\frac{900 + 273}{100} \right)^4 \left[\frac{1 - 0.926}{1 - (1 - 0.6) \times 0.926} \right]$$

$$= 0.09117 \times 18931.8 \left[\frac{0.074}{0.6296} \right] = \textbf{202.87 W. (Ans.)}$$

Example 12.15. *A shape of cavity is frustrum having 30 cm and 60 cm diameters and 75cm height, is maintained at 500° C. Find:*

(i) The heat loss from the cavity when smaller diameter is at the bottom.

(ii) The percentage change in heat loss if the bigger diameter is at the bottom.

Assume cavity is black body.

Solution. Heat lost by cavity is given by

$$Q = A_1 \varepsilon_1 \sigma T_1^4 \left[\frac{1 - F_{1-1}}{1 - (1 - \varepsilon_1) F_{1-1}} \right] \quad ...(i)$$

(i) The heat loss from the cavity : Refer Fig. 12.19 (a)

where, $$F_{1-1} = 1 - \frac{A_2}{A_1} = 1 - \frac{A_2}{A_b + A_i}$$

where, A_b = Area of the bottom surface, and

A_i = Area of inclined or curved surface

$$A_i = \pi (r_1 + r_2) \sqrt{(r_2 - r_1)^2 + h^2}$$

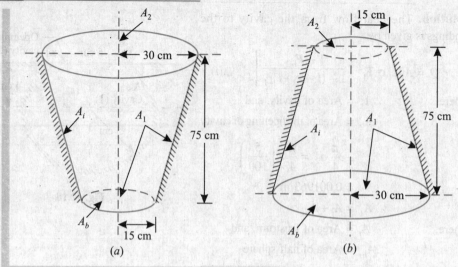

Fig. 12.19

$$= \pi (15 + 30) \sqrt{(30 - 15)^2 + 75^2} = 10813 \text{ cm}^2 = 1.0813 \text{ m}^2$$

$$A_b = \pi \times 15^2 \times 10^{-4} \text{ m}^2 = 0.0707 \text{ m}^2$$

$$A_2 = \pi \times 30^2 \times 10^{-4} \text{ m}^2 = 0.283 \text{ m}^2$$

$\therefore$ $$F_{1-1} = 1 - \frac{A_2}{A_b + A_i} = 1 - \frac{0.283}{0.0707 + 1.0813} = 0.754$$

Now substituting the values in eqn. (*i*), we get

$$Q = (A_b + A_i) \, \varepsilon_1 \, \sigma \, T_1^4 \left[\frac{1 - F_{1-1}}{1 - (1 - \varepsilon_1) \, F_{1-1}} \right]$$

$$= (0.0707 + 1.0813) \times 1 \times 5.67 \left(\frac{500 + 273}{100} \right)^4 \left(\frac{1 - 0.754}{1} \right)$$

$$= 6.532 \times 3570.4 \, (1 - 0.754) = \mathbf{5737 \ W} \textbf{ (Ans.)}$$

(*ii*) **Percentage change in heat loss :**

Refer Fig. 12.19 (*b*).

$$F_{1-1} = 1 - \frac{A_2}{A_b + A_i} = 1 - \frac{\pi \times (0.15)^2}{\pi \times (0.3)^2 + 1.0813} = 1 - \frac{0.0707}{0.283 + 1.0813}$$

$$= 1 - 0.052 = 0.948$$

$\therefore$ $$Q' = (A_b + A_i) \, \varepsilon_1 \, \sigma \, T_1^4 \left(\frac{1 - F_{1-1}}{1} \right)$$

$$= (0.283 + 1.0813) \times 1 \times 5.67 \left(\frac{500 + 273}{100} \right)^4 (1 - 0.948)$$

$$= 7.7356 \times 3570.4 \, (1 - 0.948) = 1436.2 \text{ W}$$

Percentage decrease in the second case

$$= \frac{Q - Q'}{Q} = \frac{5737 - 1436.2}{5737} = 0.7496 \text{ or } \mathbf{74.96\%} \quad \textbf{(Ans.)}$$

Example 12.16. *The filament of a 75 W light bulb may be considered a black body radiating into a black enclosure at 70° C. The filament diameter is 0.10 mm and length is 5 cm. Considering the radiation, determine the filament temperature.* **(U.P.S.C., 1998)**

Solution. *Given :* $Q = 75$ W $= 75$ J/s; $T_2 = 70 + 273 = 343$ K; $d = 0.01$ mm; $l = 5$ cm.

Filament temperature, t_1 :

$$Q := \sigma \varepsilon A (T_1^4 - T_2^4)$$

$$75 = 5.67 \times 10^{-8} \times 1 \times (\pi d l) \times (T_1^4 - T_2^4)$$

or,

$$75 = 5.67 \times 10^{-8} \times 1 \times (\pi \times 0.1 \times 10^{-3} \times 5 \times 10^{-2}) \times (T_1^4 - 343^4)$$

$$= 8.906 \times 10^{-13} (T_1^4 - 343^4)$$

or,

$$T_1^4 = \frac{75}{8.906 \times 10^{-13}} + (343)^4 = 8.42 \times 10^{13} + 343^4$$

or,

$$T_1 = (8.42 \times 10^{-13} + 343^4)^{1/4} = 3029 \text{ K}$$

or,

$$t_1 = 3029 - 273 = \mathbf{2756° C \text{ (Ans.)}}$$

Example 12.17. *Two parallel rectangular surfaces 1m × 2m are opposite to each other at a distance of 4 m. The surfaces are black and at 100° C and 200° C. Calculate the heat exchange by radiation between the two surfaces.*

Sulution. The heat flow between the two surfaces is given by

$$Q_{12} = A_1 F_{1-2} \sigma (T_1^4 - T_2^4)$$

as

$$\varepsilon_1 = \varepsilon_2 = 1$$

From Fig. 12.2, corresponding to $\dfrac{X}{L} = \dfrac{2}{4} = 0.5$

and, $\dfrac{Y}{L} = \dfrac{1}{4} = 0.25$, $F_{1-2} = 0.043$

$\therefore$ $Q_{12} = (2 \times 1) \times 0.043 \times 5.67$

$$\left[\left(\frac{200 + 273}{100} \right)^4 - \left(\frac{100 + 273}{100} \right)^4 \right]$$

$$= 0.487 [500.55 - 193.57] = \mathbf{149.5 \text{ W (Ans).}}$$

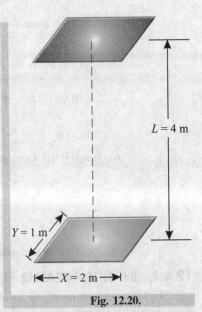

$L = 4$ m

$Y = 1$ m

$\leftarrow X = 2$ m $\rightarrow$

Fig. 12.20.

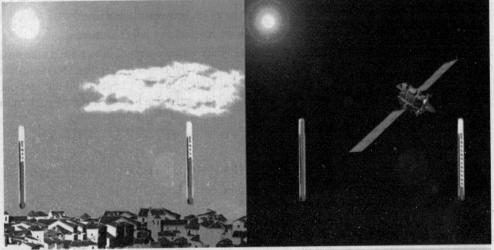

On Earth, heat travels by radiation, convection and conduction.

In space, heat travels only by radiation.

12.4. HEAT EXCHANGE BETWEEN NON-BLACK BODIES

The *black body* concept is an idealizaiton which serves as a standard for the performance of a real body. In engineering applications, most surfaces encountered do not behave like black bodies which absorb the entire incident radiation. The real surfaces (non-black) do not absorb the whole of the incident radiation; a part is reflected back to the radiating surface and this back and forth reflections between the surfaces may go on several times. As the emissivities and absorptivities are not uniform in all directions and for all wavelengths, it is worthwhile to simplify the problem to some extent by considering the bodies to be *gray* for which the emissivities and absorptivities are constant over the whole wavelength spectrum. Now we shall discuss exchange of heat for simple cases involving opaque gray bodies.

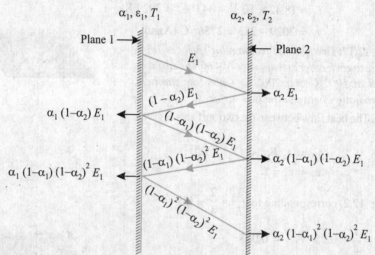

Fig. 12.21. Heat exchange (radiant) between two non-black parallel surfaces.

12.4.1. INFINITE PARALLEL PLANES

The following **assumptions** are made for the analysis of radiant heat exhange between two non-black parallel surfaces:

1. The configuration factor of either surface is unity.
2. There is non-absorbing medium (such as air) in between the surfaces.
3. The emissive and reflective properties are constant over all the surfaces.

As depicted in Fig. 12.21, the surface (plane) 1 emits radiant energy E_1 which strikes the surface (plane) 2. Here a part $\alpha_2 E_1$ is absorbed (by the surface 2) and $(1 - \alpha_2) E_1$ (remainder) is reflected back to surface 1. Here a part $\alpha_1 (1 - \alpha_2) E_1$ is absorbed (by the surface) and the remainder $(1 - \alpha_1) (1 - \alpha_2) E_1$ is refleced and so on. The amount of energy that has left surface 1 per unit time (Q_1) is given by:

$$Q_1 = E_1 - [\alpha_1 (1 - \alpha_2) E_1 + \alpha_1 (1 - \alpha_1) (1 - \alpha_2)^2 E_1 + \alpha_1 (1 - \alpha_1)^2 (1 - \alpha_2)^3 E_1 + \ldots]$$

$$= E_1 - \alpha_1 (1 - \alpha_2) E_1 [1 + (1 - \alpha_1) (1 - \alpha_2) + (1 - \alpha_1)^2 (1 - \alpha_2)^2 + \ldots]$$

$$= E_1 - \alpha_1 (1 - \alpha_2) E_1 [1 + Z + Z^2 + \ldots]$$

where
$$Z = (1 - \alpha_1) (1 - \alpha_2)$$

As $Z < 1$, the series $1 + Z + Z^2 + \ldots$, when extended to infinity gives $\dfrac{1}{1 - Z}$.

$$\therefore \qquad Q_1 = E_1 - \frac{\alpha_1 (1 - \alpha_2) E_1}{1 - Z} = E_1 \left[1 - \frac{\alpha_1 (1 - \alpha_2)}{1 - (1 - \alpha_1) (1 - \alpha_2)} \right]$$

As per Kirchhoff's law, emissivity and absorptivity of a surface are equal and so $\alpha_1 = \varepsilon_1$ and $\alpha_2 = \varepsilon_2$.

$$\therefore \quad Q_1 = E_1 \left[1 - \frac{\varepsilon_1 (1 - \varepsilon_2)}{1 - (1 - \varepsilon_1)(1 - \varepsilon_2)} \right]$$

$$= E_1 \left[\frac{1 - (1 - \varepsilon_1)(1 - \varepsilon_2) - \varepsilon_1 (1 - \varepsilon_2)}{1 - (1 - \varepsilon_1)(1 - \varepsilon_2)} \right]$$

or,
$$= E_1 \left[\frac{1 - (1 - \varepsilon_2 - \varepsilon_1 + \varepsilon_1 \varepsilon_2) - (\varepsilon_1 - \varepsilon_1 \varepsilon_2)}{1 - (1 - \varepsilon_2 - \varepsilon_1 - \varepsilon_1 \varepsilon_2)} \right]$$

$$= E_1 \left[\frac{1 - 1 + \varepsilon_2 + \varepsilon_1 - \varepsilon_1 \varepsilon_2 - \varepsilon_1 + \varepsilon_1 \varepsilon_2}{1 - 1 + \varepsilon_2 + \varepsilon_1 - \varepsilon_1 \varepsilon_2} \right]$$

or,
$$Q_1 = \frac{E_1 \varepsilon_2}{\varepsilon_1 + \varepsilon_2 - \varepsilon_1 \varepsilon_2} \qquad ...(12.18)$$

Similarly the surface 2 emits radiant energy E_2. A part $\alpha_1 E_2$ is absorbed by the surface 1 and the remainder $(1 - \alpha_1) E_2$ is reflected back to surface 2. A part $\alpha_2 (1 - \alpha_1) E_2$ is absorbed and the rest $(1 - \alpha_1)(1 - \alpha_2) E_2$ is reflected and so on. Proceeding as done earlier, we can determine that the amount of radiant energy which leaves surface 2 per unit time is given by

$$Q_2 = E_2 \left[\frac{\varepsilon_1}{\varepsilon_1 + \varepsilon_2 - \varepsilon_1 \varepsilon_2} \right] \qquad ...(12.19)$$

The net flow of heat/energy from surface 1 to surface 2 per unit time is given by

$$Q_{12} = Q_1 - Q_2$$

$$= \frac{E_1 \varepsilon_2}{\varepsilon_1 + \varepsilon_2 - \varepsilon_1 \varepsilon_2} - \frac{E_2 \varepsilon_1}{\varepsilon_1 + \varepsilon_2 - \varepsilon_1 \varepsilon_2}$$

$$= \frac{E_1 \varepsilon_2 - E_2 \varepsilon_1}{\varepsilon_1 + \varepsilon_2 - \varepsilon_1 \varepsilon_2} \qquad ...(12.20)$$

For non-black surfaces,

$$E_1 = \varepsilon_1 \sigma T_1^4 \text{ and } E_2 = \varepsilon_2 \sigma T_2^4 \qquad ... \text{By Stefan-Boltzmann law}$$

$$\therefore \quad Q_{12} = \frac{\varepsilon_1 \sigma T_1^4 \varepsilon_2 - \varepsilon_2 \sigma T_2^4 \varepsilon_1}{\varepsilon_1 + \varepsilon_2 - \varepsilon_1 \varepsilon_2}$$

or,
$$Q_{12} = \frac{\varepsilon_1 \varepsilon_2}{\varepsilon_1 + \varepsilon_2 - \varepsilon_1 \varepsilon_2} \sigma (T_1^4 - T_2^4)$$

or,
$$Q_{12} = f_{1-2} \sigma (T_1^4 - T_2^4) \qquad ...(12.21)$$

where,
$$f_{1-2} = \frac{\varepsilon_1 \varepsilon_2}{\varepsilon_1 + \varepsilon_2 - \varepsilon_1 \varepsilon_2}$$

or,
$$f_{1-2} = \frac{1}{\dfrac{1}{\varepsilon_1} + \dfrac{1}{\varepsilon_2} - 1}$$

and is called **interchange factor** for the radiation from surface 1 to surface 2.

12.4.2. INFINITE LONG CONCENTRIC CYLINDERS

Consider two concentric cylinders as shown in Fig. 12.22 of areas A_1 and A_2, emissivities ε_1 and ε_2 and their surfaces maintained at temperatures T_1 and T_2 respectively.

Now, $\qquad A_1\,F_{1-2} = A_2\,F_{2-1}$ ... By reciprocity theorem

But, $\qquad\qquad F_{1-2} = 1$ (Since all the radiations emitted by the inner cylinder are intercepted by the outer cylinder.)

$\therefore \qquad\qquad F_{2-1} = \dfrac{A_1}{A_2}$

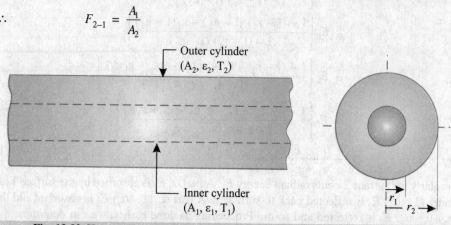

Fig. 12.22. Heat exchange (radiant) between two infinite long concentric cylinders.

Consider the energy emitted per unit area by the inner cylinder:

Inner cylinder emits energy $= E_1$

Outer cylinder absorbs energy $= \alpha_2\,E_1 = \varepsilon_2\,E_1$ $(\because \alpha_2 = \varepsilon_2)$

Outer cylinder reflects energy $= E_1 - \varepsilon_2\,E_1 = E_1\,(1 - \varepsilon_2)$

Inner cylinder absorbs energy $= E_1\,(1 - \varepsilon_2)\,F_{2-1}\,\alpha_1 = E_1\,(1 - \varepsilon_2)\,\dfrac{A_1}{A_2}\,\varepsilon_1$

Inner cylinder reflects energy $= E_1\,(1 - \varepsilon_2) - E_1\,(1 - \varepsilon_2)\,\varepsilon_1\,\dfrac{A_1}{A_2}$

$$= E_1\,(1 - \varepsilon_2)\left[1 - \varepsilon_1\,\dfrac{A_1}{A_2}\right]$$

It can be shown that the energy absorbed by the inner cylinder on the second reflection would be

$$= E_1\,(1 - \varepsilon_2)^2\,\varepsilon_1\,\dfrac{A_1}{A_2}\left[1 - \dfrac{A_1}{A_2}\,\varepsilon_1\right]$$

This absorption and reflection continue indefinitely, so we can find the net energy lost by the inner cylinder considering infinite times absorptions and reflections.

$\therefore$ Heat lost by the inner cylinder per unit area is given by

$$Q_1 = E_1 - E_1\,(1 - \varepsilon_2)\,\varepsilon_1\,\dfrac{A_1}{A_2} - E_1\,(1 - \varepsilon_2)^2\,\varepsilon_1\,\dfrac{A_1}{A_2}\left[1 - \dfrac{A_1}{A_2}\,\varepsilon_1\right] + \dots$$

$$= E_1\left[1 - \dfrac{A_1}{A_2}\,\varepsilon_1\,(1 - \varepsilon_2) - (1 - \varepsilon_2)^2\,\varepsilon_1\,\dfrac{A_1}{A_2}\left\{1 - \dfrac{A_1}{A_2}\,\varepsilon_1\right\} + \dots\right]$$

$$= E_1\left[1 - \dfrac{A_1}{A_2}\,\varepsilon_1\,(1 - \varepsilon_2)\left\{1 + (1 - \varepsilon_2)\left(1 - \dfrac{A_1}{A_2}\,\varepsilon_1\right)\right\} + \dots\right]$$

$$= E_1\left[1 - \dfrac{A_1}{A_2}\,\varepsilon_1\,(1 - \varepsilon_2)\left\{1 - (1 - \varepsilon_2)\left(1 - \dfrac{A_1}{A_2}\,\varepsilon_1\right)\right\}^{-1} + \dots\right]$$

$$= E_1 \left[1 - \frac{\dfrac{A_1}{A_2}\, \varepsilon_1\,(1 - \varepsilon_2)}{\left\{ 1 - (1 - \varepsilon_2)\left(1 - \dfrac{A_1}{A_2}\,\varepsilon_1\right)\right\}} \right]$$

or $$Q_1 = \frac{E_1\,\varepsilon_2}{\dfrac{A_1}{A_2}\,\varepsilon_1 + \varepsilon_2 - \dfrac{A_1}{A_2}\,\varepsilon_1\,\varepsilon_2} \qquad \qquad ...(12.22)$$

Similarly, net heat/energy lost by the outer cylinder per unit area would be,

$$Q_2 = \frac{\varepsilon_1\, E_2 \cdot \dfrac{A_1}{A_2}}{\dfrac{A_1}{A_2}\,\varepsilon_1 + \varepsilon_2 - \dfrac{A_1}{A_2}\,\varepsilon_1\,\varepsilon_2} \qquad \qquad ...(12.23)$$

The net radiation heat transfer between the inner and outer concentric cylinders is given by

$$Q_{12} = Q_1 - Q_2$$

$$= A_1 \left[\frac{E_1\,\varepsilon_2}{\dfrac{A_1}{A_2}\,\varepsilon_1 + \varepsilon_2 - \dfrac{A_1}{A_2}\,\varepsilon_1\,\varepsilon_2} \right] - A_2 \left[\frac{\varepsilon_1\, E_2 \cdot \dfrac{A_1}{A_2}}{\dfrac{A_1}{A_2}\,\varepsilon_1 + \varepsilon_2 - \dfrac{A_1}{A_2}\,\varepsilon_1\,\varepsilon_2} \right]$$

$$= \frac{A_1\, E_1\,\varepsilon_2 - A_1\, E_2\,\varepsilon_1}{\dfrac{A_1}{A_2}\,\varepsilon_1 + \varepsilon_2 - \dfrac{A_1}{A_2}\,\varepsilon_1\,\varepsilon_2}$$

Also, for non-black bodies

$$E_1 = \varepsilon_1\,\sigma\, T_1^4 \text{ and } E_2 = \varepsilon_2\,\sigma\, T_2^4 \qquad \qquad ...\text{By Stefan-Boltzmann law}$$

$$\therefore \qquad Q_{12} = \frac{A_1\,\varepsilon_1\,\varepsilon_2\,\sigma\, T_1^4 - A_1\,\varepsilon_1\,\varepsilon_2\,\sigma\, T_2^4}{\dfrac{A_1}{A_2}\,\varepsilon_1 + \varepsilon_2 - \dfrac{A_1}{A_2}\,\varepsilon_1\,\varepsilon_2}$$

$$= \frac{\varepsilon_1\,\varepsilon_2\, A_1\,\sigma\,(T_1^4 - T_2^4)}{\left[\dfrac{A_1}{A_2}\,\varepsilon_1\,\varepsilon_2\left(\dfrac{1}{\varepsilon_2} - 1\right)\right] + \varepsilon_2}$$

or $$Q_{12} = \frac{A_1\,\sigma\,(T_1^4 - T_2^4)}{\dfrac{1}{\varepsilon_1} + \dfrac{A_1}{A_2}\left(\dfrac{1}{\varepsilon_2} - 1\right)} \qquad \qquad ...(12.24)$$

$$= f_{1-2}\, A_1\,\sigma\,(T_1^4 - T_2^4) \qquad \qquad ...[12.24\,(a)]$$

where, $$f_{1-2} = \frac{1}{\dfrac{1}{\varepsilon_1} + \dfrac{A_1}{A_2}\left(\dfrac{1}{\varepsilon_2} - 1\right)}$$

is the **interchange factor** or **equivalent emissivity** for radiant heat exchange between infinite long concentric cylinders.

Equation (12.24) is equally applicable to concentric spheres except that for *concentric cylinders of equal length*:

$$\frac{A_1}{A_2} = \frac{2\pi\, r_1\, L}{2\pi\, r_2\, L} = \frac{r_1}{r_2}, \text{ and}$$

for concentric spheres:

$$\frac{A_1}{A_2} = \frac{4\pi\, r_1^2}{4\pi\, r_2^2} = \frac{r_1^2}{r_2^2}.$$

12.4.3. SMALL GRAY BODIES

Consider two small gray bodies (the gray bodies are said to be small if their size is very small as compared to the distance between them) 1 and 2 having emissivities ε_1, ε_2, or absorptivities α_1, α_2. The radiant energy emitted by body 1 is partly absorbed by body 2. The portion of radiation unabsorbed and thus reflected on the first incidence is considered to be lost in space (due to surfaces being small) *i.e.*, nothing returns back to surface 1.

Similar is the case with surface 2.

The energy emitted by body $1 = A_1\, \varepsilon_1\, \sigma\, T_1^4$

The energy incident on body $2 = F_{1-2}\, A_1\, \varepsilon_1\, \sigma\, T_1^4$

The energy absorbed by body $2 = \alpha_2\, F_{1-2}\, A_1 \varepsilon\, \alpha\, T_1^4$

The energy transfer from body 1 to body 2,

$$Q = \varepsilon_1\, \varepsilon_2\, A_1\, F_{1-2}\, \sigma\, T_1^4 \qquad\qquad (\because \alpha_2 = \varepsilon_2)$$

Similarly the energy transfer from body 2 to body 1,

$$Q_2 = \varepsilon_1\, \varepsilon_2\, A_2\, F_{2-1}\, \sigma\, T_2^4$$

The net radiant heat exchange between the two bodies is

$$Q_{12} = \varepsilon_1\, \varepsilon_2\, A_1\, F_{1-2}\, \sigma\, T_1^4 - \varepsilon_1\, \varepsilon_2\, A_2\, F_{2-1}\, \sigma\, T_2^4$$

But $A_1 F_{1-2} = A_2 F_{2-1}$ ...By reciprocity theorem

$\therefore$

$$Q_{12} = \varepsilon_1\, \varepsilon_2\, A_1\, F_{1-2}\, (T_1^4 - T_2^4)$$
$$= f_{1-2}\, A_1\, F_{1-2}\, (T_1^4 - T_2^4) \qquad\qquad ...(12.25)$$

where, $f_{1-2} = \varepsilon_1 \varepsilon_2$ represents the *equivalent emissivity* or *interchange factor* for radiant heat exchange between two small gray bodies.

12.4.4. SMALL BODY IN A LARGE ENCLOSURE

Consider a small body placed in a large enclosure. The large gray enclosure acts like a black body, absorbing practically all the radiation incident upon it and reflecting negligibly small energy back to the small gray body. In this case $F_{1-2} = 1$ since all the radiations emitted by the small body would be intercepted by the outer large enclosure. Thus,

Energy emitted by small body 1 and absorbed by the outer large enclosure $2 = A_1\, \varepsilon_1\, \sigma\, T_1^4$

Energy emitted by the enclosure $2 = A_2\, \varepsilon_2\, \sigma\, T_2^4$

Energy incident upon the small body $1 = F_{2-1}\, A_2\, \varepsilon_2\, \sigma\, T_2^4$

Energy absorbed by the small body $1 = \alpha_1\, F_{2-1}\, A_2\, \varepsilon_2\, \sigma\, T_2^4$

$$= \varepsilon_1\, \varepsilon_2\, A_2\, F_{2-1}\, \sigma\, T_2^4 \qquad\qquad (\because \alpha_1 = \varepsilon_1)$$

$\therefore$ The net radiant heat exchange between the small body 1 and the outer large enclosure 2,

$$Q_{12} = \varepsilon_1\, A_1\, \sigma\, T_1^4 - \varepsilon_1\, \varepsilon_2\, A_2\, F_{2-1}\, \sigma\, T_2^4$$

If $T_1 = T_2$ and $Q_{12} = 0$, we have

$$A_1 = A_2\, \varepsilon_2\, F_{2-1}; \text{ and}$$

$\therefore$

$$Q_{12} = \varepsilon_1\, A_1\, \sigma\, (T_1^4 - T_2^4)$$
$$= f_{1-2}\, A_1\, \sigma\, (T_1^4 - T_2^4) \qquad\qquad ...(12.26)$$

where, f_{1-2} ($= \varepsilon_1$) represents the *equivalent emissivity* or *interchange factor* for radiation heat exchange between a small body and a large enclosure.

Net radiation heat exchange between two gray surfaces, considering both the interchange factor f_{1-2} and geometric factor F_{1-2}, is given by:

$$Q_{net} = f_{1-2} \, F_{1-2} \, \sigma A_1 \, (T_1^4 - T_2^4) \qquad \text{...(12.27)}$$

Values of f_{1-2} and F_{1-2} for some cases/situations are given in Table 12.1.

Table 12.1. Geometric (F_{1-2}) and interchange (f_{1-2}) factors

S.No.	Configuration	Geometric factor (F_{1-2})	Interchange factor (f_{1-2})
1.	Infinite parallel planes	1	$\dfrac{1}{\dfrac{1}{\varepsilon_1} + \dfrac{1}{\varepsilon_2} - 1}$
2.	Infinitely long concentric cylinders or concentric spheres	1	$\dfrac{1}{\dfrac{1}{\varepsilon_1} + \dfrac{A_1}{A_2}\left(\dfrac{1}{\varepsilon_2} - 1\right)}$
3.	Body 1 (small) enclosed by body 2	1	ε_1
4.	Body 1(large) enclosed by body 2	1	$\dfrac{1}{\dfrac{1}{\varepsilon_1} + \dfrac{A_1}{A_2}\left(\dfrac{1}{\varepsilon_2} - 1\right)}$
5.	Two rectangles with common side at right angles to each other	1	$\varepsilon_1 \varepsilon_2$

Thermal radiation system.

12.5. ELECTRICAL NETWORK ANALOGY FOR THERMAL RADIATION SYSTEMS

An *electrical network analogy* is an alternative approach for analysing radiation heat exchange between gray or black surfaces. In this approach the two terms commonly used are *irradiation* and *radiosity*.

Irradiation (G). It is defined as the *total radiation incident upon a surface per unit time per unit area*. It is expressed in W/m².

Radiosity (J). This term is used to indicate the total radiation leaving a surface per unit time per unit area. It is also expressed in W/m².

The radiosity comprises the original emittance ϕ from the surface plus the reflected portion of any radiation incident upon it [Refer Fig. 12.23 (a)].

i.e. $\qquad J = E + \rho G$

or, $\qquad\qquad J = \varepsilon E_b + \rho G \qquad$ ...(12.28)

where, $\qquad\qquad E_b$ = Emissive power of a perfect black body at the same temperature.

Also, $\qquad\qquad \alpha + \rho + \tau = 1$

or, $\qquad\qquad \alpha + \rho = 1 \qquad\qquad$ ($\tau = 0$, the surface being opaque)

or, $\qquad\qquad \rho = 1 - \alpha$

$\therefore \qquad\qquad J = \varepsilon E_b + (1 - \alpha)\, G$

But, $\qquad\qquad \alpha = \varepsilon \qquad\qquad$ ...By Kirchhoff's law

$\therefore \qquad\qquad J = \varepsilon E_b + (1 - \varepsilon)G \qquad\qquad$ ...(12.29)

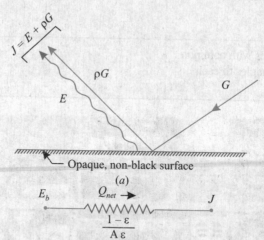

(a)

(b)

Fig. 12.23. Irradiation and radiosity.

or, $\qquad\qquad J - \varepsilon E_b = (1 - \varepsilon)\, G$

or, $$G = \frac{J - \varepsilon E_b}{1 - \varepsilon} \qquad\qquad ...(12.30)$$

The net energy leaving a surface is the difference between its radiosity and irradiation. Thus,

$$\frac{Q_{net}}{A} = J - G \qquad\qquad ...(12.31)$$

or, $$\frac{Q_{net}}{A} = J - \frac{J - \varepsilon\, E_b}{1 - \varepsilon}$$

or, $$= \frac{J\,(1 - \varepsilon) - (J - \varepsilon\, E_b)}{1 - \varepsilon} = \frac{J - J\varepsilon - J + \varepsilon\, E_b}{1 - \varepsilon} = \frac{\varepsilon\,(E_b - J)}{1 - \varepsilon}$$

or, $$Q_{net} = \frac{A\,\varepsilon\,(E_b - J)}{1 - \varepsilon} = \frac{E_b - J}{(1 - \varepsilon)/A\varepsilon} \qquad \qquad ...(12.32)$$

The representation of this equation in the form of electric network is shown in Fig. 12.23 (b). The quantity $\dfrac{1 - \varepsilon}{A\,\varepsilon}$ is known as *surface resistance*, as it is related to surface properties of the radiating body.

Now consider the exchange of radiant energy between the two surfaces (non-black) 1 and 2. Of the total radiation which leaves surface 1, the amount that reaches surface 2 is $J_1 A_1 F_{1-2}$. Similarly, the heat radiated by surface 2 and received by surface 1 is $J_2 A_2 F_{2-1}$. The net interchange of heat between the surfaces (Q_{12}) is given by

$$Q_{12} = J_1 A_1 F_{1-2} - J_2 A_2 F_{2-1} \qquad \qquad ...(12.33)$$

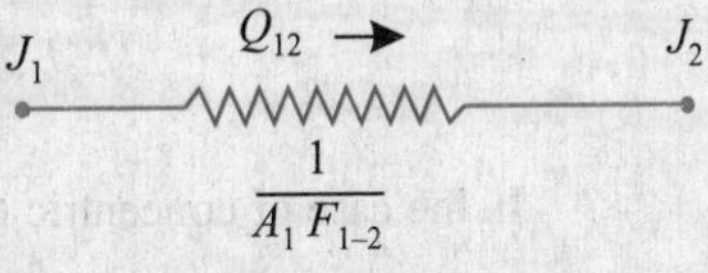

But, $$A_1 F_{1-2} = A_2 F_{2-1}$$
...By reciprocity theorem

$\therefore$ $$Q_{12} = A_1 F_{1-2}\,(J_1 - J_2)$$

or, $$Q_{12} = \frac{J_1 - J_2}{1/\,A_1\, F_{1-2}} \qquad \qquad ...(12.34)$$

Fig. 12.24

This eqn. (12.34) can be represented in the form of electric network as shown in Fig. 12.24. The quantity $\dfrac{1}{A_1\, F_{1-2}}$ is called the **space resistance** because it is due to the distance and geometry of the radiating bodies.

If the surface resistances of the two bodies and space resistance between them is considered then the net heat flow can be represented by an electric circuit as shown in Fig. 12.25. The net heat exchange between the two gray surfaces is given by

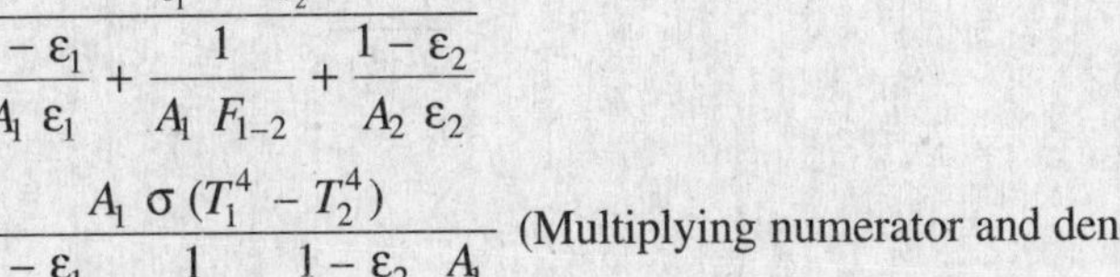

Fig. 12.25

$$(Q_{12})_{net} = \frac{E_{b_1} - E_{b_2}}{\dfrac{1 - \varepsilon_1}{A_1\, \varepsilon_1} + \dfrac{1}{A_1\, F_{1-2}} + \dfrac{1 - \varepsilon_2}{A_2\, \varepsilon_2}}$$

$$= \frac{A_1\, \sigma\, (T_1^4 - T_2^4)}{\dfrac{1 - \varepsilon_1}{\varepsilon_1} + \dfrac{1}{F_{1-2}} + \dfrac{1 - \varepsilon_2}{\varepsilon_2} \cdot \dfrac{A_1}{A_2}} \qquad \text{(Multiplying numerator and denominator by } A_1\text{)}$$

or, $$(Q_{12})_{net} = (F_g)_{1-2}\, A_1\, \sigma\, (T_1^{\,4} - T_2^{\,4}) \qquad \qquad ...(12.35)$$

where, $$(F_g)_{1-2} = \frac{1}{\dfrac{1 - \varepsilon_1}{\varepsilon_1} + \dfrac{1}{F_{1-2}} + \dfrac{1 - \varepsilon_2}{\varepsilon_2} \cdot \dfrac{A_1}{A_2}}$$

and is known as **gray body factor.**

When exchange of heat takes place between two black surfaces, the surface resistance becomes zero as $\varepsilon_1 = \varepsilon_2 = 1$; $(F_g)_{1-2}$ changes to F_{1-2} (i.e., the configuration factor) and the eqn. (12.35) reduces to

$$Q_{net} = F_{1-2} A \, \sigma \, (T_1^4 - T_2^4) \qquad \text{...for } black \ surfaces$$

Let us consider the following cases:

1. *When the radiating bodies are infinite parallel planes:*

In this case
$$A_1 = A_2 \text{ and } F_{1-2} = 1$$

$$\therefore \qquad (F_g)_{1-2} = \frac{1}{\dfrac{1-\varepsilon_1}{\varepsilon_1} + 1 + \dfrac{1-\varepsilon_2}{\varepsilon_2}} = \frac{1}{\dfrac{1}{\varepsilon_1} + \dfrac{1}{\varepsilon_2} - 1} \qquad \text{...(12.36)}$$

2. *When the radiating bodies are concentric cylinders or spheres:*

Here
$$F_{1-2} = 1$$

$$\therefore \qquad (F_g)_{1-2} = \frac{1}{\dfrac{1-\varepsilon_1}{\varepsilon_1} + 1 + \dfrac{1-\varepsilon_2}{\varepsilon_2} \cdot \dfrac{A_1}{A_2}} \qquad \text{...(12.37)}$$

In the case of concentric cylinders,

$$\frac{A_1}{A_2} = \frac{\pi \, d_1 \, l}{\pi \, d_2 \, l} = \frac{d_1}{d_2} = \frac{r_1}{r_2} \qquad \text{...(12.38)}$$

In the case of concentric spheres,

$$\frac{A_1}{A_2} = \frac{4 \, \pi \, r_1^2}{4 \, \pi \, r_2^2} = \frac{r_1^2}{r_2^2} \qquad \text{...(12.39)}$$

3. *When a small body lies inside a large enclosure:*

Here,
$$F_{1-2} = 1, A_1 \ll A_2 \qquad \text{so that } \frac{A_1}{A_2} \to 0$$

$$\therefore \qquad (F_g)_{1-2} = \frac{1}{\dfrac{1-\varepsilon_1}{\varepsilon_1} + 1} \qquad \text{...(12.40)}$$

Examples : (*i*) A pipe carrying steam in a large room, and (*ii*) A thermocouple bead located inside a duct to measure temperature of the fluid.

12.6. RADIATION HEAT EXCHANGE FOR THREE GRAY SURFACES

The network for three gray surfaces is shown in Fig. 12.26. In this case each of the body exchanges heat with the other two. The heat expressions are as follows:

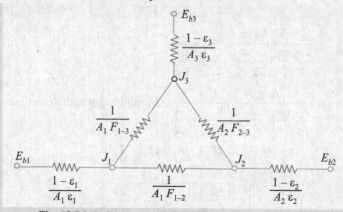

Fig. 12.26. Radiation network for three gray surfaces.

$$Q_{12} = \frac{J_1 - J_2}{1/A_1\, F_{1-2}}$$

$$Q_{13} = \frac{J_1 - J_3}{1/A_1\, F_{1-3}} \qquad \ldots(12.41)$$

$$Q_{23} = \frac{J_2 - J_3}{1/A_2\, F_{2-3}}$$

The values of Q_{12}, Q_{13} etc. are determined from the values of the radiosities which must be calculated first. The most-convenient method is the Krichhoff's law which states that the sum of the currents entering a node is zero.

12.7. RADIATION HEAT EXCHANGE FOR TWO BLACK SURFACES CONNECTED BY A SINGLE REFRACTORY SURFACE

The network for two black surfaces connected by a single refractory surface is shown in the Fig. 12.27. Here the surfaces 1 and 2 are black and R is the refractory surface. The surface R is not connected to any potential as the net radiation transfer from this surface is zero.

The total resistance between E_{b1} and E_{b2}

$$\frac{1}{R_t} = \frac{1}{1/A_1\, F_{1-2}} + \left[\frac{1}{\dfrac{1}{A_1\, F_{1-R}} + \dfrac{1}{A_R\, F_{R-2}}}\right]$$

or, $$\frac{1}{R_t} = A_1\, F_{1-2} + \left[\frac{1}{\dfrac{1}{A_1\, F_{1-R}} + \dfrac{1}{A_R\, F_{R-2}}}\right]$$

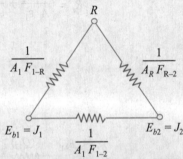

Fig. 12.27. Radiation network for two black surfaces connected by a single refractory surface.

Also $F_{1-R} + F_{1-2} = 1$

$\therefore$ $F_{1-R} = 1 - F_{1-2}$

$F_{2-R} + F_{2-1} = 1$

$\therefore$ $F_{2-R} = 1 - F_{2-1}$

$A_R\, F_{R-2} = A_2\, F_{2-R}$

$\therefore$ $$\frac{1}{R_t} = A_1\, F_{1-2} + \left[\frac{1}{\dfrac{1}{A_1\,(1 - F_{1-2})} + \dfrac{1}{A_2\,(1 - F_{2-1})}}\right]$$

$\therefore$ $$(Q_{12})_{net} = (E_{b1} - E_{b2})\left[A_1\, F_{1-2} + \left\{\frac{1}{\dfrac{1}{A_1\,(1 - F_{1-2})} + \dfrac{1}{A_2\,(1 - F_{2-1})}}\right\}\right]$$

or, $$(Q_{12})_{net} = A_1\, \bar{F}_{1-2}\,(E_{b1} - E_{b2}) = A_1\, \bar{F}_{1-2}\, \sigma\,(T_1^4 - T_2^4) \qquad \ldots(12.42)$$

$\therefore$ $$\bar{F}_{1-2} = F_{1-2} + \left[\frac{1}{\dfrac{1}{(1 - F_{1-2})} + \dfrac{A_1}{A_2}\left\{\dfrac{1}{1 - F_{2-1}}\right\}}\right] \qquad \ldots[12.42(a)]$$

Using reciprocity relation $A_1\, F_{1-2} = A_2\, F_{2-1}$ and simplifying, we get

$$\bar{F}_{1-2} = \frac{A_2 - A_1\, F_{1-2}^2}{A_1 + A_2 - 2A_1\, F_{1-2}} \qquad \ldots[12.42(b)]$$

12.8. RADIATION HEAT EXCHANGE FOR TWO GRAY SURFACES CONNECTED BY SINGLE REFRACTORY SURFACE

The network for radiation heat exchange for two gray surfaces connected by single refractory surface is shown in Fig. 12.28. The third surface influences the heat transfer process because it absorbs and re-radiates energy to the other two surfaces which exchange heat. It may be noted that, in this case, the node 3 is not connected to a radiation surface resistance because surface 3 does not exchange energy.

The total resistance between E_{b1} and E_{b2} is given by

$$R_t = \frac{1 - \varepsilon_1}{A_1 \varepsilon_1} + \frac{1 - \varepsilon_2}{A_2 \varepsilon_2} + \left[\frac{1}{A_1 F_{1-2} + \dfrac{1}{\dfrac{1}{A_1 F_{1-R}} + \dfrac{1}{A_R F_{R-2}}}} \right]$$

But $\qquad F_{1-R} = 1 - F_{1-2}$ and $F_{2-R} = 1 - F_{2-1}$

$$\therefore \qquad R_t = \frac{1 - \varepsilon_1}{A_1 \varepsilon_1} + \frac{1 - \varepsilon_2}{A_2 \varepsilon_2} + \left[\frac{1}{A_1 F_{1-2} + \dfrac{1}{\dfrac{1}{A_1 (1 - F_{1-2})} + \dfrac{1}{A_2 (1 - F_{2-1})}}} \right]$$

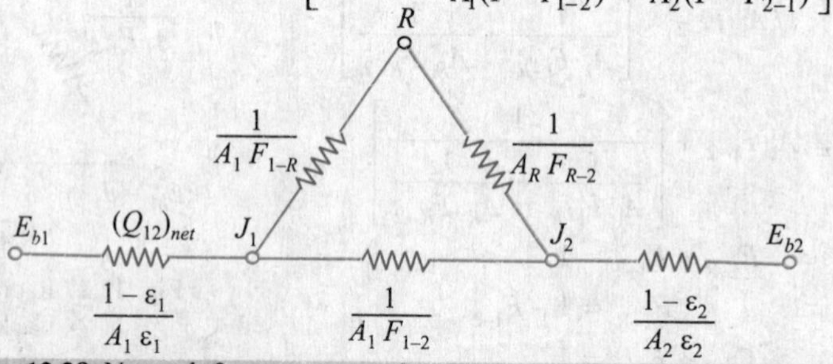

Fig. 12.28. Network for two gray surfaces connected by a refractory surface.

But from eqn. (12.42), we have

$$A_1 \bar{F}_{1-2} = A_1 F_{1-2} + \left[\frac{1}{\dfrac{1}{A_1 (1 - F_{1-2})} + \dfrac{1}{A_2 (1 - F_{2-1})}} \right]$$

or, $\qquad R_t = \dfrac{1 - \varepsilon_1}{A_1 \varepsilon_1} + \dfrac{1 - \varepsilon_2}{A_2 \varepsilon_2} + \dfrac{1}{A_1 \bar{F}_{1-2}}$

$$\therefore \qquad (Q_{12})_{net} = (E_{b1} - E_{b2}) \left[\frac{1}{\dfrac{1 - \varepsilon_1}{A_1 \varepsilon_1} + \dfrac{1 - \varepsilon_2}{A_2 \varepsilon_2} + \dfrac{1}{A_1 \bar{F}_{1-2}}} \right]$$

or, $\qquad (Q_{12})_{net} = A_1 (E_{b1} - E_{b2}) \left[\dfrac{1}{\left(\dfrac{1}{\varepsilon_1} - 1 \right) + \dfrac{A_1}{A_2} \left(\dfrac{1}{\varepsilon_2} - 1 \right) + \dfrac{1}{\bar{F}_{1-2}}} \right]$ ...(12.43)

Also, $\qquad (Q_{12})_{net} = A_1 (F_g)_{1-2} (E_{b1} - E_{b2}) = A_1 (F_g)_{1-2} \sigma (T_1^4 - T_2^4)$ ...(12.44)

$$\therefore \qquad (F_g)_{1-2} = \left[\frac{1}{\left(\dfrac{1}{\varepsilon_1} - 1 \right) + \dfrac{A_1}{A_2} \left(\dfrac{1}{\varepsilon_2} - 1 \right) + \dfrac{1}{\bar{F}_{1-2}}} \right]$$ ...[12.44 (a)]

(where, $$\bar{F}_{1-2} = \frac{A_2 - A_1 F_{1-2}^2}{A_1 + A_2 - 2A_1 F_{1-2}})$$

12.9. RADIATION HEAT EXCHANGE FOR FOUR BLACK SURFACES

The network for radiation heat exchange for four black surfaces is shown in Fig. 12.29.
The net rate of flow from surface 1 is given by

$$(Q_1)_{net} = A_1 F_{1-2}(E_{b1} - E_{b2}) + A_1 F_{1-3}(E_{b1} - E_{b3}) + A_1 F_{1-4}(E_{b1} - E_{b4})$$
$$...(12.45)$$

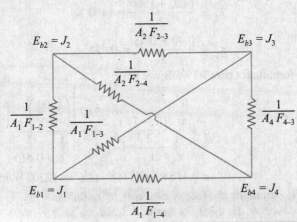

Fig. 12.29. Network for four black surfaces.

12.10. RADIATION HEAT EXCHANGE FOR FOUR GRAY SURFACES

The network for radiation heat exchange for four gray surfaces is shown in Fig. 12.30.

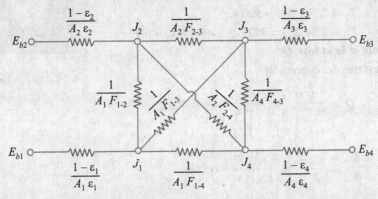

Fig. 12.30. Network for four gray surfaces.

The net rate of heat flow from the four gray surfaces is given by:

$$(Q_1)_{net} = \frac{E_{b1} - J_1}{\dfrac{1 - \varepsilon_1}{A_1 \varepsilon_1}} = A_1 F_{1-2}(J_1 - J_2) + A_1 F_{1-3}(J_1 - J_3) + A_1 F_{1-4}(J_1 - J_4) \quad ...(12.46)$$

$$(Q_2)_{net} = \frac{E_{b2} - J_2}{\dfrac{1 - \varepsilon_2}{A_2 \varepsilon_2}} = A_2 F_{2-1}(J_2 - J_1) + A_2 F_{2-3}(J_2 - J_3) + A_2 F_{2-4}(J_2 - J_4) \quad ...(12.47)$$

$$(Q_3)_{net} = \frac{E_{b3} - J_3}{\dfrac{1 - \varepsilon_3}{A_3 \varepsilon_3}} = A_3 F_{3-1}(J_3 - J_1) + A_3 F_{3-2}(J_3 - J_2) + A_3 F_{3-4}(J_3 - J_4) \quad ...(12.48)$$

$$(Q_4)_{net} = \frac{E_{b4} - J_4}{\dfrac{1 - \varepsilon_4}{A_4 \, \varepsilon_4}} = A_4 F_{4-1}(J_4 - J_1) + A_4 F_{4-2}(J_4 - J_2) + A_4 F_{4-3}(J_4 - J_3) \quad ...(12.49)$$

Example 12.18. *A refractory material which has $\varepsilon = 0.4$ at 1500 K and $\varepsilon = 0.43$ at 1420 K is exposed to black furnace walls at 1500 K. What is the rate of gain of heat radiation per m^2 area?* (M.U.)

Solution. Taking the mean temperature and mean emissivity of the heated body, we get

$$T_2 = \frac{1420 + 1500}{2} = 1460 \text{ K}$$

$$\varepsilon_2 = \frac{0.40 + 0.43}{2} = 0.415$$

Now using the formula for parallel walls, we have

$$q = \frac{\sigma \,(T_1^4 - T_2^4)}{\dfrac{1}{\varepsilon_1} + \dfrac{1}{\varepsilon_2} - 1} = \frac{5.67 \left[\left(\dfrac{1500}{100}\right)^4 - \left(\dfrac{1460}{100}\right)^4\right]}{\dfrac{1}{1} + \dfrac{1}{0.415} - 1}$$

$$= 0.415 \times 5.67 \,(15^4 - 14.6^4) = 12207 \text{ W/m}^2 = \textbf{12.2 kW/m}^2 \textbf{ (Ans.)}$$

Example 12.19. *Determine the rate of heat loss by radiation from a steel tube of outside diameter 70 mm and 3 m long at a temperature of 227° C if the tube is located within a square brick conduit of 0.3 m side and at 27° C. Take ε (steel) = 0.79 and ε (brick) = 0.93.* (AMIE Summer, 1999; P.U., 1998)

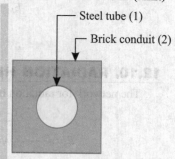

— Steel tube (1)

— Brick conduit (2)

Fig. 12.31

Solution. *Given* : $d = 70$ mm $= 0.07$ m, $L = 3$m;

$T_1 = 227 + 273 = 500$ K;

$T_2 = 27 + 273 = 300$ K; $\varepsilon_1 = 0.79$; $\varepsilon_2 = 0.93$.

The rate of heat loss, Q:

The heat transfer is given by

$$Q = \frac{A_1 \, \sigma \,(T_1^4 - T_2^4)}{\dfrac{1}{\varepsilon_1} + \left(\dfrac{1}{\varepsilon_2} - 1\right)\dfrac{A_1}{A_2}} \qquad ...(\text{Eqn.}12.24)$$

Now, $\dfrac{A_1}{A_2} = \dfrac{\pi \, d \, L}{P.L} = \dfrac{\pi \times 0.07}{4 \times 0.3} = 0.183$

Substituting the values in the above equation, we get

$$Q = \frac{(\pi \times 0.07 \times 3) \times 5.67 \left[\left(\dfrac{500}{100}\right)^4 - \left(\dfrac{300}{100}\right)^4\right]}{\dfrac{1}{0.79} + \left(\dfrac{1}{0.93} - 1\right) \times 0.183}$$

$$= \frac{3.74 \,(625 - 81)}{1.266 + 0.0138} = \textbf{1589.7 W (Ans.)}$$

Example 12.20. *An electric heating system is installed in the ceiling of a room 5 m (length) × 5 m (width) × 2.5 m (height). The temperature of the ceiling is 315 K whereas under equilibrium conditions the walls are at 295 K. If the floor is non-sensitive to radiations and the emissivities of the ceiling and wall are 0.75 and 0.65 respectively calculate the radiant heat loss from the ceiling to the walls.*

Solution. Refer to Fig. 12.32. $X = 5$ m, $Y = 5$ m, $Z = 2.5$ m, $T_1 = 315$ K, $T_2 = 295$ K, $\varepsilon_1 = 0.75$, $\varepsilon_2 = 0.65$

Radiant heat loss from the ceiling to the walls:

The rate of radiant heat exchange between the ceiling (suffix 1) and a single wall (suffix 2) is given by

$$Q_{12} = (F_g)_{1-2} A_1 \sigma (T_1^4 - T_2^4)$$

or $$Q_{12} = \dfrac{A_1 \sigma (T_1^4 - T_2^4)}{\left(\dfrac{1-\varepsilon_1}{\varepsilon_1}\right) + \dfrac{1}{F_{1-2}} + \left(\dfrac{1-\varepsilon_2}{\varepsilon_2}\right)\dfrac{A_1}{A_2}}$$

...(1)

$$\left[where \ (F_g)_{1-2} = \dfrac{1}{\dfrac{1-\varepsilon_1}{\varepsilon_1} + \dfrac{1}{F_{1-2}} + \left(\dfrac{1-\varepsilon_2}{\varepsilon_2}\right)\dfrac{A_1}{A_2}} \right]$$

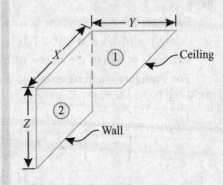

Fig. 12.32

A_1 = Area of ceiling = $5 \times 5 = 25$ m^2

A_2 = Area of single wall = $5 \times 2.5 = 12.5$ m^2

The ceiling and wall are perpendicular surfaces with common edge for which

$$\frac{Z}{X} = \frac{2.5}{5} = 0.5 \text{ and } \frac{Y}{X} = \frac{5}{5} = 1$$

Corresponding to these parameters, the shape factor F_{1-2} as read from Fig. 12.4 equals 0.15.
Substituting the values in eqn. (1), we get

$$Q_{12} = \dfrac{25 \times 5.67 \left\{\left(\dfrac{315}{100}\right)^4 - \left(\dfrac{295}{100}\right)^4\right\}}{\left(\dfrac{1-0.75}{0.75}\right) + \dfrac{1}{0.15} + \left(\dfrac{1-0.65}{0.65}\right) \times \dfrac{25}{12.5}} = \dfrac{3220.9}{0.333 + 6.667 + 1.077} = 398.77 \text{ W}$$

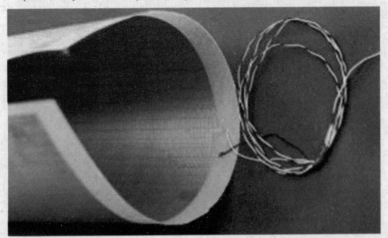

A patented thick-film flexible sensors for the measurement of heat transfer (conduction, convection and radiation) offering high sensitivity and low thermal resistance.

Total radiant heat loss from the ceiling to all the four walls

$$= 4 \times 398.77 = 1595 \text{ W or } \mathbf{1.595 \text{ kW (Ans.)}}$$

Example 12.21. *A hot ingot casting 25 cm (length) × 25 cm (width) × 1.8 m (height) at a temperature of 1200 K is stripped from its mould. The casting is made to stand on the end on the floor of a large foundry whose wall, floor and roof can be assumed to be at 290 K temperature. If the emissivity of casting material is 0.8, calculate the net heat exchange between the casting and the room.*

Solution. The rate of radiant heat exchange between the ingot and the room is given by

$$Q_{12} = (F_g)_{1-2} A_1 \sigma (T_1^4 - T_2^4)$$

where, A_1 = Area of the ingot = $(0.25 \times 0.25) + 4 \times 0.25 \times 1.8 = 1.8625 \text{ m}^2$

The configuration corresponds to a completely enclosed body, and small compared with the enclosing body, *i.e.* $A_1 << A_2$ and $F_{1-2} = 1$. Hence

$$(F_g)_{1-2} = \cfrac{1}{\left(\cfrac{1-\varepsilon_1}{\varepsilon_1}\right) + \cfrac{1}{F_{1-2}} + \left(\cfrac{1-\varepsilon_2}{\varepsilon_2}\right)\cfrac{A_1}{A_2}} = \cfrac{1}{\cfrac{1-\varepsilon_1}{\varepsilon_1} + 1 + 0} = \varepsilon_1 = 0.8$$

$$\therefore \quad Q_{12} = 0.8 \times 1.8625 \times 5.67 \left[\left(\frac{1200}{100}\right)^4 - \left(\frac{290}{100}\right)^4 \right]$$

$$= 174586 \text{ W or } \mathbf{174.586 \text{ kW (Ans.)}}$$

Example 12.22. *An enclosure is formed by three surfaces. Details of their shape factors, emissivities and temperatures are as follows :*

Surface	Shape	Emissivity	Temperature
1.	*Curved cylindrical*	*0.8*	*500° C*
2.	*One end closing disc*	*0.85*	*400° C*
3.	*Other end closing disc*	*0.85*	*400° C*

Diameters of two closing flat discs and interspacing between the two are 25 mm and 100 mm respectively. Shape factor between two identical discs is 0.05. Calculate the net rate of radiant heat flow leaving from surface 1 and reaching to each of the surfaces 2 and 3. **(P.U.)**

Solution. *Given:* $d = d_2 = d_3 = 25 \text{ mm} = 0.025 \text{ m}$; $h = 100 \text{ mm} = 0.1 \text{ m}$; $F_{2-3} = 0.05$; $\varepsilon_1 = 0.8$; $\varepsilon_2 = \varepsilon_3 = 0.85$.

The shape factor relations are:

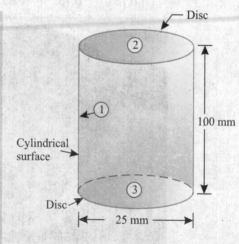

$$F_{2-1} + F_{2-3} = 1 \text{ or } F_{2-3} = 1 - F_{2-1}$$

$$F_{1-2} + F_{1-3} = 1 \text{ or } F_{1-3} = 1 - F_{1-2}$$

and, $\quad A_1 F_{1-2} = A_2 F_{2-1}$

or , $\quad F_{1-2} = \cfrac{A_2}{A_1} \times F_{2-1}$

$\therefore \quad 0.05 = 1 - F_{2-1}$

or, $\quad F_{2-1} = 1 - 0.05 = 0.95$

and, $\quad F_{1-2} =$

$$\frac{A_2}{A_1} \times 0.95 = \frac{(\pi/4)\, d^2}{\pi d h} \times 0.95 = \frac{d}{4h} \times 0.95$$

$$= \frac{0.025}{4 \times 0.1} \times 0.95 = 0.059$$

Disc

Cylindrical surface

Disc

100 mm

25 mm

Fig. 12.33

$$Q_{12} = Q_{13}$$

There is no heat flow from 2 to 3 or 3 to 2 as

$$Q_{23} = Q_{32}$$

$$\therefore \quad Q_{12} = \frac{\sigma (T_1^4 - T_2^4)}{\dfrac{1 - \varepsilon_1}{A_1 \varepsilon_1} + \dfrac{1}{A_1 F_{1-2}} + \dfrac{1 - \varepsilon_2}{A_2 \varepsilon_2}}$$

$$A_1 = \pi d h = \pi \times 0.025 \times 0.1 = 0.00785 \text{ m}^2$$

$$A_2 = \frac{\pi}{4} d^2 = \frac{\pi}{4} (0.025)^2 = 0.00049 \text{ m}^2$$

$$T_1 = 500 + 273 = 773 \text{ K}, \; T_2 = 400 + 273 = 673 \text{ K}$$

Substituting the values in the above equation, we get

$$Q_{12} = \frac{5.67 \left[\left(\dfrac{773}{100} \right)^4 - \left(\dfrac{673}{100} \right)^4 \right]}{\left(\dfrac{1 - 0.8}{0.00785 \times 0.8} \right) + \left(\dfrac{1}{0.00785 \times 0.059} \right) + \dfrac{(1 - 0.85)}{0.00049 \times 0.85}}$$

$$= \frac{5.67 \, (3570.4 - 2051.4)}{31.85 + 2159.13 + 360.14} = \mathbf{3.376 \text{ W} \; (Ans.)}$$

Example 12.23. *A short cylindrical enclosure is formed with three surfaces, a circular plane surface 1 of radius 20 cm maintained at 2000 K and having $\varepsilon_1 = 0.8$, another circular plane surface 2 of same size as 1 having $\varepsilon_2 = 0.5$ and maintained at 500 K. Surfaces 1 and 2 are parallel to each other and distance between them is 5 cm. The third surface is reradiating surface which forms an enclosure. Find:*

(i) Net heat transfer rate between 1 and 2 due to radiation, and

(ii) The temperature attained by the reradiating surface.

Use the following expression for finding the shape factor between two circular, coaxial and parallel areas.

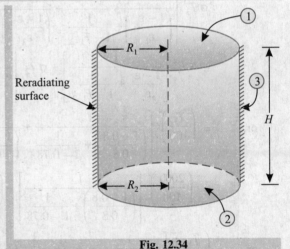
Fig. 12.34

$$F_{1-2} = \frac{1}{2B^2} \left[X - \sqrt{X^2 - 4B^2 \, C^2} \right]$$

where $\quad B = \dfrac{R_1}{H}, C = \dfrac{R_2}{H}$ and

$$X = (1 + B^2 + C^2)$$

where R_1 and R_2 are radii of the circular plates and H is the distance between them. (P.U.)

Solution. *Given:* $R_1 = R_2 = 20 \text{ cm} = 0.2 \text{ m}$ and $H = 5 \text{ cm} = 0.05 \text{ m}$; $T_1 = 2000 \text{ K}$; $T_2 = 500 \text{ K}$; $\varepsilon_1 = 0.8$; $\varepsilon_2 = 0.5$

$$B = C = \frac{0.2}{0.05} = 4$$

$$X = 1 + B^2 + C^2 = 1 + (4)^2 + (4)^2 = 33$$

$$\therefore \quad F_{1-2} = \frac{1}{2 B^2} \left[X - \sqrt{X^2 - 4B^2 \, C^2} \right]$$

$$= \frac{1}{2 \times (4)^2} \left[33 - \sqrt{(33)^2 - 4 \times (4)^2 (4)^2} \right]$$

(i) The net heat transfer rate between surfaces 1 and 2, Q_{12} :

The heat transfer between the surfaces 1 and 2 is given by

$$Q_{12} = \frac{A_1 \, \sigma \, (T_1^4 - T_2^4)}{\left(\frac{1 - \varepsilon_1}{\varepsilon_1} \right) + \left(\frac{1 - \varepsilon_2}{\varepsilon_2} \right) \frac{A_1}{A_2} + \left[\frac{A_1 + A_2 - 2A_1 \, F_{1-2}}{A_2 - A_1 \, F_{1-2}^2} \right]} \qquad \text{...(Eqn. 12.44)}$$

In this case $A_1 = A_2$

$$Q_{12} = \frac{A_1 \, \sigma \, (T_1^4 - T_2^4)}{\left(\frac{1 - \varepsilon_1}{\varepsilon_1} \right) + \left(\frac{1 - \varepsilon_2}{\varepsilon_2} \right) + \frac{2 \, (1 - F_{1-2})}{(1 - F_{1-2}^2)}} = \frac{\pi \, R_1^2 \, \sigma \, (T_1^4 - T_2^4)}{\left(\frac{1 - \varepsilon_1}{\varepsilon_1} \right) + \left(\frac{1 - \varepsilon_2}{\varepsilon_2} \right) + \frac{2}{(1 + F_{1-2})}}$$

$$= \frac{\pi \times 0.2^2 \times 5.67 \left[\left(\frac{2000}{100} \right)^4 - \left(\frac{500}{100} \right)^4 \right]}{\left(\frac{1 - 0.8}{0.8} \right) + \left(\frac{1 - 0.5}{0.5} \right) + \frac{2}{1 + 0.78}}$$

$$= \frac{0.7125 \, (160000 - 625)}{2.37} = 47913 \text{ W or } \mathbf{47.9 \text{ kW (Ans.)}}$$

(ii) The temperature attained by the reradiating surface, T_3

The temperature T_3 of the reradiating surface is given by

$$\sigma \, T_3^4 \left[\frac{1}{\left(\frac{1 - \varepsilon_1}{\varepsilon_1} \right) + \frac{1}{1 - F_{1-2}}} + \frac{1}{\left(\frac{1 - \varepsilon_2}{\varepsilon_2} \right) + \frac{1}{1 - F_{1-2}}} \right]$$

$$= \sigma \, T_1^4 \left[\frac{1}{\frac{1 - \varepsilon_1}{\varepsilon_1} + \frac{1}{1 - F_{1-2}}} \right] + \sigma \, T_2^4 \left[\frac{1}{\frac{1 - \varepsilon_2}{\varepsilon_2} + \frac{1}{1 - F_{1-2}}} \right]$$

or,
$$= \left(\frac{T_3}{100} \right)^4 \left[\frac{1}{\left(\frac{1 - 0.8}{0.8} \right) + \frac{1}{1 - 0.78}} + \frac{1}{\left(\frac{1 - 0.5}{0.5} \right) + \frac{1}{1 - 0.78}} \right]$$

$$= \left(\frac{2000}{100} \right)^4 \left[\frac{1}{\left(\frac{1 - 0.8}{0.8} \right) + \frac{1}{1 - 0.78}} \right] + \left(\frac{500}{100} \right)^4 \left[\frac{1}{\left(\frac{1 - 0.5}{0.5} \right) + \frac{1}{1 - 0.78}} \right]$$

or,
$$\left(\frac{T_3}{100} \right)^4 \left[\frac{1}{0.25 + 4.54} + \frac{1}{1 + 4.54} \right] = (20)^4 \left[\frac{1}{0.25 + 4.54} \right] + (5)^4 \left[\frac{1}{1 + 4.54} \right]$$

or,
$$\left(\frac{T_3}{100} \right)^4 \left[\frac{1}{4.79} + \frac{1}{5.54} \right] = \frac{(20)^4}{4.79} + \frac{(5)^4}{5.54}$$

or,
$$\left(\frac{T_3}{100} \right)^4 \times 0.3893 = 33402.9 + 112.8 = 33515.7$$

or,
$$\frac{T_3}{100} = \left(\frac{33515.7}{0.3893} \right)^{1/4} = 17.13$$

or,
$$T_3 = 100 \times 17.13 = \mathbf{1713 \text{ K (Ans.)}}$$

Example 12.24. *Calculate the heat transfer rate per m^2 area by radiation between the surfaces of two long cylinders having radii 100 mm and 50 mm respectively. The smaller cylinder being in the larger cylinder. The axes of the cylinders are parallel to each other and separated by a distance of 20 mm. The surfaces of inner and outer cylinders are maintained at 127° C and 27° C respectively. The emissivity of both the surfaces is 0.5.*

Assume the medium between the two cylinders is non-absorbing. (P.U.)

Solution. *Given:* $r_1 = 50$ mm $= 0.05$ m; $r_2 = 100$ mm $= 0.1$ m, $T_1 = 127 + 273 = 400$ K, $T_2 = 27 + 273 = 300$ K, $\varepsilon_1 = \varepsilon_2 = 0.5$.

The heat transfer between two concentric or eccentric cylinders is given by

$$(Q_{12})_{net} = \frac{A_1 \, \sigma \, (T_1^4 - T_2^4)}{\left(\dfrac{1-\varepsilon_1}{\varepsilon_1}\right) + \dfrac{1}{F_{1-2}} + \left(\dfrac{1-\varepsilon_2}{\varepsilon_2}\right)\dfrac{A_1}{A_2}} \qquad \text{...(Eqn. 12.35)}$$

Here $\quad F_{1-2} = 1$ and $\dfrac{A_1}{A_2} = \dfrac{2\pi r_1 L}{2\pi r_2 L} = \dfrac{r_1}{r_2}$

Substituting the values, we have

$$(Q_{12})_{net} = \frac{1 \times 5.67 \left[\left(\dfrac{400}{100}\right)^4 - \left(\dfrac{300}{100}\right)^4\right]}{\left(\dfrac{1-0.5}{0.5}\right) + 1 + \left(\dfrac{1-0.5}{0.5}\right)\times\dfrac{0.05}{0.1}} = \frac{992.25}{2.5} = \textbf{396.9 W/m}^2 \ \ \textbf{(Ans.)}$$

Example 12.25. *A long cylindrical heater 25 mm in diameter is maintained at 660° C and has surface resistivity of 0.8. The heater is located in a large room whose walls are at 27° C. How much will the radiant heat transfer from the heater be reduced if it is surrounded by a 300 mm diameter radiation shield of aluminium haivng an emissivity of 0.2? What is the temperature of the shield?* (M.U.)

Solution. *Given:* $r_1 = \dfrac{25}{2} = 12.5$ mm $= 0.0125$ m; $r_3 = \dfrac{300}{2} = 150$ mm $= 0.15$ m; $T_1 = 660 + 273 = 933$ K; $T_2 = 27 + 273 = 300$ K; $\varepsilon_1 = 0.8$, ε_3 (shield) $= 0.2$.

Considering L is the length of the heater, the heat lost by the heater to the room is given by

$$Q = A_1 \varepsilon_1 \sigma [T_1^4 - T_2^4] \qquad \text{...(i)}$$

where suffix '1' belongs to heater and T_2 is the room wall temperature.

$$\therefore \qquad Q = 2\pi r_1 L \times 0.8 \times 5.67 \left[\left(\dfrac{933}{100}\right)^4 - \left(\dfrac{300}{100}\right)^4\right]$$

$$= 2\pi \times 0.0125 \, L \times 0.8 \times 5.67 \, (9.33^4 - 3^4) = 0.356 \, L \, (7577.5 - 81)$$

or, $\qquad q' = \dfrac{Q'}{L} = 0.356 \, (7577.5 - 81) = 2668.7 \text{ W} \approx 2.67 \text{ kW/m}$

When the cylinder is enclosed in a radiation shield then the heat flow is given by

$$Q' = \frac{A_1 \, \sigma \, (T_1^4 - T_3^4)}{\dfrac{1}{\varepsilon_1} + \left(\dfrac{1}{\varepsilon_3} - 1\right)\dfrac{r_1}{r_3}} = A_3 \varepsilon_3 \sigma \, (T_3^4 - T_2^4)$$

as heat lost by heater to shield is further lost by shield to the room, where suffix 3' belongs to shield.

$$q' = \frac{Q'}{L} = \frac{2\pi r_1 \, \sigma \, (T_1^4 - T_3^4)}{\dfrac{1}{\varepsilon_1} + \left(\dfrac{1}{\varepsilon_3} - 1\right)\dfrac{r_1}{r_3}} = \frac{2\pi r_3 \, \sigma \, (T_3^4 - T_2^4)}{\dfrac{1}{\varepsilon_3}} \qquad \text{...(ii)}$$

From the above equation, first we have to find out the value of T_3

$$\frac{r_1 (T_1^4 - T_3^4)}{\frac{1}{\varepsilon_1} + \left(\frac{1}{\varepsilon_3} - 1\right)\frac{r_1}{r_3}} = \frac{r_3 (T_3^4 - T_2^4)}{\frac{1}{\varepsilon_3}}$$

Now substituting the given values in the above equation, we get

$$\frac{0.0125 (933^4 - T_3^4)}{\frac{1}{0.8} + \left(\frac{1}{0.2} - 1\right) \times \frac{0.0125}{0.15}} = \frac{0.15 (T_3^4 - 300^4)}{\frac{1}{0.2}}$$

$$\frac{0.0125 (933^4 - T_3^4)}{1.58} = 0.03 (T_3^4 - 300^4)$$

or, $\qquad 933^4 - T_3^4 = 3.792 (T_3^4 - 300^4) = 3.792\ T_3^4 - 3.792 \times 300^4$

or, $\qquad 4.792\ T_3^4 = 933^4 + 3.792 \times 300^4 = 300^4 (3.792 + 93.55)$

or, $\qquad T_3^4 = 20.3 \times (300)^4$ or $T_3 = 636.8$ K or **363.8° C (Ans.)**

Substituting this value in eqn. (ii), we get

$$q' = \frac{2\pi \times 0.15 \times 5.67 \left[\left(\frac{636.8}{100}\right)^4 - \left(\frac{300}{100}\right)^4\right]}{\frac{1}{0.2}} = 1.0688 (1644.4 - 81)$$

$$= 1670 \text{ W/m} = 1.67 \text{ kW/m}$$

∴ *Percentage reduction in heat flow*

$$= \frac{q - q'}{q} \times 100 = \frac{2.67 - 1.67}{2.67} \times 100 = \textbf{37.45\% (Ans.)}$$

Example 12.26. *Three thin walled infinitely long hollow cylinders of radii 5 cm, 10 cm and 15 cm are arranged concentrically as shown in Fig. 12.35. $T_1 = 1000$ K and $T_3 = 300$ K.*

Assuming $\varepsilon_1 = \varepsilon_2 = \varepsilon_3 = 0.05$ and vacuum in the spaces between the cylinders, calculate the steady state temperature of cylindrical surface 2 and heat flow per m^2 area of cylinder 1.

(P.U.)

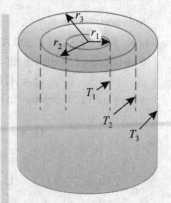

Fig. 12.35

Solution. *Given:* $r_1 = 5$ cm; $r_2 = 10$ cm; $r_3 = 15$ cm; $T_1 = 1000$ K; $T_3 = 300$ K

$$\varepsilon_1 = \varepsilon_2 = \varepsilon_3 = 0.05.$$

For steady state heat flow,

$$Q_{12} = Q_{23}$$

or,

$$\frac{A_1 \sigma (T_1^4 - T_2^4)}{\left(\frac{1 - \varepsilon_1}{\varepsilon_1}\right) + \frac{1}{F_{1-2}} + \left(\frac{1 - \varepsilon_2}{\varepsilon_2}\right)\frac{A_1}{A_2}} = \frac{A_2 \sigma (T_2^4 - T_3^4)}{\left(\frac{1 - \varepsilon_2}{\varepsilon_2}\right) + \frac{1}{F_{2-3}} + \left(\frac{1 - \varepsilon_3}{\varepsilon_3}\right)\frac{A_2}{A_3}}$$

In this case $F_{1-2} = F_{2-3} = 1$; and

$$\frac{A_1}{A_2} = \frac{r_1}{r_2} = \frac{5}{10} = 0.5$$

$$\frac{A_2}{A_3} = \frac{r_2}{r_3} = \frac{10}{15} = 0.67$$

$$\therefore \quad \frac{2\,\pi\,r_1\,L\left[\left(\dfrac{1000}{100}\right)^4 - \left(\dfrac{T_2}{100}\right)^4\right]}{\left(\dfrac{1-0.05}{0.05}\right)+1+\left(\dfrac{1-0.05}{0.05}\right)\times 0.5} = \frac{(2\,\pi\,r_2\,L\left[\left(\dfrac{T_2}{100}\right)^4 - \left(\dfrac{300}{100}\right)^4\right]}{\left(\dfrac{1-0.05}{0.05}\right)+1+\left(\dfrac{1-0.05}{0.05}\right)\times 0.67}$$

$$\frac{0.05\,(10000 - x^4)}{29.5} = \frac{0.1\,(x^4 - 81)}{32.73}$$

or, $$(1000 - x^4) = \frac{29.5 \times 0.1}{32.73 \times 0.05}\,(x^4 - 81) = 1.8\,(x^4 - 81)$$

or, $$2.8\,x^4 = 10000 - 145.8 = 9854.2$$

or, $$x = \left(\frac{9854.2}{2.8}\right)^{1/4} = 7.7$$

or, $$\frac{T_2}{100} = 7.7 \text{ or } T_2 = 770 \text{ K}$$

∴ Heat flow per m² area of cylinder 1,

$$Q_{12} = \frac{A_1\,\sigma\,(T_1^4 - T_2^4)}{\left(\dfrac{1-\varepsilon_1}{\varepsilon_1}\right)+1+\left(\dfrac{1-\varepsilon_2}{\varepsilon_2}\right)\dfrac{A_1}{A_2}}$$

$$Q_{12} = \frac{1\times 5.67\left[\left(\dfrac{1000}{100}\right)^4 - \left(\dfrac{770}{100}\right)^4\right]}{\left(\dfrac{1-0.05}{0.05}\right)+1+\left(\dfrac{1-0.05}{0.05}\right)\times 0.5}$$

$$= \frac{5.67 \times (10000 - 3515.3)}{29.5} = \textbf{1246.4 W (Ans.)}$$

Example 12.27. *Three hollow thin walled cylinders having diameters 10 cm, 20 cm and 30cm are arranged concentrically. The temperatures of the innermost and outermost cylindrical surfaces are 100 K and 300 K respectively. Assuming vacuum between the annular spaces, find the steady state temperature attained by the cylindrical surface having diameter of 20 cm.*

Take $\varepsilon_1 = \varepsilon_2 = \varepsilon_3 = 0.05.$ (M.U. 1998)

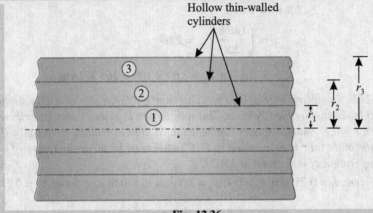

Hollow thin-walled cylinders

Fig. 12.36

Solution. *Given:* $r_1 = \dfrac{10}{2} = 5\,\text{cm}, r_2 = \dfrac{20}{2} = 10\,\text{cm}, r_3 = \dfrac{30}{2} = 15\,\text{cm}; T_1 = 100\,\text{K},$

$T_3 = 300\,\text{K}, \varepsilon_1 = \varepsilon_2 = \varepsilon_3 = 0.05.$

Temperature, T_2:

Referring to the Fig. 12.36, we can write

$$\frac{A_1\,\sigma\,(T_1^4 - T_2^4)}{\left(\dfrac{1-\varepsilon_1}{\varepsilon_1}\right) + \dfrac{1}{F_{1-2}} + \left(\dfrac{1-\varepsilon_2}{\varepsilon_2}\right)\dfrac{A_1}{A_2}} = \frac{A_2\,\sigma\,(T_2^4 - T_3^4)}{\left(\dfrac{1-\varepsilon_2}{\varepsilon_2}\right) + \dfrac{1}{F_{2-3}} + \left(\dfrac{1-\varepsilon_3}{\varepsilon_3}\right)\dfrac{A_2}{A_3}}$$

where all the areas are surface areas of the cylinders.

As
$$F_{1-2} = F_{2-3} = 1 \text{ and } \varepsilon_1 = \varepsilon_2 = \varepsilon_3 \text{ (given)} = 0.05$$

$\therefore$
$$\frac{A_1\,(T_1^4 - T_2^4)}{\dfrac{1}{\varepsilon_1} + \left(\dfrac{1}{\varepsilon_2} - 1\right)\dfrac{A_1}{A_2}} = \frac{A_2\,(T_2^4 - T_3^4)}{\dfrac{1}{\varepsilon_2} + \left(\dfrac{1}{\varepsilon_3} - 1\right)\dfrac{A_2}{A_3}} \qquad \qquad \text{...(i)}$$

$$\frac{A_1}{A_2} = \frac{r_1}{r_2} = \frac{5}{10} = 0.5 \text{ and } \frac{A_2}{A_3} = \frac{r_2}{r_3} = \frac{10}{15} = 0.67$$

Substituting the values in eqn. (*i*), we get

$$\frac{2\,\pi\,r_1\,L\,(T_1^4 - T_2^4)}{\dfrac{1}{0.05} + \left(\dfrac{1}{0.05} - 1\right) \times 0.5} = \frac{2\,\pi\,r_2\,L\,(T_2^4 - T_3^4)}{\dfrac{1}{0.05} + \left(\dfrac{1}{0.05} - 1\right) \times 0.67}$$

$$\frac{T_1^4 - T_2^4}{20 + 19 \times 0.5} = \frac{(r_2/r_1)\,(T_2^4 - T_3^4)}{20 + 19 \times 0.67}$$

$$\frac{T_1^4 - T_2^4}{29.5} = \frac{2\,(T_2^4 - T_3^4)}{32.73} = \frac{T_2^4 - T_3^4}{16.36} \qquad \left(\because \dfrac{r_2}{r_1} = 2\right)$$

or, $$\left(\frac{100}{100}\right)^4 - \left(\frac{T_2}{100}\right)^4 = \frac{29.5}{16.36}\left[\left(\frac{T_2}{100}\right)^4 - \left(\frac{300}{100}\right)^4\right]$$

$$1 - x^4 = 1.8\,(x^4 - 81) \qquad \left[\text{where } x = \dfrac{T_2}{100}\right]$$

or, $$1 - x^4 = 1.8\,x^4 - 145.8$$

or, $$2.8\,x^4 = 146.8$$

or, $$x = \left(\frac{146.8}{2.8}\right)^{1/4} = 2.69$$

or, $$\frac{T_2}{100} = 2.69 \text{ or } \boldsymbol{T_2 = 2.69 \times 100 = 269\,K} \text{ (Ans.)}$$

Example 12.28. *An electric wire of 0.25 mm diameter, $\varepsilon = 0.4$ is placed within a tube of 2.5 mm diameter, $\varepsilon = 0.6$ having negligible thickness. This tube in turn is placed concentrically within a tube of 5 mm diameter, $\varepsilon = 0.7$. Annular spaces can be assumed to be evacuated completely. If the surface temperature of the outer tube is maintained at 5° C, what must be the temperature of wire so as to maintain the temperature of inner tube at 120° C ?* (P.U. 1996)

Solution. *Given:* $d_1 = 0.25\,\text{mm}, \varepsilon_1 = 0.4; d_2 = 2.5\,\text{mm}, \varepsilon_2 = 0.6; d_3 = 5\,\text{mm}, \varepsilon_3 = 0.7; t_2 = 120°\,\text{C}, t_3 = 5°\,\text{C}.$

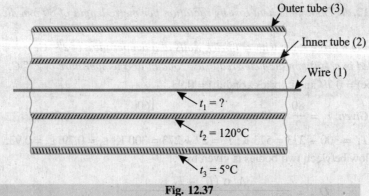

Fig. 12.37

Temperature of the wire, t_1 :

For steady state condition :

Heat lost by the wire to the inner tube by radiation

$\qquad$ = Heat lost by inner tube to the outer tube by radiation

i.e.

$$\frac{A_1 \, \sigma \, (T_1^4 - T_2^4)}{\dfrac{1-\varepsilon_1}{\varepsilon_1} + 1 + \left(\dfrac{1-\varepsilon_2}{\varepsilon_2}\right)\dfrac{A_1}{A_2}} = \frac{A_2 \, \sigma \, (T_2^4 - T_3^4)}{\left(\dfrac{1-\varepsilon_2}{\varepsilon_2}\right) + 1 + \left(\dfrac{1-\varepsilon_3}{\varepsilon_3}\right)\dfrac{A_2}{A_3}} \qquad \text{...(1)}$$

$\qquad\qquad$ As $F_{1-2} = 1$ in both cases

$$\frac{A_1}{A_2} = \frac{\pi \, d_1 \, L}{\pi \, d_2 \, L} = \frac{0.25}{2.5} = 0.1$$

$$\frac{A_2}{A_3} = \frac{\pi \, d_2 \, L}{\pi \, d_3 \, L} = \frac{2.5}{5} = 0.5$$

Now, substituting the values in eqn. (1), we get

$$\frac{\left(\pi \times \dfrac{0.25}{1000} \times 1\right) \times 5.67 \left[\left(\dfrac{T_1}{100}\right)^4 - \left(\dfrac{120+273}{100}\right)^4\right]}{\left(\dfrac{1-0.4}{0.4}\right) + 1 + \left(\dfrac{1-0.6}{0.6}\right) \times 0.1} = \frac{\left(\pi \times \dfrac{2.5}{1000} \times 1\right) \times 5.67 \left[\left(\dfrac{1206+273}{100}\right)^4 - \left(\dfrac{5+273}{100}\right)^4\right]}{\left(\dfrac{1-0.6}{0.6}\right) + 1 + \left(\dfrac{1-0.7}{0.7}\right) \times 0.5}$$

$$\frac{0.25 \left[\left(\dfrac{T_1}{100}\right)^4 - (3.93)^4\right]}{2.567} = \frac{0.25 \, [(3.93)^4 - (2.78)^4]}{1.884}$$

$$\frac{\left(\dfrac{T_1}{100}\right)^4 - 238.5}{2.567} = \frac{10 \, (238.5 - 59.7)}{1.884}$$

or,

$$\left(\frac{T_1}{100}\right)^4 = 238.5 + \frac{2.567 \times 10 \, (238.5 - 59.7)}{1.884} = 2674.7$$

or,

$$\frac{T_1}{100} = (2674.7)^{1/4} = 7.19 \text{ or } T_1 = 100 \times 7.19 = 719 \, K$$

or,

$$t_1 = 719 - 273 = \mathbf{446° \, C \, (Ans.)}$$

Example 12.29. *Determine heat lost by radiation per metre length of 80 mm diameter pipe at 300° C, if*

(i) *located in a large room with red brick walls at a temperature of 27° C;*

(ii) *enclosed in a 160 mm diameter red brick conduit at a temperature of 27° C.*   (P.U.)

Take ε(pipe) = 0.79 and ε (brick conduit) = 0.93.

Solution. *Given:* $r_1 = \dfrac{80}{2} = 40$ mm = 0.04 m; $r_2 = \dfrac{160}{2} = 80$ mm = 0.08 m;

$\quad T_1 = 300 + 273 = 573$ K; $T_2 = 27 + 273 = 300$ K, $\varepsilon_1 = 0.79$; $\varepsilon_2 = 0.93$.

The heat flow between two bodies is given by

$$Q_{12} = \frac{A_1\,\sigma\,(T_1^4 - T_2^4)}{\left(\dfrac{1-\varepsilon_1}{\varepsilon_1}\right) + \dfrac{1}{F_{1-2}} + \left(\dfrac{1-\varepsilon_2}{\varepsilon_2}\right)\dfrac{A_1}{A_2}}$$

(i) If the pipe is located in a room, then

$$Q_{12} = \frac{A_1\,\sigma\,(T_1^4 - T_2^4)}{\dfrac{1}{\varepsilon_1}} \quad \text{as } F_{1-2} = 1 \text{ and } \frac{A_1}{A_2} \ll 1$$

$$= A_1\,\varepsilon_1\,\sigma\,(T_1^4 - T_2^4)$$

$$= (2\,\pi \times 0.04 \times 1) \times 0.79 \times 5.67 \left[\left(\frac{573}{100}\right)^4 - \left(\frac{300}{100}\right)^4\right]$$

$$= 1.126\,(1078 - 81) = \mathbf{1122.6\ W/m\ (Ans.)}$$

(ii) If the pipe is located in a conduit then,

$$F_{1-2} = 1 \text{ and } \frac{A_1}{A_2} = \frac{r_1}{r_2} = \frac{0.04}{0.08} = 0.5$$

$$\therefore \qquad Q_{12} = \frac{A_1\,\sigma\,(T_1^4 - T_2^4)}{\left(\dfrac{1-\varepsilon_1}{\varepsilon_1}\right) + 1 + \left(\dfrac{1-\varepsilon_2}{\varepsilon_2}\right)\dfrac{A_1}{A_2}}$$

$$= \frac{2\,\pi \times 0.04 \times 1 \times 5.67 \left[\left(\dfrac{573}{100}\right)^4 - \left(\dfrac{300}{100}\right)^4\right]}{\left(\dfrac{1-0.79}{0.79}\right) + 1 + \left(\dfrac{1-0.93}{0.93}\right) \times 0.5} = \frac{1.126\,(1078 - 81)}{1.303}$$

$$= \mathbf{861.5\ W/m\ (Ans.)}$$

Reduction in heat flow by enclosing in conduit

$$= 1122.6 - 861.5 = 261.1\ \text{W/m}$$

Example 12.30. *A steel rod of 20 mm diameter, for the purpose of heat treatment, is mounted axially in a heat treatment muffle furnace of inside diameter 150 mm. The inside surface of the muffle is maintained at temperature of 1300 K. The emissivities of the furnace and the rod are 0.85 and 0.60 respectively. The specific heat and density of the steel rod are 0.67 kJ/kg K and 7850 kg/m^3 respectively. If the rod occupies the full length of furnace, calculate the time required to heat rod from 700 K to 800 K.*

Solution. The net radiant heat exchange between the steel rod and the furnace is given by

$$Q_{12} = (F_g)_{1-2}\,A_1\,\sigma\,(T_1^4 - T_2^4)$$

where the suffices 1 and 2 refer to steel rod and the furnace respectively.

For concentric cylinders of equal length, $F_{1-2} = 1$, hence

$$(F_g)_{1-2} = \cfrac{1}{\cfrac{1-\varepsilon_1}{\varepsilon_1} + \cfrac{1}{F_{1-2}} + \left(\cfrac{1-\varepsilon_2}{\varepsilon_2}\right)\cfrac{A_1}{A_2}} = \cfrac{1}{\cfrac{1-\varepsilon_1}{\varepsilon_1} + 1 + \left(\cfrac{1-\varepsilon_2}{\varepsilon_2}\right)\cfrac{A_1}{A_2}} = \cfrac{1}{\cfrac{1}{\varepsilon_1} + \left(\cfrac{1-\varepsilon_2}{\varepsilon_2}\right)\cfrac{A_1}{A_2}}$$

$$= \cfrac{1}{\cfrac{1}{0.6} + \left(\cfrac{1-0.85}{0.85}\right) \times \cfrac{20}{150}} = 0.592$$

$$\therefore \quad Q_{12} = 0.592 \times \left(\pi \times \frac{20}{1000} \times 1\right) \times 5.67 \times \left[\left(\frac{T_1}{100}\right)^4 - \left(\frac{T_2}{100}\right)^4\right]$$

$$= 0.21 \left[\left(\frac{T_1}{100}\right)^4 - \left(\frac{T_2}{100}\right)^4\right] \quad \text{... for unit length of the rod and furnace.}$$

Ignoring the –ve sign convention, the heat exchange in heating from 700 K, 800 K to 1300 K is

$$Q_{12} = 0.21 \left[\left(\frac{1300}{100}\right)^4 - \left(\frac{700}{100}\right)^4\right] = 5493.6 \text{ W}$$

and,

$$Q_{12} = 0.21 \left[\left(\frac{1300}{100}\right)^4 - \left(\frac{800}{100}\right)^4\right] = 5137.6 \text{ W}$$

Average heat exchange per unit length $= \dfrac{5493.6 + 5137.6}{2} = 5315.6 \text{ W}$

Heat required to raise the temperature of the rod from 700 K to 800 K is given by

$$Q = m\,c_p\,\Delta_t$$

$$= \left[\frac{\pi}{4} \times \left(\frac{20}{1000}\right)^2 \times 1 \times 7850\right] \times 0.67 \times (800 - 700) = 165.23 \text{ kJ}$$

$\therefore$ *Time required for the desired heating*

$$= \frac{165.23 \times 1000}{5315.6} = \textbf{31.08 s (Ans.)}$$

Example 12.31. *For a hemispherical furnace, the flat floor is at 700 K and has an emissivity of 0.5. The hemispherical roof is at 1000 K and has emissivity of 0.25. Find the net radiative heat transfer from roof to floor.*

Solution : *Given :* $T_1 = 700$ K; $\varepsilon_1 = 0.5$; $T_2 = 1000$ K; $\varepsilon_2 = 0.25$

Q_{12} (from floor to roof)

$$= \cfrac{A_1 \, \sigma \, (T_1^4 - T_2^4)}{\left(\cfrac{1-\varepsilon_1}{\varepsilon_1}\right) + \cfrac{1}{F_{1-2}} + \left(\cfrac{1-\varepsilon_2}{\varepsilon_2}\right)\cfrac{A_1}{A_2}}$$

In this case $A_1 = \pi r^2$ and $A_2 = \dfrac{4\pi r^2}{2} = 2\pi r^2$

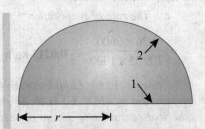

Fig. 12.38. Hemispherical furnace.

$$\therefore \quad \frac{A_1}{A_2} = \frac{\pi r^2}{2\pi r^2} = 0.5, \; F_{1-2} = 1$$

$$\therefore \quad Q_{12} = \cfrac{1 \times 5.67 \left[\left(\dfrac{700}{100}\right)^4 - \left(\dfrac{1000}{100}\right)^4\right]}{\left(\dfrac{1-0.5}{0.5}\right) + 1 + \left(\dfrac{1-0.25}{0.25}\right) \times 0.5} \; \text{W/m}^2$$

$$= \frac{1 \times 5.67 \,(2401 - 10000)}{3.5} = -12310.4 \text{ W/m}^2$$

The –ve sign indicates that *floor gains the heat.*

$\therefore$ $Q_{12} = 12310.4 \text{ W/m}^2 \text{ (Gain) (Ans.)}$

Example 12.32. *Two concentric spheres 210 mm and 300 mm diameters with the space between them evacuated are to be used to store liquid air (–153° C) in a room at 27° C. The surfaces of the spheres are flushed with aluminium ($\varepsilon = 0.03$) and latent heat of vaporization of liquid air is 209.35 kJ/kg. Calculate the rate of evaporation of liquid air.* (P.U.)

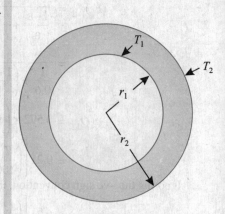

Fig. 12.39

Solution. *Given:* $r_1 = \dfrac{210}{2} = 105 \text{ mm} = 0.105 \text{ m}$;

$r_2 = \dfrac{300}{2} = 150 \text{ mm} = 0.15 \text{ m}$; $T_1 = -153 + 273 = 120 \text{ K}$;

$T_2 = 27 + 273 = 300 \text{ K}$; $\varepsilon_1 = \varepsilon_2 = 0.03$, $h_{fg} = 209.35 \text{ kJ/kg}$.

Rate of evaporation of liquid air:

The heat flow from the inner sphere surface to outer sphere surface is given by

$$Q_{12} = \frac{A_1 \, \sigma \, (T_1^4 - T_2^4)}{\left(\dfrac{1 - \varepsilon_1}{\varepsilon_1}\right) + \dfrac{1}{F_{1-2}} + \left(\dfrac{1 - \varepsilon_2}{\varepsilon_2}\right)\dfrac{A_1}{A_2}}$$

$$Q_{12} = \frac{4 \, \pi \, r_1^2 \, \sigma \, (T_1^4 - T_2^4)}{\left(\dfrac{1 - \varepsilon_1}{\varepsilon_1}\right) + 1 + \left(\dfrac{1 - \varepsilon_2}{\varepsilon_2}\right)\dfrac{r_1^2}{r_2^2}}$$

$$= \frac{4 \, \pi \times (0.105)^2 \times 5.67 \left[\left(\dfrac{120}{100}\right)^4 - \left(\dfrac{300}{100}\right)^4\right]}{\left(\dfrac{1 - 0.03}{0.03}\right) + 1 + \left(\dfrac{1 - 0.03}{0.03}\right) \times \left(\dfrac{0.105}{0.15}\right)^2}$$

$$= \frac{0.7855 \, (2.07 - 81)}{32.33 + 1 + 15.84} = \frac{-61.99}{49.17} = -1.26 \text{ W}$$

–ve sign indicates that heat is gained by the surface 1, means, heat is flowing from outside surface to inside surface.

$\therefore$ *The rate of evaporation*

$$= \frac{1.26 \times 3600}{209.35 \times 1000} = \textbf{0.0217 kg/h} \;\; \textbf{(Ans.)}$$

Example 12.33. *Liquid oxygen (boiling temperature = –182° C) is to be stored in spherical container of 30 cm diameter. The system is insulated by an evacuated space between inner space and surrounding 45 cm inner diameter concentric sphere. For both spheres $\varepsilon = 0.03$ and temperature of the outer sphere is 30° C. Estimate the rate of heat flow by radiation to the oxygen in the container.* (N.M.U., 1998)

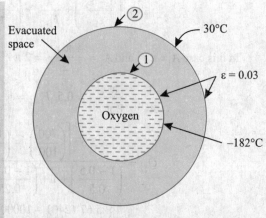

Fig. 12.40

Solution. *Given:* $T_1 = -182 + 273 = 91$K, $T_2 = 30 + 273 = 303$ K, $\varepsilon_1 = \varepsilon_2 = 0.03$
$d_1 = 30$ cm $= 0.3$ m, $d_2 = 45$ cm $= 0.45$ m.

Rate of heat flow, Q_{12}:

The heat flow between the two concentric spheres by radiation is given by

$$Q_{12} = \frac{A_1\ \sigma\ (T_1^4 - T_2^4)}{\dfrac{1-\varepsilon_1}{\varepsilon_1} + \dfrac{1}{F_{1-2}} + \left(\dfrac{1-\varepsilon_2}{\varepsilon_2}\right)\dfrac{A_1}{A_2}}$$

For concentric spheres $F_{1-2} = 1$ and $\dfrac{A_1}{A_2} = \left(\dfrac{d_1}{d_2}\right)^2 = \left(\dfrac{0.3}{0.45}\right)^2 = 0.4444$

$$A_1 = 4\,\pi\,r_1^{\,2} = 4\,\pi \times \left(\dfrac{0.3}{2}\right)^2 = 0.283 \text{ m}^2$$

Now substituting the values in the above equation, we get

$$Q_{12} = \frac{0.283 \times 5.67\left[\left(\dfrac{91}{100}\right)^4 - \left(\dfrac{303}{100}\right)^4\right]}{\left(\dfrac{1-0.03}{0.03}\right) + 1 + \left(\dfrac{1-0.03}{0.03}\right) \times 0.4444}$$

$$= \frac{0.283 \times 5.67\ (0.686 - 84.289)}{32.33 + 1 + 14.37} = -2.81 \text{ W (Ans.)}$$

−ve sign shows *heat flows from outside to inside.*

Example 12.34. *A square room 3m × 3m, has a floor heated to 27°C and has a ceiling at 10°C. The walls are assumed to be perfectly insulated. The height of the room is 2.5 m. The emissivity of all the surfaces is 0.8. Determine the following:*

(i) The net heat interchange between the floor and the ceiling;

(ii) The wall temperature.

Assume ceiling to floor shape factor as 0.25.

(M.U.)

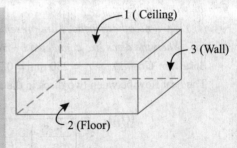

Fig. 12.41

Solution. *Given:* $\varepsilon_1 = \varepsilon_2 = \varepsilon_3 = 0.8$; $T_1 = 10 + 273 = 283$ K; $T_2 = 27 + 273 = 300$ K.

(i) **The net heat interchange between the floor and the ceiling, (Q_{12})net :**

From the Fig. 12.41, it is clear that

$$F_{1-1} = F_{2-2} = 0$$

$$F_{1-2} = F_{2-1} = 0.25$$

$F_{1-2} + F_{1-3} = 1$ or $0.25 + F_{1-3} = 1$ or $F_{1-3} = 1 - 0.25 = 0.75$

$F_{2-1} + F_{2-3} = 1$ or $0.25 + F_{2-3} = 1$ or $F_{2-3} = 1 - 0.25 = 0.75$

$$(Q_{12})_{net} = \frac{A_1\,\sigma(T_1^4 - T_2^4)}{\left(\dfrac{1-\varepsilon_1}{\varepsilon_1}\right) + \left(\dfrac{1-\varepsilon_2}{\varepsilon_2}\right)\dfrac{A_1}{A_2} + \left[\dfrac{A_1 + A_2 - 2A_1\ F_{1-2}}{A_2 - A_1\ F_{1-2}^2}\right]} \qquad \text{...[Eqn. (12.44)]}$$

$$= \frac{A_1 \, \sigma \, (T_1^4 - T_2^4)}{\left(\dfrac{1-\varepsilon_1}{\varepsilon_1}\right) \times 2 + \dfrac{2\,(1-F_{1-2})}{(1-F_{1-2}^2)}} = \frac{A_1 \, \sigma \, (T_1^4 - T_2^4)}{2\left[\dfrac{1-\varepsilon_1}{\varepsilon_1} + \dfrac{1}{1+F_{1-2}}\right]}$$

$$(\because A_1 = A_2 \text{ and } \varepsilon_1 = \varepsilon_2)$$

$\therefore$

$$(Q_{12})_{net} = \frac{(3 \times 3) \times 5.67\left[\left(\dfrac{283}{100}\right)^4 - \left(\dfrac{300}{100}\right)^4\right]}{2\left[\dfrac{1-0.8}{0.8} + \dfrac{1}{1+0.25}\right]} = \frac{51.03\,(64.14 - 81)}{2.1} = -409.7 \text{ W}$$

The −ve sign shows that the heat is gained by the ceiling.

$\therefore \qquad (Q_{12})_{net} = \textbf{409.7 W (Gain) (Ans.)}$

(*ii*) **The wall temperature, T_3:**

In this particular case, the wall tempeature is given by

$$T_3^4 = \frac{1}{2}\,(T_1^4 + T_2^4) = \frac{1}{2}\,(2.83^4 + 3^4) \times 10^8 = 72.57 \times 10^8$$

$\therefore \qquad T_3 = (72.57 \times 10^8)^{1/4} = \textbf{292 K} = \textbf{19°C. (Ans.)}$

Example 12.35. *Two black discs each of diameter 500 mm, are placed directly opposite at a distance 1 m apart. The discs are maintained at 1000 K and 500 K respectively. Calculate the heat flow between the discs:*

(*i*) *When no other surfaces are present.*

(*ii*) *When the discs are connected by right cylindrical black no-flux surface.* (P.U.)

Solution: *Given:* $r_1 = r_2 = 250$ mm $= 0.25$ m, $L = 1$m, $T_1 = 1000$ K, $T_2 = 500$ K

The heat flow between two discs in the absence of third body is given by

$$(Q_{12})_{net} = \frac{A_1 \, \sigma \, (T_1^4 - T_2^4)}{\left(\dfrac{1-\varepsilon_1}{\varepsilon_1}\right) + \dfrac{1}{F_{1-2}} + \left(\dfrac{1-\varepsilon_2}{\varepsilon_2}\right)\dfrac{A_1}{A_2}}$$

(*i*) **When no other surfaces are present:**

In this case $\varepsilon_1 = \varepsilon_2 = 1$ and $A_1 = A_2 = \pi \times 0.25^2 = 0.196$ m^2

$\therefore \qquad (Q_{12})_{net} = A_1 \, F_{1-2} \, \sigma \, (T_1^4 - T_2^4)$ ...(*i*)

From Fig. 12.3, corresponding to $\dfrac{L}{r_i} = \dfrac{1}{0.25} = 4$

and, $\qquad \dfrac{r_2}{L} = \dfrac{0.25}{1} = 0.25, \ F_{1-2} = 0.04.$

Substituting the values in eqn. (*i*), we get

$$(Q_{12})_{net} = 0.196 \times 0.04 \times 5.67\left[\left(\dfrac{1000}{100}\right)^4 - \left(\dfrac{500}{100}\right)^4\right]$$

$$= 0.0444\,(10000 - 625) = \textbf{416.25 W (Ans.)}$$

(*ii*) **When the discs are connected by right cylindrical black no-flux surface:**

The heat flow between the discs when the discs are connected by a refractory surface is given by:

$$(Q_{12})_{net} = A_1 \, (F_g)_{1-2} \, (E_{b1} - E_{b2}) = A_1 \, (F_g)_{1-2} \, \sigma \, (T_1^4 - T_2^4)$$

where, $$(F_g)_{1-2} = \left[\cfrac{1}{\left[\left(\cfrac{1}{\varepsilon_1} - 1\right) + \cfrac{A_1}{A_2}\left(\cfrac{1}{\varepsilon_2} - 1\right) + \cfrac{1}{\overline{F}_{1-2}}\right]} \right]$$ ...(Eqn. 12.44]

and, $$\overline{F}_{1-2} = \cfrac{A_2 - A_1 \, F_{1-2}^2}{A_1 + A_2 - 2A_1 \, F_{1-2}}$$ ...[Eqn. 12.42 (b)]

i.e. $$(Q_{12})_{net} = \cfrac{A_1 \, \sigma \, (T_1^4 - T_2^4)}{\left(\cfrac{1}{\varepsilon_1} - 1\right) + \cfrac{A_1}{A_2}\left(\cfrac{1}{\varepsilon_2} - 1\right) + \left[\cfrac{A_1 + A_2 - 2A_1 \, F_{1-2}}{A_2 - A_1 \, F_{1-2}^2}\right]}$$

In this case $\varepsilon_1 = \varepsilon_2 = 1$ and $A_1 = A_2$

$\therefore$ $$(Q_{12})_{net} = \cfrac{A_1 \, \sigma \, (T_1^4 - T_2^4)}{\cfrac{2A_1 \, (1 - F_{1-2})}{A_1 \, (1 - F_{1-2}^2)}} = A_1 \, \sigma \, (T_1^4 - T_2^4)\left(\cfrac{1 + F_{1-2}}{2}\right)$$

$$= 0.196 \times 5.67 \left[\left(\cfrac{1000}{100}\right)^4 - \left(\cfrac{500}{100}\right)^4\right]\left[\cfrac{1 + 0.04}{2}\right]$$

$$= 1.111 \, (10000 - 625) \times 0.52 = \textbf{5416 W (Ans.)}$$

Example 12.36. *A boiler furnace of 3 m height is made in the shape of a frustrum with bottom diameter 5 m and top diameter 6 m. The emissivities of both surfaces = 0.9. The bottom surface is at 1000° C and the top surface is at 500° C. Considering the inclined surface is refractory surface, find the radiation heat transfer from the bottom to top surface and inclined wall temperature.*

Solution. *Given:* $r_1 = 2.5$ m, $r_2 = 3$ m, H (or L) $= 3$ m; $\varepsilon_1 = \varepsilon_2 = 0.9$; $T_1 = 1000 + 273 = 1273$ K, $T_2 = 500 + 273 = 773$ K.

Central boiler outdoor wood furnace.

Radiation heat transfer from the bottom to top surface; Q_{12}:

The heat flow is given by

$$Q_{12} = \frac{A_1\ \sigma\ (T_1^4 - T_2^4)}{\frac{1-\varepsilon_1}{\varepsilon_1} + \left(\frac{1-\varepsilon_2}{\varepsilon_2}\right)\frac{A_1}{A_2} + \left(\frac{A_1 + A_2 - 2A_1\ F_{1-2}}{A_2 - A_1\ F_{1-2}^2}\right)} \qquad \ldots(1)$$

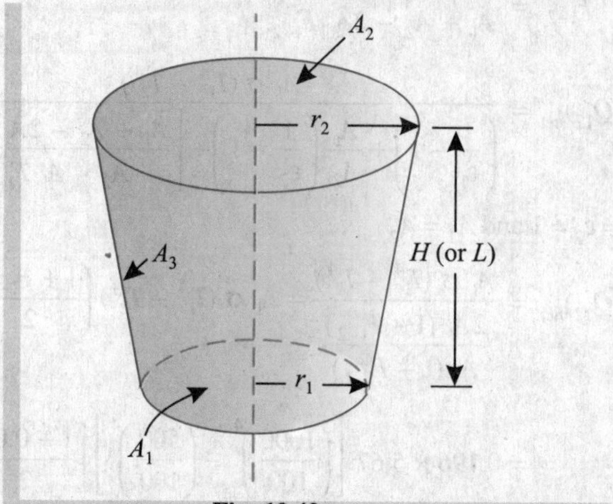

Fig. 12.42

From Fig. 12.3, corresponding to $\dfrac{L}{r_1} = \dfrac{3}{2.5} = 1.2$ and $\dfrac{r_2}{L} = \dfrac{3}{3} = 1$, we get

$$F_{1-2} = 0.4$$
$$A_1 = \pi\ r_1^2 = \pi \times 2.5^2 = 19.63 \text{ m}^2$$
$$A_2 = \pi\ r_2^2 = \pi \times 3^2 = 28.27 \text{ m}^2$$

Substituting the values, in the above equation, we get

$$Q_{12} = \frac{19.63 \times 5.67 \left[\left(\dfrac{12.73}{100}\right)^4 - \left(\dfrac{773}{100}\right)^4\right]}{\left(\dfrac{1-0.9}{0.9}\right) + \left(\dfrac{1-0.9}{0.9}\right) \times \dfrac{19.63}{28.27} + \left(\dfrac{19.63 + 28.27 - 2 \times 19.63 \times 0.4}{28.27 - 19.63 \times 0.4^2}\right)}$$

$$= \frac{19.63 \times 5.7\ (26261 - 3570.4)}{0.111 + 0.077 + 1.281}$$

$$= 1719204 \text{ W} = \textbf{1719.2 kW (Ans.)}$$

(ii) **Inclined wall (refractory) temperature, $T_{ref.}$:**

The refractory temperature is given by,

$$T_{ref.} = \left[\frac{1}{C_1 + C_2}\ (C_2\ T_1^4 + C_1\ T_2^4)\right]^{1/4} \qquad \ldots(2)$$

where, $$C_1 = \frac{1-\varepsilon_1}{A_1\ \varepsilon_1} + \frac{1}{A_1\ (1 - F_{1-2})}$$

$$= \frac{1-0.9}{19.63 \times 0.9} + \frac{1}{19.63\ (1 - 0.4)}$$

$$= 0.00566 + 0.0849 = 0.0905$$

and,
$$C_2 = \frac{1 - \varepsilon_2}{A_2\,\varepsilon_2} + \frac{1}{A_2\left[1 - \dfrac{A_1}{A_2}\cdot F_{1-2}\right]}$$

$$= \frac{1 - 0.9}{28.27 \times 0.9} + \frac{1}{28.27\left[1 - \dfrac{19.63}{28.27}\times 0.4\right]}$$

$$= 0.00393 + \frac{1}{20.42} = 0.0529$$

Now substituting the values in eqn. (2), we get

$$T_{ref.} = \left[\frac{1}{0.0905 + 0.0529}\{0.0529\,(1273)^4 + 0.0905\,(773)^4\}\right]^{1/4}$$

$$= \left[6.97 \times 10^8\,(1389.2 + 323.1)\right]^{1/4} = 1045.2\ \text{K} = \mathbf{772.2°C\ (Ans.)}$$

Example 12.37. *Two identical circular plates each with area 1m² and emissivity 0.5 are arranged facing each other in a large room. The emissive power of the plates are 30 kW/m² and 3 kW/m² respectively. The temperature of the surrounding is 27°C. The surface of the plates facing each other only are radiating energy, find*

(i) *Distance between the plates;*

(ii) *Temperature of the plates;*

(iii) *Heat transfer to the surroundings from the plates.*

Assume the shape factor between the plates as 0.6. (M.U.)

Solution: *Given:* $A_1 = A_2 = 1\text{m}^2$, $\varepsilon_1 = \varepsilon_2 = 0.5$ and $F_{1-2} = F_{2-1} = 0.6$; $E_{b1} = 30\ \text{kW/m}^2$; $E_{b2} = 3\ \text{kW/m}^2$; $T_3 = 27 + 273 = 300\ \text{K}$.

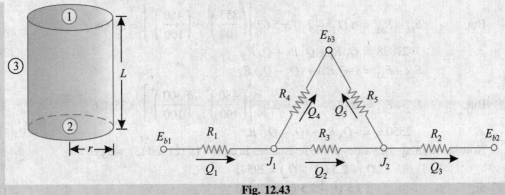

Fig. 12.43

The values of the resistances are:

$$R_1 = \frac{1 - \varepsilon_1}{A_1\,\varepsilon_1} = \frac{1 - 0.5}{1 \times 0.5} = 1$$

$$R_2 = \frac{1 - \varepsilon_2}{A_2\,\varepsilon_2} = \frac{1 - 0.5}{1 \times 0.5} = 1$$

$$R_3 = \frac{1}{A_1\,F_{1-2}} = \frac{1}{1 \times 0.6} = 1.67$$

$$F_{1-3} = F_{2-3} = 1 - F_{1-2} = 1 - 0.6 = 0.4$$

$$R_4 = \frac{1}{A_1\,F_{1-3}} = \frac{1}{1 \times 0.4} = 2.5$$

$$R_5 = \frac{1}{A_2 \, F_{2-3}} = \frac{1}{1 \times 0.4} = 2.5$$

(i) Distance between the plates, L:

The shape factor for the given configuration (from Fig. 12.3)

at $\qquad \frac{r}{L} = 2$ for $F_{1-2} = 0.6$

$$A = \pi \, r^2 = 1 \qquad \therefore r = \frac{1}{\sqrt{\pi}} = 0.564 \text{ m}$$

$$\frac{r}{L} = 2 \text{ or } L = \frac{r}{2} = \frac{0.564}{2} = 0.282 \text{ m}$$

(ii) Temperature of the plates, T_1 & T_2:

$$E_{b1} = \sigma \, T_1^4 = 5.67 \times 10^{-8} \, T_1^4 = 30 \times 1000$$

or, $\qquad T_1^4 = \dfrac{30 \times 1000 \times 10^8}{5.67} \qquad \therefore T_1 = \left(\dfrac{30 \times 1000 \times 10^8}{5.67}\right)^{1/4} \simeq \textbf{853 K (Ans.)}$

$$E_{b2} = \sigma \, T_2^4 = 5.67 \times 10^{-8} \, T_2^4 = 3 \times 1000$$

or, $\qquad T_2^4 = \dfrac{3 \times 1000 \times 10^8}{5.67} \qquad \therefore T_2 = \left(\dfrac{3 \times 1000 \times 10^8}{5.67}\right)^{1/4} = \textbf{480 K (Ans.)}$

(iii) Heat transfer to the surroundings from the plates, Q:

$$E_{b1} - E_{b3} = Q_1 \, R_1 + Q_4 \, R_4 = Q_1 \, R_1 + (Q_1 - Q_2) \, R_4$$

But, $\qquad E_{b1} - E_{b3} = \sigma \, (T_1^4 - T_3^4) = 30000 - 5.67 \times 10^{-8} \, (300)^4 = 29541$

$\therefore \qquad 29541 = Q_1 R_1 + (Q_1 - Q_2) \, R_4 \qquad\qquad\qquad \text{...(1)}$

$$E_{b1} - E_{b2} = Q_1 R_1 + Q_2 R_3 + Q_3 R_2$$

But, $\qquad E_{b1} - E_{b2} = \sigma \, (T_1^4 - T_2^4) = 5.67 \left[\left(\dfrac{853}{100}\right)^4 - \left(\dfrac{480}{100}\right)^4\right] = 27008$

$\therefore \qquad 27008 = Q_1 \, R_1 + Q_2 \, R_3 + Q_3 \, R_2 \qquad\qquad\qquad \text{...(2)}$

$$E_{b2} - E_{b3} = (-Q_3 R_2) + (Q_2 - Q_3) \, R_5$$

But, $\qquad E_{b2} - E_{b3} = \sigma \, (T_2^4 - T_3^4) = 5.67 \left[\left(\dfrac{480}{100}\right)^4 - \left(\dfrac{300}{100}\right)^4\right] = 2550.6$

$\therefore \qquad 2550.6 = -Q_3 \, R_2 + (Q_2 - Q_3) \, R_5 \qquad\qquad\qquad \text{...(3)}$

Now substituting the values of the resistances in eqns. (1), (2) and (3), we get

$$Q_1 + 2.5 \, (Q_1 - Q_2) = 29541$$

or, $\qquad 3.5 \, Q_1 - 2.5 \, Q_2 = 29541 \qquad\qquad\qquad\qquad\qquad \text{...(i)}$

$$Q_1 + 1.67 \, Q_2 + Q_3 = 27008 \qquad\qquad\qquad\qquad\qquad \text{...(ii)}$$

$$-Q_3 + 2.5 \, (Q_2 - Q_3) = 2550.6$$

or, $\qquad 2.5 \, Q_2 - 3.5 \, Q_3 = 2550.6 \qquad\qquad\qquad\qquad\qquad \text{...(iii)}$

Now solving eqns. (i), (ii) and (iii), we get

$$Q_1 = 12887 \text{ W}; \qquad Q_2 = 6228 \text{ W}; \qquad Q_3 = 3720 \text{ W}$$

$$Q_1 = \frac{E_{b1} - J_1}{R_1} \qquad \therefore J_1 = E_{b1} - Q_1 R_1 = 30000 - 12887 \times 1 = 17113$$

$$Q_2 = \frac{J_1 - J_2}{R_3} \qquad \therefore J_2 = J_1 - Q_2 \, R_3 = 17113 - 6228 \times 1.67 = 6712$$

$$Q_4 = \frac{J_1 - E_{b3}}{R_4} = \frac{17113 - 5.67\left(\frac{300}{100}\right)^4}{2.5} = 6661$$

$$Q_5 = \frac{J_2 - E_{b3}}{R_5} = \frac{6712 - 5.67\left(\frac{300}{100}\right)^4}{2.5} = 2501$$

$$\therefore \qquad Q = Q_4 + Q_5 = 6661 + 2501 = 9162 \text{ W} = \textbf{9.162 kW (Ans.)}$$

Example 12.38. *Two parallel plates of size 1.0 m × 1.0 m spaced 0.5 m apart are located in a very large room, the walls of which are maintained at a temperature of 27° C. One plate is maintained at a temperature of 900° C and the other at 400° C. Their emissivities are 0.2 and 0.5 respectively. If the plates exchange heat between themselves and surroundings, find the net heat transfer to each plate and to the room. Consider only the plate surfaces facing each other.*

Solution. In this problem three surfaces, the two plates and the room are involved. The radiation network is shown in Fig. 12.44.

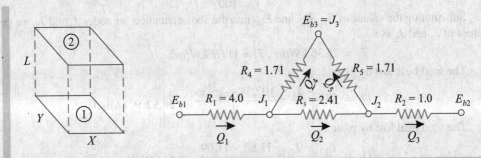

Fig. 12.44

$$X = 1 \text{ m}, Y = 1 \text{ m}, L = 0.5 \text{ m}$$

$$\therefore \qquad \frac{X}{L} = \frac{1}{0.5} = 2; \frac{Y}{L} = \frac{1}{0.5} = 2$$

Corresponding to the above parameters, the value of shape factor F_{1-2} as obtained from Fig. 12.2 equals 0.415.

Also, $\qquad F_{1-2} + F_{1-3} = 1$

or, $\qquad F_{1-3} = 1 - F_{1-2} = 1 - 0.415 = 0.585$

and, $\qquad F_{2-1} + F_{2-3} = 1$

or, $\qquad F_{2-3} = 1 - F_{2-1} = 1 - F_{1-2} = 0.585$

The values of the resistances are:

$$R_1 = \frac{1 - \varepsilon_1}{A_1 \varepsilon_1} = \frac{1 - 0.2}{(1.0 \times 1.0) \times 0.2} = 4.0$$

$$R_2 = \frac{1 - \varepsilon_2}{A_2 \varepsilon_2} = \frac{1 - 0.5}{(1.0 \times 1.0) \times 0.5} = 1.0$$

$$R_3 = \frac{1}{A_1 F_{1-2}} = \frac{1}{(1.0 \times 1.0) \times 0.415} = 2.41$$

$$R_4 = \frac{1}{A_1 F_{1-3}} = \frac{1}{(1.0 \times 1.0) \times 0.585} = 1.71$$

$$R_5 = \frac{1}{A_2 F_{2-3}} = \frac{1}{(1.0 \times 1.0) \times 0.585} = 1.71$$

Since the room is much larger in size than the plates, the surface resistance $\dfrac{1-\varepsilon_3}{A_3 \, \varepsilon_3}$ may be taken as zero and thus $E_{b3} = J_3$.

The radiosities, J_1 and J_2 can be calculated by setting the sum of the heat currents entering nodes, J_1 and J_2 to zero.

Node J_1: $\dfrac{E_{b1} - J_1}{4.0} + \dfrac{J_2 - J_1}{2.41} + \dfrac{E_{b3} - J_1}{1.71} = 0$

Node J_2: $\dfrac{J_1 - J_2}{2.41} + \dfrac{E_{b_3} - J_2}{1.71} + \dfrac{E_{b_2} - J_2}{2.0} = 0$

where $E_{b1} = \sigma T_1^4 = 5.67 \times \left(\dfrac{900 + 273}{100}\right)^4 = 107.34 \ \text{kW/m}^2$

$E_{b2} = \sigma T_2^4 = 5.67 \times \left(\dfrac{400 + 273}{100}\right)^4 = 11.63 \ \text{kW/m}^2$

$E_{b3} = \sigma T_3^4 = 5.67 \times \left(\dfrac{27 + 273}{100}\right)^4 = 0.46 \ \text{kW/m}^2$

Substituting the values of E_{b1}, E_{b2} and E_{b3} into the above equation for nodes J_1 and J_2, we get the values of J_1 and J_2 as :

$$J_1 = 25.36 \ \text{kW/m}^2, \ J_2 = 11.09 \ \text{kW/m}^2$$

The total heat lost by plate 1,

$$Q_1 = \frac{E_{b1} - J_1}{R_1} = \frac{107.34 - 25.36}{4} = \textbf{20.5 kW (Ans.)}$$

The total heat lost by plate 2,

$$Q_3 = \frac{E_{b2} - J_2}{R_2} = \frac{11.63 - 11.09}{1.0} = \textbf{0.54 kW (Ans.)}$$

The total heat received/absorbed by the room

$$= Q_4 + Q_5 = \frac{J_1 - J_3}{R_4} + \frac{J_2 - J_3}{R_5}$$

$$= \frac{25.36 - 0.46}{1.71} + \frac{11.09 - 0.46}{1.71} \qquad (\because J_3 = E_{b3})$$

$$= \textbf{20.8 kW (Ans.)}$$

> As per energy balance :
> The net energy lost by both the plates = Energy absorbed by the room.

12.11. RADIATION SHIELDS

In certain situations it is required to reduce the overall heat transfer between two radiating surfaces. This is done by either *using materials which are highly reflective or by using radiation shields between the heat exchanging surfaces. The radiation shields reduce the radiation heat transfer by effectively increasing the surface resistances without actually removing any heat from the overall system.* Thin sheets of plastic coated with highly reflecting metallic films on both sides serve as very effective radiation shields. These are used for the insulation of cryogenic storage tanks. A familiar application of radiation shields is *in the measurement of the temperature of a fluid by a thermometer or a thermocouple which is shielded to reduce the effects of radiation.*

Refer Fig. 12.45. Let us consider two parallel plates, 1 and 2, each of area A $(A_1 = A_2 = A)$ at temperatures T_1 and T_2 respectively with a radiation shield placed between them as shown in Fig. 12.45.

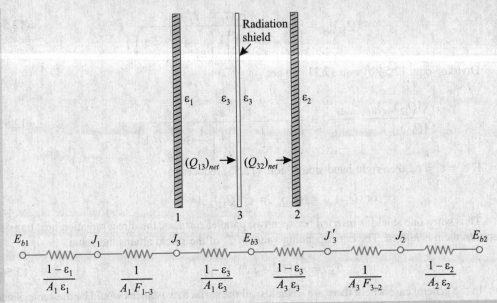

Fig. 12.45. Radiation network for two parallel infinite planes separated by one shield.

With no radiation shields, the net heat exchange between the parallel plates is given by:

$$(Q_{12})_{net} = \frac{A \, \sigma \, (T_1^4 - T_2^4)}{\dfrac{1}{\varepsilon_1} + \dfrac{1}{\varepsilon_2} - 1} \qquad \qquad ...(12.21)$$

If the emissivity of the radiation shield is ε_3, we can use this equation to find heat exchange between surfaces 1, 3 and 3, 2.

$$(Q_{13})_{net} = \frac{A \, \sigma \, (T_1^4 - T_3^4)}{\dfrac{1}{\varepsilon_1} + \dfrac{1}{\varepsilon_3} - 1} \qquad \qquad ...(12.50)$$

and,

$$(Q_{32})_{net} = \frac{A \, \sigma \, (T_3^4 - T_2^4)}{\dfrac{1}{\varepsilon_3} + \dfrac{1}{\varepsilon_2} - 1} \qquad \qquad ...(12.51)$$

Since the radiation shield does not deliver or remove heat from the system, therefore,

$$(Q_{13})net = (Q_{32})net$$

i.e.,

$$\frac{A \, \sigma \, (T_1^4 - T_3^4)}{\dfrac{1}{\varepsilon_1} + \dfrac{1}{\varepsilon_3} - 1} = \frac{A \, \sigma \, (T_3^4 - T_2^4)}{\dfrac{1}{\varepsilon_3} + \dfrac{1}{\varepsilon_2} - 1} \qquad \qquad ...(12.52)$$

Simplification of eqn. (12.52) yields

$$T_3^4 = \frac{T_1^4 \left(\dfrac{1}{\varepsilon_3} + \dfrac{1}{\varepsilon_2} - 1 \right) + T_2^4 \left(\dfrac{1}{\varepsilon_1} + \dfrac{1}{\varepsilon_3} - 1 \right)}{\left(\dfrac{1}{\varepsilon_3} + \dfrac{1}{\varepsilon_2} - 1 \right) + \left(\dfrac{1}{\varepsilon_1} + \dfrac{1}{\varepsilon_3} - 1 \right)} \qquad \qquad ...(12.53)$$

Substituting the value of T_3 in the left hand side of eqn. (12.52), we get

$$(Q_{12})_{net} = \frac{A\sigma(T_1^4 - T_2^4)}{\left(\dfrac{1}{\varepsilon_1} + \dfrac{1}{\varepsilon_3} - 1\right) + \left(\dfrac{1}{\varepsilon_3} + \dfrac{1}{\varepsilon_2} - 1\right)} \qquad ...(12.54)$$

Dividing eqn. 12.54 by eqn 12.21, we get

$$\frac{[Q_{12})_{net}]_{with\ shield}}{[Q_{12})_{net}]_{without\ shield}} = \frac{\dfrac{1}{\varepsilon_1} + \dfrac{1}{\varepsilon_2} - 1}{\left(\dfrac{1}{\varepsilon_1} + \dfrac{1}{\varepsilon_3} - 1\right) + \left(\dfrac{1}{\varepsilon_3} + \dfrac{1}{\varepsilon_2} - 1\right)} \qquad ...(12.55)$$

If $\varepsilon_1 = \varepsilon_2 = \varepsilon_3$, then right hand side of eqn. (12.55) reduces to

$$\frac{1}{2} \text{ or } (Q_{13})_{net} = (Q_{32})_{net} = \frac{1}{2}(Q_{12})_{net}$$

Thus when one shield is inserted between two parallel surfaces, the direct radiation heat transfer between them is *halved*. The corresponding value of T_3 of the shield attains the value

$$T_3^4 = \frac{1}{2}(T_1^4 + T_2^4) \qquad ...(12.56)$$

In the general case where there are n shields, all the surface resistances would be the same, since the emissivities are equal. There will be two surface resistances for each shield and one for each heat transfer surface. There will also be $(n+1)$ 'space resistances' but the configuration factor is unity for each infinite parallel plane.

$$\text{Total resistance } (R)_{n\text{-}shields} = \left[(2n+2)\left(\frac{1-\varepsilon}{\varepsilon}\right) + (n+1)(1)\right] \bigg/ A$$

$$= \left[(n+1)\left(\frac{2}{\varepsilon} - 1\right)\right] \bigg/ A \qquad ...(12.57)$$

The radiant heat transfer rate between two infinitely large parallel plates separated by n-shields is, therefore,

$$(Q)_{n\text{-}shields} = \frac{1}{(n+1)\left(\dfrac{2}{\varepsilon} - 1\right)} A\sigma(T_1^4 - T_2^4) \qquad ...(12.58)$$

Where $n = 0$ (*i.e.*, with no shields), the resistance is given by

$$(R)_{without\ shield} = \left[\frac{2}{\varepsilon} - 1\right] \bigg/ A \qquad ...(12.59)$$

and thus

$$(Q)_{without\ shield} = \frac{A\sigma(T_1^4 - T_2^4)}{\left(\dfrac{2}{\varepsilon} - 1\right)} \qquad ...(12.60)$$

From eqns. 12.57 to 12.60, we get

$$\frac{(Q)_{n\text{-}shields}}{(Q)_{without\ shield}} = \frac{(R)_{without\ shield}}{(R)_{n\text{-}shields}} = \frac{1}{n+1} \qquad ...(12.61)$$

... provided that the reduction in heat flow does not affect the wall temperatures.

Arranging the eqn. (12.55) in a slightly different form, we have

$$(Q_{12})_{net} = \frac{A\sigma(T_1^4 - T_2^4)}{\dfrac{1}{\varepsilon_1} + \dfrac{1}{\varepsilon_2} + 2\left(\dfrac{1}{\varepsilon_3}\right) - 2}$$

This equation can be generalized for a system of two parallel plates separated by n-shields of emissivity $\varepsilon_{s1}, \varepsilon_{s2} \ldots \varepsilon_{sn}$ as

$$(Q_{12})_{net} = \frac{A \, \sigma \, (T_1^4 - T_2^4)}{\dfrac{1}{\varepsilon_1} + \dfrac{1}{\varepsilon_2} + 2 \displaystyle\sum_{i=1}^{n} \dfrac{1}{\varepsilon_{si}} - (n+1)} \qquad \ldots(12.62)$$

Cylindrical radiation shields. The heat transfer rate between two long concentric cylindrical surfaces separated by a cylindrical shield can be easily shown to be given by

$$Q_1 = \frac{2 \, \pi \, r_1 \, L \, \sigma \, (T_1^4 - T_2^4)}{\dfrac{1}{\varepsilon_1} + \dfrac{r_1}{r_2}\left(\dfrac{1}{\varepsilon_2} - 1\right) + \dfrac{r_1}{r_s}\left(\dfrac{1}{\varepsilon_{s1}} + \dfrac{1}{\varepsilon_{s2}} - 1\right)}$$
$$\ldots(12.63)$$

where ε_{s1} and ε_{s2} are the surface emissivities of the shield and L is the length of the cylinders.

If the surfaces and the shield have the same emissivity ε, eqn. (12.63) becomes

$$Q_1 = \frac{2 \, \pi \, r_1 \, L \, \sigma \, (T_1^4 - T_2^4)}{\dfrac{1}{\varepsilon} + \dfrac{r_1}{r_2}\left(\dfrac{1}{\varepsilon} - 1\right) + \dfrac{r_1}{r_s}\left(\dfrac{2}{\varepsilon} - 1\right)} \qquad \ldots(12.64)$$

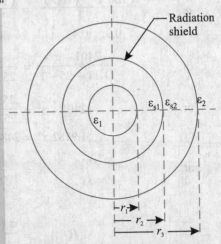

Fig. 12.46. Cylindrical radiation shield.

Example 12.39. *Calculate the net radiant heat exchange per m^2 area for two large parallel plates at temperatures of $427°$ C and $27°$ C respectively. ε (hot plate) = 0.9 and ε (cold plate) = 0.6.*

If a polished aluminium shield is placed between them, find the percentage reduction in the heat transfer; ε (shield) = 0.4.
(P.U.)

Solution. *Given :* $T_1 = 427 + 273 = 700$ K; $T_2 = 27 + 273 = 300$ K; ε_1 (hot plate) = 0.9, ε_2 (cold plate) = 0.6, ε_3 (shield) = 0.4.

Net radiant heat exchange per m^2 area:

In the absence of radiation shield the heat flow between plates 1 and 2 is given by

$$(Q_{12})_{net} = \frac{\sigma \, (T_1^4 - T_2^4)}{\dfrac{1}{\varepsilon_1} + \dfrac{1}{\varepsilon_2} - 1} \qquad \ldots\text{[Eqn. (12.21)]}$$

$$= \frac{5.67 \left[\left(\dfrac{700}{100}\right)^4 - \left(\dfrac{300}{100}\right)^4\right]}{\dfrac{1}{0.9} + \dfrac{1}{0.6} - 1}$$

$$= \frac{13154.4}{1.777} = 7402.6 \text{ W. (Ans.)}$$

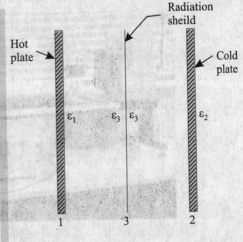

Fig. 12.47

Percentage reduction in the heat transfer flow:

When a shield is placed between the plates 1 and 2, then

$$(Q_{13})_{net} = (Q_{32})_{net}$$

$$\therefore \qquad \frac{A\,\sigma\,(T_1^4 - T_3^4)}{\dfrac{1}{\varepsilon_1} + \dfrac{1}{\varepsilon_3} - 1} = \frac{A\,\sigma\,(T_3^4 - T_2^4)}{\dfrac{1}{\varepsilon_3} + \dfrac{1}{\varepsilon_2} - 1}$$

or,
$$\frac{\left(\dfrac{700}{100}\right)^4 - \left(\dfrac{T_3}{100}\right)^4}{\dfrac{1}{0.9} + \dfrac{1}{0.4} - 1} = \frac{\left(\dfrac{T_3}{100}\right)^4 - \left(\dfrac{300}{100}\right)^4}{\dfrac{1}{0.4} + \dfrac{1}{0.6} - 1}$$

or,
$$\frac{2401 - x^4}{1.11 + 25 - 1} = \frac{x^4 - 81}{25 + 1.67 - 1} \qquad \left[\text{where } x = \frac{T_3}{100}\right]$$

or,
$$2401 - x^4 = \frac{25.11}{25.67}\,(x^4 - 81) = 0.9782 = (x^4 - 81)$$

or,
$$1.9782\,x^4 = 2480.2 \qquad\qquad \therefore x^4 = 1253.8$$

or,
$$x = \frac{T_3}{100} = (1253.8)^{1/4} = 5.95 \text{ or } T_3 = 595 \text{ K}$$

$$\therefore \qquad (Q_{13})_{net} = \frac{\sigma\,(T_1^4 - T_3^4)}{\dfrac{1}{\varepsilon_1} + \dfrac{1}{\varepsilon_3} - 1} = \frac{5.67\left[\left(\dfrac{700}{100}\right)^4 - \left(\dfrac{595}{100}\right)^4\right]}{\dfrac{1}{0.9} + \dfrac{1}{0.4} - 1}$$

$$= \frac{6507.2}{25.11} = 259.1 \text{ W}$$

$\therefore$ Reduction in heat flow due to shield

$$= (Q_{12})_{net} - (Q_{13})_{net} = 7402.6 - 259.1 = 7143.5 \text{ W}$$

or, Percentage reduction $= \dfrac{7143.5}{7402.6} \times 100 = \textbf{96.5\% (Ans.)}$

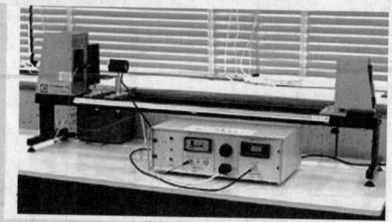

Thermal radiation unit.

Example 12.40. *Determine the radiant heat exchanger in W/m^2 between two large parallel steel plates of emissivities 0.8 and 0.5 held at temperatures of 1000 K and 500 K respectively, if a thin copper plate of emissivity 0.1 is introduced as a radiation shield between the two plates. Use $\sigma = 5.67 \times 10^{-8}$ W/m^2 K^4.*

(U.P.S.C., 1995)

Solution. *Given :* $T_1 = 1000$ K; $\varepsilon_1 = 0.8$, $T_2 = 500$ K; $\varepsilon_2 = 0.5$, $\varepsilon_3 = 0.1$.

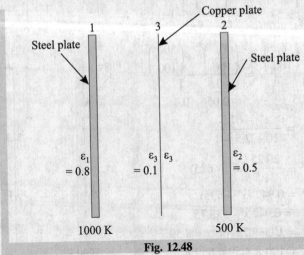

Fig. 12.48

Radiant heat exchange in W/m², $(Q_{12})_{net}$:

We know that,
$$(Q_{12})_{net} = \frac{A\sigma(T_1^4 - T_2^4)}{\left[\dfrac{1}{\varepsilon_1} + \dfrac{1}{\varepsilon_2} - 1\right] + \left[\dfrac{1}{\varepsilon_3} + \dfrac{1}{\varepsilon_2} - 1\right]} \qquad ...[\text{Eqn. (12.54)}]$$

For $A = 1$ m², we have

$$(Q_{12})_{net} = \frac{5.67\left[\left(\dfrac{1000}{100}\right)^4 - \left(\dfrac{500}{100}\right)^4\right]}{\left[\dfrac{1}{0.8} + \dfrac{1}{0.1} - 1\right] + \left[\dfrac{1}{0.1} + \dfrac{1}{0.5} - 1\right]}$$

$$= \frac{5.67\,(10000 - 625)}{(12.5 + 10 - 1) + (10 + 2 - 1)} = \textbf{2501.5 W/m² (Ans.)}$$

Example 12.41. *Consider two large parallel plates one at $t_1 = 727°C$ with emissivity $\varepsilon_1 = 0.8$ and other at $t_2 = 227°C$ with emissivity $\varepsilon_2 = 0.4$. An aluminium radiation shield with an emissivity, $\varepsilon_s = 0.05$ on both sides is placed between the plates. Calculate the percentage reduction in heat transfer rate between the two plates as a result of the shield.*

Use $\sigma = 5.67 \times 10^{-8}$ W/m² K⁴. (GATE, 1995)

Solution. *Given :* $T_1 = t_1 + 273°C = 727 + 273 = 1000$ K; $\varepsilon_1 = 0.8$;

$T_2 = t_2 + 273°C = 227 + 273 = 500$ K; $\varepsilon_2 = 0.4$;

$\varepsilon_s = \varepsilon_3 = 0.05$; $\sigma = 5.67 \times 10^{-8}$ W/m² K⁴.

Without shield, $\qquad Q$ (per unit area) $= \dfrac{\sigma(T_1^4 - T_2^4)}{\dfrac{1}{\varepsilon_1} + \dfrac{1}{\varepsilon_2} - 1}$

$$= \frac{5.67\left[\left(\dfrac{1000}{100}\right)^4 - \left(\dfrac{500}{100}\right)^4\right]}{\dfrac{1}{0.8} + \dfrac{1}{0.4} - 1} = \frac{53156}{2.75} = 19329 \text{ W}$$

Without shield, $\qquad (Q_{13})_{net} = (Q_{32})_{net}$

$$\frac{A\sigma(T_1^4 - T_3^4)}{\dfrac{1}{\varepsilon_1} + \dfrac{1}{\varepsilon_3} - 1} = \frac{A\sigma(T_3^4 - T_2^4)}{\dfrac{1}{\varepsilon_3} + \dfrac{1}{\varepsilon_2} - 1}$$

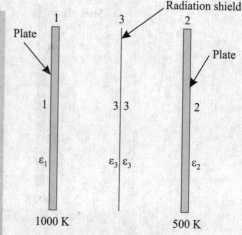

Fig. 12.49

or, $$\frac{\left(\dfrac{1000}{100}\right)^4 - \left(\dfrac{T_3}{100}\right)^4}{\dfrac{1}{0.8} + \dfrac{1}{0.05} - 1} = \frac{\left(\dfrac{T_3}{100}\right)^4 - \left(\dfrac{500}{100}\right)^4}{\dfrac{1}{0.05} + \dfrac{1}{0.4} - 1}$$

$$\frac{10000 - x^4}{1.25 + 20 - 1} = \frac{x^4 - 625}{20 + 2.5 - 1}$$

or, $$10000 - x^4 = \frac{20.25}{21.5}(x^4 - 625)$$

or, $$10000 - x^4 = 0.942(x^4 - 625)$$
$$= 0.942\,x^4 - 588.75$$

or, $$1.942\,x^4 = 10588.75 \quad\text{or}\quad x = 8.59$$

$$\therefore \qquad T_3 = 100 \times 8.59 = 859\ \text{K}$$

$$(Q_{13})_{net}\ \text{(per unit area)} = \frac{\left(\dfrac{1000}{100}\right)^4 - \left(\dfrac{859}{100}\right)^4}{\dfrac{1}{0.8} + \dfrac{1}{0.05} - 1} = \frac{4555.3}{20.25} = 224.9\ \text{W}$$

∴ Reduction in heat flow due to shield

$$(Q_{12})_{net} - (Q_{13})_{net} = 19329 - 224.9 = 19104.1\ \text{W}$$

∴ **Percentage reduction in heat transfer**

$$= \frac{19104.1}{19329} \times 100 = \mathbf{98.84\%}\ \textbf{(Ans.)}$$

Example 12.42. *The large parallel plates with emissivities 0.3 and 0.8 exchange heat. Find the percentage reduction when a polished aluminium shield of emissivity 0.04 is placed between them. Use the method of electrical analogy.*
$$\text{(P.U. Winter, 1997)}$$

Solution. *Given:* $\varepsilon_1 = 0.3$; $\varepsilon_2 = 0.8$; $\varepsilon_3 = 0.04$

Consider all resistances (surface resistances and space resistances) per unit surface area.

For steady state heat flow,

$$\frac{E_{b1} - E_{b3}}{\left(\dfrac{1-\varepsilon_1}{\varepsilon_1}\right) + 1 + \left(\dfrac{1-\varepsilon_3}{\varepsilon_3}\right)} = \frac{E_{b3} - E_{b2}}{\left(\dfrac{1-\varepsilon_3}{\varepsilon_3}\right) + 1 + \left(\dfrac{1-\varepsilon_2}{\varepsilon_2}\right)}$$

$$[\because A_1 = A_2 = A_3 = 1\text{m}^2 \text{ and } F_{1-3},\ F_{3-2} = 1]$$

or, $$\frac{\sigma(T_1^4 - T_3^4)}{\dfrac{1}{\varepsilon_1} + \dfrac{1}{\varepsilon_3} - 1} = \frac{\sigma(T_3^4 - T_2^4)}{\dfrac{1}{\varepsilon_3} + \dfrac{1}{\varepsilon_2} - 1}$$

or, $$\frac{T_1^4 - T_3^4}{\dfrac{1}{0.3} + \dfrac{1}{0.04} - 1} = \frac{T_3^4 - T_2^4}{\dfrac{1}{0.04} + \dfrac{1}{0.8} - 1}$$

or, $$\frac{T_1^4 - T_3^4}{27.33} = \frac{T_3^4 - T_2^4}{25.25}$$

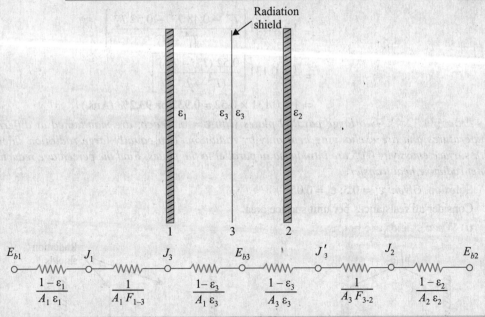

Fig. 12.50

or, $\qquad T_1^4 - T_3^4 = \dfrac{27.33}{25.25} (T_3^4 - T_2^4)$

$\qquad\qquad\qquad = 1.08 (T_3^4 - T_2^4) = 1.08\, T_3^4 - 1.08\, T_2^4$

or, $\qquad 2.08\, T_3^4 = T_1^4 + 1.08\, T_2^4$

or, $\qquad T_3^4 = \dfrac{1}{2.08} (T_1^4 + 1.08\, T_2^4) = 0.48 (T_1^4 + 1.08\, T_2^4)$ ...(i)

Q_{12} (heat flow without shield)

$$= \frac{\sigma (T_1^4 - T_2^4)}{\dfrac{1}{\varepsilon_1} + \dfrac{1}{\varepsilon_2} - 1} = \frac{\sigma (T_1^4 - T_2^4)}{\dfrac{1}{0.3} + \dfrac{1}{0.8} - 1} = \frac{\sigma (T_1^4 - T_2^4)}{3.58} \qquad ...(ii)$$

Q_{13} (heat flow with shield)

$$= \frac{\sigma (T_1^4 - T_3^4)}{\dfrac{1}{\varepsilon_1} + \dfrac{1}{\varepsilon_3} - 1} = \frac{\sigma (T_1^4 - T_3^4)}{\dfrac{1}{0.3} + \dfrac{1}{0.04} - 1} = \frac{\sigma (T_1^4 - T_3^4)}{27.33} \qquad ...(iii)$$

$\therefore$ *Percentage reduction in heat flow due to shield*

$$= \frac{Q_{12} - Q_{13}}{Q_{12}}$$

$$= 1 - \frac{Q_{13}}{Q_{12}} = 1 - \frac{\sigma (T_1^4 - T_3^4)/27.33}{\sigma (T_1^4 - T_2^4)/3.58}$$

$$= 1 - \frac{3.58}{27.33} \left[\frac{T_1^4 - T_3^4}{T_1^4 - T_2^4} \right]$$

$$= 1 - 0.131 \left[\frac{T_1^4 - 0.48 (T_1^4 + 1.08\, T_2^4)}{T_1^4 - T_2^4} \right]$$

$$= 1 - 0.131 \left[\frac{T_1^4 - 0.48\, T_1^4 - 0.52\, T_2^4}{T_1^4 - T_2^4} \right]$$

$$= 1 - 0.131 \left[\frac{0.52\, (T_1^4 - T_2^4)}{(T_1^4 - T_2^4)} \right]$$

$$= 1 - 0.131 \times 0.52 = \mathbf{0.932 \ or \ 93.2\%} \ \textbf{(Ans.)}$$

Example 12.43. *Two large parallel plates with $\varepsilon = 0.5$ each, are maintained at different temperatures and are exchanging heat only by radiation. Two equally large radiation shields with surface emissivity 0.05 are introduced in parallel to the plates. Find the percentage reduction in net radiative heat transfer.* (M.U.)

Solution. *Given:* $\varepsilon_p = 0.5$; $\varepsilon_s = 0.05$

Consider all resistances per unit surface area.

(*i*) **When shields are not used:**

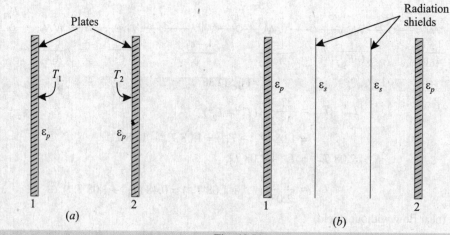

Fig. 12.51

$(Q)_{\text{without shields}}$
$$= \frac{\sigma\,(T_1^4 - T_2^4)}{\left(\dfrac{1 - \varepsilon_p}{\varepsilon_p} \right) + 1 + \left(\dfrac{1 - \varepsilon_p}{\varepsilon_p} \right)} = \frac{\sigma\,(T_1^4 - T_2^4)}{\dfrac{1}{\varepsilon_p} + \dfrac{1}{\varepsilon_p} - 1}$$

$$= \frac{C}{\dfrac{1}{0.5} + \dfrac{1}{0.5} - 1} = 0.33\ C\ [\text{where } C = \sigma\,(T_1^4 - T_2^4)]$$

(*ii*) **When shields are used :**

$(Q)_{\text{with shields}}$
$$= \frac{\sigma\,(T_1^4 - T_2^4)}{\dfrac{1}{\varepsilon_p} + \dfrac{1}{\varepsilon_p} + 2\left[\dfrac{1}{\varepsilon_s} + \dfrac{1}{\varepsilon_s} \right] - (2 + 1)} \qquad \text{...[Eqn. 12.62]}$$

$$= \frac{\sigma\,(T_1^4 - T_2^4)}{\dfrac{2}{\varepsilon_p} + \dfrac{4}{\varepsilon_s} - 3}$$

$$= \frac{C}{\dfrac{2}{0.5} + \dfrac{4}{0.05} - 3} = \frac{C}{81} = 0.012345\ C$$

$\therefore$ Percentage reduction in heat flow $= \left(\dfrac{(Q)_{without\ shields} - (Q)_{with\ shields}}{(Q)_{without\ shields}}\right) \times 100$

$= \left[1 - \dfrac{(Q)_{with\ shields}}{(Q)_{without\ shields}}\right] \times 100 = 1 - \dfrac{0.012345\ C}{0.33\ C}$

$= \textbf{96.26\%}$ **(Ans.)**

Example 12.44. *Consider two large parallel plates, one at 1000 K with emissivity 0.8 and other is at 300 K having emissivity 0.6. A radiation shield is placed between them. The shield has emissivity as 0.1 on the side facing hot plate and 0.3 on the side facing cold plate. Calculate percentage reduction in radiation heat transfer as a result of radiation shield.* (P.U. 2000)

Solution. *Given :* $T_1 = 1000$ K, $\varepsilon_1 = 0.8$, $T_2 = 300$ K, $\varepsilon_2 = 0.6$, $\varepsilon_{3h} = 0.1$, $\varepsilon_{3c} = 0.3$.

(a) The heat transfer per m^2 area between two parallel plates by radiation is given by

$$Q = \frac{\sigma\,(T_1^4 - T_2^4)}{\dfrac{1}{\varepsilon_1} + \dfrac{1}{\varepsilon_2} - 1} = \frac{5.67\left[\left(\dfrac{1000}{100}\right)^4 - \left(\dfrac{300}{100}\right)^4\right]}{\dfrac{1}{0.8} + \dfrac{1}{0.6} - 1}$$

$$= \frac{5.67\,(10^4 - 3^4)}{1.25 + 1.67 - 1} = 29292 \text{ W/m}^2 \text{ or } 29.292 \text{ kW/m}^2$$

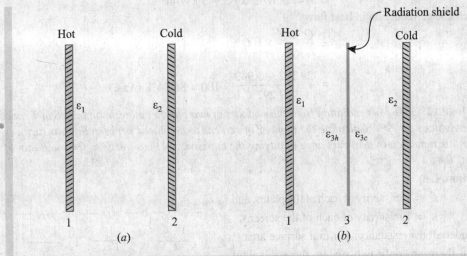

Fig. 12.52

(b) When a radiation shield is kept between two plates, then for thermal equilibrium, we can write

$$Q' = \frac{\sigma\,(T_1^4 - T_3^4)}{\dfrac{1}{\varepsilon_1} + \dfrac{1}{\varepsilon_{3h}} - 1} = \frac{\sigma\,(T_3^4 - T_2^4)}{\dfrac{1}{\varepsilon_{3c}} + \dfrac{1}{\varepsilon_2} - 1} \qquad \text{...(1)}$$

where T_3 is the temperature of the shield and ε_{3h} and ε_{3c} are the emissivities of the shield towards hot plate surface and cold plate surface.

Substituting the given values in eqn. (1), we get

$$\frac{\left(\dfrac{1000}{100}\right)^4 - \left(\dfrac{T_3}{100}\right)^4}{\dfrac{1}{0.8} + \dfrac{1}{0.1} - 1} = \frac{\left(\dfrac{T}{100}\right)^4 - \left(\dfrac{300}{100}\right)^4}{\dfrac{1}{0.3} + \dfrac{1}{0.6} - 1}$$

$$\frac{(10)^4 - x^4}{1.25 + 10 - 1} = \frac{x^4 - (3)^4}{3.33 + 1.67 - 1} \qquad \text{where } x = \frac{T_3}{100}$$

$$\frac{10000 - x^4}{10.25} = \frac{x^4 - 81}{4}$$

or, $\qquad (10000 - x^4) = \dfrac{10.25}{4}\,(x^4 - 81) = 2.56\,x^4 - 207.36$

or, $\qquad 3.56\,x^4 = 10207.36$

or, $\qquad x = \dfrac{T_3}{100} = \left(\dfrac{10207.36}{3.56}\right)^{1/4} = 7.32$

or, $\qquad T_3 = 732$ K

The heat flow per m^2 area when shield is located is given by

$$Q' = \frac{\sigma\,(T_1^4 - T_3^4)}{\dfrac{1}{\varepsilon_1} + \dfrac{1}{\varepsilon_{3h}} - 1} = \frac{5.67\left[\left(\dfrac{1000}{100}\right)^4 - \left(\dfrac{732}{100}\right)^4\right]}{\dfrac{1}{0.8} + \dfrac{1}{0.1} - 1}$$

$$= \frac{5.67\,(10^4 - 7.32^4)}{1.25 + 10 - 1} = \frac{5.67\,(10000 - 2871)}{10.25}$$

$$= 3943.5 \text{ W/m}^2 \text{ or } 3.943 \text{ kW/m}^2$$

$\therefore$ Percentage reduction in heat flow

$$= \frac{Q - Q'}{Q} \times 100$$

$$= \frac{29.292 - 3.943}{29.292} \times 100 = \mathbf{86.54\%} \text{ (Ans.)}$$

Example 12.45. *The net radiation from the surfaces of two parallel plates maintained at T_1 and T_2 is to be reduced by 99%. Calculate the number of screens to be placed between the two surfaces to achieve this reduction in heat exchange assuming the emissivity of the screens as 0.05 and that of surfaces as 0.8.*
(P.U. Winter, 1996)

Solution. Let,

ε_p = Emissivity of each of the plates, and

ε_s = Emissivity of each of the screens.

Consider all the resistances per unit surface area.

When there are only two plates, the equivalent electrical circuit is as shown in Fig. 12.53.

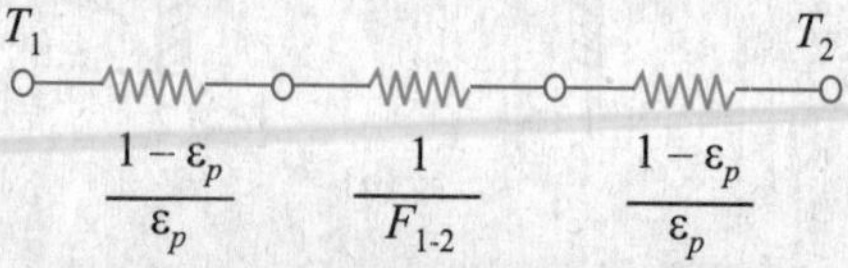

Fig. 12.53

In this case, $F_{1-2} = 1$ ... for parallel plates.

The heat transfer by radiation between two parallel plates is given by

$$(Q)_{without\ screens} = \frac{\sigma\,(T_1^4 - T_2^4)}{\dfrac{2}{\varepsilon_p} - 1} \qquad\qquad ...(1)$$

When there are 'n' screens in between the two plates, the equivalent electrical circuit is as shown in Fig. 12.54.

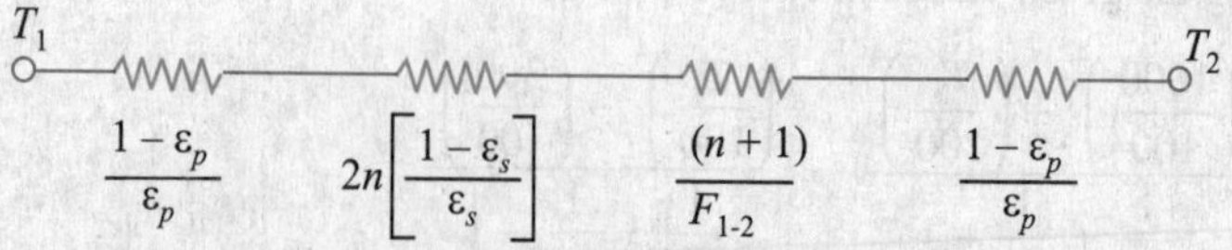

Fig. 12.54

In this case there will be $2n$ surface resistances because of n screens in addition to original two surface resistances of the plates and there will be $(n + 1)$ space resistances. The value of each space resistance is 1 as

$$F_{1-2} = F_{2-3} = F_{3-4} = \ldots\ldots = F_{(n-1)-n} = 1$$

The heat transfer by radiation between two plates when 'n' screens are placed between two plates is given by,

$$(Q)_{with\ screens} = \frac{\sigma\,(T_1^4 - T_2^4)}{2\left[\dfrac{1 - \varepsilon_p}{\varepsilon_p}\right] + \left[2n\left(\dfrac{1 - \varepsilon_s}{\varepsilon_s}\right) + (n + 1)\right]} \qquad \ldots(2)$$

But, $(Q)_{with\ screens} = (1 - 0.99)\,(Q)_{without\ screens}$ ..(Given)

Substituting the values from eqns. (1) and (2), we get

$$2\left(\frac{1 - \varepsilon_p}{\varepsilon_p}\right) + \left[2n\left(\frac{1 - \varepsilon_s}{\varepsilon_s}\right) + (n + 1)\right] = 100\left(\frac{2}{\varepsilon_p} - 1\right)$$

The given data is : $\varepsilon_p = 0.8$, $\varepsilon_s = 0.05$

Substituting these values in the above equation, we get

$$2\left(\frac{1 - 0.8}{0.8}\right) + \left[2n\left(\frac{1 - 0.05}{0.05}\right) + (n + 1)\right] = 100\left(\frac{2}{0.8} - 1\right)$$

$$0.5 + (38\,n + n + 1\,) = 150$$

$$39\,n = 148.5$$

or, $n = \dfrac{148.5}{39} \simeq 4$ (Ans.)

Example 12.46. *Determine the number of shields required to keep the temperature of the outside surface of a hollow brick lining of a furnace at 100°C when the temperature of the inside surface of the lining is 500°C. Take the emissivity of brick lining as well as for shield as 0.87.*

Heat transfer to the surroundings from the outer surface takes place by radiation and convection. The heat transfer coefficient for natural convection is given by

$$h_a = 1.44\,(\Delta t)^{0.33}\ W/m^2{}^\circ C$$

t_a (air temperature) = 25°C

Neglect the heat transfer by conduction and convection between the brick lining.   (N.U. 1999)

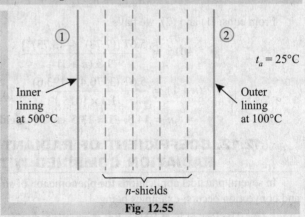

Inner lining at 500°C

Outer lining at 100°C

$t_a = 25°C$

n-shields

Fig. 12.55

Solution. *Given* : $t_a = 25°C$, $t_1 = 500°C$, $t_2 = 100°C$; $\varepsilon_1 = \varepsilon_2 = \varepsilon_s = 0.87$

Number of radiation shields required, n:

For steady state condition the heat lost by the inner lining through shields to the outer lining

= Heat lost by the outer lining to the surroundings

$$= Q_t = Q_c + Q_r$$

where Q_c and Q_r are heats lost by the outer lining to the surroundings by convection and radiation respectively.

$$Q_c = A\,h_a\,(t_2 - t_a)$$

But, $\qquad\qquad\qquad\qquad h_a = 1.44\,(100 - 25)^{0.33} = 5.99\ \text{W/m}^2\ ^\circ\text{C}$

$\therefore \qquad\qquad\qquad\qquad Q_c = 1 \times 5.99\,(100 - 25) = 449.25\ \text{W} \quad \text{where, } A = 1\text{m}^2$

$$Q_r = A\,\varepsilon\,\sigma\,(T_2^{\,4} - T_a^{\,4})$$

$$= 1 \times 0.87 \times 5.67\left[\left(\frac{100 + 273}{100}\right)^4 - \left(\frac{25 + 273}{100}\right)^4\right]$$

$$= 4.933\,(193.57 - 78.86) = 565.8\ \text{W}$$

$\therefore \qquad\qquad\qquad\qquad Q_t = 449.25 + 565.8 = 1015\ \text{W} \qquad\qquad\qquad\qquad \text{...(i)}$

This is the amount of heat radiated from the inner surface to outer surface through n-shields.

When there are n shields, the surface resistances are (2n + 2) and space resistances are (n + 1).
The space resistance for parallel plates

$$= \frac{1}{F_{1-2}} = \frac{1}{F_{2-3}} = \,.....\, = \frac{1}{F_{(n-1)-n}}$$

But, $\qquad\qquad\qquad F_{1-2} = F_{2-3} = F_{(n-1)-n} = 1$

$\therefore$ Total *space resistance*, $R_{space} = (n + 1) \times \dfrac{1}{F_{1-2}} = (n + 1)$

Total *surface resistance*, $R_{surface} = 2\,(n + 1)\left(\dfrac{1 - \varepsilon_1}{\varepsilon_1}\right)$ as $\varepsilon_1 = \varepsilon_2 = \,... \,\varepsilon_n$ (given)

where $\dfrac{1 - \varepsilon_1}{\varepsilon_1}$ is the radiation surface resistance between the two parallel surfaces, each of

1m^2 area.

$\therefore \qquad\qquad R_{surface} = 2\,(n + 1)\left(\dfrac{1 - 0.87}{0.87}\right) \approx 0.3\,(n + 1)$

$$Q_t = \frac{\sigma\,(T_1^{\,4} - T_2^{\,4})}{R_{space} + R_{surface}} = \frac{5.67\left[\left(\dfrac{500 + 273}{100}\right)^4 - \left(\dfrac{100 + 273}{100}\right)^4\right]}{(n + 1) + 0.3\,(n + 1)} \qquad \text{...(2)}$$

From eqns. (1) and (2), we have

$$1015 = \frac{5.67\,[(7.73)^4 - (3.73)^4]}{1.3\,(n + 1)}$$

$\therefore \qquad\qquad (n + 1) = \dfrac{5.67\,(3570.4 - 193.6)}{1.3 \times 1015} = 14.5$

or, $\qquad\qquad\qquad n = 14.5 - 1 = 13.5$ say **14 shields (Ans.)**

12.12. COEFFICIENT OF RADIANT HEAT TRANSFER AND RADIATION COMBINED WITH CONVECTION

In several practical applications the phenomenon of simultaneous heat exchange due to radiation and convection occurs; examples being:

(*i*)   The loss of heat from a hot steam pipe passing through a room.

(*ii*)   The flow of hot combustion products through a cooled duct.

A proper analysis of the above cases would require a simultaneous solution of convection and radiation equations which is obviously a complicated task. The total heat transfer by both convection and radiation can be calculated by the linear superposition of heat fluxes due to these modes.

i.e., $\qquad\qquad\qquad q = q_{conv.} + q_{rad.}$

$$= h_{conv.}\,(T_g - T_w) + h_{rad.}\,(T_g - T_w)$$

$$= (h_{conv.} + h_{rad.})\,(T_g - T_w)$$

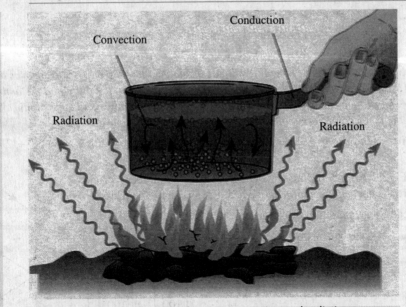

Conduction

Convection

Radiation

Radiation

Heat transfer by conduction, convection and radiation.

where T_g and T_w are the gas and wall temperatures respectively $(T_g > T_w)$ and $h_{rad.}$ is the radiation heat transfer coefficient defined by

$$h_{rad.} (T_g - t_w) = \varepsilon \sigma (T_g^4 - T_w^4)$$

or,

$$h_{rad.} = \frac{\varepsilon \sigma (T_g^4 - T_w^4)}{(T_g - T_w)} = \varepsilon \sigma (T_g^2 + T_w^2) (T_g + T_w) \qquad ...(12.65)$$

The value of $h_{rad.}$ can be calculated from the heat flux equation for any configuration. For example, the value of $h_{rad.}$ for the case of two *large parallel plates* is given by

$$\frac{Q}{A} = \frac{\sigma (T_1^4 - T_2^4)}{\dfrac{1}{\varepsilon_1} + \dfrac{1}{\varepsilon_2} - 1} = h_{rad.} (T_1 - T_2)$$

or,

$$h_{rad.} = \frac{\sigma (T_1^2 + T_2^2) (T_1 + T_2)}{\dfrac{1}{\varepsilon_1} + \dfrac{1}{\varepsilon_2} - 1} \qquad ...(12.66)$$

Example 12.47. *The heat transfer coefficient including convection radiation is 30 W/m²°C for the outer surface of the pipe in a large enclosure. Assume pipe surface is black. Calculate the radiation heat transfer coefficient if walls of the pipe surface and enclosure are at 200°C and 100°C respectively. Also find heat transfer coefficient by convection.* **(P.U.)**

Solution. *Given :* $T_1 = 200 + 273 = 473$ K; $T_2 = 100 + 273 = 373$ K,

$$h_{conv.} + h_{rad.} = 30 \text{ W/m}^2\text{°C}$$

As enclosure is large, the heat flow from the pipe is given by

$$(Q_{12})_{rad.} = A_1 \varepsilon_1 \sigma (T_1^4 - T_2^4)$$

$$= 1 \times 1 \times 5.67 \left[\left(\frac{473}{100}\right)^4 - \left(\frac{373}{100}\right)^4 \right] \qquad (\because A_1 = 1 \ m^2, \varepsilon_1 = 1)$$

$$= 1740.56 \text{ W/m}^2$$

Also, $(Q_{12})_{rad.} = A_1 h_{rad.} (t_1 - t_2)$, where $h_{rad.}$ is the radiation heat transfer coefficient.

$\therefore$ $1740.56 = 1 \times h_{rad.} \, (373 - 273)$

or, $h_{rad.} = \textbf{17.4 W/m}^2{}^\circ\textbf{C \, (Ans.)}$

$h_{conv.} = 30 - h_{rad.} = 30 - 17.4 = \textbf{12.6 W/m}^2{}^\circ\textbf{C}$ **(Ans.)**

Example 12.48. *One side of metallic plate is insulated while the other side absorbs a radiation flux of 900 W/m². The convective heat transfer coefficient between the plate and the ambient air is 10 W/m²K. The surface emissivity of the plate is 0.8. The surroundings and ambient air are at 27°C. Determine the temperature of the plate under steady state conditions.*   (M.U. 1997)

Solution. *Given :* $q_a = 900$ W/m²; $h_c = 10$ W/m² K; $\varepsilon = 0.8$, $T_a = 27 + 273 = 300$ K.

Refer Fig. 12.56. q_a is the amount of heat absorbed per m² per sec. and q_c and q_r are the convective and radiative heat fluxes lost by the plate.

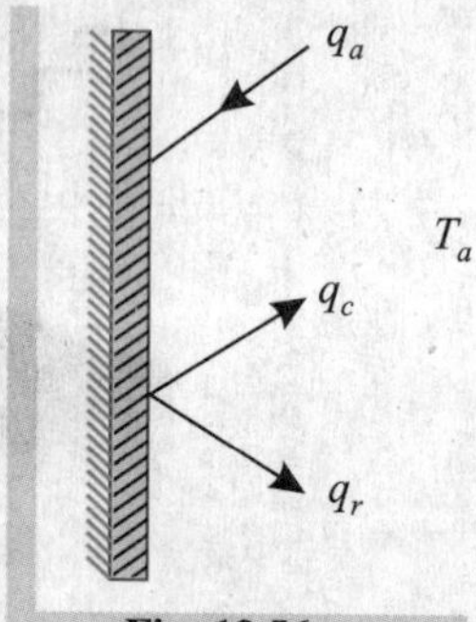

For steady state condition of the plate,

$$q_a = q_c + q_r$$
$$900 = h_c \, [\, T_p - (27 + 273)] + \varepsilon \, \sigma \, (T_p{}^4 - T_a{}^4)$$

or, $900 = 10 \, (T_p - 300) + 0.8 \times 5.67 \left[\left(\dfrac{T_p}{100} \right)^4 - \left(\dfrac{300}{100} \right)^4 \right]$

(where T_p = temperature of the plate in K)

or, $900 = 10 \, (T_p - 300) + 4.54 \left[\left(\dfrac{T_p}{100} \right)^4 - 81 \right]$

Fig. 12.56

Solving the above equation by trial and error method, we get

$$T_p = 355 \text{ K} = \textbf{82}^\circ\textbf{C \, (Ans.)}$$

Example 12.49. *A thermocouple indicates a temperature of 800°C when placed in a pipeline where a hot gas is flowing at 870°C. If the convective heat transfer coefficient between the thermocouple and gas is 60 W/m²°C, find the duct wall temperature. ε (thermocouple) = 0.5.* (P.U.)

Solution. *Given:* $T_{couple} = 800 + 273 = 1073$ K; $T_{gas} = 870 + 273 = 1143$ K;

$h_{conv.} = 60$ W/m²°C; $\varepsilon_{couple} = 0.5$

Duct wall temperature, T_{wall}:

The arrangement of thermocouple for measuring the temperature of gas flowing in a pipeline is shown in Fig. 12.57. There is convective heat flow from gas to thermocouple but a part of this heat is lost in radiation to the pipe wall. As such, the temperature indicated by a thermocouple is *always less than the actual gas temperature.*

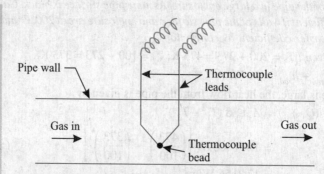

Fig. 12.57. Temperature measurement by a thermocouple.

Convective heat flow from gas to thermocouple

$$= h_{conv.} \, A \, (T_{gas} - T_{couple})$$
$$= 60 \, A \, (T_{gas} - T_{couple})$$

Heat radiated by thermocouple to pipe wall

$$= F_g \, A \, \sigma \, (T^4_{couple} - T^4_{wall})$$

The configuration factor F_g corresponds to a completely enclosed body (thermocouple), and small compared with the enclosing body (pipeline), i.e., $F_{1-2} = 1$ and $A_1 \ll A_2$.

$$\therefore \qquad F_g = \cfrac{1}{\left(\cfrac{1 - \varepsilon_1}{\varepsilon_1}\right) + \cfrac{1}{F_{1-2}} + \left(\cfrac{1 - \varepsilon_2}{\varepsilon_2}\right) \cfrac{A_1}{A_2}}$$

$$= \cfrac{1}{\left(\cfrac{1 - \varepsilon_1}{\varepsilon_1}\right) + 1 + 0} = \varepsilon_1 = 0.5$$

Under steady state conditions, $Q_{conv.} = (Q_{12})_{net}$

$$60 \, A \, (T_{gas} - T_{couple}) = 0.5 \, A \, \sigma \, [T^4_{couple} - T^4_{wall}]$$

or, $\quad 60 \, (1143 - 1073) = 0.5 \times 5.67 \left[\left(\dfrac{1073}{100}\right)^4 - \left(\dfrac{T_{wall}}{100}\right)^4\right]$

or, $\qquad\qquad 4200 = 2.835 \left[13255.6 - \left(\dfrac{T_{wall}}{100}\right)^4\right]$

or, $\qquad\qquad \left(\dfrac{T_{wall}}{100}\right)^4 = 13255.6 - \dfrac{4200}{2.835} = 11774$

$\therefore \qquad\qquad T_{wall} = (11774)^{1/4} \times 100 = 1041.7 \text{ K or } \textbf{768.7°C (Ans.)}$

Example 12.50. *A thermocouple used to measure temperature of gas flowing through a duct records 280°C. If emissivity of junction is 0.4 and film coefficient of heat transfer is 150 W/m²K*

(i) Find the true gas temperature.

(ii) What should be the emissivity of junction in order to reduce the temperature error by 30%?

The temperature of duct wall is 140°C.

(P.U. 1995)

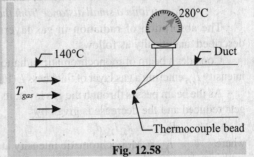

Fig. 12.58

Solution. *Given :* T_{couple} = 280 + 273 = 553 K, T_{wall} = 140 + 273 = 413 K, $h_{conv.}$ = 150 W/m² K; ε = 0.4.

(i) True gas temperature, T_{gas} **:**

Heat gained by thermocouple by convection = Heat lost by thermocouple by radiation

$$A \cdot h_{conv.} \, (T_{gas} - 553) = A \, \varepsilon \, \sigma \, (T^4_{couple} - T^4_{wall}) \qquad\qquad ...(i)$$

or, $\quad 150(T_{gas} - 553) = 0.4 \times 5.67 \left[\left(\dfrac{553}{100}\right)^4 - \left(\dfrac{413}{100}\right)^4\right]$

or, $\qquad\qquad T_{gas} = 553 + \dfrac{0.4 \times 5.67}{150} (5.53^4 - 4.13^4) = 562.74 \text{ K} = \textbf{289.74°C (Ans.)}$

(ii) Emissivity of the junction, ε :

The error in measurement = $T_{gas} - T_{couple}$ = 289.74 – 280 = 9.74°C

This error is reduced by 30%

$$= 9.74 \times 0.3 = 2.92°C$$

The error existing $= 9.74 - 2.92 = 6.82°C$

∴ New temperature record will be

$$T_{couple} = T_{gas} - 6.82°C = 289.74 - 6.82 = 282.92°C$$

Using eqn. (*i*), again, we get

$$150 \, (6.82) = \varepsilon \times 5.67 \left[\left(\frac{282.92 + 273}{100} \right)^4 - \left(\frac{413}{100} \right)^4 \right]$$

$$= 5.67 \, \varepsilon \, (955.1 - 290.94) = 3765.8 \, \varepsilon$$

or

$$\varepsilon = \frac{150 \times 6.82}{3765.8} = \mathbf{0.27 \ (Ans.)}$$

12.13. RADIATION FROM GASES, VAPOURS AND FLAMES

The phenomenon of radiation exchange between gases and heat transfer surfaces is complex one. This is so because several gases such as H_2, O_2, N_2 etc. present in flames of the furnaces are transparent to radiation at low temperatures, whereas other gases like CO, CO_2, H_2O etc., emit and absorb radiation to an appreciable extent.

The radiation from gases differs from that from solids in the following ways:

1. Gases emit or absorb radiation only between *narrow ranges or bands of wavelength whereas solids radiate at all wavelengths over the entire spectra.*

2. *The intensity of radiation, as it passes through an absorbing gas, decreases with the length of passage through the gas volume whereas in case of solids the absorption of radiation takes place within a small distance from the surface.*

The absorption of radiation in gas layers may be described analytically as follows:

Consider a beam of monochromatic radiation with an intensity $I_{\lambda o}$ entering a gas layer of thickness L (Fig. 12.59).

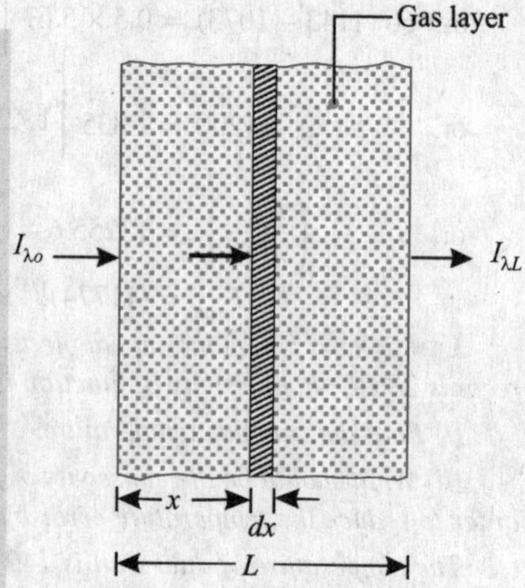

As the beam passes through the gas layer, its intensity gets reduced and the decrease is given by

Fig. 12.59. Monochromatic radiation passing through an absorbing gas.

$$dI_{\lambda x} = - k_\lambda \, I_{\lambda x} . d_x \qquad \qquad ...(12.67)$$

where

$I_{\lambda x}$ = Monochromatic intensity at a distance x, and

k_λ = a proportionality constant or mono chromatic absorption coefficient, depends on the state of gas (its temperature and pressure) and the wave-length.

Integrating eqn. (12.67) between the limits $x = 0$ and $x = L$, we get

$$\int_{x=0}^{x=L} \frac{dI_{\lambda x}}{I_{\lambda x}} = \int_{x=0}^{x=L} - k_\lambda . dx$$

or,

$$ln \frac{I_{\lambda L}}{I_{\lambda o}} = - k_\lambda . L$$

or,

$$I_{\lambda L} = I_{\lambda o} \, e^{-k_\lambda . L} \qquad \qquad ...(12.68)$$

where,

$I_{\lambda L}$ = Radiation intensity at $x = L$.

The ratio $\dfrac{I_{\lambda L}}{I_{\lambda o}}$ is the *monochromatic transmittivity* τ_λ of the gas.

In general, the gases do not reflect radiant energy *i.e.*, their reflectivity is zero, therefore,

$$\alpha_\lambda + \tau_\lambda = 1$$

or,

$$\alpha_\lambda = 1 - \tau_\lambda = 1 - e^{-k_\lambda . L}$$

Obviously the quantity $(1 - e^{-k_\lambda . L})$ represents the *monochromatic absorptivity* of the gas. According to Kirchhoff's law this will also represent the monochromatic emissivity ε_λ of the gas. When L is very large,

$$\alpha_\lambda = \varepsilon_\lambda \simeq 1$$

Thus, for very thick layers, gas radiation approaches black body radiation within the wavelength of the band. The absorptivity of a gas is a fairly complicated function of temperature, pressure, size and configuration of the gaseous region.

The following empirical relations have been suggested to workout the emissive power of CO_2 and water vapours :

For CO_2 : $E_{CO_2} = 3.5(pL)^{0.33}\left(\dfrac{T}{100}\right)^{3.5}$ ...(12.69)

For H_2O : $E_{H_2O} = 3.5\, p^{0.8}\, L^{0.6}\left(\dfrac{T}{100}\right)^{3}$ ...(12.70)

where, p = Partial pressure, and

$$L = 4 \times \frac{\text{gas volume}}{\text{enclosure area (wall)}} \quad \begin{bmatrix} L \text{ takes into consideration both} \\ \text{the size and configuration of the} \\ \text{gaseous region.} \end{bmatrix}$$

The data on the beam length for gaseous bodies of various geometrical shapes have been compiled by Hottel and the relevant graphs are available in the heat transfer hand books.

- Following formula is used to calculate the radiant heat exchange between a gas at a temperature T_g and a black surface of finite area A at temperature T_b :

$$Q = \sigma A \left(\varepsilon_g T_g^{\,4} - \alpha_g T_b^{\,4}\right) \qquad\qquad ...(12.71)$$

ε_g (emissivity of gas) is evaluated at temperature T_g and α_g (absorptivity of gas) at temperature of the surface.

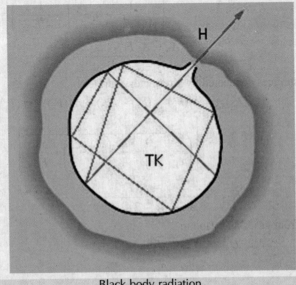

Black body radiation.

- The following formula is used to compute the net rate of heat transfer from the gas to the walls, when *inside of the enclosure is not black:*

$$Q = \sigma A \, \bar{\varepsilon}_w \, (\varepsilon_g T_g^{\,4} - \alpha_g T_w^{\,4}) \qquad\qquad ...(12.72)$$

where, $\bar{\varepsilon}_w$ = Effective surface emissivity $\left(= \dfrac{\varepsilon_w + 1}{2}\right)$ where ε_w is the emissivity of the gas at the wall temperature.

The net interchange of energy between a *flame* and its *enclosure* is given by:

$$Q_{net} = \sigma A_f F_{fw} \, \varepsilon_f \varepsilon_w \, (T_f^4 - T_w^4) \qquad\qquad ...(12.73)$$

where subscripts *f* and *w* correspond to flames and enclosure wall respectively.

HIGHLIGHTS

List of formulae :

1. $F_{1-2} = \dfrac{1}{A_1} \displaystyle\int_{A_1} \int_{A_2} \dfrac{\cos\theta_1 \, \cos\theta_2 \, dA_1 \, dA_2}{\pi r^2}$

2. $F_{1-1} + F_{1-2} + F_{1-3} + \quad ... \, F_{1-m} = 1$

3. $A_1 F_{1-2} = A_2 F_{2-1} \qquad ...$ Reciprocity theorem

4. $F_{1-1} = 0$ for convex and flat surface

5. For *two black bodies* :

$$(Q_{12})_{net} = A_1 F_{1-2} \, \sigma \, (T_1^{\,4} - T_2^{\,4})$$

6. For *two gray bodies* :

$$(Q_{12})_{net} = A_1 \, (F_g)_{1-2} \, \sigma \, (T_1^{\,4} - T_2^{\,4})$$

where $(F_g)_{1-2} = \dfrac{1}{\dfrac{1-\varepsilon_1}{\varepsilon_1} + \dfrac{1}{F_{1-2}} + \dfrac{1-\varepsilon_2}{\varepsilon_2} \cdot \dfrac{A_1}{A_2}}$

7. Two black surfaces connected by a single refractory surface :

$$(Q_{12})_{net} = A_1 \, \bar{F}_{1-2} \, (E_{b_1} - E_{b_2}) = A_1 F_{1-2} \, \sigma \, (T_1^4 - T_2^4)$$

where, $\bar{F}_{1-2} = F_{1-2} + \left[\dfrac{1}{\dfrac{1}{(1 - F_{1-2})} + \dfrac{A_1}{A_2}\left(\dfrac{1}{1 - F_{2-1}}\right)} \right]$

$$= \dfrac{A_2 - A_1 F_{1-2}^2}{A_1 + A_2 - 2A_1 F_{1-2}}$$

8. Two gray surfaces connected by a refractory surface :

$$(Q_{12})_{net} = A_1 (F_g)_{1-2} \, (E_{b1} - E_{b2}) = A_1 \, (F_g)_{1-2} \, \sigma \, (T_1^4 - T_2^4)$$

where, $(F_g)_{1-2} = \left[\dfrac{1}{\left(\dfrac{1}{\varepsilon_1} - 1\right) + \dfrac{A_1}{A_2}\left(\dfrac{1}{\varepsilon_2} - 1\right) + \dfrac{1}{\bar{F}_{1-2}}} \right]$

and, $\bar{F}_{1-2} = \dfrac{A_2 - A_1 F_{1-2}^2}{A_1 + A_2 - 2A_1 F_{1-2}}$

9. Radiation from gases and vapours

$$Q_{net} = \sigma A \, (\varepsilon_g T_g^{\,4} - \alpha_g T_w^{\,4}).$$

THEORETICAL QUESTIONS

1. Define a geometrical or shape factor.
2. Derive an expression for the shape factor in case of radiation exchange between two surfaces.
3. Derive the following relation for the radiant heat exchange between two gray surfaces, using definition of irradiation and radiosity :

$$(Q_{12})_{net} = \frac{A_1 \, \sigma \, (T_1^4 - T_2^4)}{\dfrac{1 - \varepsilon_1}{\varepsilon_1} + \dfrac{1}{\bar{F}_{1-2}} + \left(\dfrac{1 - \varepsilon_2}{\varepsilon_2}\right)\dfrac{A_1}{A_2}}$$

4. Derive expressions for the following cases, using definitions of irradiation and radiosity:
   (i) Radiation heat exchange between two black surfaces.
   (ii) Radiation heat exchange for three gray surfaces.
   (iii) Radiation heat exchange for two gray surfaces connected by single refractory surface.
   (iv) Radiation heat exchange for four gray surfaces.
5. What is a radiation shield?
6. Write a short note on radiation from gases, vapours and flames.

UNSOLVED EXAMPLES

1. Assuming the sun to radiate as a black body, calculate its temperature from the data given below:

   Solar constant = 1400 W/m²; Radius of the sun = 6.97×10^8 m; Distance between the sun and the earth = 14.96×10^{10} m. **(Ans. 5800 K)**

2. A small sphere (outside diameter = 50 mm) with a surface temperature of 277°C is located at the geometric centre of a large sphere (inside diameter = 250 mm) with an inner surface temperature of 7°C. Calculate how much of emission from the inner surface of the large sphere is incident upon the outer surface of the small sphere; assume that both sides approach black body behaviour.

   What is the net interchange of heat between the two spheres ? **(Ans. 4%, 38 W)**

3. A 60 mm thick plate with a circular hole of 30 mm diameter along the thickness is maintained at uniform temperature of 277°C. Find the loss of energy to the surroundings at 20°C, assuming that the two ends of the hole to be as parallel discs and the metallic surfaces and surroundings have black body characteristics. **(Ans. 6.3 W)**

4. Work out the shape factor of a hemispherical bowl of diameter D with respect to itself. Also calculate the radiative heat transfer from the cavity if inside temperature is 773 K and its emissivity is 0.6. The diameter of the cavity is 700 mm. **(Ans. 5.843 kW)**

5. A double walled flask may be considered equivalent to two infinite parallel planes. The emissivities of the walls are 0.3 and 0.8 respectively. The space between the walls of the flask is evacuated. Find the heat transfer per m² area when inner and outer surface temperatures are 300 K and 260 K. To reduce the heat flow, a shield of polished aluminium with $\varepsilon = 0.05$ is inserted between the walls. Find the reduction in heat transfer. **(Ans. 51.2 W/m²)**

6. The surfaces of a double-walled spherical vessel used for storing liquid oxygen are covered with a layer of silver having an emissivity of 0.03. The temperature of the outer surface of the inner wall is –153°C and the temperature of the inner surface of the outer wall is 27°C. The spheres are 21 cm and 30 cm in diameters, with the space between them evacuated. Calculate the radiation heat transfer through the walls into the vessel and the rate of the evaporation of liquid oxygen if its rate of vaporisation is 220 kJ/kg. **(Ans. 0.0824 kg/h)**

7. A steel rod of 25 mm diameter has been mounted axially in a heat treatment muffle furnace of inside diameter 200 mm. The inside surface temperature of the muffle is 1400 K and has an emissivity of 0.86, while emissivity of the surface of the rod is 0.62. Find the time required to heat the rod from 800 K to 900 K assuming that it occupies full length of the furnace. For the rod material, take specific heat as 0.67 kJ/kg K and the density as 7850 kg/m^3. (**Ans.** 28.65 s)

8. Find the heat lost by radiation per metre length of 60 mm diameter pipe at 350°C if

    (i)   it is located in a large room with red brick walls maintained at a temperature of 30°C,

    (ii) it is enclosed in a 150 mm diameter conduit of red bricks maintained at a temperature of 35°C.

    Take ε (steel tube) = 0.8, and e (brick conduit) = 0.92.

    Also calculate reduction in heat loss due to case (ii).   [**Ans.** (i) 1215.96 W; (ii) 1183 W, 32.96 W]

9. A 25 cm × 25 cm ingot casting, 1.5 m high and at 1225 K temperature, is stripped from its mould. The casting is made to stand on end on the floor of a large foundry whose wall, floor and roof can be assumed to be at 300 K temperature. If the emissivity of the casting material is 0.85, calculate the rate of radiant heat interchange between the casting and the room. (**Ans.** 171.12 kW)

10. A thermocouple is used to measure the temperature of a hot gas flowing through a pipe line which is exposed to surroundings at 650 K. The convective heat transfer coefficient from the gas to thermocouple bead is 42 W/m^{2}K. The thermocouple indicates a temperature of 750 K and it is so arranged that the heat transfer by conduction along the wires is negligible. The emissivity of thermocouple material is 0.80. Find the true gas temperature. (**Ans.** 898.9 K)

PART IV

MASS TRANSFER

Mass transfer related food processes.

Mass Transfer

13

13.1. INTRODUCTION

In a system consisting of one or more components whose concentrations vary from point to point, there is a natural tendency for the transport of different species from the region of high to those of low concentration. *This process of transfer of mass as a result of the species concentration difference in a system/mixture is called* **mass transfer.** So long as there is concentration difference mass transfer will occur.

Some *examples* of mass transfer are:

A. *Examples of industrial importance* :

1. Refrigeration by the evaporation of liquid ammonia in the atmosphere of H_2 is electrolux refrigerator.

2. Humidification of air in cooling tower.

3. Evaporation of petrol in the carburettor of an I.C. engine.

4. Neutron diffusion within nuclear reactors.

5. Estimation of depth to which carbon will penetrate in a mild steel specimen during the act of carburising.

B. *Examples of day-to-day life* :

1. Dissolution of sugar added to a cup of coffee.

2. The separation of the components of a mixture by distillation or absorption.

3. The transfer of water vapour into dry air, drying and evaporation.

4. Diffusion of smoke through tall chimneys into the environment.

13.2. MODES OF MASS TRANSFER

The mechanism of mass transfer depends greatly on the dynamics of the system in which it occurs. Like those of heat transfer, there are different *modes of mass transfer*, which are:

    (*i*)   Mass transfer by diffusion;

    (*ii*) Mass transfer by convection;

    (*iii*) Mass transfer by change of phase.

1. Mass transfer by diffusion (molecular or eddy diffusion):

The transport of water on a microscopic level as a result of diffusion from a region of high concentration to a region of low concentration in a system/mixture of liquids or gases is called **molecular diffusion.** It occurs when a substance diffuses through a layer of stagnant fluid and may be due to concentration, temperature or pressure gradients. In a gaseous mixture, molecular diffusion occurs due to random motion of the molecules.

When one of the diffusing fluids is in turbulent motion, the **eddy diffusion** takes place. Mass transfer is more rapid by eddy diffusion than by molecular diffusion. An example of an eddying diffusion process is *dissipation of smoke from a smoke stack.* Turbulence causes mixing and transfer of smoke to the ambient air.

2. Mass transfer by convection:

Mass transfer by convection involves *transfer between a moving fluid and a surface,* or *between two relatively immiscible moving fluids.* The convective mass transfer depends on the transport properties and on the dynamic (laminar or turbulent) characteristics of the flowing fluid. *Example:* The evaporation of ether.

3. Mass transfer by change of phase:

Mass transfer occurs whenever a change from one phase to another takes place. The mass transfer in such a case occurs *due to simultaneous action of convection and diffusion.* Some examples are:

    (*i*)   Hot gases escaping from the chimney rise by convection and then diffuse into the air above the chimney.

    (*ii*) Mixing of water vapour with air during evaporation of water from the lake surface (partly by convection and partly by diffusion).

    (*iii*) Boiling of water in open air — there is first transfer of mass from liquid to vapour state and then vapour mass from the liquid interface is transferred to the open air by convection as well as by diffusion.

13.3. CONCENTRATIONS, VELOCITIES AND FLUXES

13.3.1. CONCENTRATIONS

Mass concentration (or mass density). The mass concentration or mass density ρ_A of species A in a multi-component mixture is defined as the mass of A *per unit volume of the mixture.* It is expressed in kg/m^3 units.

Molar concentration (or molar density). The molar concentration C_A of species A is defined as *the number of moles of species A per unit volume of the mixture.* It is expressed in kg mole/m^3 units.

The mass concentration and molar concentration are related by the expresion,

$$C_A = \frac{\rho_A}{M_A} \qquad \qquad \text{...(13.1)}$$

where, M_A = Molecular weight of component A.

Mass fraction. The mass fraction, m_A is defined as the ratio of *mass concentration of species A to the total mass density,* ρ, *of the mixture.*

$$m_A * = \frac{\rho_A}{\rho} \qquad \qquad ...(13.2)$$

Mole fraction. The mole fraction, x_A in terms of total mole concentration of the mixture, C, is defined as

$$x_A = \frac{C_A}{C} \qquad \qquad ...(13.3)$$

In a binary mixture of A and B, by definition, the following summation rules hold good.

$$\rho_A + \rho_B = \rho \qquad \qquad ...(13.4)$$
$$C_A + C_B = C \qquad \qquad ...(13.5)$$
$$m_A^* + m_B^* = 1 \qquad \qquad ...(13.6)$$
$$x_A + x_B = 1 \qquad \qquad ...(13.7)$$

Concentrations, in the gas phase, are usually expressed as partial pressures. According to Dalton's law of partial pressures,

$$p = p_A + p_B$$

For the perfect gas law, we have

$$p_A V = n_A GT$$

Also,

$$C_A = \frac{n_A}{V} = \frac{p_A}{GT} \qquad \qquad ...(13.8)$$

$\therefore$

$$x_A = \frac{C_A}{C} = \frac{p_A / GT}{p / GT} = \frac{p_A}{p}$$

or,

$$C = C_A + C_B = \frac{p_A}{GT} + \frac{p_B}{GT} = \frac{p}{GT} \qquad \qquad ...[13.8 \, (a)]$$

where G = Universal gas constant = MR = 8314 J/kg mole K.

13.3.2. VELOCITIES

The bulk velocity of a mixture, in which different components may have different mobilities, is computed either on mass-average or molar-average basis. In a fluid mixture of two components A and B, if u_A and u_B are the mean velocities (of the components, respectively), then:

The *mass-average velocity* (u_{mass}) is defined by

$$u_{mass} = \frac{\rho_A u_A + \rho_B u_B}{\rho_A + \rho_B}$$

$$= \frac{\rho_A u_A + \rho_B u_B}{\rho} \qquad \qquad ...(13.9)$$

or,

$$u_{mass} = m_A^* u_A + m_B^* u_B \qquad \qquad ...(13.10)$$

The molar-average velocity (u_{molar}) is defined by

$$u_{molar} = \frac{u_A C_A + u_B C_B}{C_A + C_B} \qquad \qquad ...(13.11)$$

$$= \frac{u_A C_A + u_B C_B}{C}$$

or,

$$u_{molar} = x_A u_A + x_B u_B \qquad \qquad ...(13.12)$$

Let us now define two diffusion velocities (u_{mass}, u_{molar}) with respect to the two bulk velocities.

The *mass diffusion velocity* of a component is the velocity of that component relative to the mass-average velocity of the mixture. Therefore,

Mass diffusion velocity of component, $A = u_A - u_{mass}$ ...(13.13)

Mass diffusion velocity of component, $B = u_B - u_{mass}$ ...(13.14)

Similarly, the *molar-diffusion velocity* is the velocity of a component relative to the molar-average velocity of the mixture. Therefore,

Molar diffusion velocity of component $A = u_A - \bar{u}_{molar}$ ...(13.15)

Molar diffusion velocity of component $B = u_B - \bar{u}_{molar}$ ...(13.16)

13.3.3. FLUXES

Flux of mass transfer is caused by the existence of different velocities and concentrations. For species A of the multi-component mixture:

$$\text{Absolute flux} = \rho_A u_A$$

$$\text{Bulk motion flux} = \rho_A u_{mass}$$

$$\text{Diffusion flux} = \frac{m_A}{A}$$

The quantity $\dfrac{m_A}{A}$ represents *mass flow per unit area per unit time*. The absolute flux of any constituent as seen by a stations observer = Diffusion flux + bulk motion flux.

i.e.,
$$\rho_A u_A = \frac{m_A}{A} + \rho_A u_{mass}$$

or Diffusion flux,
$$\frac{m_A}{A} = \rho_A u_A - \rho_A u_{mass} = \rho_A (u_A - u_{mass})$$ ...(13.17)

Similarly, on *molar basis*,

$$\text{Diffusion flux} = m_A^* (u_A - u_{molar})$$ ...(13.18)

13.4. FICK'S LAW

In order to understand the mass diffusion (a transport process originating from molecular activity), consider a chamber in which two different gas species A and B, at the same temperature and pressure are initially separated by a partition. The left compartment has a high concentration (*i.e.*, more molecules per unit volume) of gas A (open circles) whereas the right compartment is rich in gas B (dark circles). When the partition wall is removed a driving potential comes into existence which tends to equalize the concentration difference. Mass transfer by diffusion will be in the direction of decreasing concentration and subsequently there will be a net transport of species A to the right and of species B to the left. After a sufficiently long period, equilibrium conditions prevail *i.e.*, uniform concentrations of species A and B are achieved and then the mass diffusion ceases.

It has been observed through experiments that molecular diffusion is governed by Fick's law which is expressed as

$$N_A = \frac{m_A}{A} = -D_{AB}\frac{dC_A}{dx}$$ ...(13.19)

where,
m_A = Mass flow rate of species A by diffusion, kg/s,

A = Area through which mass is flowing, m²,

$N_A = \dfrac{m_A}{A}$ = Mass flux of species A *i.e.*, amount of species A that is trans-ferred per unit time and per unit area perpendicular to the direction of transfer, kg/s-m² or kg mole/s-m²,

D_{AB} = Diffusion coefficient or mass diffusivity for binary mixture of species A and B, m²/s,

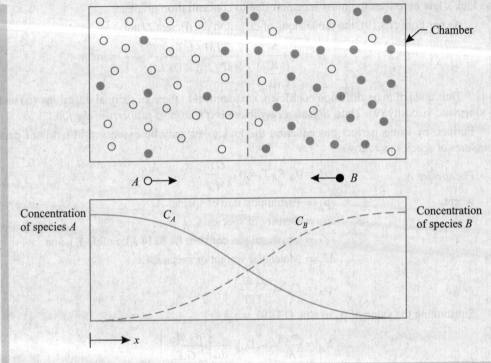

Fig. 13.1. Mass transfer by diffusion in a binary gas mixture

C_A = Concentration or molecules per unit volume of species A, kg/m³, and

$\dfrac{dC_A}{dx}$ = Concentration of gradient for species A; this acts as driving potential, kg/m³.

In Eqn. (13.19) – ve sign indicates that diffusion takes place in the direction *opposite* to that of increasing concentration.

The diffusion rate for species B is given by

$$N_B = \frac{m_B}{A} = -D_{BA} \frac{dC_B}{dx} \qquad ...(13.20)$$

It may be noted that diffusion coefficient D (*i.e.*, D_{AB} or D_{BA} in this case) is dependent upon the temperature, pressure and nature of the components of the system.

The Fick's law of diffusion is analogous to:

(*i*) Fourier law of heat conduction:

$$\frac{Q}{A} = -k\frac{dt}{dx};\text{ and}$$

(*ii*) Newton's law of viscosity :

$$\tau = \mu\frac{du}{dy}$$

By comparison of the above equations, we find that the Fourier equation describes the transport of heat energy due to temperature gradient, the shear equation describes the transport of momentum due to velocity gradient while

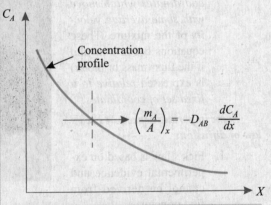

$$\left(\frac{m_A}{A}\right)_x = -D_{AB}\frac{dC_A}{dx}$$

Fig. 13.2. Concentration profile.

the Fick's law describes the mass transport due to concentration gradient.

As per Eqn. (13.19), the dimensions of diffusion coefficient D are

$$D = -\frac{N}{\left(\dfrac{dC}{dx}\right)} = \frac{(M/L^2T)}{[(M/L^3) \times (1/L)]} = \frac{L^2}{T} = m^2/s$$

Thus units of mass diffusion coefficient are identical to those of thermal diffusivity (α) and kinematic viscosity (ν). Thus, *diffusion coefficient is a transport property of the fluid.*

Further, by using perfect gas equation the Fick's law may be expressed in terms of partial pressures of species as follows:

For *species A*:
$$p_A = \rho_A R_A T = \rho_A \frac{GT}{M_A}$$

where,
p_A = Partial pressure of species A,

ρ_A = Density of species A,

G = Universal gas constant (= 8314 J/kg mole-K), and

M_A = Molecular weight of species A.

$\therefore$
$$\rho_A = C_A = \frac{p_A M_A}{GT}$$

Substituting the value of ρ_A in eqn. (13.19), we get

$$N_A = \frac{m_A}{A} = -D_{AB} \frac{d}{dx}\left[\frac{p_A M_A}{GT}\right]$$

or,
$$N_A = \frac{m_A}{A} = -D_{AB} \frac{M_A}{GT}\cdot\frac{dp_A}{dx} \qquad ...(13.21)$$

Similarly, for species B:

$$N_B = \frac{m_B}{A} = -D_{AB} \frac{M_B}{GT}\cdot\frac{dp_B}{dx} \qquad ...(13.22)$$

It may be noted that eqns. (13.21) and (13.22) are *valid only for isothermal diffusion.*

Eqns. (13.19) and (13.20) entail the following *restrictive conditions*:

(*i*) These are valid only when diffusion occurs due to concentration gradient and fail when diffusion occurs due to a temperature gradient, pressure gradient or an external force.

(*ii*) The mass or molar fluxes are measured *relative to coordinates which move with some average velocity* of the mixture. These equations become invalid if the flux (mass or molar) is expressed *relative to a fixed set of coordinates.*

Some important aspects of Fick's law of diffusion:

1. Fick's law is based on experimental evidence and cannot be derived from first principles.

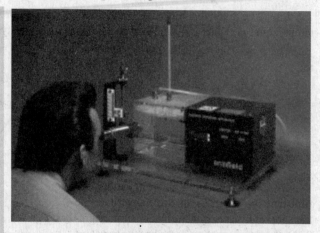

Determination of diffusion coefficient

2. Fick's law is valid for all matter irrespective of its state (*e.g.*, solid, liquid or gas).

3. The mass diffusion, besides *concentration gradient*, may occur due to a temperature gradient, a pressure gradient or an external force; however, while applying Fick's law it is assumed that these additional effects are either absent or negligibly small.

4. The movement of a diffusion substance is *in the direction of decreasing concentration*. In a diffusion process, the concentration difference is similar to temperature difference in a heat transfer process.

5. Diffusion coefficient (*D*), in general, is dependent upon temperature, pressure and nature of the system component; however, for ideal gases and dilute liquids it can be assumed to remain practically constant for a given range of temperature and pressure.

Mass diffusion coefficient:

By using kinetic theory of gases it is possible to predict the mass diffusion coefficient D_{AB}, for the binary mixture of two gases, *A* and *B*; it is of the form given below:

$$D_{AB} \sim \frac{T^{3/2}}{p} \qquad \text{...(13.23)}$$

or,
$$D_{AB} = 0.0043 \frac{(T^{3/2})}{p\,(V_A^{1/3} + V_B^{1/3})^2} \left[\frac{1}{M_A} + \frac{1}{M_B} \right]^{1/2} \qquad \text{...(13.24)}$$

p = Total pressure in atmosphere (= $p_A + p_B$),

T = Absolute temperature of the binary gas mixture, K,

V_A, V_B = Molecular volumes of constituent species at normal boiling points, cm^3/gm-mole, and

M_A, M_B = Molecular weights of species *A* and *B*.

It is evident from the above equation that diffusion coefficient (*D*) for gases depends upon temperature, pressure and other molecular properties of diffusing gases. At other temperature and pressure, we have

$$\frac{D_1}{D_2} = \left(\frac{T_1}{T_2} \right)^{3/2} \left(\frac{p_2}{p_1} \right) \qquad \text{...(13.25)}$$

D_{AB}, for liquids is wholly available from experiments. *Liquid mass diffusivities are considerably smaller than those for the gases.* This is due to high molecular density in the liquid phase. However, increase in D_{AB} with increase in temperature has been observed. *Diffusion in solids is even slower than in liquids*, only very little information in the experimental form is available.

An effective diffusivity in case of steady state diffusion through a non-diffusing, multicomponent mixture of constant composition is given by:

$$D = \frac{1}{\left(\dfrac{x_B}{D_{AB}} \right) + \left(\dfrac{x_C}{D_{AC}} \right) + \left(\dfrac{x_D}{D_{AD}} \right)} \qquad \text{...(13.26)}$$

where, x_B, x_C, x_D = Mole fraction composition of the mixture on a free basis, and

D_{AB}, D_{AC}, D_{AD} = Diffusivities of species *A* through *B*, *C*, *D*, etc.

For gas pairs of non-polar, non-reacting molecules, the diffusion coefficient is given by:

$$D_{AB} = 0.001858 \frac{T^{3/2}}{p\,(\sigma_{AB})^2\,\Omega} \left[\frac{1}{M_A} + \frac{1}{M_B} \right]^{1/2} \qquad \text{...(13.27)}$$

where, D_{AB} = Mass diffusivity of gas species *B* diffusing through another gas species *A*, cm^2/s,

T = Absolute temperature, K

p = Total pressure in atmospheres ($= p_A + p_B$),

σ_{AB} = Collision diameter in Å (Angstroms),

Ω = Collision integral, a dimensionless function of the temperature and the intermolecular potential field for one molecule of A and one molecule of B, and

M_A, M_B = Molecular weights of gas species A and B respectively.

The value of Ω (collision integral) is, in general, compiled as a function of $\dfrac{KT}{\varepsilon_{AB}}$, where K is Boltzmann's constant and ε_{AB} is the energy of molecular interaction for this binary system AB.

In case of a binary system, composed of non-polar molecule pairs, we have:

$$\sigma_{AB} = \frac{\sigma_A + \sigma_B}{2}$$

$$\varepsilon_{AB} = \sqrt{\varepsilon_A \, \varepsilon_B}$$

The diffusion coefficient for dilute liquids is calculated from the following empirical relation:

$$D_{AB} = \frac{T}{F \mu_B} \qquad \qquad ...(13.28)$$

where, D_{AB} = Diffusivity of solute A through a solvent B, m²/s,

T = Absolute temperature, K,

μ_B = Viscosity of solvent B, centipoise, and

F = A function of the molar volume of solute A, K.s/cm²; centipoise

The values of F may be obtained from the charts available.

13.5. GENERAL MASS DIFFUSION EQUATION IN STATIONARY MEDIA

The general differential equation for mass transfer of any species can be derived on the similar lines as outlined in chapter 2 for the derivation of heat transfer equations.

Consider a homogeneous medium consisting of binary mixture of species A and B. Let the medium be stationary (*i.e.*, the mass average or molar average velocity of the mixture is zero) and mass transfer may occur only by

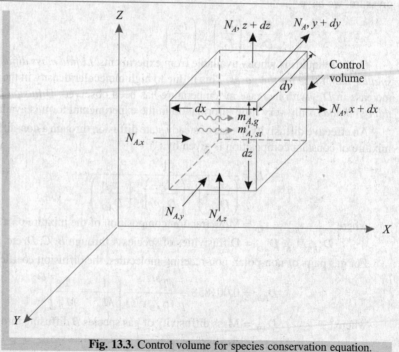

Fig. 13.3. Control volume for species conservation equation.

diffusion. Now, consider a differential control volume $dxdydz$ as shown in Fig. 13.3. The mass balance of species A diffusing through the control volume in the stationary medium B is given by:

Along X-direction :

Mass influx at the left face $= N_{A,x}.dy\,dz$ $\left(\text{where } N_A = \dfrac{m_A}{A}\right)$

Mass efflux at the right face $= N_{A,x+dx} \cdot dy\,dz$

$$= N_{A,x}.dy\,dz + \frac{\partial}{\partial x}[N_{A,x}\,dy\,dz]\,dx$$

$$= \left[N_{A,x} + \frac{\partial}{\partial x}(N_{A,x})\,dx\right]dy\,dz$$

Accumulations of mass of species A in the control volume due to its mass diffusion in the X-direction is given by the difference between the mass influx and mass efflux.

$\therefore$ Mass of species A accumulated/stored, due to diffusion, within the control volume

$$= N_{A,x}\,dy\,dz - \left[N_{A,x} + \frac{\partial}{\partial x}(N_{A,x})\,dx\right]dy\,dz$$

$$= -\frac{\partial}{\partial x}(N_{A,x})\,dx\,dy\,dz$$

Similarly the mass accumulation of species A along Y and Z directions is given by:

Along Y-direction $= -\dfrac{\partial}{\partial y}(N_{A,y})\,dx\,dy\,dz$

Along Z-direction $= -\dfrac{\partial}{\partial z}(N_{A,z})\,dx\,dy\,dz$

$\therefore$ Total or net accumulation of mass of species A

$$= -\left[\frac{\partial}{\partial x}(N_{A,x}) + \frac{\partial}{\partial y}(N_{A,y}) + \frac{\partial}{\partial z}(N_{A,z})\right]dx\,dy\,dz \qquad ...(13.29)$$

As a result of volumetric chemical reactions occurring throughout the medium, there may be a generation of species A within the control volume, which may be expressed as

$$m_{A,g} = N_{A,g} \cdot dx\,dy\,dz \qquad ...(13.30)$$

where, $N_{A,g}$ = rate of increase of the mass of species A due to chemical reactions per unit volume of the mixture, kg/s.m^3.

The total mass of species A accumulated in the control volume due to mass diffusion along the coordinate axes (Eqn. 13.29) and the mass generated within the control volume (Eqn. 13.30) serves to increase the mass concentration of species A. This increase is reflected by the time rate of change in mass concentration of species A in the control volume and is

$$= \frac{\partial C_A}{\partial \tau} \cdot dx\,dy\,dz \qquad ...(13.31)$$

Now, from mass-balance considerations, we have

$$-\left[\frac{\partial}{\partial x}(N_{A,x}) + \frac{\partial}{\partial y}(N_{A,y}) + \frac{\partial}{\partial z}(N_{A,z})\right]dx\,dy\,dz + N_{A,g}.dx\,dy\,dz = \frac{\partial C_A}{\partial \tau} \cdot dx\,dy\,dz$$

Dividing both sides by $dx\,dy\,dz$, we get

$$-\left[\frac{\partial}{\partial x}(N_{A,x}) + \frac{\partial}{\partial y}(N_{A,y}) + \frac{\partial}{\partial z}(N_{A,z})\right] + N_{A,g} = \frac{\partial C_A}{\partial \tau}$$

For a stationary medium, using Fick's law, the above Eqn. reduces to

$$\frac{\partial}{\partial x}\left(D_{AB}\frac{\partial C_A}{\partial x}\right) + \frac{\partial}{\partial y}\left(D_{AB}\frac{\partial C_A}{\partial y}\right) + \frac{\partial}{\partial z}\left(D_{AB}\frac{\partial C_A}{\partial z}\right) + N_{A,g} = \frac{\partial C_A}{\partial \tau} \qquad ...(13.32)$$

If D_{AB} and C are constant the above equation becomes

$$\frac{\partial^2 C_A}{\partial x^2} + \frac{\partial^2 C_A}{\partial y^2} + \frac{\partial^2 C_A}{\partial z^2} + \frac{N_{A,g}}{D_{AB}} = \frac{1}{D_{AB}}\frac{\partial C_A}{\partial \tau} \qquad ...(13.33)$$

The above equation is analogous to the heat conduction equation. A few typical boundary conditions are:

1. *Specified boundary concentration:* $\qquad C_A = C_{A0}$ at $x = 0$

2. *Impermeable surface at boundary:* $\qquad \dfrac{\partial C_A}{\partial x} = 0$ at $x = 0$

3. *Specified mass flux at a surface:* $\qquad N_A = \dfrac{m_A}{A} = -D_{AB}\dfrac{\partial C_A}{\partial x}$ at $x = 0$

4. *Specified mass transfer coefficient* $\qquad N_A = h_m(C_{As} - C_{A\infty})$
   (convection) at surface:

   where, h_m = Convective mass transfer coefficient,

   C_{As} = Concentrations in the fluid adjacent to the surface, and

   $C_{A\infty}$ = Bulk concentration in the fluid stream.

13.6. STEADY STATE DIFFUSION THROUGH A PLAIN MEMBRANE

Consider mass diffusion of fluid A through a plain membrane whose thickness L is small in comparison with other dimensions. The mass concentrations of the fluid at the opposite wall faces are C_{A1} and C_{A2} respectively. Considering the diffusion along X-axis (Fig. 13.4), then the controlling equation is

$$\frac{d^2 C_A}{dx^2} = 0$$

Upon integration, we have

$$\frac{dC_A}{dx} = C_1 \text{ and}$$

$$C_A = C_1 x + C_2 \qquad ...(i)$$

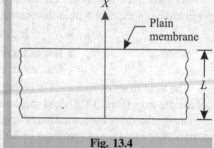

Fig. 13.4

Using the boundary conditions, we have

$$C_A = C_{A1} \text{ at } x = 0, \quad C_A = C_{A2} \text{ at } x = L$$

$$\therefore \qquad C_2 = C_{A1} \text{ and } C_1 = \left[\frac{C_{A2} - C_{A1}}{L}\right]$$

Substituting these values in eqn. (i), we get

$$C_A = (C_{A2} - C_{A1})\frac{x}{L} + C_{A1}$$

The mass transfer rate is given by

$$\frac{m_A}{A} = -D\frac{dC_A}{dx}$$

$$= -D_1\frac{d}{dx}\left[(C_{A2} - C_{A1})\frac{x}{L} + C_{A1}\right]$$

$$= -D \left(\frac{C_{A2} - C_{A1}}{L} \right)$$

or, $$\frac{m_A}{A} = \frac{D}{L} (C_{A1} - C_{A2}) \qquad \qquad ...(13.34)$$

or, $$\frac{m_A}{A} = \frac{(C_{A1} - C_{A2})}{(L/D)}$$

(L/D) is known as *diffusional resistance*.

The above expression can be used for solving the problems on composite membranes.

The diffusion rate in the radial direction of a *cylindrical system* of inner and outer radii of r_1 and r_2 respectively and length L is

$$m_A = \frac{D (C_{A1} - C_{A2})}{\Delta x} A_m \qquad \qquad ...(13.35)$$

where, $$\Delta x = (r_2 - r_1) \text{ and } A_m = \frac{2\pi L (r_2 - r_1)}{\ln (r_2 / r_1)}$$

Further, $$\Delta x = (r_2 - r_1) \text{ and } A_m = 4\pi r_1 r_2$$

... in case of a spherical system.

13.7. STEADY STATE EQUIMOLAR COUNTER DIFFUSION

Equimolar counter diffusion between species A and B of a binary gas mixture is defined as an *isothermal diffusion process in which each molecule of component A is replaced by each molecule of constituent B and vice-versa.* Consider two large chambers A and B, connected by a passage (Fig. 13.5) in such a way that each molecule of gas A is replaced by a molecule of gas B, and *vice versa*. The total pressure $p = p_A + p_B$ is uniform throughout and the species concentrations are maintained constant in each of the chambers.

Using Fick's law, the molar diffusion rates of species A and B are given by

$$N_A = \frac{m_A}{A} = -D_{AB} \frac{A}{G.T} \cdot \frac{dp_A}{dx} \qquad \qquad ...(13.36)$$

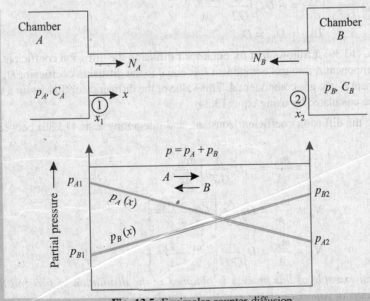

Fig. 13.5. Equimolar counter diffusion.

and,
$$N_B = \frac{m_B}{A} = -D_{BA}\frac{A}{G.T}\cdot\frac{dp_B}{dx} \qquad ...(13.37)$$

where, p_A, p_B = Partial pressures, and

N_A, N_B = Molar diffusion rates of the gases/species A and B respectively.

It is evident from Fig. 13.5 that species A and B are diffusing in the direction of their decreasing concentration gradient (*i.e.*, opposite direction).

As per Dalton's law of partial pressures, the total pressure (p) is equal to the sum of the partial pressures of the constituents (p_A, p_B).

i.e.,
$$p = p_A + p_B$$

Differentiating with respect to x, we obtain
$$\frac{dp}{dx} = \frac{dp_A}{dx} + \frac{dp_B}{dx}$$

Since the total pressure of the system remains constant under steady conditions, therefore,
$$\frac{dp}{dx} = \frac{dp_A}{dx} + \frac{dp_B}{dx} = 0$$

or,
$$\frac{dp_A}{dx} = -\frac{dp_B}{dx} \qquad ...(13.38)$$

Further, under steady state conditions, the total molar flux, relative to stationary coordinates, must be zero. Thus,
$$N_A + N_B = 0$$

or,
$$N_A = -N_B$$

or,
$$-D_{AB}\frac{A}{G.T}\cdot\frac{dp_A}{dx} = +D_{BA}\frac{A}{G.T}\cdot\frac{dp_B}{dx}$$

Replacing $\dfrac{dp_B}{dx}$ in terms of $\dfrac{dp_A}{dx}$ as given by eqn. (13.38), we have
$$-D_{AB}\frac{A}{G.T}\cdot\frac{dp_A}{dx} = -D_{BA}\frac{A}{G.T}\cdot\frac{dp_B}{dx}$$

or,
$$D_{AB} = D_{BA} = D \qquad ...(13.39)$$

From eqn. (13.39) it follows that for equimolar diffusion the diffusion coefficient D_{AB} for diffusion of gas component A into gas component B is equal to the diffusion coefficient D_{BA} for diffusion of gas component B into gas component A. This value of the diffusion coefficient for a binary mixture of gases can be calculated by using eqn. (13.24).

Assuming the diffusion coefficient constant, and integrating Eqn. (13.36) between two points, we get,
$$N_A = \frac{m_A}{A} = -D\frac{A}{G.T}\int_1^2\frac{dp_A}{dx}$$

or,
$$N_A = \frac{m_A}{A} = D\frac{A}{G.T}\left[\frac{p_{A1} - p_{A2}}{x_2 - x_1}\right] \qquad ...(13.40)$$

and,
$$N_B = \frac{m_B}{A} = D\frac{A}{G.T}\left[\frac{p_{B1} - p_{B2}}{x_2 - x_1}\right] \qquad ...(13.41)$$

A *practical example of this process is obtained in the distillation of two constituents whose molar latent heats of vaporisation are essentially equal.*

13.8. ISOTHERMAL EVAPORATION OF WATER INTO AIR FROM A SURFACE

Let us consider isothermal evaporation of water from a surface and its subsequent diffusion through the stagnant layer of air over it as shown in Fig. 13.6. For the analysis of this type of mass diffusion following **assumptions** are made:

1. The system is under steady state and isothermal conditions.
2. The total pressure within the system remains constant.
3. Air as well as water vapour behaves as an ideal gas.
4. There is a slight air movement over the top of the tank to remove the water vapour which diffuses to that point; however, this movement does not disturb the concentration profile of air in the tank.
5. The water concentration at the surface of water is much more compared to that at the top of the tank (*i.e.*, $C_{w1} > C_{w2}$ or $C_{a2} > C_{a1}$).

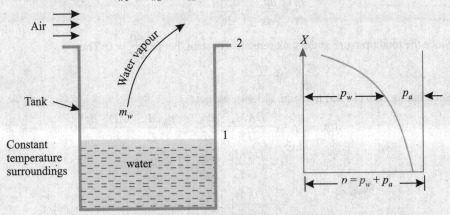

Fig. 13.6. Diffusion of water vapour through air.

Under steady state conditions the upward movement of water must be balanced by a downward diffusion of air so that concentration at any distance from the water surface remains constant. Mass diffusion of air in the downward direction is given by

$$(m_a)_{down} = -D\,\frac{A\,m_a}{GT}\cdot\frac{dp_a}{dx} \qquad\qquad ...(13.42)$$

where, A = Cross-sectional area of the tank, and

$\dfrac{dp_a}{dx}$ = Partial pressure gradient of air.

Since, there is no mass movement of air downward at the surface of a water, there will be a bulk mass movement upwards with a velocity just large enough to compensate for the mass diffusion of the air downward.

Bulk mass transfer of air upward, $(m_a)_{up} = -\rho_a\,Au = -pa\,\dfrac{M_a}{GT}\,Au$ $\qquad$ ...(13.43)

where, u = Bulk velocity upward.

Equating eqns. (13.42) and (13.43), we get

$$D\,\frac{A M_a}{G.T}\cdot\frac{dp_A}{dx} = p_a\,\frac{M_a}{GT}\,Au$$

or, $$u = \frac{D}{p_a}\cdot\frac{dp_a}{dx}$$

The total mass transport of water vapour, $(m_w)_{total}$

$$= \text{Upward mass diffusion of water, } (m_w)_{diffusion} + \text{water vapour}$$
carried along with bulk movement of air, $(m_w)_{bulk}$

or,
$$(m_w)_{total} = -D \frac{A M_w}{G.T} \cdot \frac{dp_w}{dx} + \rho_w Au$$

$$= -D \frac{A M_w}{G.T} \cdot \frac{dp_w}{dx} + \frac{p_w M_w}{G.T} Au$$

or,
$$(m_w)_{total} = -D \frac{A M_w}{G.T} \cdot \frac{dp_w}{dx} - \frac{p_w M_w}{G.T} \cdot \frac{AD}{p_a} \cdot \frac{dp_a}{dx} \qquad ...(13.44)$$

According to Dalton's law of partial pressures,

$$p = p_a + p_w$$

Differentiating, we get

$$\frac{dp}{dx} = \frac{dp_a}{dx} + \frac{dp_w}{dx}$$

Since the total pressure in the tank remains constant, hence $\dfrac{dp}{dx} = 0$. Thus

$$\frac{dp_a}{dx} = -\frac{dp_w}{dx} \qquad\qquad ...(13.45)$$

Substituting eqn. (13.45) into eqn. (13.44), we get

$$(m_w)_{total} = -\frac{DA M_w}{G.T.} \cdot \frac{dp_w}{dx} - \frac{p_w M_w}{G.T.} \cdot \frac{AD}{p_a} \cdot \frac{dp_w}{dx}$$

$$= -\frac{DA M_w}{G.T.} \cdot \frac{dp_w}{dx} \left(1 + \frac{p_w}{p_a} \right)$$

$$= -\frac{DA M_w}{G.T.} \cdot \frac{dp_w}{dx} \left(\frac{p_a + p_w}{p_a} \right)$$

or,
$$(m_w)_{total} = -\frac{DA M_w}{G.T.} \cdot \frac{dp_w}{dx} \left(\frac{p}{p - p_w} \right) \qquad ...(13.46)$$

Equation (13.46) is known as **Stefan's law for diffusion** *of an ideal gaseous component through a practically stagnant and ideal constituent of the binary system.*

Integrating eqn. (13.46) between x_1 and x_2, we have

$$(m_w)_{total} \int_{x_1}^{x_2} dx = -\frac{DA M_w}{G.T.} \cdot p \int_{p_{w1}}^{p_{w2}} \frac{dp_w}{p - p_w}$$

or,
$$(m_w)_{total} (x_2 - x_1) = \frac{DA M_w}{G.T} p \ln \left[\frac{p_{w2} - p}{p_{w1} - p} \right]$$

or,
$$(m_w)_{total} = \frac{DA M_w}{G.T} \cdot \frac{p}{(x_2 - x_1)} \ln \left[\frac{p - p_{w2}}{p - p_{w1}} \right] \qquad ...(13.47)$$

or,
$$(m_w)_{total} = \frac{DA M_w}{G.T} \cdot \frac{p}{(x_2 - x_1)} \ln \left(\frac{p_{a2}}{p_{a1}} \right) \qquad ...[13.47\ (a)]$$

The distribution of partial pressures of air and water vapour with distance x in the medium is illustrated in Fig. 13.7.

Introducing the concept of *log mean partial pressure of air* (*LMPa*), we have

$$LMPa = \frac{p_{a2} - p_{a1}}{\ln (p_{a2} / p_{a1})}$$

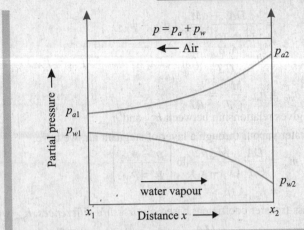

Fig. 13.7. Distribution of partial pressures of air and water vapour.

$$= \frac{(p - p_{w2}) - (p - p_{w1})}{\ln (p_{a2} / p_{a1})}$$

or, $\ln \left(\dfrac{p_{a2}}{p_{a1}} \right) = \dfrac{p_{a2} - p_{a1}}{LMPa} = \dfrac{p_{w1} - p_{w2}}{LMPa}$ ...(13.48)

The equation (13.47) may be rewritten as

$$(m_w)_{total} = \frac{DAM_w}{G.T.} \cdot \frac{p}{(x_2 - x_1)} \cdot \frac{p_{a2} - p_{a1}}{LMPa} \qquad ...(13.49)$$

$$= \frac{DAM_w}{G.T.} \cdot \frac{p}{x_2 - x_1} \cdot \frac{p_{w1} - p_{w2}}{LMPa} \qquad ...(13.50)$$

When there is no appreciable change in the pressure of water vapour compared with the total pressure of water vapour and air mixture, then the mass of water vapour transported may be calculated without appreciable error by using arithmetic mean partial pressure of air $\left(\dfrac{p_{a1} + p_{a2}}{2} \right)$ instead of log mean partial pressure.

13.9. MASS TRANSFER COEFFICIENT

Mass transfer coefficient h_{mc}, similar to convective heat transfer coefficient, h may also be defined of species A as follows:

$$m_A = \frac{DA (C_{A1} - C_{A2})}{(x_2 - x_1)} = h_{mc} . A (C_{A1} - C_{A2}) \qquad ...(13.51)$$

where, h_{mc} = Diffusion mass transfer coefficient of species A based on concentration difference, m/s

$$= \frac{D}{x_2 - x_1},$$

A = Area of cross-section, m², and

C_{A1}, C_{A2} = Fluid concentrations at the two faces.

The mass transfer coefficient can also be expressed in terms of partial pressure differences for species A.

$$m_A = DA \frac{M_A}{G.T} \frac{(p_{A1} - p_{A2})}{(x_2 - x_1)}$$

$$= \frac{DA}{(x_2 - x_1)} \cdot \frac{M_A}{G.T} (p_{A1} - p_{A2})$$

$$= h_{mc} \frac{A.M_A}{G.T} (p_{A1} - p_{A2}) = h_{mp} A (p_{A1} - p_{A2})$$

or,
$$h_{mp} = h_{mc} \cdot \frac{M_A}{G.T} = \frac{h_{mc}}{RT} \qquad \qquad ...(13.52)$$

Equation (13.52) gives relationship between h_{mp} and h_{mc}.

For diffusion of water vapour through a layer of stagnant air, we have

$$m_w = \frac{DA}{G.T} \frac{M_w P}{(x_2 - x_1)} \ln \left[\frac{p - p_{w2}}{p - p_{w1}} \right]$$

$$= h_{mp} A (p_{w1} - p_{w2})$$

Therefore, the mass transfer coefficient based on *pressure differences*, h_{mp} works out to be

$$h_{mp} = \frac{D p}{(x_2 - x_1)(p_{w1} - p_{w2})} \cdot \frac{M_w}{G.T} \ln \left[\frac{p - p_{w2}}{p - p_{w1}} \right] \qquad ...(13.53)$$

The corresponding expression for mass transfer coefficient based upon *concentration difference* is given by:

$$h_{mc} = \frac{D p}{(x_2 - x_1)(p_{w1} - p_{w2})} \cdot \ln \left[\frac{p - p_{w2}}{p - p_{w1}} \right] \qquad ...(13.54)$$

13.10. CONVECTIVE MASS TRANSFER

Whereas molecular diffusion mass transfer is analogous to conduction heat transfer (during molecular diffusion, the bulk velocities are insignificant and only diffusion velocities are considered), the convective mass transfer is analogous to convective heat transfer (this is particularly true for low concentrations of mass in the fluid and low mass transfer rates). Mass transfer by convection takes place in cases *where the bulk velocity is appreciable or when both the species, in a binary mixture, are moving with significant velocities.* Mass convection, like heat convection, may occur under *free* or *forced* conditions. The buoyancy force causing circulation in free convection mass transfer results from the differences in density of the vapour-air mixtures of varying compositions.

The evaporation of alcohol is an example of *free convection* mass transfer, whereas the evaporation of water from an ocean when *air blows over it* is a case of *forced convection* mass transfer.

The fluid flow may be *laminar* or *turbulent*. If the fluid flow is laminar then all of the transport between the surface and moving fluid will be by molecular means. On the other hand, if the fluid flow is turbulent, there will be physical movement of the material across streamlines, transported by eddies present

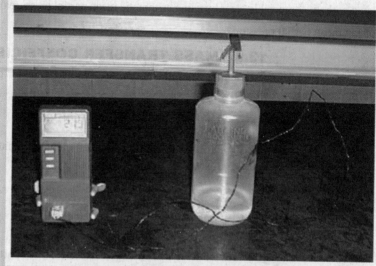

When alcohol is skirted on skin, your skin feels cooler. This is because as the alcohol evaporates from the skin, it removes heat from the skin and transfers it to the air.

in the turbulent flow. As in the case of heat transfer, higher mass transfer rates are associated with turbulent conditions. Therefore, in any convective situation, the distribution between laminar or turbulent flow will be an important consideration.

Mass transfer by convection involves the transportation of material between a boundary surface and a moving fluid or between two immiscible moving fluids. It is expressed as :

$$\frac{m_A}{A} = h_m \ (\Delta C_A) \qquad \qquad ...(13.55)$$

where,　　　$\dfrac{m_A}{A}$ = Mass flux which occurs in the direction of decreasing concentration,

and

h_m = Mass transfer coefficient of component A.

13.11. CORRELATIONS FOR CONVECTIVE MASS TRANSFER

The equations for conservation of momentum and energy for the boundary layer development on a flat plate are:

$$u \frac{\partial u}{\partial x} + v \frac{\partial u}{\partial y} = v \frac{\partial^2 u}{\partial y^2}$$

and

$$u \frac{\partial t}{\partial x} + v \frac{\partial t}{\partial y} = \alpha \frac{\partial^2 t}{\partial y^2}$$

Similarly, the concentration equation may be written as

$$u \frac{\partial C}{\partial x} + v \frac{\partial C}{\partial y} = D \frac{\partial^2 C}{\partial y^2}$$

where,　　　C = Concentration of the component which is diffusing through the boundary layer, and

D = Diffusion coefficient.

In the correlations the following parameters are used:

1. *Prandtl number* (*Pr*) :

Prandtl number, $Pr = \dfrac{v}{\alpha}$. It forms the connecting link between velocity and temperature profiles; these profiles become identical when $Pr = 1$.

2. *Schmidt number* (*Sc*) :

Schmidt number, $(Sc) = \dfrac{v}{D}$. It forms the connecting link between velocity and concentration profiles; these profiles show the identical behaviour when $Sc = 1$.

3. *Lewis number* (*Le*) :

Lewis number, $Le = \dfrac{\alpha}{D}$. It forms a connecting link between the temperature and concentration profiles; these profiles become identical when $Le = 1$.

4. *Sherwood number* (*Sh*) :

Sherwood number,　　　$Sh = \dfrac{h_{mc} \cdot x}{D} = f \ (Re.Sc)$ 　　　...(13.56)

Based on analogy with heat transfer, the following *empirical relations*, under different flow conditions, have been suggested :

A. Flow over a flat plate :

The local mass transfer coefficient for laminar and turbulent boundary layer flows past a flat plate oriented at zero angle of incidence is given by

$$Sh_x = \frac{h_m \cdot x}{D} = 0.332 \ (Re_x)^{0.8} \ (Sc)^{0.33} \qquad \text{(For laminar flow)} \quad ...(13.57)$$

$$Sh_x = \frac{h_m \cdot x}{D} = 0.0288 \ (Re_x)^{0.8} \ (Sc)^{0.33} \qquad \text{(For turbulent flow)} \quad ...(13.58)$$

In case of *average values*, the values will be *doubled*.

For mixed boundary layer conditions with transition occurring at a critical Reynolds number of $Re_c = 5 \times 10^5$, the correlation is

$$\overline{Sh} = (0.037 \ Re_L^{0.8} - 870) \ Sc^{0.33} \qquad\qquad ...(13.59)$$

B. Flow in tubes :

Gilliland proposed the following correlation for *forced mass convection through a tube* :

$$Sh = 0.023 \ (Re)^{0.83} \ (Sc)^{0.44} \qquad\qquad ...(13.60)$$

for $2000 < Re < 35 \times 10^3$ and $0.6 < Sc < 2.5$

Example 13.1. *The molecular weights of the two components A and B of a gas mixture are 24 and 28 respectively. The molecular weight of gas mixture is found to be 30. If the mass concentration of the mixture is 1.2 kgm³, determine the following:*

(i) Molar fractions,   *(ii) Mass fractions, and*

(iii) Total pressure if the temperature of the mixture is 290 K.

Solution. *Given:* $M_A = 24$, $M_B = 48$, $M = 30$, $\rho = 1.2$ kg/m³, $T = 290$ K

Mole concentration of the mixture, $C = \dfrac{\rho}{M} = \dfrac{1.2}{30} = 0.04$

Also, $C_A + C_B = C$ ...[Eqn. (13.5)]

or, $C_A + C_B = 0.04$ ...(i)

and, $\rho_A = M_A \ C_A = 24 \ C_A;\ \rho_B = M_B \ C_B = 48 \ C_B$

But, $\rho_A + \rho_B = \rho$ ...[Eqn. (13.4)]

$\therefore$ $24 \ C_A + 48 \ C_B = 1.2$ ...(ii)

Solving eqns. (i) and (ii), we get

$\therefore$ $C_A = 0.03$ kg mole/m³   and $C_B = 0.01$ kg mole/m³

$\rho_A = M_A \ C_A = 24 \times 0.03 = 0.72$ kg/m³; and

$\rho_B = M_B \ C_B = 48 \times 0.01 = 0.48$ kg/m³

(i) Molar fractions, x_A **and** x_B**:**

$$x_A = \frac{C_A}{C} = \frac{0.03}{0.04} = \mathbf{0.75} \ \textbf{(Ans.)}$$

$$x_B = \frac{C_B}{C} = \frac{0.01}{0.04} = \mathbf{0.25} \ \textbf{(Ans.)}$$

(ii) Mass fractions, m_A^***,** m_B^* **:**

$$m_A^* = \frac{\rho_A}{\rho} = \frac{0.72}{1.2} = \mathbf{0.6} \ \textbf{(Ans.)}$$

$$m_B^* = \frac{\rho_B}{\rho} = \frac{0.48}{1.2} = \mathbf{0.4} \ \textbf{(Ans.)}$$

(iii) **Total pressure at** $T = 290$ K, p:

Using the perfect gas equation for the mixture, we get

$$pV = mRT$$

or,

$$p = \frac{m}{V} RT = \rho \frac{G}{M} T$$

[G (universal gas constant) $= MR = 8.314$ kJ/kg mole K]

or,

$$p = 1.2 \times \frac{8.314}{30} \times 290 = \mathbf{96.4 \ kPa} \ \textbf{(Ans.)}$$

Example 13.2. *A vessel contains a binary mixture of O_2 and N_2 with partial pressures in the ratio 0.21 and 0.79 at 15°C. The total pressure of the mixture is 1.1 bar. Calculate the following:*

(i) Molar concentrations,   *(ii) Mass densities,*

(iii) Mass fractions, and   *(iv) Molar fractions of each species.*

Solution. *Given :* $T = 15 + 273 = 288$ K, $p = 1.1$ bar $= 1.1 \times 10^5$ N/m^2.

(i) **Molar concentrations,** C_{O_2} **and** C_{N_2} **:**

$$C_{O_2} = \frac{p_{O_2}}{GT} = \frac{0.21 \times 1.1 \times 10^5}{8314 \times 288} = \mathbf{0.00965 \ kg \ mole/m^3} \ \textbf{(Ans.)}$$

...[Eqn. (13.8)]

$$C_{N_2} = \frac{p_{N_2}}{GT} = \frac{0.79 \times 1.1 \times 10^5}{8314 \times 288} = \mathbf{0.0363 \ kg \ mole/m^3} \ \textbf{(Ans.)}$$

(ii) **Mass densities** ρ_{O_2} **and** ρ_{N_2} **:**

The mass densities of O_2 and N_2, as calculated from the relation $\rho = MC$ [Eqn. (13.1)] are:

$$\rho_{O_2} = M_{O_2} \times C_{O_2} = 32 \times 0.00965 = \mathbf{0.309 \ kg/m^3} \ \textbf{(Ans.)}$$

$$\rho_{N_2} = M_{N_2} \times C_{N_2} = 28 \times 0.0363 = \mathbf{1.016 \ kg/m^3} \ \textbf{(Ans.)}$$

(iii) **Mass fractions,** x_{O_2} **and** x_{N_2} **:**

Now, overall mass density, $\rho = \rho_{O_2} + \rho_{N_2}$

$$= 0.309 + 1.016 = 1.325 \ \text{kg/m}^3$$

$$x_{O_2} = \frac{\rho_{O_2}}{\rho} = \frac{0.309}{1.325} = \mathbf{0.233} \ \textbf{(Ans.)}$$

$$x_{N_2} = \frac{\rho_{N_2}}{\rho} = \frac{1.016}{1.325} = \mathbf{0.767} \ \textbf{(Ans.)}$$

(iv) **Molar fractions of each species,** $m_{O_2}^*$, $m_{N_2}^*$ **:**

$$C = C_{O_2} + C_{N_2} = 0.00965 + 0.0363 = 0.046 \ \text{kg mole/m}^3$$

$$\therefore \quad m_{O_2}^* = \frac{C_{O_2}}{C} = \frac{0.00965}{0.046} = \mathbf{0.21} \ \textbf{(Ans.)}$$

$$m_{N_2}^* = \frac{C_{N_2}}{C} = \frac{0.0363}{0.046} = \mathbf{0.79} \ \textbf{(Ans.)}$$

(The molar fractions are equal to the partial pressures fraction).

Example 13.3. *From the data given below, calculate the diffusion coefficient for NH_3 in air at 27°C temperature and atmospheric pressure:*

NH_3 (Gas A) : Molecular weight = 17   *Molecular volume = 26.43 cm^3/gm mole*

Air (Gas B): Molecular weight = 29   *Molecular volume = 30.6 cm^3/gm mole.*

Solution. *Given:* $M_A = 17$, $V_A = 26.43$ cm³/gm mole; $M_B = 29$, $V_B = 30.6$ cm³/gm mole, $T = 27 + 273 = 300$ K, $p = 1$ atmosphere.

Diffusion coefficient, D_{AB}:

The diffusion coefficient for binary gaseous mixture is calculated from the relaton:

$$D_{AB} = 0.0043 \frac{(T)^{3/2}}{p\,(V_A^{1/3} + V_B^{1/3})^2} = \left[\frac{1}{M_A} + \frac{1}{M_B}\right]^{1/2} \qquad \text{...[Eqn. (13.24)]}$$

Substituting the appropriate values, we obtain,

$$D_{AB} = 0.0043 \frac{(300)^{3/2}}{1\,(26.43^{1/3} + 30.6^{1/3})^2} \left[\frac{1}{17} + \frac{1}{29}\right]^{1/2}$$

$$= 0.0043 \times \frac{5196.15}{(2.978 + 3.128)^2} \, [(0.0588 + 0.0345)]^{1/2} = \mathbf{0.183 \ cm^2/s.} \quad \textbf{(Ans.)}$$

Example 13.4. *From the following data calculate the diffusion coefficient of CO_2 in air at a temperature of 25°C and atmospheric pressure.*

CO_2 *(Gas A):* $\sigma = 3.996$ Å ; $\dfrac{\varepsilon}{K} = 190$ K

Air (Gas B): $\sigma = 3.167$ Å ; $\dfrac{\varepsilon}{K} = 97$ K

The table given below may be used to estimate collision integral Ω.

$\dfrac{kT}{\varepsilon}$	2.00	2.10	2.20	2.30
Ω	1.075	1.057	1.041	1.026

Solution. *Given:* $\sigma_A = 3.996$ Å, $\dfrac{\varepsilon_A}{K} = 190$ K, $M_A = 44$; $\sigma_B = 3.167$ Å, $\dfrac{\varepsilon_B}{K} = 97$ K, $M_B = 29$

Diffusion Coefficient, D_{AB}:

The diffusion coefficient may be calculated using the following relation :

$$D_{AB} = 0.001858 \frac{T^{3/2}}{p\,(\sigma_{AB})^2 \Omega} \left[\frac{1}{M_A} + \frac{1}{M_B}\right]^{1/2} \qquad \text{...[Eqn. (13.27)]}$$

Here, $\sigma_{AB} = \dfrac{\sigma_A + \sigma_B}{2} = \dfrac{3.996 + 3.167}{2} = 3.5815$ Å

$$\frac{\varepsilon_{AB}}{K} = \sqrt{\frac{\varepsilon_A}{K} \times \frac{\varepsilon_B}{K}} = \sqrt{190 \times 97} = 135.76 \text{ K}$$

or, $\dfrac{\varepsilon_{AB}}{KT} = \dfrac{135.76}{(25 + 273)} = 0.4556$

or, $\dfrac{KT}{\varepsilon_{AB}} = \dfrac{1}{0.4556} = 2.195$

Corresponding to $\dfrac{KT}{\varepsilon_{AB}} = 2.195$, the collision integral Ω

$$= 1.057 - \left[\frac{1.057 - 1.041}{2.20 - 2.10}\right] \times (2.195 - 2.10) = 1.0418$$

Substituting the various values in the above equation, we get

$$D_{AB} = 0.001858 \times \frac{(298)^{3/2}}{1 \times (3.5815)^2 \times 1.0418} \left[\frac{1}{44} + \frac{1}{29}\right]^{1/2}$$

$$= 0.001858 \times \frac{5144.28}{13.363}(0.02273 + 0.03448)^{1/2} = \textbf{0.171 cm}^2\textbf{/s} \ \ (\textbf{Ans.})$$

Example 13.5. *A steel rectangular container having walls 16 mm thick is used to store gaseous hydrogen at elevated pressure. The molar concentrations of hydrogen in the steel at the inside and outside surfaces are 1.2 kg mole/m³ and zero respectively. Assuming the diffusion coefficient for hydrogen in steel as 0.248×10^{-12} m²/s, calculate the molar diffusion flux for hydrogen through the steel.*

Solution. Given: $L = 16$ mm $= 0.016$ m, $C_{A1} = 1.2$ kg mole/m³, $C_{A2} = 0$, $D_A = 0.248 \times 10^{-12}$ m²/s.

Molar diffusion flux rate, N_A:

Assuming one dimensional and steady state condition, the molar diffusion flux rate through the steel is given by Fick's law of diffusion.

$$N_A = \frac{m_A}{A} = D_A\left(\frac{C_A - C_{A2}}{L}\right) \qquad \text{...Eqn. (13.34)}$$

$$= 0.248 \times 10^{-12}\left(\frac{1.2 - 0}{0.016}\right) = \textbf{18.6} \times \textbf{10}^{-12} \textbf{ kg mole/s.m}^2.$$

Example 13.6. *Hydrogen gas is maintained at pressures of 2.4 bar and 1 bar on opposite sides of a plastic membrane 0.3 mm thick. The binary diffusion coefficient of hydrogen in the plastic is 8.6×10^{-8} m²/s and solubility of hydrogen in the membrane is 0.00145 kg mole/m³-bar. Calculate, under uniform temperature conditions of 24°C, the following:*

(i) *Molar concentrations of hydrogen at the opposite faces of the membrane, and*

(ii) *Molar and mass diffusion flux of hydrogen through the membrane.*

Solution. *Given*: Solubility, $S = 0.00145$ kg mole/m³-bar; Pressures = 2.4 bar and 1 bar, $L = 0.3$ mm $= 0.0003$ m; $D = 8.6 \times 10^{-8}$ m²/s.

(i) **Molar concentrations of hydrogen, C_{h1} and C_{h2}:**

The molar concentration (C), the total pressure (p) and solubility (S) of the diffusing gas are related to each other by the relation,

$$C = S.p$$

Therefore, molar concentrations of *hydrogen* at the opposite faces of the plastic membrane are:

$$C_{h1} = 0.00145 \times 2.4 = \textbf{0.00348 kg mole/m}^3 \ (\textbf{Ans.})$$
$$C_{h2} = 0.00145 \times 1 = \textbf{0.00145 kg mole/m}^3. \ (\textbf{Ans.})$$

(ii) **Molar and mass diffusion flux:**

The molar diffusion flux of hydrogen through the *membrane* is calculated from the relation,

$$N_h = \frac{m_h}{A} = \frac{D(C_{h1} - C_{h2})}{(x_2 - x_1)} = D\left(\frac{C_{h1} - C_{h2}}{L}\right)$$

(The subscripts h and p refer to hydrogen and plastic, respectively)

or, $$N_h = 8.6 \times 10^{-8}\left(\frac{0.00348 - 0.00145}{0.0003}\right) = \textbf{58.19} \times \textbf{10}^{-8} \textbf{ kg mole/s - m}^2. \ (\textbf{Ans.})$$

(where, M_h = molecular weight of hydrogen = 2 kg/kg mole)

Example 13.7. *Ammonia and air are in equimolar diffusion in a cylindrical tube of 3.5 mm diameter and 25 m length. The total pressure is 1 atmosphere and the temperature is 27°C. One end of the tube is connected to a large reservoir of ammonia and the other end of the tube is open to the atmosphere. If the mass diffusivity for the mixture is 0.3 × 10⁻⁴ m²/s, calculate the mass transfer rates of ammonia and air through the tube.*

Solution. *Given:* $(x_2 - x_1) = 25$ m; $p_{A1} = 1$ atmosphere $= 1.0132 \times 10^5$ N/m²; $p_{A2} = 0$; $D = 0.3 \times 10^{-4}$ m²/s $= 0.3 \times 10^{-4} \times 3600 = 0.108$ m²/h; $T = 27 + 273 = 300$ K.

Let the suffixes A and B refer to NH_3 and air respectively.

Mass flow rates of NH_3 and air through the tube:

Using eqn. (13.40), we get the rate of diffusion N_A as

$$N_A = \frac{DA}{G.T}\left[\frac{p_{A1} - p_{A2}}{x_2 - x_1}\right] \qquad (\because D_{AB} = D_{BA} = D)$$

$$= \frac{0.108 \times \left(\frac{\pi}{4} \times 0.0035^2\right)}{8314 \times (27 + 273)}\left[\frac{1.0132 \times 10^5 - 0}{25}\right]$$

$$= 1.688 \times 10^{-9} \text{ kg mole/h}$$

Since molecular weights of NH_3 and air are 17 and 29 respectively, therefore,

The mass flow rate of NH_3

$$= 1.688 \times 10^{-9} \times 17$$

$$= \mathbf{28.696 \times 10^{-9} \text{ kg/h (Ans.)}}$$

The mass flow rate of air

$$= -1.688 \times 10^{-9} \times 29$$

$$= -\mathbf{48.952 \times 10^{-9} \text{ kg/h (Ans.)}}$$

$(\because N_A + N_B = 0$ or $N_B = -N_A$, where A and B are species of the binary gas mixture).

Example 13.8. *A 30 mm deep pan is filled with water to a level of 15 mm and is exposed to dry air at 40°C. Assuming the mass diffusivity as 0.25 × 10⁻⁴ m²/s, calculate the time required for all the water to evaporate.*

Solution. *Given:* $(x_2 - x_1) = 15$ mm $= 0.015$ m; $T = 40 + 273 = 313$K; $D = 0.25 \times 10^{-4}$ m²/s.

In this case we have,

p_{w1} = Partial pressure of water vapour corresponding to saturation temperature of 40°C = 0.07384 bar (at the water surface, *i.e.*, $x_1 = 0$), and

Mass transfer in bubble columns

p_{w2} = 0 (at the top of the pan, $x_2 = 15$ mm), as air is dry and there is no water vapour.

Since water is diffusing into air, using Eqn. (13.47), we have

$$(m_w)_{total} = \frac{DAM_w}{G.T} \cdot \frac{p}{x_2 - x_1} \ln\left(\frac{p_{a2}}{p_{a1}}\right)$$

or, $(m_w)_{total} = \dfrac{DAM_w}{G.T} \cdot \dfrac{p}{(x_2 - x_1)} \; \ln\left[\dfrac{p - p_{w2}}{p - p_{w1}}\right]$

(where M_w = molecular weight of water = 18 and $p = 1.0132$ bar; $A = 1$ m^2)

Substituting the appropriate values, we get

$(m_w)_{total} = \dfrac{0.25 \times 10^{-4} \times 1 \times 18 \times (1.0132 \times 10^5)}{8314 \times 313 \times 0.015} \; \ln\left[\dfrac{1.0132 - 0}{1.0132 - 0.07384}\right]$

$= 1.168 \times 10^{-3} \times 0.07567 = 8.838 \times 10^{-5}$ kg/m^{2}s

The total amount of water to be evaporated per m^2 area

$= (0.015 \times 1) \times 1000 = 15$ kg/m^2 area

∴ The time required $= \dfrac{15}{8.838 \times 10^{-5}} \times \dfrac{1}{3600}$ h = **47.14 h (Ans.)**

Example 13.9. *An open tank 5.5 m in diameter contains 1 mm deep layer of benzene (molecular weight = 78) at its bottom. The vapour pressure of benzene in the tank is 0.13 bar. The diffusion of benzene takes place through a stagnant air film 2.8 mm thick. The system is operating at 1 atm and 20°C and under these conditions the diffusivity of benzene is 8.3 × 10⁻⁶ m²/s. Assuming the density of benzene as 880 kg/m³, calculate the time taken for the entire benzene to evaporate.*

Solution. Let suffixes b and a refer to benzene and air respectively. The partial pressures of benzene and air at inlet and outlet of air film are given as:

$p_{b1} = 0.13$ bar   and $p_{b2} = 0$ (since beyond air film there is no diffusion)

$p_{a1} = p - p_{b1} = 1.03 - 0.13 = 0.883$ bar

$p_{a2} = p - p_{b2} = 1.013 - 0 = 1.013$ bar

The diffusion rate of benzene through a stagnant air film is given by

$m_b = \dfrac{DAM_b}{G.T} \cdot \dfrac{p}{(x_2 - x_1)} \; \ln\left[\dfrac{p_{a2}}{p_{a1}}\right]$

$= \dfrac{8.3 \times 10^{-6} \times \left(\dfrac{\pi}{4} \times 5.5^2\right) \times 78 \times (1.013 \times 10^5)}{8314 \times (20 + 273) \times (2.8 \times 10^{-3})} \times \ln\left(\dfrac{1.013}{0.883}\right)$

$= 0.03137$ kg/s

The mass of benzene to be evaporated

$= \left(\dfrac{\pi}{4} \times 5.5^2 \times 1 \times 10^{-3}\right) \times 880 = 20.91$ kg

Hence, time taken for entire benzene to evaporate

$= \dfrac{20.9}{0.03137} = 666.24$ s or **11.1 min. (Ans.)**

Example 13.10. *Air at 1 atm and 25°C, containing small quantities of iodine, flows with a velocity of 6.2 m/s inside a 35 mm diameter tube. Calculate mass transfer coefficient for iodine. The thermophysical properties of air are:*

$v = 15.5 \times 10^{-6}$ m²/s; $D = 0.82 \times 10^{-5}$ m²/s.

Solution. *Given:* $U = 6.2$ m/s; $d = 35$mm $= 0.035$m; $v = 15.5 \times 10^{-6}$ m²/s; $D = 0.82 \times 10^{-5}$ m²/s.

Mass transfer coefficient of iodine, h_m:

Schmidt number, $Sc = \dfrac{\mu}{\rho D} = \dfrac{v}{D} = \dfrac{15.5 \times 10^{-6}}{0.82 \times 10^{-5}} = 1.89$

Reynolds number, $$Re = \frac{\rho L U}{\mu} = \frac{dU}{\nu} = \frac{0.035 \times 6.2}{15.5 \times 10^{-6}} = 14000$$

Obviously the flow is turbulent and thus,

Sherwood number, $$Sh = 0.023 \, (Re)^{0.83} \, (Sc)^{0.44}$$

$$= 0.023 \, (14000)^{0.83} \, (1.89)^{0.44} = 84.07$$

Also, $$Sh = \frac{h_m d}{D}$$

$\therefore$ $$h_m = \frac{Sh.D}{d} = \frac{84.07 \times 0.82 \times 10^{-5}}{0.036} = \textbf{0.0197 m/s. (Ans.)}$$

Example 13.11. *Air at 20°C ($\rho = 1.205$ kg/m³; $\nu = 15.06 \times 10^{-6}$ m²/s; $D = 4.166 \times 10^{-5}$ m²/s) flows over a tray (length = 320 mm, width = 420 mm) full of water with a velocity of 2.8 m/s. The total pressure of moving air is 1 atm and the partial pressure of water present in the air is 0.0068 bar. If the temperature on the water surface is 15°C, calculate the evaporation rate of water.*

Solution. *Given :* $U = 2.8$ m/s; $L = 320$ mm $= 0.32$ m; $\rho = 1.205$ kg/m³; $\nu = 15.06 \times 10^{-6}$ m²/s, $D = 4.166 \times 10^{-5}$ m²/s.

In order to ascertain the type of flow, let us first find Reynolds number.

$$Re = \frac{\rho L U}{\mu} = \frac{L U}{\nu} = \frac{0.3 \times 2.8}{15.06 \times 10^{-6}} = 0.558 \times 10^5$$

The flow of air may be treated as flow over flat plate and since $Re < 5 \times 10^5$, the flow is *laminar* in nature and for this,

Sherwood number, $$Sh = \frac{h_m . L}{D} = 0.664 \, (Re)^{0.5} \, (Sc)^{0.33}$$

But, Sc (Schmidt number) $$= \frac{\nu}{D} = \frac{15.06 \times 10^{-6}}{4.166 \times 10^{-5}} = 0.3615$$

$\therefore$ $$\frac{h_m \times 0.32}{4.166 \times 10^{-5}} = 0.664 \, (0.558 \times 10^5)^{0.5} \, (0.3615)^{0.33} = 112.11$$

or, $$h_m = \frac{112.11 \times 4.166 \times 10^{-5}}{0.32} = 0.0146 \text{ m/s}$$

The partial pressure of water over the water surface,

p_{w1} (saturation pressure of water at 15°C) = 0.017 bar

Mass transfer coefficient based on pressure difference is given by

$$h_{mp} = \frac{h_{mc}}{RT}$$ ...[Eqn. (13.52)]

$$= \frac{0.0146}{287 \times (15 + 273)} = 1.766 \times 10^{-7} \text{ m/s}$$

The mass diffusion of water is given by

$$m_w = h_{mp} \, A \, (p_{w1} - p_{w2})$$

$$= 1.766 \times 10^{-7} \times (0.32 \times 0.42) \, (0.017 - 0.0068) \times 10^5$$

$$= 2.421 \times 10^{-5} \text{ kg/s or } \textbf{0.087 kg/h. (Ans.)}$$

TYPICAL EXAMPLES

Example 13.12. *A distillation column containing a mixture of benzene and toluene is at a temperature of 105°C and a pressure of 1 bar. The liquid and vapour phases contain 20% mole of benzene and 55% mole of toluene respectively. At 105°C the vapour pressure of toluene is 0.72 bar and its diffusivity is 5.2 × 10⁻⁶ m²/s. Assuming the equimolar diffusion, calculate the molar diffusion flux of toluene if the diffusion zone is 0.35 m thick.*

Solution. Let subscripts b and t refer to benzene and toluene and suffixes 1 and 2 denote the liquid and vapour planes respectively.

At the liquid plane 1, the partial pressure of toluene is,

$$p_{t1} = \text{Molar concentration} \times \text{vapour pressure}$$
$$= (1 - 0.2) \times 0.72 = 0.576 \text{ bar}$$

At the vapour plane 2,

$$p_{t2} = (1 - 0.55) \times 1 = 0.45 \text{ bar}$$

For the equimolar diffusion, the molar diffusion flux of toluene is

$$N_t = \frac{m_t}{A} = \frac{D}{GT} \frac{(p_{t1} - p_{t2})}{(x_2 - x_1)} \qquad \text{...(Eqn. 13.40)}$$

$$= \frac{(5.2 \times 10^{-6})}{8314 \times (105 + 273)} \left[\frac{(0.576 - 0.45) \times 10^5}{0.35 \times 10^{-3}} \right]$$

$$= \textbf{5.956} \times \textbf{10}^{-5} \textbf{ kg mole/s.m}^2 \textbf{ (Ans.)}$$

Example 13.13. *Hydrogen gas at 25°C and 2.5 atmosphere flows through a rubber tubing of 12 mm inside radius and 24 mm outside radius. The binary diffusion coefficient of hydrogen is 2.1 × 10⁻⁸ m²/s and the solubility of hydrogen is 0.055 m³ of hydrogen per m³ of rubber at 1 atmosphere. If the gas constant for hydrogen is 4160 J/kg K and the concentration of hydrogen at the outer surface of tubing is negligible, calculate the diffusion flux rate of hydrogen per metre length of rubber tubing.*

Solution. *Given :* $p = 2.5 \times 10^5$ N/m²; $r_1 = 12$ mm $= 0.012$ m, $r_2 = 24$ mm $= 0.024$ m

$$T = 25 + 273 = 298 \text{ K}, R = 4160 \text{ J/kg K}$$

Diffusion flux rate of hydrogen, m:

The solubility of hydrogen at a pressure of 2.5 atmospheres is $S = 0.055 \times 2.5 = 0.1375$ m³/m³ rubber tubing $= V =$ volume of hydrogen in m³/m³ of rubber.

From perfect gas law,

$$pV = mRT$$

or, $$m = \frac{pV}{RT} = \text{concentration} = C$$

or, $$m = \frac{2.5 \times 10^5 \times 0.1375}{4160 \times 298} = C_{h1} = 0.02773 \text{ kg/m}^3 \text{ of rubber tubing}$$

(at the inner surface of the pipe)

and, $$C_{h2} = 0 \text{ (as the resistance to diffusion is stated to be negligible at the outer surface of the tube).}$$

The diffusion flux through the cylinder is given by

$$m = \frac{D (C_{h1} - C_{h2})}{\Delta x} A_m$$

where,
$$\Delta x = (r_2 - r_1) = 0.024 - 0.012 = 0.012 \text{ m}$$
$$A_m = \frac{2\pi L (r_2 - r_1)}{\ln (r_2/r_1)} = \frac{2\pi \times 1 \times 0.012}{\ln (0.024/0.012)} = 0.1088 \text{ m}^2$$

$\therefore$
$$m = \frac{2.1 \times 10^{-8} (0.02773 - 0)}{0.012} \times 0.1088 = \mathbf{0.528 \times 10^{-8} \text{ kg/s.m}}.$$

Example 13.14. *Air is contained in a tyre tube of surface area 0.5 m² and wall thickness 10 mm. The pressure of air drops from 2.2 bar to 2.18 bar in a period of 6 days. The solubility of air in the rubber is 0.072 m³ of air per m³ of rubber at 1 bar. Determine the diffusivity of air in rubber at the operating temperature of 300 K if the volume of air in the tube is 0.028 m³.*

Solution. *Given* : $A = 0.5 \text{ m}^2$, $p_i = 2.2 \text{ bar}$, $p_f = 2.18 \text{ bar}$, $T = 300 \text{ K}$, $S = 0.072 \text{ m}^3$,
$$V = 0.028 \text{ m}^3, \text{ and } L = 10 \text{ mm} = 0.01 \text{ m}$$

Diffusivity of air in rubber, D:

Initial mass of air in the tube,
$$m_i = \frac{p_i \, V}{R \, T} = \frac{2.2 \times 10^5 \times 0.028}{287 \times 300} = 0.0715 \text{ kg}$$

Final mass of air in the tube,
$$m_f = \frac{p_f \, V}{R \, T} = \frac{2.18 \times 10^5 \times 0.028}{287 \times 300} = 0.07089 \text{ kg}$$

Mass of air escaped $= 0.0715 - 0.07089 = 0.00061 \text{ kg}$

$\therefore$ The mass flux of air escaped is given by
$$N_a = \frac{m_a}{A} = \frac{\text{Mass of air escaped}}{\text{Time elapsed} \times \text{area}} = \frac{0.00061}{(6 \times 24 \times 3600) \times 0.5} = 0.35 \times 10^{-9} \text{ kg/s.m}^2$$

The solubility of air should be calculated at the mean operating pressure, which is
$$= \frac{2.2 + 2.18}{2} = 2.19 \text{ bar}$$

The solubility of air *i.e.*, volume at the mean inside pressure is
$$S = 0.072 \times 2.19 = 0.1577 \text{ m}^3/\text{m}^3 \text{ of rubber}$$

The air which escapes to atmosphere will be at 1 bar pressure and its solubility will remain at 0.72 m³ of air per m³ of rubber.

The corresponding mass concentrations at the inner and outer surfaces of the tube, from characteristic gas equation, are calculated as :
$$C_{a1} = \frac{p_1 \, V_1}{R \, T_1} = \frac{2.19 \times 10^5 \times 0.1577}{287 \times 300} = 0.4011 \text{ kg/m}^3$$
$$C_{a2} = \frac{p_2 \, V_2}{R \, T_2} = \frac{1 \times 10^5 \times 0.072}{287 \times 300} = 0.0836 \text{ kg/m}^3$$

The diffusion flux rate of air through the rubber is given by
$$N_a = \frac{m_a}{A} = \frac{D \, (C_{a1} - C_{a2})}{(x_2 - x_1)} = \frac{D \, (C_{a1} - C_{a2})}{L}$$

or,
$$2.35 \times 10^{-9} = \frac{D \, (0.4011 - 0.0836)}{0.01}$$

or,
$$D = \frac{2.35 \times 10^{-9} \times 0.01}{(0.4011 - 0.0836)} = \mathbf{0.74 \times 10^{-10} \text{ m}^2/\text{s.}} \text{ (Ans.)}$$

Example 13.15. *Oxygen is diffusing through stagnant carbon monoxide at 0°C and 760 mm Hg pressure under steady state conditions. The partial pressure of oxygen at two planes 3.5 mm apart is 90 mm of Hg and 20 mm of Hg respectively. Calculate the rate of diffusion of oxygen in gm-mole/s through cm² area. Assume diffusivity of oxygen in carbon monoxide = 0.17 cm²/s and gas constant = 82.06 cm² atm/gm mole K.*

Mass transfer test vessel

Solution. $T = 0 + 273 = 273$ K, $D = 0.17$ cm²/s, $R_A = 82.06$ cm² atm/gm mole K.

Let suffices A and B refer to oxygen and carbon monoxide respectively.

Partial pressures of oxygen on the given planes are :

$$p_{A1} = \frac{90}{760} = 0.1184 \text{ atm}$$

$$p_{A2} = \frac{20}{760} = 0.0263 \text{ atm}$$

Partial pressures of carbon monoxide are :

$$p_{B1} = 1 - 0.1184 = 0.8816 \text{ atm}$$
$$p_{B2} = 1 - 0.0263 = 0.9737 \text{ atm}$$

Log mean partial pressure for non-diffusing carbon is given by :

$$LMPB = \frac{p_{B2} - p_{B1}}{\ln (p_{B2} / p_{B1})} \qquad \text{...[Eqn. (13.48)]}$$

$$= \frac{(0.9737 - 0.8816)}{\ln (0.9737/0.8816)} = 0.927 \text{ atm}$$

The rate of diffusion of oxygen is given by

$$N_A = \frac{D A M_A}{G T} \cdot \frac{p}{(x_2 - x_1)} \left[\frac{p_{A1} - p_{A2}}{LM \, PB} \right] \qquad \text{...[Eqn. (13.50)]}$$

$$= \frac{D A}{R_A T} \cdot \frac{p}{(x_2 - x_1)} \left[\frac{p_{A1} - p_{A2}}{LM \, PB} \right] \qquad \left(\because R_A = \frac{G}{M_A} \right)$$

$$= \frac{0.17 \times 1}{82.06 \times 273} \times \frac{1}{3.5 \times 10^{-3}} \left[\frac{0.1184 - 0.0263}{0.927} \right]$$

$$= \mathbf{2.154 \times 10^{-4} \text{ gm mole/s.}}$$

Alternatively:

$$N_A = \frac{D A}{R_A T} \cdot \frac{p}{x_2 - x_1} \times \ln \frac{p_{B2}}{p_{B1}} \qquad \text{...[Eqn. 13.47 (a)]}$$

$$= \frac{0.17 \times 1}{82.06 \times 273} \times \frac{1}{3.5 \times 10^{-3}} \ln \left(\frac{0.9737}{0.8816} \right) = 2.154 \times 10^4 \text{ gm mole/s.}$$

Example 13.16. *Nitrogen gas diffuses through a 12 mm layer of non-diffusing gaseous mixture containing $C_2H_4 = 20\%$, $C_2H_6 = 10\%$, $C_4H_{10} = 70\%$, under steady state condition. The operating temperature and pressure of the system are 25°C and 1 atm respectively and at this condition the partial pressures of nitrogen at two planes are 0.15 bar and 0.08 bar respectively. The diffusivity of nitrogen through C_2H_4, C_2H_6 and C_4H_{10} are 16×10^{-6} and 14×10^{-6} and 9×10^{-6} m²/s respectively. Determine the diffusion rate of nitrogen across the two planes.*

Solution. The *effective diffusivity* of gas through a non-diffusing multi-component mixture of constant composition, under steady state condition, is given by

$$D = \frac{1}{\left(\dfrac{x_B}{D_{AB}}\right) + \left(\dfrac{x_C}{D_{AC}}\right) + \left(\dfrac{x_D}{D_{AD}}\right)} \qquad \qquad ...\text{[Eqn. 13.26]}$$

where, x_B, x_C, x_D = Mole fraction compositions of the mixture, and

D_{AB}, D_{AC}, D_{AD} = Diffusivities of species A (Nitrogen) through species B (C_2H_4), C (C_2H_6) and D (C_4H_{10}).

Substituting the appropriate values we get

$$D = \frac{1}{\dfrac{0.20}{16 \times 10^{-6}} + \dfrac{0.1}{14 \times 10^{-6}} + \dfrac{0.7}{9 \times 10^{-6}}} = \frac{10^6}{0.0125 + 0.00714 + 0.0777}$$

$$= 10.27 \times 10^{-6} \text{ m}^2/\text{s}$$

Let suffices N and M refer to nitrogen and gaseous mixture respectively.

The partial pressures of nitrogen and gaseous mixture at two planes are :

$$p_{N1} = 0.15 \text{ bar and } p_{N2} = 0.08 \text{ bar}$$

$$\therefore \qquad p_{M1} = p - p_{N1} = 1.013 - 0.15 = 0.863 \text{ bar}$$

$$p_{M2} = p - p_{N2} = 1.013 - 0.08 = 0.933 \text{ bar}$$

The diffusion rate of gaseous mixture is given by

$$m_N = \frac{D A M_N}{G.T} \cdot \frac{p}{(x_2 - x_1)} \ln\left(\frac{p_{M2}}{p_{M1}}\right) \qquad \qquad ...\text{[Eqn. 13.47 (a)]}$$

$$= \frac{10.27 \times 10^{-6} \times 1 \times 28}{8314 \times (25 + 273)} = \frac{1.013 \times 10^5}{12 \times 10^{-3}} \ln\left(\frac{0.933}{0.863}\right) = \mathbf{7.64 \times 10^{-5} \text{ kg/m}^2 \text{ (Ans.)}}$$

Example 13.17. *Due to accidental opening of a valve, the water has been split out on the floor of an industrial plant. The water level is 1.2 mm and temperature 25°C. The temperature and pressure of air are 25°C and 1 bar respectively. The specific humidity of air is 1.8 g/kg of dry air. Assuming D = 0.25 × 10⁻⁴ m²/s and the evaporation takes place by molecular diffusion through an air film 6 mm thick, determine the time required to evaporate the complete water.*

Solution. *Given:* $(x_2 - x_1) = 6$ mm $= 0.006$ m, $T = 25 + 273 = 298$ K, $p = 1$ bar, $D = 0.25 \times 10^{-4}$ m²/s, specific humidity of air, $W = 1.8$ g/kg of dry air.

Time required to evaporate the complete water:

Here, $p_{w1} = 0.03169$ bar (corresponding to saturation temperature 25°C)

p_{w2} is obtained from the expression of specific humidity which is given by

$$W = \frac{0.622 \, p_{w2}}{p - p_{w2}}$$

or, $$1.8 \times 10^{-3} = \frac{0.622 \times p_{w2}}{1 - p_{w2}}$$

or, $$1.8 \times 10^{-3} (1 - p_{w2}) = 0.622 \, p_{w2}$$

or, $$0.0018 - 0.0018 \, p_{w2} = 0.622 \, p_{w2}$$

or, $$p_{w2} = 0.00288 \text{ bar}$$

Using eqn. (13.47), we get

$$(m_w)_{total} = \frac{D A M_w}{G.T.} \cdot \frac{p}{(x_2 - x_1)} \ln\left[\frac{p - p_{w2}}{p - p_{w1}}\right]$$

$$= \frac{0.25 \times 10^{-4} \times 1 \times 18}{8314 \times 298} \times \frac{1 \times 10^5}{0.006} \ln \left[\frac{1 - 0.00288}{1 - 0.03169} \right]$$

$$= 0.003027 \ln \left(\frac{0.997}{0.968} \right)$$

$$= 8.935 \times 10^{-5} \text{ kg/s.m}^2$$

The total amount of water to be evaporated per m^2 of area

$$= 1 \times \frac{1.2}{1000} \times 1000 = 1.2 \text{ kg}$$

$\therefore$ Time required $= \dfrac{1.2}{8.935 \times 10^{-5}} s = \dfrac{1.2}{8.935 \times 10^{-5} \times 3600} h = \textbf{3.73 } \textbf{\textit{h}} \textbf{ (Ans.)}$

HIGHLIGHTS

1. The process of transfer of mass as a result of the species concentration difference in a system/mixture is called *mass transfer*.

2. Modes of mass transfer are : Diffusion, convection and change of phase.

3. Flux of mass transfer is caused by the existence of different velocities and concentrations.

4. Liquid mass diffusivities are considerably smaller than those for gases. Diffusion in solids is even slower than in liquids.

5. Equimolar counter diffusion between species A and B of a binary gas mixture is defined as isothermal diffusion process in which each molecule of component A is replaced by each molecule of constituent B and *vice-versa*.

List of formulae:

(i) $$N_A = \frac{m_A}{A} = D_{AB} \left[\frac{C_{A1} - C_{A2}}{x_2 - x_1} \right]$$

(ii) $$D_{AB} = 0.0043 \frac{T^{3/2}}{p \, (V_A^{1/3} + V_B^{1/3})^2} \left[\frac{1}{M_A} + \frac{1}{M_B} \right]^{1/2}$$

(iii) $$\frac{D_1}{D_2} = \left(\frac{p_2}{p_1} \right) \left(\frac{T_1}{T_2} \right)^{3/2}$$

(iv) $$D = \frac{1}{\left(\dfrac{x_B}{D_{AB}} \right) + \left(\dfrac{x_C}{D_{AC}} \right) + \left(\dfrac{x_D}{D_{AD}} \right)}$$

(v) $$D_{AB} = 0.001858 \frac{T^{3/2}}{p \, (\sigma_{AB})^2 \, \Omega} \left[\frac{1}{M_A} + \frac{1}{M_B} \right]^{1/2}$$

where, D_{AB} = Mass diffusivity of gas species B diffusing through another gas species A, cm^2/s,

T = Absolute temperature, K,

p = Total pressure in atmospheres = $(p_A + p_B)$,

σ_{AB} = Collision diameter in Å (Angstroms),

Ω = Collision integral, and

M_A, M_B = Molecular weights of gas species A and B respectively.

(vi) $$\sigma_{AB} = \frac{\sigma_A + \sigma_B}{2}$$

(vii) $\varepsilon_{AB} = \sqrt{\varepsilon_A\,\varepsilon_B}$

(viii) $\dfrac{m_A}{A} = \dfrac{C_{A1} - C_{A2}}{(L/D_A)}$ ... Diffusion through a plain membrane

L/DA is known as *diffusional resistance*.

(ix) $N_A = \dfrac{m_A}{A} = D \cdot \dfrac{A}{GT}\left[\dfrac{p_{A1} - p_{A2}}{x_2 - x_1}\right]$

$(m_w)_{total} = \dfrac{DAM_w}{G.T.} \cdot \dfrac{p}{(x_2 - x_1)} \cdot \dfrac{(p_{w1} - p_{w2})}{LMPa}$ ... Evaporation of water into air.

where *LMPa* means log mean partial pressure of air.

(x) $h_{mc} = \dfrac{D}{x_2 - x_1}$

(xi) $h_{mp} = \dfrac{h_{mc}}{RT}$

(xii) $Sh_x = 0.332\,(Re_x)^{0.5}\,(Sc)^{0.33}$
$\left.\begin{array}{l} \\ \end{array}\right]$
$Sh = 0.664\,(Re)^{0.5}\,(Sc)^{0.33}$ ... For laminar flow.

$Sh_x = 0.0288\,(Re_x)^{0.8}\,(Sc)^{0.33}$
$Sh = 0.0576\,(Re)^{0.8}\,(Sc)^{0.33}$ ... For turbulent flow

$Sh = 0.023\,(Re)^{0.83}\,(Sc)^{0.44}$ for $2000 < Re < 35 \times 10^3$ and $0.6 < Sc < 2.5$
... For flow in tubes.

THEORETICAL QUESTIONS

1. Explain briefly the term 'mass transfer'.
2. Enumerate applications of mass transfer.
3. List the various modes of mass transfer.
4. State Fick's law of diffusion. What are its limitations?
5. What do you mean by equimolar counter diffusion?
6. Derive the general mass transfer equation in cartesian coordinates.

UNSOLVED EXAMPLES

1. The molecular weights of the two components A and B of a gas mixture are 20 and 40 respectively. The molecular weight of the gas mixture is found to be 25. If the mass concentration of the mixture is 1 kg/m³, determine the following:

   (i)   Molar fractions,   (ii)   Mass fractions, and

   (iii)   Total pressure if the temperature of the mixture is 27°C.

   [**Ans.** (i) 0.75, 0.25; (ii) 0.6, 0.4, (iii) 99.8 kPa]

2. A vessel contains a binary mixture of oxygen and nitrogen with partial pressures in the ratio 0.21 and 0.79 at 27°C. The total pressure of the mixture is 1 bar. Determine :

   (i)   Molar concentrations,   (ii)   Mass densities,

   (iii)   Mass fractions, and   (iv)   Molar fractions of each species.

   [**Ans.** (i) 0.00842 kg mole/m³, 0.03167 kg mole/m³, (ii) 0.269 kg/m³, 0.887 kg/m³,

   (iii) 0.233, 0.767, (iv) 0.21, 0.79]

3. A steel rectangular container having walls 15 mm thick is used to store gaseous hydrogen at elevated pressure. The molar concentrations of hydrogen in the steel at the inside and outside surfaces are

1 kg mole/m^3 and zero respectively. Assuming the diffusion coefficient for hydrogen in steel as 25 × 10^{-12} m^2/s, calculate the molar diffusion flux for hydrogen through the steel.

[**Ans.** 16.66 × 10^{-12} kg mole/s.m^2]

4. A plastic membrane 0.25 mm thick has hydrogen gas maintained at pressures of 2.5 bar and 1 bar on its opposite sides. The binary diffusion coefficient of hydrogen in the plastic is 8.5 × 10^{-8} m^2/s and the solubility of hydrogen in the membrane is 0.0015 kg mole/m^2-bar. Under the uniform conditions of 25°C, calculate :
   (*i*) The molar concentrations of hydrogen at the opposite faces of the membrane, and
   (*ii*) The molar and mass diffusion flux of hydrogen through the membrane.

   [**Ans.** (*i*) 0.00375 and 0.0015 kg mole/m^3; (*ii*) 76.5 × 10^{-8} kg mole/s-m^2; 153 × 10^{-8} kg/s-m^2]

5. A 20 mm deep pan is filled with water to a level of 10 mm and is exposed to dry air at 40°C. Determine the time required for all the water to evaporate. Assume the mass diffusivity as 2.6 × 10^{-5} m^2/s.

   [**Ans.** 55.74 h]

6. Calculate the rate of diffusion of water vapour from a pool of water at the bottom of a well which is 6 m deep and 2.5 m diameter to dry ambient air over the top of the well. The entire system may be assumed at 30°C and one atmospheric pressure. The diffusion coefficient is 2.5 × 10^{-5} m^2/s.

   [**Ans.** 0.00233 kg/h]

7. An open tank 5 m in diameter contains 1 mm deep layer of benzene (molecular weight = 78) at its bottom. The vapour pressure of benzene in the tank is 14 kPa. Diffusion of benzene takes place only through a stagnant air film 3 mm thick. The operating pressure and temperature of the system are 1 atm and 20°C and at this condition, the diffusivity of benzene is 8.5 × 10^{-6} m^2/s. Calculate the time taken for the entire benzene to evaporate. Take the density of benzene as 880 kg/m^3. [**Ans.** 10.73 min]

8. Air at 25°C and 1 atm, containing small quantities of iodine (v = 15.5 × 10^{-6} m^2/s, D = 0.82 × 10^{-5} m^2/s), flows with a velocity of 5.25 m/s inside a 30 mm diameter tube. Calculate mass transfer coefficient for iodine. [**Ans.** 0.0176 m/s]

9. Air at 20°C flows over a tray (length = 0.3 m and width = 0.4 m) full of water. The total pressure of moving air is 1 atm and partial pressure of water present in air is 0.007 bar. If the temperature on the water surface is 15°C, calculate evaporation rate of water. The thermophysical properties of air are: ρ = 1.205 kg/m^3, v = 15.06 × 10^{-6} m^2/s and D = 4.166 × 10^{-5} m^2/s. [**Ans.** 0.84 kg/h]

10. Hydrogen gas at 47°C and 3 atmosphere flows through a rubber tubing of 1.5 cm inner radius and 2.5 cm outer radius. The diffusivity of hydrogen through rubber is stated to be 0.792 × 10^{-4} m^2/s and the solubility of hydrogen is 0.06 m^3 of hydrogen/m^3 of rubber at 1 atmosphere. If the gas constant for hydrogen is 4160 kJkg and the concentration of hydrogen at the outer surface of tubing is negligible, calculate the diffusion flux rate of hydrogen per metre length of rubber tubing.

   [**Ans.** 0.395 × 10^{-4} kg/h.m]

11. Air is contained in a tyre tube of surface area 0.5 m^2 and wall thickness 1 cm. The pressure of air drops from 2 bar to 1.99 bar in a period of 5 days. The solubility of air in the rubber is 0.07 m^3 of air per m^3 of rubber at 1 bar. Determine the diffusivity of air rubber at the operating temperature of 27°C if the volume of air in the tube is 0.025 m^3. [**Ans.** 0.55 × 10^{-10} m^2/s]

12. Due to accidental opening of a valve, the water has been split out on the floor of an industrial plant. The water level is 1 mm and temperature 20°C. The temperature and pressure of air are 20°C and 1 atm respectively. Assuming D = 0.26 × 10^{-4} m^2/s and evaporation takes place by molecular diffusion through an air film 5 mm thick, determine the time required to evaporate the complete water.

   The specific humidity of air is 2g/kg of dry air. [**Ans.** 2.56 *h*]

ADDITIONAL/TYPICAL WORKED EXAMPLES

(Questions Selected from Universities and Competitive Examinations)

CONDUCTION

Example A-1. (a) *What are the objectives of conduction analysis?*

(b) *Explain "Guarded hot plate method" of measuring thermal conductivity.*

Ans. (a) Conduction analysis is carried out to achieve the following *objectives* :

1. To determine the temperature distribution, variation of temperature with time and position.

2. To make computation for heat transfer etc.

(b) **Measurement of thermal conductivity by 'Guarded hot plate method':**

Guarded hot plate method is a steady state absolute method suitable for : (*i*) materials which can be laid between two parallel plates; (*ii*) loose fill materials which can be filled between such plates.

It is the *most dependable and reproducible method for the measurement of thermal conductivity of insulating materials.*

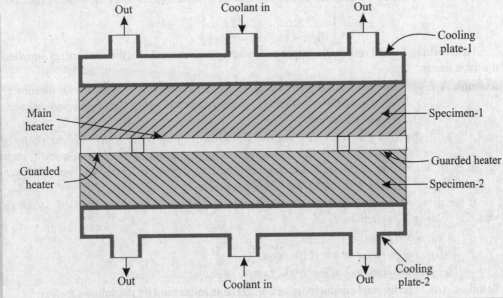

Fig. 1. Guarded hotplate method for measuring thermal conductivity.

The thermal conductivity can be *estimated* by having the following :

(*i*) A one-dimensional heat flow through the flat specimen.

(*ii*) An arrangement for maintaining the faces of the specimen at constant temperature.

(*iii*) Some metering method to measure the heat flux through a known area.

Fig. 1 shows the schematic arrangement of experimental set up for the guarded hot plate method.

- The **main heater** is incorporated at the centre of the unit and is maintained at a fixed *temperature* (by the electrical energy which can be metered).

- The **guarded heater**, which surrounds the main heater on its ends, is supplied adequate electrical energy to maintain its temperature same as that of the main heater. This arrangement ensures unidirectional heat flow and eliminates the distorion caused by edge losses.

— The main and guarded heaters are made up of mica sheets in which Nichrome wire is wound closely spaced. Invariably, these heaters are surrounded longitudinally by copper surface plates so that temperature is uniformly distributed.

- Test specimens '1' and '2' are placed on both sides of the heater or copper surface plates, as the case may be. At the hot and cold faces of the specimens thermocouples are attached.

The following *measurements* are made :

Q = Heat flow from the main heater through a test specimen (it will be half of the total electrical energy supplied to the main heater)

A = Area of heat flow (= Area of main heater + area of one-half of air gap between it and the guarded heater),

L = Thickness of the test-specimen, and

$(t_h - t_c)$ = Temperature drop across the specimen; subscripts h and c refer to hot and cold faces respectively.

The thermal conductivity (k) is then found out as follows :

$$k = \frac{Q}{A} \frac{L}{(t_h - h_c)} \qquad \left[\because Q = -kA \frac{dt}{dx} = kA \frac{(t_h - h_c)}{L} \right]$$

However, when the specimens are of different thicknesses, the respective temperatures at the hot and cold surfaces would be different and in that case K will be evaluated by the follows relation :

$$k = \frac{Q}{A} \left[\frac{L_1}{(t_{h1} - t_{c1})} + \frac{L_2}{(t_{h2} - t_{c2})} \right]$$

Here suffices 1 and 2 refer to the upper and lower specimens and Q is the total energy supplied to the main heater.

Example A-2. (a) *List the various factors which influence the thermal conductivity a substance. In what way, the conductivity is affected by the solid, liquid and gaseous phases of the substance?*

(b) *The flow of heat occurs along the axis of the solid which has the shape of a truncated cone with circumferential surface insulated. The base is at 360°C and the area of the section at distance x measured from the base of the cone is given by :*
$A = 1.2 (1 - 1.5 x) \, m^2$ *where x is in meters.*

If the plane at x = 0.2 m is maintained at 120°C and the thermal conductivity of the solid material is 3W/m°C, determine :

(i) *Heat flow,*

(ii) *Temperature at x = 0.1 m, and*

(iii) *Temperature gradient at the two faces and at x = 0.1 m.*

Solution. (a). The thermal conductivity of a material is influenced by the follows *factors* :

1. Homogeneous and non-homogeneous character of the material.
2. Crystalline, amsorphous and porous structure of the substance.
3. Chemical composition of the substance (or substances) of which it is composed.
4. Gaseous, liquid and solid phases in which the substance exists,
5. Temperature and pressure to which the substance is subjected.

The factors with the *greatest influence* are :

- Chemical composition,
- Phase change, and
- Temperature.

Generally a liquid is better conductor than a gas, and a solid is a better conductor than a liquid.

(b) *Given* : $t_1 = 360°C$; $t_2 = 120°C$; $A = 1.2 (1 - 1.5\, x)$ m^2 ; $k = 3$ W/m°C

Refer Fig. 2.

(i) Heat flow, Q :

The insulated circumferential surface implies that the situation corresponds to *one-dimensional conduction* in the $x =$ direction, for which we have :

$$Q = -kA \frac{dt}{dx}$$

$$= -k\,[1.2\,(1-1.5x)]\,\frac{dt}{dx}$$

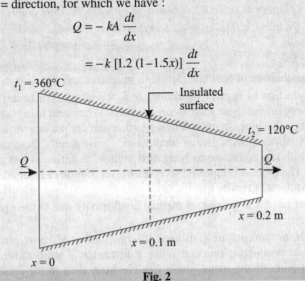

Fig. 2

Separating the variables and upon integration, we get

$$Q \int \frac{dx}{(1-1.5x)} = -1.2\,k \int dt$$

or

$$Q\left[-\frac{1}{1.5}\,ln\,(1-1.5x)\right]_{x_1}^{x_2} = -1.2\,k\,(t_2 - t_1)$$

∴

$$Q = -\frac{1.2 \times 1.5\,k\,(t_1 - t_2)}{ln\,\{1 - 1.5\,(x_2 - x_1)\}}$$

$$= -\frac{1.2 \times 1.5 \times 3\,(360 - 120)}{ln\,[1 - 1.5\,(0.2 - 0)]} = \textbf{3633.6 W (Ans.)}$$

(ii) Temperature x = 0.1 m :

$$3633.6 = -\frac{1.2 \times 1.5 \times 3\,(360 - t)}{ln\,\{1 - 1.5\,(0.1 - 0)\}} = \frac{5.4\,(360 - t)}{0.1625}$$

∴

$$t = 360 - \frac{3633.6 \times 0.1625}{5.4} = \textbf{250.6°C (Ans.)}$$

(iii) Temperature gradient at the two faces and at x = 0.1 m :

The temperature gradient at a section may be written as :

$$\frac{dt}{dx} = -\frac{Q}{kA}$$

- At $x = 0$; $A = 1.2\,(1 - 1.5\,x) = 1.20$ m^2

∴

$$\frac{dt}{dx} = -\frac{3633.6}{3 \times 1.2} = \textbf{-1009.3°C/m (Ans.)}$$

- At $x = 0.1$ m; $A = 1.2 (1 - 1.5 \times 0.1) = 1.02$ m^2

$$\therefore \qquad \frac{dt}{dx} = -\frac{3633.6}{3 \times 1.02} = 1187.4°C/m \text{ (Ans.)}$$

- At $x = 0.2$ m; $A = 1.2 (1 - 1.5 \times 0.2) = 0.84$ m^2

$$\therefore \qquad \frac{dt}{dx} = -\frac{3633.6}{3 \times 0.84} = 1441.9°C/m \text{ (Ans)}$$

Example. A-3.(a) *How does the heat conduction in insulators and metals take place?*

(b) *A 3.6 cm diameter pipe at 105°C is losing heat at the rate of 120 W/m length of pipe to the surrounding air at 15°C. This is to be reduced to a minimum value by providing insulation. The following insulation materials are available :*

Insulation A : Quantity = 0.00372 m³/m length of pipe; Thermal conductivity = 5 W/m°C

Insulation B : Quantity = 0.0048 m³/m length of pipe; Thermal conductivity = 1 W/m°C

Determine the position of better insulating layer relative to the pipe and percentage saving in heat loss.

Solution. (a) The mechanism of heat conduction in insulators and metals is as follows :

- The conduction of heat in **insulators** (e.g. wood, glass, asbestos) take place *due to vibration of atoms about their mean positions.* When heat is imparted to one part of an insulating substance, atoms belonging to that part are put in a violent state of agitation and start vibrating with greater amplitudes. Consequently these more active particles collide with less active atoms lying next to them, resulting in less active atoms getting excited. The process is repeated layer after layer of molecules/atoms until the other part of the insulator is reached.

- Insulators have a low value of thermal conductivity due to their porosity, which may contain air.

- In **metals**, *besides atomic vibrations, a large number of free electrons also participate in the heat conduction process.* When a difference of temperature exists between the different parts of the metal, these free electrons drift in the direction of decreasing temperature. It is due to this drift of free electrons that metals behave better conductors than other solids. The observed proportionality between the thermal and electrical conductivities of pure metals is on account of these free electrons.

— The electrons do not contribute to heat conductivity in the insulator since these are *not free but fixed in the valence band.*

(b) Thermal resistance due to pipe material,

$$R_{th-p} = \frac{\Delta t}{Q} = \frac{105 - 15}{120} = 0.75°C/W$$

For a pipe with two layers of insulation,

$$\Sigma R_{th} = R_{th-p} + R_{th-1} + R_{th-2}$$

$$= 0.75 + \frac{1}{2\pi k_1 l} \ln\left(\frac{r_2}{r_1}\right) + \frac{1}{2\pi k_2 l} \ln\left(\frac{r_3}{r_2}\right)$$

Arrangement-I. The *insulation material A is placed inside. i.e., next to the pipe :*

$$r_1 = 0.018 \text{ m}$$

Now, $\pi\left(r_2^2 - r_1^2\right) \times 1 = 0.00372 \qquad \therefore r_2 = 0.0388$ m

Also, $\pi\left(r_3^2 - r_2^2\right) \times 1 = 0.0048 \qquad \therefore r_3 = 0.055$ m

$$\therefore \qquad \Sigma R_{th} = 0.75 + \frac{1}{2\pi \times 5 \times 1} \ln\left(\frac{0.0388}{0.018}\right) + \frac{1}{2\pi \times 1 \times 1} \ln\left(\frac{0.055}{0.0388}\right)$$

$$= 0.75 + 0.02445 + 0.0555 = 0.8299°C/W$$

$$\therefore \qquad \text{Heat loss, } Q = \frac{\Delta t}{\Sigma R_{th}} = \frac{105 - 15}{0.8299} = 108.45 \text{ W}$$

Arrangement-II. The *insulation material B is placed inside*, i.e., *next to the pipe*.

$$r_1 = 0.018 \text{ m}$$

Now, $\pi\,(r_2^2 - 0.018^2) = 0.0048 \qquad \therefore r_2 = 0.043 \text{ m}$

Also, $\pi\,(r_3^2 - 0.043^2) = 0.00372 \qquad \therefore r_3 = 0.055 \text{ m}$

$$\therefore \qquad \Sigma R_{th} = 0.75 + \frac{1}{2\pi \times 1 \times 1} \ln\left(\frac{0.043}{0.018}\right) + \frac{1}{2\,\pi \times 5 \times 1} \ln\left(\frac{0.055}{0.043}\right)$$

$$= 0.75 + 0.1386 + 0.00783 = 0.8964 °C/W$$

$$\therefore \qquad \text{Heat loss, } Q = \frac{105 - 15}{0.8964} = 100.4 \text{ W}$$

Obviously the *heat loss is small when insulation material B is placed next to pipe*.

$$\%\text{age saving in heat loss} = \frac{108.45 - 100}{100} \times 100 = \textbf{8.45 \% (Ans.)}$$

Example. A-4. (a) *List some of the situations where poor conductivity of air helps to restrict the heat transmission by conduction.*

   (b) *A hemispherical oven of 72 cm internal radius is lagged with 12 cm thick fire bricks covering surrounded by a magnesia layer of thickness 6 cm. An electric heater is placed at the centre and under steady state conditions, the inner surface is maintained at 815°C. The system is a room for which the ambient temperature is 15°C and outside unit convective coefficient is 8.75 W/m² °C. Thermal conductivities of fire bricks and magnesia are 0.315 W/m °C and 0.0525 W/°C respectively. Neglecting any thermal resistance due to the oven material, determine :*

   (i) *The heat loss through the oven and the wattage required of the heater filament to be placed inside to affect the same heat transfer.*

   (ii) *The temperature at a point halfway through the fire brick covering.*

Solution. (a) Following are the few situations where poor conductivity of air helps to restrict the heat transmission by conduction :

   1. Two thin blankets are warmer than a single blanket of double the thickness since the two blankets enclose between them a layer of air.

   2. Woolen fibres are rough and hence have fine pores filled with air. Both wool and air are bad conductors of heat and do not permit the body heat to flow to the atmosphere.

   3. Birds often swell their feathers to enclose air and thus prevent the outflow of heat of the body.

   4. Eskimos make double walled glass houses; air is enclosed between the walls which reduces the outflow of heat from the inside of the houses.

   (b) *Given* : $r_1 = 72$ cm or 0.72 m; $r_2 = 72 + 12 = 84$ cm or 0.84 m; $r_3 = 84 + 6 = 90$ cm or 0.9 m.

$$\Delta t = 815 - 15 = 800°C; \; h_0 = 8.75 \text{ W/m}^2 °C; \; k_{fb} = 0.315 \text{ W/m°C}; \; k_{mag} = 0.0525 \text{ W/m°C}$$

(i) **The heat loss from the oven and the wattage required :**

Thermal resistance for a spherical body is given by,

$$R_{th} = \frac{r_0 - r_i}{4\pi k\, r_0\, r_i}$$

and for a hemisphere, it equals half of this value.

$$\therefore \qquad \text{Resistance of fire brick, } R_{th-fb} = \frac{1}{2} \times \frac{(0.84 - 0.72)}{4\pi \times 0.315 \times 0.84 \times 0.72} = 0.02506 °C/W$$

$$\text{Resistance of magnesia, } R_{th-mg} = \frac{1}{2} \times \frac{(0.9 - 0.84)}{4\pi \times 0.0525 \times 0.9 \times 0.84} = 0.06015 °C/W$$

Resistance of outside air film $R_{th-af} = \dfrac{1}{2} \times \dfrac{1}{h_0 \, A_0}$

$$= \dfrac{1}{2} \times \dfrac{1}{8.75 \times 4\pi \times (0.9)^2} = 0.005614 \text{ °C/W}$$

Total thermal resistance, $\Sigma R_{th} = 0.02506 + 0.06015 + 0.005614 = 0.0908$ °C/W

$\therefore$ Heat lost from oven $= \dfrac{\Delta t}{\Sigma R_{th}} = \dfrac{800}{0.0908} = \textbf{8810.6 W (Ans.)}$

Required filament wattage $= \textbf{8.81 kW (Ans.)}$

(ii) The temperature at a point halfway through the fire brick covering, t :

Radius at mid-plane of the fire brick lining,

$$r = \dfrac{r_1 + r_2}{2} = \dfrac{0.72 + 0.84}{2} = 0.78 \text{ m}$$

Thermal resistance of fire bricks upto its mid-plane

$$= \dfrac{1}{2} \times \dfrac{(0.78 - 0.72)}{4\pi \times 0.315 \times 0.78 \times 0.72} = 0.0135 \text{ °C/W}$$

Since the heat flowing through each section is same,

$$8810.6 = \dfrac{815 - t}{0.0135}$$

$\therefore$ $\qquad t = 815 - 8810.6 \times 0.0135 = \textbf{696°C (Ans.)}$

Example A-5. *A 7.8 m diameter vertical kiln has a hemispherical dome at the top; the dome is fabricated from a 30 cm thick layer of chrome brick which has a thermal conductivity of 1.16 W/m °C. The kiln dome has inside temperature of 880°C, and 25°C atmospheric air results into 11.4 W/m² °C heat transfer coefficient between the dome and air. Determine :*

(i) *The outside surface temperature of the dome and the heat loss from the kiln.*

(ii) *The percentage reduction in heat loss that would result by using a flat dome fabricated from the same material and with kiln operating under identical temperature conditions.*

Solution. *Given :* $r_1 = \dfrac{7.8}{2} = 3.9$ m; $r_2 = 3.9 + 0.3 = 4.2$ m; $k = 1.16$ W/m°C

$h = 11.4$ W/m² °C ; $t_1 = 880$°C; $t_a = 25$°C

(i) Outside surface temperature (t_2) and heat loss (Q) :

Conduction heat loss from a spherical body

$$= 4\pi k \, (t_1 - t_2) \times \dfrac{r_1 \, r_2}{r_2 - r_1} \qquad \qquad ...[\text{Eqn. 2.76}]$$

and for a hemisphere it equals half of this value.

$\therefore$ Conduction heat loss from the hemispherical dome

$$= 2\pi \times 1.16 \, (880 - t_2) \times \dfrac{3.9 \times 4.2}{4.2 - 3.9}$$

$$= 397.95 \, (880 - t_2) \qquad \qquad ...(i)$$

Convective heat flow outside surface of dome to the surrounding air

$$= hA \, (t_2 - t_a)$$

$$= 11.4 \times \left(\dfrac{1}{2} \times 4\pi \times 4.2^2 \right) \times (t_2 - 25)$$

$$= 1263.52 \, (t_2 - 25) \qquad \qquad ...(ii)$$

Under steady state conditions,

$$397.95 \, (880 - t_2) = 1263.52 \, (t_2 - 25)$$

$$350196 - 397.95 t_2 = 1263.52 \, t_2 - 31588$$

∴ $$t_2 = \frac{(350196 + 31588)}{(397.95 + 1283.52)} = 229.8°C \text{ (Ans.)}$$

Heat loss from the dome = 397.95 (880 − 229.8) = **258.747 kW (Ans.)**

(*ii*) **Percentage heat lost by using flat dome :**

For a dome with flat top,

$$\frac{kA \, (t_1 - t_2)}{L} = hA \, (t_2 - t_a)$$

The area (*A*) for conduction and convection heat-flow will be same.

∴ $$\frac{1.16 \, (880 - t_2)}{0.3} = 11.4 \, (t_2 - 25)$$

or, $$(880 - t_2) = 2.948 \, t_2 - 73.7$$

∴ $$t_2 = \frac{880 + 73.7}{2.948 + 1} = 241.56°C$$

∴   Heat loss from the dome $= \dfrac{kA \, (t_1 - t_2)}{L}$

$$= \frac{1.16 \times (\pi \times 3.9^2) \times (880 - 241.56)}{0.3}$$

$$= 117960 \text{ W or } 117.96 \text{ kW}$$

%age reduction in heat loss $= \dfrac{258.747 - 117.96}{258.747} \times 100 = \textbf{54.4\% (Ans.)}$

Example A-6. (*Variable conductivity*) *The thermal conductivity of an insulating material used over a 200 mm diameter pipe carrying a hot fluid varies as : k = 0.065 (1 + 0.0015 t), where 't' is in "°C' and 'k' is in W/m°C.*

The temperatures at the pipe surface and at the outside of insulation are 250°C and 60°C respectively. If the thickness of the insulation is 60 mm, determine :

   (*i*)   *The heat flow from the hot fluid and temperature at mid thickness of insulation.*

   (*ii*) *The slopes of temperature profile at inside surface, mid plane and outside surface.*

Solution. *Given :* $r_1 = \dfrac{200}{2} = 100$ mm or 0.1 m; $r_2 = 0.1 + 0.06 = 0.16$ m; $k = 0.065 \, (1 + 0.0015t)$;

$t_1 = 250°C; \, t_2 = 60°C$

(*i*) **The heat flow and the temperature at the mid thickness:**

As *the dependence of thermal conductivity on temperature is linear, the mean thermal conductivity corresponds to thermal conductivity taken at mean wall temperature.*

$$k_m = 0.065 \left[1 + 0.0015 \left(\frac{250 + 60}{2} \right) \right] = 0.08 \text{ W/m°C}$$

The heat flow through a cylindrical surface with radii r_1 and r_2 is given by

$$Q = \frac{(t_1 - t_2)}{\left[\dfrac{\ln (r_2 / r_1)}{2 \pi k L} \right]}$$ ...[(2.60)]

$$= \frac{(250 - 60)}{\left[\dfrac{\ln (0.16/0.1)}{2\pi \times 0.08 \times 1}\right]} = 203.2 \textbf{ W/m length (Ans.)}$$

Let 't' be the temperature at mid plane ($r_m = 0.1 + 0.03 = 0.13$ m)

$$k_m = 0.065 \left[1 + 0.0015 \left(\frac{250 + t}{2}\right)\right] = 0.065 \left[1 + 0.00075 (250 + t)\right]$$

$$Q = \frac{250 - t)}{\left[\dfrac{\ln (0.13/0.1)}{2\pi \times 0.065 \{1 + 0.00075 (250 + t)\} \times 1}\right]}$$

$$= \frac{(250 - t)\left[2\pi \times 0.065 \{1 + 0.00075 (250 + t)\} \times 1\right]}{\ln (0.13/0.1)}$$

For steady state heat conduction, heat passing through each section of the pipe is same.

$$\therefore \quad 203.2 = \frac{(250 - t)\left[2\pi \times 0.065 \{1 + 0.00075 (250 + t) \times 1\}\right]}{\ln (0.13/0.1)}$$

or,
$$203.2 = \frac{(250 - t)\left[0.4084 (1 + 0.1875 + 0.00075\, t)\right]}{0.2624}$$

$$53.32 = (250 - t)(0.485 + 0.0003063t)$$

$$= 121.25 + 0.0766\, t - 0.485\, t - 0.000\, 3063\, t^2$$

or,
$$0.0003063\, t^2 + 0.4084\, t - 67.93 = 0$$

or,
$$t^2 + 1333.33t - 221776 = 0$$

or,
$$t = \frac{-1333.33 \pm \sqrt{(1333.33)^2 + 4 \times 221776}}{2}$$

$$= \frac{-1333.33 \pm 1632.44}{2} = \textbf{149.56°C (Ans.)}$$

(ii) The Slopes of the temperature profiles :

The slopes of the temperature profiles are calculated from the following relation:

$$\frac{dt}{dx} = -\frac{Q}{kA} \quad \text{(Fourier law)}$$

● *Inside surface* : $A = 2\pi\, r_1\, L = 2\pi \times 0.1 \times 1 = 0.628$ m^2

$$k = 0.065 (1 + 0.0015 \times 250) = 0.0894 \text{ W/m°C}$$

$$\therefore \quad \frac{dt}{dx} = -\frac{203.2}{0.0894 \times 0.628} = -\textbf{3619.3°C/m (Ans.)}$$

● *Mid-plane* : $A = 2\pi r_m l = 2\pi \times 0.13 \times 1 = 0.8168$ m^2

$$k = 0.065 (1 + 0.0015 \times 149.56) = 0.0796 \text{ W/m°C}$$

$$\therefore \quad \frac{dt}{dx} = -\frac{203.2}{0.0796 \times 0.8168} = -\textbf{3125.3°C/m (Ans.)}$$

● *Outside surface* : $A = 2\pi\, r_2 l = 2\pi \times 0.16 \times 1 = 1.005$ m^2

$$k = 0.065 (1 + 0.0015 \times 60) = 0.07085 \text{ W/m°C}$$

$$\therefore \quad \frac{dt}{dx} = -\frac{203.2}{0.07085 \times 1.005} = -\textbf{2853.8°C/m (Ans.)}$$

Example A-7. *(Critical thickness of insulation).* A heat exchanger of outside radius 150 mm is to be insulated with glass wool of thermal conductivity 0.0825 W/m°C. The temperature at the surface of shell is 280°C and it can be assumed to remain constant after the layer of insulation has been applied to the shell. The convective film coefficient between the outside surface of slag wool and the surrounding air is estimated to be 8W/m²°C. Further, it is specified that the temperature at the outer surface of insulation must not exceed 30°C and the loss of heat per metre length of the shell should not be greater than 200 W.

Would the slag wool serve the intended purpose to restrict the heat loss? If yes, what should be the thickness of insulating material to suit the prescribed conditions.

Solution. *Given :* $r = 150$ mm $= 0.15$ m; $k = 0.0825$ W/m°C; $t_i = 280$°C; $t_o = 30$°C; $h_o = 8$W/m² °C; $Q = 200$ W.

The critical radius of insulation is given by,

$$r_c = \frac{k}{h_o} \qquad \text{...[Eqn. 2.86]}$$

$$= \frac{0.0825}{8} = 0.01031 \text{ m or } 10.31 \text{ mm}$$

Since the critical radius ($r_c = 10.31$ mm) is considerably smaller than the radius $r = 150$ mm of the shell; therefore, the *use of slag wool as insulating material would serve the intended purpose to restrict heat loss.* (**Ans.**)

Loss of heat from a cylindrical shell is given by,

$$Q = \frac{2\pi L (t_i - t_o)}{\dfrac{1}{h_o r_o} + \dfrac{ln (r_o / r_i)}{k}} \qquad \text{...[Eqn. (2.69)]}$$

or,

$$\frac{Q}{L} = \frac{2\pi (t_i - t_o)}{\dfrac{1}{h_o r_o} + \dfrac{ln (r_o / r_i)}{k}}$$

Inserting the appropriate values, we get

$$200 = \frac{2\pi(280 - 30)}{\dfrac{1}{8 r_o} + \dfrac{ln (r_0 / 0.15)}{0.0825}}$$

or,

$$200 = \frac{1570.8}{\dfrac{0.125}{r_0} + 12.12 \, ln (r_o / 0.15)}$$

or,

$$\frac{0.125}{r_0} + 12.12 \, ln (r_o / 0.15) = 7.854$$

By trial and error, we get

$$r_o = 0.275 \text{ m or } 275 \text{ mm}$$

∴ **Thickness of insulation** $= 275 - 150 = 125$ **mm** (**Ans.**)

Example A-8. *(Critical thickness of insulation)* An electric cable of 6 mm radius is applied a uniform sheathing of plastic insulation ($k = 0.187$ W/m°C). The convective film coefficient on the surface of bare cable as well as insulated cable was estimated as 11.7 W/m² °C and a surface temperature of 60°C was noted when the cable was directly exposed to ambient air at 20°C. Determine :

(i) The thickness of insulation, for keeping the wire as cool as possible.

(ii) The surface temperature of insulated cable if the intensity of current carried by the conductor remains unchanged.

Solution. *Given:* $r_1 = 6$ mm $= 0.006$ m; $k = 0.187$ W/m°C; $h_o = 11.7$ W/m^2 °C; $t_1 = 60$°C, $t_a = 20$°C

(*i*) **Thickness of insulation :**

For keeping the wire *as cool as possible* the required condition corresponds to that for critical radius of insulation, *i.e.*,

$$r_2 = r_c = \frac{k}{h_o} = \frac{0.187}{11.7} = 0.016 \text{ m} = 16 \text{ mm}$$

∴   Thickness of insulation $= r_2 - r_1 = 16 - 6 = $ **10 mm (Ans.)**

(*ii*) **The surface temperature, t_2 :**

For a base (un-insulated) wire, the heat flow,

$$Q_1 = hA\,(t_1 - t_a)$$
$$= 11.7 \times (2\pi \times 0.006 \times 1)\,(60 - 20) = 17.64 \text{ W/m length}$$

For the sheathed (insulated) cable,

$$Q_2 = \frac{2\pi\,(t_2 - 20)}{\dfrac{1}{h_0\,r_2} + \dfrac{\ln\,(r_2/r_1)}{k}} \text{ W/m length}$$

$$= \frac{2\pi\,(t_2 - 20)}{\dfrac{1}{11.7 \times 0.016} + \dfrac{\ln\,(0.016/0.006)}{0.187}} \text{ W/m length}$$

$$= \frac{6.283\,(t_0 - 20)}{5.342 + 5.245} = 0.593\,(t_2 - 20) \text{ W/m length}$$

If the intensity of current carried by the conductor remains unchanged, then

$$Q_1 = Q_2 = I^2 R$$

or, $17.64 = 0.593\,(t_2 - 20)$

∴ $t_2 = $ **49.75°C   (Ans.)**

Example A-9. (*a*) (*Critical thickness of insulation*) *Derive the following relation for heat dissipation from an electric cable which has been provided with critical insulation:*

$$Q = \frac{2\pi k L\,(t_i - t_o)}{1 + \ln\,(k/h_o\,r_i)}$$

The symbols have their usual meanings and subscripts 'i' and 'o' refers to the conditions at the inner and outer surfaces respectively.

(*b*) *An electric cable of 6 mm outer radius has a sheathing of rubber insulation for which thermal conductivity is 0.16 W/m°C. When current flows through the cable, heat is generated and surface temperature of 75°C is anticipated for the cable. This cable is laid in an environment having a temperature 15°C and the total coefficient associated with convection and radiation between the cable and environment is 8 W/m^2 °C. Determine :*

(*i*) *The most economical thickness and corresponding increase in heat dissipation due to insulation.*

(*ii*) *The increase in current carrying capacity of the cable by providing critical thickness of insulation.*

Solution. (*a*) The heat transmitted from the cable to the environment is given by,

$$Q = \frac{2\pi L\,(t_o - t_i)}{\dfrac{1}{h_o\,r_o} + \dfrac{\ln\,(r_o/r_i)}{k}}$$

When critical thickness (a thickness which gives the maximum heat dissipation from the cable surface) is provided; $r_c = r_o = \dfrac{k}{h_o}$

Then,
$$Q = \frac{2\pi L\,(t_o - t_i)}{\dfrac{1}{h_o \times (k/h_o)} + \dfrac{ln\,(k/h_o\,r_i)}{k}}$$

$$= \frac{2\pi k L\,(t_o - t_i)}{1 + ln\,(k/h_o\,r_i)} \qquad \text{.....Proved.}$$

(b)　Given : $r_i = 6$ mm $= 0.006$ m; $k = 0.16$ W/m°C; $t_i = 75$°C; $t_a = 15$°C; $h_o = 8$ W/m² °C

(i)　**The most economical thickness and increase in heat dissipation :**

Substituting the various values in the eqn., we get

$$\left(\frac{Q}{L}\right)_{insulated} = \frac{2\pi \times 0.16\,(75 - 15)}{1 + ln\,\{0.16/(8 \times 0.006)\}}$$

$$. = 27.37 \text{ W/m length}$$

For a bare cable, the heat dissipation would be,

$$\left(\frac{Q}{L}\right)_{bare} = 2\pi r_i h\,(t_i - t_o)$$

Assuming that the surface temperature of the cable and the outside connective coefficent in the bare condition are same as those in insulated coadition,

$$\left(\frac{Q}{L}\right)_{bare} = 2\pi \times 0.006 \times 8\,(75 - 15)$$

$$= 18.09 \text{ W/m length}$$

%age increase in heat dissipation

$$= \frac{27.37 - 18.09}{18.09} \times 100 = \textbf{51.3\%} \textbf{ (Ans.)}$$

This increase in heat dissipation would occur when critical insulation has been applied to the cable.

$$\text{Critical radius, } r_c = \frac{k}{h_o} = \frac{0.16}{8} = 0.02 \text{ m} = 20 \text{ mm}$$

∴　Thickness of insulation $= 20 - 6 = \textbf{14 mm (Ans.)}$

(ii)　**Percentage increase in current carrying capacity :**

$$Q = I^2 R$$

where,
$$I = \text{Current capacity, and}$$
$$R = \text{Electrical resistance of the cable.}$$

Now,
$$Q_1 = I_1^2\,R \text{ ...Bare cable}$$
$$Q_2 = I_2^2\,R \text{ ...Insulated cable}$$

∴
$$\frac{I_2}{I_1} = \sqrt{\frac{Q_2}{Q_1}} = \sqrt{\frac{27.37}{18.09}} = 1.23$$

∴　%age increase in current carrying capacity

$$= \frac{1.23\,I_1 - I_1}{I_1} \times 100 = \textbf{23\% (Ans.)}$$

Example A-10.(a) (*Critical insulation*) *Derive the following relation which will keep the insulated wire at the same temperature as if it were bare (uninsulated) :*

$$ln\left(\frac{r_o}{r_i}\right) = \frac{k}{h_o\,r_i}\left(1 - \frac{r_i}{r_o}\right)$$

The symbols have their usual meanings and subscripts i and o refer to the conditions at the inside and outside surfaces respectively.

(b) *An electric cable of 7.5 mm radius is applied a uniform sheathing 2.5 mm thick of plastic insulation ($k = 0.15$ W/m°C). The convective film coefficient between the surface of plastic and surrounding air is estimated as 10 W/m² °C.*

Does the insulation serve to augment heat loss and thus help in cooling of wire? Also, find out the outer radius of insulation which will keep the insulation at the same temperature as if it were bare.

Solution. (a) For a bare (uninsulated) wire the heat flow,

$$Q_1 = 2\pi\, r_i L h_o\, (t_i - t_o) = \frac{2\pi L\, (t_i - t_o)}{\dfrac{1}{h_o\, r_i}}$$

For the insulated wire,

$$Q_2 = \frac{2\pi L\, (t_i - t_o)}{\dfrac{1}{h_o\, r_o} + \dfrac{\ln(r_o/r_i)}{k}}$$

The condition to keep the insulated wire at the same temperature as if it were bare inherently stipulates that heat flow from the wire is same in both the situations. Thus,

$$Q_1 = Q_2$$

or,

$$\frac{1}{h_o\, r_i} = \frac{1}{h_o\, r_o} + \frac{\ln\,(r_o/r_i)}{k}$$

or,

$$\ln\left(\frac{r_o}{r_i}\right) = k\left(\frac{1}{h_o\, r_i} - \frac{1}{h_o\, r_o}\right)$$

or,

$$\ln\left(\frac{r_o}{r_i}\right) = \frac{k}{h_o\, r_i}\left(1 - \frac{r_i}{r_o}\right) \qquad \text{...Proved.}$$

(b) *Given* : $r_i = 7.5$ mm $= 0.0075$ m; $r_o = 7.5 + 2.5 = 10$ mm or 0.01 m;

$k = 0.15$ W/m°C; $h = 10$ W/m² °C

The critical radius of insulation,

$$r_c = \frac{k}{h_o} = \frac{0.15}{10} = 0.015 \text{ m} = 15 \text{ mm}$$

Since r_c is *greater than the outer radius* r_o *(i.e.* 10 mm) of the insulated wire; the *sheathing helps to dissipate more heat* and thus *help in the cooling of the wire.* **(Ans.)**

Substituting appropriate values in the above relation, we have

$$\ln\left(\frac{r_o}{r_i}\right) = \frac{0.15}{10 \times 0.0075}\left(1 - \frac{r_i}{r_o}\right) = 2\left(1 - \frac{r_i}{r_o}\right)$$

By trial and error,

$$\frac{r_o}{r_i} = 5$$

∴   Outer radius, $r_o = 5 \times r_i = 5 \times 0.0075 = 0.0375$ m $=$ **37.5 mm (Ans.)**

ExampleA-11. *(Fins) Determine the energy input required to solder together two very long pieces of bare copper wire 1.7 mm in diameter with a solder that melts at 190°C. The wires are positioned vertically in air at 25°C and the heat transfer coefficient on the wire surface is 16 W/m² °C. For the wire alloy, take the thermal conductivity as 330 W/m °C.*

Solution. *Given* : $d = 1.7$ mm or 0.0017 m; $t_o = 190$°C; $t_a = 25$°C; $h = 16$ W/m² °C; $k = 330$ W/m °C.

Energy input required to solder two long pieces :

The physical situation approximates as two *infinite fins* with a bare temperature of 190°C in an environment of 25°C with the given value of surface coefficient.

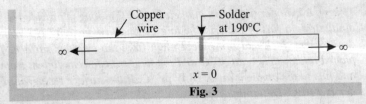

Fig. 3

Area of cross-section, $\quad A_{cs} = \dfrac{\pi}{4} d^2 = \dfrac{\pi}{4} \times (0.0017)^2 = 2.27 \times 10^{-6} \text{ m}^2$

Perimeter, $\quad\quad\quad\quad P = \pi d = \pi \times 0.0017 = 0.00534 \text{ m}$

$$m = \sqrt{\dfrac{hP}{kA_{cs}}} = \sqrt{\dfrac{16 \times 0.00534}{330 \times 2.27 \times 10^{-6}}} = 10.68$$

Heat dissipation from an infinitely long fin,

$$Q_{fin} = k\,A_{cs}\,m\,(t_o - t_a)$$

$$= 330 \times 2.27 \times 10^{-6} \times 10.68\,(190 - 25) = 1.32 \text{ W}.$$

∴ Energy input required for two wires $= 2 \times 1.32 = \mathbf{2.64\ W}$ **(Ans.)**

Example A-12. *(Fins) The Fig. 4 shows a 60 mm diameter rod, 1m long, which is having its lower face ground smooth. The remainder of the rod is exposed to the 25°C room air and a surface coefficient heat transfer equal to 7.1 W/m² °C exists between the rod surface and the room air. The grinder dissipates mechanical energy at the rate of 40 W. If thermal conductivity of rod material is 42.4 W/m °C, find the temperature of the rod at the point where grinding is taking place.*

Solution. *Given:* $d = 60$ mm $= 0.06$ m; $l = 1$m; $t_a = 25°C$; $h = 7.1$ W/m² °C; $Q_{fin} = 40$W; $k = 42.4$ W/m °C.

Temperature of the rod at the point of grinding, t_o :

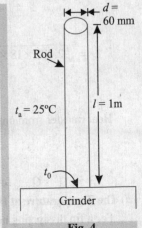

In this case, the entire dissipated energy goes into the rod at its lower face and is then transferred by convection from the outside surface area of the rod to the surrounding air.

Treating the rod as a *fin losing heat at the tip*, the heat flow through the rod is given by,

$$Q_{fin} = \sqrt{Phk\,A_{cs}}\ (t_o - t_a) \left[\dfrac{\tanh\,(ml) + \dfrac{h}{km}}{1 + \dfrac{h}{km}\ .\ \tanh\,(ml)} \right] \text{...Eqn. (2.135)}$$

Here, $P = \pi d = \pi \times 0.06 = 0.1885$ m

$$A_{cs} = \dfrac{\pi}{4} \times (0.06)^2 = 0.00283 \text{ m}^2$$

where, $\quad m = \sqrt{\dfrac{hP}{kA_{cs}}} = \sqrt{\dfrac{7.1 \times 0.1885}{42.4 \times 0.00283}} = 3.34 \text{ m}^{-1}$

$ml = 3.34 \times 1 = 3.34$

$\dfrac{h}{km} = \dfrac{7.1}{42.4 \times 3.34} = 0.05$

Inserting the appropriate values in the above eqn., we get.

$$40 = \sqrt{0.1885 \times 7.1 \times 42.4 \times 0.00283}\ (t_o - 25) \left[\dfrac{\tanh\,(3.34) + 0.05}{1 + 0.05 \tanh\,(3.34)} \right]$$

$$= 0.4\,(t_o - 25) \left[\dfrac{0.9975 + 0.05}{1 + 0.05 \times 0.9975} \right]$$

$$= 0.3991\,(t_o - 25)$$

or, $\quad t_o = \mathbf{125.2\ °C}$ **(Ans.)**

Example A-13. *(Fins). A cylinder 60 mm in diameter and 1.2 m long is provided with 10 longitu-dinal straight fins of material having thermal conductivity 115 W/m °C. The fins are 0.9 mm thick and protrude 15 mm from the cylinder surface. The system is placed in atmosphere at 30°C and the heat transfer coefficient from the cylinder and fins to the ambient air is 18 W/m² °C. If the surface temperature of the cylinder is 140°C. Determine :*

(i) *The rate of heat transfer.*

(ii) *The temperature at the end of fins.*

Consider the fin to be of finite length.

Solution. *Given* : $d = 60$ mm $= 0.06$ m; $b = 1.2$ m ; $n = 10$; $k = 115$ W/m °C ; $y = 0.9$ mm $= 0.0009$ m; $l = 15$ mm $= 0.015$ m; $h = 18$ W/m² °C; $t_o = 140$°C, $t_a = 30$°C.

For a fin of rectangular cross-section,

$$A_{cs} = b \times y = 1.2 \times 0.0009 = 0.00108 \text{ m}^2$$
$$P = 2\,(b + y) = 2\,(1.2 + 0.0009) = 2.402 \text{ m}$$

$$m = \sqrt{\frac{hP}{k\,A_{cs}}} = \sqrt{\frac{18 \times 2.402}{115 \times 0.00108}} = 18.66 \text{ m}^{-1}$$

$$ml = 18.66 \times 0.015 = 0.28$$

$$\frac{h}{km} = \frac{18}{115 \times 18.66} = 0.00839$$

(i) The rate of heat transfer :

$$Q_{fin} = \sqrt{Ph\,k\,A_{cs}}\,(t_o - t_a) \left[\frac{\tanh\,(ml) + \dfrac{h}{km}}{1 + \dfrac{h}{km} \times \tanh\,(ml)} \right]$$

$$= \sqrt{2.402 \times 18 \times 115 \times 0.00108}\,(140 - 30) \left[\frac{\tanh\,(0.28) + 0.00839}{1 + 0.00839 \times \tanh\,(0.28)} \right]$$

$$= 2.32 \times 110 \times \left[\frac{0.273 + 0.00839}{1 + 0.00839 \times 0.273} \right] = 71.65 \text{ W per fin}$$

Heat transfer from unfinned (base) surface

$$= h\left[\pi d \times 1.2 - n \times A_{cs}\right] \times (t_o - t_a)$$

$$= 18\,(\pi \times 0.06 \times 1.2 - 10 \times 0.00108) \times (140 - 30) = 426.5 \text{ W}$$

Q_{total} for 10 fins $= 426.5 + 10 \times 71.65 = $ **1143 W (Ans.)**

(ii) The Temperature at the end of fins :

For a fin dissipating heat to the surroundings from its tip end,

$$\frac{\theta}{\theta_o} = \frac{t - t_a}{t_o - t_a} = \frac{\cosh\,\{m\,(l - x)\} + \dfrac{h}{km}\,[\sinh\,\{m\,(l-x)\}]}{\cosh\,(ml) + \dfrac{h}{km}\,[\sinh\,(ml)]} \qquad ...\text{[Eqn. (2.136)]}$$

At $x = l$, the above eqn. reduces to

$$\frac{t_l - t_a}{t_o - t_a} = \frac{1}{\cosh\,(ml) + \dfrac{h}{km}\,[\sinh\,(ml)]}$$

or,

$$\frac{t_l - 30}{140 - 30} = \frac{1}{\cosh\,(0.28) + 0.00839\,\sinh\,(0.28)} = 0.9598$$

$$\therefore \qquad t_l = (140 - 30) \times 0.9598 + 30 = \textbf{135.6 °C (Ans.)}$$

Example A-14. *(Fins). The cylindrical head of an engine is 1.2 m long and has an outside diameter of 60 mm. Under typical operating conditions, the outer surface of the head is at a temperature of 160°C and is exposed to ambient air at 35°C with a convective coefficient of 85 kJ /m²h °C. The head has been provided with 10 longitudinal straight fins which are 0.9 mm thick and protrude 30 mm from the cylindrical surface. Assuming that the fins have insulated tips and that the thermal conductivity of the cylinder head and fin material is 265 kJ/ m-h-°C. Determine:*

(i) *The increase in heat dissipation due to addition of fins.*

(ii) *The temperature at the centre of the fin.*

Solution. *Given :* $d = 60$ mm $= 0.06$ m; $b = 1.2$ m; $t_o = 150$°C; $t_a = 35$°C; $h = 85$ kJ/ m² - h-°C; $n = 10$; $y = 0.9$ mm $= 0.000\,9$ m; $l = 30$ mm $= 0.03$ m; $k = 265$ kJ / m-h-°C.

For a straight rectangular fin,

$$\frac{P}{A_{cs}} = \frac{2(b+y)}{b \times y} \approx \frac{2b}{b \times y} = \frac{2}{y} \quad \text{since } y \ll b$$

$$m = \sqrt{\frac{hp}{kA_{cs}}} = \sqrt{\frac{2h}{ky}}$$

$$= \sqrt{\frac{2 \times 85}{265 \times 0.0009}} = 26.7 \text{ m}^{-1}$$

$$ml = 26.7 \times 0.03 = 0.801$$

(i) The increase in heat dissipation due to addition of fins :

For a fin with insulated tip,

$$Q_{fin} = k A_{cs} \, m \, (t_o - t_a) \tanh (ml) \qquad \qquad \text{...[Eqn (2.135)]}$$

$$= 265 \times (1.2 \times 0.0009) \times 26.7 \times (150 - 35) \tanh (0.801) = 584 \text{ kJ/h}$$

For 10 fins the heat dissipation

$$= 10 \times 584 = 5840 \text{ kJ/h}$$

Surface area of the cylinder head not occupied by the fins,

$$A = [\pi \times 0.06 \times 1.2 - (10 \times 1.2 \times 0.0009)] = 0.2154 \text{ m}^2$$

Heat dissipation from this surface by convection,

$$Q_{conv} = h A (t_o - t_a)$$

$$= 85 \times 0.2154 \times (150 - 35) = 2105.5 \text{ kJ/h}$$

$$Q_{total} = 5840 + 2105.5 = 7945.5 \text{ kJ/h}$$

Had the cylinder been *bare*, then heat transfer would have been,

$$Q_{bare} = h A (t_o - t_a)$$

$$= 85 \times (\pi \times 0.06 \times 1.2) (150 - 35) = 2211 \text{ kJ/h}$$

∴ %age increase in heat dissipation due to addition of fins

$$= \frac{7945.5 - 2211}{2211} \times 100 = \mathbf{259.4 \ \%} \text{ (Ans.)}$$

(ii) The Temperature at the centre of the fin; *t* **:**

The expression for temperature distribution is given by

$$\frac{\theta}{\theta_o} = \frac{t - t_a}{t_o - t_a} = \frac{\cosh \{m(l - x)\}}{\cosh (ml)}$$

Substituting $x = \dfrac{l}{2} = 0.015$ m and other appropriate values, we get

$$\frac{t - 35}{150 - 35} = \frac{\cosh\{26.7\ (0.03 - 0.015)\}}{\cosh\ (0.801)} = \frac{1.08}{1.338} = 0.807$$

∴ $$t = (150 - 35) \times 0.807 + 35 = \textbf{127.8}\,°C\ \textbf{(Ans.)}$$

ExampleA-15. *Derive a generalised equation for fins.*

Solution. Refer fig. 5

Consider a fin having cross-sectional area (A_{cs}) and surface area (A_s) varying along the heat flow direction (X-direction). Then, a heat balance for an elemental cross-section of thickness dx at a distance x from the base wall is given by;

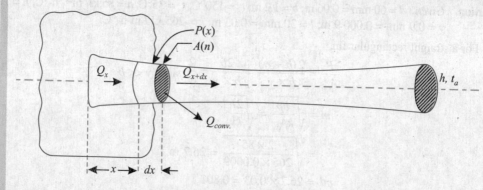

Fig. 5 A general fin of varying cross-section.

$$Q_x = Q_{x + dx} + Q_{conv.}$$

$$= Q_x + \frac{d}{dx}\ (Q_x)\ dx + Q_{conv.}$$

or, $$\frac{d}{dx}\ (Q_x)\ dx + Q_{conv.} = 0$$

or, $$\frac{d}{dx}\left(- kA_{cs}\ \frac{dt}{dx}\right) dx + h \times A_s\ (t - t_a) = 0$$

Here it has been presumed that the temperature of the fin is uniform and non-variant for the infinitesimal element. Further, assuming the thermal conductivity of the fin material to be constant within the considered temperature range, we have

$$- k\ A_{cs}\ \frac{dt^2}{dx^2} \cdot dx - k\ \frac{d\ A_{cs}}{dx} \cdot \frac{dt}{dx} \cdot dx + h \times dA_s\ (t - t_a) = 0$$

Dividing both sides by $k\,A_{cs}\ dx$, we get

$$\frac{d^2 t}{dx^2} + \frac{1}{A_{cs}}\ \frac{dA_{cs}}{dx} \cdot \frac{dt}{dx} - \frac{h}{k\ A_{cs}} \times \frac{dA_s}{dx}\ (t - t_a) = 0 \qquad \text{...(i)}$$

Also, excess temperature $\theta = t - t_a$; by differentiation, we get

$$\frac{d\theta}{dx} = \frac{dt}{dx} \qquad\qquad [\because\ t_a\ \text{(ambient temperature) is constant}]$$

Eqn. (*i*) can now be written as

$$\frac{d^2 \theta}{dx^2} + \frac{1}{A_{cs}} \times \frac{dA_{cs}}{dx} \times \frac{d\theta}{dx} - \frac{h}{k\ A_{cs}} \times \frac{dA_s}{dx}\ \theta = 0$$

The term $\dfrac{dA_s}{dx}$ represents perimeter P of the surface at the section under consideration.

$$\therefore \qquad \frac{d^2\theta}{dx^2} + \frac{1}{A_{cs}} \times \frac{dA_{cs}}{dx} \times \frac{d\theta}{dx} - \frac{hP}{kA_{cs}}\theta = 0$$

The above equation provides a *general form of the energy equation for steady, one-dimensional heat dissipation for a fin of any cross-section.*

When the fin is of constant cross-sectional area, the term $\dfrac{dA_{cs}}{dx}$ vanishes and the equation reduces to,

$$\frac{d^2\theta}{dx^2} - \frac{hP}{kA_{cs}}\theta = 0$$

or, $\qquad\qquad \dfrac{d^2\theta}{dx^2} - m^2\theta = 0 \qquad\qquad\qquad\qquad$ (same as eqn. 2.130)

where, $\qquad\qquad m = \sqrt{\dfrac{hP}{kA_{cs}}}$

Example A-16. *(**Fins**) Both ends of a 6 mm diameter U-shaped copper (k = 285 W/m °C) rod are rigidly fixed to a vertical wall which is at 110°C temperature. The length of U-shaped rod is 600 mm and it is exposed to air at 20°C. The combined radiative and convective heat transfer coefficient for the rod is 24 W/m² °C. Determine :*

    (i)   *The temperature at the centre of U-shaped rod.*

    (ii) *The heat transfer rate.*

Solution. Refer Fig 6. *Given :* $d = 6$ mm $= 0.006$ m; $k = 285$ W/m °C; $t_w = 110$°C; $l = 600$ mm $= 0.6$m; $t_a = 20$°C; $h = 24$ W/m² °C.

(i) The temperature at the centre of U-shaped rod ; t :

The temperature 't' can be worked out from the relation :

$$\theta = 2\theta_w \times \frac{\sinh(ml/2)}{\sinh(ml)}$$

...[From eqn 2.168, for $x = \dfrac{l}{2}$]

where, $\theta = t - t_a$; $\theta_w = t_w - t_a$

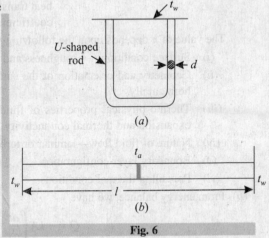

$$m = \sqrt{\frac{hP}{kA_{cs}}} = \sqrt{\frac{h \times \pi d}{k \times \frac{\pi}{4}d^2}} = \sqrt{\frac{4h}{kd}}$$

$$= \sqrt{\frac{4 \times 24}{285 \times 0.006}} = 7.493 \text{ m}^{-1}$$

$$ml = 7.493 \times 0.6 = 4.496$$

$$\frac{ml}{2} = \frac{4.496}{2} = 2.248$$

$$\therefore \quad t - 20 = 2(110 - 20) \times \frac{\sinh(2.248)}{\sinh(4.496)} = 18.8$$

or, $\qquad\qquad\qquad t = \textbf{38.8°C (Ans.)}$

(a)

(b)

Fig. 6

(ii) The heat transfer rate; Q :

The heat transfer rate from the fin can be worked out by considering two fins of 0.3 m length each with *insulated tip.*

$$Q = 2\sqrt{hPkA_{cs}}(t_o - t_a)\tanh(ml)$$

$$= 2 \sqrt{24 \times (\pi \times 0.006) \times 285 \times \left(\frac{\pi}{4} \times 0.006^2\right)(110 - 20)} \text{ tanh } (4.496)$$

$$= 2 \times 0.0604 \times 90 \times 0.9997 = \textbf{10.87 W} \quad \textbf{(Ans.)}$$

CONVECTION

Example A-17. (a) *Explain briefly Newton-Rikhman Law. Write also the factors on which the value of film coefficient depends.*

(b) *In a thermal boundary layer, the temperature profile at a particular location is given by an expression,*

$$t(y) = A - By + Cy^2$$

where A, B and C are constants. Derive an expression for the corresponding heat transfer coefficient.

Solution. (a) Irrespective of the particular nature (free or forced), the appropriate rate equation for the connective heat transfer between a surface and an adjacent fluid is presented by *Newton's law of cooling,*

$$Q = hA\,(t_s - t_f)$$

where,

Q = Convective heat flow rate,

A = Surface area exposed is heat transfer,

t_s = Surface temperature of solid,

t_f = Undisturbed temperature of the fluid, and

h = Constant of proportionality, also referred to as convective heat transfer coefficient, the surface conductance or the film coefficient.

The value of h depends upon the following *factors* :

  (*i*) Surface conditions — roughness and cleanliness.

  (*ii*) Geometry and orientation of the surface—plate, tube and cylinder placed vertically or horizontally.

  (*iii*) Thermo-physical properties of fluid—density, viscosity, specific heat, coefficient of expansion and thermal conductivity.

  (*iv*) Nature of fluid flow—laminar or turbulent.

  (*v*) Boundary layer configuration.

  (*vi*) Prevailing thermal conditions.

(b) From energy balance, we have

$$Q = - kA \left(\frac{dt}{dy}\right)_{y=o} = hA\,(t_s - t_\infty)$$

or,

$$h = - \frac{k}{(t_s - t_\infty)} \left(\frac{dt}{dy}\right)_{y=o}$$

From the given boundary layer temperature profile,

$$t = A - By + Cy^2;$$

$$\frac{dt}{dy} = - B + 2Cy$$

and,

$$\left(\frac{dt}{dy}\right)_{y=o} = - B$$

$$\therefore \qquad h = \frac{-k}{(t_s - t_\infty)}(-B) = \frac{Bk}{(t_s - t_\infty)} \quad \text{(Ans.)}$$

Example A-18. *(Boiling)* In a nucleate boiling of saturated water at 101.32 kN/m², vapour bubbles rise at an average velocity of 2.8 m/s. The average diameter of the bubbles is 3.2 mm. Using the following empirical relation for fluid flow over a single sphere :

$$\frac{hD}{k} = (1.2 + 0.53\, R_e^{0.54})\, P_r^{0.3} \left(\frac{\mu_\infty}{\mu_r}\right)^{0.25},$$

valid over the range $1 < Re < 2 \times 10^5$; and all properties except μ_s are evaluated at the free stream temperature, determine :

(i) The average heat transfer coefficient.

(ii) The drop in vapour temperature as the bubble moves up through a distance of 0.25 m.

Solution. *Given :* $p_v = 101.32$ kN/m²; $V_\infty = 2.8$ m/s; $D = 3.2$ mm; Distance by which the bubble moves up = 0.25 m.

(i) The average heat transfer coefficient; h :

For saturated water at 101.32 kN/m², the free stream temperature is 100°C and the corresponding thermo-physical properties are :

$$\rho_\infty = 958.4 \text{ ks/m}^3;\ k_\infty = 0.682 \text{ W/m °C};\ \nu_\infty = 0.297 \times 10^{-6} \text{ m}^2/\text{s};$$
$$\mu_\infty = \mu_s = \rho\nu = 2.78 \times 10^{-4} \text{ Ns/m}^2;\ Pr = 1.75;\ c_p = 4220 \text{ J/kg K}$$

Reynolds number, $Re = \dfrac{V_\infty D}{\nu_\infty} = \dfrac{2.8 \times (3.2 \times 10^{-3})}{0.297 \times 10^{-6}} = 30168$

Since $Re < 2 \times 10^5$, the given relation applies.

Substituting the appropriate values, we get

$$\frac{hD}{k_\infty} = \left[1.2 + 0.53 \times (30168)^{0.54}\right] \times (1.75)^{0.3} \times 1 = 165.9$$

$$\therefore \qquad h = 165.9 \times \frac{k_\infty}{D} = 165.9 \times \frac{0.682}{3.2 \times 10^{-3}} = \mathbf{35.36 \times 10^3\ W/m^2\,°C \ (Ans.)}$$

(ii) The drop in vapour temperature as the bubble moves up through a distance of 0.25 m :

By an energy balance, and assuming no phase change, we have

$$hA\,(T_v - T_{sat})\,\tau = m\,c_p \Delta T = (\rho V c_p)\,\Delta T$$

where, $\qquad \tau = \dfrac{\text{Distance}}{\text{Velocity}} = \dfrac{0.25}{2.8} = 0.0893\ s$

$$A = 4\pi R^2 = \pi D^2 = \pi \times (3.2 \times 10^{-3})^2 = 32.17 \times 10^{-6}\ m^2$$

$$V = \frac{\pi}{6} D^3 = \frac{\pi}{6} \times (3.2 \times 10^{-3})^3 = 1.716 \times 10^{-8}\ m^3$$

Assuming the bubbles contain no condensable gas,

$$T_v - T_{sat} = \frac{2\sigma}{r}\left[\frac{R_v\,T_{sat}^2}{\rho_v\,h_{fg}}\right] \qquad \qquad \text{...[Eqn. (9.5)]}$$

$$= \frac{2 \times 0.058}{(3.2 \times 10^{-3}/2)}\left[\frac{462 \times 373^2}{(101.32 \times 10^3) \times 2257 \times 10^3}\right] = 0.0204°C$$

$\therefore$ Vapour bubble temperature rise,

$$\Delta T = \frac{hA\,(T_v - T_{sat})\,\tau}{\rho V c_p}$$

$$= \frac{35.36 \times 10^3 \times 32.17 \times 10^{-6} \times 0.0204 \times 0.0893}{958.4 \times 1.716 \times 10^{-8} \times 4220} = \mathbf{0.0298°C \ (Ans.)}$$

Example A-19. (*Heat exchanger*) (*a*) *Is it better to arrange for flow in a heat exchanger to be parallel or counter-flow?*

(*b*) *In a counter-flow heat exchanger, oil* (c_p = 2.8 kJ/kg K) *at the rate of 1350 kg/h is cooled from 90°C to 20°C by water that enters at 15°C at the rate of 1250 kg/h.*

(*i*) *Determine the heat exchanger area for an overall heat transfer coefficient of 3800 W/m²-h-K.*

(*ii*) *Derive a relationship between oil and water temperatures at any section of the heat exchanger.*

Solution. (*a*) When a choice has to be made between parallel flow and counter-flow arrangement, the counter-flow design is usually *preferred* for the following *reasons* :

(*i*) The exchange of heat may raise the temperature of the cold fluid to *more nearly the initial temperature of the hot fluid.*

(*ii*) LMTD (Log-mean temperature difference) is higher and accordingly more heat can be transferred. Conversely, a *smaller surface area is required for the same rate of heat transfer.*

(*b*) Given : c_{ph} = 2.8 kJ/kg K; m_h = 1350 kg/h; t_{h1} = 90°C; t_{h2} = 20°C; t_{c1} = 15°C; m_c = 1250 kg/h; U = 3800 W/m²-h-K.

(*i*) **Heat exchange area, A :**

Heat lost by hot fluid = Heat gained by cold fluid

$$m_h \times c_{ph} \times (t_{h1} - t_{h2}) = m_c \times c_{pc} \times (t_{c2} - t_{c1})$$
$$1350 \times 2.8 \times (90 - 20) = 1250 \times 4.186 \times (t_{c2} - 15)$$

∴ $$t_{c2} = 65.6°C$$

$$LMTD, \ \theta_m = \frac{\theta_1 - \theta_2}{\ln (\theta_1 / \theta_2)}$$

$$= \frac{(t_{h1} - t_{c2}) - (t_{h2} - t_{c1})}{\ln \left[(t_{h1} - t_{c2}) / (t_{h2} - t_{c1}) \right]}$$

$$\frac{(90 - 65.6) - (20 - 15)}{\ln \left[(90 - 65.6)/(20 - 15) \right]} = \frac{19.4}{\ln (24.4/5)} = 12.24°C$$

Heat exchanged, $Q = UA\theta_m$

or, Heat exchanger area, $$A = \frac{Q}{U\theta_m} = \frac{m_h \times c_{ph} (t_{h1} - t_{h2})}{U\theta_m}$$

$$= \frac{1350 \times 2.8 (90 - 20)}{3800 \times 12.24} = \mathbf{5.69 \ m^2 \ (Ans.)}$$

(*ii*) At any section of the heat exchanger, we have

$$m_h \times c_{ph} \times (90 - t_h) = m_c \times c_{pc} (65.6 - t_c)$$
$$1350 \times 2.8 \times (90 - t_h) = 1250 \times 4.186 (65.6 - t_c)$$

or, $$(90 - t_h) = 1.384 (65.6 - t_c)$$

or, $$t_h = 90 - 1.384 (65.6 - t_c) = 1.384 \ t_c - 0.79 \ \mathbf{(Ans.)}$$

Example A-20. (*Heat exchanger*) *A feed water heater with steam outside and water inside the tubes is required to heat water from a temperature 't_1' to temperature 't_2'. The overall heat transfer coefficient is anticipated to be* $\left[\dfrac{m}{(m + Ba)} \right]$ *kJ/m²-s-°C, where 'a' is the total cross-sectional area of water flow in m², 'm' is the mass flow rate of water per tube in kg/s and 'B' is a dimensional constant. Derive the following relation between length 'l' and diameter 'd' of the tube :*

$$\frac{4l}{d} = c\left(B + \frac{m}{a}\right) \ln\left(\frac{t_s - t_1}{t_s - t_2}\right)$$

where 'c' is the specific heat of water and t_s is the temperature of condensing steam.

Solution. An energy balance on the coolant (water) gives the heat exchange rate as,

$$Q = N \times m \times c \times (t_2 - t_1)$$

where, N = No. of tubes, and

m = Mass flow rate of water per tube.

The overall heat exchange rate is also given by

$$Q = UA\theta_m = UA\left[\frac{\theta_1 - \theta_2}{\ln(\theta_1/\theta_2)}\right]$$

$$= UA\left[\frac{(t_s - t_1) - (t_s - t_2)}{\ln\{(t_s - t_1)/(t_s - t_2)\}}\right]$$

Also $A = N \times \pi\,d\,l$

$$\therefore \qquad N \times m \times c \times (t_2 - t_1) = \left(\frac{m}{m + Ba}\right) \times (N \times \pi dl) \times \left[\frac{(t_2 - t_1)}{l_n\{(t_s - t_1)/(t_s - t_2)\}}\right]$$

$$\pi\,d\,l = c\,(m + Ba)\ln\left(\frac{t_s - t_1}{t_s - t_2}\right)$$

Dividing both sides by the flow area $a = \dfrac{\pi d^2}{4}$

$$\frac{4l}{d} = c\left(B + \frac{m}{a}\right)\ln\left(\frac{t_s - t_1}{t_s - t_2}\right) \quad \textbf{...Required Expression (Ans.)}$$

RADIATION

Example A-21.   *A boiler furnace is laid from fire clay brick with outside lagging from plate steel; the distance between the two is quite small compared with the size of the furnace. The brick setting is at an average temperature of 380 K while the steel lagging is at 300 K. The emissivity values are :* $\varepsilon_{(brick)} = 0.84$ *and* $\varepsilon_{(steel)} = 0.64$.

Determine :

   (i)   *The radiant flux.*

   (ii) *The reduction in heat loss if a steel screen having an emissivity value of 0.62 on both sides is placed between the brick and steel setting. Also calculate the desired emissivity of screen if the radiation loss is to be limited to 90 W/m².*

Solution. *Given :* $T_1 = 380$ K; $T_2 = 300$ K; $\varepsilon_{(brick)} = 0.84$; $\varepsilon_{(steel)} = 0.64$.

(i) The radiant flux; Q_{12} :

The rate of heat interchange between brick setting (suffix 1) and steel logging (suffix 2) is given by,

$$Q_{12} = (F_g)_{1-2}\,A_1\,\sigma\left(T_1^4 - T_2^4\right)$$

The gray factor, $(F_g)_{1-2} = \dfrac{1}{\left(\dfrac{1 - \varepsilon_1}{\varepsilon_1}\right) + \dfrac{1}{F_{1-2}} + \left(\dfrac{1 - \varepsilon_2}{\varepsilon_2}\right)\dfrac{A_1}{A_2}}$

For infinite long parallel plates which see each other and nothing else,

$$F_{1-2} = 1,\, A_1 = A_2$$

$$\therefore \qquad (F_g)_{1-2} = \cfrac{1}{\left(\cfrac{1}{\varepsilon_1} - 1\right) + 1 + \left(\cfrac{1}{\varepsilon_2} - 1\right)} = \cfrac{1}{\cfrac{1}{\varepsilon_1} + \cfrac{1}{\varepsilon_2} - 1}$$

$$= \cfrac{1}{\cfrac{1}{0.84} + \cfrac{1}{0.64} - 1} = 0.57$$

$$\therefore \qquad Q_{12} = 0.57 \times 1 \times 5.67 \left[\left(\frac{380}{100}\right)^4 - \left(\frac{300}{100}\right)^4\right]$$

$$= \textbf{412.1 W/m}^2 \textbf{ (Ans.)}$$

(ii) The reduction in heat loss :

When a screen (suffix 3) is inserted between the brick (suffix 1) and steel lagging (suffix 2),

$$\left(F_g\right)_{1-2} = \cfrac{1}{\left[\left(\cfrac{1 - \varepsilon_1}{\varepsilon_1}\right) + \cfrac{1}{F_{1-2}} + \left(\cfrac{1 - \varepsilon_3}{\varepsilon_3}\right)\cfrac{A_1}{A_3}\right] + \left[\left(\cfrac{1 - \varepsilon_3}{\varepsilon_3}\right) + \cfrac{1}{F_{3-2}} + \left(\cfrac{1 - \varepsilon_2}{\varepsilon_2}\right)\cfrac{A_3}{A_2}\right]}$$

For given arrangement,

$$A_1 = A_2 = A_3 \text{ and } F_{1-2} = F_{3-2} = 1$$

$$\therefore \qquad \left(F_g\right)_{1-2} = \cfrac{1}{\cfrac{1}{\varepsilon_1} + \cfrac{1}{\varepsilon_2} + \cfrac{2}{\varepsilon_3} - 2}$$

$$= \cfrac{1}{\cfrac{1}{0.84} + \cfrac{1}{0.64} + \cfrac{2}{0.62} - 2} = 0.25$$

$$\therefore \qquad Q_{12} = 0.25 \times 1 \times 5.67 \left[\left(\frac{380}{100}\right)^4 - \left(\frac{300}{100}\right)^4\right] = \textbf{180.75 W/m}^2 \textbf{ (Ans.)}$$

Hence the reduction is heat loss due to placement of steel screen

$$= 412.1 - 180.75 = \textbf{231.35 W/m}^2 \textbf{ (Ans.)}$$

Emissivity of screen for reducing loss to 90 W/m²; ε_3:

If radiant heat loss is to be limited to 90 W/m², then

$$90 = (F_g)_{1-2} \times 1 \times 5.67 \left[\left(\frac{380}{100}\right)^4 - \left(\frac{300}{100}\right)^4\right]$$

$$= (F_g)_{1-2} \times 723$$

$$\therefore \qquad (F_g)_{1-2} \times 0.1245$$

Also,

$$\cfrac{1}{(F_g)_{1-2}} = \cfrac{1}{\varepsilon_1} + \cfrac{1}{\varepsilon_2} + \cfrac{2}{\varepsilon_3} - 2$$

or,

$$\cfrac{1}{0.1245} = \cfrac{1}{0.84} + \cfrac{1}{0.64} + \cfrac{2}{\varepsilon_3} - 2$$

$$8.032 = 1.1905 + 1.5625 + \cfrac{2}{\varepsilon_3} - 2$$

Desired emissivity of screen, $\varepsilon_3 = \textbf{0.275 (Ans.)}$

Example A-22. *A 12 mm outside diameter pipe carries a cryogenic fluid at 90 K. Another pipe of 15 mm outside diameter and at 290 K surrounds it coaxially and the space between the pipes is completely evacuated.*

    (i) *Determine the radiant heat flow for 3.5 m length of pipe if the surface emissivity for both surfaces is 0.25.*

    (ii) *Calculate the percentage reduction in heat flow if a shield of 13.5 mm diameter and 0.06 surface emissivity is placed between the pipes.*

Solution. *Given :* $d_1 = 12$ mm $= 0.012$ m; $T_1 = 90$ K ; $d_2 = 15$ mm $= 0.015$ m; $T_2 = 290$ K; $l = 3.5$ m; $\varepsilon_1 = \varepsilon_2 = 0.25$; $d_s = 13.5$ mm $= 0.0135$ m, $\varepsilon_s = 0.06$

(i) Radiant heat flow:

The rate of heat interchange between the inner (suffix 1) and outer (suffix 2) pipes is given by,

$$Q_{12} = (F_g)_{1-2} \, A_1 \, \sigma (T_1^4 - T_2^4)$$

The gray body factor,

$$(F_g)_{1-2} = \cfrac{1}{\left(\dfrac{1}{\varepsilon_1} - 1\right) + \dfrac{1}{F_{1-2}} + \left(\dfrac{1}{\varepsilon_2} - 1\right)\dfrac{A_1}{A_2}}$$

For the given configuration: $F_{1-2} = 1$

$$(F_g)_{1-2} = \cfrac{1}{\dfrac{1}{\varepsilon_1} + \left(\dfrac{1}{\varepsilon_2} - 1\right)\dfrac{A_1}{A_2}}$$

Now,
$$Q_{12} = \cfrac{A_1 \sigma (T_1^4 - T_2^4)}{\dfrac{1}{\varepsilon_1} + \left(\dfrac{1}{\varepsilon_2} - 1\right)\dfrac{A_1}{A_2}}$$

For 3.5 m length of pipe, the pipe areas are :

$$A_1 = \pi \, d_1 \, l = \pi \times 0.012 \times 3.5 = 0.1319 \text{ m}$$

$$A_2 = \pi \, d_2 \, l = \pi \times 0.015 \times 3.5 = 0.1649 \text{ m}$$

$$\frac{A_1}{A_2} = \frac{\pi d_1 l}{\pi d_2 l} = \frac{d_1}{d_2} = \frac{0.012}{0.015} = 0.8$$

Inserting the appropriate values in the above eqn., we get.

$$Q_{12} = \cfrac{0.1319 \times 5.67 \left[\left(\dfrac{90}{100}\right)^4 - \left(\dfrac{290}{100}\right)^4\right]}{\dfrac{1}{0.25} + \left(\dfrac{1}{0.25} - 1\right) \times 0.8}$$

$$= -\frac{52.4}{6.4} = \mathbf{-8.188 \text{ W}}$$

The *negative sign implies that heat flows from outer pipe to inner pipe.* (**Ans.**)

(ii) %age reduction in heat flow due to insertion of a shield :

When a radiation shield is placed between the two pipes,

$$(F_g)_{1-2} = \cfrac{1}{\left[\left(\dfrac{1}{\varepsilon_1} - 1\right) + \dfrac{1}{F_{1-s}} + \left(\dfrac{1}{\varepsilon_s} - 1\right)\dfrac{A_1}{A_s}\right] + \left[\left(\dfrac{1}{\varepsilon_s} - 1\right) + \dfrac{1}{F_{s-2}} + \left(\dfrac{1}{\varepsilon_2} - 1\right)\dfrac{A_s}{A_s}\right]}$$

Here $F_{1-s} = F_{s-2} = 1$,

$$(F_g)_{1-2} = \cfrac{1}{\cfrac{1}{\varepsilon_1} + \left(\cfrac{1}{\varepsilon_s} - 1\right)\cfrac{A_1}{A_s} + \cfrac{1}{\varepsilon_s} + \left(\cfrac{1}{\varepsilon_2} - 1\right)\cfrac{A_s}{A_2}}$$

A_s (shield pipe area) $= \pi d_s l = \pi \times 0.0135 \times 3.5 = 0.1484 \text{ m}^2$

$$\frac{A_1}{A_s} = \frac{d_1}{d_s} = \frac{0.013}{0.0135} = 0.963$$

$$\frac{A_s}{A_2} = \frac{d_s}{d_2} = \frac{0.0135}{0.015} = 0.9$$

$\therefore$

$$Q_{12} = \cfrac{A_1 \, \sigma \left(T_1^4 - T_2^4\right)}{\cfrac{1}{\varepsilon_1} + \left(\cfrac{1}{\varepsilon_s} - 1\right)\cfrac{A_1}{A_s} + \cfrac{1}{\varepsilon_s} + \left(\cfrac{1}{\varepsilon_2} - 1\right)\cfrac{A_s}{A_2}}$$

$$= \cfrac{0.1319 \times 5.67 \left[\left(\cfrac{90}{100}\right)^4 - \left(\cfrac{290}{100}\right)^4\right]}{\cfrac{1}{0.25} + \left(\cfrac{1}{0.06} - 1\right) \times 0.963 + \cfrac{1}{0.06} + \left(\cfrac{1}{0.25} - 1\right) \times 0.9}$$

$$= -\frac{52.4}{4 + 15.087 + 16.67 + 2.7} = -1.362 \text{ W}$$

Hence percentage reduction in heat flow

$$= \frac{8.188 - 1.362}{8.188} \times 100 = \textbf{83.37 \% (Ans.)}$$

PART V

OBJECTIVE TYPE QUESTIONS BANK

(With Answers)

A. Choose the Correct Answer
B. Match List I with List II
C. Competitive Examinations (UPSC, etc.) Questions
    (With Solutions – Comments)

ADDITIONAL QUESTIONS
(With Answers)

OBJECTIVE TYPE QUESTIONS

(With Answers)

1. The Fourier's law of heat transfer by conduction is expressed as

   (a) $Q = kA \dfrac{dt}{dx}$ (b) $-kA \dfrac{dt}{dx}$

   (c) $Q = kA \dfrac{dx}{dt}$ (d) $-kA \dfrac{dx}{dt}$

2. The heat transfer is constant when

   (a) temperature remains constant with time
   (b) temperature decreases with time
   (c) temperature increases with time.

3. The coefficient of thermal conductivity is defined as

   (a) Quantity of heat transfer per unit area per one degree drop in temperature
   (b) Quantity of heat transfer per one degree temperature drop per unit area
   (c) Quantity of heat transfer per unit time per unit area
   (d) Quantity of heat transfer per unit time per unit area per one degree temperature drop per unit length.

4. The thermal conductivity is expressed as

   (a) W/mK (b) W/m^{2}K
   (c) W/hmK (d) W/h^{2}m^{2}K.

5. Heat transfer from higher temperature to low temperature takes place accroding to

   (a) Fourier law
   (b) First law of thermodynamics
   (c) Second law of thermodynamcis
   (d) Zeroth law of thermodynamics.

6. Conduction through flat composite wall is given by :

   (a) $Q = \dfrac{t_1 - t_4}{\dfrac{x_1}{k_1 A} + \dfrac{x_2}{k_2 A} + \dfrac{x_3}{k_3 A}}$

   (b) $Q = \dfrac{t_1 - t_4}{\dfrac{k_1 A}{x_1} + \dfrac{k_2 A}{x_2} + \dfrac{k_3 A}{x_3}}$

   (c) $Q = \dfrac{(t_1 - t_4)\, A}{\dfrac{k_1}{x_1} + \dfrac{k_2}{x_2} + \dfrac{k_3}{x_3}}$

   (d) $Q = \dfrac{\dfrac{k_1 A}{x_1} + \dfrac{k_2 A}{x_2} + \dfrac{k_3 A}{x_3}}{(t_1 - t_4)}$

   where Q = heat transfer, t_1, t_2, t_3 and t_4 temperatures on surfaces of composite wall, x_1, x_2, x_3, x_4 thicknesses of different composite wall layers.

7. Conduction through hollow, radial one dimensional heat transfer is expressed as

   (a) $Q = \dfrac{2\pi l\,(t_1 - t_2)\,k}{\log_e r_2 / r_1}$

   (b) $Q = \dfrac{2\pi l\,(t_1 - t_2)}{k\,(r_2 - r_1)}$

   (c) $Q = \dfrac{2\pi l\,\log_e (t_1 / t_2)}{(r_2 - r_1)\,k}$

   (d) $Q = \dfrac{2\pi l\,(t_1 - t_2)\,k}{\log_e r_2 / r_1}$.

8. The radial heat transfer rate through hollow cylinder increases as the ratio of outer radius to inner radius
   (a) decreases   (b) increases
   (c) constant   (d) none of the above.

9. Stefan-Boltzmann's law is expressed as
   (a) $Q = s\,AT^4$ (b) $Q = s\,A^2T^4$
   (c) $Q = s\,AT^2$ (d) $Q = AT^4$

10. The quantity of heat radiation is dependent on
    (a) area of the body only
    (b) shape of the body only
    (c) temperature of the body only
    (d) on all (a), (b) and (c).

11. Conduction is a process of heat transfer from
    (a) a hot body to a cold body, in a straight line, without affecting the intervening medium
    (b) one particle of the body to another without the actual motion of the particles
    (c) one particle of the body to another by the actual motion of the heated particles
    (d) none of the above.

12. The amount of heat flow through a body by conduction is
    (a) dependent upon the material of the body
    (b) directly proportional to the surface area of the body
    (c) directly proportional to the temperature difference on the two faces of the body
    (d) inversely proportional to the thickness of the body
    (e) all of the above.

13. Thermal conductivity of solid metals .... with rise in temperature.
    (a) decreases   (b) increases
    (c) remains same   (d) unpredictable.

14. Thermal diffusivity of a substance is
    (a) directly proportional to the thermal conductivity
    (b) inversely proportional to density of substance
    (c) inversely proportinal to specific heat
    (d) all the the above.

15. The overall coefficient of heat transfer is used in the problems of
    (a) radiation
    (b) conduction
    (c) convection
    (d) conduction and convection.

16. Thermal conductivity of non-metallic amorphous solids .... with decrease in temperature.
    (a) decreases   (b) increases
    (c) remains constant   (d) unpredictable.

17. Heat transfer takes place as per .... law of thermodynamics.
    (a) Zeroth   (b) first
    (c) second   (d) none of the above.

18. Heat is closely related with ....
    (a) energy   (b) entropy
    (c) enthalpy   (d) temperature.

19. Heat flowing from one side to other does not depend directly on
    (a) thermal conductivity
    (b) face area
    (c) temperature difference
    (d) thickness.

20. .... has least value of conductivity.
    (a) Rubber   (b) Air
    (c) Water   (d) Glass
    (e) Plastic.

21. .... has maximum value of thermal conductivity.
    (a) Lead   (b) Copper
    (c) Steel   (d) Aluminium
    (e) Brass.

22. Heat conduction in gases is due to
    (a) electromagnetic waves
    (b) motion of electrons
    (c) mixing motion of the different layers of the gas
    (d) elastic impact of molecules.

23. Due to which of the following reasons most metals are good conductors of heat ?
    (a) Capacity to absorb free energy of electrons
    (b) Energy transport due to molecular vibration
    (c) Lattice defects
    (d) Migration of neutrons from hot end to cold end.
    (e) Presence of many free electrons and frequent collision of atoms.

24. In which of the following cases most unsteady heat flow occurs?
    (a) Through the walls of a furnace
    (b) Through lagged pipes carrying steam
    (c) Through the wall of a refrigerator
    (d) During annealing of castings.

25. In which of the following cases, molecular transmission of heat is smallest?

    (a) Solids   (b) Alloys

    (c) Gases   (d) Liquids.

26. Due to which of the folowing reasons cork is a good insulator?

    (a) It is porous   (b) Its density is low

    (c) It can be powdered (d) All of the above.

27. .... is the most widely used heat insulating material for pipelines carrying steam.

    (a) Sawdust

    (b) Cotton

    (c) Asbestos

    (d) 85% magnesia cement and glass wool.

28. With regard to 'thermal diffusivity' which of the following statements is *incorrect*?

    (a) It is a dimensionless quantity

    (b) It represents a physical property of the material

    (c) It is an important characteristic for unsteady heat conduction

    (d) None of the above.

29. The temperature distribution for a plane wall, for steady state heat flow and constant value of thermal conductivity, is

    (a) logarithmic   (b) parabolic

    (c) linear   (d) any of the above.

30. The relation $\nabla^2 T = 0$ is referred to as .... equation.

    (a) Poisson's

    (b) Laplace

    (c) Fourier heat conduction

    (d) none of the above.

31. If k is the thermal conductivity, ρ is the mass density and c is the specific heat then the thermal diffusivity of substance is given by

    (a) $\dfrac{\rho c}{k}$ (b) $\dfrac{k}{\rho c}$

    (c) $\dfrac{kc}{\rho}$ (d) $\dfrac{k\rho}{c}$.

32. .... is expected to have highest thermal conductivity.

    (a) Water   (b) Melting ice

    (c) Solid ice   (d) Steam.

33. In the heat flow equation $Q = kA\,(t_1 - t_2)/x$, the term $(t_1 - t_2)/x$ is known as

    (a) thermal conductivity

    (b) thermal coefficient

    (c) thermal resistance

    (d) temperature gradient.

34. In the heat flow equation $Q = kA\,(t_1 - t_2)/x$, the term x/kA is known as

    (a) temperature gradient

    (b) thermal coefficient

    (c) thermal resistance

    (d) thermal coductivity.

35. Film coefficient is defined as

    (a) thermal conductivity / equivalent thickness of film

    (b) inside diamter of tube / equivalent thickness of film

    (c) (specific heat × viscosity) / thermal conductivity

    (d) none of the above.

36. Why are fins provided on heat transferring surface?

    (a) To increase temperature gradient

    (b) To increase heat transfer coefficient

    (c) To increase heat transfer area

    (d) All of the above.

37. When the thickness of insulation on a pipe exceeds the critical value

    (a) the heat flow rate decreases

    (b) the heat flow rate increases

    (c) the heat flow rate remains constant

    (d) none of the above.

38. For spheres, the critical thickness of insulation is given by

    (a) $\dfrac{h}{2k}$ (b) $\dfrac{2k}{h}$

    (c) $\dfrac{k}{h}$ (d) $\dfrac{k}{2\pi h}$

    where k = thermal conductivity, h = convective heat transfer coeffecient.

39. It is considered appropriate that area of cross-section, for a finned surface, be

    (a) reduced along the length

    (b) increased along the length

    (c) maintained constant along the length

    (d) none of the above.

40. What does transient conduction mean?

    (a) Heat transfer for a short time

    (b) Conduction when the temperature at a point varies with time

(c) Very little heat transfer

(d) Heat transfer with a very small temperature difference.

41. How can the temperature drop in a plane wall with uniformly distributed heat generation be decreased?

(a) By reducing thermal conductivity of wall material

(b) By reducing wall thickness

(c) By reducing convection coefficient at the surface

(d) By reducing heat generation rate.

42. The temperature variation with time, in the lumped parameter model, is

(a) exponential   (b) sinusoidal

(c) cubic   (d) linear.

43. In transient heat conduction, the two significant dimensionless parameters are .... number and .... number.

(a) Fourier, Reynolds

(b) Reynolds, Prandtl

(c) Biot, Fourier

(d) Reyonlds, Biot.

44. .... number is relevant in transient heat condition.

(a) Reynolds   (b) Fourier

(c) Grashoff   (d) Prandtl.

45. .... number is generally associated with natural convection heat transfer.

(a) Prandtl   (b) Weber

(c) Nusselt   (d) Grashoff.

46. The degree of approach, in heat exchangers, is defined as the difference between temperatures of

(a) hot medium outlet and cold water outlet

(b) hot medium outlet and cold water inlet

(c) cold water inlet and outlet

(d) hot medium inlet and outlet.

47. Two insulating materials (put over each other) are used to insulate a steam pipe, best result would be obtained if

(a) inferior insulation is put over pipe and better one over it

(b) better insulation is put over pipe and inferior one over it

(c) both may be put in any order

(d) none of the above.

48. Compared to parallel flow heat exchanger, LMTD in case of counter-flow heat exchanger is

(a) lower   (b) higher

(b) same   (d) unpredictable.

49. Thermal diffusivity is a

(a) dimensionless parameter

(b) mathematical formula only

(c) physical property of the material

(d) function of temperature.

50. Transient heat flow occurs in

(a) melting of ice

(b) heating and cooling of buildings due to sun

(c) insulated pipes carrying superheated steam

(d) all of the above.

51. Transmission of heat by molecular collision is

(a) scattering   (b) conduction

(c) convection   (d) radiation.

52. In which of the following cases heat is transferred by conduction, convection and radiation?

(a) Boiler furnaces

(b) Refrigerator freezer coils

(c) Melting of ice

(d) All of the above.

53. .... is generally used to measure the temperature inside a furnance.

(a) Gas thermometer

(b) Optical pyrometer

(c) Alcohol thermometer

(d) Mercury thermometer.

54. .... is not the assumption of Fourier's equation of heat conduction.

(a) Constant temperature difference

(b) Uniform area of cross-section

(c) Steady heat flow

(d) Homogeneous substance.

55. A substance above critical temperature exists as

(a) liquid   (b) solid

(c) gas   (d) wet vapour.

56. .... is a non-dimensional number which generally finds application in mass transfer problem.

(a) Grashoff number   (b) Mach number

(c) Stanton number   (d) Weber number.

57. By which of the following modes of heat transfer heat is mainly transferred from an insulated pipe to the surrounding still air ?

(a) Radiation (b) Free convection

(c) Forced convection (d) Conduction.

58. .... will radiate heat to a large extent.

   (a) Black polished surface

   (b) White rough surface

   (c) White polished surface

   (d) Black rough surface.

59. When metallic surfaces are oxidised the emissivity

   (a) decreases (b) increases

   (c) remains unaltered (d) unpredictable.

60. Shape of an ideal thermometer should be ....

   (a) cubical (b) rectangular

   (c) spherical (d) cylindrical.

61. Planck's law of radiation is applicable to .... radiation.

   (a) monochromatic (b) thermal

   (c) temperature (d) none of the above.

62. Which of the folowing factors affect nucleate pool boiling?

   (a) Pressure

   (b) Material of heating surface

   (c) Physical properties of liquid

   (d) Surface condition of heating surface

   (e) All of the above.

63. The monochromatic emissivity of a white body at all wavelengths and temperatures is equal to

   (a) zero (b) 0.1 to 0.4

   (c) 0.6 (d) unity.

64. A .... body reflects entire radiation incident on it.

   (a) transparent (b) black

   (c) gray (d) white.

65. .... method is used to find the thermal conductivity of rubber.

   (a) Searle's (b) Lee's disc

   (c) Cylindrical shell (d) Laby and Hercus

66. "All bodies above absolute zero temperature emit radiation". This statement is based on

   (a) Stefan's law (b) Planck's law

   (c) Prevost theory (d) Wien's law.

67. An automobile radiator is .... type of heat exchanger.

   (a) cross-flow (b) regenerator

   (c) counter-flow (d) recuperator.

68. The wavelength for maximum emissive power is given by

   (a) Kirchhoff's law

   (b) Stefan Boltzmann's law

   (c) Fourier's law

   (d) Wien's law.

69. The emissive power of a body depends on

   (a) physical nature

   (b) nature of body

   (c) temperature of body

   (d) all of the above.

70. A hollow sphere with uniform interior temperature and a small hole behaves very nearly as a .... body.

   (a) black (b) opaque

   (c) white (d) transport.

71. .... rays have the least wavelength.

   (a) Infrared (b) Ultraviolet

   (c) Radio (d) Cosmic.

72. Dropwise condensation occurs on a .... surface.

   (a) oily (b) smooth

   (c) glazed (d) coated.

73. Why are floating heads provided in heat exchangers?

   (a) To regulate the flow

   (b) To increase the pressure drop

   (c) To decrease the pressure drop

   (d) To avoid deformation of tubes due to thermal expansion.

74. Why is entrainment separator used in evaporators?

   (a) To separate liquid droplets from vapour

   (b) To prevent foaming

   (c) To increase the boiling point

   (d) To decrease the boiling point.

75. Least value of Prandtl number can be expected in case of

   (a) water (b) liquid metals

   (c) salt solution (d) sugar solution.

76. Agitated film evaporator is suitable for concentrating .... liquids.

   (a) viscous (b) low temperature

   (c) corrosive (d) high temperature.

77. The multiple pass heat exchangers are used to

   (a) increase the rate of heat transfer

(b) reduce pressure drop

(c) increase pressure drop

(d) reduce fluid flow friction losses.

78. "The boiling point of a solution is a linear function of water at the same pressure." This statement is associated with

    (a) Fick's rule   (b) Reynolds law

    (c) Dubring's rule   (d) none of the above.

79. A correction of LMTD is necessary in case of .... heat exchanger.

    (a) cross flow   (b) parallel flow

    (c) counter current   (d) all of the above.

80. Pecelet number is the ratio of .... number to .... number.

    (a) Reynolds, Schemdit

    (b) Prandtl, Weber

    (c) Prandtl, Schemdit

    (d) Reynolds, Prandtl.

81. The temperature of sun can be measured by using a

    (a) radiation pyrometer

    (b) standard thermometer

    (c) mercury thermometer

    (d) none of the above.

82. An increase in convective coefficient over a fin .... effectiveness.

    (a) decreases   (b) increases

    (c) does not influence   (d) none of the above.

83. An increase in fin effectiveness is caused by high value of

    (a) thermal conductivity

    (b) circumference

    (c) both (a) and (b)

    (d) sectional area.

84. At higher temperatures, the energy distribution of an ideal reflector is largely in the range of

    (a) longer wavelength

    (b) shorter wavelength

    (c) remains same at all wavelengths

    (d) unpredictable.

85. Thermal diffusivity of a substance is .... proportional to ....

    (a) inversely, specific heat

    (b) inversely, density of substance

    (c) directly, thermal conductivity

    (d) all of the above.

86. "The ratio of the emissive power and absorptive power of all bodies is the same and is equal to the emissive power of a perfectly black body". This statement is known as.

    (a) Planck's law   (b) Stefan's law

    (c) Kirchhoff's law   (d) Black body law.

87. Which of the follwing properties of air does not increase with rise in temperature?

    (a) Thermal diffusivity

    (b) Dynamic viscosity

    (c) Density

    (d) Thermal conductivity.

88. According to Wien's law, the wavelength corresponding to maximum energy is proportional to

    (a) T (b) T^2

    (c) T^3 (d) T^4

    (where T is the absolute temperature).

89. At thermal equilibrium absorptivity is .... emissivity.

    (a) greater than   (b) lesser than

    (c) equal to   (d) none of the above.

90. The total emissivity power is defined as the total amount of radiation emitted by a black body ....

    (a) per unit time

    (b) per unit temperature

    (c) per unit area

    (d) per unit thickness.

91. .... is the ratio of the energy absorbed by the body to total energy falling on it.

    (a) Emissivity

    (b) Emissive power

    (c) Absorptive power

    (d) Absorptivity.

92. A gray body is one whose absorptivity

    (a) varies with temperature

    (b) varies with the wavelength of incident ray

    (c) varies with temperature and wavelength of incident ray

    (d) does not vary with temperature and wavelength of incident ray.

93. How does heat transfer take place in regenerator type heat exchanger?

    (a) By generation of heat again and again

    (b) By indirect transfer

    (c) By direct mixing of hot and cold fluids

    (d) By flow of hot and cold fluids alternately over a surface.

94. Planck's law holds good for .... bodies.
    - (a) polished
    - (b) black
    - (c) all coloured
    - (d) any of the above.

95. On which of the following factors does the amount of radiation mainly depend?
    - (a) Temperature of body
    - (b) Type of surface of body
    - (c) Nature of body
    - (d) All of the above.

96. On which of the following factors does the emissive power of a body depend?
    - (a) Wavelength
    - (b) Temperature
    - (c) Physical nature
    - (d) All of the above.

97. For a cylinderical rod with uniformly distributed heat sources, the thermal gradient dt/dr at half the radius location will be ....of that at the surface.
    - (a) one-fourth
    - (b) one-half
    - (c) twice
    - (d) four times.

98. Which of the following is the notable example of uniform generation of heat within the conducting medium?
    - (a) Resistance heating in electrical appliances
    - (b) Energy generated in the fuel element of a nuclear reactor
    - (c) Liberation of energy due to some exothermic chemical reactions
    - (d) All of the above.

99. Thermal radiations occur in the portion of electromagnetic spectrum between the wavelengths
    - (a) 10^{-2} to 10^{-4} micron
    - (b) 10^{-1} to 10^{-2} micron
    - (c) 0.1 to 10^2 micron
    - (d) none of the above.

100. Gases have poor ....
    - (a) transmissivity
    - (b) absorptivity
    - (c) reflectivity
    - (d) all of the above.

101. .... is the ratio of total emissive power of body to total emissive power of a black body at the same temperature.
    - (a) Emissivity
    - (b) Absoptivity
    - (c) Transmissivity
    - (d) Reflectivity.

102. In which of the following cases, heat transfer by radiation is encountered least ?
    - (a) Electric bulb
    - (b) Nuclear reactor
    - (c) Boiler furnace
    - (d) Insulated steam pipe.

103. For a perfectly black body
    - (a) $\alpha = 1, \rho = 0, \tau = 0$
    - (b) $\alpha = \tau = 0, \rho = 1$
    - (c) $\alpha = \rho = 0, \tau = 1$
    - (d) none of the above.

    where α = absorptivity, ρ = reflectivity and τ = transmissivity.

104. The emissivity is likely to be higher in case of
    - (a) iron oxide
    - (b) paper
    - (c) carbon
    - (d) rubber.

105. In the formulation of Stefan-Boltzmann's law, which of the following parameters does not appear?
    - (a) Radiation flux
    - (b) Emissivity
    - (c) Absorptivity
    - (d) Radiating area.

106. For solar collectors, what combination of surface characteristics is required ?
    - (a) High absorptivity and high reflectivity.
    - (b) High reflectivity and high emissivity
    - (c) High emissivity and low absorptivity
    - (d) High absorptivity and low emissivity.

107. The value of radiation shape factor for the same type of shapes will be higher when surfaces are ....
    - (a) large and held closer
    - (b) moved futrher apart
    - (c) more closer
    - (d) smaller and held closer.

108. For a radiation shield which of the following parameters should be highest?
    - (a) Emissivity
    - (b) Reflectivity
    - (c) Absorptivity
    - (d) Transmissivity.

109. The receprocity theorem states that
    - (a) $A_1 F_{1-2} = A_2 F_{2-1}$
    - (b) $A_2 F_{1-2} = A_1 F_{2-1}$
    - (c) $F_{1-2} = F_{2-1}$
    - (d) $a_1 F_{1-2} = a_2 F_{2-1}$

110. Which of the following statements is *incorrect* ?
    - (a) At thermal equilibrium, the emissivity and absorptivity are same
    - (b) Glasses are transparent to thermal radiations at short wavelengths
    - (c) The emissivity of a smooth surface is lower compared to a rough surface of the same material
    - (d) Selective surfaces have same value of emissivity throughout the entire range of wavelength.

111. For infinite parallel planes with emissivities e_1 and e_2, the interchange factor for radiation from surface 1 to surface 2 is

    (a) $\dfrac{1}{\varepsilon_1 + \varepsilon_2}$

    (b) $\varepsilon_1 + \varepsilon_2$

    (c) $\varepsilon_1 - \varepsilon_2$

    (d) $\dfrac{\varepsilon_1\, \varepsilon_2}{\varepsilon_1 + \varepsilon_2 - \varepsilon_1 \varepsilon_2}$.

112. The intensity of solar radiation on earth is .... kW/m^2.

    (a) 1

    (b) 3

    (b) 6

    (d) 8

113. The relationship $\lambda_{max}\, T$ = constant, between the temperature of a black body and the wavelength at which maximum value of monochromatic emissive power occurs is known as .... law.

    (a) Lambert's

    (b) Kirchhoff's

    (c) Planck's

    (d) Wien's displacement.

114. For a gray surface which of the following statements is correct ?

    (a) Reflectivity equals emissivity

    (b) Emissivity is constant

    (c) Absorptivity equals reflectivity

    (d) Emissivity equals transmittivity.

115. With regard to a diathermanous body which of the following statements is correct ?

    (a) It allows all the incident radiation to pass through it

    (b) It shines as a result of incident radiation

    (c) It gets heated up as a result of absorption of incident radiation

    (d) It partly absorbs and partly reflects the incident radiation.

116. A body which partly absorbs and partly reflects but does not allow any radiation to pass through it is called

    (a) specular

    (b) gray

    (c) Opaque

    (d) none of the above.

117. Which one of the following approximates to the black body condition?

    (a) Lamp black

    (b) Water

    (c) Ice

    (d) All of the above.

118. With regard to 'Fouling factor' which of the following statements is correct ?

    (a) It is used when a liquid exchanges heat with a gas

    (b) It is used only in case of Newtonian fluids

    (c) It is dimensionless

    (d) It is virtually a factor of safety in heat exchanger design.

119. In a shell and tube heat exchanger, the corrosive liquid is normally passed through

    (a) tube side

    (b) shell side

    (c) either of the above

    (d) none of the above.

120. In .... flow maximum heat transfer rate can be expected.

    (a) laminar

    (b) turbulent

    (c) counter current

    (d) co-current.

121. The nusselt number, in case of natural convection, is a function of

    (a) Weber number and Mach number

    (b) Grashoff's number and Prandtl number

    (c) Reynolds number

    (d) Reynolds number and Prandtl number.

122. When the bubbles formed on a submerged hot surface get absorbed in the mass of liquid, the process of boiling is known as .... boiling.

    (a) film

    (b) pool

    (c) nucleate

    (d) none of the above.

123. .... provides maximum contact surface for a liquid vapour system.

    (a) Packed tower

    (b) Wetted wall column

    (c) Bubble cap tower

    (d) None of the above.

124. What does 1-2 heat exchanger mean?

    (a) Two tubes of hot fluid pass through one tube of cold fluid

    (b) Single pass on tube side and double pass on shell side

    (c) Single pass on shell side and double pass on tube side

    (d) None of the above.

125. Why are baffles provided in heat exchangers ?

    (a) To reduce heat transfer rate

    (b) To increase heat transfer rate

    (c) To remove dirt

    (d) To reduce vibrations.

126. Which of the following evaporators will be preferred for handling severly scaling liquids ?

    (a) Agitated film type

    (b) Short vertical tube type

    (c) Horizontal tube type

    (d) Long vertical tube type.

127. The emissivity of a gray body is

    (a) 0.5

    (b) 1

    (c) less than 1

    (d) more than 1.

128. What does a high value of Prandtl number indicate?

   (a) Rapid heat transfer by forced convection to natural convection.

   (b) Rapid diffusion of momentem by viscous action compared to diffusion of energy.

   (c) Relative heat transfer by conduction to convection.

   (d) All of the above.

129. For gases, Prandtl number is

   (a) near unity

   (b) between 5 and 50

   (c) between 60 and 100

   (d) between 150 and 300.

130. .... number is the ratio of heat transfer coefficient to the flow of heat per unit temperature rise due to the velocity of the fluid.

   (a) Grashoff   (b) Weber

   (c) Stanton   (d) Prandtl.

131. In .... ablation heat transfer method is used.

   (a) nuclear war heads   (b) satellites

   (c) rockets   (d) none of the above.

132. Which mode of heat transfer plays insignificant role in a cooling tower?

   (a) Radiation

   (b) Evaporative cooling

   (c) Convective cooling

   (d) All of the above.

133. In which of the following heat exchange processes the value of overall heat transfer coefficient will be highest?

   (a) Steam to oil   (b) Steam condensers

   (c) Air to heavy tars   (d) Air to CO_2.

134. How can radiation heat transfer between two surfaces be reduced?

   (a) By bringing the surfaces closer together

   (b) By introducing radiation shield between the surfaces

   (c) By polishing the surfaces

   (d) All of the above.

135. .... correlates the relative thickness of the hydrodynamic and thermal boundary layers.

   (a) Mach number   (b) Nusselt number

   (c) Grashoff number   (d) Prandtl number.

136. .... number can be used for convective heat trnasfer.

   (a) Mach   (b) Froude

   (c) Nusselt   (d) None of the above.

137. The ratio of thermal conductivity ice to that of water is nearly

   (a) 2   (b) 3

   (c) 4   (d) 6

138. Which of the following can be used to a measure a temperature around – 45°C?

   (a) Thermocouple

   (b) Mercury thermometer

   (c) Alcohol thermometer

   (d) None of the above.

139. Which of the following statements is incorrect ?

   (a) Black surfaces are better absorbers than white ones

   (b) Black surfaces are better radiators than white ones

   (c) Rough surfaces are better radiators than smooth surfaces

   (d) Highly polished mirror like surfaces are very good radiators.

140. Due to which of the following reasons hydrogen cannot be liquified at room temperature?

   (a) It is diatomic gas

   (b) It has high specific heat

   (c) Its critical temperature is less than the room temperature

   (d) All of the above.

141. .... have the same units.

   (a) Planck's constant and angular momentum

   (b) Planck's constant and Stefan's constant

   (c) Boltzmann's constant and Planck's constant

   (d) Stefan's constant and Boltzmann's constant

142. In air preheater for boiler, heat is least transferred by

   (a) radiation

   (b) conduction

   (c) convectioin

   (d) conduction and convection.

143. In which of the following cases non-isotropic conductivity is exhibited?.

   (a) Lead   (b) Wood

   (c) Copper   (d) Brass.

144. .... is suitable for low temperature applications.

   (a) Fused alumina bricks

   (b) Asbestos paper

   (c) Cork

   (d) Diatomaceous earth.

145. A dimensionless number which is the ratio of kinematic viscosity to thermal diffusivity is known as ..... number.
   (a) Grashoff
   (b) Prandtl
   (c) Mach
   (d) Nusselt.

146. In Boltzmann's law which of the following quantities does not figure?
   (a) Absorptivity
   (b) Radiating area
   (c) Absolute temperature
   (d) Radiant flux
   (e) Emissivity.

147. A perfect black body is the one which
   (a) is coated with lamp black
   (b) absorbs most of the incident radiation
   (c) absorbs all incident radiation
   (d) reflects all incident radiation.

148. Which of the following statements is correct?
   (a) A substance will emit radiation at a particular wavelength only
   (b) All substances emit radiation, the quality and quantity depend on the absolute temperature and the properties of the material composing the radiating body
   (c) Only some substances emit radiation
   (d) Bodies black in colour are known as black bodies.

149. The radiation from flames consists which of the following?
   (a) Non-equilibrium radiation associated with the combustion process
   (b) Continuous radiation from burning soot particles of microscopic and submicroscopic dimensions
   (c) Infrared radiation from water vapour and CO_2
   (d) Radiation from suspended larger particles of coal, coke, or ash contributing to flame luminosity
   (e) All of the above.

150. A perfect .... surface is the surface which diffusely reflects and emits the same amount of energy which it receives by radiation.
   (a) radiating
   (b) gray
   (c) black
   (d) white.

151. If ε is the emissivity of surfaces and shields and n is the number of shields introduced between the two surfaces, then overall emissivity is given by

   (a) n/ε
   (b) $n\varepsilon$
   (c) $1/(2n - \varepsilon)$
   (d) $\varepsilon/[(n + 1)(2 - \varepsilon)]$.

152. Pyrometers which react to all wavelengths of incident radiant energy are known as .... pyrometers.
   (a) polarising
   (b) total radiation
   (c) optical
   (d) disappearing filament type.

153. Fog is formed due to
   (a) humidity
   (b) low pressure
   (c) temperature fall of atmosphere
   (d) all of above.

154. Which of the following is a very good insulator?
   (a) Saw dust
   (b) A hard wood board
   (c) An asbestos sheet
   (d) A porcelain sheet.

155. Thermal conductivity of liquids can be determined by
   (a) Searles method
   (b) Guarded plate method
   (c) Laby and Hercas method
   (d) None of the above.

156. .... is likely to have highest thermal conductivity.
   (a) Boiling water
   (b) Steam
   (c) Solid ice
   (d) Rain water.

157. The phenomenon of boiling the milk in an open container when milk spills over the vessel is termed as .... boiling.
   (a) subcooled
   (b) pool
   (c) film
   (d) nuclear.

158. ......body transmits all the radiations falling on it.
   (a) Transparent
   (b) Gray
   (c) Black
   (d) White.

159. A radiation shield should have
   (a) high emissivity
   (b) low reflectivity
   (c) high reflectivity
   (d) none of the above.

160. ...... are generally diathermanous.
   (a) Gases
   (b) Liquids
   (c) Solids
   (d) All of the above.

161. The reflectance of a black body is
   (a) zero
   (b) less than 1.0
   (c) 1.0
   (d) infinity.

162. Grashoff number has significant role in heat transfer by .....

(a) conduction   (b) radiation

(c) natural convection   (d) forced convection.

163. Heat transfer in liquids and gases takes place by

(a) conduction

(b) convection

(c) radiation

(d) conduction and radiation.

164. Metals are good conductors of heat because

(a) they contain free electrons

(b) they have high density

(c) their atoms collide frequently

(d) all of the above.

165. Temperature of steam around 550°C can be measured by ....

(a) thermopile

(b) thermocouple

(c) thermometer

(d) radiation pyrometer.

166. Flow of heat from one body to other takes place when they have different ....

(a) specific heats   (b) heat contents

(c) temperatures   (d) all of the above.

167. Due to which of the following reasons thermal conductivity of glass wool varies from sample to sample?

(a) Variation in porosity

(b) Variation in density

(c) Variation in composition

(d) Variation in structure.

168. In which of the following cases heat is transferred by all three modes of heat transfer, viz., conduction, convection and radiation?

(a) Steam condenser   (b) Boiler

(c) Electric heater   (d) None of the above.

169. .... is the rate of energy emission from unit surface area through unit solid angle, along a normal to the surface.

(a) Absorptivity

(b) Transmissivity

(c) Intensity of radiation

(d) Emissivity.

170. For which of the following cases Fourier's law of heat conduction in valid ?

(a) Irregular surfaces

(b) One dimensional cases only

(c) Two dimensional cases only

(d) Three dimensional cases only.

171. Compared to parallel flow heat changer log mean temperature diffirence (LMTD) in case of counter flow heat exchanger will be

(a) less   (b) same

(c) more   (d) impredictable.

172. A gray body is one whose absorptivity ....

(a) is equal to its emissivity

(b) varies with temperature

(c) varies with wavelength of the incident ray

(d) none of the above.

173. Joule-sec. is the unit of ....

(a) thermal conductivity

(b) kinematic viscosity

(c) universal gas constant

(d) Planck's constant.

174. Compared to black body, total emissivity of polished silver is

(a) very much lower   (b) same

(c) very much higher   (d) more or less same.

175. The heat transfer equation $\dfrac{\partial^2 t}{\partial x^2} + \dfrac{\partial^2 t}{\partial y^2} + \dfrac{\partial^2 t}{\partial z^2} = 0$

is known as

(a) General equation of heat transfer

(b) Poisson's equation

(c) Fourier's equation

(d) Laplace's equation.

176. Absorptivity of a body will be equal to its emissivity

(a) at critical temperature

(b) for a polished body

(c) at all temperatures

(d) when the system is under thermal equilibrium.

177. Which of the follwing statements is incorrect?

(a) A temperature gradient must exist for heat exchange

(b) Heat flow is always from a higher temperature to a lower temperature in accordance with the second law of thermodynamics

(c) A material medium is always necessary for heat transmission

(d) The process of heat transfer is thermodynamically an irreversible process.

178. The material medium between the heat source and receiver is not affected during the process of heat transmission by

    (a) convection
    (b) radiation
    (c) conduction
    (d) conduction as well as convection.

179. With regard to the Fourier's law, which of the following statements is incorrect?

    (a) It helps to define thermal conductivity of the heat conducting medium
    (b) It is valid for all matter regardless of its state
    (c) It is a vector representation indicating heat flow in the direction of decreasing temperature
    (d) It can be derived from first principles.

180. The rate of heat transfer per unit area per unit thickness of wall when a unit temperature difference is maintained across the opposite faces of the wall is called ....

    (a) heat flux
    (b) thermal resistance
    (b) thermal loading
    (d) thermal conductivity.

181. The average thermal conductivities of water and air conform to the ratio

    (a) 8 : 1   (b) 12 : 1
    (c) 25 : 1   (d) 40 : 1

182. Which of the following statements is incorrect ?

    (a) Thermal conductivity decreases with increase in the density of the substance
    (b) Heat treatment causes considerable variation in thermal conductivity
    (c) Thermal conductivity is always higher in the purest form of metal
    (d) Thermal conductivity of a damp material is considerably higher than the thermal conductivity of the dry material and water taken individually.

183. The steady state temperature distribution in the very large thin plate with uniform surface temperature will be

    (a) logarithmic   (b) parabolic
    (c) hyperbolic   (d) linear.

184. The thermal resistance for heat conduction through a hollow sphere of inner radius r_1 and outer radius r_2 is

    (a) $\dfrac{4\pi k (r_2 - r_1)}{r_1 \, r_2}$ (b) $\dfrac{r_2 - r_1}{4\pi k \, r_1 \, r_2}$

    (c) $\dfrac{(r_2 - r_1) \, r_1 \, r_2}{4\pi k}$ (d) none of the above.

    (where k is the thermal conductivity of the material of the sphere)

185. Which of the following statements is incorrect?

    (a) A certain thickness of lagging on a steam pipe may increase the rate of heat flow rather than reduce it
    (b) Addition of insulation does not always bring about a decrease in the heat transfer rate for geometries with non-constant cross-sectional area
    (c) Critical radius of insulation refers to the outer radius of insulation for which there is maximum thermal resistance and consequently maximum heat flow rate.
    (d) Rubber insulated wires can carry more current than a bare wire for the same rise in temperature.

186. With regard to 'fin effectiveness' which of the following statements is incorrect?

    (a) It is improved if the fin is made from a material of low thermal conductivity
    (b) It represents the ratio of heat transfer rate from the fin to the heat that would be dissipated if the entire fin surface area were maintained at the base temperature
    (c) both (a) and (b)
    (d) It is imprved by having thin but closely spaced fins.

187. .... number gives an indication of the ratio of internal (conduction) resistance to the surface (convection) resistance.

    (a) Stanton   (b) Biot
    (c) Nusselt   (d) Fourier.

188. The characteristic length, in the non-dimensional Biot number, is the ratio of

    (a) perimeter to surface area of solid
    (b) volume of solid to its surface area
    (c) surface area to perimeter of solid
    (d) none of the above.

189. Heat transfer by radiation is characterised by

    (a) circulation of fluid motion by buoyancy effects
    (b) movement of discrete packets of energy as electromagnetic waves
    (c) energy transport as a result of bulk fluid motion
    (d) all of the above.

190. With regard to `thermal radiations' which of the following statements is *incorrect*?

    (a) These occur in the portion of electromagnetic spectrum between the wavelengths 10^{-2} to 10^{-4} micron.

    (b) These travel in space with a velocity 3×10^8 m/s.

    (c) These are electromagnetic waves

    (d) None of the above.

191. Which of the following heat flow situations pertains to free or natural convection?

    (a) Cooling of billets in atmosphere

    (b) Cooling of I.C. engines

    (c) Flow of water inside the condenser tubes

    (d) All of the above.

192. .... causes forced convection in a liquid bath.

    (a) Flow of electrons in a random fashion

    (b) Intense stirring by an external agency

    (c) Molecular energy interaction

    (d) All of the above.

193. .... number has a significant role in forced convection.

    (a) Mach   (b) Reynolds

    (c) Prandtl   (d) Peclet.

194. In convective heat transfer, the Nusselt number

    (a) represents the ratio of viscous to inertia force

    (b) signifies the velocity gradient at the surface

    (c) is the ratio of molecular momentum diffusivity to thermal diffusivity

    (d) is the ratio of conduction to convection resistance.

195. Nusselt number, for forced convection, is a function of ..... number and ...... number.

    (a) Reynolds, Prandtl

    (b) Reynolds, Grashoff

    (c) Prandtl, Grashoff

    (d) None of the above.

196. In case of laminar flow over a plate, the convective heat transfer co-efficient

    (a) decreases with increase in free stream velocity

    (b) increases with distance

    (c) increases if a higher viscosity fluid is used

    (d) increases if a denser fluid is used.

197. The temperature gradient in the fluid flowing over a heated plate will be

    (a) zero at the top of thermal boundry layer

    (b) very steep at the surface

    (c) zero at the plate surface

    (d) positive at the surface.

198. The ratio of hydrodynamic to thermal boundary layer thicknesses

    (a) varies as one-third power of Prandtl number

    (b) varies as two-third power of Stanton number

    (c) varies as four-fifth power of Nusselt number

    (d) varies as root of Prandtl number.

199. When Prandtl number is equal to .... the hydrodynamic and thermal boundary layers are identical.

    (a) 0.2   (b) 1

    (c) 15   (d) 30.

200. The convective coefficients for boiling and condensation usually lie in the range

    (a) 50-500 W/m^{2}K

    (b) 200-2500 W/m^{2}K

    (c) 300-5000 W/m^{2}K

    (d) 2500–10000 W/m^{2}K.

201. With which of the following `Leiden-frost effect' is associated?

    (a) Condensation of vapour on a cold surface

    (b) Boiling of liquid on a hot surface

    (c) Evaporation of a solution

    (d) Exchange of heat between two fluids

    (e) None of the above.

202. On which of the following factors does the heat flux in nucleate pool boiling depend?

    (a) Material of the surface only

    (b) Material and roughness of the surface

    (c) Liquid properties and material of the surface

    (d) Liquid properties, material and condition of the surface.

203. How is the requirement of transfer of a large heat usually met?

    (a) By decreasing the diameter of tube

    (b) By increasing the length of tube

    (c) By increasing the number of tubes

    (d) By having multiple tube or shell passes.

204. Why are multipass heat exchangers used?

    (a) To obtain high heat transfer coefficient

    (b) To reduce the pressure drop

    (c) To get a compact unit

    (d) All of the above.

205. .... does not pertain to transient heat conduction.

(a) Fourier number   (b) Interchange factor

(c) Error function   (d) Biot number.

206. Due to which of the following reasons heat flux increases with temperature excess beyond the Leiden-fost point?

(a) Radiation effect becomes predominant

(b) Occurence of subcooled boiling

(c) Promotion of nucleate boiling

(d) None of the above.

207. Which of the following statements is incorrect?

(a) Film boiling region is usually avoided in commercial equipment

(b) In subcooled boiling, the temperature of the heating surface is more than the boiling point of the liquid

(c) There occurs transition from nucleate to film boiling at burn-out point on the boiling curve

(d) Nucleate boiling gets promoted on a smooth surface.

208. The steam condenser in a thermal power plant is a heat exchanger of the type

(a) recuperator   (b) direct contact

(c) regenerator   (d) none of the above.

209. Why are expansion bellows provided in the shell of a tubular heat exchanger ?

(a) To reduce the pressure drop

(b) To impart structural strength to exchanger

(c) To facilitate increase in length of boiler shell

(d) To account for uneven expansion of shell and tube bundles.

210. Which of the following terms does not pertain to radiation heat transfer?

(a) Configuration factor

(b) Spectral distribution

(c) Solid angle

(d) Reynolds analogy.

211. The value of convection coefficient, in condensation over a vertical surface, varies as

(a) $k^{0.5}$ (b) $k^{0.35}$

(c) $k^{0.75}$ (d) $k^{0.9}$.

(where k is the thermal conductivity of the liquid).

NUMERICAL QUESTIONS

*212. The inner surface of a plane brick wall is at 50°C and the outer surface is at 25°C. Calculate the rate of heat transfer per m^2 of the surface area of the wall, which is 220 mm thick. The thermal conductivity of the bricks is 0.51 W/m K.

(a) 20.65 W/m^2 (b) 32.75 W/m^2

(c) 47.62 W/m^2 (d) 57.95 W/m^2.

*213. A mild steel tank of wall thickness 12 mm contains water at 100°C. Calculate the rate of heat loss per m^2 of tank surface area when the atmospheric temperature is 20°C. The thermal conductivity of mild steel is 50 W/m K, and the heat transfer coefficients for the inside and outisde the tank are 2850 and 10 W/m^2 K, respectively. Calculate also the temperature of the outside surface of the tank.

(a) 300.5 W/m^2, 45.5°C

(b) 495.2 W/m^2, 67.6°C

(c) 602.6 W/m^2, 80.6°C

(d) 795.2 W/m^2, 99.52°C.

*214. A spherical shaped vessel of 1.4 m diameter is 90 mm thick. Find the rate of heat leakage, if the temperaturre difference between the inner and outer surfaces is 220°C. Thermal

conductivity of the material of the sphere is 0.083 W/mK.

(a) 0.2 kW   (b) 0.5 kW

(c) 1.0886 kW   (d) 1.6 kW.

215 Liquid air at –147° C is stored in the space of two concentric spheres of 0.2 m and 0.3 m diameters. The surface emissivities are 0.028. Assume the outer surface temperature is 25° C. Considering only

(a) W/m-s-K   (b) cal/m-s-°C.

215. Choose the *wrong* statement about thermal diffusivity :

(a) It represents a physical property of the material

(b) It is a dimensionless quantity.

(c) It is an important characteristic for unsteady heat conduction

(d) It is the ratio of thermal conductivity to thermal storage capacity of a material.

216. A body which partly absorbs and partly reflects but does not allow any radiation to pass through it (a + r = 1 and t = 0) is called

(a) diamthermanous   (b) opaque

(c) gray   (d) specular.

217. The heat flow equation through a cylinder of inner radius r_1 and other radius r_2 is desired to be written in the same form as that for heat flow through a plane wall. For wall thickness ($r_2 - r_1$), the equivalent area A_m would be

(a) $\dfrac{A_1 + A_2}{2}$ (b) $\dfrac{A_1 + A_2}{2 \log_e (A_2 / A_1)}$

(c) $\dfrac{A_2 - A_1}{\log_e (A_2 / A_1)}$ (d) $\dfrac{A_2 - A_1}{2 \log_e (A_2 / A_1)}$.

where A_1 and A_2 are the inner and outer surface areas of the cylindrical tube.

218. A gas turbine blade (idealised as a flat plate of surface area A, thickness d and thermal conductivity k) has hot gases at temperature T_1 on one side and cooling air ar temperature T_2 on the other side. If h_1 and h_2 are the corresponding surface coefficients of heat transfer, then the overall heat transfer coefficient U is given by

(a) $\dfrac{1}{U} = \dfrac{1}{h_1} + \dfrac{\delta}{k} + \dfrac{1}{h_2}$

(b) $\dfrac{1}{U} = \dfrac{1}{h_1} + \dfrac{k}{\delta} + \dfrac{1}{h_2}$

(c) $U = h_1 + \dfrac{\delta}{k} + h_2$

(d) $U = \dfrac{1}{h_1} + \dfrac{\delta}{k} + \dfrac{1}{h_2}$.

219. Which of the following is the wrong value of characteristic length l which appears in the Biot number hl/k and the Fourier number at / l^2 ?

(a) $l = R/3$ in case of a sphere of radius R
(b) $l = R/2$ in case of a cylinder of radius R and length L
(c) $l = R/6$ in case of a cube with each side of length L
(d) $l = b/2$ for a flat plate of thickness d breadth b and height h.

220. A solid cement wall of a building having thermal conductivity k and thickness d is heated by convection on the inner side and cooled by convection on the outside. The heat flux through the wall can be expressed as

(a) $\dfrac{(t_1 - t_2)}{1/h_1 + \delta/k + 1/h_2}$ (b) $\dfrac{(t_1 - t_2)}{h_1 + \delta/k + h_2}$

(c) $\dfrac{k\,(t_1 - t_2)\,(h_1 + h_2)}{\delta}$ (d) none of the above.

221. The heat dissipation from an infinitely long find is given by

(a) $\sqrt{PkhA_{cs}}\,(t_o - t_a)$
(b) $hPl\,(t_o - t_a)$
(c) $\sqrt{PkhA_{cs}}\,(t_o - t_a)\tanh ml$
(d) $\sqrt{PkhA_{cs}}\,(t_o - t_a)\,\dfrac{\tanh ml + (h/k)\,m}{l + (h/km)\tanh ml}$

The symbols have their usual meanings.

222. The heat flow equation through a sphere of inner radius r_1 and outer radius r_2 is to be written in the same form as that for heat flow through a plane wall. For wall thickness ($r_2 - r_1$), the equivalent mean radius for the spherical shell is

(a) $\dfrac{r_1 + r_2}{2}$ (b) $r_1 r_2$

(c) $\sqrt{r_1 / r_2}$ (d) $\dfrac{r_1 + r_2}{\log_e (r_2 / r_1)}$.

223. The variation in thermal conductivity of a wall material is stated to conform to the relation $k = k_o$ $(1 + aT)$. In that case the temperature at the mid-plane of the heat conducting wall would be

(a) average of the temperatures at the wall faces
(b) more than the average of the temperatures at the wall faces
(c) less than the average of the temperatures at the wall faces
(d) depends upon the temperature difference between the wall faces.

224. The Fourier's conduction heat equation $Q = - KA$ dt/dx presumes

(a) steady state, one-dimensional heat flow
(b) constant value of thermal conductivity
(c) constant and uniform temperatures at the wall surfaces
(d) all of the above.

225. A hollow sphere has inner and outer surface areas of 2 m^2 and 8 m^2 respectively. For a given temperature difference across the surfaces, it is desired to calculate heat flow by considering the material of the sphere as a plane wall of the same thickness. The equivalent mean area normal to the direction of heat flow should be

(a) 6 m^2 (b) 5 m^2
(c) 4 m^2 (d) 3 m^2.

226. The relation $\nabla^2 t = 0$ is referred to as

(a) Fourier heat conduction equation

(b) Laplace equation

(c) Poisson's equation

(d) Lumped parameter solution for transient conduction.

227. Heat is transferred from a hot fluid (temperature T_1 and heat transfer coefficient h_2) through a plane wall of thickness d, surface area A and thermal conductivity k. The thermal resistance for the set up is

(a) $\dfrac{1}{A}\left(\dfrac{1}{h_1} + \dfrac{\delta}{k} + \dfrac{1}{h_2}\right)$

(b) $A\left(\dfrac{1}{h_1} + \dfrac{\delta}{k} + \dfrac{1}{h_2}\right)$

(c) $\dfrac{1}{A}\left(h_1 + \dfrac{k}{\delta} + h_2\right)$

(d) $A\left(h_1 + \dfrac{k}{\delta} + h_2\right)$.

228. Which of the following is *not a correct* statement?

(a) The dimensions of thermal conductivity are $MLT^{-3}\,\theta^{-1}$

(b) The thermal conductivity of glass wool varies from sample to sample because of variation in its structure, composition and porosity etc.

(c) Metals and gases have a relativitely small value of thermal conductivity where as this parameter is relatively large for non-metallic solids and liquids

(d) Thermal conductivity is the ability of solids to conduct heat, and thermal diffusivity is a measure of thermal inertia.

229. Considering a composite wall comprising two layers of thermal conductivities k and 2k, and equal surface areas normal to the direction of heat flow. The outer surfaces of the composite wall are maintained at 100°C and 200°C respectively. If surface temperature at the junction is desired to be 150°C and conduction is the only mode of heat transfer, then ratio of thickness should be

(a) 1:1   (b) 2:1

(c) 1:2   (d) 2:3

230. Most unsteady heat flow occurs

(a) through the wall of a refrigerator

(b) during annealing of castings

(c) through the walls of a furnace

(d) through lagged (insulated) pipes carrying steam.

231. A thin cylinder of radius r is lagged to an outer radius r_o with an insulating layer of thermal conductivity k. If h_o is the film coefficient at the outer surface of lagging, then minimum resistance and consequently maximum heat flow rate occurs when r_o equals

(a) $\sqrt{kh_o}$ (b) $\dfrac{k}{h_o}$

(c) $\dfrac{2k}{h_o}$ (d) $\dfrac{h_o}{k}$.

232. For a long cylindere of radius R with uniformly distributed heat sources, the temperature distribution in the dimensionless form is

(a) $\dfrac{t - t_w}{t_{max} - t_w} = 1 - \dfrac{r}{R}$

(b) $\dfrac{t - t_w}{t_{max} - t_w} = 1 - \left(\dfrac{r}{R}\right)^2$

(c) $\dfrac{t - t_w}{t_{max} - t_w} = 1 - \left(\dfrac{r}{R}\right)^3$

(d) $\dfrac{t - t_w}{t_{max} - t_w} = 1 - \left(\dfrac{r}{R}\right)^4$.

where t_w is the temperature at the outer surface of the cylinder and t_{max} is the temperature along the cylinder axis.

233. The temperature distribution during transient heat conduction in a solid does not depend upon

(a) location of point within the solid

(b) Biot number hl/k

(c) Prandtl number $\mu\, c_p/k$

(d) Fourier number $\alpha\tau/l^2$.

234. Two long parallel surfaces, each of emissivity 0.7, are maintained at different temperatures and accordingly have radiation heat exchange between them. It is desired to reduce 75% of this radiant heat transfer by inserting thin parallel shields of emissivity on both sides. The number of shields should be

(a) one   (b) two

(c) three   (d) four.

235. For laminar conditions, the thickness of thermal boundary layer increases with its distance from the leading edge in proportion to

(a) x   (b) $x^{1/2}$

(c) $x^{1/3}$ (d) $x^{1/4}$.

236. The intensity of Solar radiation on earth is

(a) 1 kW/m^2 (b) 2 kW/m^2

(c) 4 kW/m^2 (d) 8 kW/m^2.

237. For a transport of diathermanous body

    (a) absorptivity $\alpha = 1$. transmissivity $\tau = 0$ and reflectivity $\rho = 0$

    (b) $\rho = 1$ and $\alpha = \tau = 0$

    (c) $\tau = 1$ and $\alpha = \rho = 0$

    (d) $\alpha + \rho = 1$ and $\tau = 0$

238. Choose the *false* statement :

    (a) The unit of heat transfer coefficient is kcal/ m²-hr-°C

    (b) The overall heat transfer coefficient has units of W/m²-deg

    (c) In M-L-T-θ system, the dimensions of convective heat transfer coefficient and the overall heat transfer coefficient are $MT^{-3}\,\theta^{-1}$

    (d) The overall heat transfer coefficient is the reciprocal of overall thermal resistance to heat flow.

239. Three fins of equal length and diameter but made of aluminium, brass and cost iron are heated to 200°C at one end. If the fins dissipate heat to the surrounding air at 25°C, the temperature at the free end will be least in case of

    (a) aluminium fin

    (b) brass fin

    (c) cast iron fin

    (d) each fin will have the same temperature at the free end.

240. Which of the following heat flow situations pertains to free or natural convection ?

    (a) Cooling of internal combustion engines

    (b) Flow of water inside the condenser tubes

    (c) Cooling of billets in atmosphere

    (d) Air-conditioning installations and nuclear reactors.

241. The requirement of transfer of a large heat is usually met by

    (a) increasing the length of tube

    (b) decreasing the diameter of tube

    (c) increasing the number of tubes

    (d) having multiple tube or shell passes.

242. Which of the following parameters does not appear in the formulation of Stefan-Boltzman law?

    (a) Absorptivity   (b) Emissivity

    (c) Radiating area   (d) Radiation flux.

243. Heisler charts are used to determine the transient heat flow rate and temperature distribution when

    (a) solids possess infinitely large thermal conductivity

    (b) internal conduction resistance is small and the convective resistance is large

    (c) internal conduction resistance is large and the convective resistance is small

    (d) both conduction and convection resistance are almost of equal importance.

244. A body cooling from 80°C to 70°C takes 10 minutes when left exposed to environmental conditions. If the body is to cool further from 70°C to 60°C under the same external conditions, it will take

    (a) same time of 10 minutes

    (b) more than 10 minutes

    (c) less than 10 minutes

    (d) time will depend upon the environmental conditions.

245. The dimensionless parameter $(b\,g\,r^2\,l^3\,D\,t)/m^2$ is referred to as

    (a) Stanton number   (b) Schmidt number

    (c) Grashoff number   (d) Peclet number.

246. For a plane wall of thickness l with uniformly distributed heat generation q_s per unit volume, the temperature t_o at the mid-plane is given by

    (a) $t_o = \dfrac{q_g\,l^2}{2k} + t_w$ (b) $t_o = \dfrac{q_g\,l^2}{4k} + t_w$

    (c) $t_o = \dfrac{q_g\,l^2}{8k} + t_w$ (d) $t_o = \dfrac{q_g\,l^2}{16k} + t_w$.

where t_w is the temperature on either side of the wall and k is the thermal conductivity of the wall material.

247. The temperature distribution $(t - t_a)/(t_o - t_a)$ for a fin with insulated tip is given by

    (a) $\exp(-mx)$

    (b) $\dfrac{\exp(mx) + \exp(-mx)}{2}$

    (c) $\dfrac{\cosh m\,(l - x)}{\cosh ml}$

    (d) $\cosh m\,(l - x) + \cosh ml$.

The symbols have their usual meanings.

248. The Nusselt number for convective heat transfer between a horizontal tube and water surrounding it is prescribed by the relation

$$Nu = 0.52\,(Gr.Pr)^{0.25}$$

For a 4 cm diameter tube, the heat transfer coefficient is stated to be 1412 kcal/m²-hr-deg. Subsequently the tube is replaced by one with 16 cm diameter tube. If temperature and surface of the fluid remains same, the heat transfer coefficient will change to

(a) 706

(b) 1000

(c) 2824

(d) 5648 kcal/m²-hr-°C

249. Radiation heat transfer is characterised by

(a) energy transport as a result of bulk fluid motion

(b) thermal energy transfer as vibrational energy in the lattice structure of the material

(c) movement of discrete packets of energy as electromagnetic waves

(d) circulation of fluid motion by bouyancy effects.

250. Choose the *false* statement :

(a) Thermal conductivity is always higher in the purest form of metal

(b) Heat treatment causes considerable variation in thermal conductivity

(c) Thermal conductivity of a damp material is considerably higher than the thermal conductivity of the dry material and water taken individually

(d) Thermal conductivity decreases with increase in the density of the substance.

251. The emissive power is multiplied with the factor ... to obtain the intensity of normal radiation for a unit surface.

(a) $\dfrac{1}{\sqrt{\pi}}$

(b) $\dfrac{1}{\pi}$

(c) $\dfrac{1}{2\pi}$

(d) $\sqrt{\pi}$.

252. Thermal radiations occur in the portion of electromagnetic spectrum between the wavelengths

(a) 10^{-2} to 10^{-4} micron

(b) 10^{-1} to 10^{-2} micron

(c) 0.1 to 10^2 micron

(d) 10^2 micron onwards.

253. The thermal radiation propagates in the forum of discrete quanta; each quanta having an energy of $E = hv$ where v is the frequency of quantum. The Planck's constant k has the dimensions.

(a) MLT

(b) MLT^{-1}

(c) MLT^{-2}

(d) ML^2T^{-1}.

254. Identify the *wrong* statement with respect to boiling heat transfer :

(a) Boiling occurs when a heated surface is exposed to a liquid and maintained at a temperature lower than the saturation temperature of the liquid.

(b) The steam boilers employing natural convection have steam raised through pool boiling.

(c) The nucleation boiling is characterised by the formation of bubbles at the nucleation sites and the resulting liquid agitation.

(d) "Leidenfrost effect" refers to the phenomenon of stable film boiling.

(e) The boiling crisis or the burn out point on the boiling curve (surface heat flux as a function of excess temperatures) represents the maximum heat flux at which transition occurs from nucleate to film boiling.

255. Two walls of same thickness and cross-sectional area have thermal conductivities in the ratio 1:2. If same temperature difference is maintained across the wall faces, the ratio of heat flow Q_1/Q_2 will be

(a) 1/2

(b) 1

(c) 2

(d) 4.

256. Consider development of laminar thermal boundary layer for a moving non-reacting fluid in contact with a flat plate of length l along the flow direction. The average value of heat transfer coefficient can be obtained by multiplying the local heat transfer coefficient at the trailing edge by the factor

(a) 0.75

(b) 1.0

(c) 1.5

(d) 2.0.

257. The emissivity and the absorptivity of a real surface are equal for radiation with identical temperature and wavelength. This law is referred to as

(a) Lambert's law

(b) Kirchhoff's law

(c) Planck's law

(d) Wien's displacement law.

258. The unit of thermal diffusivity is

(a) $m^2/hr°C$

(b) $kcal/m^2-hr$

(c) $m/hr°C$

(d) m^2/hr.

259. Choose the *wrong statement* with respect to Nusselt number and convective heat transfer coefficient :

(a) Nusselt number represents the ratio of temperature gradient at the surface to an overall or reference temperature gradient.

(b) Nusselt number represents the dimensionless slope of the temperature distribution curve at the surface.

(c) The convective coefficient can be evaluated from a knowledge of fluid temperature. distribution in the neighbourhood of the surface.

(d) For a given Nusselt number, the convective coefficient is inversely proportional to thermal conductivity of the fluid.

260. The law governing the distribution of radiant energy over wavelength for a black body at fixed temperature is referred to as

(a) Planck's law   (b) Wien's formula
(c) Kirchhoff's law   (d) Lambert's law.

261. The convective coefficients for boiling and condensation usually lie in the range

(a) 30-300
(b) 60-3000
(c) 300-10000
(d) 2500-10000 W/m^{2}K.

262. In M-L-T-q system, the dimensions of thermal diffusivity are

(a) L^2T^{-1} (b) $LT^{-1}q^{-1}$
(c) ML^2T^{-1} (d) $L^2T^{-1}q^{-1}$.

263. Choose the *false* statement :

(a) The monochromatic emissive power is the rate of energy radiated per unit area of the surface per unit wavelength.

(b) The distribution of monochromatic emissive power across the wavelength is continuous but non-uniform.

(c) At elevated temperatures, much of the energy is emitted in shorter wavelengths.

(d) The area under the monochromatic emissive power versus wavelength curve represents the total emissive power per unit area radiated from the surface.

(e) None of the above.

264. A thermally transparent surface of transmissivity 0.15 receives 500 kcal/min of radiation and reflects back 200 kcal/min out of it. The emissivity of the surface is then

(a) 0.15   (b) 0.4
(c) 0.45   (d) 0.55.

265. Peclet number is defined as

(a) $\dfrac{\text{kinematic viscosity}}{\text{thermal diffusivity}}$

(b) $\dfrac{\text{convective heat transfer viscosity}}{\text{conduction heat transfer}}$

(c) $\dfrac{\text{bouyancy force} \times \text{inertia force}}{\text{viscous force}}$

(d) $\dfrac{\text{wall heat transfer rate}}{\text{convection heat transfer}}$.

266. Which of the following is anisotropic, *i.e.*, exhibits change in thermal conductivity due to directional preferences ?

(a) Wood   (b) Glass wool
(c) Concrette   (d) Masonry brick.

267. The temperature of a body at any time during newtonian heating or cooling is stated as

(a) $\dfrac{t - t_a}{t_i - t_a} = \exp\left(- B_i F_o\right)$

(b) $\dfrac{t - t_a}{t_i - t_a} = \exp\left[(- B_i F_o)/2\right]$

(c) $\dfrac{t - t_a}{t_i - t_a} = \exp\left[- \sqrt{B_i F_o}\,\right]$

(d) $\dfrac{t - t_a}{t_i - t_a} = \exp\left[- (B_i F_o)^2\right]$.

where t_i is the body temperature at the commencement of heating or cooling process, t_a is the temperature of the surroundings, B_i and F_o are the non-dimensional Biot number and Fourier number respectively.

268. In a convective heat transfer situation, Reynolds number is very large but the Prandtl number is so small that the product $(Re . Pr)$ is less than one. In such a situation

(a) thermal boundary layer does not exist

(b) viscous boundary layer thickness equals the thermal boundary layer thickness

(c) viscous boundary layer thickness is less than the thermal boundary layer thickness

(d) viscous boundary layer thickness is greater than the thermal boundary layer thickness.

269. All the three modes of transmission are involved in

(a) melting of ice

(b) cooling of a small metal casting in a quenching bath

(c) heat flow through the walls of a refrigerator

(d) automobile engine equipped with a thermo-syphon cooling system.

270. Mark the wrong statement with respect to laminar film condensation on a vertical plate :

    (a) The rate of condensation heat transfer is maximum at the upper edge of the plate and progressively decreases as the lower edge is approached.

    (b) At a definitte point on the heat transfer surface, the film coefficient is directly proportional to thermal conductivity and inversely proportional to thickness of film at that point.

    (c) The average heat transfer coefficient is two-third of the local heat transfer coefficient at the lower edge of the plate.

271. A heat exchanger with heat transfer surface area A and overall heat transfer coefficient U handles two fluids of heat capacities C_{max} and C_{min}. The parameter NTU (number of transfer units) used in the analysis of heat exchanger is specified as

    (a) $\dfrac{AU}{C_{min}}$

    (b) AUC_{min}

    (c) $\dfrac{U}{AC_{min}}$

    (d) $\dfrac{AC_{min}}{U}$.

272. Which of the following is a *wrong* statement ?

    (a) Addition of insulation does not always bring about a decrease in the heat transfer rate for geometries with non-constant cross-section.

    (b) Rubber insulated wires can carry more current than a bare wire for the same rise in temperature.

    (c) A certain thickness of lagging on a steam pipe may increase the rate of heat flow rather than reduce it.

    (d) Critical radius of insulation refers to the outer radius of insulation for which there is maximum thermal resistance and consequently maximum heat flow rate.

273. Consider natural convection heat transfer between a vertical tube surface and a fluid surrounding it. For dimensional analysis of the problem, the characteristic length corresponds to

    (a) length of the tube

    (b) diameter of the tube

    (c) perimeter of the tube

    (d) either length or diameter of the tube.

274. Finned surfaces have improved rate of dissipation due to

    (a) decrease in ambient temperature

    (b) increase in the surface area exposed to the surroundings

    (c) increase in the convective film coefficient

    (d) all of the above.

275. The relationship, $l_{max} \, T$ = constant, between the temperature of a black body and the wavelength at which maximum value of monochromatic emissive power occurs is known as

    (a) Planck's law

    (b) Wien's displacement law

    (c) Kirchhoff's law

    (d) Lambert's law.

276. Steady state heat flow implies

    (a) negligible flow of heat

    (b) no difference of temperature between the bodies

    (c) constant heat flow rate, *i.e.*, heat flow rate independent of time

    (d) uniform rate in temperature rise of a body.

277. The Nusselt number in natural heat transfer is a function of fluid Prandtl number and

    (a) Stanton number   (b) Biot number

    (c) Grashoff number   (d) Reynolds number.

278. Pick the odd one out :

    (a) Open feed water heaters

    (b) Jet condensers

    (c) De-super heater

    (d) Surface condenser.

279. Which of the following forms of water will have the highest value of thermal conductivity ?

    (a) Boiling water   (b) Steam

    (c) Solid ice   (d) Melting ice.

280. Most metals are good conductor of heat because of

    (a) energy transport due to molecular vibration

    (b) migration of neutrons from hot end to cold end

    (c) lattice defects such as dislocations

    (d) presence of many free electrons and frequent collision of atoms

    (e) capacity to absorb free energy of electrons.

281. The metal walls of same wall thickness and cross-sectional area have thermal conductivities k, $2k$ and $3k$ respectively. For the same heat transfer, the temperature drops across the wall will be in the ratio

    (a) $1:2:3$

    (b) $3:2:1$

    (c) $1:1:3$

    (d) temperature drops ratios cannot be worked out as the given data is insufficient.

282. During the process of boiling and condensation, only a phase change takes place and one fluid remains at constant temperature throughout the heat exchanger. In terms of number of transfer units (*NTU*), the effectiveness of such an exchanger would be

(a) $\dfrac{NTU}{1 + NTU}$

(b) $1 - \exp(-NTU)$

(c) $\dfrac{1 - \exp(-2\,NTU)}{2}$

(d) cannot be worked out as the heat capacities are not known.

283. Mark the matter with least value of thermal conductivity :

(a) Air   (b) Water

(c) Ash   (d) Window glass.

284. Choose the correct statement with respect to a counter flow heat exchanger :

(a) Both the fluids at inlet are in their coldest state.

(b) Both the fluids at exit are in their hottest state.

(c) Both the fluids at inlet are in their hottest state.

(d) One fluid is hottest and the other is coldest at inlet.

285. In a double pipe parallel flow heat exchanger, there occurs condensation of saturated steam over the inner tube. Subsequently, the entrance and exit connections of the cooling medium are interchanged. The ratio of steam condensation

(a) will increase

(b) will decrease

(c) will remain unchanged

(d) may increase or decrease depending upon saturated temperature of steam and inlet temperature of cooling medium.

286. For an ideal reflector, the energy distribution at higher temperature is at

(a) shorter wavelength

(b) longer wavelength

(c) remains same at all wavelength

(d) depends upon factors other than wavelength.

287. The grey body shape factor for radiant heat exchanger between a small body (emissivity 0.4) in a large enclosure (emissivity 0.5) is

(a) 0.1   (b) 0.2

(c) 0.5   (d) 0.5.

288. Molecular transmission of heat is smallest in case of

(a) gases   (b) liquids

(c) solids   (d) alloys.

289. Heat transfer by radiation is encountered least in

(a) boiler furnace

(b) insulated steam pipe

(c) electric bulb

(d) nuclear reactor.

290. Heat conduction in gases is due to :

(a) motion of electrons

(b) elastic impact of molecules

(c) mixing motion of the different layers of the gas

(d) electromagnetic waves.

291. A thin shield of emissivity ε_3 (on both sides) is placed between two infinite parallel plates of emissivities ε_1 and ε_2, and temperatures T_1 and T_2 respectively. If $\varepsilon_1 = \varepsilon_2 = \varepsilon_3$ then the fraction radiant energy transfer without shield/with shield takes the value

(a) 0.25   (b) 0.50

(c) 0.75   (d) 0.82.

292. A straight fin of cross-sectional area A for all along its length and made of a material of thermal conductivity k serves to dissipates heat to the surroundings from a surface held at a constant temperature. What additional data is required to workout the rate of heat dissipation ?

(a) The root and tip temperatures

(b) The temperature gradient at the root

(c) The temperature gradient at the tip

(d) The convective heat transfer coefficient and the fin perimeter.

293. The temperature of a radiating surface changes from 400°K to 1200°K. The ratio of total emissive powers at the higher and lower temperatures would be

(a) 3   (b) 9

(c) 27   (d) 81.

294. The steam condenser in a thermal power plant is a heat exchanger of the type

(a) direct contact   (b) regenerator

(c) recuperator   (d) none of these.

295. What happens when the thickness of insulation on a pipe exceeds the critical value ?

(a) There is decrease in the heat flow rate.

(b) There is increase in the heat flow rate.

(c) The heat flow rate remains constant.

(d) The temperature at the junction between pipe and insulation rises.

296. For infinite parallel planes with emissivities e_1 and e_2 the interchange factor for radiation from surface 1 to surface 2 is

(a) $\varepsilon_1 \varepsilon_2$

(b) $\varepsilon_1 + \varepsilon_2$

(c) $\dfrac{1}{\varepsilon_1} + \dfrac{1}{\varepsilon_2}$

(d) $\dfrac{\varepsilon_1 \varepsilon_2}{\varepsilon_1 + \varepsilon_2 - \varepsilon_1 \varepsilon_2}$.

297. Dropwise condensation usually occurs on

(a) glazed surface

(b) smooth surface

(c) oily surface

(d) coated surface.

298. A perfectly black body

(a) absorbs all the incident radiation

(b) allows all the incident radiation to pass through it

(c) reflects all the incident radiation

(d) has its surface coated with lamp black or graphite.

299. Forced convection in a liquid bath is caused by

(a) density difference brought about by temperature gradients

(b) molecular energy interaction

(c) flow of electrons in a random fashion

(d) intense stirring by an external agency.

300. Which of the following is a *wrong* statement with respect to the Fourier's heat conduction equation?

(a) Fourier law is valid for all matter regardless of its state.

(b) Fourier law is a vector expression indicating heat flow in the direction of decreasing temperature.

(c) Fourier law can be derived from first principles.

(d) Fourier law helps to define thermal conductivity of the heat conducting medium.

301. Solar radiation is mainly scattered or transmitted but not absorbed by the atmosphere. This characteristic manifests because

(a) solar radiation is mainly in the visible spectrum for which the atmosphere has very low absorptivity

(b) solar radiation is very intense

(c) most of solar radiation is scattered and little remains for absorption

(d) atmospheric air has a very small density.

302. Choose the *false* statement :

(a) Snow is nearly black to thermal radiation.

(b) Absorption of radiation occurs in a very thin layer of material near the surface.

(c) Transmissivity varies with wavelength of incident radiation, *i.e.*, a material may be non-transport for a certain wavelength band and transparent for another.

(d) Most of the engineering materials have rough surfaces, and these rough surfaces give regular (specular) reflections.

303. The normal automobile radiator is a heat exchanger of the type

(a) direct contact

(b) parallel-flow

(c) counter-flow

(d) cross-flow.

304. Saturated steam is allowed to condense over a vertical flat surface and the condensate film flows down the surface. The local coefficient of heat transfer for condensation

(a) remains constant at all heights of the surface

(b) decreases with increasing distance from the top of the suface

(c) increases with increasing thickness of condensate film

(d) increases with increasing temperature differential between the surface and vapour.

305. Which dimensionless number has a significant role in forced convection ?

(a) Prandtl number

(b) Reynolds number

(c) Mach number

(d) Peclet number.

306. Gases have poor

(a) absorptivity

(b) reflectivity

(c) transmissivity

(d) absorptivity as well as transmissivity.

307. Identify the very good insulator :

(a) Saw dust

(b) Glass wool

(c) Cork

(d) Asbestos sheet.

308. A fin protrudes from a surface which is held at a temperature higher than that of its environments. The heat transferred away from the fin is

(a) heat escaping from the tip of the fin

(b) heat conducted along the fin length

(c) convective heat transfer from the fin surface

(d) sum of heat conducted along the fin length and that convected from the surface.

309. For an absolutely white or specular body.

(a) asborptivity $\alpha = 1$, reflectivity $\rho = 0$ and transmissivity $\tau = 0$

(b) $\rho = 1$ and $\alpha = \tau = 0$

(c) $\tau = 1$ and $\alpha = \rho = 0$

(d) $\alpha + \rho = 1$ and $\tau = 0$

310. Cork is a good insulator because

(a) it is flexible and can be cast into rolls

(b) it can be powdered

(c) it is porous

(d) its density is low.

311. The free convection heat transfer is significantly affected by

(a) Reynolds number

(b) Grashoff number

(c) Prantdtl number

(d) Stanton number.

312. The material medium between the heat source and receiver is not affected during the process of heat transmission by

(a) conduction

(b) convection

(c) radiation

(d) conduction as well as convection.

313. Milk spills over when it is boiled in an open vessel. The boiling of milk at this instant is referred to as

(a) interface evaporation

(b) subcooled boiling

(c) film boiling

(d) saturated nucleate boiling.

314. Mark the system where in heat transfer is by forced convection :

(a) Chilling effect of cold wind on warm body

(b) Fluid passing through the tubes of a condenser and other heat exchanger equipment

(c) Heat flow from a hot pavement to surrounding atmosphere

(d) Heat exchanger on the outside of cold and warm pipes.

315. Notable examples of uniform generation of heat within the conducting medium are :

(a) Energy generated in the fuel element of a nuclear reactor.

(b) Liberation of energy due to some exothermic chemical reactions.

(c) Resistance heating in electrical appliances.

(d) All of the above.

316. The thermal conductivity k and the electrical conductivity of a metal at absolute temperature T are related as

(a) $\dfrac{k}{\sigma}$ = constant

(b) $\dfrac{k}{\sigma T}$ = constant

(c) $\dfrac{k \sigma}{T}$ = constant

(d) $\dfrac{kT}{\sigma}$ = constant.

317. Heat transmission is directly linked with the transport of medium itself, *i.e.*, there is actual motion of heated particles during

(a) conduction only

(b) convection only

(c) radiation only

(d) conduction as well as radiation.

318. Lumped parameter analysis of transient heat conduction in solids stipulates

(a) infinite thermal conductivity

(b) negligible temperature gradient, *i.e.*, practically uniform temperature within the solid

(c) small conduction resistance

(d) predominance of convective resistance

(e) all of the above.

319. For steady state and constant value of thermal conductivity, the temperature distribution associated with radial conduction through a cylinder has a

(a) linear

(b) logarithmic

(c) parabolic

(d) exponential variation.

320. The essential condition for the transfer of heat from one body to another is

(a) both bodies must be in physical contact

(b) heat content of one body must be more than that of the other

(c) one of the bodies must have a high value of thermal conductivity

(d) there must exist a temperature difference between the bodies.

321. For a perfectly black body

(a) absorptivity $\alpha = 1$, reflectivity $\rho = 0$ and transmissivity $\tau = 0$

(b) $\tau = 1$ and $\alpha = \tau = 0$

(c) $\tau = 1$ and $\alpha = \rho = 0$

(d) $\alpha + \tau = 1$ and $\rho = 0$

322. Identify the *wrong* statement :

(a) The process of heat transfer is thermodynamically an irreversible process.

(b) A material medium is always necessary for heat transmission.

(c) For heat exchange, a temperature gradient must exist.

(d) Heat flow is always from a higher temperature to a lower temperature in accordance with the second law of thermodynamics.

323. The ratio of the emissive power of a body to that of a black body at the same temperature, *i.e.*, emissivity is constant for all wavelengths. Such a body is called

(a) white   (b) transparent

(c) grey   (d) diathermanous.

324. The roof of a house has been given a coating of shining metallic paint. Consequently the temperature inside the room will

(a) fall

(b) rise

(c) remain unaffected

(d) cannot be decided as it depends on factors other than the type of paint.

325. The emissivity is likely to be higher in case of

(a) rubber   (b) paper

(c) carbon   (d) iron oxide.

326. A radiation shield should

(a) have high transmissivity

(b) absorb all the radiations

(c) have high reflective power

(d) partly absorb and partly transmit the incident radiation.

327. Thermal conductivity is defined as the heat flow per unit time

(a) when temperature gradient is unity

(b) when a unit temperature difference is maintained across the opposite faces of the wall

(c) through a unit thickness of the wall

(d) across unit area when temperature gradient is unity

328. A surface for which emissivity is constant at all temperatures and throughout the entire range of wavelength is called

(a) opaque   (b) grey

(c) specular   (d) diathermanous.

329. Indicate the metal with highest value of thermal conductivity

(a) Steel   (b) Silver

(c) Copper   (d) Aluminium.

330. The direction of heat transfer is in accordance with

(a) first law of thermodynamics

(b) second law of thermodynamics

(c) Faraday's law

(d) Stefan's law.

331. The emissivity of white polished body

(a) is lower than black body

(b) is higher than black body

(c) depends upon area of body

(d) same.

332. Planck's law is true for

(a) all coloured bodies

(b) black bodies only

(c) polished bodies

(d) bodies having equal conductivities.

333. In SI system, the unit of thermal diffusivity is

(a) $kcal/m^2$-sec^2;   (b) kcal/m-sec;

(c) m-sec^2;   (d) m^2-sec.

334. In SI system the unit of thermal conductivity is

(a) W/m-°C   (b) W/m-hr-°C

(c) W/m^2-hr-°C   (d) None of these.

335. Fourier's law of heat transfer is applicable for

(a) conduction only

(b) convection only

(c) both conduction and convection

(d) none of these.

336. Electrical analogy for heat transfer coefficient is

(a) resistance   (b) inductance

(c) unit conductance   (d) none of these.

337. 'Peclet number' used in laminar flow heat transfer coefficients is the product of

(a) Prandtl number and Grashoff number

(b) Reynolds number and Prandtl number

(c) Reynolds number and Grashoff number

(d) none of these.

338. Fourier number may be expressed as

(a) ratio of buoyancy to viscous force

(b) ratio of internal thermal resistance of a solid to the boundary layer thermal resistance

(c) ratio of gravitational and surface tension forces

(d) ratio of heat conduction rate to the rate of thermal energy storage in solid.

339. In a two-fluid heat exchanger, the inlet and outlet temperatures of the hot fluid are 65°C and 40°C respectively. For the cold fluid, these are 15°C and 42°C. The heat exchanger is a

(a) parallel flow heat exchanger;

(b) counter flow heat exchanger;

(c) heat exchanger device where both parallel flow and counter flow operations are possible;

(d) none of the above.

340. randtl number of a flowing fluid less than unity indicates

(a) thermal boundary layer thickness is greater than hydrodynamic boundary layer thickness

(b) hydrodynamic boundary layer thickness is greater than thermal boundary layer thickness;

(c) hydrodynamic and thermal boundary layer thickness are same;

(d) none of the above.

341. Loss of heat from unlagged steam pipe to the ambient air is by

(a) conduction   (b) convection

(c) radiation   (d) all (a), (b), (c).

342. Thermal diffusivity is given by

(a) $\dfrac{k}{\rho\,c_p}$ (b) $\dfrac{\rho}{k\,c_p}$

(c) $\dfrac{\mu}{k\,c_p}$ (d) none of these.

343. Which of the following has the highest thermal conductivity ?

(a) Air   (b) Water

(c) Silver   (d) Brick.

344. Reynolds analogy states that

(a) $St = \dfrac{f}{2}$ (b) $St = \dfrac{f}{4}$

(c) $St = 4f$ (d) $St = \sqrt{f}$.

where, S_t = Stanton number, f = friction factor in the Fanning equation.

345. Economy of an evaporator is influenced by

(a) steam pressure

(b) temperature of the feed and number of effects

(c) either of the above

(d) none of the above.

346. Prandtl number is the ratio of

(a) momentum diffusivity to mass diffusivity

(b) momentum diffusivity to thermal diffusivity

(c) none of these.

347. Wavelength corresponding to the maximum energy is inversely proportional to the absolute temperature. This is

(a) Stefan's law   (b) Kirchhoff's law

(c) Wien's law   (d) none of these.

348. Correction is applied to *LMTD* for

(a) parallel flow   (b) counter flow

(c) cross-flow   (d) none of these.

349. A body is called grey if the monochromatic emissivity of the body is

(a) 0

(b) 1

(c) same for all wavelengths

(d) different for all wavelengths.

350. Heat transfer coefficient in transition region between laminar and turbulent

(a) can be determined by Colburn factor (J_H) *vs* Reynold's number plot

(b) can be determined by $Nu = 0.023\,Re\,0.8\,Pr^{1/3}$

(c) cannot be determined by any method

(d) any of the above.

351. The velocity and temperature distribution in a pipe flow are given by $u\,(r)$ and $T\,(r)$. If u_m is the mean velocity at any section of the pipe, the bulk-mean temperature at that section is

(a) $\int_0^{r_0} u\,(r)\,T\,(r)\,r^2\,dr$

(b) $\int_0^{r_0} \dfrac{u\,(r)}{3r} \cdot \dfrac{T\,(r)}{2r}\,dr$

(c) $\dfrac{4\int_0^{r_0} u\,(r)\,T\,(r)\,dr}{2\pi\,r_0^{3}}$

(d) $\dfrac{2}{u_m\,r_0^{2}}\int_0^{r_0} u\,(r)\,T\,(r)\,r\,dr.$

352. The units of thermal resistance are

(a) $\dfrac{m^2\,{}^\circ C}{W}$ (b) $\dfrac{m^2}{W}$

(c) $\dfrac{m\,{}^\circ C}{W}$ (d) none of these.

353. The conductivity of glass wool varies from sample to sample because of variation in

(a) composition   (b) structure

(c) porosity   (d) all of the above.

354. The time constant of a thermocouple is

(a) time taken to attain 50% of initial temp. difference

(b) time taken to attain 99% of initial temp. difference

(c) time taken to attain 36.8% of initial temp. difference

(d) not defined.

355. Thermal diffusivity is

(a) $\dfrac{\rho \, c_p}{k}$

(b) $\dfrac{k}{\rho \, c_p}$

(c) $\dfrac{\rho \, k}{c_p}$

(d) $\dfrac{c_p}{\rho \, k}$.

356. For heating of a flat plate the hydrodynamic boundary layer is thinner than thermal boundary layer. The value of Prandtl number is

(a) greater than one

(b) less than one

(c) equal to one

(d) can be less than or greater than one depending upon the value of Reynolds number.

357. Nusselt number is

(a) a dimensionless temperature gradient

(b) the ratio of two temperature gradients

(c) none of the above two

(d) both of the above two, *i.e.*, (a) and (b).

358. Stanton number is equal to

(a) $Re \cdot Pr$

(b) $Gr \cdot Pr$

(c) $\dfrac{Re}{Pr}$

(d) $\dfrac{Nu}{Re \cdot Pr}$.

359. The total emissive power E of a diffuse surface is related to radiation intensity I as, E equal to

(a) $\dfrac{\pi}{4} I$

(b) πI

(c) $\pi^2 I$

(d) $4\pi I$.

360. The absorptivity of a whitewashed wall is close to

(a) 0.1

(b) 0.3

(c) 0.5

(d) 0.9.

361. The rate of heat transfer is constant if

(a) temperature decreases with time

(b) temperature increases with time

(c) temperature is constant

(d) none of the above.

362. Fourier's law is based on assumption that

(a) heat flow is one-dimensional

(b) heat flow is steady

(c) both (a) and (b)

(d) none of the above.

363. The term $\dfrac{\Delta x}{kA}$ in the equation

$$Q = kA \, \dfrac{t_1 - t_2}{\Delta x} \quad \text{is known as :}$$

(a) thermal resistance

(b) thermal conductance

(c) thermal loading

(d) none of the above.

364. Critical radius of a hollow cylinder is defined as:

(a) inner radius which would give maximum heat flow

(b) outer radius which would give minimum heat flow

(c) outer radius which would give maximum heat flow

(d) none of the above.

365. The average temperature difference between the two fluids in case of counterflow heat exchanger as compared to parallel flow heat exchange is :

(a) more

(b) less

(c) same

(d) none of the above.

NUMERICAL QUESTIONS

*366. The inner surface of a plane brick wall is at 50°C and the outer surface is at 25°C. Calculate the rate of heat transfer per m^2 of the surface area of the wall, which is 220 mm thick. The thermal conductivity of the bricks is 0.51 W/m K.

(a) 20.65 W/m^2

(b) 32.75 W/m^2

(c) 47.62 W/m^2

(d) 57.95 W/m^2.

*367. A mild steel tank of wall thickness 12 mm contains water at 100°C. Calculate the rate of heat loss per m^2 of tank surface area when the atmospheric temperature is 20°C. The thermal conductivity of mild steel is 50 W/m K, and the heat transfer coefficients for the inside and outside the tank are 2850 and 10 W/m^2 K,

respectively. Calculate also the temperature of the outside surface of the tank.

(a) 300.5 W/m^2, 45.5°C

(b) 495.2 W/m^2, 67.6°C

(c) 602.6 W/m^2, 80.6°C

(d) 795.2 W/m^2, 99.52°C.

*368. A spherical shaped vessel of 1.4 m diameter is 90 mm thick. Find the rate of heat leakage, if the temperature difference between the inner and outer surfaces is 220°C. Thermal conductivity of the material of the sphere is 0.083 W/mK.

(a) 0.2 kW

(b) 0.5 kW

(c) 1.0886 kW

(d) 1.6 kW.

*369. Liquid air at –147°C is stored in the space of two concentric spheres of 0.2 m and 0.3 m diameters. The surface emissivities are 0.028. Assume the outer surface temperature is 25°C. Considering only radiation heat transfer and taking the latent heat of liquid air of 210 kJ/kg, find the rate of evaporation.

Take $\sigma = 204 \times 10^{-4}$ kJ/h-m^2-K^4

  (a) 16.25 kg/h   (b) 18.22 hg/h
  (c) 23.25 kg/h   (d) 30.65 kg/h.

*370. A body at 1000°C in black surroundings at 500°C has an emissivity of 0.42 at 1000°C and an emissivity of 0.72 at 500°C. Calculate the rate of heat loss by radiation per m^2.

(i) When the body is assumed to be grey with $\varepsilon = 0.42$

(ii) When the body is not grey.

    Assume that the absorptivity is independent of the surface temperature.

  (a) 20.6 kW, 18.5 kW
  (b) 32.6 kW, 28.5 kW
  (c) 54.893 kW, 47.962 kW
  (d) 68.96 kW, 52.9 kW.

B. MATCH LIST I WITH LIST II AND SELECT CORRECT ANSWER USING THE CODES GIVEN BELOW THE LISTS:

371.

	List I		List II
A.	Non-isotropic thermal conductivity is exhibited in case of	1.	molecular
B.	Conduction is the transmission of heat by .... collision.	2.	four
C.	The thermal conductivity of ice is nearly .... times the thermal conductivity of water.	3.	porous
D.	Cork is a good insulator because it is	4.	wood.

Codes	A	B	C	D
(a)	4	2	3	1
(b)	4	1	2	3
(c)	1	2	3	4
(d)	3	4	2	1.

372.

	List I		List II
A.	The process of heat transfer during entry of satellites and missiles, at very high speeds, into earth's surface is known as	1.	Prevost theory
B.	Radiation heat transfer between two surfaces can be reduced by introducing .... between the surfaces.	2.	ablation
C.	Gases have poor	3.	radiation shield
D.	All bodies above absolute zero emit radiations. This statement is based on .... of heat exchange.	4.	reflectivity.

Codes:

	A	B	C	D
(a)	1	2	3	4
(b)	4	3	2	1
(c)	3	4	1	2
(d)	2	3	4	1

373.

	List I		List II
A.	A body which absorbs heat radiations of all wavelengths falling on it, is called	1.	emisivity
B.	.... is the ratio of emissive power of a body to the emissive power of a perfectly black body	2.	black body
C.	.... is the ratio of thermal conductivity to the equivalent thickness of the film of fluid	3.	absorptive power
D.	Ratio of energy absorbed by a body to the total energy falling on it is	4.	film coefficient.

Codes:

	A	B	C	D
(a)	2	1	4	3
(b)	1	2	3	4
(c)	3	4	2	1
(d)	4	2	3	1.

374.

	List I		List II
A.	Radiation heat transfer	1.	Wien displacement law
B.	Conduction heat transfer	2.	Fourier number
C.	Forced convection	3.	Fourier law
D.	Transient heat flow	4.	Stanton number.

Codes:

	A	B	C	D
(a)	4	3	1	2
(b)	3	4	2	1
(c)	1	3	4	2
(d)	4	2	1	3.

375.

	List I		List II
A.	Free convection	1.	$\dfrac{hd}{k}$
B.	Nusselt number	2.	$\dfrac{2k}{h_o}$
C.	Thermal diffusivity	3.	$\dfrac{k}{\rho c_p}$
D.	Critical radius of insulation	4.	Grashoff number.

Codes:

	A	B	C	D
(a)	1	2	3	4
(b)	4	1	3	2
(c)	2	3	4	1
(d)	4	2	3	1.

376.

	List I		List II
A.	LMTD correction is applied in case of .... heat exchanger.	1.	highly polished
B.	Dropwise condensation occurs on .... surfaces.	2.	cross flow
C.	Grashoff number has significant role in heat transfer by	3.	liquid metals
D.	Least value of Prandtl number can be expected in case of	4.	free convection.

Codes:

	A	B	C	D
(a)	2	1	4	3
(b)	1	2	3	4
(c)	4	3	2	1
(d)	3	4	2	1

COMPETITIVE EXAMINATIONS QUESTIONS–U.P.S.C.
(WITH SOLUTIONS – COMMENTS)

377. Upto the critical radius of insulation
(a) added insulation will increase heat loss (b) added insulation will decrease heat loss
(c) convection heat loss will be less than conduction heat loss
(d) heat flux will decrease.

*378. A designer chooses the values of fluid flow ranges and specific heats in such a manner that the heat capacities of the two fluids are equal. A hot fluid enters the counterflow heat exchanger at 100°C and leaves at 60°C. The cold fluid enters the heat exchanger at 40°C. The mean temperature difference between the two fluids is:
(a) $(100 + 60 + 40)/3$°C
(b) 60°C
(b) 40°C
(d) 20°C.

*379. For infinite parallel planes with emissivities, e_1 and e_2, the interchange factor for radiation from surface 1 to surface 2 is given by
(a) $\dfrac{\varepsilon_1 \varepsilon_2}{\varepsilon_1 + \varepsilon_2 - \varepsilon_1 \varepsilon_2}$
(b) $\dfrac{1}{\varepsilon_1} + \dfrac{1}{\varepsilon_2}$
(c) $\varepsilon_1 + \varepsilon_2$
(d) $\varepsilon_1 \varepsilon_2$.

*380. A furnace is made of a red brick wall of thickness 0.5 m and conductivity 0.7 W/mK. For the same heat loss and temperature drop, this can be replaced by a layer of diatomite earth of conductivity 0.14 W/mK and thickness
(a) 0.05 m
(b) 0.1 m
(c) 0.2 m
(d) 0.5 m.

381. The thicknesses of thermal and hydrodynamic boundary layers are equal if (Pr = Prandtl Number, Nu = Nusselt Number)
(a) $Pr = 1$
(b) $Pr > 1$
(c) $Pr < 1$
(d) $Pr = Nu$.

382. A heat exchanger with heat transfer surface area A and overall heat transfer coefficient U handles two fluids of heat capacities C_{max} and C_{min}. The parameter NTU (number of transfer units) used in the analysis of heat exchanger is specified as
(a) $\dfrac{A\,C_{min}}{U}$
(b) $\dfrac{U}{A\,C_{min}}$
(c) AUC_{min}
(d) $\dfrac{AU}{C_{min}}$

383. ε-NTU method is particularly useful in thermal design of heat exchangers when
    (a) the outlet temperature of the fluid streams is not known as a priori
    (b) outlet temperature of the fluid streams is known as a priori
    (c) the outlet temperature of the hot fluid streams is known but that of the cold fluid streams is not known as a priori
    (d) inlet temperatures of the fluid streams are known as a priori.

384. Thermal boundary layer is a region where
    (a) inertia terms are of the same order of magnitude as convection terms
    (b) convection terms are of the same order of magnitude as dissipation terms
    (c) convection terms are of the same order of magnitude as conduction terms
    (d) dissipation is negligible.

385. For evaporators and condensers, for the given conditions, the logarithmic mean temperature difference (LMTD) for parallel flow is
    (a) equal to that for counterflow
    (b) greater than that for counterflow
    (c) smaller than that for counterflow counterflow.
    (d) very much smaller than that for

386. A thin flat plate 2 m by 2 m is hanging freely in air. The temperature of the surroundings is 25°C. Solar radiation is falling on one side of the plate at the rate of 500 W/m². The temperature of the plate will remain constant at 30°C, if the convective heat transfer coefficient (in W/m²°C) is
    (a) 25   (b) 50
    (c) 100   (d) 200.

*387. A composite slab has two layers of different materials with thermal conductivity k_1 and k_2. If each layer had the same thickness, the equivalent thermal conductivity of the slab would be
    (a) $k_1 + k_2$ (b) $\dfrac{(k_1 + k_2)}{(k_1 \, k_2)}$
    (c) $\dfrac{(2 \, k_1 \, k_2)}{(k_1 + k_2)}$ (d) $k_1 k_2$.

*388. Which one of the following modes of heat transfer would take place predominantly, from boiler furnace to water wall ?
    (a) Convection
    (b) Conduction
    (c) Radiation
    (d) Conduction and convection.

*389. Given the following data:
    Inside heat transfer coeficient = 25 W/m²K
    Outside heat transfer coefficient = 25 W/m²K
    Thermal conductivity of bricks (15 cm thick) = 0.15 W/mK,
    The overall heat transfer coefficient (in W/m²K) will be closer to the
    (a) inverse of heat transfer coefficient
    (b) heat transfer coefficient
    (c) thermal conductivity of bricks
    (d) heat transfer coefficient based on the thermal conductivity of the bricks alone.

390. Match List I with List II and select the correct answer using the codes given below the lists:

	List I		List II
	(Dimensionless quantity)		(Application)
A.	Stanton number	1.	Natural convection for ideal gases
B.	Grashoff number	2.	Mass transfer
C.	Peclet number	3.	Forced convection
D.	Schmidt number	4.	Forced convection for small Prandtl number.

Codes:	A	B	C	D
(a)	2	4	3	1
(b)	3	1	4	2
(c)	3	4	1	2
(d)	2	1	3	4.

391. The burnout heat flux in the nucleate boiling regime is a function of which of the following properties?

1. Heat of evaporation
2. Temperature difference
3. Density of vapour
4. Density of liquid
5. Vapour-liquid surface tension.

Select the corrct answer using the codes given below:

Codes:

(*a*) 1, 2, 4 and 5   (*b*) 1, 2, 3 and 5

(*c*) 1, 3, 4 and 5   (*d*) 2, 3 and 4.

*392. Which of the following are the reasons for the volumetric efficiency of reciprocating compressor being less than 100% ?

1. Deviations from isentropic process
2. Pressure drop across the valves
3. Superheating in compressor
4. Cearance volume
5. Deviations from isothermal process
6. Leakages.

Select the correct answer from the codes given below:

Codes:

(*a*) 1, 2, 3 and 5   (*b*) 2, 3, 4 and 5

(*c*) 1, 4, 5 and 6   (*d*) 2, 3, 4 and 6.

ESE – 1996

*393. It is desired to increase the heat dissipation rate over the surface of an electronic device of spherical shape of 5 mm radius exposed to convection with $h = 10$ W/m^{2}K by encasing it in a spherical sheath of conductivity 0.04 W/m K. For maximum heat flow, the diameter of the sheath should be

(*a*) 18 mm   (*b*) 16 mm

(*c*) 12 mm   (*d*) 8 mm.

395. A pipe carrying saturated steam is covered with a layer of insulation and exposed to ambient air. The thermal resistances are as shown in the following figure :

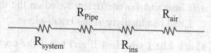

Which one of the following statements is *correct* in this regard ?

(*a*) R_{steam} and R_{pipe} are negligible as compared to R_{ins} and R_{air}

(*b*) R_{pipe} and R_{air} are negligible as compared to R_{ins} and R_{steam}

(*c*) R_{steam} and R_{air} are negligible as compared to R_{pipe} and R_{ins}

(*d*) No quantitative data is provided, therefore no comparison is possible.

395. Which one of the following statements is *correct*?

(*a*) Laminar flow is greater than that for turbulent flow

(*b*) Turbulent flow is greater than that for laminar flow

(*c*) Laminar flow is equal to that for turbulent flow

(*d*) A given flow can be determined only if the Prandtl number is known.

395. Match List I with List II and select the correct answer using the codes given below the lists :

List I		List II	
A.	Reynolds number	1.	Film coefficient, pipe diameter, thermal conductivity
B.	Prandtl number	2.	Flow velocity, acoustic velocity
C.	Nusselt number	3.	Heat capacity, dynamic viscosity, thermal conductivity
D.	Match number	4.	Flow velocity, pipe diameter, kinematic viscosity

Codes:	A	B	C	D
(*a*)	4	1	3	2
(*b*)	4	3	1	2
(*c*)	2	3	1	4
(*d*)	2	1	3	4

397. Match List I with List II and select the correct answer using the codes given below the lists :

List I		List II	
A.	Window glass	1.	Emissivity independent of wavelength
B.	Grey surface	2.	Emission and absorption limited of wavelength
C.	Carbon dioxide	3.	Rate at which radiation leaves a surface
D.	Radiosity	4.	Transparency to shortwave radiation.

Codes:	A	B	C	D
(a)	1	4	2	3
(b)	4	1	3	2
(c)	4	1	2	3
(d)	1	4	3	2

398. Match List I and List II and select the correct answer using the codes given below the lists :

List I		List II	
A.	Momentum transfer	1.	Thermal diffusivity
B.	Mass transfer	2.	Kinematic viscosity
C.	Heat transfer	3.	Diffusion coefficient.

Codes:	A	B	C
(a)	2	3	1
(b)	1	3	2
(c)	3	2	1
(d)	1	2	3.

399. A counterflow heat exchanger is used to heat water from 20°C to 80°C by using hot exhaust gas entering at 140°C and leaving at 80°C. The log mean temperature difference for the heat exchanger is

(a) 80°C

(b) 60°C

(c) 110°C

(d) not determinable as zero/zero is involved.

400. A heat exchanger with transfer surface area A and overall heat transfer coefficient U handles two fluids of heat capacities C_1 and C_2 such that $C_1 > C_2$. The NTU of the heat exchanger is given by

(a) AU/C_2

(b) (b) $e^{-\left(\frac{AU}{C_2}\right)}$

(c) $e^{-(AU/C_1)}$

(d) AU/C_1.

401. Consider the following statements regarding condensation heat transfer :

1. For a single tube, horizontal position is preferred over vertical position for better heat transfer

2. Heat transfer coefficient decreases if the vapour stream moves at high velocity

3. Condensation of steam on an oily surface is dropwise

4. Condensation of pure benzene vapour is always dropwise.

Of these statements

(a) 1 and 2 are correct

(b) 2 and 4 are correct

(c) 1 and 3 are correct

(d) 3 and 4 are correct.

402. Consider the following statements pertaining to heat transfer through fins :

1. Fins are equally effective irrespective of whether they are on the hot side or cold side of the fluid.

2. The temperature along the fin is variable and hence the rate of heat transfer varies along the elements of the fin.

3. The fins may be made of materials that have a higher thermal conductivity than the material of the wall.

4. Fins must be arranged at right angles to the direction of flow of the working fluid.

Of these statements :

(a) 1 and 2 are correct (b) 2 and 4 are correct

(c) 1 and 3 are correct (d) 2 and 3 are correct.

403. Consider the following statements :

1. Under certain conditions, an increase in thickness of insulation may increase the heat loss from a heated pipe.

2. The heat loss from a insulated pipe reaches a maximum when the outside radius insulation is equal to the ratio of thermal conductivity to the surface coefficient.

3. Small diameter tubes are invariably insulated.

4. Economic insulation is based on minimum heat loss from pipe.

Of these statements :

(a) 1 and 3 are correct (b) 2 and 4 are correct

(c) 1 and 2 are correct (d) 3 and 4 are correct.

404. Addition of fin to the surface increases the heat transfer if $\sqrt{hA/kP}$ is

(a) equal to one

(b) greater than one

(c) less than one

(d) greater than one but less than two.

405. Consider the development of laminar boundary layer for a moving non-reacting fluid in contact with a flat plate of length '1' along the flow direction. The average value of heat transfer coefficient can be obtained by multiplying the local heat transfer coefficient at the trailing edge by the factor

(a) 0.75   (b) 1.0

(c) 1.5   (d) 2.0.

406. A solid copper ball of mass 500 grams, when quenched in a water bath at 30°C cools from 530°C to 430°C in 10 seconds. What will be the temperature of the ball after the next 10 seconds?

(a) 300°C

(b) 320°C

(c) 350°C

(d) Not determinable for want of sufficient data.

407. A steam pipe is covered with two layers of insulating materials, with the better insulating material forming the outer part. If the two layers are interchanged, the heat conducted

(a) will decrease

(b) will increase

(c) will remain unaffected

(d) may increase or decrease depending upon the thickness of each layer.

408. In a large plate, the steady temperature distribution is as shown in the given figure. If no heat is generated in the plate, the thermal conductivity 'k' will vary as (T is temperature and is a constant).

(a) $k_o (1 + at)$ (b) $k_o (1 - aT)$

(c) $k_o + aT$ (d) $k_o - aT$

409. The time constant of a thermocouple is the time taken to attain

(a) the final value to be measured

(b) 50% of the value of the initial temperature difference

(c) 63.2% of the value of the initial temperature difference

(d) 98.8% of the value of the initial temperature difference.

410. When there is a flow of fluid over a flat plate of length 'L', the average heat transfer coefficient is given by (Nu_x = local Nusselt number; other symbols have the usual meaning).

(a) $\displaystyle\int_0^L h_x\, dx$ (b) $\dfrac{d}{dx}(h_x)$

(c) $\dfrac{1}{L}\displaystyle\int_0^L hx\, dx$ (d) $\dfrac{k}{L}\displaystyle\int_0^L Nu_x\, dx$.

411. When all the conditions are identical, in the case of flow through pipes with heat transfer, the velocity profiles will be identical for

(a) liquid heating and liquid cooling

(b) gas heating and gas cooling

(c) liquid heating and gas cooling

(d) heating and cooling of any fluid.

412. In the case of turbulent flow through a horizontal isothermal cylinder of diameter 'D', free convection heat transfer coefficient from the cylinder will

(a) be independent of diameter

(b) vary as $D^{3/4}$

(c) vary as $D^{1/4}$

(d) vary as $D^{1/2}$.

*413. Sun's surface at 5800 K emits radiation at a wavelength of 0.5 m. A furnace at 300°C will emit through a small opening, radiation at a wavelength of nearly

(a) 10 μ   (b) 5 μ

(c) 0.25 μ   (d) 0.025 μ.

414. Consider the following statements :
If the surface is pock-marked with a number of cavities, then as compared to a smooth surface

1. radiation will increase
2. nucleate boiling will increase
3. conduction will increase
4. covection will increase.

Of these statements :

(a) 1, 2 and 3 are correct
(b) 1, 2, and 4 are correct
(c) 1, 3, and 4 are correct
(d) 2, 3, and 4 are correct.

415. Consider two infinitely long blackbody concentric cylinders with a diameter ratio $D_2/D_1 = 3$. The shape for the outer cylinder with itself will be

(a) 0   (b) 1/3
(c) 2/3   (d) 1.

416. Consider the following phenomena :
1. Boiling

2. Free convection in air
3. Forced convection
4. Conduction in air.

Their correct sequence in increasing order of heat transfer coefficient is :

(a) 4, 2, 3, 1   (b) 4, 1, 3, 2
(c) 4, 3, 2, 1   (d) 3, 4, 1, 2.

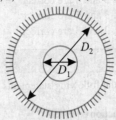

417. A thermocouple in a thermowell measures the temperature of hot gas flowing through the pipe. For the most accurate measurement of temperature, the thermowell should be made of

(a) steel   (b) brass (c)
    copper   (d) aluminium.

ESE-1997

418. Consider the following statements :

The flow configuration in a heat exchanger, whether counterflow or otherwise, will NOT matter if

1. a liquid is evaporating
2. a vapour is condensing
3. mass flow rate of one of the fluids is far greater.

Of these statements :

(a) 1 and 2 are correct
(b) 1 and 3 are correct
(c) 2 and 3 are correct
(d) 1, 2 and 3 are correct.

419. Which one of the following diagrams correctly shows the temperature distribution for a gas-to-gas counter-flow heat exchanger ?

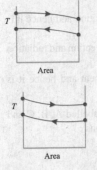

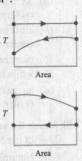

420. Consider the following statements :

The effect of fouling in a water-cooled steam condensers is that it

1. reduces the heat transfer coefficient of water.
2. reduces the overall heat transfer coefficient.
3. reduces the area available for heat transfer.
4. increases the pressure drop of water.

Of these statements :

(a) 1, 2 and 4 are correct
(b) 2, 3 and 4 are correct
(c) 2 and 4 are correct
(d) 1 and 3 are correct.

421. The given figure shows a pool-boiling curve. Consider the following statements in this regard:

1. Onset of nucleation causes a marked change in slope.
2. At the point B, heat transfer coefficient is the maximum.

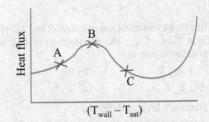

3. In an electrically heated wire submerged in the liquid, film heating is difficult to achieve.

4. Beyond the point C, radiation becomes significant.

Of these statements :

(a) 1, 2 and 4 are correct

(b) 1, 3 and 4 are correct

(c) 2, 3 and 4 are correct

(d) 1, 2 and 3 are correct.

422. A composite wall consists of two layers of different materials having conductivities k_1 and k_2. For equal thickness of the two layers, the equivalent thermal conductivity of the slab will be

(a) $k_1 + k_2$

(b) $k_1 k_2$

(c) $\dfrac{2k_1 k_2}{k_1 + k_2}$

(d) $\dfrac{k_1 + k_2}{k_1 k_2}$

ESE-1998

423. Consider the following statements : The Fourier heat conduction equation $Q = - kA \dfrac{dt}{dx}$ presumes

1. steady-state conditions.

2. constant value of thermal conductivity.

3. uniform temperatures at the wall surfaces.

4. one-dimensional heat flow.

Of these statements :

(a) 1, 2, and 3 are correct

(b) 1, 2, and 4 are correct

(c) 2, 3, and 4 are correct

(d) 1, 3, and 4 are correct.

424. The temperature variation in a large plate, as shown in the figure, would correspond to which of the following condition(s)?

1. Unsteady heat.

2. Steady-state with variation of k.

3. Steady-state with heat generation.

Select the correct answer using the codes given below :

Codes :

(a) 2 alone

(b) 1 and 2

(c) 1 and 3

(d) 1, 2 and 3.

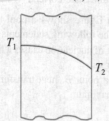

425. In a long cylindrical rod of radius R and a surface heat flux of q_o, the uniform internal heat generation rate is

(a) $2q_o/R$

(b) $2q_o$

(c) q_o/R

(d) q_o/R^2.

426. Boundary layer is defined as

(a) a thin layer at the surface where gradients of both velocity and temperature are small

(b) a thin layer at the surface where velocity and velocity gradients are large

(c) a thick layer at the surface where velocity and temperature gradients are large

(d) a thin layer at the surface where gradients of both velocity and temperature are large.

427. A large spherical enclosure has a small opening. The rate of emission of radiative flux through this opening is 7.35 kW/m^2. The temperature at the inner surface of the sphere will be about (assume Stefan Boltzmann constant, s = 5.67 × 10^{-8} W/m^2 K^4)

(a) 600°C

(b) 330°C

(c) 373 K

(d) 1000 K.

428. Consider the following statements :

1. For metals, the value of absorptivity is high.

2. For non-conducting materials, reflectivity is low.

3. For polished surfaces, reflectivity is high.

4. For gases, reflectivity is very low.

Of these statements :

(a) 2, 3 and 4 are correct

(b) 3 and 4 are correct

(c) 1, 2 and 4 are correct

(d) 1 and 2 are correct.

429. On a summer day, a scooter rider feels more comfortable while on the move than while at a stop light because

(a) an object in motion captures less solar radiation

(b) air is transparent to radiation and hence it is cooler than the body

(c) more heat is lost by convection and radiation while in motion

(d) air has a low specific heat and hence it is cooler.

430. Match the velocity profiles labelled A, B, C and D with the following situations :

1. Natural convection

2. Condensation

3. Forced convection
4. Bulk viscosity wall viscosity.
5. Flow in pipe entrance.

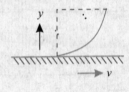
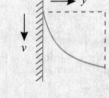
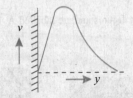
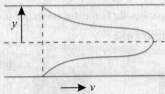

Select the correct answer using the codes given below :

Codes:	A	B	C	D
(a)	3	2	1	5
(b)	1	4	2	3
(c)	3	2	1	4
(d)	2	1	5	3.

431. Heat is mainly transferred by conduction, convection and radiation in
(a) insulated pipes carrying hot water
(b) refrigerator freezer coil
(c) boiler furnaces
(d) condensation of steam in a condenser.

432. Consider the following statements :
1. If a condensing liquid does not wet a surface dropwise, then condensation will take place on it.
2. Dropwise condensation gives a higher heat transfer rate than film-wise condensation.
3. Reynolds number of condensing liquid is based on its mass flow rate.
4. Suitable coating or vapour additive is used to promote film-wise condensation.

Of these statements :
(a) 1 and 2 are correct
(b) 2, 3 and 4 are correct
(c) 4 alone is correct
(d) 1, 2 and 3 are correct.

433. A furnace wall is constructed as shown in the figure. The interface temperature t_i will be
(a) 5600°C

1000°C

(b) 200°C

t_i

Outer casing

$k_1 = 3$ W/m K

(c) 920°C

$k_2 = 0.3$ W/m K   120°C

(d) 1120°C

$t_\infty = 40°C$

← 0.3 m → ← 0.3 m →

434. Solar energy is absorbed by the wall of a building as shown in the figure. Assuming that the ambient temperature inside and outside are equal and considering steady-state, the equivalent circuit will be as shown in the figure (a, b, c, d).

(symbols : $R_{CO} = R_{\text{convection, outside}}$, $R_{CI} = R_{\text{convection, inside}}$ and $R_w = R_{\text{wall}}$)

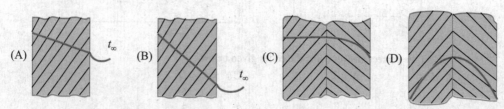

435. Temperature profiles for four cases are shown in the following figures and are labelled A, B, C and D. Match the above figures with :

(A)   (B)   (C)   (D)

1. High conductivity fluid.
2. Low conductivity fluid.
3. Insulating body.
4. Guard heater.

Select the correct answer using the codes given below :

Codes:	A	B	C	D
(a)	1	2	3	4
(b)	2	1	3	4
(c)	1	2	4	3
(d)	2	1	4	3.

436. The heat flow equation through a cylinder of inner radius 'r_1' and outer radius 'r_2' is desired in the same form as that for heat flow through a plane wall. The equivalent area A_m is given by:

(a) $\dfrac{A_1 + A_2}{\log_e\left(\dfrac{A_2}{A_1}\right)}$

(b) $\dfrac{A_1 + A_2}{2\log_e\left(\dfrac{A_2}{A_1}\right)}$

(c) $\dfrac{A_2 - A_1}{2\log_e\left(\dfrac{A_2}{A_1}\right)}$

(d) $\dfrac{A_2 - A_1}{\log_e\left(\dfrac{A_2}{A_1}\right)}$.

*437. A steel plate of thickness 5 cm and thermal conductivity 20 W/mK is subjected to a uniform heat flux of 800 W/m^2 on one surface 'A' and transfers heat by convection with a heat transfer co-efficient of 80 W/m^{2}K from the other surface 'B' into ambient air t_a of 25°C. The temperature of the surface 'B' transferring heat by convection is

(a) 25°C   (b) 35°C
(c) 45°C   (d) 55°C

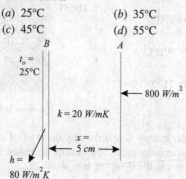

438. The hydrodynamic boundary layer thickness is defined as the distance from the surface where the

(a) velocity equals the local external velocity

(b) velocity equals the approach velocity

(c) momentum equals 99% of the momentum of the free stream

(d) velocity equals 99% of the local external velocity.

*439. Heat is lost from a 100 mm diameter steam pipe placed horizontally in ambient at 30°C. If the Nusselt number is 25 and thermal conductivity of air is 0.03 W/mK, then the heat transfer co-efficient will be

(a) 7.5 W/m²K   (b) 16.2 W/m²K

(c) 25.2 W/m² K   (d) 30 W/m²K.

*440. If the temperature of a solid surface changes

from 27°C to 627°C, then its emissive power will increase in the ratio of

(a) 3   (b) 9

(c) 27   (d) 81.

*441. A spherical aluminium shell of inside diameter 2 m is evacuated and used as a radiation test chamber. If the inner surface is coated with carbon black and maintained at 600 K, the irradiation on a small test surface placed inside the chamber is (Stefan-Boltzmann constant $\sigma = 5.67 \times 10^{-8}$ W/m²K⁴)

(a) 1000 W/m²   (b) 3400 W/m²

(c) 5680 W/m²   (d) 7348 W/m².

*442. Match List-I with List-II and select the correct answer using the codes given below the lists.

	List-I		List-II
A.	Stefan-Boltzmann law	1.	$q = hA\,(T_1 - T_2)$
B.	Newton's law of cooling	2.	$E = \alpha E_b$
C.	Fourier's law	3.	$q = \dfrac{kA}{L}\,(T_1 - T_2)$
D.	Kirchoff's law	4.	$q = \sigma A\,(T_1^4 - T_2^4)$
		5.	$q = kA\,(T_1 - T_2)$

Codes :

	A	B	C	D			A	B	C	D
(a)	4	1	3	2		(b)	4	5	1	2
(c)	2	1	3	4		(d)	2	5	1	4

*443. A cross-flow type air-heater has an area of 50 m². The overall heat transfer coefficient is 100 W/m²K and heat capacity of both hot and cold stream is 1000 W/K. The value of NTU is

(a) 1000   (b) 500

(c) 5   (d) 0.2.

444. Saturated steam is allowed to condense over a vertical flat surface and the condensate film flows down the surface. The local heat transfer coefficient for condensation

(a) remains constant at all locations of the surface

(b) decreases with increasing distance from the top of the surface

(c) increases with increasing thickness of condensate film

(d) increases with decreasing temperature differential between the surface and vapour.

445. A fin of length 'l' protrudes from a surface held at temperature t_0 greater than the ambient

temperature t_a. The heat dissipation from the free end of the fin is assumed to be negligible. The temperature gradient at the fin tip $\left(\dfrac{dt}{dx}\right)_{x=l}$ is

(a) zero   (b) $\dfrac{t_l - t_a}{t_o - t_a}$

(c) $h\,(t_o - t_l)$ (d) $\dfrac{t_a - t_l}{l}$

*446. A furnace wall is constructed as shown in the given figure. The heat transfer coefficient across the outer casing will be

(a) 80 W/m²K   (b) 40 W/m²K

(c) 20 W/m²K   (d) 10 W/m²K.

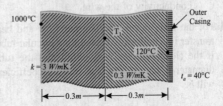

*447. For laminar flow over a flat plate, the local heat transfer coefficient 'h_x' varies as $x^{-1/2}$, where x is the distance from the leading edge ($x = 0$) of the plate. The ratio of the average coefficient 'h_a' between the leading edge and some location 'A' at $x = x$ on the plate to the local heat transfer coefficient 'h_x' at A is

(a) 1
(b) 2
(c) 4
(d) 8

*448. A heat pump operating on Carnot cycle pumps heat from a reservoir at $300\ K$ to a reservoir at $600\ K$. The coefficient of performance is

(a) 1.5
(b) 0.5
(c) 2
(d) 1

ESE–2000

449. Consider the following statements :

The reheat cycle helps to reduce

1. fuel consumption 2. steam flow
3. the condenser size

Which of these statements are *correct* ?

(a) 1 and 2
(b) 1 and 3
(c) 2 and 3
(d) 1, 2 and 3

450. The outer surface of a long cylinder is maintained at constant temperature. The cylinder does not have any heat source.

The temperature in the cylinder will

(a) increase linearly with radius
(b) decreases linearly with radius
(c) be independent of radius
(d) vary logarithmically with radius.

451. A composite plane wall is made up of two different materials of the same thickness and having thermal conductivities of k_1 and k_2 respectively. The equivalent thermal conductivity of the slab is

(a) $k_1 + k_2$
(b) $k_1 k_2$
(c) $\dfrac{k_1 + k_2}{k_1 k_2}$
(d) $\dfrac{2k_1 k_2}{k_1 + k_2}$

452. A copper wire of radius 0.5 mm is insulated with a sheathing of thickness 1 mm having a thermal conductivity of 0.5 $W/m - K$. The outside surface convective heat transfer coefficient is 10 $W/m^2 - K$. If the thickness of insulation sheathing is raised by 10 mm, then the electrical current-varrying capacity of the wire will

(a) increase
(b) decrease
(c) remain the same
(d) vary depending upon the electrical conductivity of the wire.

453. For the fully developed laminar flow and heat transfer in a uniformly heated long circular tube, if the flow velocity is doubled and the tube diameter is halved, the heat transfer coefficient will be

(a) double of the original value
(b) half of the original value
(c) same as before
(d) four times of the original value

454. Heat transfer by radiation between two grey bodies of emissivity ε is proportional to (notations have their usual meanings)

(a) $\dfrac{(E_b - J)}{(1 - \varepsilon)}$
(b) $\dfrac{(E_b - J)}{(1 - \varepsilon)/\varepsilon}$
(c) $\dfrac{(E_b - J)}{(1 - \varepsilon)^2}$
(d) $\dfrac{(E_b - J)}{(1 - \varepsilon^2)}$.

455. Solar radiation of 1200 W/m^2 falls perpendicularly on a grey opaque surface of emissivity 0.5. If the surface temperature is 50° C and surface emissive power 600 W/m^2, the radiosity of that surface will be

(a) 600 W/m^2
(b) 1000 W/m^2
(c) 1200 W/m^2
(d) 1800 W/m^2.

456. The overall heat transfer coefficient U for a plane composite wall of n layers is given by (the thickness of the ith layer is t_i , thermal conductivity of the ith layer is k_i, convective heat transfer coefficient is h)

(a) $\dfrac{1}{\dfrac{1}{h_1} + \sum\limits_{i=1}^{n} \dfrac{t_i}{k_i} + \dfrac{1}{h_n}}$
(b) $h_1 + \sum\limits_{i=1}^{n} \dfrac{t_i}{k_i} + h_n$

(c) $h_1 + \dfrac{1}{\sum\limits_{i=1}^{n} \dfrac{t_i}{k_i}} + h_n$
(d) $\dfrac{1}{h_1} + \sum\limits_{i=1}^{n} \dfrac{t_i}{k_i} + \dfrac{1}{h_n}$

457. The equation of effectiveness $\varepsilon = 1 - e^{-NTU}$ of a heat exchanger is valid (NTU is number of transfer units) in the case of

(a) boiler and condenser for parallel-flow
(b) boiler and condenser for counter-flow
(c) boiler and condenser for both parallel-flow and counter-flow
(d) gas turbine for both parallel flow and counter-flow.

458. Match List I with List II and select the correct answer using the codes given below the Lists (notations have their usual meanings) :

	List I		List II
A.	Fin	1.	$\dfrac{UA}{C_{min}}$
B.	Heat exchanger	2.	$\dfrac{x}{2\sqrt{\alpha t}}$
C.	Transient conduction	3.	$\sqrt{\dfrac{hP}{kA}}$
D.	Heisler chart	4.	hl/k

Codes :

	A	B	C	D		A	B	C	D
(a)	3	1	2	4	(b)	2	1	3	4
(c)	3	4	2	1	(d)	2	4	3	1.

459. The Nusselt number is related to Reynolds Number in laminar and turblent flows respectively as

(a) $Re^{-1/2}$ and $Re^{0.8}$ (b) $Re^{1/2}$ and $Re^{0.8}$
(c) $Re^{-1/2}$ and $Re^{-0.8}$ (d) $Re^{1/2}$ and $Re^{-0.8}$.

460. In respect of free convection over a vertical flat plate the Nusselt number varies with Grashoff number 'Gr' as

(a) Gr and $Gr^{1/4}$ for laminar and turblent flows respectively

(b) $Gr^{1/2}$ and $Gr^{1/3}$ for laminar and turbulent flows respectively

(c) $Gr^{1/4}$ and $Gr^{1/3}$ for laminar and turbulent flows respectively

(d) $Gr^{1/3}$ and $Gr^{1/4}$ for laminar and turbulent flows respectively.

461. Consider the following conditions for heat transfer (thickness of thermal boundary layer is δ_t, velocity of boundary layer is d and Prandtl number is Pr) :

1. $\delta_t (x) = \delta (x)$ if $Pr = 1$
2. $\delta_t (x) \gg \delta (x)$ if $Pr \ll 1$
3. $\delta_t (x) \ll \delta (x)$ if $Pr \gg 1$

Which of these conditions apply for convective heat transfer?

(a) 1 and 2   (b) 2 and 3
(c) 1 and 3   (d) 1, 2 and 3.

ESE–2001

462. A plane wall of thickness 2L has a uniform volumetric heat source q^* (W/m³). It is exposed to local ambinet temperature T_∞ at both the ends $(x = \pm L)$. The surface temperature T_s of the wall under steady-state condition (where h and k have their usual meanings) is given by

(a) $T_s = T_\infty + \dfrac{q^* L}{h}$ (b) $T_s = T_\infty + \dfrac{q^* L^2}{2k}$

(c) $T_s = T_\infty + \dfrac{q^* L^2}{h}$ (d) $T_s = T_\infty + \dfrac{q^* L^3}{2k}$.

463. A flat plate has thickness 5 cm, thermal conductivity 1 W/(mK), convective heat transfer coefficients on its two flat faces of 10 W/(m²K) and 20 W/(m²K). The overall heat transfer co-efficient for such a flat plate is

(a) 5 W/(m²K)   (b) 6.33 W/(m²K)
(c) 20 W/(m²K)   (d) 30 W/(m²K).

464. The efficiency of a pin fin with insulated tip is

(a) $\dfrac{\tan h\, mL}{(hA/kP)^{0.5}}$ (b) $\dfrac{\tan h\, mL}{mL}$

(c) $\dfrac{mL}{\tan h\, mL}$ (d) $\dfrac{(hA/kP)^{0.5}}{\tan h\, mL}$.

465. A cylinder made of a metal of conductivity 40 W/(mK) is to be insulated with a material of conductivity 0.1 W/(mK). If the convective heat transfer coefficient with the ambient atmosphere is 5W/(m²K), the critical radius of insulation is

(a) 2 cm   (b) 4 cm
(c) 8 cm   (d) 50 cm.

466. Nusselt number for fully developed turbulent flow in a pipe is given by $Nu = CRe^a\, Pr^b$. The values of a and b are

(a) $a = 0.5$ and $b = 0.33$ for heating and cooling both

(b) $a = 0.5$ and $b = 0.4$ for heating and $b = 0.3$ for cooling

(c) $a = 0.8$ and $b = 0.4$ for heating and $b = 0.3$ for cooling

(d) $a = 0.8$ and $b = 0.3$ for heating and $b = 0.4$ for cooling.

467. For natural convective flow over a vertical flat plate as shown in the given figure, the governing differential equation for momentum is

$$\left(u \frac{\partial u}{\partial x} + v \frac{\partial u}{\partial y} \right) = g\beta \, (T - T_\infty) + \gamma \frac{\partial^2 u}{\partial y^2}$$

If equation is nondimentionalized by $U = \dfrac{u}{U_\infty}$,

$V = \dfrac{u}{U_\infty}$, $X = \dfrac{x}{L}$, $Y = \dfrac{y}{L}$ and $\theta = \dfrac{T - T_\infty}{T_s - T_\infty}$

then the term $g\,\beta\,(T - T_\infty)$, is equal to

(a) Grashoff number

(b) Prandtl number

(c) Rayleigh number

(d) $\dfrac{\text{Grashof number}}{(\text{Reynolds number})^2}$

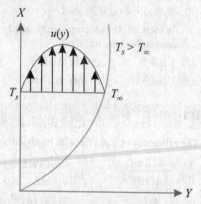

468. The shape factor of a hemispherical body placed on a flat surface with respect to itself is

(a) zero   (b) 0.25

(c) 0.5   (d) 1.0.

469. Which one of the following heat exchangers gives parallel straight line pattern of temperature distribution for both cold and hot fluids ?

(a) Parallel-flow with unequal heat capacities

(b) Counter-flow with equal heat capacities

(c) Parallel-flow with equal heat capacities

(d) Counter-flow with unequal heat capacities.

470. In a counter-flow heat exchanger, the hot fluid is cooled from 110° C to 80° C by a cold fluid which gets heated from 30° C to 60° C. LMTD for the heat exchanger is

(a) 20° C   (b) 30° C

(c) 50° C   (d) 80° C.

471. In a counterflow heat exchanger, the product of specific heat and mass flow rate is same for the hot and cold fluids. If NTU is equal to 0.5, then the effectiveness of the heat exchanger is

(a) 1.0   (b) 0.5

(c) 0.33   (d) 0.2.

472. For flow over a flat plate the hydrodynamic boundary layer thickness is 0.5 mm. The dynamic viscosity is 25×10^{-6} Pa s, specific heat is 2.0 kJ/(kg K) and thermal conductivity is 0.05 W/(m-K). The thermal boundary layer thickness would be

(a) 0.1 mm   (b) 0.5 mm

(c) 1 mm   (d) 2 mm.

473. An enclosure conists of the four surfaces 1, 2, 3 and 4. The view factors for radiation heat transfer (where the subscripts 1, 2, 3, 4 refer to the respective surfaces) are $F_{11} = 0.1$, $F_{12} = 0.4$ and $F_{13} = 0.25$. The surface areas A_1 and A_4 are 4 m^2 and 2 m^2 respctively. The view factor F_{41} is

(a) 0.75   (b) 0.50

(c) 0.25   (d) 0.10.

ESE–2002

*474. A 0.5 m thick plane wall has its two surfaces kept at 300°C and 200°C. Thermal conductivity of the wall varies linearly with temperature and its values at 300°C and 200°C are 25 W/mK and 15 W/mK, respectively. Then the steady heat flux through the wall is

(a) 8 kW/m^2 (b) 5 kW/m^2

(c) 4 kW/m^2 (d) 3 kW/m^2.

*475. A 320 cm high vertical pipe at 150°C wall temperature is in a room with still air at 10°C. This pipe supplies heat at the rate of 8 kW into the room air by natural convection. Assuming laminar flow, the height of the pipe needed to supply 1 kW only is

(a) 10 cm   (b) 20 cm

(c) 40 cm   (d) 80 cm.

*476. The average Nusselt number in laminar natural convection from a vertical wall at 180°C with still air at 20°C is found to be 48. If the wall temperature becomes 30°C, all other parameters remaining same, the average Nusselt number will be

(a) 8   (b) 16
(c) 24   (d) 32.

*477. A fluid of thermal conductivity 1.0 W/m-K flows in fully developed flow with Reynolds number of 1500 through a pipe of diameter 10 cm. The heat transfer coefficient for uniform heat flux and uniform wall temperature boundary conditions are, respectively,

(a) 36.57 and 43.64 $\dfrac{W}{m^2K}$

(b) 43.64 and 36.57 $\dfrac{W}{m^2K}$

(c) 43.64 $\dfrac{W}{m^2K}$ for both the cases

(d) 36.57 $\dfrac{W}{m^2K}$ for both the cases .

*478. Two large parallel grey plates with a small gap, exchange radiation at the rate of 1000 W/m² when their emissivities are 0.5 each. By coating one plate, its emissivity is refuced to 0.25. Temperatures remain unchanged. The new rate of heat exchange shall become

(a) 500 W/m²   (b) 600 W/m²
(c) 700 W/m²   (d) 800 W/m².

*479. Two long parallel plates of same emissivity 0.5 are maintained at different temperatures and have radiation heat exchange between them. The radiation shield of emissivity 0.25 placed in the middle will reduce radiation heat exchange to

(a) $\dfrac{1}{2}$ (b) $\dfrac{1}{4}$
(c) $\dfrac{3}{10}$ (d) $\dfrac{3}{5}$.

480. Match List-I (Type of radiation) with List-II (Characteristic) and select the correct answer using the codes given below the lists :

List I		List II	
(Type of radiation)		*(Characteristic)*	
A.	Black body	1.	Emissivity does not depend on wavelength
B.	Grey body	2.	Mirror like reflection
C.	Specular	3.	Zero reflectivity
D.	Diffuse	4.	Intensity same in all directions

Codes :

	A	B	C	D		A	B	C	D
(a)	2	1	3	4	(b)	3	4	2	1
(c)	2	4	3	1	(d)	3	1	2	4

481. Match List-I (Type of heat transfer) with List-II (Governing dimensionless parameter) and select the correct answer using the codes given below the lists :

List I		List II	
(Type of heat transfer)		*(Governing dimensionless parameter)*	
A.	Forced convection	1.	Reynolds, Grashoff and Prandtl number
B.	Natural convection	2.	Reynolds and Prandtl number
C.	Combined free and forced convection	3.	Fourier modulus and Biot number
D.	Unsteady conduction with convection at surface	4.	Prandtl number and Grashoff number

Codes :

	A	B	C	D		A	B	C	D
(a)	2	1	4	3	(b)	3	4	1	2
(c)	2	4	1	3	(d)	3	1	4	2

*482. The insulated tip temperature of a rectangular longitudinal fin having an excess (over ambient) root temperature of θ_o is

(a) $\theta_o \tanh (ml)$

(b) $\dfrac{\theta_o}{\sinh (ml)}$

(c) $\dfrac{\theta_o \tanh (ml)}{(ml)}$

(d) $\dfrac{\theta_o}{\cosh (ml)}$.

*483. Consider the following statements pertaining to large heat transfer rate using fins :
   1. Fins should be used on the side where heat transfer coefficient is small.
   2. Long and thick fins should be used.
   3. Short and thin fins should be used.
   4. Thermal conductivity of fin material should be large.
   Which of the above statements are *correct* ?
   (a) 1, 2 and 3   (b) 1, 2 and 4   (c) 2, 3 and 4   (d) 1, 3 and 4.

484. Using thermal-electrical analogy in heat transfer, match List-I (Electrical quantities) with List-II (Thermal quantities) and select the correct answer using the codes given below the lists :

	List I						List II			
	(Electrical quantities)						(Thermal quantities)			
A.	Voltage					1.	Thermal resistance			
B.	Current					2.	Thermal capacity			
C.	Resistance					3.	Heat flow			
D.	Capacitance					4.	Temperature			

Codes :

	A	B	C	D		A	B	C	D
(a)	2	3	1	4	(b)	4	1	3	2
(c)	2	1	3	4	(d)	4	3	1	2

485. Pandtl number of a flowing fluid greater than unity indicates that hydrodynamic boundary layer thickness is
   (a) greater than thermal boundary layer thickness
   (b) equal to thermal boundary layer thickness
   (c) greater than hydrodynamic boundary layer thickness
   (d) independent of thermal boundary layer thickness.

ANSWERS

A. CHOOSE THE CORRECT ANSWER :

1. (b)	2. (a)	3. (d)	4. (a)	5. (c)
6. (a)	7. (a)	8. (a)	9. (a)	10. (c)
11. (b)	12. (e)	13. (a)	14. (d)	15. (d)
16. (a)	17. (c)	18. (d)	19. (d)	20. (b)
21. (b)	22. (d)	23. (e)	24. (d)	25. (c)
26. (a)	27. (d)	28. (a)	29. (c)	30. (b)
31. (b)	32. (c)	33. (d)	34. (c)	35. (a)
36. (c)	37. (b)	38. (b)	39. (a)	40. (b)
41. (b)	42. (a)	43. (d)	44. (b)	45. (d)

46. (a)	47. (b)	48. (b)	49. (c)	50. (b)
51. (c)	52. (a)	53. (b)	54. (b)	55. (c)
56. (c)	57. (b)	58. (c)	59. (b)	60. (c)
61. (a)	62. (e)	63. (a)	64. (d)	65. (b)
66. (c)	67. (a)	68. (d)	69. (d)	70. (a)
71. (d)	72. (a)	73. (d)	74. (a)	75. (c)
76. (a)	77. (a)	78. (c)	79. (a)	80. (d)
81. (a)	82. (a)	83. (c)	84. (b)	85. (a)
86. (c)	87. (c)	88. (a)	89. (c)	90. (a)
91. (d)	92. (d)	93. (d)	94. (b)	95. (d)
96. (d)	97. (b)	98. (d)	99. (c)	100. (c)
101. (a)	102. (d)	103. (a)	104. (b)	105. (c)
106. (d)	107. (a)	108. (b)	109. (a)	110. (d)
111. (d)	112. (a)	113. (d)	114. (b)	115. (a)
116. (c)	117. (d)	118. (d)	119. (a)	120. (b)
121. (c)	122. (b)	123. (b)	124. (c)	125. (b)
126. (c)	127. (c)	128. (b)	129. (a)	130. (c)
131. (b)	132. (a)	133. (b)	134. (b)	135. (d)
136. (c)	137. (c)	138. (c)	139. (d)	140. (c)
141. (a)	142. (a)	143. (b)	144. (d)	145. (b)
146. (a)	147. (c)	148. (b)	149. (e)	150. (a)
151. (d)	152. (b)	153. (c)	154. (a)	155. (b)
156. (c)	157. (c)	158. (a)	159. (c)	160. (a)
161. (a)	162. (c)	163. (b)	164. (c)	165. (b)
166. (c)	167. (e)	168. (b)	169. (c)	170. (b)
171. (c)	172. (a)	173. (d)	174. (a)	175. (d)
176. (d)	177. (c)	178. (b)	179. (d)	180. (d)
181. (c)	182. (a)	183. (d)	184. (b)	185. (c)
186. (c)	187. (b)	188. (b)	189. (b)	190. (a)
191. (a)	192. (b)	193. (b)	194. (d)	195. (a)
196. (d)	197. (a)	198. (a)	199. (b)	200. (d)
201. (b)	202. (d)	203. (d)	204. (a)	205. (b)
206. (a)	207. (d)	208. (a)	209. (d)	210. (d)
211. (c)	212. (d)	213. (d)	214. (c)	215. (b)
216. (b)	217. (c)	218. (a)	219. (d)	220. (a)
221. (a)	222. (c)	223. (b)	224. (d)	225. (c)

226. (b)	227. (a)	228. (c)	229. (c)	230. (b)
231. (b)	232. (b)	233. (c)	234. (c)	235. (b)
236. (a)	237. (c)	238. (d)	239. (a)	240. (c)
241. (d)	242. (a)	243. (d)	244. (b)	245. (c)
246. (c)	247. (c)	248. (b)	249. (c)	250. (d)
251. (b)	252. (c)	523. (d)	254. (a)	255. (a)
256. (d)	257. (b)	258. (d)	259. (d)	260. (a)
261. (d)	262. (a)	263. (e)	264. (c)	265. (b)
266. (a)	267. (a)	268. (c)	269. (d)	270. (c)
271. (a)	272. (d)	273. (a)	274. (b)	275. (b)
276. (c)	277. (c)	278. (d)	279. (c)	280. (d)
281. (b)	282. (b)	283. (a)	284. (c)	285. (c)
286. (a)	287. (c)	288. (a)	289. (b)	290. (b)
291. (b)	292. (b)	293. (d)	294. (c)	295. (b)
296. (d)	297. (c)	298. (a)	299. (d)	300. (c)
301. (c)	302. (d)	303. (d)	304. (b)	305. (b)
306. (b)	307. (b)	308. (c)	309. (b)	310. (c)
311. (b)	312. (c)	313. (c)	314. (c)	315. (d)
316. (b)	317. (b)	318. (e)	319. (b)	320. (d)
321. (a)	322. (b)	323. (c)	324. (a)	325. (b)
326. (a)	327. (d)	328. (b)	329. (b)	330. (b)
331. (a)	332. (a)	333. (d)	334. (a)	335. (a)
336. (c)	337. (b)	338. (d)	339. (b)	340. (a)
341. (d)	342. (a)	343. (c)	344. (a)	345. (b)
346. (b)	347. (c)	348. (c)	349. (c)	350. (a)
351. (d)	352. (a)	353. (c)	354. (c)	355. (b)
356. (b)	357. (d)	358. (d)	359. (b)	360. (d)
361. (d)	362. (c)	363. (a)	364. (c)	365. (a)
366. (d)	367. (d)	368. (c)	369. (b)	370. (c)

B. MATCH LIST I WITH LIST II

371. (b)	372. (d)	373. (a)	374. (b)	375. (a)
376. (a)				

C. COMPETITIVE EXAMINATIONS QUESTIONS (WITH SOLUTIONS – COMMENTS)

377. (b)	378. (d)	379. (a)	380. (b)	381. (d)
382. (d)	383. (a)	384. (b)	385. (c)	*386. (a)

387. (b)	388. (c)	389. (d)	390. (b)	391. (a)
392. (d)	*393. (a)	394. (a)	395. (a)	396. (b)
397. (c)	398. (a)	399. (b)	400. (a)	401. (c)
402. (b)	403. (c)	404. (b)	405. (d)	406. (c)
407. (a)	408. (a)	409. (c)	410. (c)	411. (d)
412. (c)	*413. (b)	414. (b)	415. (a)	416. (b)
417. (c)	418. (d)	419. (b)	420. (b)	421. (a)
422. (c)	423. (d)	424. (a)	425. (a)	426. (d)
427. (a)	428. (a)	429. (d)	430. (a)	431. (c)
432. (b)	433. (c)	434. (a)	435. (a)	436. (d)
437. (b)	438. (d)	439. (a)	440. (d)	441. (d)
442. (c)	443. (c)	444. (a)	445. (a)	446. (d)
447. (b)	448. (c)	449. (a)	450. (c)	451. (c)
452. (c)	453. (b)	454. (b)	455. (c)	456. (a)
457. (d)	458. (a)	459. (b)	460. (a)	461. (d)
462. (a)	463. (a)	464. (b)	465. (a)	466. (d)
467. (c)	468. (d)	469. (b)	470. (b)	471. (d)
472. (d)	473. (c)	474. (c)	475. (b)	476. (c)
477. (b)	478. (b)	479. (c)	480. (d)	481. (c)
482. (c)	483. (d)	484. (a)	485. (a)	

SOLUTIONS–COMMENTS

*366. Temperature of the inner surface of the wall, $t_1 = 50°C$
Temperature of the outer surface of the wall, $t_2 = 25°C$
The thickness of the wall, $x = 220$ mm $= 0.22$ m
Thermal conductivity of the brick, $k = 0.51$ W/m K
The *rate of heat transfer per unit area*,

$$\therefore \quad q = \frac{Q}{A} = \frac{k}{x}(t_1 - t_2)$$

$$= \frac{0.51}{0.22} \times (50 - 25)$$

$$\left[\because Q = \frac{kA}{x}(t_1 - t_2) \right.$$
$$\left. \text{and } q = \frac{Q}{A} = \frac{k}{x}(t_1 - t_2) \right]$$

$$= 57.95 \text{ W/m}^2.$$

*367. Refer to Fig. 1, Thickness of mild steel tank wall, $x = 12$ mm $= 0.012$ m; Temperature of water, $t_A = 100°C$; Temperature of air, $t_B = 20°C$; Thermal conductivity of mild steel, $k = 50$ W/m K.
Heat transfer coefficients ;

$$\left[\text{Inside, } h_A = 2850 \; W/m^2 \, K \right.$$
$$\left. \text{Outside, } h_B = 10 \; W/m^2 \, K \right]$$

(i) Rate of heat loss per m² of tank surface, q:

$$q = U(t_A - t_B)$$

The overall heat transfer coefficient, U is found from relation:

$$\frac{1}{U} = \frac{1}{h_A} + \frac{x}{k} + \frac{1}{h_B}$$

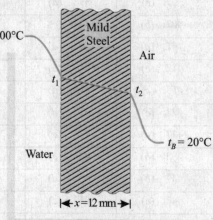

$t_A = 100°C$

Mild Steel

Air

t_1

t_2

Water

$t_B = 20°C$

$\leftarrow x = 12\,mm \rightarrow$

Fig. 1

$$= \frac{1}{2850} + \frac{0.012}{50} + \frac{1}{10}$$

$$= 0.0003508 + 0.00024 + 0.1$$

$$= 0.1006$$

$\therefore \quad U = \dfrac{1}{0.1006} = 9.94 \text{ W/m}^2\text{ K}$

$\therefore \quad q = 9.94 \times (100 - 20)$

$$= 795.2 \text{ W/m}^2.$$

i.e., *Rate of heat loss per m² of surface area*

$$= 795.2 \text{ W/m}^2.$$

(ii) **Temperature of the outside surface of the tank, t_2 :**

Now, $\qquad q = h_B(t_2 - t_B)$

$\therefore \qquad 795.2 = 10(t_2 - 20)$

or, $\qquad t_2 = \dfrac{795.2}{10} + 20 = 99.52°C$

i.e., *Temperature of outside surface of the tank* = **99.52°C.**

*368. $r_2 = 0.7$ m, $r_1 = 0.7 - 0.09 = 0.61$ m

$$t_1 - t_2 = 220°C, \ k = 0.083 \text{ W/mK}$$

Now, $\qquad Q = \dfrac{t_1 - t_2}{\left(\dfrac{r_2 - r_1}{4\pi k r_1 r_2}\right)} = \dfrac{220}{\left(\dfrac{0.7 - 0.61}{4\pi \times 0.083 \times 0.61 \times 0.7}\right)}$

$$= 1088.6 \text{ W or } 1.0886 \text{ kW}$$

i.e., *Rate of heat leakage* = **1.0886 kW.**

*369. Temperature of liquid air, $\qquad T_1 = 273 + (-147) = 126$ K

Temperature of outer surface, $\qquad T_2 = 273 + 25 = 298$ K

Latent heat of liquid air $\qquad = 210$ kJ/kg

Stefan Boltzmann constant, $\qquad \sigma = 2.04 \times 10^{-4}$ kJ/h-m² K⁴

Emissivity $\qquad \varepsilon_1 = \varepsilon_2 = 0.028$

Rate of evaporation:

The heat transfer through the concentric sphere by radiation is given by

$$Q = \frac{A_c \, \sigma \, (T_1^4 - T_2^4)}{\dfrac{1}{\varepsilon_1} + \dfrac{A_1}{A_2}\left(\dfrac{1}{\varepsilon_2} - 1\right)}$$

$$= \frac{4\pi \times 0.1^2 \times 2.04 \times 10^{-4}\,[(126)^4 - (298)^4]}{\left[\dfrac{1}{0.028} + \left(\dfrac{0.2}{0.3}\right)^2\left(\dfrac{1}{0.028} - 1\right)\right]}$$

$$= \frac{-195703.25}{(35.71 + 0.444 \times 34.71)} = 3828.2 \text{ kJ/h}$$

$\therefore \quad$ Rate of evaporation $= \dfrac{3828.2}{210} = $ **18.22 kg/h**

*370. (i) When the body is grey with $\varepsilon = 0.42$:
$$T_1 = 1000 + 273 = 1273 \text{ K}$$
$$T_2 = 500 + 273 = 773 \text{ K}$$
$$\varepsilon \text{ at } 1000°C = 0.42$$
$$\varepsilon \text{ at } 500°C = 0.72$$
$$\sigma = 5.67 \times 10^{-8}$$

Heat loos per m^2 by radiation,
$$q = \varepsilon\sigma (T_1^4 - T_2^4)$$
$$= 0.42 \times 10^{-8} [(1273)^4 - (773)^4] = 54893 \text{ W}$$

i.e., Heat loos per m^2 by radiation = **54.893 kW.**

(ii) **When the body is not grey:**

Absorptivity when source is at 500°C = Emissivity when body is at 500°C

i.e., Absorptivity, $\quad \alpha = 0.72$

Then, energy emitted $\quad = \varepsilon\sigma T_1^4 = 0.42 \times 5.67 \times 10^{-8} \times (1273)^4$

and , Energy absorbed $\quad = \alpha\sigma T_2^4 = 0.72 \times 5.67 \times 10^{-8} \times (773)^4$

i.e., $\quad q$ = Energy emitted – energy absorbed
$$= 0.42 \times 5.67 \times 10^{-8} \times (1273)^4 - 0.72 \times 5.67 \times 10^8 \times (773)^4$$
$$= 62538 - 14576 = 47962 \text{ W}$$

i.e., Heat loss per m^2 by radiation = **47.962 kW.**

*378. Mean temperature difference = Temperature of hot fluid (at exit) – Temperature of of cold fluid
$$\text{(at entry)}$$
$$= 60 - 40 = 20°C$$

Hence (*d*) is the correct answer.

*379. In case of infinite parallel planes having emissivities ε_1 and ε_2 respectively, the interchange factor (or effective emissivity coefficient)

$$= \frac{1}{\dfrac{1}{\varepsilon_1} + \dfrac{1}{\varepsilon_2} - 1} = \frac{\varepsilon_1 \varepsilon_2}{\varepsilon_1 + \varepsilon_2 - \varepsilon_1 \varepsilon_2}$$

Hence correct choice is (*a*).

*380. Heat loss for a thick plate homogeneous wall $= kA \cdot \dfrac{dt}{dx}$

$$\therefore \quad \left(0.7 \times A \times \frac{dt}{0.5}\right)_{red\ bricks} = \left(0.14 \times A \frac{dt}{dx}\right)_{diatomite}$$

or, $\quad dx = \dfrac{0.14}{0.7} \times 0.5 = \textbf{0.1 m}$

Hence (*b*) in the correct choice.

*386. Area, $A = 2 \times 2 = 4 \text{ m}^2$, Rate of solar radiation falling on one side of the plate, $Q = 500 \text{ W/m}^2$, $dt = 30 - 25 = 5°C$. Convective heat transfer coefficient, h :

Heat transfer by convection, $Q = h.A.dt$ (where $Q = 500 \times A$ or $500 \times 4 = 2000 \text{ W}$)

or, $\quad 2000 = h \times 4 \times 5$ or $h = \dfrac{2000}{4 \times 5} = \textbf{100 W/m}^2\textbf{°C}$

*388. The energy from flame, in bolier, is transmitted mainly by *radiation* to water wall and radiant superheater. Hence correct answer is (*c*).

*389. Overall heat transfer coefficient (U) in W/m^2 K is expressed as

$$\frac{1}{U} = \frac{1}{h_i} + \frac{dx}{k} + \frac{1}{h_o},$$

where, $h_i = 25$ W/m^{2}K, $h_o = 25$ W/m^{2}K, and $k = 0.15$ W/mK

or, $\frac{1}{U} = \frac{1}{25} + \frac{0.15}{0.15} + \frac{1}{25} = \frac{27}{25}$ or $U = \frac{25}{27}$

which is closer to the heat transfer coefficient based on the bricks alone.

Thus (d) is the correct choice.

*392. The volumetric efficiency of reciprocating compressor in less than 100 per cent due to the following reasons: Pressure drop across the valves, superheating in compressor, clearance volume and leakages.

Thus (d) is the correct choice.

*393. For the spherical sheath, critical radius,

$$r_c = \frac{2k_o}{h_o} = \frac{2 \times 0.04}{10} = 0.008 \text{ m} = 8 \text{ mm}$$

$\therefore$ Diameter of the sheath $= 2 \times r_c = 2 \times 8 = 16$ **mm.**

*399. In case where the numerator and denominator of *LMTD* expression are equal to zero,

LMTD = Temperature difference at any end which in this case is either

140 – 80 or 80 – 20 = 60°C.

437. Ans. (b) $800 = \frac{t_B - t_o}{1/h} = \frac{t_B - 25}{1/80}$, $10 = t_B - 25$ and $t_B = 35$°C.

439. Ans. (a) $\frac{hl}{k} = Nu$, or $h = \frac{25 \times 0.03}{0.1} = 7.5$ W/m^{2}K

440. Ans. (d) Emissive power is proportional to T^4 *i.e.* $\alpha \left(\frac{627 + 273}{27 + 273}\right)^4 \alpha\, 3^4\, \alpha\, 81$.

441. Ans. (d) Irradiation on a small test surface placed inside a hollow black spherical chamber $= \sigma T^4$
$= 5.67 \times 10^{-8} \times 600^4 = 7348$ W/m^2.

443. Ans. (c) NTU $= \frac{AU}{C_{min}}$, A = area = 50 m^2, U = overall heat transfer coefficient = 100 W/m^{2}K

C_{min} = Heat capacity = 1000 W/K $\quad \therefore$ NTU $= \frac{50 \times 100}{1000} = 5$.

446. Ans. (d) For two insulating layers,

$$\frac{Q}{A} = \frac{t_1 - t_2}{\frac{\Delta x_1}{k_1} + \frac{\Delta x_2}{k_2}} = \frac{1000 - 120}{\frac{0.3}{3} + \frac{0.3}{0.3}} = \frac{880}{1.1} = 880$$

For outer casing, $\frac{Q}{A} = \frac{120 - 40}{1/h}$, or $800 \times \frac{1}{h} = 80$, and $h = \frac{800}{80} = 10$ W/m^{2}K

447. Ans. (b) Say at $x = 0$, $h_0 = h$, at $x = x$, $h_x = \frac{h}{\sqrt{x}}$

Average $= \frac{1}{x} \int_0^x \frac{h}{\sqrt{x}} dx = 2h\sqrt{x}$ $\quad \therefore$ Ratio $= \frac{1}{x} \cdot \frac{2h\sqrt{x}\sqrt{x}}{h} = 2$.

448. Ans. (c) C.O.P. of heat pump $= \frac{T_2}{T_2 - T_1} = \frac{600}{600 - 300} = 2$

474. Ans. (c) Average thermal conductivity $k_m = \frac{25 + 15}{2} = 20$ W/mK

$$\frac{Q}{A} = \frac{k_m (t_1 - t_2)}{\Delta x} = \frac{20 \times (300 - 200)}{0.5} = 4 \text{ kW/m}^2$$

475. Ans. (b) $Q \propto h \times l$, and $h \propto \left(\dfrac{\Delta T}{l}\right)^{1/4}$; $\quad \therefore Q \propto l^{3/4}$; or $\dfrac{8}{1} = \left(\dfrac{320}{L}\right)^{3/4}$ and $L = 20$ cm.

476. Ans. (c) $Nu_{av} \propto Gr^{1/4}$ and $Gr \propto \Delta T$

Thus ratio of Grashoff number in two cases is $\propto \dfrac{30-20}{180-20} \propto \dfrac{1}{16}$

$\therefore \quad Nu_{av} \propto \left(\dfrac{1}{16}\right)^{\frac{1}{4}} \propto \dfrac{1}{2}$, $\qquad \therefore \qquad Nu_{av}$ for second case $= \dfrac{48}{2} = 24$.

477. Ans. (b) For constant heat flux as per Bayley, $h = 4.364\,\dfrac{k}{D} = 4.364 \times \dfrac{1.0}{0.1} = 43.64\,\dfrac{W}{m^2 K}$, and for constant

wall surface temperature, $h = 3.66\,\dfrac{k}{D} = 3.66 \times \dfrac{1.0}{0.1} = 3.66\,\dfrac{W}{m^2 K}$

478. Ans. (b) $Q = 1000 \times \dfrac{\dfrac{2}{\varepsilon_1} - 1}{\left(\dfrac{1}{\varepsilon_1} - 1\right) + \left(\dfrac{1}{\varepsilon_2} - 1\right) + 1} = \dfrac{1000 \times \left(\dfrac{2}{0.5} - 1\right)}{\dfrac{1}{0.5} - 1 + \dfrac{1}{0.25} - 1 + 1} = \dfrac{3 \times 10^3}{5} = 600\,\dfrac{W}{m^2}$

479. Ans. (c) Reduction in radiation heat exchange due to introduction of shield

$$\dfrac{\dfrac{2}{\varepsilon_1} - 1}{2\left(\dfrac{1-\varepsilon_1}{\varepsilon_1}\right) + 2\left(\dfrac{1-\varepsilon_2}{\varepsilon_2}\right) + 2} = \dfrac{\dfrac{2}{0.5} - 1}{2 \times \dfrac{0.5}{0.5} + 2 \times \dfrac{0.75}{0.25} + 2} = \dfrac{3}{10}$$

482. Ans. (c)   Insulated tip temperature $= \dfrac{\theta_0 \tan h\,(ml)}{(ml)}$.

483. Ans. (d)   Only wrong statement is that long and thick fins should be used.

484. Ans. (a)   If $Pr > 1$, then hydrodynamic boundary layer thickness > thermal boundary layer thickness.

ADDITIONAL QUESTIONS (WITH ANSWERS)
AMIE EXAMINATIONS QUESTIONS

A. CHOOSE THE CORRECT ANSWER:

1. This dimensionless number is relevant in transient heat conduction
   - (a) Fourier number
   - (b) Grashoff number
   - (c) Weber number
   - (d) Archmedes number.

2. Fins are provided on heat transfer surface so as to increase
   - (a) heat transfer coefficient
   - (b) mechanical strength to the equipment
   - (c) heat transfer area
   - (d) level of turblence.

3. The velocity profile for fully developed laminar flow in a tube is
   - (a) parabolic
   - (b) hyperbolic
   - (c) linear
   - (d) exponential.

4. For steady flow and constant value of conductivity, the temperature distribution for a hollow cylinder of radii r_1 and r_2 is
   - (a) linear
   - (b) parabolic
   - (c) logarithmin function of radii
   - (d) cubic.

5. The critical radius of insulation for sphere is equal to
   - (a) $2\,k \times h$
   - (b) $\dfrac{2h}{k}$
   - (c) $\dfrac{h}{2k}$
   - (d) $\sqrt{2kh}$.

6. In case of heat exchanger, the value of logarithmic mean temperature difference should be
   - (a) as small as possible
   - (b) as large as possible
   - (c) constant
   - (d) none of the above.

7. For a free convection, Nusselt number is a function of
   - (a) Prandtl and Grashoff number
   - (b) Reynolds and Grashoff number
   - (c) Reynolds number only
   - (d) Reynolds and Prandtl number.

8. If the ratio of emission of a body to that of a black body at a given temperature is constant for all wavelengths, the body is called
   - (a) black body
   - (b) grey body
   - (c) white body
   - (d) opaque body.

9. Kirchhoff's law is applicable to
   - (a) monochromatic ratiation
   - (b) total radiation
   - (c) both (a) and (b)
   - (d) neither (a) nor (b).

10. Stefan and Boltzmann's law is applicable to
   - (a) grey body
   - (b) white body
   - (c) black body
   - (d) all of the above.

11. For an opaque body sum of absorptivity and reflectivity is
   - (a) 0
   - (b) 1.0
   - (c) 0.5
   - (d) 0.8.

12. According to Kirchhoff's law the ratio of total radiating power to the absorptivity of the body is dependent on
   - (a) temperature of the body
   - (b) nature of the body
   - (c) wavelength of radiation
   - (d) none of these.

13. Fins are usually provided to a heat exchanger surface
   - (a) to augment heat transfer by increasing the heat transfer coefficient
   - (b) to augment heat transfer by increasing the surface area
   - (c) to augment heat transfer by increasing the temperature difference
   - (d) to augment heat transfer by increasing turbulence.

14. A good absorber of thermal radiation is also a good emitter. It is called
   - (a) Wien's law
   - (b) Planck's law
   - (c) Stefan's law
   - (d) Kirchhoff's law.

15. In a concentric double-pipe heat exchanger where one of the fluids undergoes phase change
   - (a) the two fluids should flow opposite to each other
   - (b) the two fluids should flow parallel to each other
   - (c) the two fluids should flow normal to each other
   - (d) the directions of flow of the two fluids are of no consequence.

16. For natural convection heat transfer, Nusselt number is a function of
   - (a) Prandtl number and Grashoff number
   - (b) Reynolds number and Greshoff number
   - (c) Reynolds number and Prandtl number
   - (d) Stanton number and Peclet number.

17. A fluid is a substance that
   - (a) always expands until it fills any container
   - (b) is incompressible
   - (c) cannot remain at rest under action of any shear force
   - (d) cannot be subjected to shear forces.

18. The water pipeline, in cold countries, is laid at a certain depth from the earth surface in order to
   - (a) supply warm water
   - (b) prevent water from freezing
   - (c) reduce frictional losses
   - (d) none of the above.

19. A cold liquid is stored in spherical vessel in order to
   - (a) reduce rate of heat transfer
   - (b) increase rate of heat transfer
   - (c) prevent the liquid from freezing
   - (d) none of the above.

20. In a heat exchanger, for a given heat flow rate and also same inlet and outlet temperatures, the heat transfer area will be minimum for
   - (a) counter-flow type
   - (b) parallel-flow, type
   - (c) cross-flow
   - (d) none of the above.

21. The total average emissivity at a given temperature is given by
   - (a) $\int_0^\infty \varepsilon_\lambda E_{b\lambda}\, d\lambda \Big/ \int_0^\infty E_{b\lambda}\, d\lambda$
   - (b) $\int_0^\lambda \varepsilon_\lambda E_{b\lambda}\, d\lambda \Big/ \int_0^\infty E_{b\lambda}\, d\lambda$
   - (c) $\int_0^\infty \varepsilon_\lambda E_{b\lambda}\, d\lambda \Big/ \int_0^\lambda E_{b\lambda}\, d\lambda$
   - (d) $\int_0^\lambda \varepsilon_\lambda E_{b\lambda}\, d\lambda \Big/ \int_0^\lambda E_{b\lambda}\, d\lambda$.

22. The heat transfer rate becomes maximum towards the end of
    (a) free convection boiling regime
    (b) nucleat boiling regime
    (c) film boiling regime
    (d) none of the above.

23. The thickness of thermal boundary layer is equal to hydrodynamic boundary layer when Pradtl number is equal to
    (a) 0   (b) 0.1
    (c) 0.5   (d) 1.0.

24. The heat transfer coefficient, in free convection, is a function of
    (a) Reynolds number   (b) Mach number
    (c) Grashoff number   (d) none of the above.

25. A radiation shlied is used around thermocouples in order to measure more accurately the temperature of
    (a) solids   (b) gases
    (c) boiling liquids (d) condensing liquids

26. The fouling factor
    (a) increases the overall heat transfer coefficient
    (b) decreases the overall heat transfer coefficient
    (c) is equal to the overall heat transfer coefficient
    (d) none of the above.

27. The analogy of conductivity in heat transfer to fluid flow is
    (a) velocity of fluid
    (b) density of fluid
    (c) viscosity of fluid
    (d) dielectric constant of fluid.

28. Heat flows from higher temperature to lower temperature in case of
    (a) conduction only
    (b) convection only
    (c) radiation only
    (d) all the above cases.

29. High transfer rate is high in
    (a) film boiling
    (b) nucleate boiling
    (c) both in film and nucleate boiling
    (d) in simple convection.

30. Radiation heat from a substance
    (a) takes place at all temperatures
    (b) takes place only above 273°C

(c) takes place only above room temperature
(d) depends on surrounding temperature.

31. In case of a black body
    (a) transmittivity is one
    (b) absorptivity is zero
    (b) reflectivity is one
    (d) none of the above.

32. Conventionally, heat transfer area is obtained by
    (a) increasing the diameter of the tube
    (b) increasing the length of the tube
    (c) adding fins to the tube
    (d) decreasing the thickness of the tube.

33. In metals heat transfer by conduction happens by
    (a) the movements of the atoms
    (b) the movements of the free electrons
    (c) the bombardment of atoms with each other
    (d) none of the above.

34. Radiation heat transfer occurs at a speed of
    (a) sound   (b) light
    (c) 60000 km/h   (d) 3000 m/h.

B. FILL IN THE BLANKS:

1. Dropwise condensation occurs on ....surface.

2. The critical radius of insulation is given to be a ratio of ....and overall heat transfer coefficient.

3. A body, which absorbs all the radiations falling on it, is called ....

4. The unit of thermal conductivity in SI units is ....

5. Fins are used to .... the heat flow from the surface.

6. Cold feed should be fed .... in a multifaced evaporator.

7. The expression for logarithmic mean radius is ....

8. For heating air by steam .... heat exchangers are recommended.

9. Natural convection is caused due to ....

10. In evaporators, to separate liquid droplets from the vapour .... is used.

11. A gas does not .... any thermal radiation.

12. The unit of heat transfer coefficient in SI units is ....

13. Prandtl number is a ratio of kinematic viscosity and .... of a fluid.

C. MATCH THE SETS :

1.

	Set A		Set B
(i)	Reciprocity theorem	(a)	Transient condition
(ii)	Inertia force/surface tension force	(b)	Reynolds number
(iii)	Inertia force/gravitational force	(c)	Convective heat transfer
(iv)	Inertia force/viscous force	(d)	Froude number
(v)	Biot number	(e)	Radiant heat exchange.

2.

	Set A		Set B
(i)	Fourier law	(a)	Forced convection
(ii)	Fourier number	(b)	Free convection
(iii)	Grashoff number	(c)	Conduction heat transfer
(iv)	Wien displacement law	(d)	Transient heat flow.
(v)	Stanton number	(e)	Radiation heat transfer.

3.

	Set A		Set B
(i)	Planck's law	(a)	Turbulent flow
(ii)	Stanton number	(b)	Heat exchanger
(iii)	NTU	(c)	Radiation heat transfer
(iv)	Eddy viscosity	(d)	Capillarity
(v)	Surface tension	(e)	Forced convection

ANSWERS

A. CHOOSE THE CORRECT ANSWER :

1. (a)	2. (c)	3. (a)	4. (c)	5. (b)
6. (b)	7. (a)	8. (b)	9. (c)	10. (c)
11. (b)	12. (d)	13. (b)	14. (d)	15. (d)
16. (a)	17. (c)	18. (b)	19. (a)	20. (a)
21. (a)	22. (b)	23. (d)	24. (c)	25. (b)
26. (b)	27. (c)	28. (d)	29. (c)	30. (a)
31. (d)	32. (c)	33. (b)	34. (b).	

B. FILL IN THE BLANKS :

1.	contaminated	2.	thermal conductivity	3.	black body
4.	W/m°C	5.	increase	6.	from bottom

7. $\dfrac{r_2 - r_1}{\ln (r_2 / r_1)}$ 8. surface   9. density difference

10.	baffle plate	11.	reflect	12.	W/m²°C
13.	thermal diffusivity.				

C. MATCH THE SETS :

1.	(i) (e)	(ii) (c)	(iii) (d)	(iv) (b)	(v) (a)
2.	(i) (c)	(ii) (d)	(iii) (b)	(iv) (e)	(v) (a)
3.	(i) (c)	(ii) (e)	(iii) (b)	(iv) (a)	(v) (d).

INDEX